Linear Models and Regression with R

An Integrated Approach

SERIES ON MULTIVARIATE ANALYSIS

Editor: M M Rao **ISSN: 1793-1169**

Published

Vol. 1: Martingales and Stochastic Analysis
J. Yeh

Vol. 2: Multidimensional Second Order Stochastic Processes
Y. Kakihara

Vol. 3: Mathematical Methods in Sample Surveys
H. G. Tucker

Vol. 4: Abstract Methods in Information Theory
Y. Kakihara

Vol. 5: Topics in Circular Statistics
S. R. Jammalamadaka and A. SenGupta

Vol. 6: Linear Models: An Integrated Approach
D. Sengupta and S. R. Jammalamadaka

Vol. 7: Structural Aspects in the Theory of Probability
A Primer in Probabilities on Algebraic-Topological Structures
H. Heyer

Vol. 8: Structural Aspects in the Theory of Probability (Second Edition)
H. Heyer

Vol. 9: Random and Vector Measures
M. M. Rao

Vol. 10: Abstract Methods in Information Theory (Second Edition)
Y. Kakihara

Vol. 11: Linear Models and Regression with R: An Integrated Approach
D. Sengupta and S. R. Jammalamadaka

Series on
Multivariate Analysis
Vol. 11

Linear Models and Regression with R
An Integrated Approach

Debasis Sengupta
Indian Statistical Institute, India

Sreenivasa Rao Jammalamadaka
University of California, Santa Barbara, USA

World Scientific

NEW JERSEY • LONDON • SINGAPORE • BEIJING • SHANGHAI • HONG KONG • TAIPEI • CHENNAI • TOKYO

Published by

World Scientific Publishing Co. Pte. Ltd.

5 Toh Tuck Link, Singapore 596224

USA office: 27 Warren Street, Suite 401-402, Hackensack, NJ 07601

UK office: 57 Shelton Street, Covent Garden, London WC2H 9HE

Library of Congress Cataloging-in-Publication Data

Names: Sengupta, Debasis, 1949– author. | Jammalamadaka, S. Rao, author. |
Sengupta, Debasis, 1949– . Linear models.

Title: Linear models and regression with R : an integrated approach /
Debasis Sengupta, Sreenivasa Rao Jammalamadaka.

Description: New Jersey : World Scientific, [2019] | Series: Series on multivariate analysis, 1793-1169 ; Vol. 11 | "This book is an expanded, updated, and reorganized version of 'Linear Models: An Integrated Approach', published sixteen years ago." | Includes bibliographical references and indexes.

Identifiers: LCCN 2019024346 | ISBN 9789811200403 (hardcover)

Subjects: LCSH: Linear models (Statistics) | Regression analysis. |
Linear models (Statistics)--Data processing. | R (Computer program language)

Classification: LCC QA279 .S462 2019 | DDC 519.5/360285513--dc23

LC record available at https://lccn.loc.gov/2019024346

British Library Cataloguing-in-Publication Data

A catalogue record for this book is available from the British Library.

First published 2020 (Hardcover)

Reprinted 2020 (in paperback edition)

ISBN 978-981-122-928-2 (pbk)

For any available supplementary material, please visit
https://www.worldscientific.com/worldscibooks/10.1142/11282#t=suppl

To the memory of my guru in linear models,
Pochiraju Bhimasankaram

DS

To the memory of my parents,
Seetharamamma and Ramamoorthy, Jammalamadaka

SRJ

Preface

This book is an expanded, updated, and reorganized version of "*Linear Models: An Integrated Approach*", published sixteen years ago. As the new title suggests, the scope of this book is considerably broader, with many illustrative examples, applications with data sets, and their implementation in R.

Although an elementary discussion of linear models is part of any typical undergraduate course on regression analysis at most universities, a systematic treatment of the linear model is usually deferred until the graduate level. This book aims to cater to students and courses at both these levels.

A first course in regression generally aims to discuss the basic theory with focus on different applications. However, to go beyond such superficial data analysis, one needs to develop a stronger background with a clear understanding of the theoretical underpinnings of the models and methods used. One should also learn about a variety of issues that come up in practice. Our goal in this book is to provide in one single place, these different types of resources, namely the basic material, the underlying theory, and solutions to various practical issues that come up. To motivate and illustrate the key ideas, we use several real data examples and show how one could use relevant R codes to carry out various tasks of interest.

A graduate course in linear models typically relies on the matrix-vector formulation and draws heavily from tools of linear algebra. We do use algebra — but the emphasis is on telling the story through simple statistical ideas. We develop most of the theory using essentially two statistical concepts namely, the "linear zero function" (a linear analogue of an ancillary statistic), and the principle of "decorrelation". The insights provided by these concepts are particularly helpful in understanding the decomposition of sum of squares, say in designed experiments. More importantly, these simple concepts allow us to extend the theory that one uses in the more common homoscedastic linear model, to the case of a general linear model with possibly singular error dispersion matrix — hence the phrase "An Integrated Approach" in the title of the book.

The approach based on linear zero functions and decorrelation also provides easy access to several advanced topics in linear models, such as models with random effects or serial/spatial correlation, inclusion or exclusion of observations or parameters, multivariate linear model, and foundations of distribution-free linear inference.

After introducing the basic ideas about a linear model along with several examples in Chapter 1, we describe in Chapter 2 the probability background for regression, and properties of the multivariate normal distribution that would be used in later chapters. In the next two chapters, we consider the basic linear model with uncorrelated errors with equal variance. Chapter 3 develops the theory of linear estimation, followed by a discussion of confidence regions, testing, and prediction in Chapter 4. Chapter 5 which is a major chapter in the book, is devoted to model building, regression diagnostics, remedial measures, and the generalized linear model. Analysis of variance and covariance in designed experiments is considered in Chapter 6. The results of Chapters 3 and 4 are then extended to the case of the general linear model with an arbitrary dispersion matrix, in Chapter 7. Chapter 8 develops the case when the error dispersion matrix is misspecified or partially specified. We deal with updates in the general linear model in Chapter 9, and with multivariate response in Chapter 10. The final Chapter discusses the statistical foundations of linear inference, alternative linear estimators, a geometric perspective, and concludes with some large sample results. A summary of the algebraic and the statistical results used in the book are given in Appendices A and B, respectively.

The book contains 181 examples and 379 end-of-the-chapter exercises, which involve analysis of 28 real data sets and numerous other data sets synthesized for illustrating specific points. The exercises are meant to (a) further illustrate the material covered, (b) supplement some results with proofs, interpretations and extensions, (c) introduce or expand ideas that are related to the particular chapter, and (d) give glimpses of interesting research issues. Solutions to most of the theoretical exercises are given in Appendix C. A good number of exercises are left unsolved, so that they can be used as homework assignments when this is used as a textbook. Solutions to these additional exercises are available to instructors on request from the authors.

Copies of the data sets and some R functions used in the book are available and can be downloaded as part of the package `lmreg`, which can be installed from CRAN.

The book is meant primarily for students and researchers in statistics. Engineers and scientists who need a thorough understanding of linear models for their work will also find it useful. Practitioners of regression methods, who wish to look under the hood, would find structured treatment of the tools they need and use — such as leverages, residuals, deletion diagnostics, indicators of collinearity and various plots. We also hope that researchers will find stimulus for further work from the perspective of current research, discussed in the later chapters and the leads provided in some of the exercises.

A one-quarter or one-semester undergraduate course on regression can be taught covering Chapters 1–5 along with the data sets and analyses using R, while skipping the starred sections among these chapters. A one-semester graduate-level course on linear models can cover Chapters 1–6 including the starred sections, and selected topics from the other chapters. A follow-up course for a second semester can cover many of the advanced topics from Chapters 7–11. Some starred sections in Chapters 3–8 may still be omitted during a first reading, depending on the background of the readers. For students who have already had a first course in linear models/regression elsewhere, a second course may be taught by going through Chapters 3–7, with additional topics selected from Chapters 8–11.

A word about the notations. In the book, we do not make a distinction between lemmas, theorems, and corollaries — all of them being labeled as propositions. The propositions, definitions, remarks, and examples are numbered consecutively within a section, in a common sequence. Equations are also numbered consecutively within a section. Throughout the book, vectors are represented by lowercase and boldface letters, while uppercase and boldface letters are used to denote matrices. No notational distinction is made between a random vector and a particular realization of it.

The approach adopted in this book has its roots in the lecture notes of R.C. Bose (1949). It was conceived in its present form by P. Bhimasankaram, who also provided extensive suggestions on the manuscript at various stages.

Debasis Sengupta
Sreenivasa Rao Jammalamadaka

Contents

Preface vii

Glossary of Abbreviations xix

Glossary of Matrix Notations xxi

1. Introduction 1

- 1.1 The linear model 3
- 1.2 Why a linear model? 9
- 1.3 Uses of the linear model 10
- 1.4 Description of the linear model and notations 14
- 1.5 Scope of the linear model 17
- 1.6 Related models* 19
- 1.7 A tour through the rest of the book 21
- 1.8 Complements/Exercises 24

2. Regression and the Normal Distribution 29

- 2.1 Multivariate normal and related distributions 30
  - 2.1.1 Matrix of variances and covariances 30
  - 2.1.2 The multivariate normal distribution 31
  - 2.1.3 The conditional normal distribution 32
  - 2.1.4 Related distributions 34
- 2.2 The case of singular dispersion matrix* 36
- 2.3 Regression as best prediction 39
  - 2.3.1 Mean regression 39
  - 2.3.2 Median and quantile regression* 45
  - 2.3.3 Regression with multivariate response 47

2.4 Linear regression as best linear prediction 48
2.5 Multiple correlation coefficient* 53
2.6 Decorrelation* 55
2.7 Complements/Exercises 57

3. Estimation in the Linear Model 61

3.1 Least squares estimation 62
3.2 Fitted values and residuals 65
3.3 Variances and covariances 72
3.4 Estimation of error variance 74
3.5 Linear estimation: some basic facts 76
3.5.1 Linear functions of the response 76
3.5.2 Estimability and identifiability 79
3.6 Best linear unbiased estimation 82
3.7 Maximum likelihood estimation 88
3.8 Error sum of squares and degrees of freedom* 89
3.9 Reparametrization* 94
3.10 Linear restrictions* 96
3.11 Nuisance parameters* 102
3.12 Information matrix and Cramer-Rao bound* 104
3.13 Collinearity in the linear model 109
3.14 Complements/Exercises 112

4. Further Inference in the Linear Model 121

4.1 Distribution of the estimators 121
4.2 Tests of linear hypotheses 122
4.2.1 Significance of regression coefficients 122
4.2.2 Testability of linear hypotheses* 131
4.2.3 Hypotheses with a single degree of freedom 135
4.2.4 Decomposing the sum of squares* 138
4.2.5 GLRT and ANOVA table* 140
4.2.6 Power of the generalized likelihood ratio test* . . 146
4.2.7 Multiple comparisons* 147
4.2.8 Nested hypotheses* 150
4.3 Confidence regions 151
4.3.1 Confidence interval for a single LPF 151
4.3.2 Confidence region for a vector LPF* 153
4.3.3 Simultaneous confidence intervals* 155

4.3.4 Confidence band for regression surface* 159
4.4 Prediction in the linear model 161
4.4.1 Best linear unbiased predictor 162
4.4.2 Prediction interval 163
4.4.3 Simultaneous prediction intervals* 166
4.4.4 Tolerance interval* 167
4.5 Consequences of collinearity* 169
4.6 Complements/Exercises 171

5. Model Building and Diagnostics in Regression 181

5.1 Selection of regressors 184
5.1.1 Too many and too few regressors 184
5.1.2 Some criteria for subset selection 192
5.1.3 Methods of subset selection 198
5.1.4 Selection bias 200
5.2 Leverages and residuals 202
5.3 Checking for violation of assumptions 207
5.3.1 Nonlinearity 207
5.3.2 Heteroscedasticity 213
5.3.3 Correlated observations 224
5.3.4 Non-normality 229
5.4 Casewise diagnostics 237
5.4.1 Diagnostics for parameter estimates 238
5.4.2 Diagnostics for fit 239
5.4.3 Precision diagnostics 240
5.4.4 Spotting unusual cases graphically 242
5.4.5 Dealing with discordant observations 245
5.5 Collinearity 246
5.5.1 Indicators of collinearity 248
5.5.2 Strategies for collinear data 254
5.6 Biased estimators with smaller dispersion* 255
5.6.1 Principal components estimator 256
5.6.2 Ridge estimator 258
5.6.3 Shrinkage estimator 259
5.7 Generalized linear model 260
5.7.1 Maximum likelihood estimation 263
5.7.2 Logistic regression 265
5.8 Complements/Exercises 270

6. Analysis of Variance 281

6.1 Optimal designs . . . 283
6.2 One-way classified data . . . 284
6.2.1 The model . . . 284
6.2.2 Estimation of model parameters . . . 287
6.2.3 Analysis of variance . . . 291
6.2.4 Multiple comparisons of group means . . . 294
6.3 Two-way classified data . . . 296
6.3.1 Single observation per cell . . . 297
6.3.2 Interaction in two-way classified data . . . 304
6.3.3 Multiple observations per cell: balanced data . . . 309
6.3.4 Unbalanced data . . . 315
6.4 Multiple treatment/block factors . . . 317
6.5 Nested models . . . 318
6.6 Analysis of covariance . . . 322
6.6.1 The model . . . 322
6.6.2 Uses of the model . . . 323
6.6.3 Estimation of parameters . . . 324
6.6.4 Tests of hypotheses . . . 327
6.6.5 ANCOVA table and adjustment for covariates* . . 330
6.7 Complements/Exercises . . . 333

7. General Linear Model 341

7.1 Why study the singular model? . . . 342
7.2 Special considerations with singular models . . . 343
7.2.1 Checking for model consistency* . . . 344
7.2.2 LUE, LZF, estimability and identifiability* . . . 345
7.3 Best linear unbiased estimation . . . 348
7.3.1 BLUE, fitted values and residuals . . . 348
7.3.2 Dispersions . . . 352
7.3.3 The nonsingular case . . . 354
7.4 Estimation of error variance . . . 355
7.5 Maximum likelihood estimation . . . 357
7.6 Weighted least squares estimation . . . 358
7.7 Some recipes for obtaining the BLUE* . . . 361
7.7.1 'Unified theory' of least squares estimation . . . 361
7.7.2 The inverse partitioned matrix approach . . . 363
7.7.3 A constrained least squares approach . . . 365

7.8 Information matrix and Cramer-Rao bound* 366
7.9 Effect of linear restrictions 369
7.9.1 Linear restrictions in the general linear model . . 369
7.9.2 Improved estimation through restrictions 372
7.9.3 Stochastic restrictions* 373
7.9.4 Inequality constraints* 375
7.10 Model with nuisance parameters 377
7.11 Tests of hypotheses 379
7.12 Confidence regions 381
7.13 Prediction 383
7.13.1 Best linear unbiased predictor 383
7.13.2 Prediction and tolerance intervals 384
7.13.3 Inference in finite population sampling* 385
7.14 Complements/Exercises 388

8. Misspecified or Unknown Dispersion 395

8.1 Misspecified dispersion matrix 396
8.1.1 Tolerable misspecification* 398
8.1.2 Efficiency of least squares estimators* 404
8.1.3 Effect on the estimated variance of LSEs* 410
8.2 Unknown dispersion: the general case 412
8.2.1 An estimator based on prior information* 412
8.2.2 Maximum likelihood estimator 413
8.2.3 Translation invariance and REML 415
8.2.4 A two-stage estimator 417
8.3 Mixed effects and variance components 419
8.3.1 Identifiability and estimability 420
8.3.2 ML and REML methods 422
8.3.3 ANOVA methods 428
8.3.4 Minimum norm quadratic unbiased estimator . . . 430
8.3.5 Best quadratic unbiased estimator 435
8.3.6 Further inference in the mixed model* 436
8.4 Other special cases with correlated error 437
8.4.1 Serially correlated observations 437
8.4.2 Models for spatial data 439
8.5 Special cases with uncorrelated error 441
8.5.1 Combining experiments: meta-analysis 441
8.5.2 Systematic heteroscedasticity 443

8.6 Some problems of signal processing 444
8.7 Complements/Exercises 446

9. Updates in the General Linear Model 451

9.1 Inclusion of observations 452
9.1.1 A simple case 452
9.1.2 General case: linear zero functions gained 454
9.1.3 General case: update equations 457
9.1.4 Application to model diagnostics 462
9.1.5 Design augmentation 462
9.1.6 Recursive prediction and Kalman filter 466
9.2 Exclusion of observations 473
9.2.1 A simple case 473
9.2.2 General case: linear zero functions lost 475
9.2.3 General case: update equations 477
9.2.4 Deletion diagnostics 479
9.2.5 Missing plot substitution 482
9.3 Exclusion of explanatory variables 484
9.3.1 A simple case 485
9.3.2 General case: linear zero functions gained 486
9.3.3 General case: update equations 488
9.3.4 Consequences of omitted variables 489
9.3.5 Sequential linear restrictions 490
9.4 Inclusion of explanatory variables 490
9.4.1 A simple case 490
9.4.2 General case: linear zero functions lost 492
9.4.3 General case: update equations 493
9.4.4 Application to regression model building 494
9.5 Data exclusion and variable inclusion 494
9.6 Complements/Exercises 495

10. Multivariate Linear Model 499

10.1 Description of the multivariate linear model 500
10.2 Best linear unbiased estimation 501
10.3 Unbiased estimation of error dispersion 506
10.4 Maximum likelihood estimation 510
10.4.1 Estimator of mean 510
10.4.2 Estimator of error dispersion 510

10.4.3 REML estimator of error dispersion 512

10.5 Effect of linear restrictions 512

10.5.1 Effect on estimable LPFs, LZFs and BLUEs . . . 512

10.5.2 Change in error sum of squares and products . . . 513

10.5.3 Change in 'BLUE' and MSE matrix 514

10.6 Tests of linear hypotheses 515

10.6.1 Generalized likelihood ratio test 515

10.6.2 Roy's union-intersection test 517

10.6.3 Other tests 518

10.6.4 A more general hypothesis 524

10.6.5 Multiple comparisons 526

10.6.6 Test for additional information 526

10.7 Linear prediction and confidence regions 527

10.8 Applications 530

10.8.1 One-sample problem 530

10.8.2 Two-sample problem 530

10.8.3 Multivariate ANOVA 531

10.8.4 Growth models 532

10.9 Complements/Exercises 533

11\. Linear Inference — Other Perspectives 537

11.1 Foundations of linear inference 538

11.1.1 General theory 538

11.1.2 Basis set of BLUEs 543

11.1.3 A decomposition of the response 545

11.1.4 Estimation and error spaces 550

11.2 Admissible, Bayes and minimax linear estimators 552

11.2.1 Admissible linear estimator 552

11.2.2 Bayes linear estimator 555

11.2.3 Minimax linear estimator 558

11.3 Other linear estimators 565

11.3.1 Biased estimators revisited 565

11.3.2 Best linear minimum bias estimator 565

11.3.3 'Consistent' estimator 567

11.4 A geometric view of BLUE in the linear model 567

11.4.1 The homoscedastic case 568

11.4.2 The effect of linear restrictions 569

11.4.3 The general linear model 570

11.5 Large sample properties of estimators 575

11.6 Complements/Exercises 579

Appendix A Matrix and Vector Preliminaries 583

A.1 Matrices and vectors 583
A.2 Generalized inverse 590
A.3 Vector space and projection 593
A.4 Column space 597
A.5 Matrix decompositions 603
A.6 Löwner order 609
A.7 Solutions of linear equations 610
A.8 Optimization of quadratic forms and functions 611
A.9 Complements/Exercises 614

Appendix B Review of Statistical Theory 617

B.1 Basic concepts of inference 617
B.2 Point estimation 621
B.3 Bayesian estimation 628
B.4 Tests of hypotheses 631
B.5 Confidence region 634
B.6 Complements/Exercises 635

Appendix C Solutions to Selected Exercises 637

Bibliography and Author Index 713

Index 735

Glossary of Abbreviations

(Abbreviations used in more than one section or subsection of the book)

Abbreviation	Full form	Described on page
AIC	Akaike's information criterion	194
ALE	admissible linear estimator	552
ANOVA	analysis of variance	141
ANCOVA	analysis of covariance	323
AR	autoregressive	20
ARMA	autoregressive moving average	20
BLE	Bayes linear estimator	555
BLP	best linear predictor	49
BLUE	best linear unbiased estimator	82
BLUP	best linear unbiased predictor	162
CRD	completely randomized design	284
GLM	generalized linear model	261
GLRT	generalized likelihood ratio test	633
IVIF	intercept augmented variance inflation factor	249
LPF	linear parametric function	76
LSE	least squares estimator	62
LUE	linear unbiased estimator	76
LZF	linear zero function	76
MILE	Minimax linear estimator	558
MINQUE	minimum norm quadratic unbiased estimator	432
ML	maximum likelihood	624
MLE	maximum likelihood estimator	624
MSE	mean squared error	621
MSEP	mean squared error of prediction	161
NLZF	normalized linear zero function	506
OLS	ordinary least squares	217
RBD	randomized block design	297
REML	restricted/residual maximum likelihood	416
SSE	sum of squares due to error	92
UMVUE	uniformly minimum variance unbiased estimator	622
VIF	variance inflation factor	249
WLS	weighted least squares	217

Glossary of Matrix Notations

Notation	Meaning	Defined on page
$a_{i,j}$	(i,j)th element of the matrix $\boldsymbol{A}$	583
$((a_{i,j}))$	the matrix whose (i,j)th element is $a_{i,j}$	583
$\boldsymbol{AB}$	product of the matrix $\boldsymbol{A}$ with the matrix $\boldsymbol{B}$	584
$\boldsymbol{A}'$	transpose of the matrix $\boldsymbol{A}$	584
$\text{tr}(\boldsymbol{A})$	trace of the matrix $\boldsymbol{A}$	584
$\boldsymbol{I}$	identity matrix	585
$\boldsymbol{0}$	matrix of zeroes	585
$\boldsymbol{1}$	(column) vector of ones	585
$\rho(\boldsymbol{A})$	rank of the matrix $\boldsymbol{A}$	586
$\boldsymbol{A}^{-1}$	inverse of the matrix $\boldsymbol{A}$	586
$\text{vec}(\boldsymbol{A})$	vector obtained by successively concatenating the columns of the matrix $\boldsymbol{A}$	588
$\lVert\boldsymbol{A}\rVert_F$	Frobenius (Euclidean) norm of the matrix $\boldsymbol{A}$	588
$\boldsymbol{A}\otimes\boldsymbol{B}$	Kronecker product of $\boldsymbol{A}$ with $\boldsymbol{B}$	588
$\boldsymbol{A}^{-L}$	a left-inverse of the matrix $\boldsymbol{A}$	590
$\boldsymbol{A}^{-R}$	a right-inverse of the matrix $\boldsymbol{A}$	590
$\boldsymbol{A}^{-}$	a g-inverse of the matrix $\boldsymbol{A}$	591
$\boldsymbol{A}^{+}$	Moore-Penrose inverse of the matrix $\boldsymbol{A}$	591
$\mathcal{C}(\boldsymbol{A})$	column space of the matrix $\boldsymbol{A}$	597
$\mathcal{C}(\boldsymbol{A})^{\perp}$	orthogonal complement of $\mathcal{C}(\boldsymbol{A})$	594
$\dim(\mathcal{C}(\boldsymbol{A}))$	dimension of $\mathcal{C}(\boldsymbol{A})$	594
$\boldsymbol{P}_{A}$	orthogonal projection matrix of $\mathcal{C}(\boldsymbol{A})$	600
$\lvert\boldsymbol{A}\rvert$	determinant of the matrix $\boldsymbol{A}$	585
$\lVert\boldsymbol{A}\rVert$	largest singular value of the matrix $\boldsymbol{A}$	613
$\lambda_{max}(\boldsymbol{A})$	largest eigenvalue of the symmetric matrix $\boldsymbol{A}$	404
$\lambda_{min}(\boldsymbol{A})$	smallest eigenvalue of the symmetric matrix $\boldsymbol{A}$	404

Chapter 1

Introduction

It is in human nature to try and understand the physical and natural phenomena that occur around us. For example, all of us know that death is a certainty and that it is only the time of death that is not known beforehand. People have tried to understand the time of death as much as possible, by quantifying the chances of this event at various ages. In the mid-nineteenth century, William Guy published a series of articles (see e.g. Guy, 1859) on comparative studies of the duration of life among persons of different professions. Figure 1.1 depicts a part of the age-at-death data published by him, where the deceased person's profession has been classified into eight categories: 'historians', 'poets', 'painters', 'musicians', 'mathematicians and astronomers', 'chemists and natural philosophers', 'naturalists' and 'engineers, architects and surveyors'. Despite the variation in ages at death within each category, it would be interesting to know whether people in these various professions generally live for the same duration. For instance, do mathematicians live significantly longer than poets or historians? This is not merely a matter of casual curiosity. Today actuaries routinely classify potential customers for life insurance by various characteristics that are perceived to have a bearing on the hazard of death. Since it is very difficult to identify a large group of people exactly matching the profile of a specific customer, we look for a broader picture. We seek to describe the probable lifetimes of individuals through a mathematical model that is applicable for the entire set of data, covering all the categories and other relevant characteristics that might affect a lifetime.

Similarly a mother who wants to check if her daughter is growing normally, say in terms of height, is looking to see if the child fits an overall pattern, subject to individual variations. In order to determine what is a 'normal' height for a particular age, it is common practice to collate a large

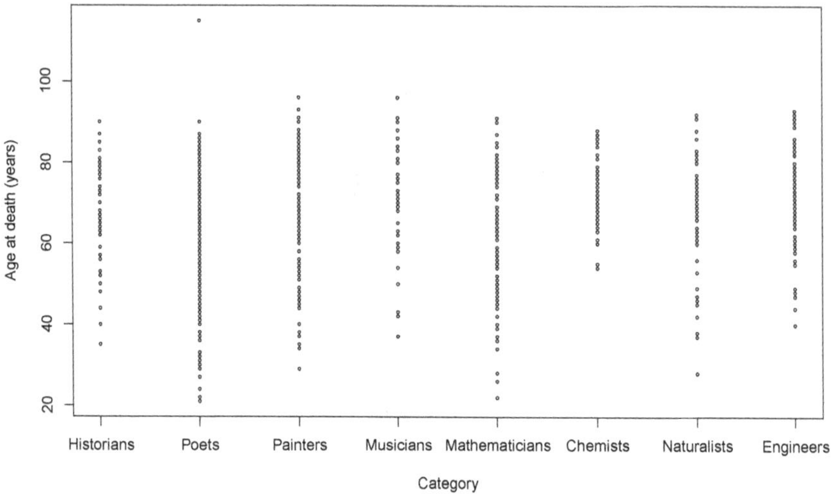

Fig. 1.1 Age at death of people in different professions (Source: Guy, 1859)

amount of data on the heights of children at different ages. A typical data set is represented in the scatter plot of Figure 1.2, which shows the heights of adolescent girls between the ages 7 and 12.[1] In a carefully planned study like this one, one generally measures the heights of girls on or around their birthdays (i.e. at integer values of age), and there is not much data for non-integer values of age. Thus, in order to get an idea of the 'normal' range of heights for any given age (say, 10 years and 3 months), one has to use a model based on all available data. Even if the goal is to find 'normal' height at integer values of age, a suitable model can help us draw better inferences by considering information from adjacent age categories.

A model is generally a simplistic attempt to capture the essentials in a given context. Either because we lack all the facts or in order to keep it simple, we often leave some relevant factors out of the model. Also, models need to be validated through measurement, and measurements often come with error. In order to account for the measurement or observational errors as well as the factors that may have been left out, one needs a *statistical* model which allows some amount of uncertainty.

[1]The data used here is a part of a larger data set, collected from school going children in the southern part of Kolkata, India around the year 2008 (Dasgupta, 2015).

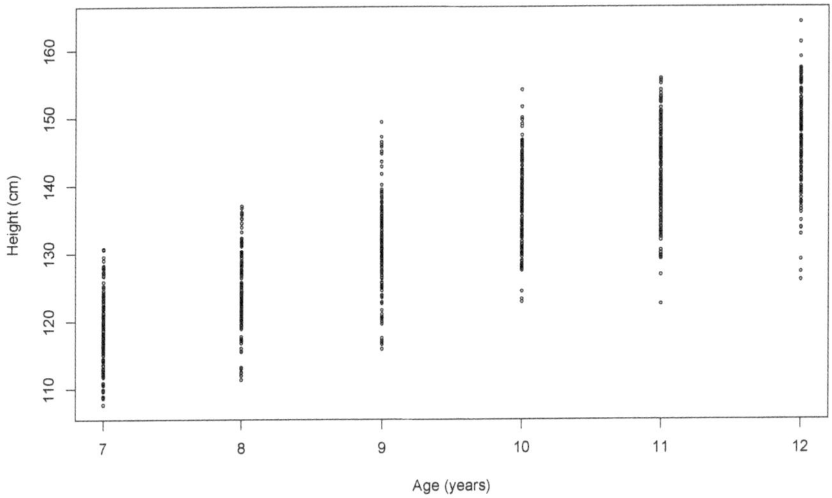

Fig. 1.2 Height of adolescent girls at various ages (Source: Dasgupta, 2015)

1.1 The linear model

In the two examples mentioned above, the basic question that one would like to answer through a statistical model is the following: How can an observed quantity y be explained by a number of other quantities, $x_1, x_2, \ldots, x_k$? Perhaps the simplest model that is used to answer this question is the so-called *linear model*

$$y = \beta_0 + \beta_1 x_1 + \beta_2 x_2 + \cdots + \beta_k x_k + \varepsilon, \tag{1.1}$$

where $\beta_0, \beta_1, \ldots, \beta_k$ are unknown constants and ε is an error term that accounts for uncertainties. We shall refer to y as the *response variable* or simply *response*. It is also referred to as the *dependent variable*, *endogenous variable* or *criterion variable*. We shall refer to $x_1, x_2, \ldots, x_k$ as *explanatory variables*. These are also called *independent variables* or *exogenous variables*. In some special contexts these are called *regressors*, *predictors* or *factors*. The coefficients $\beta_0, \beta_1, \ldots, \beta_k$ are the *parameters* of the model. Note that the right-hand side of (1.1) is not only a linear function of the explanatory variables; it is a linear function of the model parameters as well.

We now provide a few examples of the linear model.

Example 1.1. (Growth of girls) In the growth data example, the age of a girl can be used as the only explanatory variable (x_1), and her height as the dependent variable (y). The resulting special case of the linear model (1.1) is

$$y = \beta_0 + \beta_1 x_1 + \varepsilon.$$

Here, the error ε mostly captures the person-to-person variation from $\beta_0 + \beta_1 x_1$, regarded as the central value of height for age x_1. Since the model does not make any specific provision for error in measuring the height, that error is also included in ε. The parameter β_1 represents the increase in the central value of the height y per year of age. If this rate were to change from year to year, the linear model would not be accurate. The linear model would then serve only as an approximation to a function that is possibly nonlinear in x_1. In such a case, the error term ε would include the approximation error also. The parameter β_0 in the above model represents the height at age zero. However, this interpretation need not be literally interpreted as the typical height of a newborn girl. The plot of Figure 1.2 spans only the age range 7 to 12. The above linear model is meant to be a straight line approximation to this plot. The parameter β_0 is the intercept of that straight line with the vertical axis. If height data for younger ages had been available, the plot in that region might have been quite different from this straight line. □

Example 1.2. A well-known result in optics is the *Snell's law* which relates the angle of incidence (θ_1) with the angle of refraction (θ_2), when light crosses the boundary between two media. According to this law,

$$\sin\theta_2 = \kappa \sin\theta_1,$$

where κ is the ratio of refractive indices of the two media. If the refractive index of one medium is known, the refractive index of the other can be estimated by observing θ_1 and θ_2. However, any measurement will involve some amount of error. Thus, the following special case of the model (1.1) may be used:

$$y = \beta_1 x_1 + \varepsilon,$$

where $\beta_1 = \kappa$, $y = \sin\theta_2$, $x_1 = \sin\theta_1$ and θ_1 and θ_2 are the *measured* angles of incidence and refraction, respectively. □

Example 1.3. (Galton's data on family heights) Children of taller parents are often found to be taller. Can heights be indefinitely improved through successive generations of selective breeding? In order to explore this possibility, Sir Francis Galton (1886) recorded the heights of a number of parents and their mature offspring. Figure 1.3 shows the scatter plot of the mature height of the first born son against the height of his father (which is only a part of Galton's data). It is indeed observed that the heights of first-born sons are positively associated with the heights of their fathers. Improvement of height over a generation could have been inferred if the points at the *right side of the plot* had been mostly above the 45° line drawn on the plot. However, it is found that most of these points lie *below* that line. This finding indicates that taller fathers tend to have taller sons, but these taller sons are not generally as tall as their fathers. Likewise, first born sons of shorter fathers are generally shorter than others, but taller than their respective fathers. Galton referred to this phenomenon as 'regression towards mediocrity through hereditary structure'. The term *regression* owes its origin to this work of Galton.

While the father's height has been used here for a simplified description of the problem, the mother's height should also be factored in for a more

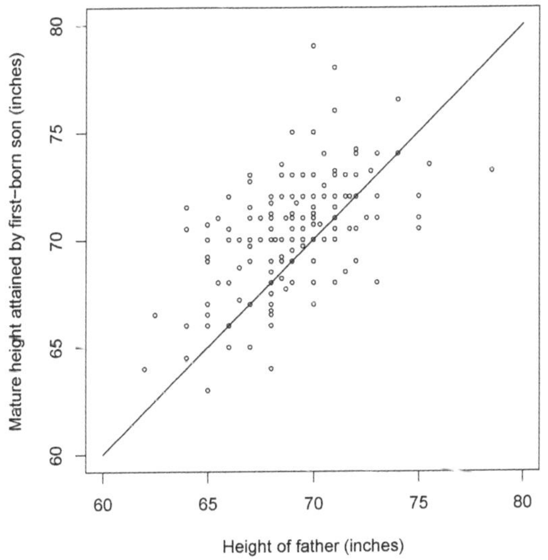

Fig. 1.3 Heights of mature first-born sons of fathers with different heights

meaningful analysis. This may be achieved by using the following model.

$$y = \beta_0 + \beta_1 x_1 + \beta_2 x_2 + \varepsilon. \tag{1.2}$$

Here, y is the mature height of the first-born son, x_1 is the height of his father and x_2 is the height of his mother. The error term ε includes all deviations from an exact linear relationship, including measurement error, individual variations arising from whatever reason and any departure from the linear relation. According to this model, the parameter β_1 may be interpreted as the expected difference between the mature heights of two first-born sons having equally tall mothers, and fathers having an inch of difference in height. The parameter β_2 has a similar interpretation. As in the previous example, we can interpret the parameter β_0 mathematically as the intercept and leave it at that, as the search for a physical meaning would have to evoke the rather difficult concept of the height of a son born to parents of zero height! □

Example 1.4. (Age at death) For the data set mentioned at the beginning of this chapter, one may represent the age at death (y) as a linear function of several binary variables,

$$y = \beta_0 + \beta_1 x_1 + \beta_2 x_2 + \beta_3 x_3 + \beta_4 x_4 + \beta_5 x_5 + \beta_6 x_6 + \beta_7 x_7 + \varepsilon,$$

where x_1 is 1 if the dead person was a 'poet' and 0 otherwise, and likewise x_2, x_3, x_4, x_5, x_6 and x_7 are indicators of the dead person being a 'painter', a 'musician', and 'mathematician or astronomer', a 'chemist or natural philosopher' and an 'engineer, architect or surveyor', respectively. Note that we do not need an eighth binary indicator variable corresponding to the profession 'historian' as it can be associated with the case when all these 7 binary variables are 0. This model would only be applicable to persons belonging to these eight professions. The parameter β_0 represents the mean age at death of historians. The parameter β_1 is the excess of the mean age at death of poets over historians. This 'excess' can be negative. The other parameters have similar interpretation. The error ε represents the person-to-person variation in the age at death, which is presumed to be of the same order for any particular professional category. □

Example 1.5. (Birth weight of babies) It is suspected that a newborn baby may be underweight if the mother is a smoker. The weight of a baby may also depend on the ethnic group and a number of health factors of the mother. Figure 1.4 represents a part of a data set, collected at Baystate

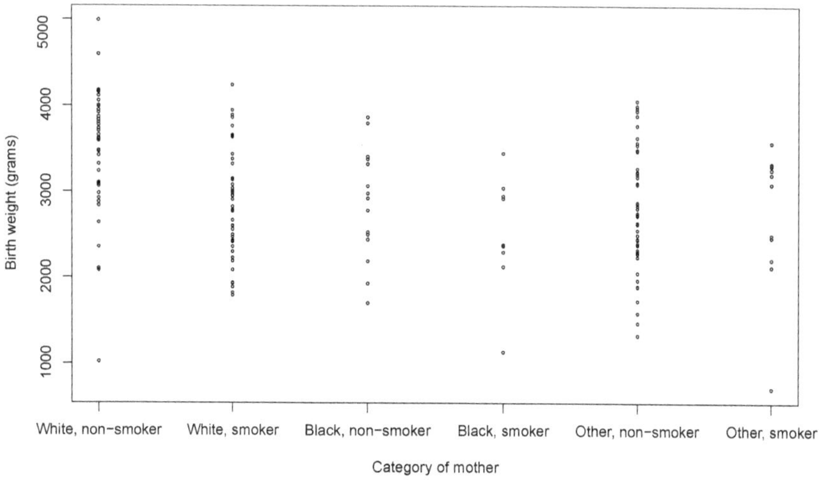

Fig. 1.4 Birth weight of babies for different categories of mothers

Medical Center, Springfield, Massachusetts during 1986 and published in Hosmer et al. (2013), that includes the birth weight of newborn babies together with the mother's smoking status and ethnic category. A simple model that can relate the variables is

$$y = \beta_0 + \tau_1 x_1 + \beta_1 x_2 + \beta_2 x_3 + \varepsilon,$$

where y is the birth weight of a baby, x_1 is a binary variable that is 1 if the mother is smoker and 0 if she is not, x_2 is a binary variable that is equal to 1 if the mother is white and 0 otherwise, and x_3 is a third binary variable indicating whether the mother is black. The error term represents all the risk factors that are not specifically included, such as the mother's age, bodyweight and health parameters, and natural variation among babies. This model is a special case of (1.1), though we have used slightly different notations for the parameters, τ_1 for the smoking status and β_1, β_2 for the ethnic categories, in order to differentiate their roles. Some additional risk factors available in the data set may also be included in the model. □

Example 1.6. (Treatment of leprosy) Snedecor and Cochran (1967, p. 421), reported data arising from the testing of two antibiotic drugs among leprosy patients at the Eversley Childs Sanitarium in the Phillippines. The

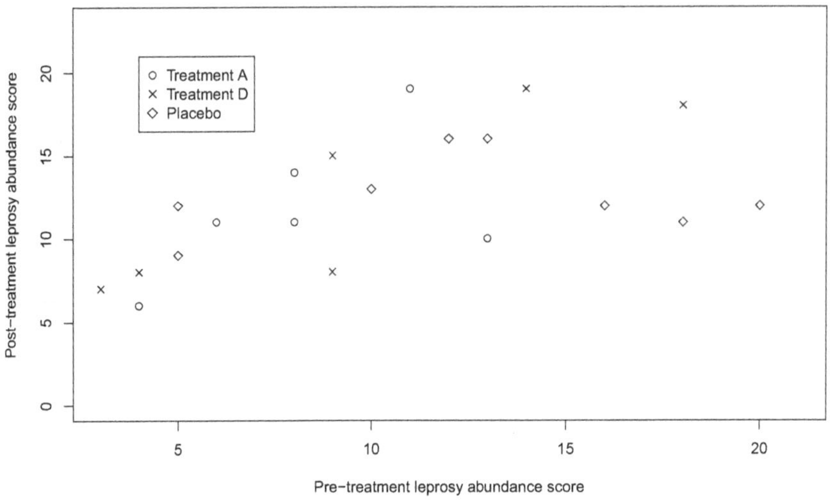

Fig. 1.5 Pre- and post-treatment leprosy scores of patients under three treatments

patients had been randomly allocated to treatment by either of the two antibiotics (A and D) or to a dummy treatment (referred to treatment F or as placebo). The data consist of the pre- and post-treatment scores on the abundance of leprosy bacilli at pre-selected sites in the body. Figure 1.5 shows the plot of the scores for the three groups. While the efficacy of the treatments should be judged on the basis of the post-treatment scores (smaller score being better), one cannot disregard the condition of the patient prior to the treatment. Therefore, the following linear model for the post-treatment score (y) may be used.

$$y = \beta_0 + \tau_1 x_1 + \tau_2 x_2 + \eta z + \varepsilon.$$

Here, x_1 and x_2 are binary variables indicating the use of the drugs A and D, respectively, and z is the pre-treatment score. The parameters τ_1 and τ_2 are the expected (hopefully negative) amounts by which drugs A and D are able to 'increase' the score over the placebo group. The better drug should have a more negative value of the parameter. The parameters η and β_0 represents the slope and the intercept of the straight-line relation between the post- and pre-treatment scores. The model implies that the effect of either drug is only on the intercept. The error term represents the diversity in the individual patient's response to the treatments and any imprecision of the scores in capturing that response. □

The foregoing discussion indicates that the explanatory variables in a linear model can be stochastic or deterministic (fixed), or even a combination of the two. The error term in the model can arise from a variety of sources, including (i) variation in the response even for a given set of fixed values of the explanatory variables, (ii) imperfection of measurements, (iii) approximation arising from using a linear equation to model an inherently nonlinear type of dependence and (iv) explanatory variables that fail to be included in the model.

1.2 Why a linear model?

The model (1.1) is just one of many possible models that can be used to explain the response in terms of the explanatory variables. Some of the reasons why we study the linear model in detail are as follows.

(a) Because of its simplicity, the linear model is better understood and easier to interpret than most other competing models, and the methods of analysis and inference are better developed. Therefore, if there is no particular reason to presuppose another model, the linear model may be used at least as a first step, or as the default.

(b) The linear model formulation is useful even for certain nonlinear models which can be reduced to the form (1.1) by means of a transformation. Examples of such models are given in Section 1.5.

(c) Results obtained for the linear model serve as a stepping stone for the analysis of a much wider class of related models such as mixed effects model, state-space and other time series models. These are outlined in Section 1.6.

(d) Suppose the response is modelled as a nonlinear function of the explanatory variables plus error. In many practical situations only a part of the domain of this function is of interest, where a local linear approximation might suffice. For example, in a manufacturing process, one is interested in a narrow region centered around the operating point. If the above function is reasonably smooth in this region, a linear model serves as a good first order approximation to what may be globally a nonlinear model.

(e) Certain probability models for the response and the explanatory variables imply that the response should be centered around a linear function of the explanatory variables. If there is any reason to believe in a joint probability model of this kind, the linear model is the natural choice. A good example is the multivariate normal distribution. Sometimes the assumption of this distribution is justified by invoking the *central limit theorem*, particularly when the variables are themselves aggregates or averages of a large collection of other quantities.

1.3 Uses of the linear model

An important application of the linear model is in regression analysis where the average response is explained via other observed variables (called *regressors* in this context). Building a working model to describe the relationship among the variables is sometimes an end in itself.

Example 1.7. (Receding galaxies) Edwin Hubble (1929) discovered that faraway galaxies appear to move away from us faster than the nearer ones. This conclusion was based on indirect measurements of the speed of 24 galaxies and their distances from Earth. By drawing a scatter plot similar to Figure 1.6, Hubble showed that there is a proportional relation between the distance and the speed. This discovery had a profound impact on Physicists' understanding of an expanding universe. □

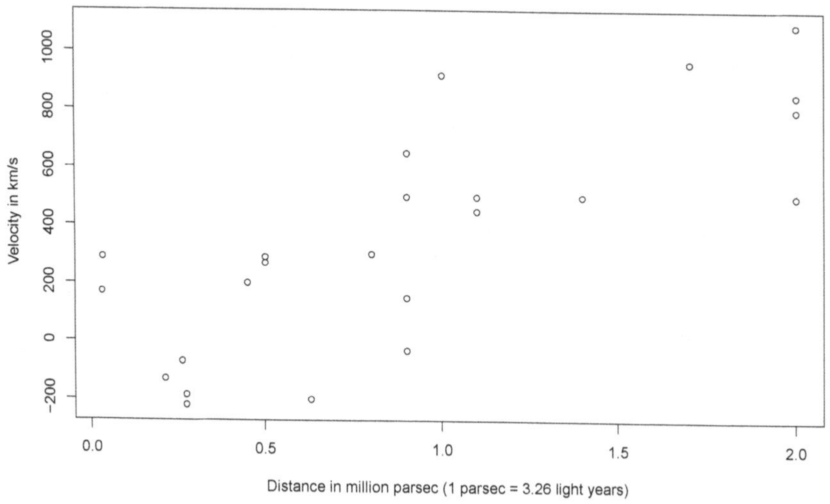

Fig. 1.6 Velocity of galaxies at various distances from the Earth

Apart from the purpose of capturing the actual relationship among variables in a given context, the linear model may be used as a vehicle for various types of analyses. The law of refraction of light is now universally accepted. Yet material with new optical properties continue to evolve, and their refractive index needs to be measured. This task amounts to fitting the linear model of Example 1.2 to data on angles of incidence and refraction, with the purpose of estimating β_1. The same requirement arises in other fields also, as the next example shows.

Example 1.8. (Inflated price of drugs) It is well known that pharmaceutical companies sell trade-marked medicines at much higher prices than the manufacturing cost. A drug sold under a brand name is often several times costlier than the same composition sold under its generic name. The ratio of the prices vary from drug to drug and from place to place. In order to have a clear understanding of this phenomenon, the World Health Organization (WHO) had commissioned a study covering a number of developing countries. For comparability, the price in a particular region is expressed as a ratio (called median price ratio or MPR) with respect to the organization's drug price indicator median values. Table 1.1 shows the across-country median of these ratios in respect of 13 medicines, most of which are in the WHO list of essential medicines. The factor by which

Table 1.1 Across-countries median of median price ratio (MPR) of some medicines available in the private market under the generic name and the brand name of the originator (data object `drugprice` in R package `lmreg`, source: Gelders et al., 2005)

Drug	Quantity	Originator MPR	Generic MPR
Beclometasone inhaler	50 mcg/dose	3.32	1.43
Salbutamol inhaler	0.1 mg/dose	2.7	1.2
Glibenclamide	5 mg tab/cap	32.09	6.06
Metformin	500 mg tab/cap	5.04	1.28
Atenolol	50 mg tab/cap	33.98	5.28
Captopril	25 mg tab/cap	14.54	3.07
Hydrochlorothiazide	25 mg tab/cap	49.48	11.22
Losartan	50 mg tab/cap	1.35	0.11
Nifedipine retard	20 mg	23.74	2.71
Carbamazepine	200 mg tab/cap	7.97	2.63
Phenytoin	100 mg tab/cap	9.92	3.95
Amitriptyline	25 mg tab/cap	7.16	3.93
Fluoxetine	20 mg tab/cap	58.86	5.32

the branded drug price (of the originator company) differs from the generic drug price may be computed by fitting the model

$$y = \beta_1 x_1 + \varepsilon$$

to the median of originator MPR (y) and median of generic MPR (x_1) data and estimating the coefficient β_1. □

The issue of estimating one of the coefficients in the linear model with multiple explanatory variables arises frequently in econometrics and clinical trial. Methods of obtaining such an estimate and its standard error are discussed in Chapters 3 and 7.

Regression analysis on the basis of a linear model is also carried out in order to statistically examine certain beliefs or hypotheses regarding the model. For instance, assuming the model (1.2) for Galton's family data, one may wish to check the notion that the father's height affects the first born son's height more than the mother's height does. The quantitative form of this statement is the hypothesis $\beta_1 > \beta_2$, which may be tested on the basis of available data. As mentioned in Example 1.3, Galton and many others in the nineteenth century were more interested in the question of possible improvement in certain traits (such as mature height) in consecutive generations. In the context of the model (1.2), this question may be formulated as the hypothesis $\beta_0 + \beta_1 x_{1m} + \beta_2 x_{2m} > x_{1m}$ for some minimum heights of the father (x_{1m}) and the mother (x_{2m}). In the case of the birth weight data of Example 1.5, the purpose of the analysis could be to check if smoking has any adverse effect on the birth weight (i.e. whether $\tau_1 < 0$), even as the mother's ethnicity and health condition have an impact on it too. Tests of statistical hypotheses are discussed in Chapters 4 and 7.

Another important use of regression analysis through the linear model is in the area of prediction. It is the need for prediction that motivates studies on human height at different ages, such as the one described in Example 1.1. There is need to predict, at every stage of the physical development of a child, not only the expected height and weight but also the normal range of height and weight. If a child is too short (stunted) or underweight, early detection can lead to timely intervention. Prediction is also necessitated in other contexts. The value of the main variable of interest (the response variable) may be impossible to obtain at the time of analysis or may involve expensive measurement. One or more readily available variables may be used as a proxy. A case in point is Example 4.36 of Chapter 4, where the amount of body fat (assessed directly through the measurements of lower abdominal adipose tissue) is sought to be predicted through waist circumference. The latter variable is more readily measurable, and may be regarded as the explanatory variable. Once the relation between the 'response' (namely, extent of adipose tissue) and the waist circumference is established through a suitable linear model, one can proceed to predict the response by simply measuring the waist circumference and using it as input to the model. See Chapters 4 and 7 for methods of prediction in the linear model. Sometimes unobserved values of the 'explanatory variables' are predicted on the basis of the corresponding response and a fitted model. This reverse prediction problem is called *calibration* (see Brown, 1993).

The linear model can also be used for comparing the means of several groups. This can be done in an observational study where there is no control over the sample size in each group, as the case may have been for the age at death of people with different professions (Example 1.4). The comparison can also be made in a designed set-up, such as the experiment to compare the efficacy of two drugs for leprosy (see Example 1.6). This example also involved a somewhat uncontrolled variable, namely the pre-treatment score, which might have a bearing on the response. There are situations where multiple influential factors are combined in a measured way to form different scenarios, so that the differential effects of the factors on the response may be identified by making use of a suitable linear model.

Example 1.9. (Abrasion of denim jeans) Jeans subjected to three types of denim treatments (pre-washed, stone-washed and enzyme washed) and three levels of laundry cycles (0, 5 and 25 cycles) were given score on abrasion resistance, where a lower score indicates higher damage. There were ten replicates for each combination of denim treatment and laundry cycles. The data, published by Card et al. (2006) are depicted in the three dimensional scatter plot of Figure 1.7. The linear model was used by the authors to identify the differential effects of the denim treatments and laundry cycles on the abrasion score. □

Chapter 6 briefly outlines the basic issues of experimental design and the analysis of data arising from such experiments.

If one of the explanatory variables is controllable, then one might ask: Which value of this variable will produce a desired level of response (within a certain margin of error)? This task, which is related to calibration, is called the *problem of control*. The linear model provides a framework for solving this problem (see Press, 2005, Chapter 14).

A somewhat related question in polynomial regression (see Example 1.10 below) is the following: How should one choose the explanatory variable(s)

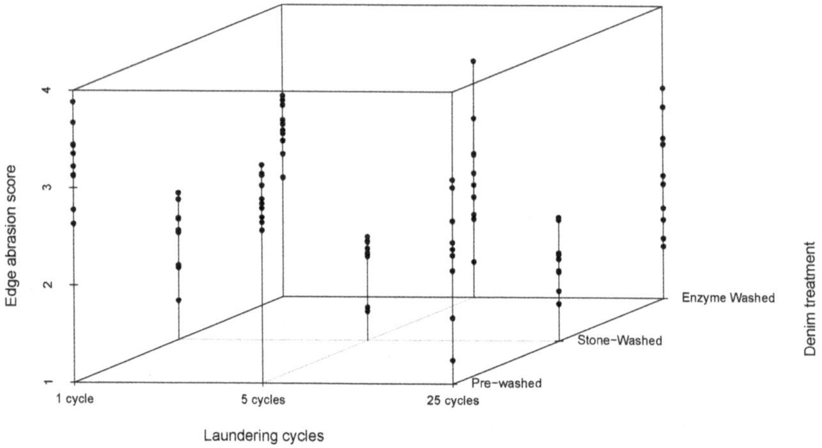

Fig. 1.7 Edge abrasion of denim jeans under different manufacturing conditions

so that the expected response is optimized? A similar question may be asked when the response is modelled as a polynomial in *several* variables. Typically there are constraints on the range of the explanatory variables. In the context of the assumed model, the problem reduces to finding the maximum or minimum of the estimated *response surface* within a certain range of the variables. An example without range constraints is given in Exercise 1.18. Various methods for response surfaces are described in detail by Khuri and Cornell (1996) and Box and Draper (1987).

The linear model is also used as a basis for imputation of missing data. The idea is to fill in the missing value using information from related variables, as in the case of prediction (see Titterington and Sedransk, 1987, for details). Diagnostic tools developed in the context of a linear model are sometimes used to detect other problems with the data such as bad or incorrect data (see Section 5.4.5).

1.4 Description of the linear model and notations

Using model (1.1) for a set of n observations of the response and explanatory variables, the equations would take the explicit form

$$y_i = \beta_0 + \beta_1 x_{i1} + \beta_2 x_{i2} + \cdots + \beta_p x_{ip} + \varepsilon_i, \quad i = 1, \ldots, n, \tag{1.3}$$

where for each i, y_i is the ith observation of the response, x_{ij} is the ith observation of the jth explanatory variable ($j = 1, 2, \ldots, k$), and ε_i is the unobservable error corresponding to this observation. For $j = 1, \ldots, k$, the parameter β_j may be interpreted as the rate of change in the average value of the response with a unit change in the jth explanatory variable, when the values of the other explanatory variables remain the same. The parameter β_0, called the intercept, may be interpreted as the average response when all the explanatory variables are zero — an interpretation that makes sense where such a model with all explanatory variables set to zero, is thought to be meaningful. Otherwise, the intercept may be regarded simply as an additional parameter that adds flexibility to the model.

The above set of n equations can be written in the following compact form using matrix and vector notations.[2]

$$\boldsymbol{y} = \boldsymbol{X}\boldsymbol{\beta} + \boldsymbol{\varepsilon}. \tag{1.4}$$

In this model

$$\boldsymbol{y} = \begin{pmatrix} y_1 \\ y_2 \\ \vdots \\ y_n \end{pmatrix}, \quad \boldsymbol{X} = \begin{pmatrix} 1 & x_{11} & \cdots & x_{1k} \\ 1 & x_{21} & \cdots & x_{2k} \\ \vdots & \vdots & \ddots & \vdots \\ 1 & x_{n1} & \cdots & x_{nk} \end{pmatrix}, \quad \boldsymbol{\beta} = \begin{pmatrix} \beta_0 \\ \beta_1 \\ \vdots \\ \beta_k \end{pmatrix}, \quad \boldsymbol{\varepsilon} = \begin{pmatrix} \varepsilon_1 \\ \varepsilon_2 \\ \vdots \\ \varepsilon_n \end{pmatrix}.$$

In order to complete the description of the model, some assumptions about the nature of the errors are necessary. It is assumed that the errors have zero mean and their variances and covariances are known up to a scale factor. These assumptions are summarized in the matrix-vector form as

$$E(\boldsymbol{\varepsilon}) = \boldsymbol{0}, \quad D(\boldsymbol{\varepsilon}) = \sigma^2 \boldsymbol{V}, \tag{1.5}$$

where the notation E stands for expected value and D represents the dispersion (or variance-covariance) matrix. The vector $\boldsymbol{0}$ denotes a vector with zero elements (in this case n elements) and $\boldsymbol{V}$ is a known matrix of order $n \times n$. The parameter σ^2 is unspecified, along with the vector parameter $\boldsymbol{\beta}$. The elements of $\boldsymbol{\beta}$ are real-valued, while σ^2 is nonnegative.

We shall use the triplet

$$(\boldsymbol{y}, \boldsymbol{X}\boldsymbol{\beta}, \sigma^2 \boldsymbol{V}) \tag{1.6}$$

as a shorthand for the linear model (1.4)–(1.5). When the errors $\varepsilon_1, \ldots, \varepsilon_n$ are uncorrelated and each has variance σ^2, we have the special case $\boldsymbol{V} = \boldsymbol{I}$,

[2]Matrices and vectors, reviewed in Appendix A, are represented by boldface letters, with uppercase letters reserved for matrices and lowercase letters for vectors. Notations introduced in that appendix are summarized in page xxi and used throughout the book.

the $n \times n$ identity matrix. We call the model $(\boldsymbol{y}, \boldsymbol{X\beta}, \sigma^2\boldsymbol{I})$ the *homoscedastic* linear model. Whenever it is necessary to stress the more general nature of the model $(\boldsymbol{y}, \boldsymbol{X\beta}, \sigma^2\boldsymbol{V})$ as compared to the homoscedastic model, we shall refer to the former model as the *general linear model.*

The values of the explanatory variables, x_{ij}, $j = 1, \ldots, k$, $i = 1, \ldots, n$ can sometimes be controlled at the time of conducting an experiment, as one would expect in the optics experiment of Example 1.2 or the conditions under which the jeans are manufactured as in Example 1.9. These could also be observed quantities beyond the control of the observer, as in the case of the heights of the parents in Example 1.3 or the pre-treatment score of leprosy patients in Example 1.6. When observed without control, the x_{ij}s may be assumed to be random, and the model (1.4)–(1.5) may be interpreted as the conditional model of $\boldsymbol{y}$ given $\boldsymbol{X}$. An explicit representation of the conditional model is

$$E(\boldsymbol{y}|\boldsymbol{X}) = \boldsymbol{X\beta}, \quad D(\boldsymbol{y}|\boldsymbol{X}) = \sigma^2\boldsymbol{V}. \tag{1.7}$$

Thus, the error term $\boldsymbol{\varepsilon}$ in (1.4) is the difference $\boldsymbol{y} - E(\boldsymbol{y}|\boldsymbol{X})$. The mean and dispersion of the error given in (1.5) should be interpreted as conditional on $\boldsymbol{X}$. The representation (1.7) is called the *linear regression model.* In this context $\boldsymbol{\beta}$ is called the vector of regression parameters or regression coefficients (see Section 2.3 for a discussion on regression).

When the matrix $\boldsymbol{X}$ in the model (1.4) has only nonstochastic elements (as one would expect in designed experiments such as Examples 1.2 and 1.9), it is generally referred to as the *design matrix.* Since this model can arise in a regression set-up, where the elements of $\boldsymbol{X}$ may be stochastic, we would prefer to use the less specific term, *model matrix.*

An important requirement of the linear regression model is that the errors $\boldsymbol{y} - E(\boldsymbol{y}|\boldsymbol{X})$ must be uncorrelated with $\boldsymbol{X}$ (see Proposition 2.15). As we noted in some examples of Section 1.1, the error term may include the effects of variables that could not be included in the model. In some other examples, imprecision of measurement is an important source of error. Thus, it is assumed that the aggregate of these effects (over and above the effect of $\boldsymbol{X}$) is uncorrelated with the included variables. This assumption is referred to as *exogeneity* in econometrics. Any violation of this assumption (*endogeneity*) has been shown to have serious consequences on inference based on the model 1.7 (see Verbeek, 2017, Chapter 5).

Suppose the observations $(y_i, x_{i1}, \ldots, x_{ip})$ for $i = 1, 2, \ldots, n$ are statistically independent (in which case $\boldsymbol{V} = \boldsymbol{I}$). Then the conditional model (1.7) can be written in the simpler form

$$\begin{aligned} E(y|x_1, x_2, \ldots, x_k) &= \beta_0 + \beta_1 x_1 + \cdots + \beta_k x_k, \\ Var(y|x_1, \ldots, x_k) &= \sigma^2, \end{aligned} \tag{1.8}$$

where $Var(\cdot)$ indicates variance, y stands for *any* of the observed responses and $x_1, \ldots, x_k$ are the corresponding explanatory variables.

1.5 Scope of the linear model

Apart from the cases where a linear model is directly applicable, as in Examples 1.2–1.9, there are other situations where it can be used after some modifications.

Example 1.10. (Polynomial regression) When there is a single explanatory variable, sometimes the mean response is sought to be explained as a polynomial function of the explanatory variable. In other words, the model is

$$y = \beta_0 + \beta_1 x + \beta_2 x^2 + \cdots + \beta_k x^k + \varepsilon,$$

where y and x are the response and the explanatory variable, respectively. This is known as the *polynomial regression model.* This model can be viewed as a special case of (1.1) with $x_j = x^j$, $j = 1, 2, \ldots, k$. Therefore, the methodology to be developed for the model (1.1) will be applicable to the polynomial regression model. □

Remark 1.11. The linear model of Example 1.10 can be viewed as a conditional model mentioned in (1.7). Once x is fixed, the mean response is being explained through the higher order power terms of this x to add flexibility. This example as well as Example 1.2 bring up an important point about a linear model. Note that the right-hand side of (1.1) is linear both in the parameters as well as in the explanatory variables. However, it is the linearity in the parameters which makes it a linear model. A model of the form (1.1) is called a linear model as long as the right-hand side is linear in the parameters — even if it is not linear in the explanatory variables.

Nonlinearity in the explanatory variables can sometimes be removed by transforming the response. A transformation which makes the model linear in the explanatory variables is called *linearization.* □

Example 1.12. (Accelerated failure time) Studies in reliability and survival analysis deal with time to failure of mechanical or biological entities.

An important problem in this area is to analyse the effect of various explanatory variables (also called *covariates* in this context) on the time to failure. A popular model stipulates that the effect of every covariate is to accelerate (or decelerate) the time to failure (t) by a factor. Specifically, $\log t$ is modelled as

$$\log t = \beta_0 + \beta_1 x_1 + \cdots + \beta_k x_k + \varepsilon,$$

where $x_1, \ldots, x_k$ are the covariates. This model is clearly of the form (1.1). The problem of inference for the accelerated failure time model is often compounded by incompleteness of the data and dependence of the covariates on time. □

Example 1.13. (Nonlinear regression) The Michaelis-Menten model for enzymic reactions states that the rate of reaction (v) is given by the formula

$$v = \frac{\kappa_0 \cdot s}{\kappa_1 + s}, \tag{1.9}$$

where s is the substrate concentration and κ_0 and κ_1 are constants. The presence of measurement error and unaccounted factors mean that the above expression for v would hold only in the approximate sense. If the approximation error is explicitly represented by an additive error term, we have the model

$$v = \frac{\kappa_0 \cdot s}{\kappa_1 + s} + \varepsilon, \tag{1.10}$$

which is not a special case of (1.1). However, if we let $y = 1/v$ and $x = 1/s$, then the approximate version of (1.9) can be rewritten as

$$y = \beta_0 + \beta_1 x + \delta, \tag{1.11}$$

where $\beta_0 = 1/\kappa_0$, $\beta_1 = \kappa_1/\kappa_0$, and δ is the approximation error. The latter model is of the form (1.1). □

Note that in the above example, the models (1.10) and (1.11) are *not* equivalent. The error in model (1.10) is $\varepsilon = v - E(v|s)$, while it is $\delta = 1/v - E(1/v|s)$ in model (1.11). If ε has zero mean, there is no reason why δ should have zero mean (see Exercise 1.3 for evidence to the contrary). If one assumes the model (1.10), then fitting this model to data would require *nonlinear regression*, which involves iterative methods. The quality of the initial iterate is often crucial to the convergence of an iterative method. A solution obtained by fitting the approximate model (1.11) may serve to produce useful initial values for κ_0 and κ_1 in this case. This method of finding initial values may be considered whenever the nonlinear model under consideration can be approximately linearized by means of a transformation. General methodology for nonlinear regression will not be discussed in this book. The interested reader may use for instance, the books by Bates and Watts (1988) or Seber and Wild (2003).

Example 1.14. (Generalized linear model) Sometimes a nonlinear function $\eta(\cdot)$ of the expected response (given the explanatory variables) is modelled as a linear function of the regression parameters. A typical model takes the form

$$\eta(E(y|x_1,\ldots,x_k)) = \beta_0 + \beta_1 x_1 + \cdots + \beta_k x_k. \tag{1.12}$$

This model is known as the *generalized linear model*, and the function η is called the *link function*, which is assumed to be known. One can define $z = \eta(y)$ and use the model

$$z = \beta_0 + \beta_1 x_1 + \cdots + \beta_k x_k + \varepsilon,$$

where the error term represents not only the errors due to measurement or ignored factors, but also the error arising from the above process of linearization. However, sometimes it may not be possible to linearize the model (see Exercise 1.16). □

The linearized model of this example is not directly used for fitting (1.12). As in the case of nonlinear regression, fitting a generalized linear model often requires iterative methods (see Section 5.7). The linearized model may be fitted in order to produce reasonable initial iterates for such a procedure.

1.6 Related models*

The term *linear model* is sometimes used in a more general sense than what we have considered here so far. From a broader perspective, any model which connects variables or their transformed versions through a linear relationship is a linear model. This description fits the generalized linear model, mentioned in the previous section. Additional examples are given below.

Example 1.15. (Autoregressive model for time series) When observations are collected sequentially at regular time intervals, the pattern of temporal dependence can be represented by the model

$$x_t = \phi_1 x_{t-1} + \phi_2 x_{t-2} + \cdots + \phi_p x_{t-p} + \varepsilon_t, \quad t \text{ is an integer}, \tag{1.13}$$

where x_t is the observation at time t, $\phi_1, \phi_2, \ldots, \phi_p$ are unspecified parameters, and ε_t is the unobservable model error at time t, which is assumed to be uncorrelated with the errors at other times. The errors are assumed to have an unspecified but constant variance. The form of the model (1.13) is very similar to (1.1). In fact, (1.13) can be viewed as a regression model where the explanatory variables are a collection of past values of the 'response' itself. Hence, it is known as the *autoregressive* model of order p, or simply AR(p). This model serves as a vehicle for *linear prediction*, that is, prediction of the future values of a variable in terms of a linear combination of its past values. The model has a wide range of applications, in areas such as economics, geology, speech and signal processing. □

A more general linear model for time series data is the *autoregressive moving average* model of order (p, q), also known as ARMA(p, q) and given by

$$x_t = \phi_1 x_{t-1} + \phi_2 x_{t-2} + \cdots + \phi_p x_{t-p} + \theta_0 \varepsilon_t + \theta_1 \varepsilon_{t-1} + \cdots + \theta_q \varepsilon_{t-q}, \quad (1.14)$$

where t is an integer.

Example 1.16. (State-space model for time series) Another important model for time series data is the state-space model, described by the pair of equations

$$\begin{aligned} \boldsymbol{x}_t &= \boldsymbol{B}_t \boldsymbol{x}_{t-1} + \boldsymbol{u}_t, \\ \boldsymbol{z}_t &= \boldsymbol{H}_t \boldsymbol{x}_t + \boldsymbol{v}_t, \end{aligned} \qquad t \text{ is an integer.} \quad (1.15)$$

Here, $\boldsymbol{z}_t$ is a vector observed at time t (the *measurement vector*), $\boldsymbol{x}_t$ is an unobservable *state vector* at time t, $\boldsymbol{B}_t$ and $\boldsymbol{H}_t$ are known matrices and $\boldsymbol{u}_t$ and $\boldsymbol{v}_t$ are vectors of model errors at time t. The first of these two equations is referred to as the *state update equation* and the second one, the *measurement equation*. This model has many important applications and will be discussed further in Section 9.1.6. □

Example 1.17. (Mixed effects linear model) In Example 1.3, we had ignored a part of Galton's data that contained heights of sons who were not first born. Mature heights of brothers could have correlation not only due the common heights of their parents, but also because of their shared upbringing. In order to account for this commonality, we can include in the model (1.2) the effect of the family. The expanded model for the matured height of a son may be written in the form

$$y = \beta_0 + \beta_1 x_1 + \beta_2 x_2 + u_1 \gamma_1 + \cdots + u_q \gamma_q + \varepsilon,$$

where q is the total number of families, and for $j = 1, 2, \ldots, q$, u_j is a binary variable indicating whether the son belongs to the jth family and γ_j is the incremental contribution of the jth family to his mature height. Note that unlike β_0, β_1 and β_2, the parameters $\gamma_1, \ldots, \gamma_q$ are themselves random. Determination of the extent of family-to-family variation in the mature height — rather than the specific values of $\gamma_1, \ldots, \gamma_q$ — may be the objective of a study. Since this model involves a combination of fixed and random parameters, it is called a *mixed effects linear model.* A general form of this model is discussed in Section 8.3. □

Example 1.18. (Simultaneous equations model) A model for the demand for food (d) is

$$d = \beta_0 + \beta_1 r + \beta_2 r_o + \beta_3 s + \varepsilon, \tag{1.16}$$

where r is the price of food, r_o is the price of other commodities, s is the income and ε is an error term. Likewise, the price r can be modelled as

$$r = \alpha_0 + \alpha_1 d + \alpha_2 w + \delta, \tag{1.17}$$

where w is an indicator of weather condition and δ is another error term. Note that both the equations are important for the study of demand and price of food, and the roles of response and explanatory variables are interchanged in the two equations. Models described by simultaneous linear equations of this kind are very important in econometrics. We shall not deal with such models in this book. The interested reader may refer to Fomby et al. (1984, Chapters 19–24). □

Inference related to the models described in this section has a close connection with that for the model (1.1). Several other issues such as model building, diagnostics, and validation are also common to all these 'linear models'. The model (1.1) — by virtue of being the simplest — serves as a common reference or benchmark for the other models.

1.7 A tour through the rest of the book

In Chapter 2 we deal with the probabilistic aspect of regression. We introduce the multivariate and the conditional normal distributions and the related distributions that are needed for inference on linear models. Subsequently we present regression as the optimal solution to a prediction problem, a linear version of this formulation and the concept of multiple correlation. We end the chapter by describing the principle of decorrelation, which would serve as a key theoretical tool in several other chapters.

In Chapter 3 we consider estimation of linear functions of $\boldsymbol{\beta}$ in the linear model $(\boldsymbol{y}, \boldsymbol{X\beta}, \sigma^2\boldsymbol{I})$. After addressing the question of estimability of linear functions of $\boldsymbol{\beta}$, we develop the theory of optimal estimation of these functions by means of linear functions of $\boldsymbol{y}$. The theory is built around linear zero functions (LZFs) — linear functions of $\boldsymbol{y}$ which have zero mean. We also show the connection of the optimal estimator with estimators obtained by the least squares method, and provide statistical interpretations of the residual sum of squares. Subsequently we introduce the ideas of reparametrization, nuisance parameters, linear restrictions and collinearity in the linear model.

While continuing with the model $(\boldsymbol{y}, \boldsymbol{X\beta}, \sigma^2\boldsymbol{I})$ in Chapter 4, we obtain confidence intervals/regions for parametric functions and tests of linear hypotheses. To this end, we discuss the sampling distribution of the estimated model parameters, and examine which linear hypotheses are testable. The generic test statistic is motivated via an intuitive decomposition of the sum of squares in terms of LZFs. Finally, we discuss the problem of prediction on the basis of the linear model, and the effect of collinearity on various aspects of inference.

Chapter 5, the biggest chapter of the book, is devoted to regression model building and diagnostics. After dealing with the issue of selection of subsets in detail, we investigate the building blocks of diagnostics, namely leverages and residuals. We use them to build diagnostic tools for violation of various assumptions of the linear model, and discuss ways of dealing with such violations. We also consider casewise diagnostics and diagnostics for detecting collinearity. Subsequently we discuss some biased estimators that are often preferred for data with collinearity. We wrap up the chapter with a section on the generalized linear model, and in particular, the logistic regression model.

In Chapter 6 we deal with the analysis of designed experiments. Some standard designs and their analyses are put in the context of the model $(\boldsymbol{y}, \boldsymbol{X\beta}, \sigma^2\boldsymbol{I})$, and the explained sum of squares is decomposed further in terms of interpretable LZFs. The chapter ends with a discussion of models where controllable and other factors are present simultaneously. Discussion in this chapter is confined to a few basic designs.

Chapter 7, which deals with the model $(\boldsymbol{y}, \boldsymbol{X\beta}, \sigma^2\boldsymbol{V})$, runs somewhat parallel to the developments of Chapters 3 and 4. We explain the importance of the general linear model, and in particular, the singular linear model. We show how the ideas used in Chapters 3 and 4 can also be used in the general case, leading to analogous results. LZFs continue to play a key role in the development and interpretations.

An issue with the analysis discussed in Chapter 7 is that the error dispersion matrix is assumed to be known, up to a constant. In Chapter 8 we relax this assumption by allowing the dispersion matrix to be known up to a few parameters. We discuss some general estimation methods in this context. Special attention is given to the cases of block diagonal error dispersion matrix, serial and spatial correlation of errors, variance components and mixed effects model. We also identify some special cases where the lack of knowledge of the error dispersion matrix may not matter very much.

We deal with updates in the general linear model in Chapter 9, as some observations are either included in or excluded from the model. We characterize the changes in terms of LZFs, which in turn throw light on the changes that take place in the statistical quantities of interest. We also outline applications of these results in various areas such as diagnostics, design and recursive prediction. Subsequently, we consider inclusion or exclusion of one or more predictors in the general linear model.

In Chapter 10 we generalize the main results of Chapter 7 to the case of the multivariate general linear model with possibly singular dispersion matrix. LZFs once again facilitate the interpretations which are similar to those given in Chapters 3, 4 and 7.

The foundational issues related to linear inference in the linear model are taken up in Chapter 11. This theoretical development parallels the classical theory of parametric inference, although no distributional assumption is necessary here. The chapter is then wrapped up with a discussion of alternative linear estimators in the linear model, geometric interpretation of optimal linear estimators in the linear model (including the singular dispersion case) and large sample properties of the estimator of Chapter 7.

Appendices A and B provide a brief summary of various linear-algebraic and statistical concepts that are needed for reading the various chapters of the book. The summary is meant to be a refresher as well as a reference for those who have already studied these topics elsewhere. We tried to make the material somewhat self-contained, so that the reader does not have to constantly refer to other sources for these basic results.

Answers to selected exercises are given in Appendix C.

1.8 Complements/Exercises

Exercises with solutions given in Appendix C

1.1 Give some examples of data sets that can be collected if needed, where the linear model may be used

(a) to predict a variable y in terms of another variable x that is more easily accessible than y;
(b) to understand the relation between two variables, x and y;
(c) to determine whether a variable x has any effect whatsoever on the mean value of a variable of interest, y;
(d) to measure the effect of a variable x_1 on the mean value of another variable y, in the presence of a third variable x_2 that might also have an effect on the mean value of y.

The answer should be in terms of four hypothetical examples for the four parts.

1.2 Consider the *piecewise linear model*

$$y = \begin{cases} \alpha_0 + \alpha_1 x + \varepsilon & \text{if } x \le x_0, \\ \beta_0 + \beta_1 x + \varepsilon & \text{if } x > x_0. \end{cases}$$

Show that if x_0 is known, this model can be rewritten as a linear model — with a suitable choice of explanatory variables. [Usually the *change point* x_0 is unknown and treated as a parameter, which means the piecewise linear model is in fact a nonlinear model.]

1.3 Consider the models (1.10) and (1.11) of Example 1.13. Show that the errors ε and δ both have zero mean only if v and $1/v$ are uncorrelated. Is this condition likely to hold?

1.4 *Cobb-Douglas model.* This model for production function postulates that the production (q) is related to labour (l) and capital (k) via the equation

$$q = a l^{\alpha} k^{\beta} \cdot u,$$

where a, α and β are unspecified constants and u is the (multiplicative) model error. The model is transformed to a linear model via a logarithmic (log) transformation of both sides of the equation. Assume that the additive error of the transformed model has zero mean. If δ is defined as $q - a l^{\alpha} k^{\beta}$, the additive error of the original model, show that this error has larger variance when the mean response of the transformed model is larger.

1.5 *Errors in variables.* Suppose for a given value of the random explanatory variable x, the response (y) is given by the linear model

$$y = \beta_0 + \beta_1 x + \varepsilon.$$

Suppose x is observed with some random error, and the observation x_o is represented by the model

$$x_o = x + \delta,$$

where δ has zero mean and is independent of ε and x.

(a) A model involving y and x_o may be obtained by eliminating x from the two equations. Show that this model is *not* a special case of (1.1), by calculating the correlation between the model error and x_o.

(b) Is the model represented by the original pair of equations a special case of any of the models considered in this chapter?

1.6 Suppose the effectiveness of a new drug (for which there is no competitor) is studied in the following way. A random sample of 10 clinics is selected without replacement from all the clinics in the country, and a random sample of 10 patients is selected without replacement from these clinics. The selected patients are administered the drug and the 'improvement in status' is recorded. The model for this response is

$$y_{ij} = \mu + \delta_i + \varepsilon_{ij}, \quad i, j = 1, \ldots, 10,$$

where μ is a constant, δ_i is the effect of the ith clinic, and ε_{ij} is a random term corresponding to the jth patient of the ith clinic. The objective of the study is to measure the average 'improvement in status', irrespective of the clinic. Should the δ_is be modelled as fixed parameters or random quantities? Which parameter of this model should be the focus of inference? Identify the model from among all those considered in this chapter for which the above model is a special case.

Additional exercises

1.7 The salary (y) of an employee in an organization is modelled as

$$y = \beta_0 + \beta_1 x_1 + \beta_2 x_2 + \beta_3 x_3 + \beta_4 x_4 + \varepsilon,$$

where x_1 and x_2 are binary indicators of graduation from high-school and college, respectively, x_3 is the indicator of at least one post-graduate degree, x_4 is the number of years in service and ε is the error term of the model.

(a) What are the possible sources of the model error?
(b) Interpret the parameters $\beta_0, \ldots, \beta_4$.
(c) Which constraints on the parameters correspond to the hypothesis: 'salary does not depend on the educational background'?

1.8 For the polynomial regression model of Example 1.10, interpret the parameter β_0. What does the hypothesis $\beta_2 = 0$ signify?

1.9 *Signal detection.* An important problem of optical and electrical communication is to detect whether a 'signal' is present in a sequence of observations, which is modelled as

$$y_t = a\cos(2\pi f t + \phi) + \varepsilon_t, \quad t = 1, 2, \ldots, n,$$

where t is the time index, $a\cos(2\pi f t + \phi)$ is a sinusoidal function of t (called *signal*) having amplitude a, frequency f and phase ϕ, and ε_t is the error at time t (called *noise*). If a is zero, the observations consist only of noise, i.e. there is no signal. Assuming that the frequency is known, show that the above *signal plus noise model* with unspecified amplitude and phase reduces to (1.3) after a suitable transformation of the parameters. What are the explanatory variables of this linear model? Formulate the hypothesis of 'no signal' in terms of the parameters of the linear model.

1.10 Table 1.2 gives men's and women's world record times for various outdoor running distances, recognized by the International Association of Athletics Federations (IAAF) as of 17 November, 2017. It may be

Table 1.2 World record running times data (data object `worldrecord` in R package `lmreg`, source: International Association of Athletics Federations, `https://www.iaaf.org/records/by-category/world-records`)

Running distance (meters)	Men's record (seconds)	Women's record (seconds)
100	9.58	10.49
200	19.19	21.34
400	43.03	47.60
800	100.91	113.28
1000	131.96	148.98
1500	206.00	230.07
2000	284.79	323.75
3000	440.67	486.11
5000	757.35	851.15
10000	1577.53	1757.45

assumed that the log of the record time is approximately a linear function of the log of the running distance.

(a) Identify the matrix and vectors of (1.4) if a linear model is used for the men's log-record times and another one for the women's log-record times.

(b) Construct a single 'grand model' with four parameters which can be used as a substitute for these two models, and identify the corresponding matrix and vectors.

1.11 (a) If a single linear model is used for all the log-record times for the data of Table 1.2, and the gender effect is represented by an additional (binary) explanatory variable, then identify the matrix and vectors of (1.4).

(b) Identify a constraint on the parameters of the 'grand model' of Exercise 1.10 which would make it equivalent to the model of part (a).

1.12 Table 1.3 gives the midyear population of the world for the years 1981–2000. Suppose a linear model is used to express the world population approximately in terms of the year. Identify the matrix and vectors of (1.4), and interpret the parameters β_0 and β_1.

1.13 If the linear model of Exercise 1.2 is used for the world population data of Table 1.3 with x_0 chosen as the year 1990, and the model is expressed as (1.4), identify the matrix and the vectors.

1.14 According to the piecewise linear model of Exercise 1.2, $E(y|x)$ may be discontinuous at x_0. Observe that the discontinuity disappears if the

Table 1.3 World population data (data object `worldpop` in R package `lmreg`, source: U.S. Census Bureau, International Data Base, `http://www.census.gov/ipc/ www/idbnew.html`)

Year	Population (billion)	Year	Population (billion)
1981	4.533	1991	5.367
1982	4.613	1992	5.450
1983	4.694	1993	5.531
1984	4.774	1994	5.611
1985	4.855	1995	5.691
1986	4.938	1996	5.769
1987	5.024	1997	5.847
1988	5.110	1998	5.925
1989	5.196	1999	6.003
1990	5.284	2000	6.080

restriction $\beta_0 - \alpha_0 = (\alpha_1 - \beta_1)x_0$ is imposed. Rewrite this continuous, piecewise linear model as another linear model — with a suitable choice of explanatory variables.

1.15 If the linear model of Exercise 1.14 is used for the world population data of Table 1.3 with x_0 chosen as the year 1990, and the model is expressed as (1.4), identify the matrix and vectors.

1.16 *Logistic regression model.* Suppose the response is a binary variable whose conditional mean (π) given the explanatory variables $x_1, \ldots, x_k$ is given by the equation

$$\log\left(\frac{\pi}{1-\pi}\right) = \beta_0 + \beta_1 x_1 + \cdots + \beta_k x_k.$$

Is this model a special case of any of the models discussed in this chapter? Can it be linearized by a suitable transformation of the response?

1.17 The manufacturer of a medicine for common cold claims that this medicine provides 30% longer relief than that provided by a competing brand. In order to test this claim, an experiment is conducted with a number of adult volunteers who were given a standard dose of one medicine or the other. The duration of relief was measured, and other possibly influencing factors such as gender were recorded too. Is it possible to formulate the problem in such a way that the manufacturer's claim amounts to a simple condition on the parameters of a linear model which may be fitted to the above data?

1.18 *Response surface.* Consider the quadratic regression model

$$y = \beta_0 + \beta_1 x + \beta_2 x^2 + \varepsilon, \quad Var(\varepsilon) = \sigma^2,$$

with independent observations. If $\beta_2 > 0$, determine the value of x which will minimize the expected response.

[See Exercise 4.12 for estimation of this value from data.]

Chapter 2

Regression and the Normal Distribution

The regression method may be considered as a way of approximating a random variable of interest, as a function of several other related random variables. This task can only be effective if there is some sort of dependence between the variable of interest (called the response) and the approximating (or explanatory) variables. We will assume here that there is such a stochastic dependence, and that the realized values of the explanatory variables are observed, while the corresponding value of the response is unknown and is to be assessed. In such a situation, we try to identify the best possible approximation, and study its properties under certain assumptions.

As we shall see in this chapter, the nature of the 'best' approximation depends on the joint distribution of the response and the explanatory variables. In many cases, the functional form of the approximation may be known or surmised structurally (e.g. as a linear function), although the specific function in a given case may still involve a few unknown quantities, called the parameters. These parameters need to be inferred empirically from the data. This crucial exercise of inferring the parameters, when this functional form is linear, is done in the next two chapters.

The multivariate normal distribution is sometimes used as an overarching model controlling the pattern of dependence between the response and the explanatory variables. Therefore we begin with a discussion of the multivariate normal distribution as a prelude to studying regression. In this chapter, as well as throughout the book, we do not make a notational distinction between a random vector and a particular realization of it, just to keep the notations simple.

2.1 Multivariate normal and related distributions

2.1.1 *Matrix of variances and covariances*

For a given random vector $\boldsymbol{u}$, we denote the expected value and variance-covariance matrix (also known as the dispersion matrix) as $E(\boldsymbol{u})$ and $D(\boldsymbol{u})$, respectively. For an ordered pair of random vectors $\boldsymbol{u}$ and $\boldsymbol{v}$, we denote[1] the matrix of covariances by $Cov(\boldsymbol{u}, \boldsymbol{v})$, that is,

$$Cov(\boldsymbol{u}, \boldsymbol{v}) = E[\{\boldsymbol{u} - E(\boldsymbol{u})\}\{\boldsymbol{v} - E(\boldsymbol{v})\}'].$$

According to this notation, $D(\boldsymbol{u}) = Cov(\boldsymbol{u}, \boldsymbol{u})$, and $Cov(\boldsymbol{v}, \boldsymbol{u}) = Cov(\boldsymbol{u}, \boldsymbol{v})'$. It is easy to see that $Cov(\boldsymbol{A}\boldsymbol{u}, \boldsymbol{B}\boldsymbol{v}) = \boldsymbol{A}Cov(\boldsymbol{u}, \boldsymbol{v})\boldsymbol{B}'$ and $D(\boldsymbol{A}\boldsymbol{u}) = \boldsymbol{A}D(\boldsymbol{u})\boldsymbol{A}'$.

In particular, for any constant (nonrandom) vector $\boldsymbol{l}$ having the same order as $\boldsymbol{u}$, the variance of $\boldsymbol{l}'\boldsymbol{u}$ (denoted by $Var(\boldsymbol{l}'\boldsymbol{u})$) is $\boldsymbol{l}'D(\boldsymbol{u})\boldsymbol{l}$. Since this variance is nonnegative for any constant vector $\boldsymbol{l}$, all dispersion matrices are nonnegative definite. Also, as the interchange between any pair of random variables does not change the covariance between them, a dispersion matrix is symmetric. Symmetric and nonnegative matrices have a spectral decomposition with nonnegative eigenvalues. Consequently, every dispersion matrix can be factored as $\boldsymbol{C}\boldsymbol{C}'$ (see Section A.5 for decompositions of matrices). If a dispersion matrix is of full rank, then it is positive definite, and the matrix $\boldsymbol{C}$ in the above decomposition is invertible. A singular dispersion matrix is positive semidefinite. Some useful properties of singular dispersion matrices will be discussed in Section 2.2.

Suppose

$$\boldsymbol{u} = \begin{pmatrix} u_1 \\ u_2 \\ \vdots \\ u_m \end{pmatrix}, \quad D(\boldsymbol{u}) = \boldsymbol{\Sigma} = \begin{pmatrix} \sigma_1^2 & \sigma_{12} & \cdots & \sigma_{1m} \\ \sigma_{21} & \sigma_2^2 & \cdots & \sigma_{2m} \\ \vdots & \vdots & \ddots & \vdots \\ \sigma_{m1} & \sigma_{m2} & \cdots & \sigma_m^2 \end{pmatrix}.$$

Then for $i, j = 1, 2, \ldots, m$, $Cov(u_i, u_j) = \sigma_{ij} = \sigma_{ji}$, and the correlation between u_i and u_j is $\rho_{ij} = \sigma_{ij}/(\sigma_i\sigma_j)$. It follows that $\boldsymbol{\Sigma}$ can be factored as

$$\boldsymbol{\Sigma} = \begin{pmatrix} \sigma_1 & 0 & \cdots & 0 \\ 0 & \sigma_2 & \cdots & 0 \\ \vdots & \vdots & \ddots & \vdots \\ 0 & 0 & \cdots & \sigma_m \end{pmatrix} \begin{pmatrix} 1 & \rho_{12} & \cdots & \rho_{1m} \\ \rho_{21} & 1 & \cdots & \rho_{2m} \\ \vdots & \vdots & \ddots & \vdots \\ \rho_{m1} & \rho_{m2} & \cdots & 1 \end{pmatrix} \begin{pmatrix} \sigma_1 & 0 & \cdots & 0 \\ 0 & \sigma_2 & \cdots & 0 \\ \vdots & \vdots & \ddots & \vdots \\ 0 & 0 & \cdots & \sigma_m \end{pmatrix}. \tag{2.1}$$

[1]The matrix and vector notations used in this book is summarized in page xxi.

The matrix in the middle of the right-hand side is the correlation matrix of $\boldsymbol{u}$, which is multiplied on both sides with the diagonal matrix consisting of the standard deviations, to get $\boldsymbol{\Sigma}$.

2.1.2 *The multivariate normal distribution*

Definition 2.1. The random vector $\boldsymbol{y}$ is said to have the multivariate normal distribution if, for every fixed vector $\boldsymbol{t}$ having the same order as $\boldsymbol{y}$, the random variable $\boldsymbol{t}'\boldsymbol{y}$ has the univariate normal distribution. □

Suppose the random vector $\boldsymbol{y}$ has the multivariate normal distribution, such that $E(\boldsymbol{y}) = \boldsymbol{\mu}$ and $D(\boldsymbol{y}) = \boldsymbol{\Sigma}$. It follows from the definition that for any fixed vector $\boldsymbol{t}$ having order n, $\boldsymbol{t}'\boldsymbol{y}$ is univariate normal with mean $\boldsymbol{t}'\boldsymbol{\mu}$ and variance $\boldsymbol{t}'\boldsymbol{\Sigma t}$, so that the characteristic function of $\boldsymbol{y}$ is $E(\exp[i\boldsymbol{t}'\boldsymbol{y}]) = \exp[i\boldsymbol{t}'\boldsymbol{\mu} - \boldsymbol{t}'\boldsymbol{\Sigma t}/2]$. Thus, the multivariate normal distribution is completely characterized by the mean vector and the dispersion matrix. We use the notation $\boldsymbol{y} \sim N(\boldsymbol{\mu}, \boldsymbol{\Sigma})$ to indicate that $\boldsymbol{y}$ has the multivariate normal distribution with mean $\boldsymbol{\mu}$ and dispersion matrix $\boldsymbol{\Sigma}$.

When $\boldsymbol{\Sigma} = \sigma^2\boldsymbol{I}$, the characteristic function of $\boldsymbol{y} \sim N(\boldsymbol{\mu}, \boldsymbol{\Sigma})$ factorizes into the characteristic functions of the univariate normal distributions of the elements of $\boldsymbol{y}$. Therefore, in this case, the elements of $\boldsymbol{y}$ are independent normal variates. Let $\boldsymbol{y} = (y_1 \cdots y_n)'$ and $\boldsymbol{\mu} = (\mu_1 \cdots \mu_n)$. Then, the density of $\boldsymbol{y}$ is the product of their marginal densities,

$$\begin{aligned} f(\boldsymbol{y}) &= \prod_{j=1}^{n} \frac{1}{(2\pi\sigma^2)^{1/2}} \exp\left[-\frac{(y_i - \mu_i)^2}{2\sigma^2}\right] \\ &= (2\pi\sigma^2)^{-n/2} \exp[-\tfrac{1}{2}\sigma^{-2}(\boldsymbol{y} - \boldsymbol{\mu})'(\boldsymbol{y} - \boldsymbol{\mu})]. \end{aligned} \tag{2.2}$$

In general, $\boldsymbol{\Sigma}$ can be any nonnegative definite matrix (not necessarily of the form $\sigma^2\boldsymbol{I}$). Assuming that $\boldsymbol{\Sigma}$ is full-rank, i.e. nonsingular, it can be factored as $\boldsymbol{CC}'$, where $\boldsymbol{C}$ is also a nonsingular matrix. It is easy to see that $\boldsymbol{C}^{-1}\boldsymbol{y} \sim N(\boldsymbol{C}^{-1}\boldsymbol{\mu}, \boldsymbol{I})$. The density of $\boldsymbol{y}$, obtained by linear transformation from the density of $\boldsymbol{C}^{-1}\boldsymbol{y}$, is (see Exercise 2.1)

$$f(\boldsymbol{y}) = (2\pi)^{-n/2}|\boldsymbol{\Sigma}|^{-1/2} \exp[-\tfrac{1}{2}(\boldsymbol{y} - \boldsymbol{\mu})'\boldsymbol{\Sigma}^{-1}(\boldsymbol{y} - \boldsymbol{\mu})]. \tag{2.3}$$

Example 2.2. (Bivariate normal distribution) Suppose the pair of random variables x and y have the bivariate normal distribution, with

$$\boldsymbol{y} = \begin{pmatrix} x \\ y \end{pmatrix}, \qquad \boldsymbol{\mu} = \begin{pmatrix} \mu_x \\ \mu_y \end{pmatrix}, \qquad \boldsymbol{\Sigma} = \begin{pmatrix} \sigma_x^2 & \sigma_{xy} \\ \sigma_{xy} & \sigma_y^2 \end{pmatrix}.$$

The parameters of the marginal distributions can be written as

$$E(x) = \mu_x, \quad E(y) = \mu_y, \quad Var(x) = \sigma_x^2, \quad Var(y) = \sigma_y^2,$$

and the correlation between x and y is $\rho = \sigma_{xy}/(\sigma_x\sigma_y)$. It follows that

$$|\boldsymbol{\Sigma}| = \sigma_x^2\sigma_y^2 - \sigma_{xy}^2 = \sigma_x^2\sigma_y^2(1-\rho^2),$$

$$\boldsymbol{\Sigma}^{-1} = \frac{1}{|\boldsymbol{\Sigma}|}\begin{pmatrix} \sigma_y^2 & -\sigma_{xy} \\ -\sigma_{xy} & \sigma_x^2 \end{pmatrix} = \frac{1}{1-\rho^2}\begin{pmatrix} \frac{1}{\sigma_x^2} & -\frac{\rho}{\sigma_x\sigma_y} \\ -\frac{\rho}{\sigma_x\sigma_y} & \frac{1}{\sigma_y^2} \end{pmatrix}.$$

Therefore,

$$(\boldsymbol{y}-\boldsymbol{\mu})'\boldsymbol{\Sigma}^{-1}(\boldsymbol{y}-\boldsymbol{\mu}) = \frac{1}{1-\rho^2}\left[\left(\frac{x-\mu_x}{\sigma_x}\right)^2 + \left(\frac{y-\mu_y}{\sigma_y}\right)^2 - 2\rho\left(\frac{x-\mu_x}{\sigma_x}\right)\left(\frac{y-\mu_y}{\sigma_y}\right)\right].$$

Thus, the bivariate normal density function is given by

$$f(x,y) = \frac{1}{2\pi\sigma_x\sigma_y\sqrt{1-\rho^2}}\exp\left[-\frac{1}{2(1-\rho^2)}\left\{\left(\frac{x-\mu_x}{\sigma_x}\right)^2 + \left(\frac{y-\mu_y}{\sigma_y}\right)^2 - 2\rho\left(\frac{x-\mu_x}{\sigma_x}\right)\left(\frac{y-\mu_y}{\sigma_y}\right)\right\}\right]. \quad (2.4)$$

When $\rho = 0$, $f(x,y)$ reduces to the product of the marginal densities. Thus, uncorrelated random variables, if jointly normal, are independent. □

2.1.3 *The conditional normal distribution*

Let $\boldsymbol{y} \sim N(\boldsymbol{\mu}, \boldsymbol{\Sigma})$ and

$$\boldsymbol{y} = \begin{pmatrix} \boldsymbol{y}_1 \\ \boldsymbol{y}_2 \end{pmatrix}, \quad \boldsymbol{\mu} = \begin{pmatrix} \boldsymbol{\mu}_1 \\ \boldsymbol{\mu}_2 \end{pmatrix}, \quad \boldsymbol{\Sigma} = \begin{pmatrix} \boldsymbol{\Sigma}_{11} & \boldsymbol{\Sigma}_{12} \\ \boldsymbol{\Sigma}_{21} & \boldsymbol{\Sigma}_{22} \end{pmatrix},$$

where the partitions correspond to one another. If $\boldsymbol{\Sigma}_{11}$ is nonsingular, then it can be shown that the conditional distribution of $\boldsymbol{y}_2$ given $\boldsymbol{y}_1$ is normal with mean and dispersion given by (see Proposition 2.14 below for the proof of a more general result)

$$E(\boldsymbol{y}_2|\boldsymbol{y}_1) = \boldsymbol{\mu}_2 + \boldsymbol{\Sigma}_{21}\boldsymbol{\Sigma}_{11}^{-1}(\boldsymbol{y}_1 - \boldsymbol{\mu}_1), \quad (2.5)$$

$$D(\boldsymbol{y}_2|\boldsymbol{y}_1) = \boldsymbol{\Sigma}_{22} - \boldsymbol{\Sigma}_{21}\boldsymbol{\Sigma}_{11}^{-1}\boldsymbol{\Sigma}_{12}. \quad (2.6)$$

We would denote this conditional distribution as

$$\boldsymbol{y}_2|\boldsymbol{y}_1 \sim N(\boldsymbol{\mu}_2 + \boldsymbol{\Sigma}_{21}\boldsymbol{\Sigma}_{11}^{-1}, \boldsymbol{\Sigma}_{22} - \boldsymbol{\Sigma}_{21}\boldsymbol{\Sigma}_{11}^{-1}).$$

Observe that the conditional mean is linear in $\boldsymbol{y}_1$, while the conditional dispersion does not depend on $\boldsymbol{y}_1$. If $\boldsymbol{\Sigma}_{12} = \mathbf{0}$, this density does not depend on $\boldsymbol{y}_1$ (thus coinciding with the unconditional density of $\boldsymbol{y}_2$). This confirms that two random vectors, which are jointly multivariate normal, happen to be independent of one another if and only if they are uncorrelated.

Example 2.3. (Bivariate normal distribution, continued) By identifying $\boldsymbol{y}_1$ and $\boldsymbol{y}_2$ with x and y, respectively, and using the notations of Example 2.2, we have (2.5) and (2.6) simplifying to

$$E(y|x) = \mu_y + \rho\frac{\sigma_y}{\sigma_x}(x - \mu_x), \tag{2.7}$$

$$Var(y|x) = (1 - \rho^2)\sigma_y^2. \tag{2.8}$$

The conditional variance of y given x is generally smaller than the unconditional variance σ_y^2, and these are equal when $\rho = 0$. In that case, the conditional mean is the same as the unconditional mean. □

Example 2.4. Consider the conditional distribution of the random variable y given the random vector $\boldsymbol{x}$, derived from their joint distribution, assumed to be normal. Using the notations $\boldsymbol{\mu}_x$, μ_y, $\boldsymbol{\Sigma}_{xx}$ $\boldsymbol{\sigma}_{xy}$ and σ_y^2 for $E(\boldsymbol{x})$, $E(y)$, $D(\boldsymbol{x})$, $Cov(\boldsymbol{x}, y)$ and $Var(y)$, respectively, we have (2.5) and (2.6) reducing to

$$E(y|\boldsymbol{x}) = \mu_y + \boldsymbol{\sigma}_{xy}'\boldsymbol{\Sigma}_{xx}^{-1}(\boldsymbol{x} - \boldsymbol{\mu}_x), \tag{2.9}$$

$$Var(y|\boldsymbol{x}) = \sigma_y^2 - \boldsymbol{\sigma}_{xy}'\boldsymbol{\Sigma}_{xx}^{-1}\boldsymbol{\sigma}_{xy}. \tag{2.10}$$

Once again, the conditional variance of y given $\boldsymbol{x}$ is generally smaller than the unconditional variance σ_y^2, except when $\boldsymbol{\sigma}_{xy} = 0$, in which case $E(y|\boldsymbol{x}) = \mu_y$. As in (2.8), the conditional variance (2.10) may be expressed as a fraction of the unconditional variance, i.e. as $(1 - \rho^2)\sigma_y^2$. The fraction

$$\rho^2 = \frac{\boldsymbol{\sigma}_{xy}'\boldsymbol{\Sigma}_{xx}^{-1}\boldsymbol{\sigma}_{xy}}{\sigma_y^2},$$

which is analogous to the squared correlation in (2.8), is called the squared multiple correlation coefficient of y with the random vector $\boldsymbol{x}$. This concept will be discussed further in Section 2.5. □

The conditional dispersion matrix (2.6) can be factored, in the manner described in Section 2.1.1, into matrices consisting of standard deviations and correlations. The correlations arising from this conditional covariance matrix (2.6) are different from the (unconditional) correlations among the pairs of members of $\boldsymbol{y}_2$, and are called *partial correlations* given $\boldsymbol{y}_1$. These partial correlations are attributes of the joint dispersion matrix $\boldsymbol{\Sigma}$ and are well-defined even when the joint distribution is not normal.

Example 2.5. Let the dispersion matrix of the random variables y_1, y_2 and y_3 be

$$\begin{pmatrix} 1 & 0.5 & 0.5 \\ 0.5 & 1 & 0.25 \\ 0.5 & 0.25 & 1 \end{pmatrix},$$

where the correlation matrix is the dispersion matrix itself. It follows from (2.6) that the partial correlation between y_2 and y_3 given y_1 is 0, even though their correlation is 0.25.

On the other hand, if the correlation between y_2 and y_3 is 0 (rather than 0.25), and the other parameters are as above, then the partial correlation between y_2 and y_3 given y_1 turns out to be $-1/3$. □

2.1.4 *Related distributions*

If $\boldsymbol{y} \sim N(\boldsymbol{\mu}, \boldsymbol{\Sigma})$ and $\boldsymbol{L}$ is a nonrandom matrix with n columns, then it follows from the definition of the multivariate normal distribution that $\boldsymbol{Ly}$ is multivariate normal with with mean and dispersion that can be easily calculated. Indeed, one can write the characteristic function of $\boldsymbol{Ly}$ as

$$\begin{aligned} E(\exp[i\boldsymbol{t}'\boldsymbol{Ly}]) = E(\exp[i(\boldsymbol{L}'\boldsymbol{t})'\boldsymbol{y}]) &= \exp[i(\boldsymbol{L}'\boldsymbol{t})'\boldsymbol{\mu} - (\boldsymbol{L}'\boldsymbol{t})'\boldsymbol{\Sigma}(\boldsymbol{L}'\boldsymbol{t})/2] \\ &= \exp[i\boldsymbol{t}'(\boldsymbol{L\mu}) - \boldsymbol{t}'(\boldsymbol{L\Sigma L}')\boldsymbol{t})/2]. \end{aligned}$$

This shows, $\boldsymbol{Ly} \sim N(\boldsymbol{L\mu}, \boldsymbol{L\Sigma L}')$. Other functions of $\boldsymbol{y}$ lead to several important distributions, that would be useful later.

Definition 2.6. A random variable q is said to have the chi-square distribution with n degrees of freedom (written formally as $q \sim \chi^2_n$) if q can be written as $\boldsymbol{y}'\boldsymbol{y}$, where $\boldsymbol{y}_{n\times 1} \sim N(\boldsymbol{0}, \boldsymbol{I})$. □

Definition 2.7. A random variable u is said to have the student's t-distribution with n degrees of freedom (written formally as $u \sim t_n$) if u can be written as $y/\sqrt{z/n}$, where $y \sim N(0,1)$, $z \sim \chi^2_n$ and y and z are independent random variables. □

Definition 2.8. A random variable v is said to have the F distribution with n_1 and n_2 degrees of freedom (written formally as $v \sim F_{n_1,n_2}$) if v can be written as $\frac{z_1/n_1}{z_2/n_2}$, where $z_1 \sim \chi^2_{n_1}$, $z_2 \sim \chi^2_{n_2}$ and z_1 and z_2 are independent random variables. □

Remark 2.9. *(Noncentral distributions)* If the normal distribution mentioned in definitions 2.6–2.7 has nonzero mean, then the resulting distributions are said to be *noncentral.* Specifically, if $\boldsymbol{y}_{n\times 1} \sim N(\boldsymbol{\mu}, \boldsymbol{I})$, then $q = \boldsymbol{y}'\boldsymbol{y}$ is said to have the noncentral chi-square distribution with n degrees of freedom and noncentrality parameter $\boldsymbol{\mu}'\boldsymbol{\mu}$ (written formally as $q \sim \chi^2_n(\boldsymbol{\mu}'\boldsymbol{\mu})$). If $y \sim N(\mu, 1)$, $z \sim \chi^2_n$ and y and z are independent then $u = y/\sqrt{z/n}$ is said to have the noncentral student's t-distribution with n degrees of freedom and noncentrality parameter μ (written formally as $u \sim t_n(\mu)$). Finally, if $z_1 \sim \chi^2_{n_1}(c)$, $z_2 \sim \chi^2_{n_2}$ and z_1 and z_2 are independent random variables, then $v = \frac{z_1/n_1}{z_2/n_2}$ is said to have the noncentral F distribution with n_1 and n_2 degrees of freedom and noncentrality parameter c (written formally as $v \sim F_{n_1,n_2}(c)$). □

The next two propositions show that the chi-squares distribution arises not only from a sum of squares of normal random variables with unit variance, but also from certain quadratic forms involving a vector of normal random variables.

Proposition 2.10. (Fisher-Cochran Theorem)*Let $\boldsymbol{y}_{n\times 1} \sim N(\boldsymbol{\mu}, \boldsymbol{I})$ and $\boldsymbol{y}'\boldsymbol{A}_1\boldsymbol{y}, \ldots, \boldsymbol{y}'\boldsymbol{A}_r\boldsymbol{y}$ be quadratic forms whose sum is equal to $\boldsymbol{y}'\boldsymbol{y}$. Then $\boldsymbol{y}'\boldsymbol{A}_i\boldsymbol{y} \sim \chi^2_{\rho(A_i)}(\lambda_i)$ for $i = 1, \ldots, r$ and are independent if and only if $\sum_{i=1}^r \rho(\boldsymbol{A}_i) = n$, in which case $\lambda_i = \boldsymbol{\mu}'\boldsymbol{A}_i\boldsymbol{\mu}$, $i = 1, \ldots, r$, and $\sum_{i=1}^r \lambda_i = \boldsymbol{\mu}'\boldsymbol{\mu}$.*

Proof. Suppose $\boldsymbol{y}'\boldsymbol{A}_i\boldsymbol{y} \sim \chi^2_{\rho(A_i)}(\lambda_i)$ for $i = 1, \ldots, r$ and are independent. It follows that for $i = 1, \ldots, r$ there is $\boldsymbol{x}_i \sim N(\boldsymbol{\mu}_i, \boldsymbol{I})$ such that $\boldsymbol{x}_i'\boldsymbol{x}_i = \boldsymbol{y}'\boldsymbol{A}_i\boldsymbol{y}$ and $\lambda_i = \boldsymbol{\mu}_i'\boldsymbol{\mu}_i$. Let $\boldsymbol{x} = (\boldsymbol{x}_1' : \cdots : \boldsymbol{x}_r')'$. Then

$$\boldsymbol{x}'\boldsymbol{x} \sim \chi^2_{\sum_{i=1}^r \rho(A_i)}\left(\sum_{i=1}^r \lambda_i\right) \quad \text{and } \boldsymbol{y}'\boldsymbol{y} \sim \chi^2_n(\boldsymbol{\mu}'\boldsymbol{\mu}).$$

Since $\boldsymbol{x}'\boldsymbol{x} = \boldsymbol{y}'\boldsymbol{y}$, by comparing the distributions of these we conclude that $\sum_{i=1}^r \rho(\boldsymbol{A}_i) = n$.

To prove the converse, let $\sum_{i=1}^r \rho(\boldsymbol{A}_i) = n$ and $\boldsymbol{B}_i\boldsymbol{C}_i'$ be a rank-factorization of $\boldsymbol{A}_i$, $i = 1, \ldots, r$. Also let $\boldsymbol{B} = (\boldsymbol{B}_1 : \cdots : \boldsymbol{B}_r)$ and $\boldsymbol{C} = (\boldsymbol{C}_1 : \cdots : \boldsymbol{C}_r)$. The condition $\sum_{i=1}^r \rho(\boldsymbol{A}_i) = n$ ensures that $\boldsymbol{B}$ and $\boldsymbol{C}$ are $n \times n$ matrices. Further,

$$\boldsymbol{y}'\boldsymbol{y} = \sum_{i=1}^r \boldsymbol{y}'\boldsymbol{A}_i\boldsymbol{y} = \sum_{i=1}^r \boldsymbol{y}'\boldsymbol{B}_i\boldsymbol{C}_i'\boldsymbol{y} = \boldsymbol{y}'\boldsymbol{B}\boldsymbol{C}'\boldsymbol{y} \quad \forall\, \boldsymbol{y}.$$

We can assume without loss of generality that $\boldsymbol{A}_1, \ldots, \boldsymbol{A}_r$ are symmetric. Hence, $\boldsymbol{BC}'$ is symmetric. Choosing $\boldsymbol{y}$ in the above equation as one eigenvector of $\boldsymbol{BC}'$ at a time, it is easily seen that all the eigenvalues of this matrix are equal to 1. Therefore, $\boldsymbol{BC}' = \boldsymbol{I}$, i.e. $\boldsymbol{C}' = \boldsymbol{B}^{-1}$. It follows that $\boldsymbol{C}'\boldsymbol{B} = \boldsymbol{I}$. By comparing the blocks of the two sides of this matrix identity, we conclude that $\boldsymbol{C}_i'\boldsymbol{B}_i = \boldsymbol{I}$ for $i = 1, \ldots, r$. Consequently, $\boldsymbol{B}_i\boldsymbol{C}_i'\boldsymbol{B}_i\boldsymbol{C}_i' = \boldsymbol{B}_i\boldsymbol{C}_i'$, i.e. $\boldsymbol{A}_1, \ldots, \boldsymbol{A}_r$ are symmetric and idempotent matrices. Without loss of generality we can choose $\boldsymbol{C}_i = \boldsymbol{B}_i$ for $i = 1, \ldots, r$. Since $\boldsymbol{BB}' = \boldsymbol{BC}' = \boldsymbol{I}$, $\boldsymbol{B}$ is an orthogonal matrix. Consequently, $\boldsymbol{B}'\boldsymbol{y} \sim N(\boldsymbol{B}'\boldsymbol{\mu}, \boldsymbol{I})$. It follows that $\boldsymbol{B}_i'\boldsymbol{y} \sim N(\boldsymbol{B}_i'\boldsymbol{\mu}, \boldsymbol{I})$ for $i = 1, \ldots, r$ and that these are independent. Independence and the stated distributions of $\boldsymbol{y}'\boldsymbol{A}_1\boldsymbol{y}, \ldots, \boldsymbol{y}'\boldsymbol{A}_r\boldsymbol{y}$ follow from Remark 2.9, which also implies the facts that $\lambda_i = \boldsymbol{\mu}'\boldsymbol{A}_i\boldsymbol{\mu}$, $i = 1, \ldots, r$. Finally,

$$\sum_{i=1}^{r} \boldsymbol{\mu}'\boldsymbol{A}_i\boldsymbol{\mu} = \sum_{i=1}^{r} \boldsymbol{\mu}'\boldsymbol{B}_i\boldsymbol{B}_i'\boldsymbol{\mu} = \boldsymbol{\mu}'\boldsymbol{BB}'\boldsymbol{\mu} = \boldsymbol{\mu}'\boldsymbol{\mu}. \qquad \square$$

Proposition 2.11. *Suppose* $\boldsymbol{y}_{n\times 1} \sim N(\boldsymbol{\mu}, \boldsymbol{I})$, $\boldsymbol{A}$ *and* $\boldsymbol{B}$ *are idempotent matrices of order* $n \times n$ *and* $\boldsymbol{C}$ *is any matrix of order* $m \times n$.

(a) $\boldsymbol{y}'\boldsymbol{A}\boldsymbol{y} \sim \chi^2_{\rho(A)}(\boldsymbol{\mu}'\boldsymbol{A}\boldsymbol{\mu})$.
(b) $\boldsymbol{y}'\boldsymbol{A}\boldsymbol{y}$ *and* $\boldsymbol{y}'\boldsymbol{B}\boldsymbol{y}$ *are independently distributed if and only if* $\boldsymbol{AB} = \boldsymbol{0}$.
(c) $\boldsymbol{y}'\boldsymbol{A}\boldsymbol{y}$ *and* $\boldsymbol{C}\boldsymbol{y}$ *are independently distributed if and only if* $\boldsymbol{CA} = \boldsymbol{0}$.

Proof. See Exercise 2.3. $\square$

Remark 2.12. If $\boldsymbol{y}_{n\times 1} \sim N(\boldsymbol{\mu}, \boldsymbol{\Sigma})$ and $\boldsymbol{\Sigma}$ is nonsingular, then $\boldsymbol{\Sigma}$ can be factored as $\boldsymbol{CC}'$, where $\boldsymbol{C}$ is also square and nonsingular. Therefore, $\boldsymbol{C}^{-1}\boldsymbol{y} \sim N(\boldsymbol{C}^{-1}\boldsymbol{\mu}, \boldsymbol{I})$. It follows from the above proposition that $\boldsymbol{y}'\boldsymbol{C}^{-1'}\boldsymbol{C}^{-1}\boldsymbol{y}$, which can also be written as $\boldsymbol{y}'\boldsymbol{\Sigma}^{-1}\boldsymbol{y}$, has the $\chi^2_n(\boldsymbol{\mu}'\boldsymbol{\Sigma}^{-1}\boldsymbol{\mu})$ distribution. See Exercise 2.2 for a similar result for singular $\boldsymbol{\Sigma}$. $\square$

2.2 The case of singular dispersion matrix*

The matrix $\boldsymbol{\Sigma}$ is singular (i.e. positive semidefinite) if and only if there is a nonzero vector $\boldsymbol{l}$ such that $Var(\boldsymbol{l}'\boldsymbol{y}) = 0$, that is, $\boldsymbol{l}'\boldsymbol{y}$ is a degenerate random variable. In the last five chapters of this book we shall have occasion to deal with random vectors which may have a singular dispersion matrix. A major difficulty in working with a singular dispersion matrix is that a random vector having such a dispersion matrix is not free to have all conceivable values. The restriction on its possible values is governed by the column space of the dispersion matrix. In this context the next proposition provides two results that would allow us to understand and accommodate these restrictions.

Proposition 2.13. *If $\boldsymbol{u}$ and $\boldsymbol{v}$ are random vectors with finite mean and dispersion matrices, then*

(a) $[\boldsymbol{u} - E(\boldsymbol{u})] \in \mathcal{C}(D(\boldsymbol{u}))$ *with probability 1,*
(b) $\mathcal{C}(Cov(\boldsymbol{u}, \boldsymbol{v})) \subseteq \mathcal{C}(D(\boldsymbol{u}))$.

Proof. Let $\boldsymbol{y} = (\boldsymbol{I} - \boldsymbol{P}_{D(u)})[\boldsymbol{u} - \boldsymbol{E}(\boldsymbol{u})]$. It is easy to see that $E(\boldsymbol{y}) = \boldsymbol{0}$ and $D(\boldsymbol{y}) = \boldsymbol{0}$. Therefore the random variable $\|\boldsymbol{y}\|^2$ satisfies the condition

$$\begin{aligned} E(\|\boldsymbol{y}\|^2) = E(\boldsymbol{y}'\boldsymbol{y}) &= E(\text{tr}(\boldsymbol{y}\boldsymbol{y}')) = \text{tr}E(\boldsymbol{y}\boldsymbol{y}') \\ &= \text{tr}E[\{E(\boldsymbol{y}) + (\boldsymbol{y} - E(\boldsymbol{y}))\}\{E(\boldsymbol{y}) + (\boldsymbol{y} - E(\boldsymbol{y}))\}'] \\ &= \text{tr}[E(\boldsymbol{y})E(\boldsymbol{y}')] + \text{tr}D(\boldsymbol{y}) = 0. \end{aligned}$$

It follows by a standard argument of probability theory (see, for instance, Theorem 15.2(ii) of Billingsley (2012)), that any nonnegative random variable with zero expected value, must be zero with probability 1. Therefore, the vector $\boldsymbol{y}$ is almost surely a zero vector.[2] This proves part (a).

Part (b) is obtained by applying part (b) of Proposition A.19 to the combined dispersion matrix of $\boldsymbol{u}$ and $\boldsymbol{v}$. □

Now suppose $\boldsymbol{y} \sim N(\boldsymbol{\mu}, \boldsymbol{\Sigma})$, where $\boldsymbol{\Sigma}$ is singular, i.e. positive semi-definite. The matrix $\boldsymbol{\Sigma}$ has a rank factorization of the form $\boldsymbol{C}\boldsymbol{C}'$, where the number of columns of the matrix $\boldsymbol{C}$ is $\rho(\boldsymbol{\Sigma})$, the rank of $\boldsymbol{\Sigma}$. The density function of $\boldsymbol{y}$ turns out to be (Exercise 2.1)

$$f(\boldsymbol{y}) = \begin{cases} (2\pi)^{-\rho(\Sigma)/2}|\boldsymbol{C}'\boldsymbol{C}|^{-1/2}\exp[-\frac{1}{2}(\boldsymbol{y}-\boldsymbol{\mu})'\boldsymbol{\Sigma}^{-}(\boldsymbol{y}-\boldsymbol{\mu})] & \\ & \text{if } (\boldsymbol{I}-\boldsymbol{P}_{\Sigma})(\boldsymbol{y}-\boldsymbol{\mu}) = \boldsymbol{0}, \\ 0 & \text{if } (\boldsymbol{I}-\boldsymbol{P}_{\Sigma})(\boldsymbol{y}-\boldsymbol{\mu}) \neq \boldsymbol{0}. \end{cases} \quad (2.11)$$

The choice of the g-inverse does not matter. This density reduces to (2.3) when $\boldsymbol{\Sigma}$ is nonsingular, and to (2.2) when $\boldsymbol{\Sigma} = \sigma^2\boldsymbol{I}$.

Let us now suppose $\boldsymbol{y}$ is partitioned as $(\boldsymbol{y}_1' \ \boldsymbol{y}_2')'$. The next proposition shows that the conditional distribution of $\boldsymbol{y}_2$ given $\boldsymbol{y}_1$ is also normal.

Proposition 2.14. If $\boldsymbol{y}_1$ and $\boldsymbol{y}_2$ are random vectors that jointly have the normal distribution with mean and dispersion

$$E\begin{pmatrix}\boldsymbol{y}_1\\ \boldsymbol{y}_2\end{pmatrix} = \begin{pmatrix}\boldsymbol{\mu}_1\\ \boldsymbol{\mu}_2\end{pmatrix}, \qquad D\begin{pmatrix}\boldsymbol{y}_1\\ \boldsymbol{y}_2\end{pmatrix} = \begin{pmatrix}\boldsymbol{\Sigma}_{11} & \boldsymbol{\Sigma}_{12}\\ \boldsymbol{\Sigma}_{21} & \boldsymbol{\Sigma}_{22}\end{pmatrix},$$

[2] We shall use the phrase *with probability 1* interchangeably with *almost surely*.

then the conditional distribution of $\boldsymbol{y}_2$ given $\boldsymbol{y}_1$ is normal with mean and dispersion given by

$$E(\boldsymbol{y}_2|\boldsymbol{y}_1) = \boldsymbol{\mu}_2 + \boldsymbol{\Sigma}_{21}\boldsymbol{\Sigma}_{11}^{-}(\boldsymbol{y}_1 - \boldsymbol{\mu}_1), \tag{2.12}$$

$$D(\boldsymbol{y}_2|\boldsymbol{y}_1) = \boldsymbol{\Sigma}_{22} - \boldsymbol{\Sigma}_{21}\boldsymbol{\Sigma}_{11}^{-}\boldsymbol{\Sigma}_{12}, \tag{2.13}$$

and the above expressions almost surely do not depend on the choice of the g-inverse.

Proof. Suppose $\boldsymbol{\Sigma}_{11}^{-}$ is a g-inverse of $\boldsymbol{\Sigma}_{11}$, and

$$\boldsymbol{y}_3 = \boldsymbol{y}_2 - \boldsymbol{\Sigma}_{21}\boldsymbol{\Sigma}_{11}^{-}(\boldsymbol{y}_1 - \boldsymbol{\mu}_1).$$

Note that the joint distribution of $\boldsymbol{y}_1$ and $\boldsymbol{y}_3$ may be obtained from the joint distribution of $\boldsymbol{y}_1$ and $\boldsymbol{y}_2$, and vice versa, since $\boldsymbol{y}_2 = \boldsymbol{y}_3 + \boldsymbol{\Sigma}_{21}\boldsymbol{\Sigma}_{11}^{-}(\boldsymbol{y}_1 - \boldsymbol{\mu}_1)$. Further, since $\boldsymbol{y}_1$ and $\boldsymbol{y}_3$ are linear combinations of $\boldsymbol{y}_1$ and $\boldsymbol{y}_2$, they jointly have a normal distribution. Observe that

$$Cov(\boldsymbol{y}_3, \boldsymbol{y}_1) = Cov(\boldsymbol{y}_2 - \boldsymbol{\Sigma}_{21}\boldsymbol{\Sigma}_{11}^{-}(\boldsymbol{y}_1 - \boldsymbol{\mu}_1), \boldsymbol{y}_1) = \boldsymbol{\Sigma}_{21} - \boldsymbol{\Sigma}_{21}\boldsymbol{\Sigma}_{11}^{-}\boldsymbol{\Sigma}_{11} = \boldsymbol{0}.$$

It follows that the characteristic function of the joint distribution of $\boldsymbol{y}_1$ and $\boldsymbol{y}_3$ factor into characteristic functions of the marginal distributions of $\boldsymbol{y}_1$ and $\boldsymbol{y}_3$. Therefore, $\boldsymbol{y}_3$ and $\boldsymbol{y}_1$ are independent. Thus, the conditional distribution of $\boldsymbol{y}_3$ given $\boldsymbol{y}_1$ is the same as the unconditional distribution of $\boldsymbol{y}_3$, which is normal with mean $E(\boldsymbol{y}_3) = \boldsymbol{\mu}_2$ and dispersion

$$\begin{aligned}
D(\boldsymbol{y}_3) &= Cov(\boldsymbol{y}_2 - \boldsymbol{\Sigma}_{21}\boldsymbol{\Sigma}_{11}^{-}(\boldsymbol{y}_1 - \boldsymbol{\mu}_1), \boldsymbol{y}_2 - \boldsymbol{\Sigma}_{21}\boldsymbol{\Sigma}_{11}^{-}(\boldsymbol{y}_1 - \boldsymbol{\mu}_1)) \\
&= D(\boldsymbol{y}_2) - Cov(\boldsymbol{\Sigma}_{21}\boldsymbol{\Sigma}_{11}^{-}(\boldsymbol{y}_1 - \boldsymbol{\mu}_1), \boldsymbol{y}_2) \\
&\quad - Cov(\boldsymbol{y}_2, \boldsymbol{\Sigma}_{21}\boldsymbol{\Sigma}_{11}^{-}(\boldsymbol{y}_1 - \boldsymbol{\mu}_1)) + D(\boldsymbol{\Sigma}_{21}\boldsymbol{\Sigma}_{11}^{-}(\boldsymbol{y}_1 - \boldsymbol{\mu}_1)) \\
&= \boldsymbol{\Sigma}_{22} - \boldsymbol{\Sigma}_{21}\boldsymbol{\Sigma}_{11}^{-}\boldsymbol{\Sigma}_{12} - \boldsymbol{\Sigma}_{21}\boldsymbol{\Sigma}_{11}^{-}\boldsymbol{\Sigma}_{12} + \boldsymbol{\Sigma}_{21}\boldsymbol{\Sigma}_{11}^{-}S_{11}S_{11}^{-}\boldsymbol{\Sigma}_{12} \\
&= \boldsymbol{\Sigma}_{22} - \boldsymbol{\Sigma}_{21}\boldsymbol{\Sigma}_{11}^{-}\boldsymbol{\Sigma}_{12}.
\end{aligned}$$

When $\boldsymbol{y}_1$ is fixed, $\boldsymbol{y}_2$ differs from $\boldsymbol{y}_3$ only by the constant vector $\boldsymbol{\Sigma}_{21}\boldsymbol{\Sigma}_{11}^{-}(\boldsymbol{y}_1 - \boldsymbol{\mu}_1)$. Therefore, the conditional distribution of $\boldsymbol{y}_2$ given $\boldsymbol{y}_1$ is normal with mean $\boldsymbol{\mu}_2 + \boldsymbol{\Sigma}_{21}\boldsymbol{\Sigma}_{11}^{-}(\boldsymbol{y}_1 - \boldsymbol{\mu}_1)$ and dispersion $\boldsymbol{\Sigma}_{22} - \boldsymbol{\Sigma}_{21}\boldsymbol{\Sigma}_{11}^{-}\boldsymbol{\Sigma}_{12}$. It follows from Theorem 2.13 that $\mathcal{C}(\boldsymbol{\Sigma}_{12}) \subseteq \mathcal{C}(\boldsymbol{\Sigma}_{11})$ and $(\boldsymbol{y}_1 - \boldsymbol{\mu}_1) \in \mathcal{C}(\boldsymbol{\Sigma}_{11})$ with probability one, which means the expression for the conditional dispersion does not depend on the choice of the g-inverse, while the conditional mean also has this invariance property almost surely. □

The singular normal distribution is encountered when there is a deterministic relationship among the random components of $\boldsymbol{y}$. Even if no explicit relationship is known, an implied one can always be found. Specifically, if $\boldsymbol{B}\boldsymbol{B}'$ is a rank-factorization of $\boldsymbol{I} - \boldsymbol{P}_{\Sigma}$, then the linear relationship $\boldsymbol{B}'\boldsymbol{y} = \boldsymbol{B}\boldsymbol{\mu}$ holds with probability 1.

2.3 Regression as best prediction

2.3.1 *Mean regression*

Let y be the random variable of interest (response) and $\boldsymbol{x}$ be the set of explanatory random variables. If y is to be approximated by the function $g(\boldsymbol{x})$ of $\boldsymbol{x}$, then the meaning of this approximation, more commonly referred to as prediction, has to be clarified. The prediction error, $y - g(\boldsymbol{x})$, is a random variable. Therefore, it is unlikely that the error would be small in every realization. A more realistic requirement is that the error should have a small magnitude, or that the squared error should be small, on the average. Thus, the predictor $g(\boldsymbol{x})$ may be said to be good if the *mean squared error* (MSE) of prediction, $E[(y - g(\boldsymbol{x}))^2]$, is small. This *minimum mean squared error* (MMSE) criterion is the one commonly used for prediction. The next proposition shows that the best predictor in this sense happens to be the conditional mean, $E(y|\boldsymbol{x})$.

Proposition 2.15. *Let $L_g(y, \boldsymbol{x}) = (y - g(\boldsymbol{x}))^2$ be the squared error of prediction of the random variable y by a function $g(\boldsymbol{x})$ of the random vector $\boldsymbol{x}$. Suppose $g_0(\boldsymbol{x}) = E(y|\boldsymbol{x})$. Then,*
(a) $E(y|\boldsymbol{x})$ is MMSE predictor of y, that is, $E[L_{g_0}(y, \boldsymbol{x})] \leq E[L_g(y, \boldsymbol{x})]$,
(b) The MMSE predictor is unbiased, that is, $E(g_0(\boldsymbol{x})) = E(y)$.
(c) The prediction error of the MMSE predictor $y - E(y|\boldsymbol{x})$ is uncorrelated with every function of $\boldsymbol{x}$.
(d) The minimized value of the MSE of prediction is $E[Var(y|\boldsymbol{x})]$.

Proof. We shall prove part (a) later. Part (b) follows from the fact that

$$\begin{aligned} E(y) - E(g_0(\boldsymbol{x})) &= E[E(y - g_0(\boldsymbol{x})|\boldsymbol{x})] \\ &= E[E(y|\boldsymbol{x}) - g_0(\boldsymbol{x})] = E(0) = 0. \end{aligned}$$

Also, for any function $g(\boldsymbol{x})$ of $\boldsymbol{x}$,

$$\begin{aligned} Cov(y - g_0(\boldsymbol{x}), g(\boldsymbol{x})) &= E[E\{(y - g_0(\boldsymbol{x}))(g(\boldsymbol{x}) - E(g(\boldsymbol{x})))|\boldsymbol{x}\}] \\ &= E[(E(y|\boldsymbol{x}) - g_0(\boldsymbol{x}))(g(\boldsymbol{x}) - E(g(\boldsymbol{x})))] = 0. \end{aligned}$$

This proves part (c). By making use of this result, it is observed that

$$\begin{aligned} &E[L_g(y, \boldsymbol{x})] \\ &= E[(y - g(\boldsymbol{x}))^2] = E[(y - g_0(\boldsymbol{x}) + g_0(\boldsymbol{x}) - g(\boldsymbol{x}))^2] \\ &= E[(y - g_0(\boldsymbol{x}))^2] + E[(g_0(\boldsymbol{x}) - g(\boldsymbol{x}))^2] + 2E[(y - g(\boldsymbol{x}))(g_0(\boldsymbol{x}) - g(\boldsymbol{x}))] \\ &= E[(y - g_0(\boldsymbol{x}))^2] + E[(g_0(\boldsymbol{x}) - g(\boldsymbol{x}))^2] \\ &= E[L_{g_0}(y, \boldsymbol{x})] + E[(g_0(\boldsymbol{x}) - g(\boldsymbol{x}))^2] \leq E[L_{g_0}(y, \boldsymbol{x})], \end{aligned}$$

which proves part (a). Part (d) is proved by observing

$$E[L_{g_0}(y, \boldsymbol{x})] = E[E\{(y - E(y|\boldsymbol{x}))^2|\boldsymbol{x}\}] = E[Var(y|\boldsymbol{x})]. \qquad \square$$

The inequality in the last part of the proof shows that if $g(\boldsymbol{x})$ is any predictor with the same mean squared error as $g_0(\boldsymbol{x})$, then $E[(g_0(\boldsymbol{x}) - g(\boldsymbol{x}))^2] = 0$, which implies $g(\boldsymbol{x})$ must be almost surely equal to $g_0(\boldsymbol{x})$. In this sense the MMSE predictor is unique.

The conditional mean $E(y|\boldsymbol{x})$ is referred to as *the regression of y on $\boldsymbol{x}$*. It is sometimes called the *regression function*, in order to emphasize the fact that the conditional mean varies as a function of $\boldsymbol{x}$. Proposition 2.15 shows why the description and modeling of the conditional mean is important. The next few examples would show how certain joint or conditional distributions lead to some explicit forms of the conditional mean and variance. In some cases, the conditional mean turns out to be a linear function of $\boldsymbol{x}$. However, none of these models need to hold for the regression to be linear. The regression function can be modeled (linearly or otherwise) without any distributional assumption on the conditional or joint distribution. In fact, direct modeling of the regression function generally involves fewer assumptions.

Example 2.16. (Bivariate normal distribution, continued) Suppose the pair of random variables x and y have the bivariate normal distribution, with

$$E(x) = \mu_x, \quad E(y) = \mu_y, \quad Var(x) = \sigma_x^2, \quad Var(y) = \sigma_y^2$$

and correlation coefficient ρ. It was shown in Example 2.3 that the conditional distribution of y given x is univariate normal with

$$E(y|x) = \mu_y + \rho\frac{\sigma_y}{\sigma_x}(x - \mu_x),$$
$$Var(y|x) = \sigma_y^2(1 - \rho^2).$$

Thus, the regression of y on x is $\mu_y + \rho\frac{\sigma_y}{\sigma_x}(x - \mu_x)$. Since the conditional variance does not depend on x, the minimized value of the MSE of prediction is $\sigma_y^2(1 - \rho^2)$.

When $\rho = 0$, the regression of y on x is $E(y|x) = \mu_y$, which does not depend on x at all. This would also be the MMSE predictor of y in terms of a constant (i.e. in the absence x)!

Figure 2.1 shows the scatter plots of 100 sets of paired data (x, y) simulated from the bivariate normal distribution with $\mu_x = 20$, $\sigma_x = 1$, $\mu_y = 5$,

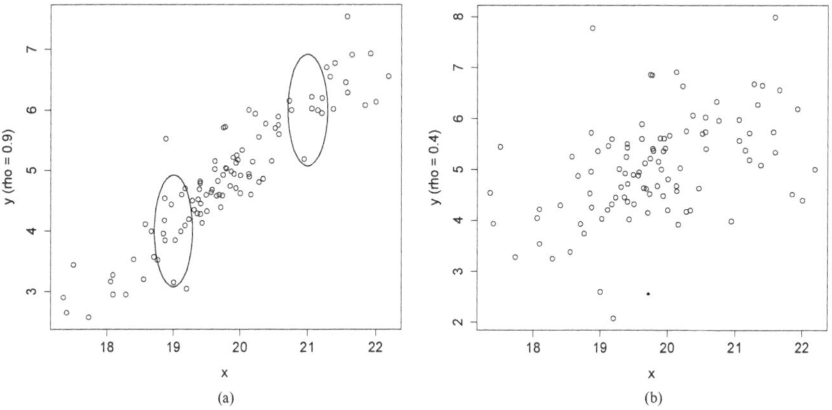

Fig. 2.1 Scatter plots of bivariate normal data for (a) $\rho = 0.9$ and (b) $\rho = 0.4$

$\sigma_y = 1$ and two values of ρ. The plots in the left and right panels correspond to $\rho = 0.9$ and $\rho = 0.4$, respectively. Both the scatter plots show that the generated values of y are centered at about 5. Therefore, if one has to guess where another value of y would lie, a good guess would be 5, though the actual value of y may be as small as 2 or as large as 8. However, if $\rho = 0.9$ and one knows that $x = 21$, then the MMSE predictor of y works out to be 5.9. This is a better guess than 5, as the values of y corresponding to values of x around 21 (encircled in the left panel of the figure) are near 5.9. Going by the observed scatter, the actual values of y corresponding to $x \approx 21$ are not too far from 5.9. This finding confirms that for this example, the MSE of prediction by the value 5.9 is only 0.19, whereas the variance of y is 1. Likewise, When x is known to be 19, the MMSE predictor of y is $E(y|x) = 4.1$, which is commensurate with the observed values of y corresponding to x near about 19 (also encircled in the scatter plot of the left panel). The points in this region are about as widely scattered as the earlier set of points, which confirms that the conditional variance remains the same, 0.19.

Thus, it makes sense to take into account the value of x, where available, if one has to predict y.

The right panel of Figure 2.1 shows that the benefit of knowing x is much less when $\rho = 0.4$. In this case the minimized mean squared prediction error is 0.64, which is 64% of the variance of y. Thus, there can only be a moderate gain from the use of x to predict y. Interestingly, in this case, the MMSE predictors of y for $x = 21$ and $x = 19$ happen to be 5.4 and 4.6, respectively. These values are much closer to 5, which would be the MMSE predictor of y in the absence of x. In other words, the larger value of the minimized mean square error means that one would be more conservative about departing from 5 while making prediction based on x. □

Example 2.17. Suppose x is a binary random variable with $P(x = 1) = \pi_1$ and $P(x = 0) = 1 - \pi_1$, and the conditional distribution of y given x is univariate normal with

$$E(y|x) = \begin{cases} \mu_1 & \text{if } x = 1, \\ \mu_0 & \text{if } x = 0, \end{cases}$$
$$Var(y|x) = \sigma^2.$$

Note that the marginal distribution of y is not normal, rather it is a mixture of normal distributions. Here, the regression of y on x, described above, can be alternatively expressed as

$$E(y|x) = \mu_0 + (\mu_1 - \mu_0)x.$$

The MSE of prediction is σ^2. □

Example 2.18. Suppose x and y are independent and have the standard normal distribution, and (r, θ) are the polar coordinates of the point on the plane represented by the cartesian coordinates (x, y), i.e. $x = r\cos\theta$ and $y = r\sin\theta$. It can be checked that r and θ are independent, $E(\sin^2\theta) = E(\cos^2\theta) = 1/2$, $E(r^2) = 2$, and $E(r) = \sqrt{\frac{\pi}{2}}$. Therefore, the regression of y on θ is

$$E(y|\theta) = E(r\sin\theta|\theta) = E(r)\sin\theta = \sqrt{\frac{\pi}{2}}\sin\theta.$$

Further,

$$E(y^2|\theta) = E(r^2\sin^2\theta|\theta) = E(r^2)\sin^2\theta = 2\sin^2\theta.$$

Therefore,

$$Var(y|\theta) = 2\sin^2\theta - \frac{\pi}{2}\sin^2\theta = \left(2 - \frac{\pi}{2}\right)\sin^2\theta.$$

It follows that the MSE of prediction is $E[Var(y|\theta)] = 1 - \pi/4$. □

Example 2.18 shows that the regression function can be nonlinear. It also illustrates that one should generally expect the conditional variance of the response to depend on the explanatory variable. Exception to this rule is a feature of regression models derived from a multivariate normal distribution, as the next example shows.

Example 2.19. (Multivariate normal distribution, continued) Suppose $\boldsymbol{x}$ and y jointly have the multivariate normal distribution with mean vector and dispersion matrices

$$E\begin{pmatrix}\boldsymbol{x}\\ y\end{pmatrix} = \begin{pmatrix}\boldsymbol{\mu}_x\\ \mu_y\end{pmatrix}; \qquad D\begin{pmatrix}\boldsymbol{x}\\ y\end{pmatrix} = \begin{pmatrix}\boldsymbol{\Sigma}_{xx} & \boldsymbol{\sigma}'_{xy}\\ \boldsymbol{\sigma}_{xy} & \sigma_y^2\end{pmatrix}.$$

It was shown in Example 2.4 that the conditional distribution is univariate normal with mean and variance

$$E(y|\boldsymbol{x}) = \mu_y + \boldsymbol{\sigma}'_{xy}\boldsymbol{\Sigma}_{xx}^{-1}(\boldsymbol{x} - \boldsymbol{\mu}_x),$$
$$Var(y|\boldsymbol{x}) = \sigma_y^2 - \boldsymbol{\sigma}'_{xy}\boldsymbol{\Sigma}_{xx}^{-1}\boldsymbol{\sigma}_{xy},$$

assuming $\boldsymbol{\Sigma}_{xx}$ is nonsingular. Thus, the regression of y on $\boldsymbol{x}$ is $\mu_y + \boldsymbol{\sigma}'_{xy}\boldsymbol{\Sigma}_{xx}^{-1}(\boldsymbol{x} - \boldsymbol{\mu}_x)$, and the MSE of prediction is $\sigma_y^2 - \boldsymbol{\sigma}'_{xy}\boldsymbol{\Sigma}_{xx}^{-1}\boldsymbol{\sigma}_{xy}$.

The regression function in this example may be expressed as

$$E(y|\boldsymbol{x}) = \beta_0 + \beta_1 x_1 + \cdots + \beta_p x_k, \tag{2.14}$$

where

$$\boldsymbol{x} = \begin{pmatrix}x_1\\ \vdots\\ x_k\end{pmatrix}, \qquad \beta_0 = \mu_y - \boldsymbol{\sigma}'_{xy}\boldsymbol{\Sigma}_{xx}^{-1}\boldsymbol{\mu}_x, \qquad \begin{pmatrix}\beta_1\\ \vdots\\ \beta_k\end{pmatrix} = \boldsymbol{\Sigma}_{xx}^{-1}\boldsymbol{\sigma}_{xy}.$$

This equation has the form of (1.8). The expression is a linear function of $\boldsymbol{x}$ plus a constant, i.e. an affine function of $\boldsymbol{x}$. The parameter σ^2 in (1.8) may be identified with the conditional variance, $\sigma_y^2 - \boldsymbol{\sigma}'_{xy}\boldsymbol{\Sigma}_{xx}^{-1}\boldsymbol{\sigma}_{xy}$. □

The model (1.8) accounts for a single observation in a special case of the model (1.7), where the observations are conditionally independent. We end this section with a proposition which shows how even the general linear model (1.7) follows from a multivariate normal distribution of the variables. We shall denote by vec($\boldsymbol{A}$) the vector obtained by successively concatenating the columns of the matrix $\boldsymbol{A}$, and use $\boldsymbol{1}$ to denote a vector of 1s.

Proposition 2.20. *Let the random vector $\boldsymbol{y}_{n\times 1}$ and the random matrix $\boldsymbol{X}_{n\times(k+1)}$ be such that $\boldsymbol{X} = (\boldsymbol{1} : \boldsymbol{Z})$,*

$$\text{vec}(\boldsymbol{y} : \boldsymbol{Z}) \sim N\left(\begin{pmatrix}\mu_y\\ \boldsymbol{\mu}_x\end{pmatrix}_{(k+1)\times 1} \otimes \boldsymbol{1}_{n\times 1},\ \boldsymbol{\Sigma}_{(k+1)\times(k+1)} \otimes \boldsymbol{V}_{n\times n}\right),$$

and the matrix

$$\boldsymbol{\Sigma} = \begin{pmatrix} \sigma_y^2 & \boldsymbol{\sigma}'_{xy} \\ \boldsymbol{\sigma}_{xy} & \boldsymbol{\Sigma}_{xx} \end{pmatrix}$$

is possibly singular. Then

$$E(\boldsymbol{y}|\boldsymbol{X}) = \boldsymbol{X}\boldsymbol{\beta}, \qquad D(\boldsymbol{y}|\boldsymbol{X}) = \sigma^2\boldsymbol{V},$$

where

$$\begin{aligned} \boldsymbol{\beta} &= \begin{pmatrix} \mu_y - \boldsymbol{\sigma}'_{xy}\boldsymbol{\Sigma}^-_{xx}\boldsymbol{\mu}_x \\ \boldsymbol{\Sigma}^-_{xx}\boldsymbol{\sigma}_{xy} \end{pmatrix}, \\ \sigma^2 &= \sigma_y^2 - \boldsymbol{\sigma}'_{xy}\boldsymbol{\Sigma}^-_{xx}\boldsymbol{\sigma}_{xy}. \end{aligned}$$

Proof. Since $\boldsymbol{X} = (\boldsymbol{1} : \boldsymbol{Z})$, conditioning with respect to $\boldsymbol{X}$ is equivalent to conditioning with respect to $\boldsymbol{Z}$. The stated formulae would follow from (2.12) and (2.13). Let $\boldsymbol{x} = \mathrm{vec}(\boldsymbol{Z})$. It follows that

$$\begin{aligned} D(\boldsymbol{y}|\boldsymbol{X}) &= D(\boldsymbol{y}|\boldsymbol{x}) \\ &= \sigma_{yy}\boldsymbol{V} - (\boldsymbol{\sigma}'_{xy} \otimes \boldsymbol{V})(\boldsymbol{\Sigma}_{xx} \otimes \boldsymbol{V})^-(\boldsymbol{\sigma}_{xy} \otimes \boldsymbol{V}) \\ &= \sigma_{yy}\boldsymbol{V} - (\boldsymbol{\sigma}'_{xy} \otimes \boldsymbol{V})(\boldsymbol{\Sigma}^-_{xx} \otimes \boldsymbol{V}^-)(\boldsymbol{\sigma}_{xy} \otimes \boldsymbol{V}) \\ &= \sigma_{yy}\boldsymbol{V} - (\boldsymbol{\sigma}'_{xy}\boldsymbol{\Sigma}^-_{xx}\boldsymbol{\sigma}_{xy} \otimes \boldsymbol{V}\boldsymbol{V}^-\boldsymbol{V}) \\ &= (\sigma_{yy} - \boldsymbol{\sigma}'_{xy}\boldsymbol{\Sigma}^-_{xx}\boldsymbol{\sigma}_{xy})\boldsymbol{V}. \end{aligned}$$

This is of the form given in the proposition.

Using the properties of the Kronecker product described in Sections A.1 and A.2, and the fact that $\boldsymbol{x} - E(\boldsymbol{x}) = (\boldsymbol{\Sigma}_{xx} \otimes \boldsymbol{V})\boldsymbol{l}$ for some vector $\boldsymbol{l}$ of size kn (see Proposition 2.13(a)), we can also write

$$\begin{aligned} E(\boldsymbol{y}|\boldsymbol{X}) &= E(\boldsymbol{y}|\boldsymbol{x}) \\ &= \mu_y\boldsymbol{1} + (\boldsymbol{\sigma}'_{xy} \otimes \boldsymbol{V})(\boldsymbol{\Sigma}_{xx} \otimes \boldsymbol{V})^-(\boldsymbol{x} - \boldsymbol{\mu}_x \otimes \boldsymbol{1}) \\ &= \mu_y\boldsymbol{1} + (\boldsymbol{\sigma}'_{xy} \otimes \boldsymbol{V})(\boldsymbol{\Sigma}_{xx} \otimes \boldsymbol{V})^-(\boldsymbol{\Sigma}_{xx} \otimes \boldsymbol{V})\boldsymbol{l} \\ &= \mu_y\boldsymbol{1} + [(\boldsymbol{\sigma}'_{xy}\boldsymbol{\Sigma}^-_{xx}\boldsymbol{\Sigma}_{xx}) \otimes (\boldsymbol{V}\boldsymbol{V}^-\boldsymbol{V})]\boldsymbol{l} \\ &= \mu_y\boldsymbol{1} + [(\boldsymbol{\sigma}'_{xy}\boldsymbol{\Sigma}^-_{xx}\boldsymbol{\Sigma}_{xx}) \otimes \boldsymbol{V}]\boldsymbol{l} \\ &= \mu_y\boldsymbol{1} + [(\boldsymbol{\sigma}'_{xy}\boldsymbol{\Sigma}^-_{xx}) \otimes \boldsymbol{I}](\boldsymbol{\Sigma}_{xx} \otimes \boldsymbol{V})\boldsymbol{l} \\ &= \mu_y\boldsymbol{1} + [(\boldsymbol{\sigma}'_{xy}\boldsymbol{\Sigma}^-_{xx}) \otimes \boldsymbol{I}](\boldsymbol{x} - \boldsymbol{\mu}_x \otimes \boldsymbol{1}) \\ &= (\mu_y - \boldsymbol{\sigma}'_{xy}\boldsymbol{\Sigma}^-_{xx}\boldsymbol{\mu}_x)\boldsymbol{1} + [(\boldsymbol{\sigma}'_{xy}\boldsymbol{\Sigma}^-_{xx}) \otimes \boldsymbol{I}]\boldsymbol{x} \\ &= (\mu_y - \boldsymbol{\sigma}'_{xy}\boldsymbol{\Sigma}^-_{xx}\boldsymbol{\mu}_x)\boldsymbol{1} + \boldsymbol{Z}\boldsymbol{\Sigma}^-_{xx}\boldsymbol{\sigma}_{xy}, \end{aligned}$$

which coincides with the expression given in the proposition. □

Note that since $\boldsymbol{\Sigma}_{xx}$ is allowed to be singular, nonrandom explanatory variables may be included in $\boldsymbol{X}$ with no additional technical problems. If $\boldsymbol{\Sigma}_{xx}$ is singular, $\boldsymbol{\beta}$ is not uniquely defined — as it depends on the selection of $\boldsymbol{\Sigma}_{xx}^{-}$. However, $E(\boldsymbol{y}|\boldsymbol{X})$ is uniquely defined.

The result in Proposition 2.20 hinges crucially on the special structure of the joint covariance matrix of $\boldsymbol{y}$ and $\boldsymbol{Z}$. The assumed form of this matrix, $\boldsymbol{\Sigma} \otimes \boldsymbol{V}$, ensures that the first element of $E(\boldsymbol{y}|\boldsymbol{X})$ depends only on the first row of $\boldsymbol{X}$, the second element depends on the second row, and so on. Further, the assumptions $E(\boldsymbol{y}) = \mu_y \boldsymbol{1}$ and $E(\boldsymbol{Z}) = \boldsymbol{1} \otimes \boldsymbol{\mu}_x'$ ensure that the constant part of $E(\boldsymbol{y}|\boldsymbol{X})$ is the same for all the elements. These two simplifications mean that the regression model has a manageable number of parameters for inference. As mentioned in Section 1.4, usually $\boldsymbol{V}$ is assumed to be known and $\boldsymbol{\beta}$ and σ^2 are estimated from the data. We shall continue to make these assumptions in Chapters 3–7. The case of partially known $\boldsymbol{V}$ will be discussed in Chapter 8.

2.3.2 *Median and quantile regression**

In Proposition 2.15, the best approximation has been achieved by minimizing the mean of the squared error loss function. While this is a commonly used criterion, it is by no means the only possibility. Another commonly used measure of approximation error is the mean of the absolute error loss function, $L_g(y, \boldsymbol{x}) = |y - g(\boldsymbol{x})|$. The next proposition shows that the best predictor according to this criterion is the conditional median of y given $\boldsymbol{x}$.

Proposition 2.21. *Let $L_g(y, \boldsymbol{x}) = |y - g(\boldsymbol{x})|$ be the absolute error of prediction of the random variable y by a function $g(\boldsymbol{x})$ of the random vector $\boldsymbol{x}$. Suppose $g_0(\boldsymbol{x})$ is the median of the conditional distribution of y given $\boldsymbol{x}$. Then,*
(a) $g_0(\boldsymbol{x})$ is the minimum mean absolute error (MMAE) predictor of y, that is, $E[L_{g_0}(y, \boldsymbol{x})] \le E[L_g(y, \boldsymbol{x})]$,
(b) The median of the prediction error is zero.

Proof. For part (a), it is sufficient to prove that $E[L_{g_0}(y, \boldsymbol{x})|\boldsymbol{x}] \le E[L_g(y, \boldsymbol{x})|\boldsymbol{x}]$ for every fixed $\boldsymbol{x}$. This inequality, in turn, would follow if we can show that for any distribution of y (conditional or otherwise) having median m, $E(|y - m|) \le E(|y - c|)$ for any constant c.

For any $c > m$, we have (using the notation $I(A)$ for the indicator of an event A)

$$
\begin{aligned}
&|y-c|-|y-m| \\
&= (c-m)I(y \le m) + (m-c)I(y > c) + [(c-y)-(y-m)]I(m < y \le c) \\
&= (c-m)I(y \le m) + (m-c)I(y > c) + [(m-c)+2(c-y)]I(m < y \le c) \\
&= (c-m)I(y \le m) + (m-c)I(y > m) + 2(c-y)I(m < y \le c) \\
&\ge (c-m)I(y \le m) + (m-c)I(y > m).
\end{aligned}
$$

For any $c < m$, we have

$$
\begin{aligned}
&|y-c|-|y-m| \\
&= (c-m)I(y \le c) + (m-c)I(y > m) + [(y-c)-(m-y)]I(c < y \le m) \\
&= (c-m)I(y \le c) + (m-c)I(y > m) + [(c-m)+2(y-c)]I(c < y \le m) \\
&= (c-m)I(y \le m) + (m-c)I(y > m) + 2(y-c)I(c < y \le m) \\
&\ge (c-m)I(y \le m) + (m-c)I(y > m).
\end{aligned}
$$

Thus, we have the same inequality for all values of c on either side of the median m. By taking expected values of the two sides, we obtain

$$E(|y-c|) - E(|y-m||) \ge (c-m)P(y \le m) + (m-c)P(y > m) = 0$$

when m is the median, proving part (a). To prove part (b), note that subtraction of the median from any random variable makes the median of the difference equal to zero. Therefore, for every fixed $\boldsymbol{x}$, the conditional probability of the prediction error (corresponding to the optimal predictor obtained in part (a)) being positive is 0.5. The unconditional probability must also be 0.5. Therefore, the median of the prediction error is zero. □

The optimal solutions obtained through Propositions 2.15 and 2.21 are the mean and the median, respectively, of the conditional distribution of the response given the explanatory variables. Thus, the conditional distribution plays a key role in prediction. An important consequence of this finding is that one does not have to assume a model for the joint distribution of the response and the explanatory variables, to be able to carry out prediction. It is enough to model the conditional distribution. One can even restrict the modeling assumption to some aspect of the conditional distribution, such as a location parameter. A model for the conditional median is generally called a median regression model. A model for the conditional mean, which is more common, is called a mean regression model, or simply a regression model. It is well known that these two measures of location can differ only when the distribution is asymmetric. Therefore, median regression is an important option for asymmetric response. Even for symmetric data, median regression is recognized as a tool for robust inference, since the sample median is known to be less sensitive to outliers than the sample mean.

Whether or not the response is asymmetric, a positive value of prediction error may have a different cost than a negative prediction error of equal magnitude. A simple loss function that takes into account this asymmetry is

$$a \cdot (g(\boldsymbol{x}) - y)I(y \leq g(\boldsymbol{x})) + b \cdot (y - g(\boldsymbol{x}))I(y > g(\boldsymbol{x})),$$

where a and b are positive constants. As far as minimization of the expected loss is concerned, a scale change of the loss function does not matter. Thus, one can divide the above function by $a + b$, set $\tau = b/(a + b)$, and work with the equivalent loss function

$$L_g(y, \boldsymbol{x}; \tau) = (1 - \tau)(g(\boldsymbol{x}) - y)I(y \leq g(\boldsymbol{x})) + \tau(y - g(\boldsymbol{x}))I(y > g(\boldsymbol{x})).$$

It can be shown that the optimum function g that minimizes the above loss function is the τ-quantile of the conditional distribution of y given $\boldsymbol{x}$. In other words, if $g_\tau(\boldsymbol{x})$ is defined by the relation $P(y \leq g_\tau(\boldsymbol{x})|\boldsymbol{x}) = \tau$, then

$$E[L_{g_\tau}(y, \boldsymbol{x}; \tau)] \leq E[L_g(y, \boldsymbol{x}; \tau)], \tag{2.15}$$

for any function $g(\boldsymbol{x})$.

Note that when $\tau = 0.5$, $L_g(y, \boldsymbol{x}; \tau)$ is a multiple of the loss function $L_g(y, \boldsymbol{x})$ used in Proposition 2.21, and the τ-quantile is the median. Thus, part (a) of that proposition is a special case of the inequality (2.15).

Many models and methods are available for quantile regression in general and also specifically for median regression (see Koenker, 2005; Bloomfield, 1983). In this book however, we would focus on mean regression.

2.3.3 *Regression with multivariate response*

If the response to be predicted through the random vector $\boldsymbol{x}$ is another random vector $\boldsymbol{y}$, the approximating function should also be vector-valued, with number of elements matching that of $\boldsymbol{y}$. Let $\boldsymbol{g}(\boldsymbol{x})$ be such a function. The corresponding prediction error, $\boldsymbol{y} - \boldsymbol{g}(\boldsymbol{x})$, is a random vector also. In order that the prediction error is generally small, one can try and minimize $E(\|\boldsymbol{y} - \boldsymbol{g}(\boldsymbol{x})\|^2)$. A more general criterion for minimization is $E[(\boldsymbol{y} - \boldsymbol{g}(\boldsymbol{x}))'\boldsymbol{W}(\boldsymbol{x})(\boldsymbol{y} - \boldsymbol{g}(\boldsymbol{x}))]$, where $\boldsymbol{W}$ is an arbitrary, positive definite matrix that may depend on $\boldsymbol{x}$. The positive definiteness of the matrix would ensure that the criterion takes positive values only. When $\boldsymbol{W}$ is chosen as the identity matrix, the criterion simplifies to $E(\|\boldsymbol{y} - \boldsymbol{g}(\boldsymbol{x})\|^2)$. It turns out that as long as the matrix $\boldsymbol{W}$ is positive definite, the choice of the matrix does not matter. The optimal solution is always the conditional mean vector, $\boldsymbol{g}(\boldsymbol{x}) = E(\boldsymbol{y}|\boldsymbol{x})$ (Exercise 2.8). As in the scalar case, this optimal predictor happens to be unbiased, and its prediction error is uncorrelated with any function of the predictor $\boldsymbol{x}$. It is easy to see that the dispersion matrix of the prediction error is $E[D(\boldsymbol{y}|\boldsymbol{x})]$.

Example 2.22. (Multivariate normal distribution) Suppose $\boldsymbol{x}$ and $\boldsymbol{y}$ together have the multivariate normal distribution with mean vector and dispersion matrices

$$E\begin{pmatrix}\boldsymbol{x}\\ \boldsymbol{y}\end{pmatrix} = \begin{pmatrix}\boldsymbol{\mu}_x\\ \boldsymbol{\mu}_y\end{pmatrix}; \qquad D\begin{pmatrix}\boldsymbol{x}\\ \boldsymbol{y}\end{pmatrix} = \begin{pmatrix}\boldsymbol{\Sigma}_{xx} & \boldsymbol{\Sigma}_{xy}'\\ \boldsymbol{\Sigma}_{xy} & \boldsymbol{\Sigma}_{yy}\end{pmatrix}.$$

We have seen in Section 2.1.3 that the conditional distribution of y given $\boldsymbol{x}$ is multivariate normal with mean vector and dispersion matrix

$$E(\boldsymbol{y}|\boldsymbol{x}) = \boldsymbol{\mu}_y + \boldsymbol{\Sigma}_{xy}'\boldsymbol{\Sigma}_{xx}^{-1}(\boldsymbol{x} - \boldsymbol{\mu}_x),$$
$$D(\boldsymbol{y}|\boldsymbol{x}) = \boldsymbol{\Sigma}_{yy} - \boldsymbol{\Sigma}_{xy}'\boldsymbol{\Sigma}_{xx}^{-1}\boldsymbol{\Sigma}_{xy}.$$

Thus, the regression of $\boldsymbol{y}$ on $\boldsymbol{x}$ is $\boldsymbol{\mu}_y + \boldsymbol{\Sigma}_{xy}'\boldsymbol{\Sigma}_{xx}^{-1}(\boldsymbol{x} - \boldsymbol{\mu}_x)$, and the dispersion matrix of the prediction error is $\boldsymbol{\Sigma}_{yy} - \boldsymbol{\Sigma}_{xy}'\boldsymbol{\Sigma}_{xx}^{-1}\boldsymbol{\Sigma}_{xy}$. As seen in Section 2.2, whenever $\boldsymbol{\Sigma}_{xx}$ is singular, the inverse in all these expressions may be replaced by any g-inverse. □

2.4 Linear regression as best linear prediction

We have seen in the previous section that the 'best prediction' of a response in terms of explanatory variables, going by the mean squared error criterion, is the conditional mean of the response given the explanatory variables. In order to find the conditional mean, one has to know at least the conditional distribution (if not the joint distribution). A great deal of simplification occurs in the normal case, where the conditional mean is linear in the explanatory variables. We now show that even if one does not assume multivariate normality, the optimal predictor obtained in the normal case (see Example 2.19) is still the best predictor, if we restrict attention to linear predictors. Further, identification of this 'best' predictor requires only the knowledge of the mean vector and variance-covariance matrix of the response and the explanatory variables, rather than the knowledge of any joint or conditional distribution.

Suppose we wish to predict the response y through the vector of explanatory variables $\boldsymbol{x}$, using the affine function $\boldsymbol{l}'\boldsymbol{x} + c$, where c is a constant and

$\boldsymbol{l}$ is a vector of constants having the same dimension as $\boldsymbol{x}$. The solution to the minimization problem

$$\min_{\boldsymbol{l},c} E[y - \boldsymbol{l}'\boldsymbol{x} - c]^2$$

may be called the *linear* regression of y on $\boldsymbol{x}$. It is known more commonly as the *best linear predictor* (BLP) of y given $\boldsymbol{x}$. We denote it by $\widehat{E}(y|\boldsymbol{x})$.

We identify the BLP and its properties in the next proposition.

Proposition 2.23. *Let*

$$E\begin{pmatrix}\boldsymbol{x}\\ y\end{pmatrix} = \begin{pmatrix}\boldsymbol{\mu}_x\\ \mu_y\end{pmatrix} \quad \text{and} \quad D\begin{pmatrix}\boldsymbol{x}\\ y\end{pmatrix} = \begin{pmatrix}\boldsymbol{\Sigma}_{xx} & \boldsymbol{\sigma}_{xy}\\ \boldsymbol{\sigma}'_{xy} & \sigma_y^2\end{pmatrix},$$

where $\boldsymbol{\Sigma}_{xx}$ is nonsingular. Then,
(a) the BLP is $\widehat{E}(y|\boldsymbol{x}) = \mu_y + \boldsymbol{\sigma}'_{xy}\boldsymbol{\Sigma}_{xx}^{-1}(\boldsymbol{x} - \boldsymbol{\mu}_x)$;
(b) the prediction error of the BLP, $y - \widehat{E}(y|\boldsymbol{x})$, is uncorrelated with every linear function of $\boldsymbol{x}$;
(c) the BLP is unbiased, that is, $E[\widehat{E}(y|\boldsymbol{x})] = \mu_y$;
(d) the MSE of prediction of the BLP is $E[y - \widehat{E}(y|\boldsymbol{x})]^2 = \sigma_y^2 - \boldsymbol{\sigma}'_{xy}\boldsymbol{\Sigma}_{xx}^{-1}\boldsymbol{\sigma}_{xy}$.

Proof. It is easy to see that $y - \mu_y - \boldsymbol{\sigma}'_{xy}\boldsymbol{\Sigma}_{xx}^{-1}(\boldsymbol{x} - \boldsymbol{\mu}_x)$ has zero mean and is uncorrelated with $\boldsymbol{x} - \boldsymbol{\mu}_x$. Hence, it must be uncorrelated with every linear function of $\boldsymbol{x}$. It follows that for any $\boldsymbol{l}$ and c

$$\begin{aligned} E[y - \boldsymbol{l}'\boldsymbol{x} - c]^2 &= E[y - \mu_y - \boldsymbol{\sigma}'_{xy}\boldsymbol{\Sigma}_{xx}^{-1}(\boldsymbol{x} - \boldsymbol{\mu}_x)]^2 \\ &\quad + E[\mu_y + \boldsymbol{\sigma}'_{xy}\boldsymbol{\Sigma}_{xx}^{-1}(\boldsymbol{x} - \boldsymbol{\mu}_x) - \boldsymbol{l}'\boldsymbol{x} - c]^2. \end{aligned}$$

Clearly the left-hand side is minimized by choosing $\boldsymbol{l}$ and c in a way that makes the second term on the right-hand side equal to zero. This proves part (a). The remaining parts are consequences of part (a). □

If the matrix $\boldsymbol{\Sigma}_{xx}$ is singular, the inverse $\boldsymbol{\Sigma}_{xx}^{-1}$ in the above proposition has to be replaced by any g-inverse. The proof goes through with this substitution, and Proposition 2.13 ensures that the choice of the g-inverse does not matter.

Let $\boldsymbol{x} = (x_1 : \cdots : x_k)'$. It follows from Proposition 2.23 that we can write y as

$$y = \beta_0 + \beta_1 x_1 + \cdots + \beta_k x_k + \varepsilon, \tag{2.16}$$

where

$$\beta_0 = \mu_y - \boldsymbol{\sigma}'_{xy}\boldsymbol{\Sigma}_{xx}^{-1}\boldsymbol{\mu}_x, \qquad \begin{pmatrix}\beta_1\\ \vdots\\ \beta_k\end{pmatrix} = \boldsymbol{\Sigma}_{xx}^{-1}\boldsymbol{\sigma}_{xy} \tag{2.17}$$

and $\varepsilon = y - \widehat{E}(y|\boldsymbol{x})$. According to Proposition 2.23, ε has mean zero and variance $\sigma^2 = \sigma_y^2 - \boldsymbol{\sigma}'_{xy}\boldsymbol{\Sigma}_{xx}^{-1}\boldsymbol{\sigma}_{xy}$, and is uncorrelated with $\boldsymbol{x}$. Therefore, (2.16) is a special case of (1.4)–(1.5) for a single observation. However, the explanatory variables in (2.16) are in general random and are only uncorrelated with (not necessarily independent of) ε. Even though the model (2.16) applies to any y and $\boldsymbol{x}$ having the moments described in Proposition 2.23, the model may not always be interpretable as a conditional one (given the explanatory variables). Methods of inference that require the model errors to be independent of the explanatory variables can only be used for the model (2.16) if that assumption is explicitly made.

We now present some additional properties of the BLP that would prove useful.

Proposition 2.24. *The best linear predictor has the following properties.*
(a) The BLP is a linear operator, that is, $\widehat{E}(ay_1 + by_2|\boldsymbol{x}) = a\widehat{E}(y_1|\boldsymbol{x}) + b\widehat{E}(y_2|\boldsymbol{x})$.
(b) The BLP is invariant to linear transformation of the explanatory variables, that is, $\widehat{E}(y|\boldsymbol{L}\boldsymbol{x} + \boldsymbol{c}) = \widehat{E}(y|\boldsymbol{x})$ *for any constant nonsingular matrix* $\boldsymbol{L}$ *and any constant vector* $\boldsymbol{c}$ *with appropriate dimensions.*
(c) If $\boldsymbol{x} = (x_1 : \boldsymbol{x}_2')'$, $y^* = y - \widehat{E}(y|\boldsymbol{x}_2)$ *and* $x_1^* = x_1 - \widehat{E}(x_1|\boldsymbol{x}_2)$, *then the BLP* $\widehat{E}(y|\boldsymbol{x})$ *can be decomposed as*

$$\widehat{E}(y|\boldsymbol{x}) = \widehat{E}(y|\boldsymbol{x}_2) + \widehat{E}(y^*|x_1^*).$$

(d) If $\boldsymbol{x}$, x_1^* *and* y^* *are as in part (c), then the MSE of prediction of the BLP* $\widehat{E}(y|\boldsymbol{x})$ *is the same as that of the BLP* $\widehat{E}(y^*|x_1^*)$.

Proof. Part (a) is a consequence of part (a) of Proposition 2.23, while part (b) follows from the definition of the BLP.

To prove part (c), observe from part (a) of Proposition 2.23 that x_1^* can be written as $x_1 - \boldsymbol{a}'\boldsymbol{x}_2 - b$, where $\boldsymbol{a}$ is a constant vector and b is another constant. Therefore,

$$\begin{pmatrix} x_1^* \\ \boldsymbol{x}_2 \end{pmatrix} = \begin{pmatrix} 1 & -\boldsymbol{a}' \\ \boldsymbol{0} & \boldsymbol{I} \end{pmatrix} \begin{pmatrix} x_1 \\ \boldsymbol{x}_2 \end{pmatrix} + \begin{pmatrix} -b \\ \boldsymbol{0} \end{pmatrix},$$

which is of the form $\boldsymbol{L}\boldsymbol{x} + \boldsymbol{c}$ with a nonsingular matrix $\boldsymbol{L}$. It follows from part (a) of this proposition that

$$\widehat{E}(y|\boldsymbol{x}) = \widehat{E}\left(y \,\middle|\, \begin{pmatrix} x_1^* \\ \boldsymbol{x}_2 \end{pmatrix}\right).$$

Further, from part (b) of Proposition 2.23, y^* and x_1^* are both uncorrelated with $\boldsymbol{x}_2$. Therefore,

$$D\begin{pmatrix} x_1^* \\ \boldsymbol{x}_2 \end{pmatrix}^{-1} = \begin{pmatrix} 1/E[(x_1^*)^2] & \mathbf{0} \\ \mathbf{0} & [D(\boldsymbol{x}_2)]^{-1} \end{pmatrix},$$

and

$$\widehat{E}\left(y^* \middle| \begin{pmatrix} x_1^* \\ \boldsymbol{x}_2 \end{pmatrix}\right) = \widehat{E}(y^*|x_1^*).$$

Note that $\widehat{E}(y|\boldsymbol{x}_2)$, being a linear function of $\boldsymbol{x}_2$, is uncorrelated with x_1^*, and so

$$\widehat{E}\left(\widehat{E}(y|\boldsymbol{x}_2) \middle| \begin{pmatrix} x_1^* \\ \boldsymbol{x}_2 \end{pmatrix}\right) = \widehat{E}(\widehat{E}(y|\boldsymbol{x}_2)|\boldsymbol{x}_2) = \widehat{E}(y|\boldsymbol{x}_2).$$

By putting the last two identities together and using the fact that $y = \widehat{E}(y|\boldsymbol{x}_2) + y^*$, we have the result in part (c).

This result implies that

$$y^* - \widehat{E}(y^*|x_1^*) = y - \widehat{E}(y|\boldsymbol{x}_2) - \widehat{E}(y^*|x_1^*) = y - \widehat{E}(y|\boldsymbol{x}),$$

that is, the respective prediction errors of the BLPs $\widehat{E}(y|\boldsymbol{x})$ and $\widehat{E}(y^*|x_1^*)$ are identical. Part (d) follows from this fact. □

The result in part (c) of the above proposition has an important implication for the model (2.16). By defining $\boldsymbol{x}_2 = (x_2 : \cdots : x_k)'$, it is observed that the parameter β_1 in (2.17) is the coefficient of x_1^* in $\widehat{E}(y^*|x_1^*)$. In fact, since both y^* and x_1^* have zero mean, we have

$$\widehat{E}(y^*|x_1^*) = \beta_1 x_1^*.$$

The above expression may be referred to as the partial linear regression of y on x_1, after the linear effect of $\boldsymbol{x}_2$ has been controlled. Thus, β_1 in (2.17) may be interpreted as the slope parameter in the simplified model

$$y^* = \beta_1 x_1^* + \varepsilon, \tag{2.18}$$

where the error ε is identical to the error term in (2.16). As in Example 2.16, it can be written as

$$\beta_1 = \rho_{yx_1 \cdot x_2} \frac{\sigma_{y \cdot x_2}}{\sigma_{x_1 \cdot x_2}}, \tag{2.19}$$

where $\sigma_{x_1 \cdot x_2}$ and $\sigma_{y \cdot x_2}$ are standard deviations of y^* and x_1^*, respectively, and $\rho_{yx_1 \cdot x_2}$ is the partial correlation of y and x_1, after the linear effect of $\boldsymbol{x}_2$

has been corrected for (see also Exercise 2.7). If y and $\boldsymbol{x}$ have the multivariate normal distribution, then the BLP may be interpreted as conditional mean, and $\sigma_{x_1 \cdot x_2}$ and $\sigma_{y \cdot x_2}$ may be interpreted as the conditional standard deviations of x_1 and y respectively, given $\boldsymbol{x}_2$.

All the coefficients of (2.16) may be interpreted similarly. The model (2.18) forms the basis of the added variable plot or partial regression plot, to be discussed in Sections 3.11 and 5.3.1.

The results of Proposition 2.23 can be extended to derive the general model (1.4)–(1.5). The task involves linear prediction of a response vector $\boldsymbol{y}$ in terms of a matrix of explanatory variables, $\boldsymbol{X}$. As an intermediate step, let us consider the prediction of $\boldsymbol{y}$ in terms of another random vector $\boldsymbol{x}$. As in Section 2.3.3, we set our objective as minimizing the mean square error of prediction, where the predictor is linear in $\boldsymbol{x}$. Specifically, we denote by $\widehat{E}(\boldsymbol{y}|\boldsymbol{x})$ the linear predictor $\boldsymbol{L}\boldsymbol{x} + \boldsymbol{c}$ that minimizes the MSE $E\left(\|\boldsymbol{y} - \boldsymbol{L}\boldsymbol{x} - \boldsymbol{c}\|^2\right)$, with respect to the matrix $\boldsymbol{L}$ and the vector $\boldsymbol{c}$. The solution to the optimization problem and its properties are discussed in the next proposition, which can be viewed as a multivariate extension of Proposition 2.23.

Proposition 2.25. *Let the random vectors $\boldsymbol{x}$ and $\boldsymbol{y}$ have mean and dispersion given by*

$$E\begin{pmatrix}\boldsymbol{x}\\ \boldsymbol{y}\end{pmatrix} = \begin{pmatrix}\boldsymbol{\mu}_x\\ \boldsymbol{\mu}_y\end{pmatrix}, \qquad D\begin{pmatrix}\boldsymbol{x}\\ \boldsymbol{y}\end{pmatrix} = \begin{pmatrix}\boldsymbol{\Sigma}_{xx} & \boldsymbol{\Sigma}_{xy}\\ \boldsymbol{\Sigma}'_{xy} & \boldsymbol{\Sigma}_{yy}\end{pmatrix}.$$

Then,
(a) the BLP is $\widehat{E}(\boldsymbol{y}|\boldsymbol{x}) = \boldsymbol{\mu}_y + \boldsymbol{\Sigma}'_{xy}\boldsymbol{\Sigma}_{xx}^{-1}(\boldsymbol{x} - \boldsymbol{\mu}_x)$;
(b) the prediction error of the BLP, $\boldsymbol{y} - \widehat{E}(\boldsymbol{y}|\boldsymbol{x})$, is uncorrelated with every linear function of $\boldsymbol{x}$;
(c) the BLP is unbiased, that is, $E[\widehat{E}(\boldsymbol{y}|\boldsymbol{x})] = \boldsymbol{\mu}_y$;
(d) the dispersion matrix of the prediction error of the BLP is $D(\boldsymbol{y} - \widehat{E}(\boldsymbol{y}|\boldsymbol{x})) = \boldsymbol{\Sigma}_{yy} - \boldsymbol{\Sigma}'_{xy}\boldsymbol{\Sigma}_{xx}^{-1}\boldsymbol{\Sigma}_{xy}$.

Proof. Write $\boldsymbol{y}$, $\boldsymbol{L}$, $\boldsymbol{c}$, $\boldsymbol{\mu}_y$ and $\boldsymbol{\Sigma}_{xy}$ as

$$\boldsymbol{y} = \begin{pmatrix} y_1\\ y_2\\ \vdots\\ y_m\end{pmatrix}, \quad \boldsymbol{L} = \begin{pmatrix} \boldsymbol{l}'_1\\ \boldsymbol{l}'_2\\ \vdots\\ \boldsymbol{l}'_m\end{pmatrix}, \quad \boldsymbol{c} = \begin{pmatrix} c_1\\ c_2\\ \vdots\\ c_m\end{pmatrix}, \quad \boldsymbol{\mu}_y = \begin{pmatrix} \mu_{y_1}\\ \mu_{y_2}\\ \vdots\\ \mu_{y_m}\end{pmatrix}$$

and $\boldsymbol{\Sigma}_{xy} = (\boldsymbol{\sigma}_{xy_1} \;\; \boldsymbol{\sigma}_{xy_2} \;\; \cdots \;\; \boldsymbol{\sigma}_{xy_m})$. It is clear that

$$E\left(\|\boldsymbol{y} - \boldsymbol{L}\boldsymbol{x} - \boldsymbol{c}\|^2\right) = \sum_{i=1}^{m} E(y_i - \boldsymbol{l}'_i\boldsymbol{x} - c_i)^2.$$

It follows from Proposition 2.23 that the ith term of the summation on the right-hand side is minimized when $\boldsymbol{l}_i\boldsymbol{x} + c_i$ is chosen as $\widehat{E}(y_i|\boldsymbol{x}) = \mu_{y_i} + \boldsymbol{\sigma}'_{xy_i}\boldsymbol{\Sigma}_{xx}^{-1}(\boldsymbol{x} - \boldsymbol{\mu}_x)$. Since $\boldsymbol{l}_i$ and c_i appear only in the ith term of the summation, this choice is optimal. By combining these univariate optimal predictors as a vector, we have the result in part (a). In view of this fact, parts (b) and (c) are restatements of the corresponding parts of Proposition 2.23, while part (d) follows from straightforward calculation. □

If $\boldsymbol{\Sigma}_{xx}$ is singular, the statement and the proof of this proposition remain valid after $\boldsymbol{\Sigma}^{-1}$ is replaced by any g-inverse, $\boldsymbol{\Sigma}^{-}$.

As in the case of the best predictor obtained in Section 2.3.3, it can be shown that the BLP obtained in the above proposition continues to be the optimal linear predictor if one uses $E[(\boldsymbol{y} - \boldsymbol{L}\boldsymbol{x} - \boldsymbol{c})'\boldsymbol{W}(\boldsymbol{x})(\boldsymbol{y} - \boldsymbol{L}\boldsymbol{x} - \boldsymbol{c})]$ as the criterion of optimization, where $\boldsymbol{W}$ is an arbitrary, positive definite matrix that may depend on $\boldsymbol{x}$ (see Exercise 2.9). This criterion reduces to $E\left(\|\boldsymbol{y} - \boldsymbol{L}\boldsymbol{x} - \boldsymbol{c}\|^2\right)$ when $\boldsymbol{W}$ is chosen as the identity matrix. See Exercise 2.10 for another optimal property of the BLP. Yet another optimality is established in the next Section.

By adapting the result in Proposition 2.25 to the set-up of Proposition 2.20, while avoiding any distributional assumption, the BLP of the response vector $\boldsymbol{y}$ in terms of the matrix $\boldsymbol{X}$ can be shown to lead to a general model similar to (1.4)–(1.5). This work is left as Exercise 2.11.

2.5 Multiple correlation coefficient*

Often one attempts to predict a response y with a single explanatory variable x. According to Proposition 2.23, the best linear predictor of y in terms of x is

$$\widehat{E}(y|x) = \mu_y + \frac{\sigma_{xy}}{\sigma_x^2}(x - \mu_x) = \mu_y + \rho\sigma_y\left(\frac{x - \mu_x}{\sigma_x}\right), \tag{2.20}$$

where the symbols have their usual meaning (see Example 2.2). Thus, if a single explanatory variable x is available for predicting y, and the parameters μ_x, μ_y, σ_x^2, σ_y^2 and ρ are known, the above equation gives the best predictor. Interestingly, the BLP depends on x through its standardized version $(x - \mu_x)/\sigma_x$. Therefore, any affine function of x, which clearly has the same standardized version and the same correlation with y, would produce exactly the same linear predictor through (2.20).

This single explanatory variable can in fact be a summary obtained from several explanatory variables. Let $\boldsymbol{x}$ be the vector of explanatory variables.

If we restrict ourselves to a linear summary of the form $\boldsymbol{l}'\boldsymbol{x}$, a reasonable choice of the summary would be one which has a high correlation with y. Suppose we choose $\boldsymbol{l}$ such that $\boldsymbol{l}'\boldsymbol{x}$ has the *largest possible correlation with* y, and use $x = \boldsymbol{l}'\boldsymbol{x}$ to obtain the predictor in (2.20). The question is: will this predictor be inferior to the BLP computed directly from $\boldsymbol{x}$?

In order to answer this question, we have to characterize a linear combination of $\boldsymbol{x}$ with largest possible correlation with y. The next proposition provides such a characterization and implies that the proposed predictor would indeed be the same as the BLP.

Proposition 2.26. *Let*

$$E\begin{pmatrix}\boldsymbol{x}\\ y\end{pmatrix} = \begin{pmatrix}\boldsymbol{\mu}_x\\ \mu_y\end{pmatrix} \quad \textit{and} \quad D\begin{pmatrix}\boldsymbol{x}\\ y\end{pmatrix} = \begin{pmatrix}\boldsymbol{\Sigma}_{xx} & \boldsymbol{\sigma}_{xy}\\ \boldsymbol{\sigma}'_{xy} & \sigma_y^2\end{pmatrix}.$$

Suppose $\boldsymbol{\Sigma}_{xx}$ *is nonsingular. Then,*
(a) the linear function $\boldsymbol{l}'\boldsymbol{x}$ *has the largest possible correlation with* y *if and only if it differs at most by an additive constant from a positive multiple of the BLP,* $\widehat{E}(y|\boldsymbol{x}) = \mu_y + \boldsymbol{\sigma}'_{xy}\boldsymbol{\Sigma}_{xx}^{-1}(\boldsymbol{x} - \boldsymbol{\mu}_x)$;
(b) the correlation of the BLP with y *is* $\sqrt{\boldsymbol{\sigma}'_{xy}\boldsymbol{\Sigma}_{xx}^{-1}\boldsymbol{\sigma}_{xy}/\sigma_y^2}$.

Proof. Consider the linear function $\boldsymbol{l}'\boldsymbol{x}$. Its correlation with $\boldsymbol{y}$ is

$$\frac{\boldsymbol{l}'\boldsymbol{\sigma}_{xy}}{\sqrt{\boldsymbol{l}'\boldsymbol{\Sigma}_{xx}\boldsymbol{l}\sigma_y^2}}.$$

Factorize $\boldsymbol{\Sigma}_{xx}$ as $\boldsymbol{B}\boldsymbol{B}'$, where $\boldsymbol{B}$ is a nonsingular matrix. It follows that

$$\boldsymbol{l}'\boldsymbol{\sigma}_{xy} \le |\boldsymbol{l}'\boldsymbol{\sigma}_{xy}| = \sqrt{(\boldsymbol{l}'\boldsymbol{B}\boldsymbol{B}^{-1}\boldsymbol{\sigma}_{xy})^2} = \sqrt{((\boldsymbol{B}'\boldsymbol{l})'\boldsymbol{B}^{-1}\boldsymbol{\sigma}_{xy})^2},$$

which, by the Cauchy-Schwartz inequality, is less than or equal to

$$\sqrt{(\boldsymbol{B}'\boldsymbol{l})'(\boldsymbol{B}'\boldsymbol{l})(\boldsymbol{B}^{-1}\boldsymbol{\sigma}_{xy})'(\boldsymbol{B}^{-1}\boldsymbol{\sigma}_{xy})} = \sqrt{\boldsymbol{l}'\boldsymbol{\Sigma}_{xx}\boldsymbol{l}\cdot\boldsymbol{\sigma}'_{xy}\boldsymbol{\Sigma}_{xx}^{-1}\boldsymbol{\sigma}_{xy}}.$$

It follows that

$$\frac{\boldsymbol{l}'\boldsymbol{\sigma}_{xy}}{\sqrt{\boldsymbol{l}'\boldsymbol{\Sigma}_{xx}\boldsymbol{l}\sigma_y^2}} \le \sqrt{\frac{\boldsymbol{\sigma}'_{xy}\boldsymbol{\Sigma}_{xx}^{-1}\boldsymbol{\sigma}_{xy}}{\sigma_y^2}}.$$

This inequality would hold with equality if and only if $\boldsymbol{B}\boldsymbol{l}$ is a positive multiple of $\boldsymbol{B}^{-1}\boldsymbol{\sigma}_{xy}$, i.e. $\boldsymbol{l}$ is a positive multiple of $\boldsymbol{\Sigma}_{xx}^{-1}\boldsymbol{\sigma}_{xy}$.

The proves part (a). The expression in part (b) is the highest value obtained on the right side of the above equation. □

The *multiple correlation coefficient* of y with $\boldsymbol{x}$ is the maximum value of the correlation between y and any linear function of $\boldsymbol{x}$. It follows from Proposition 2.26 that the multiple correlation coefficient of y with $\boldsymbol{x}$ is

$$\rho_{yx} = \sqrt{\frac{\boldsymbol{\sigma}'_{xy}\boldsymbol{\Sigma}_{xx}^{-1}\boldsymbol{\sigma}_{xy}}{\sigma_y^2}}. \tag{2.21}$$

Part (d) of Proposition 2.23 shows that the MSE of prediction of the BLP is $\sigma_y^2(1-\rho_{yx}^2)$. In contrast, σ_y^2 is the MSE of prediction of y by the best constant, namely, the mean μ_y. Thus, $1-\rho_{yx}^2$ represents the factor by which the minimum MSE can be reduced by making use of $\boldsymbol{x}$ as a linear predictor.

Remark 2.27. If the matrix $\boldsymbol{\Sigma}_{xx}$ in Proposition 2.26 is singular, the statement and the proof of the above proposition goes through if we replace $\boldsymbol{\Sigma}_{xx}^{-1}$ by any g-inverse $\boldsymbol{\Sigma}_{xx}^{-}$ and $\boldsymbol{B}^{-1}$ by any left-inverse, $\boldsymbol{B}^{-L}$. The choice of the g-inverse or the left-inverse does not matter, as $\boldsymbol{\sigma}_{xy}$ lies in the column space of $\boldsymbol{B}$. In this case there are many ways of choosing $\boldsymbol{l}$ so that the Cauchy-Schwartz inequality holds with equality. Specifically, one can generate new choices by adding any vector from the null-space of $\boldsymbol{\Sigma}_{xx}$. However, Proposition 2.13 ensures that these modifications would not alter any linear function of $(\boldsymbol{x}-\boldsymbol{\mu}_x)$. Thus, the statement of Proposition 2.26 would continue to hold in the singular case with $\boldsymbol{\Sigma}_{xx}^{-1}$ replaced by $\boldsymbol{\Sigma}_{xx}^{-}$. □

2.6 Decorrelation*

Propositions 2.25 and 2.26 imply that the vector $\boldsymbol{y}$ can be decomposed as

$$\boldsymbol{y} = [\boldsymbol{\mu} + \boldsymbol{\Sigma}'_{xy}\boldsymbol{\Sigma}_{xx}^{-1}(\boldsymbol{x}-\boldsymbol{\mu}_x)] + [\boldsymbol{y} - \boldsymbol{\Sigma}'_{xy}\boldsymbol{\Sigma}_{xx}^{-1}(\boldsymbol{x}-\boldsymbol{\mu}_x) - \boldsymbol{\mu}],$$

where each of the elements of the first vector (the BLP of $\boldsymbol{y}$ in terms of $\boldsymbol{x}$) has the largest possible correlation with the corresponding element of $\boldsymbol{y}$ and the second vector is uncorrelated with $\boldsymbol{x}$. Even where prediction is not required, such a decomposition is useful for decorrelating one random vector from another. The next proposition gives a characterization of the linear adjustment needed for decorrelation in a somewhat general set-up.

Proposition 2.28. *Let $\boldsymbol{u}$ and $\boldsymbol{v}$ be random vectors having first and second order moments such that $E(\boldsymbol{v}) = \boldsymbol{0}$. Then the linear compound $\boldsymbol{u} - \boldsymbol{B}\boldsymbol{v}$ is uncorrelated with $\boldsymbol{v}$ if and only if*

$$\boldsymbol{B}\boldsymbol{v} = Cov(\boldsymbol{u},\boldsymbol{v})[D(\boldsymbol{v})]^{-}\boldsymbol{v} \quad \textit{with probability 1.}$$

Proof. The 'if' part is easy to prove. To prove the 'only if' part, let $Cov(\boldsymbol{u} - \boldsymbol{Bv}, \boldsymbol{v}) = \boldsymbol{0}$. It follows that $\boldsymbol{B}D(\boldsymbol{v}) = Cov(\boldsymbol{u}, \boldsymbol{v})$, or $D(\boldsymbol{v})\boldsymbol{B}' = Cov(\boldsymbol{v}, \boldsymbol{u})$. According to part (c) of Proposition A.23, $\boldsymbol{B}'$ must be of the form $\boldsymbol{V}^{-}Cov(\boldsymbol{v}, \boldsymbol{u}) - (\boldsymbol{I} - \boldsymbol{V}^{-}\boldsymbol{V})\boldsymbol{G}$, where $\boldsymbol{V} = D(\boldsymbol{v})$ and $\boldsymbol{G}$ is an arbitrary matrix. Since $E(\boldsymbol{v}) = \boldsymbol{0}$, part (a) of Proposition 2.13 implies that $\boldsymbol{v} \in \mathcal{C}(\boldsymbol{V})$ almost surely. We can choose $\boldsymbol{V}^{-}$ as a symmetric matrix without loss of generality, and the value of $Cov(\boldsymbol{u}, \boldsymbol{v})\boldsymbol{V}^{-}\boldsymbol{v}$ does not depend on the choice of the g-inverse. Consequently, $\boldsymbol{v}'\boldsymbol{B}' = \boldsymbol{v}'\boldsymbol{V}^{-}Cov(\boldsymbol{v}, \boldsymbol{u}) - \boldsymbol{0}$, i.e. $\boldsymbol{Bv} = Cov(\boldsymbol{u}, \boldsymbol{v})\boldsymbol{V}^{-}\boldsymbol{v}$ with probability 1. □

Part (b) of Proposition 2.13 ensures that the value of $\boldsymbol{Bv}$ in Proposition 2.28 does not depend on the choice of the g-inverse.

We shall refer to the result in Proposition 2.28 as the *decorrelation principle.* It plays an important role in the derivation of several results of this book. The principle can be understood from the diagram of Figure 2.2, where the random vectors $\boldsymbol{u}$ and $\boldsymbol{v}$ are represented by arrows. Vectors at right angles to each other signify zero correlation. Parallel vectors have correlation 1 or -1. In general $\boldsymbol{u}$ and $\boldsymbol{v}$ are correlated, that is, these vectors are not at right angles to one another. The vector $\boldsymbol{Bv}$ described in Proposition 2.28 can be interpreted as the component of $\boldsymbol{u}$ in the direction of $\boldsymbol{v}$. The remaining part, $\boldsymbol{u} - \boldsymbol{Bv}$, is at right angles (uncorrelated) with $\boldsymbol{v}$. The random vectors $\boldsymbol{Bv}$ and $\boldsymbol{u} - \boldsymbol{Bv}$ constitute a decomposition of $\boldsymbol{u}$ into uncorrelated components.

Given a set of correlated random variables, the above construction may

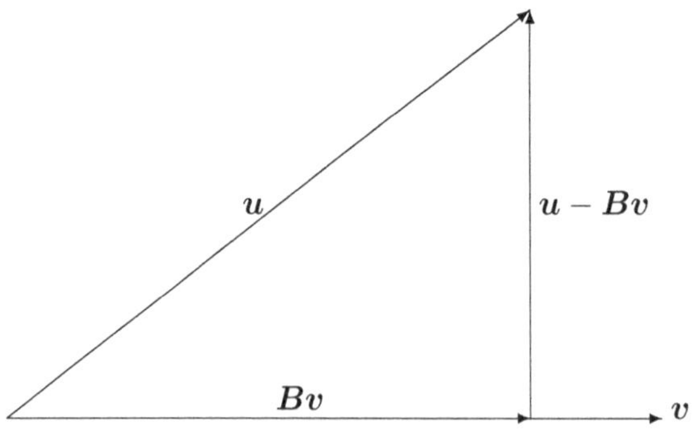

Fig. 2.2 A geometric view of decorrelation

be used iteratively to form a minimal or basis set of uncorrelated random variables, so that all the original variables are linear functions of the variables in the basis set. One can arrange the given random variables in any arbitrary serial order, and pick the first one as the initial basis set. At any stage of the iteration, one has to pick the first available variable in the original list, which is not a linear combination of the variables already included in the basis set. Once this variable is identified, it has to be decorrelated from the existing basis set using the formula of Proposition 2.28, and then added to the basis set. The process continues till there no remaining variable in the original list, which is not a linear function of the basis set. This principle is more commonly used for obtaining a set of orthogonal vectors from an arbitrary set of vectors of common order, and is known as Gram-Schmidt orthogonalization (see Golub and Van Loan, 2013). It can be shown that the number of uncorrelated random variables in the basis set is equal to the rank of the dispersion matrix of the original set of variables.

2.7 Complements/Exercises

Exercises with solutions given in Appendix C

2.1 Suppose $\boldsymbol{y} \sim N(\boldsymbol{\mu}, \boldsymbol{\Sigma})$. Show that

(a) if $\boldsymbol{\Sigma}$ is nonsingular, the joint density of $\boldsymbol{y}$ is given by (2.3).
(b) if $\boldsymbol{\Sigma}$ is singular, the joint density of $\boldsymbol{y}$ is given by (2.11).

2.2 If $\boldsymbol{z} \sim N(\boldsymbol{0}, \boldsymbol{\Sigma})$, then show that the quadratic form $\boldsymbol{z}'\boldsymbol{\Sigma}^{-}\boldsymbol{z}$ almost surely does not depend on the choice of the g-inverse, and has the chi-square distribution with $\rho(\boldsymbol{\Sigma})$ degrees of freedom.

2.3 Prove Proposition 2.11.

2.4 Prove the following converse of part (a) of Proposition 2.11: If $\boldsymbol{y} \sim N(\boldsymbol{\mu}, \boldsymbol{I})$, and $\boldsymbol{y}'\boldsymbol{A}\boldsymbol{y}$ has a chi-square distribution then $\boldsymbol{A}$ is an idempotent matrix, in which case the chi-square distribution has $\rho(\boldsymbol{A})$ degrees of freedom and noncentrality parameter $\boldsymbol{\mu}'\boldsymbol{A}\boldsymbol{\mu}$. [See Rao (1973c, p. 186) for a more general result.]

2.5 Show that part (b) of Proposition 2.11 (for $\boldsymbol{\mu} = \boldsymbol{0}$) holds under the weaker assumption that $\boldsymbol{A}$ and $\boldsymbol{B}$ are nonnegative definite matrices (not necessarily idempotent).

2.6 Prove (2.15).

2.7 Prove algebraically that the right-hand side of (2.19) is indeed equal to the β_1 in (2.17).

2.8 Let $\boldsymbol{y}$ and $\boldsymbol{x}$ be random vectors and $\boldsymbol{W}(\boldsymbol{x})$ be a positive definite matrix for every value of $\boldsymbol{x}$.

   (a) Show that the vector function $\boldsymbol{g}(\boldsymbol{x})$ that minimizes $E[(\boldsymbol{y} - \boldsymbol{g}(\boldsymbol{x}))'\boldsymbol{W}(\boldsymbol{x})(\boldsymbol{y} - \boldsymbol{g}(\boldsymbol{x})]$ is $\boldsymbol{g}(\boldsymbol{x}) = E(\boldsymbol{y}|\boldsymbol{x})$.

   (b) What happens when $\boldsymbol{W}(\boldsymbol{x})$ is positive semidefinite?

2.9 Modify the results of Exercise 2.8 under the constraint that $g(\boldsymbol{x})$ is of the form $\boldsymbol{Lx} + \boldsymbol{c}$.

2.10 Let $\boldsymbol{x}$ and $\boldsymbol{y}$ be random vectors with finite first and second order moments such that

$$E\begin{pmatrix}\boldsymbol{x}\\ \boldsymbol{y}\end{pmatrix} = \begin{pmatrix}\boldsymbol{\mu}_x\\ \boldsymbol{\mu}_y\end{pmatrix}, \quad D\begin{pmatrix}\boldsymbol{x}\\ \boldsymbol{y}\end{pmatrix} = \begin{pmatrix}\boldsymbol{\Sigma}_{xx} & \boldsymbol{\Sigma}_{xy}\\ \boldsymbol{\Sigma}_{yx} & \boldsymbol{\Sigma}_{yy}\end{pmatrix}.$$

Show that the best linear predictor (BLP) of $\boldsymbol{y}$ in terms of $\boldsymbol{x}$, which minimizes (in the sense of the Löwner order) the mean squared prediction error matrix $E[(\boldsymbol{y} - \boldsymbol{Lx} - \boldsymbol{c})(\boldsymbol{y} - \boldsymbol{Lx} - \boldsymbol{c})']$ with respect to $\boldsymbol{L}$ and $\boldsymbol{c}$, is unique and is given by

$$\widehat{E}(\boldsymbol{y}|\boldsymbol{x}) = \boldsymbol{\mu}_y + \boldsymbol{\Sigma}_{yx}\boldsymbol{\Sigma}_{xx}^{-}(\boldsymbol{x} - \boldsymbol{\mu}_x).$$

What is the minimized value of the mean squared prediction error matrix?

2.11 Let the random vector $\boldsymbol{y}_{n\times 1}$ and the random matrix $\boldsymbol{X}_{n\times(k+1)}$ be such that $\boldsymbol{X} = (\boldsymbol{1} : \boldsymbol{Z})$,

$$E(\boldsymbol{y} : \boldsymbol{Z}) = \boldsymbol{1} \otimes (\mu_y : \boldsymbol{\mu}_x'),$$
$$D(\text{vec}(\boldsymbol{y} : \boldsymbol{Z})) = \boldsymbol{\Sigma}_{(k+1)\times(k+1)} \otimes \boldsymbol{V}_{n\times n},$$

for some nonnegative definite matrices $\boldsymbol{V}$ and $\boldsymbol{\Sigma}$, and that $\boldsymbol{\Sigma}$ can be partitioned as

$$\boldsymbol{\Sigma} = \begin{pmatrix}\sigma_y^2 & \boldsymbol{\sigma}_{xy}'\\ \boldsymbol{\sigma}_{xy} & \boldsymbol{\Sigma}_{xx}\end{pmatrix}.$$

Show that $\boldsymbol{y}$ can be decomposed as

$$\boldsymbol{y} = \boldsymbol{X\beta} + \boldsymbol{\varepsilon},$$

where $E(\boldsymbol{\varepsilon}) = \boldsymbol{0}$, $D(\boldsymbol{\varepsilon}) = \sigma^2\boldsymbol{V}$, $\boldsymbol{\varepsilon}$ is uncorrelated with the elements of $\boldsymbol{X}$, and

$$\boldsymbol{\beta} = \begin{pmatrix}\mu_y + \boldsymbol{\sigma}_{xy}'\boldsymbol{\Sigma}_{xx}^{-}\boldsymbol{\mu}_x\\ \boldsymbol{\Sigma}_{xx}^{-}\boldsymbol{\sigma}_{xy}\end{pmatrix},$$
$$\sigma^2 = \sigma_y^2 - \boldsymbol{\sigma}_{xy}'\boldsymbol{\Sigma}_{xx}^{-}\boldsymbol{\sigma}_{xy}.$$

Can it be said that $\boldsymbol{y}$ follows the model (1.4) along with (1.5)?

2.12 Prove the following facts about decorrelation.

(a) If $\boldsymbol{u}$ and $\boldsymbol{v}$ are random vectors with known first and second order moments such that $E(\boldsymbol{v}) \in \mathcal{C}(D(\boldsymbol{v}))$, and $\boldsymbol{B}$ is chosen so that $\boldsymbol{u} - \boldsymbol{B}\boldsymbol{v}$ is uncorrelated with $\boldsymbol{v}$, show that $D(\boldsymbol{u} - \boldsymbol{B}\boldsymbol{v}) \leq D(\boldsymbol{u})$ (that is, decorrelation reduces the dispersion of a vector in the sense of the Löwner order).

(b) Let $\boldsymbol{u}$, $\boldsymbol{v}$ and $\boldsymbol{B}$ be as above, $\boldsymbol{v} = (\boldsymbol{v}_1' : \boldsymbol{v}_2')'$ and $\boldsymbol{B}_1$ be chosen such that $\boldsymbol{l}'(\boldsymbol{u} - \boldsymbol{B}_1\boldsymbol{v}_1)$ is uncorrelated with $\boldsymbol{v}_1$. Show that $D(\boldsymbol{u} - \boldsymbol{B}_1\boldsymbol{v}_1) \geq D(\boldsymbol{u} - \boldsymbol{B}\boldsymbol{v})$ (that is, by expanding the size of $\boldsymbol{v}$, one can reduce the dispersion of the decorrelated vector).

Additional exercises

2.13 Derive the conditional distribution in Example 2.3 directly from Equation (2.4), by multiplying $\left(\frac{x-\mu_x}{\sigma_x}\right)^2$ in the exponent with $[(1-\rho^2)+\rho^2]$ and splitting it into two parts, so that the marginal density can be factored out.

2.14 If $\boldsymbol{y} \sim N(\boldsymbol{0}, \boldsymbol{I})$, and $\boldsymbol{A}$ and $\boldsymbol{B}$ be nonnegative definite matrices such that $\boldsymbol{y}'\boldsymbol{A}\boldsymbol{y} \sim \chi^2_{\rho(A)}$ and $\boldsymbol{y}'(\boldsymbol{A}+\boldsymbol{B})\boldsymbol{y} \sim \chi^2_{\rho(A+B)}$, then show that $\boldsymbol{y}'\boldsymbol{B}\boldsymbol{y} \sim \chi^2_{\rho(B)}$.

2.15 Suppose the random variables x and y have the bivariate normal distribution with $E(x) = 2$, $E(y) = -4$, $Var(x) = 1$, $Var(y) = 4$ and $Cov(x, y) = 1$.

(a) What is the regression of y on x?

(b) What is the error variance in the linear regression model $y = \beta_0 + \beta_1 x + \varepsilon$?

(c) Which fraction of the variance of y is not explained by x?

(d) If $z = \frac{x}{10} - 1$, what would be the regression of y on z?

2.16 Determine the regression of y on x if

(a) $f(x, y) = xe^{-x(y+1)}$ for $x \geq 0$, $y \geq 0$ and 0 elsewhere.

(b) $f(x, y) = 2$ for $x \geq 0$, $y \geq 0$, $x + y \leq 1$, and 0 elsewhere.

2.17 If the random variables x and y are as in Example 2.17, determine whether the regression of x on y is also linear in y.

2.18 Find an affine function of the random vector $\boldsymbol{x}$, written as $\boldsymbol{l}'\boldsymbol{x} + c$, that has the most negative correlation with a random variable y.

2.19 If an affine function of the random vector $\boldsymbol{x}$, written as $\boldsymbol{l}'\boldsymbol{x} + c$, has the largest possible correlation with a random variable y, is it necessary that $\boldsymbol{l}'\boldsymbol{x} + c$ is the BLP of y?

2.20 Suppose the joint distribution of the random variables y, x_1 and x_2 is multivariate normal, the correlation of y with $\beta_0 + \beta_1 x_1 + \beta_2 x_2$ is equal to the multiple correlation of y with x_1 and x_2, and $E(y) = E(\beta_0 + \beta_1 x_1 + \beta_2 x_2)$. Can it be said that $\beta_0 + \beta_1 x_1 + \beta_2 x_2$ is the regression of y on x_1 and x_2? Explain.

2.21 Suppose the joint dispersion matrix of $\boldsymbol{x}$ and y be as in Proposition 2.26. By factorizing this dispersion in the manner of (2.1), derive an expression of the multiple correlation coefficient of y with $\boldsymbol{x}$ in terms of the correlation matrix of y and $\boldsymbol{x}$

Chapter 3

Estimation in the Linear Model

Consider the homoscedastic linear model

$$y = X\beta + \varepsilon; \qquad E(\varepsilon) = \mathbf{0}, \quad D(\varepsilon) = \sigma^2 I$$

which we represent by $(y, X\beta, \sigma^2 I)$. This is a special case of the model described in (1.4)–(1.5), with the restrictions that the model errors (elements of the vector ε) have a common variance and are uncorrelated. We assume that y is a vector of n elements, X is an $n \times p$ matrix with $n > p$ and β is a vector of p elements. The unknown parameters of this model are the coefficient vector β and the error variance σ^2. In this chapter we deal with the problem of estimation of these parameters from the observables y and X.

The first few sections concern the well-known method called least squares estimation. We discuss the fitted values of the response, the corresponding residuals, variances and covariances of the estimators, and finally the estimation of the error variance σ^2. A closer examination of the estimation problem may reveal difficulty in the estimation of some of the model parameters. For example, if one has ten observations, all of them measuring the combined weight of an apple and an orange, one cannot hope to estimate the weight of the orange alone from these measurements. As demonstrated by this example, in general, only some functions of the model parameters and not all, can be estimated from the data. We discuss this issue in Section 3.5.

If it is possible to estimate a given parameter, the next question is how to estimate it in the best possible way. This leads us to the theory of best linear unbiased estimation, discussed in Section 3.6. An elegant and unified development of this theory is based on an important tool, namely the set of "linear zero functions", — linear functions of the response y which have zero expectation for all possible parameter values. In Section 3.7 we present the *maximum likelihood estimator* (MLE), under a distributional assumption for the errors. Subsequent sections deal with some variations to the linear model, and issues and problems which arise in such estimation.

3.1 Least squares estimation

In the linear model $(\boldsymbol{y}, \boldsymbol{X\beta}, \sigma^2\boldsymbol{I})$, the response vector consists of the sum of two parts: a systematic part, $\boldsymbol{X\beta}$, and the random error part, $\boldsymbol{\varepsilon}$. Estimation of the vector parameter $\boldsymbol{\beta}$ is to find its value from the available data ($\boldsymbol{y}$ and $\boldsymbol{X}$). If $\widehat{\boldsymbol{\beta}}$ were to be an estimate of $\boldsymbol{\beta}$, the difference $\boldsymbol{y} - \boldsymbol{X}\widehat{\boldsymbol{\beta}}$ would account for model error. One would expect $\boldsymbol{y} - \boldsymbol{X}\widehat{\boldsymbol{\beta}}$ to be small if $\widehat{\boldsymbol{\beta}}$ is a good estimate of $\boldsymbol{\beta}$. Therefore, it makes sense to estimate the value of $\boldsymbol{\beta}$ so as to minimize the sum of squared elements of this error vector. Such an estimator is called a *least squares estimator* (LSE) of $\boldsymbol{\beta}$. Formally, an LSE is

$$\widehat{\boldsymbol{\beta}}_{LS} = \arg\min_{\boldsymbol{\beta}} \|\boldsymbol{y} - \boldsymbol{X\beta}\|^2 = \arg\min_{\boldsymbol{\beta}} [\boldsymbol{y}'\boldsymbol{y} - 2\boldsymbol{y}'\boldsymbol{X\beta} + \boldsymbol{\beta}'\boldsymbol{X}'\boldsymbol{X\beta}]. \quad (3.1)$$

By differentiating the quadratic function with respect to $\boldsymbol{\beta}$ and setting it to zero, we have

$$\boldsymbol{X}'\boldsymbol{X\beta} = \boldsymbol{X}'\boldsymbol{y}. \quad (3.2)$$

The above equation is traditionally referred to as the *normal equation*. Proposition A.23 indicates that although there is always a solution to the normal equation, it is uniquely defined if and only if $\boldsymbol{X}'\boldsymbol{X}$ is nonsingular, i.e. if $\boldsymbol{X}$ has full column rank. In such a case, the unique LSE of $\boldsymbol{\beta}$ is

$$\widehat{\boldsymbol{\beta}}_{LS} = (\boldsymbol{X}'\boldsymbol{X})^{-1}\boldsymbol{X}'\boldsymbol{y}. \quad (3.3)$$

Remark 3.1. By differentiating the quadratic function $\|\boldsymbol{y} - \boldsymbol{X\beta}\|^2$ twice with respect to $\boldsymbol{\beta}$, we obtain the matrix $2\boldsymbol{X}'\boldsymbol{X}$, which is nonnegative definite (see Proposition A.25). It follows that the solution to the normal equation actually *minimizes* the sum of squared errors. To see this more directly, we write

$$\begin{aligned}
&\|\boldsymbol{y} - \boldsymbol{X\beta}\|^2 \\
&= \|\boldsymbol{y} - \boldsymbol{X}\widehat{\boldsymbol{\beta}} + \boldsymbol{X}\widehat{\boldsymbol{\beta}} - \boldsymbol{X\beta}\|^2 \\
&= \|\boldsymbol{y} - \boldsymbol{X}\widehat{\boldsymbol{\beta}}\|^2 + \|\boldsymbol{X}\widehat{\boldsymbol{\beta}} - \boldsymbol{X\beta}\|^2 + 2(\boldsymbol{y} - \boldsymbol{X}(\boldsymbol{X}'\boldsymbol{X})^{-1}\boldsymbol{X}'\boldsymbol{y})'\boldsymbol{X}(\widehat{\boldsymbol{\beta}} - \boldsymbol{\beta}) \\
&= \|\boldsymbol{y} - \boldsymbol{X}\widehat{\boldsymbol{\beta}}\|^2 + \|\boldsymbol{X}\widehat{\boldsymbol{\beta}} - \boldsymbol{X\beta}\|^2 + 2\boldsymbol{y}'(\boldsymbol{X} - \boldsymbol{X}(\boldsymbol{X}'\boldsymbol{X})^{-1}\boldsymbol{X}'\boldsymbol{X})(\widehat{\boldsymbol{\beta}} - \boldsymbol{\beta}) \\
&= \|\boldsymbol{y} - \boldsymbol{X}\widehat{\boldsymbol{\beta}}\|^2 + \|\boldsymbol{X}\widehat{\boldsymbol{\beta}} - \boldsymbol{X\beta}\|^2 \\
&\geq \|\boldsymbol{y} - \boldsymbol{X}\widehat{\boldsymbol{\beta}}\|^2.
\end{aligned}$$

□

Remark 3.2. If $\boldsymbol{X}'\boldsymbol{X}$ is singular, a general solution to (3.2) is of the form $(\boldsymbol{X}'\boldsymbol{X})^{-}\boldsymbol{X}'\boldsymbol{y}$, where $(\boldsymbol{X}'\boldsymbol{X})^{-}$ is *any* g-inverse of $\boldsymbol{X}'\boldsymbol{X}$ (see Remark A.24). In such a case, the (nonunique) quantity

$$\widehat{\boldsymbol{\beta}}_{LS} = (\boldsymbol{X}'\boldsymbol{X})^{-}\boldsymbol{X}'\boldsymbol{y} \tag{3.4}$$

may be called a least squares estimator of $\boldsymbol{\beta}$. The inequality $\|\boldsymbol{y} - \boldsymbol{X}\boldsymbol{\beta}\|^2 \geq \|\boldsymbol{y} - \boldsymbol{X}\widehat{\boldsymbol{\beta}}\|^2$ is proved in the same manner, using the fact that $\boldsymbol{X}(\boldsymbol{X}'\boldsymbol{X})^{-}\boldsymbol{X}'\boldsymbol{X} = \boldsymbol{X}$. □

Whenever the inverse of $\boldsymbol{X}'\boldsymbol{X}$ exists, the unique LSE is unbiased, since

$$E(\widehat{\boldsymbol{\beta}}_{LS}) = (\boldsymbol{X}'\boldsymbol{X})^{-1}\boldsymbol{X}'E(\boldsymbol{y}) = (\boldsymbol{X}'\boldsymbol{X})^{-1}\boldsymbol{X}'\boldsymbol{X}\boldsymbol{\beta} = \boldsymbol{\beta}.$$

When there is only one explanatory variable, $\boldsymbol{x}$, the linear model becomes

$$\boldsymbol{y} = \beta_0\mathbf{1} + \beta_1\boldsymbol{x} + \boldsymbol{\varepsilon}, \tag{3.5}$$

where $\mathbf{1}$ is a vector with all the elements equal to 1. This model is known as the *simple linear regression* model (in contrast with the *multiple linear regression* model, or simply the *multiple regression* model, for multiple explanatory variables). Here, $\boldsymbol{X} = (\mathbf{1} : \boldsymbol{x})$ and $\boldsymbol{\beta} = (\beta_0 : \beta_1)'$, $\boldsymbol{x} = (x_1 : x_2 : \cdots : x_n)'$, $\boldsymbol{y} = (y_1 : y_2 : \cdots : y_n)'$ and $\boldsymbol{\varepsilon} = (\varepsilon_1 : \varepsilon_2 : \cdots : \varepsilon_n)'$. Thus, the unique LSE of $\boldsymbol{\beta}$ is

$$\widehat{\boldsymbol{\beta}}_{LS} = \begin{pmatrix} n & n\bar{x} \\ n\bar{x} & \|\boldsymbol{x}\|^2 \end{pmatrix}^{-1} \begin{pmatrix} n\bar{y} \\ \boldsymbol{x}'\boldsymbol{y} \end{pmatrix},$$

where $\bar{x} = n^{-1}\mathbf{1}'\boldsymbol{x}$ and $\bar{y} = n^{-1}\mathbf{1}'\boldsymbol{y}$. After some algebraic manipulation the LSEs of β_1 and β_0 simplify to

$$\widehat{\beta}_1 = \frac{\boldsymbol{x}'\boldsymbol{y} - n\cdot\bar{x}\cdot\bar{y}}{\|\boldsymbol{x}\|^2 - n\cdot\bar{x}^2} = \frac{(\boldsymbol{x} - \bar{x}\mathbf{1})'\boldsymbol{y}}{\|\boldsymbol{x} - \bar{x}\mathbf{1}\|^2} = \frac{\sum_{i=1}^n (x_i - \bar{x})(y_i - \bar{y})}{\sum_{i=1}^n (x_i - \bar{x})^2}, \tag{3.6}$$

$$\widehat{\beta}_0 = \bar{y} - \widehat{\beta}_1\bar{x}. \tag{3.7}$$

Example 3.3. (Receding galaxies, continued) For the galactic objects data of Table 3.1, let y_i be the velocity of the ith galaxy at distance x_i from Earth, and assume the linear model $y_i = \beta_0 + \beta_1 x_i + \varepsilon_i$, which is another form of the model (3.5). The least squares estimates of the parameters are obtained by evaluating the expressions given in (3.6)–(3.7).

In order to carry out these computations in R, one has to invoke the R package `lmreg` through the command `library(lmreg)` and load the data through the command `data(stars1)`. The variable names and the first few cases in the data set can be viewed by using the command `head(stars1)`. The estimates of the coefficients are obtained through the following additional commands.

Table 3.1 Distance of galactic objects from Earth and their velocities (data object **stars1** in R package **lmreg**, source: Hubble, 1929)

Object name	Distance (mpc)*	Velocity (km/s)
SMC	0.032	170
LMC	0.034	290
NGC 6822	0.214	–130
NGC 598	0.263	–70
NGC 221	0.275	–185
NGC 224	0.275	–220
NGC 5357	0.45	200
NGC 4736	0.5	290
NGC 5194	0.5	270
NGC 4449	0.63	–200
NGC 4214	0.8	300
NGC 3031	0.9	–30
NGC 3627	0.9	650
NGC 4826	0.9	150
NGC 5236	0.9	500
NGC 1068	1	920
NGC 1055	1.1	450
NGC 7331	1.1	500
NGC 4258	1.4	500
NGC 4151	1.7	960
NGC 4382	2	500
NGC 4472	2	850
NGC 4486	2	800
NGC 4649	2	1090

*mpc = million parsec; 1 parsec = 3.26 light years

```
lmstars <- lm(Velocity ~ Distance, data=stars1)
lmstars$coef
```

It is found that $\widehat{\beta}_0 = -68.15$ and $\widehat{\beta}_1 = 465.9$. Thus, the fitted model is

$$y = -68.15 + 465.9x.$$

The graph of the straight line represented by the above equation is shown together with the scatter plot in Figure 3.1. The vertical distance of a typical point from the corresponding point on the line is also shown. The LSEs of β_1 and β_0 (representing the slope and intercept of the line, respectively) are such that they minimize the sum of squares of these vertical distances of all the points from the line. □

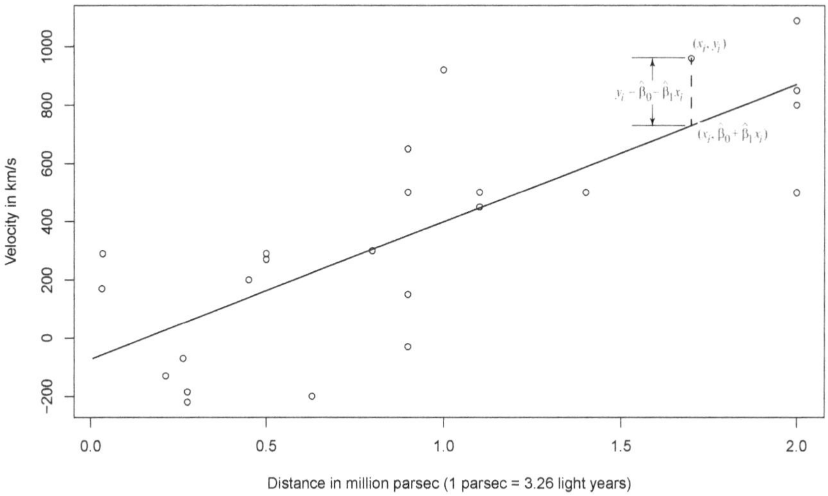

Fig. 3.1 Estimated linear relation between velocities of galaxies and their distances from the Earth

3.2 Fitted values and residuals

As mentioned at the beginning of the previous section, the goal of least squares estimation is to choose the vector parameter $\boldsymbol{\beta}$ in such a way that the response vector $\boldsymbol{y}$ is approximated as closely as possible by its systematic part, $\boldsymbol{X\beta}$. If the least squares estimator is $\widehat{\boldsymbol{\beta}}_{LS}$, the best approximation of $\boldsymbol{y}$ would be $\boldsymbol{X}\widehat{\boldsymbol{\beta}}_{LS}$. This approximation simplifies to $\boldsymbol{X}(\boldsymbol{X}'\boldsymbol{X})^{-1}\boldsymbol{X}'\boldsymbol{y}$. We formally define the vector of *fitted values* of the response $\boldsymbol{y}$ as

$$\widehat{\boldsymbol{y}} = \boldsymbol{H}\boldsymbol{y}, \tag{3.8}$$

where

$$\boldsymbol{H} = \boldsymbol{X}(\boldsymbol{X}'\boldsymbol{X})^{-1}\boldsymbol{X}'. \tag{3.9}$$

When $\boldsymbol{X}'\boldsymbol{X}$ is singular, the inverse above is replaced by the corresponding g-inverse. Since the matrix $\boldsymbol{H}$ turns $\boldsymbol{y}$ into $\widehat{\boldsymbol{y}}$, it is often referred to as the *hat*-matrix. It is also called the *prediction* matrix.

The remaining part of $\boldsymbol{y}$ that could not be captured by the systematic part is

$$\boldsymbol{e} = \boldsymbol{y} - \widehat{\boldsymbol{y}} = (\boldsymbol{I} - \boldsymbol{H})\boldsymbol{y}. \tag{3.10}$$

This part is called the *residual* vector. The ith elements of the vectors $\widehat{\boldsymbol{y}}$ and $\boldsymbol{e}$ are the fitted value ($\widehat{y}_i$) and the residual (e_i), respectively, of the ith observation. If we denote the ith row of the prediction matrix $\boldsymbol{X}$ by $\boldsymbol{x}_i'$, then

$$\widehat{y}_i = \boldsymbol{x}_i'\widehat{\boldsymbol{\beta}}_{LS},$$
$$e_i = y_i - \boldsymbol{x}_i'\widehat{\boldsymbol{\beta}}_{LS}.$$

In the special case of the simple linear regression model of (3.5), these expressions simplify to

$$\widehat{y}_i = \widehat{\beta}_0 + \widehat{\beta}_1 x_i,$$
$$e_i = y_i - \widehat{\beta}_0 - \widehat{\beta}_1 x_i.$$

An interesting fact is that even if $\boldsymbol{X}'\boldsymbol{X}$ is singular, the vector of fitted values is uniquely defined, irrespective of the choice of the g-inverse. A common way that singularity of $\boldsymbol{X}'\boldsymbol{X}$ may arise is through redundancy in the specification of parameters.

Example 3.4. (Age at death, continued) William Guy's data on the age at death of persons belonging to different professions (available as the data object `lifelength`) was described in the example of page 6. We present here an apparently different model for the same data set, where the age at death of the ith deceased person of the jth profession is given by

$$y_{ij} = \mu + \tau_i + \varepsilon_{ij}, \quad i = 1, \ldots, n_j, \quad j = 1, \ldots, 8.$$

This is the *one-way classified data* model. Here, μ is the overall mean age at death and τ_i is the additional mean age at death for the ith profession, the professions being labeled as 1 = historian, 2 = poet, and so on. The number of observations for the jth profession is n_j. The connection with the model presented in Example 1.4 is that $\beta_0 = \mu + \tau_1$, and $\beta_i = \tau_{i+1} - \tau_1$ for $i = 1, \ldots, 7$. In the present formulation, the meaning of μ (overall mean age at death) is open to interpretation. It could be the mean age at death of the entire population, the mean age at death of the sample at hand, or any plausible 'general mean'. Whatever that is, $\mu + \tau_i$ is clearly the mean age at death for the ith profession. If one subtracts a constant (say, 1 year) from μ and adds the same constant to each τ_i, this adjustment would not alter the value of $\mu + \tau_i$ for any i. Therefore, the model explaining the data remains unchanged by this alteration. Assuming all the errors (ε_{ij}) to be uncorrelated, this is a special case of the model $(\boldsymbol{y}, \boldsymbol{X\beta}, \sigma^2\boldsymbol{I})$, where

$\boldsymbol{y} = (\boldsymbol{y}_1 : \boldsymbol{y}_2 : \cdots : \boldsymbol{y}_8)'$, $\boldsymbol{y}_j = (y_{1j} : y_{2j} : \cdots : y_{n_j j})'$ for $j = 1, 2, \ldots, 8$, $\boldsymbol{\beta} = (\mu : \tau_1 : \tau_2 : \cdots : \tau_8)'$ and

$$\boldsymbol{X} = \begin{pmatrix} \mathbf{1}_{n_1\times1} & \mathbf{1}_{n_1\times1} & \mathbf{0}_{n_1\times1} & \mathbf{0}_{n_1\times1} & \mathbf{0}_{n_1\times1} & \mathbf{0}_{n_1\times1} & \mathbf{0}_{n_1\times1} & \mathbf{0}_{n_1\times1} & \mathbf{0}_{n_1\times1} \\ \mathbf{1}_{n_2\times1} & \mathbf{0}_{n_2\times1} & \mathbf{1}_{n_2\times1} & \mathbf{0}_{n_2\times1} & \mathbf{0}_{n_2\times1} & \mathbf{0}_{n_2\times1} & \mathbf{0}_{n_2\times1} & \mathbf{0}_{n_2\times1} & \mathbf{0}_{n_2\times1} \\ \mathbf{1}_{n_3\times1} & \mathbf{0}_{n_3\times1} & \mathbf{0}_{n_3\times1} & \mathbf{1}_{n_3\times1} & \mathbf{0}_{n_3\times1} & \mathbf{0}_{n_3\times1} & \mathbf{0}_{n_3\times1} & \mathbf{0}_{n_3\times1} & \mathbf{0}_{n_3\times1} \\ \mathbf{1}_{n_4\times1} & \mathbf{0}_{n_4\times1} & \mathbf{0}_{n_4\times1} & \mathbf{0}_{n_4\times1} & \mathbf{1}_{n_4\times1} & \mathbf{0}_{n_4\times1} & \mathbf{0}_{n_4\times1} & \mathbf{0}_{n_4\times1} & \mathbf{0}_{n_4\times1} \\ \mathbf{1}_{n_5\times1} & \mathbf{0}_{n_5\times1} & \mathbf{0}_{n_5\times1} & \mathbf{0}_{n_5\times1} & \mathbf{0}_{n_5\times1} & \mathbf{1}_{n_5\times1} & \mathbf{0}_{n_5\times1} & \mathbf{0}_{n_5\times1} & \mathbf{0}_{n_5\times1} \\ \mathbf{1}_{n_6\times1} & \mathbf{0}_{n_6\times1} & \mathbf{0}_{n_6\times1} & \mathbf{0}_{n_6\times1} & \mathbf{0}_{n_6\times1} & \mathbf{0}_{n_6\times1} & \mathbf{1}_{n_6\times1} & \mathbf{0}_{n_6\times1} & \mathbf{0}_{n_6\times1} \\ \mathbf{1}_{n_7\times1} & \mathbf{0}_{n_7\times1} & \mathbf{0}_{n_7\times1} & \mathbf{0}_{n_7\times1} & \mathbf{0}_{n_7\times1} & \mathbf{0}_{n_7\times1} & \mathbf{0}_{n_7\times1} & \mathbf{1}_{n_7\times1} & \mathbf{0}_{n_7\times1} \\ \mathbf{1}_{n_8\times1} & \mathbf{0}_{n_8\times1} & \mathbf{0}_{n_8\times1} & \mathbf{0}_{n_8\times1} & \mathbf{0}_{n_8\times1} & \mathbf{0}_{n_8\times1} & \mathbf{0}_{n_8\times1} & \mathbf{0}_{n_8\times1} & \mathbf{1}_{n_8\times1} \end{pmatrix}.$$

The last seven columns of this matrix may be identified as the values of the binary variables $x_1, \ldots, x_7$ defined in Example 1.4. The second column contains the values of another binary variable that is 1 for historians and 0 for others.

The data for this example may be loaded and $\boldsymbol{y}$ and $\boldsymbol{X}$ matrices may be generated through the following code. This code makes use of the function `binaries` of the R package `lmreg`, which stacks up values of all the binary variables that can be associated with different levels of a categorical variable.

```
data(lifelength)
attach(lifelength)
y <- Lifelength; X <- cbind(1,binaries(Category))
detach(lifelength)
```

Once the matrices are defined, it follows that

$$\boldsymbol{X}'\boldsymbol{X} = \begin{pmatrix} \sum_{j=1}^{b} n_j & n_1 & n_2 & \cdots & n_8 \\ n_1 & n_1 & 0 & \cdots & 0 \\ n_2 & 0 & n_2 & \cdots & 0 \\ \vdots & \vdots & \vdots & \ddots & \vdots \\ n_8 & 0 & 0 & \cdots & n_8 \end{pmatrix}; \qquad \boldsymbol{X}'\boldsymbol{y} = \begin{pmatrix} \sum_{j=1}^{8} \sum_{i=1}^{n_j} y_{ij} \\ \sum_{i=1}^{n_1} y_{i1} \\ \sum_{i=1}^{n_2} y_{i2} \\ \vdots \\ \sum_{i=1}^{n_8} y_{i8} \end{pmatrix}.$$

The numerical values of these matrices can be obtained by using the R commands `t(X)%*%X` and `t(X)%*%y`, respectively. The matrix $\boldsymbol{X}'\boldsymbol{X}$ would be singular, because it has dependent columns. In particular, the first column is the sum of the other columns. (This dependence originates from $\boldsymbol{X}$, whose first column is also the sum of the other columns.) It may be verified that the following matrix is a g-inverse of $\boldsymbol{X}'\boldsymbol{X}$

$$(\boldsymbol{X}'\boldsymbol{X})^- = \begin{pmatrix} 0 & 0 & 0 & \cdots & 0 \\ 0 & \frac{1}{n_1} & 0 & \cdots & 0 \\ 0 & 0 & \frac{1}{n_2} & \cdots & 0 \\ \vdots & \vdots & \vdots & \ddots & \vdots \\ 0 & 0 & 0 & \cdots & \frac{1}{n_8} \end{pmatrix} + \begin{pmatrix} 1 \\ -1 \\ -1 \\ \vdots \\ -1 \end{pmatrix} (a:0:0:0:0:0:0:0:0),$$

for any constant a. The corresponding LSE of $\boldsymbol{\beta}$ is

$$\begin{pmatrix} \hat{\mu} \\ \hat{\tau}_1 \\ \hat{\tau}_2 \\ \vdots \\ \hat{\tau}_8 \end{pmatrix} = \begin{pmatrix} a\sum_{j=1}^{8}\sum_{i=1}^{n_j} y_{ij} \\ n_1^{-1}\sum_{i=1}^{n_1} y_{i1} - a\sum_{j=1}^{8}\sum_{i=1}^{n_j} y_{ij} \\ n_2^{-1}\sum_{i=1}^{n_2} y_{i2} - a\sum_{j=1}^{8}\sum_{i=1}^{n_j} y_{ij} \\ \vdots \\ n_8^{-1}\sum_{i=1}^{n_8} y_{i8} - a\sum_{j=1}^{8}\sum_{i=1}^{n_j} y_{ij} \end{pmatrix}.$$

The estimator is not unique, because a can be arbitrarily chosen. However, the fitted values are

$$\hat{y}_{ij} = \hat{\mu} + \hat{\tau}_j = n_j^{-1}\sum_{i=1}^{n_j} y_{ij}, \quad i = 1, \ldots, n_j, \quad j = 1, \ldots, 8. \tag{3.11}$$

One can use the R function `lm` to obtain the fitted values, as follows.

```
data(lifelength)
lmlife <- lm(Lifelength~factor(Category), data = lifelength)
fitted <- lmlife$fit
```

The vector `fitted` would contain the same fitted value for all cases in a particular category. One can obtain the category-wise fitted values in an array, without duplication, by directly using the computational formula (3.11), as follows.

```
attach(lifelength)
fitage <- array(0,dim=length(unique(Category)))
for (i in unique(Category)) fitage[i] <- mean(Lifelength[Category==i])
detach(lifelength)
```

Alternatively, the following computational shortcut can be used.

```
fitage <- aggregate(Lifelength~Category, data = lifelength, mean)
```

Subsequently the fitted values for various categories are displayed through the following code.

```
catnames <- c(" Historians", " Poets", " Painters", " Musicians", #
            " Mathematicians and astronomers", #
            " Chemists and natural philosophers", #
            " Naturalists", " Engineers, architects and surveyors")
data.frame(fitage, row.names = catnames)
```

This code produces the following list of fitted ages at death for different categories.

```
                                     fitage
 Historians                        67.36170
 Poets                             58.10314
 Painters                          64.19820
 Musicians                         69.44444
 Mathematicians and astronomers    63.13415
 Chemists and natural philosophers 72.60465
 Naturalists                       67.34921
 Engineers, architects and surveyors 70.76316
```

The linear dependence of the columns of $\boldsymbol{X}$ stems from the redundancy of the parameter specifications, as mentioned above. The parameters cannot be identified separately, unless one imposes an additional constraint, such as $\tau_1 + \tau_2 + \cdots + \tau_8 = 0$ or $n_1\tau_1 + n_2\tau_2 + \cdots + n_8\tau_8 = 0$. □

Example 3.5. (Abrasion of denim jeans, continued) Consider the abrasion score of jeans, mentioned in Example 1.9, which was measured repeatedly for three types of denim treatments and three levels of laundry cycles (ten observations for each combination). The data are given in Table 3.2. Let us use the following linear model for the abrasion score of the lth observation for the ith denim treatment and the jth laundry cycle:

$$y_{ijl} = \mu + \tau_i + \beta_j + \varepsilon_{ijl},$$

where i and j run from 1 to 3 and l runs from 1 to 10.

This designed set-up, known as the *two-way classified data* model, is typical in industrial and agricultural experiments where several treatments are applied to various blocks of experimental units. The experiment is often conducted to assess the differential impact of the treatments. Here, the parameter μ represents the general mean abrasion score that is not specific to any treatment or laundry cycle (a general effect which is present in all the observations), τ_i is the effect of the ith treatment on the mean abrasion score, and β_j is the effect of the j laundry cycle (or block) on the mean abrasion score. The observed response has the combined effect of

Table 3.2 Data on abrasion score of jeans (data object `denim` in R package `lmreg`, Card et al., 2006)

Pre-washed			Stone-washed			Enzyme-washed		
Number of laundry cycles			Number of laundry cycles			Number of laundry cycles		
0	5	25	0	5	25	0	5	25
3.2218	3.1506	3.0114	2.2389	1.3373	1.7170	2.6790	1.8032	1.5333
3.3547	3.0300	3.0123	2.4392	2.0123	2.2421	2.9687	2.1526	1.8093
3.1334	2.7948	2.3802	2.0989	1.9434	1.8357	2.7750	2.4623	2.2600
2.6289	2.5685	3.0909	1.7627	2.0190	1.8986	3.0185	2.2728	1.9291
3.8816	3.2388	2.3173	2.1132	1.2970	1.3799	2.2233	1.8494	2.6441
3.4383	3.1351	2.1572	2.1229	1.8800	1.8926	2.4641	2.4745	1.6144
2.7742	2.7016	1.6737	2.5048	2.0632	2.2674	2.8179	2.0292	2.5819
3.4454	2.8420	1.2398	2.2467	2.0151	1.8818	2.6048	3.4265	3.1609
3.6696	2.8887	2.4494	1.4007	1.8988	1.5106	2.7132	1.3626	2.1734
3.1223	2.6499	2.6677	1.7422	1.8638	1.7043	3.0655	2.8369	2.9636

μ, the particular block where it comes from and the particular treatment received. We shall revisit this example several times in this chapter in order to understand various concepts.

This model has too many parameters. One can add a constant to μ and subtract that constant from either all the τ_i's or all the β_j's without changing the mean response in any single case. Assuming all the errors (ε_{ijk}) to be uncorrelated, this is a special case of the model $(\boldsymbol{y}, \boldsymbol{X\beta}, \sigma^2\boldsymbol{I})$, where

$$\begin{aligned}
\boldsymbol{y} &= (\boldsymbol{y}_{11}' : \boldsymbol{y}_{12}' : \boldsymbol{y}_{13}' : \boldsymbol{y}_{21}' : \boldsymbol{y}_{22}' : \boldsymbol{y}_{23}' : \boldsymbol{y}_{31}' : \boldsymbol{y}_{32}' : \boldsymbol{y}_{33}')',\\
\boldsymbol{y}_{ij} &= (y_{ij1}\ y_{ij2}\ \cdots\ y_{ij(10)}) \text{ for } i,j = 1,2,3,\\
\boldsymbol{X} &= \begin{pmatrix}
\mathbf{1}_{10\times1} & \mathbf{1}_{10\times1} & \mathbf{0}_{10\times1} & \mathbf{0}_{10\times1} & \mathbf{1}_{10\times1} & \mathbf{0}_{10\times1} & \mathbf{0}_{10\times1}\\
\mathbf{1}_{10\times1} & \mathbf{1}_{10\times1} & \mathbf{0}_{10\times1} & \mathbf{0}_{10\times1} & \mathbf{0}_{10\times1} & \mathbf{1}_{10\times1} & \mathbf{0}_{10\times1}\\
\mathbf{1}_{10\times1} & \mathbf{1}_{10\times1} & \mathbf{0}_{10\times1} & \mathbf{0}_{10\times1} & \mathbf{0}_{10\times1} & \mathbf{0}_{10\times1} & \mathbf{1}_{10\times1}\\
\mathbf{1}_{10\times1} & \mathbf{0}_{10\times1} & \mathbf{1}_{10\times1} & \mathbf{0}_{10\times1} & \mathbf{1}_{10\times1} & \mathbf{0}_{10\times1} & \mathbf{0}_{10\times1}\\
\mathbf{1}_{10\times1} & \mathbf{0}_{10\times1} & \mathbf{1}_{10\times1} & \mathbf{0}_{10\times1} & \mathbf{0}_{10\times1} & \mathbf{1}_{10\times1} & \mathbf{0}_{10\times1}\\
\mathbf{1}_{10\times1} & \mathbf{0}_{10\times1} & \mathbf{1}_{10\times1} & \mathbf{0}_{10\times1} & \mathbf{0}_{10\times1} & \mathbf{0}_{10\times1} & \mathbf{1}_{10\times1}\\
\mathbf{1}_{10\times1} & \mathbf{0}_{10\times1} & \mathbf{0}_{10\times1} & \mathbf{1}_{10\times1} & \mathbf{1}_{10\times1} & \mathbf{0}_{10\times1} & \mathbf{0}_{10\times1}\\
\mathbf{1}_{10\times1} & \mathbf{0}_{10\times1} & \mathbf{0}_{10\times1} & \mathbf{1}_{10\times1} & \mathbf{0}_{10\times1} & \mathbf{1}_{10\times1} & \mathbf{0}_{10\times1}\\
\mathbf{1}_{10\times1} & \mathbf{0}_{10\times1} & \mathbf{0}_{10\times1} & \mathbf{1}_{10\times1} & \mathbf{0}_{10\times1} & \mathbf{0}_{10\times1} & \mathbf{1}_{10\times1}
\end{pmatrix} \text{ and } \boldsymbol{\beta} = \begin{pmatrix} \mu\\ \tau_1\\ \tau_2\\ \tau_3\\ \beta_1\\ \beta_2\\ \beta_3 \end{pmatrix}.
\end{aligned}$$

The vector $\boldsymbol{y}$ and the matrix $\boldsymbol{X}$ can be obtained after reading the relevant data, by using the function `binaries` of the package `lmreg`, through the following code.

```
data(denim)
attach(denim)
y <- Abrasion
X <- cbind(1,binaries(Denim),binaries(Laundry))
```

The matrix $\boldsymbol{X}'\boldsymbol{X}$ would be singular, because $\boldsymbol{X}$ has dependent columns. For example, the first column is the sum of the next three columns, and also equal to the sum of the last three columns. Therefore, the LSE of $\boldsymbol{\beta}$ is not uniquely defined. However, irrespective of the LSE chosen, the fitted values work out to be, for $i, j = 1, 2, 3$, $l = 1, \ldots, 10$,

$$\hat{y}_{ijl} = \frac{1}{30}\sum_{j'=1}^{3}\sum_{l'=1}^{10} y_{ij'l'} + \frac{1}{30}\sum_{i'=1}^{3}\sum_{l'=1}^{10} y_{i'jl'} - \frac{1}{90}\sum_{i'=1}^{3}\sum_{j'=1}^{3}\sum_{l'=1}^{10} y_{i'j'l'}.$$

While the above formula can be used to compute the fitted values, it is easier to obtain them by using the R function `lm` as follows.

```
washnames <- c("0 laundry cycles", "5 laundry cycles",
     "25 laundry cycles")
Laundrycat <- factor(Laundry, label = washnames)
denimnames <- c("Pre-washed", "Stone-washed", "Enzyme-washed")
Denimcat <- factor(Denim, label = denimnames)
lmjeans <- lm(Abrasion~Laundrycat+Denimcat)
fitted <- lmjeans$fit
fits <- array(0, dim = c(3,3))
for (i in 1:3) {
    for (j in 1:3) fits[i,j] <- mean(fitted[(Denim==i)&(Laundry==j)])
}
colnames(fits) <- washnames
as.data.frame(fits, row.names = denimnames)
detach(denim)
```

The fitted values of abrasion scores for the different categories are found to be as given below.

Denim treatment	no laundry cycle	5 laundry cycles	25 laundry cycles
pre-washed	3.1483	2.7927	2.6260
stone-washed	2.2037	1.8480	1.6813
enzyme washed	2.7150	2.3593	2.1927

Redundancy of the parameter specifications, which leads to the dependence among the columns of $\boldsymbol{X}$, may be removed by imposing additional constraints, such as $\tau_1 + \tau_2 + \tau_3 = 0$ and $\beta_1 + \beta_2 + \beta_3 = 0$. □

3.3 Variances and covariances

It follows from (3.3) that when $\boldsymbol{X}'\boldsymbol{X}$ is nonsingular, the variance-covariance matrix of $\widehat{\boldsymbol{\beta}}_{LS}$ is

$$D\left(\widehat{\boldsymbol{\beta}}_{LS}\right) = \sigma^2(\boldsymbol{X}'\boldsymbol{X})^{-1}. \tag{3.12}$$

When $\boldsymbol{X}'\boldsymbol{X}$ happens to be singular, the dispersion matrix is $D\left(\widehat{\boldsymbol{\beta}}_{LS}\right) = \sigma^2(\boldsymbol{X}'\boldsymbol{X})^{-}\boldsymbol{X}'\boldsymbol{X}(\boldsymbol{X}'\boldsymbol{X})^{-}$, which is not unique. In the case of the simple linear regression model of (3.5), the matrix simplifies to

$$D\left(\widehat{\boldsymbol{\beta}}_{LS}\right) = \sigma^2 \begin{pmatrix} n & n\bar{x} \\ n\bar{x} & \|\boldsymbol{x}\|^2 \end{pmatrix}^{-1} = \frac{\sigma^2}{n\|\boldsymbol{x}\|^2 - n^2\bar{x}^2} \begin{pmatrix} \|\boldsymbol{x}\|^2 & -n\bar{x} \\ -n\bar{x} & n \end{pmatrix}. \tag{3.13}$$

In particular,

$$Var(\widehat{\beta}_0) = \frac{\sigma^2}{n}\left(1 + \frac{\bar{x}^2}{\frac{1}{n}\sum_{i=1}^n (x_i - \bar{x})^2}\right),$$

$$Var(\widehat{\beta}_1) = \frac{\sigma^2}{\sum_{i=1}^n (x_i - \bar{x})^2}.$$

It is clear that both the variances are smaller when the sample variance of the x_is is large, i.e. the values of the explanatory variable is well spread out. If the sample variance of the x_is do not change much with sample size, then both the variances reduce in inverse proportion with increase in sample size. Also, the variance of $\widehat{\beta}_0$ is always larger than $\frac{\sigma^2}{n}$, the value it would have if the explanatory variable had not been there in the model (i.e. the response had been modeled with the best fitting constant).

Further from (3.8) and (3.10) it follows that

$$D(\widehat{\boldsymbol{y}}) = \sigma^2\boldsymbol{H}, \tag{3.14}$$

$$D(\boldsymbol{e}) = \sigma^2(\boldsymbol{I} - \boldsymbol{H}), \tag{3.15}$$

$$Cov(\widehat{\boldsymbol{y}}, \boldsymbol{e}) = \boldsymbol{0}, \tag{3.16}$$

where $\boldsymbol{H} = \boldsymbol{X}(\boldsymbol{X}'\boldsymbol{X})^{-1}\boldsymbol{X}'$, as defined in (3.9). In particular, the fitted values $\widehat{y}_1, \ldots, \widehat{y}_n$ are uncorrelated with the residuals $e_1, \ldots, e_n$ and these have variances

$$Var(\widehat{y}_i) = \sigma^2 h_i, \qquad i = 1, \ldots, n, \tag{3.17}$$

$$Var(e_i) = \sigma^2(1 - h_i), \qquad i = 1, \ldots, n, \tag{3.18}$$

where h_i is the ith diagonal element of $\boldsymbol{H}$ and is commonly known as the ith *leverage*.

Example 3.6. (Receding galaxies, continued) For the galactic objects data of Table 3.1, analysed under the linear model of Example 3.3, the variance-covariance matrix of the estimators turns out to be

$$D\begin{pmatrix}\widehat{\beta}_0\\ \widehat{\beta}_1\end{pmatrix} = \sigma^2(\boldsymbol{X}'\boldsymbol{X})^{-1} = \sigma^2\begin{pmatrix}0.12834 & -0.09510\\ -0.09510 & 0.10435\end{pmatrix}.$$

The matrix $(\boldsymbol{X}'\boldsymbol{X})^{-1}$ is computed through the additional line of command `vcov(lmstars)/summary(lmstars)$sig^2`. (See Example 3.10 below for an explanation of the R command.) Thus, $Var(\widehat{\beta}_0) = 0.12834\sigma^2$, $Var(\widehat{\beta}_1) = 0.10435\sigma^2$ and the correlation coefficient of the estimators is -0.82179. □

Example 3.7. (Age at death, continued) For the age at death example previously considered on page 66, the additional lines of code given below produce the standard deviation of the fitted values as multiples of σ, the standard deviation of the errors ε_{ij} in the model of Example 3.4.

```
attach(lifelength); sd <- sqrt(hatvalues(lmlife))
sdval <- NULL
for (i in unique(Category)) sdval <- c(sdval,(sd[Category==i])[1])
as.data.frame(sdval, row.names = catnames); detach(lifelength)
```

The standard deviation of the fitted value for age at death of historians is found to be 0.1459σ years. For the other categories, the multipliers of σ are: 0.0670 (poets), 0.0949 (painters), 0.1491 (musicians), 0.1104 (mathematicians and astronomers), 0.1525 (chemists and natural philosophers), 0.1260 (naturalists) and 0.1147 (engineers, architects and surveyors) years. The smallest standard deviation is observed in the case of poets, while there is much larger standard deviation for chemists and natural philosophers. This pattern is *not* in line with the spread of the data in these categories, seen in Figure 1.1. The spread is indicative of the respective standard deviations of the observed ages at death in the different categories. In contrast, the standard deviations reported here are based on the linear model of Example 3.4, which presumes equal variance of the model errors in all the categories. The formula for variance of the fitted values (3.17) depends only on the categories. The larger variance of the fitted values for chemists and natural philosophers is only because of the fact that the number of observations in that category is only 43, while there are as many as 223 poets represented in the data. □

Example 3.8. (Abrasion of denim jeans, continued) For the data on abrasion score of jeans, previously considered in the example of page 69, the variances of the fitted values for all the observations would be the same and equal to $\sigma^2/18$. This is because of the symmetry of the values of the explanatory variables (i.e. all combinations of τ_i's and β_j's occurring equal number of times). One can also use the additional lines of R code given below to confirm this fact.

```
attach(denim); vars <- hatvalues(lmjeans)
varval <- array(0, dim = c(3,3)); colnames(varval) <- washnames
for (i in 1:3) {
  for (j in 1:3) varval[i,j] <- (vars[(Denim==i)&(Laundry==j)])[1]
}
as.data.frame(varval, row.names = denimnames); detach(denim)
```
□

3.4 Estimation of error variance

The variances of the LSE, the fitted values or the residuals, described in the previous section, are all expressed as multiples of σ^2, the variance of the model error. This parameter needs to be estimated. Since the model errors $\varepsilon_1, \ldots, \varepsilon_n$ have zero mean, the expected value of each of the squared errors $\varepsilon_1^2, \ldots, \varepsilon_n^2$ is σ^2. Therefore, any one of these squared errors is an unbiased estimator of σ^2. Their average should also be an unbiased and even better estimator. However, this average of squares cannot be used as an estimator, since the model errors are not observed.

Interestingly, a linear function of the unobserved error vector $\boldsymbol{\varepsilon}$ can be computed directly from the observations. That function is the vector of residuals, which can be written as

$$\boldsymbol{e} = \boldsymbol{y} - \boldsymbol{H}\boldsymbol{y} = \boldsymbol{X}\boldsymbol{\beta} + \boldsymbol{\varepsilon} - \boldsymbol{X}(\boldsymbol{X}'\boldsymbol{X})^{-1}\boldsymbol{X}'\boldsymbol{X}\boldsymbol{\beta} - \boldsymbol{H}\boldsymbol{\varepsilon} = (\boldsymbol{I} - \boldsymbol{H})\boldsymbol{\varepsilon}.$$

Thus, even though $\boldsymbol{\varepsilon}$ is not observed, one can make use of $(\boldsymbol{I}-\boldsymbol{H})\boldsymbol{\varepsilon}$, which is completely free of $\boldsymbol{\beta}$. Sum of squares of this residual vector, if appropriately scaled, should yield an unbiased estimator of σ^2. In order to determine the requisite scaling factor, we calculate the expected value of the sum of squares.

$$\begin{aligned} E[\|\boldsymbol{e}\|^2] = E[\boldsymbol{\varepsilon}'(\boldsymbol{I}-\boldsymbol{H})\boldsymbol{\varepsilon}] &= E[\mathrm{tr}\{(\boldsymbol{I}-\boldsymbol{H})\boldsymbol{\varepsilon}\boldsymbol{\varepsilon}'\}] \\ = \mathrm{tr}[E\{(\boldsymbol{I}-\boldsymbol{H})\boldsymbol{\varepsilon}\boldsymbol{\varepsilon}'\}] &= \mathrm{tr}[(\boldsymbol{I}-\boldsymbol{H})(\sigma^2\boldsymbol{I})] \\ = \sigma^2\mathrm{tr}(\boldsymbol{I}-\boldsymbol{H}) &= \sigma^2[n - \mathrm{tr}(\boldsymbol{X}(\boldsymbol{X}'\boldsymbol{X})^-\boldsymbol{X}')] \\ = \sigma^2[n - \rho(\boldsymbol{X}(\boldsymbol{X}'\boldsymbol{X})^-\boldsymbol{X}')] &= (n-\rho(X))\sigma^2. \end{aligned}$$

The crucial fact used in the above simplification is that $\boldsymbol{X}(\boldsymbol{X}'\boldsymbol{X})^-\boldsymbol{X}'$ is an orthogonal projection matrix, for which the trace is equal to the rank (see page 607). For nonsingular $\boldsymbol{X}'\boldsymbol{X}$, the expression simplifies to $(n-p)\sigma^2$. [In this case the expression can also be justified by the simpler argument that $\text{tr}(\boldsymbol{X}(\boldsymbol{X}'\boldsymbol{X})^{-1}\boldsymbol{X}') = \text{tr}((\boldsymbol{X}'\boldsymbol{X})^{-1}\boldsymbol{X}'\boldsymbol{X}) = \text{tr}(\boldsymbol{I}) = p$.] It follows that an unbiased estimator of σ^2 is

$$\widehat{\sigma^2} = \frac{\boldsymbol{e}'\boldsymbol{e}}{n-r}, \tag{3.19}$$

where $\boldsymbol{e}$ is the vector of residuals and $r = \rho(\boldsymbol{X})$.

The MLE of σ^2 in the normal case is $\boldsymbol{e}'\boldsymbol{e}/n$ (see Section 3.7), which is a biased estimator.

Remark 3.9. Although $\widehat{\sigma^2}$ is not the MLE in the normal case, it has another very important property: it is the UMVUE of σ^2. To see this, note that the exponent of the density function of $\boldsymbol{y}$ (given $\boldsymbol{X}$) can be written as

$$-\frac{1}{2\sigma^2}\left[\|\boldsymbol{X\beta} - \boldsymbol{X}\widehat{\boldsymbol{\beta}}_{LS}\|^2 + \boldsymbol{e}'\boldsymbol{e}\right].$$

By factorization theorem, $\boldsymbol{X}\widehat{\boldsymbol{\beta}}_{LS}$ and $\boldsymbol{e}'\boldsymbol{e}$ are jointly sufficient for $\boldsymbol{X\beta}$ and σ^2. It can be shown that these are also complete (see Exercise 3.39). Since $\boldsymbol{X}\widehat{\boldsymbol{\beta}}_{LS}$ and $\widehat{\sigma^2}$ are both unbiased, and are complete sufficient for $\boldsymbol{X\beta}$ and σ^2, these are the UMVUEs of these parameters. □

Other optimal properties of $\widehat{\sigma^2}$ will be discussed in Chapter 8 (see Section 8.2.3 and Exercise 8.22).

By substituting σ^2 with $\widehat{\sigma^2}$ in (3.12), one can get an unbiased estimate of the variance-covariance matrix of $\widehat{\boldsymbol{\beta}}_{LS}$. The square-roots of the diagonal elements of this matrix are the estimated standard deviations of the elements of $\widehat{\boldsymbol{\beta}}_{LS}$, commonly known as *standard error.*

Example 3.10. (Receding galaxies, continued) Consider the galactic objects data of Table 3.1, analysed in Examples 3.3 and 3.6. The estimate of σ, obtained as the square-root of (3.19) through the additional command `summary(lmstars)$sigma`, is 250.61. Substitution of (3.19) in (3.12) produces an estimated variance-covariance matrix of the regression coefficients. In the present case, this computation is obtained by the command `vcov(lmstars)`, which produces the matrix

$$\widehat{D}\begin{pmatrix}\widehat{\beta}_0\\ \widehat{\beta}_1\end{pmatrix} = \widehat{\sigma^2}(\boldsymbol{X}'\boldsymbol{X})^{-1} = \begin{pmatrix} 8060.4 & -5972.8\\ -5972.8 & 6553.7\end{pmatrix}.$$

The standard errors of $\widehat{\beta}_0$ and $\widehat{\beta}_1$, obtained directly through the command `summary(lmstars)$coeff[,2]`, are 89.78 and 80.95, respectively. □

3.5 Linear estimation: some basic facts

In the linear model of Example 3.4, the excess mean life of a musician over the mean life of a mathematician is represented by the difference $\tau_4 - \tau_5$. In Example 3.5, the differential effect of enzyme wash over stone wash in respect of mean abrasion of jeans is $\tau_3 - \tau_2$. These are examples of linear combinations of the parameters of a linear model, which may have to be estimated. Another example — a generic one — is the mean response corresponding to a specific profile of explanatory variables, which may not have been encountered in the data set available for estimation. A linear function of the vector parameter $\boldsymbol{\beta}$ in the linear model $(\boldsymbol{y}, \boldsymbol{X\beta}, \sigma^2\boldsymbol{I})$ is called a *linear parametric function* (LPF). If $\boldsymbol{p}'\boldsymbol{\beta}$ is an LPF, we may estimate it with $\boldsymbol{p}'\widehat{\boldsymbol{\beta}}_{LS}$. This estimator is a linear function of the response vector $\boldsymbol{y}$. Since $\boldsymbol{y}$ itself is related to $\boldsymbol{\beta}$ through a linear function (according to the assumed model), it seems reasonable that we would look for a linear function of $\boldsymbol{y}$ as an estimator of any LPF. Is it possible to find a linear estimator of $\boldsymbol{p}'\boldsymbol{\beta}$, which is better than $\boldsymbol{p}'\widehat{\boldsymbol{\beta}}_{LS}$? Before we get a firm answer to this question, we need to study various linear functions of $\boldsymbol{y}$ and their inter-relationship, under the linear model $(\boldsymbol{y}, \boldsymbol{X\beta}, \sigma^2\boldsymbol{I})$.

3.5.1 *Linear functions of the response*

Suppose $\boldsymbol{l}'\boldsymbol{y}$ is a linear function of $\boldsymbol{y}$. It follows immediately from the model that $E(\boldsymbol{l}'\boldsymbol{y}) = \boldsymbol{l}'\boldsymbol{X\beta}$. Therefore, we can call $\boldsymbol{l}'\boldsymbol{y}$ an unbiased estimator of the LPF $\boldsymbol{l}'\boldsymbol{X\beta}$. In the exceptional case when $\boldsymbol{l}'\boldsymbol{X\beta}$ is identically zero, $\boldsymbol{l}'\boldsymbol{y}$ is not an estimator of anything but zero itself.

Definition 3.11. The statistic $\boldsymbol{l}'\boldsymbol{y}$ is said to be a *linear unbiased estimator* (LUE) of the LPF $\boldsymbol{p}'\boldsymbol{\beta}$ if $E(\boldsymbol{l}'\boldsymbol{y}) = \boldsymbol{p}'\boldsymbol{\beta}$ for all possible values of $\boldsymbol{\beta}$. □

Definition 3.12. A linear function of the response, $\boldsymbol{l}'\boldsymbol{y}$ is called a *linear zero function* (LZF) if $E(\boldsymbol{l}'\boldsymbol{y}) = 0$ for all possible values of $\boldsymbol{\beta}$. □

It follows from the above discussion that every linear function $\boldsymbol{l}'\boldsymbol{y}$ is either an LUE of some LPF of the form $\boldsymbol{p}'\boldsymbol{\beta}$, or an LZF. Interestingly, by adding an LZF to an LUE of $\boldsymbol{p}'\boldsymbol{\beta}$, we get another LUE of $\boldsymbol{p}'\boldsymbol{\beta}$. This makes the problem of estimation more interesting. There is no shortage of LZFs in a linear model. In fact, all residuals are LZFs, and so are linear combinations of residuals. Thus, by adding different LZFs to any LUE of an LPF, we can produce many other LUEs of that LPF. Therefore we need to understand the nature of these LZFs to be able to navigate through this plethora of unbiased estimators.

Example 3.13. (A trivial example) Suppose an orange and an apple with (unknown) weights α_1 and α_2, respectively, are weighed separately with a crude scale. Each measurement is followed by a 'dummy' measurement with nothing on the scale, in order to get an idea about typical measurement errors. Let us assume that the measurements satisfy the linear model

$$\begin{pmatrix} y_1 \\ y_2 \\ y_3 \\ y_4 \end{pmatrix} = \begin{pmatrix} 1 & 0 \\ 0 & 0 \\ 0 & 1 \\ 0 & 0 \end{pmatrix} \begin{pmatrix} \alpha_1 \\ \alpha_2 \end{pmatrix} + \begin{pmatrix} \varepsilon_1 \\ \varepsilon_2 \\ \varepsilon_3 \\ \varepsilon_4 \end{pmatrix},$$

with the usual assumption of homoscedastic errors with variance σ^2.

The observations y_2 and y_4, being direct measurements of error, may be used to estimate the error variance. These are LZFs. The other two observations carry information about the two parameters. There are several unbiased estimators of α_1, such as y_1, $y_1 + y_2$ and $y_1 + y_4$. It appears that y_1 would be a natural estimator of α_1 since it is free from the baggage of any LZF. We shall formalize this heuristic argument later. □

In reality we seldom have information about the requisite LPFs and the errors as nicely segregated as in Example 3.13. Our aim is to achieve this segregation for any linear model, so that the task of choosing an unbiased estimator becomes easier.

Before proceeding further, let us characterize the LUEs and LZFs algebraically. Recall that $\boldsymbol{H} = \boldsymbol{X}(\boldsymbol{X}'\boldsymbol{X})^{-1}\boldsymbol{X}'$, as defined in (3.9).

Proposition 3.14. *In the linear model* $(\boldsymbol{y}, \boldsymbol{X\beta}, \sigma^2\boldsymbol{I})$, *the linear statistic* $\boldsymbol{l}'\boldsymbol{y}$ *is*

(a) an LUE of the LPF $\boldsymbol{p}'\boldsymbol{\beta}$ *if and only if* $\boldsymbol{X}'\boldsymbol{l} = \boldsymbol{p}$,
(b) an LZF if and only if $\boldsymbol{X}'\boldsymbol{l} = \boldsymbol{0}$, *that is,* $\boldsymbol{l}$ *is of the form* $(\boldsymbol{I} - \boldsymbol{H})\boldsymbol{m}$ *for some vector* $\boldsymbol{m}$.

Proof. In order to prove part (a), note that $\boldsymbol{l}'\boldsymbol{y}$ is an LUE of $\boldsymbol{p}'\boldsymbol{\beta}$ if and only if $E(\boldsymbol{l}'\boldsymbol{y}) = \boldsymbol{l}'\boldsymbol{X\beta}$, i.e. the relation $\boldsymbol{l}'\boldsymbol{X\beta} = \boldsymbol{p}'\boldsymbol{\beta}$ must hold as an identity for *all* $\boldsymbol{\beta}$. This is equivalent to the condition $\boldsymbol{X}'\boldsymbol{l} = \boldsymbol{p}$.

The special case of part (a) for $\boldsymbol{p} = \boldsymbol{0}$ indicates that $\boldsymbol{l}'\boldsymbol{y}$ is an LZF if and only if $\boldsymbol{X}'\boldsymbol{l} = \boldsymbol{0}$. Since $\boldsymbol{H} = \boldsymbol{P}_{\boldsymbol{X}}$, the orthogonal projection matrix for $\mathcal{C}(\boldsymbol{X})$, the latter condition is equivalent to requiring $\boldsymbol{l}$ to be of the form $(\boldsymbol{I} - \boldsymbol{P}_X)\boldsymbol{m}$ for some vector $\boldsymbol{m}$. □

Remark 3.15. Proposition 3.14(b) implies that every LZF is a linear function of the residual vector $\boldsymbol{e} = (\boldsymbol{I}-\boldsymbol{H})\boldsymbol{y}$ found from least squares estimation, and can be written as $\boldsymbol{m}'(\boldsymbol{I}-\boldsymbol{H})\boldsymbol{y}$ for some vector $\boldsymbol{m}$. This fact will be used extensively hereafter. Proposition 3.14 will have to be modified somewhat for the more general model $(\boldsymbol{y}, \boldsymbol{X\beta}, \sigma^2\boldsymbol{V})$ (see Section 7.2.2). However, the characterization of LZFs as linear functions of $(\boldsymbol{I} - \boldsymbol{P}_X)\boldsymbol{y}$ continues to hold for such models. □

Remark 3.16. Consider the explicit form of the model considered here,

$$\boldsymbol{y} = \boldsymbol{X\beta} + \boldsymbol{\varepsilon}. \tag{1.4}$$

As observed above, any LZF can be written as $\boldsymbol{l}'(\boldsymbol{I}-\boldsymbol{H})\boldsymbol{y}$, which is the same as $\boldsymbol{l}'(\boldsymbol{I}-\boldsymbol{H})\boldsymbol{\varepsilon}$. Thus, the LZFs do not depend on $\boldsymbol{\beta}$ at all, and are functions of the model errors only. This is why LZFs are sometimes referred to as *linear error functions*. The converse is also true. Suppose $\boldsymbol{m}'\boldsymbol{\varepsilon}$ is any linear function of the errors that is observable (i.e. expressible as a linear function of $\boldsymbol{y}$). Since its mean must be zero, it is an LZF. Thus, all observable linear functions of the model errors are LZFs. □

Example 3.17. (Trivial example, continued) In the case of Example 3.13,

$$\boldsymbol{H} = \begin{pmatrix} 1\,0\,0\,0 \\ 0\,0\,0\,0 \\ 0\,0\,1\,0 \\ 0\,0\,0\,0 \end{pmatrix}, \quad \text{so that } (\boldsymbol{I} - \boldsymbol{H})\boldsymbol{y} = \begin{pmatrix} 0 \\ y_2 \\ 0 \\ y_4 \end{pmatrix}.$$

Thus, every LZF is a linear function of y_2 and y_4. □

Example 3.18. (Age at death, continued) The vector of least squares fitted values for the age at death data of Example 3.4 had been calculated (see page 68). By subtracting it from the response vector, we get the vector of residuals. It turns out that the elements of this vector are the age at death of different individuals minus the average age at death of individuals of the same group (historians, poets and so on). Therefore, every LZF is a linear function of these mean-corrected ages of death. □

Example 3.19. (Abrasion of denim jeans, continued) The design matrix for this two-way classified data model is given on page 70. Each of the first ten observations (y_1 to y_{10}) is an unbiased estimator of the LPF $(\mu+\tau_1+\beta_1)$.

Here, $\boldsymbol{p} = (1:1:0:0:1:0:0)'$ and the first observation (y_1) can be written as $\boldsymbol{l}'\boldsymbol{y}$ where $\boldsymbol{l}$ is the first column of $\boldsymbol{I}_{90\times 90}$. The reader may try to identify the LPFs for which LUEs can be found from the last eighty observations.

The difference $(y_i - y_j)$ is an LZF for $1 \leq i,j \leq 10$, $i \neq j$. It can be easily verified that $y_i - y_j = \boldsymbol{l}'\boldsymbol{y}$ where $\boldsymbol{l}$ is the difference between the ith and jth columns of $\boldsymbol{I}_{90\times 90}$, and these LZFs satisfy the condition $\boldsymbol{X}'\boldsymbol{l} = \boldsymbol{0}$. The reader is encouraged to look for other LZFs in this model. □

3.5.2 *Estimability and identifiability*

Proposition 3.14(a) provides a condition not only on $\boldsymbol{l}$, but also on $\boldsymbol{p}$. If $\boldsymbol{p}$ does not lie in $\mathcal{C}(\boldsymbol{X}')$, the column space of $\boldsymbol{X}'$, there is no $\boldsymbol{l}$ satisfying the condition $\boldsymbol{X}'\boldsymbol{l} = \boldsymbol{p}$. Thus, some LPFs may not have an LUE.

Definition 3.20. An LPF is said to be *estimable* if it has an LUE. □

Since the existence of *linear* unbiased estimator is all that is required, such a function would have been better described as a *linearly estimable* one. However, the less specific term 'estimable' is used almost universally to describe this. The following proposition says that $\boldsymbol{p}'\boldsymbol{\beta}$ is estimable if and only if $\boldsymbol{p}'$ is any row or linear combination of rows of the $\boldsymbol{X}$ matrix.

Proposition 3.21. *A necessary and sufficient condition for the estimability of an LPF* ($\mathbf{p}'\boldsymbol{\beta}$) *is that* $\mathbf{p} \in \mathcal{C}(\boldsymbol{X}')$.

Proof. Suppose $\boldsymbol{p} \in \mathcal{C}(\boldsymbol{X}')$, i.e. there is a vector $\boldsymbol{l}$ such that $\boldsymbol{p} = \boldsymbol{X}'\boldsymbol{l}$. It is easy to see that $\boldsymbol{l}'\boldsymbol{y}$ is an LUE of $\boldsymbol{p}'\boldsymbol{\beta}$, which means the latter is estimable. Conversely, if we assume the estimability of $p'\boldsymbol{\beta}$, then there must be a vector $\boldsymbol{l}$ such that $\boldsymbol{l}'\boldsymbol{y}$ is an LUE of $\boldsymbol{p}'\boldsymbol{\beta}$. Therefore, $E(\boldsymbol{l}'\boldsymbol{y}) = \boldsymbol{l}'\boldsymbol{X}\boldsymbol{\beta} = \boldsymbol{p}'\boldsymbol{\beta}$ for all $\boldsymbol{\beta}$. It follows that $\boldsymbol{p} = \boldsymbol{X}'\boldsymbol{l}$, i.e. $\boldsymbol{p} \in \mathcal{C}(\boldsymbol{X})$. □

The result of Proposition 3.21 is just one of the numerous characterizations of estimability that can be found in the literature. Alalouf and Styan (1979) give a catalogue of fifteen other equivalent conditions. See Exercise 3.5 for an easily verifiable characterization.

Remark 3.22. A vector LPF, $\boldsymbol{A\beta}$, is estimable if and only if $\mathcal{C}(\boldsymbol{A}') \subseteq \mathcal{C}(\boldsymbol{X}')$. The entire vector $\boldsymbol{\beta}$ is estimable if and only if $\rho(\boldsymbol{X})$ is equal to p, the number of parameters. In such a case all LPFs are estimable (Exercise 3.2). □

Example 3.23. (Trivial example, continued) The rank of $\boldsymbol{X}$ in Example 3.13 is 2, which means every LPF of this model is estimable. Indeed, for arbitrary p_1 and p_2, an LUE of the LPF $p_1\alpha_1 + p_2\alpha_2$ is $p_1y_1 + p_2y_3$. □

Example 3.24. (Age at death, continued) It was mentioned in Example 3.4 that the first column is equal to the sum of the remaining columns. Therefore, all parameters would not be estimable. The LPF $\tau_1 - \tau_2$ can be written as $\boldsymbol{p}'\boldsymbol{\beta}$, where $\boldsymbol{p}' = (0:1:-1:0:0:0:0:0:0)$. This happens to be the difference of the first and (n_1+1)th row of $\boldsymbol{X}$. Therefore, $\tau_1 - \tau_2$ is estimable. In particular, $y_1 - y_{n_1+1}$ is an LUE of this LPF. If we write μ as $\boldsymbol{p}'\boldsymbol{\beta}$, then $\boldsymbol{p}' = (1:0:0:0:0:0:0)$. This vector can never be obtained from linear operations of the rows of $\boldsymbol{X}$. This parameter is not estimable.

We now use the functions `binaries` and `is.included` of the R package `lmreg` to check whether $\boldsymbol{p} \in \mathcal{C}(\boldsymbol{X}')$, i.e. whether $\boldsymbol{p}'\boldsymbol{\beta}$ is estimable.

```
data(lifelength); attach(lifelength)
X <- cbind(1, binaries(Category))
p <- c(0,1,-1,0,0,0,0,0,0)
is.included(p,t(X)); detach(lifelength)
```

The output is `TRUE`. However, if we use `p = c(1,0,0,0,0,0,0,0,0)`, the output becomes `FALSE`. □

Example 3.25. (Abrasion of denim jeans, continued) Consider the model of Example 3.5. Here, there first column is equal to the sum of the next three columns, and the last column is equal to that sum minus the sum of the fifth and sixth columns. Except for these two dependent columns, which do not contribute to the rank, the middle five columns are linearly independent. While there are seven columns, $\rho(\boldsymbol{X})$ is only 5. Hence, we cannot expect all the parameters to be estimable. The LPF $\tau_1 - \tau_2$ is estimable, because the corresponding $\boldsymbol{p}'$ is $(0:1:-1:0:0:0:0)$, which is the difference of the first and eleventh row of $\boldsymbol{X}$. (We can also cite a specific LUE, such as $y_1 - y_{11}$.) However, μ is not estimable, since $(1:0:0:0:0:0:0)' \notin \mathcal{C}(\boldsymbol{X}')$.

As in the previous example, we can also check estimability of an LPF through the functions `binaries` and `is.included`, using the code given below.

```
data(denim); attach(denim)
X <- cbind(1,binaries(Denim),binaries(Laundry))
p <- c(0,1,-1,0,0,0,0)
is.included(p,t(X)); detach(denim)
```

The output is `TRUE`. If we use `p = c(0,1,0,0,0,0,0)` in the above code, the output becomes `FALSE`. □

Definition 3.20 may seem to suggest that the *only* defect of a non-estimable LPF is that there is no linear and unbiased estimator. It appears as if a non-estimable LPF might be reasonably estimated by a biased and/or nonlinear estimator. However, this is not the case. Consider the model of Example 3.5. If one subtracts 2 from μ and adds 1 to each of τ_1, τ_2, τ_3, β_1, β_2 and β_3, this alternative set of values has the same mean and variance of all the observations. There is no way to distinguish one set of candidate values from the other, on the basis of the observables $y_1, \ldots, y_{90}$. In this sense μ cannot even be identified on the basis of the observations.

The above example illustrates the difficulty in 'estimating' a non-estimable function. This interpretation of non-estimability holds quite generally: given a non-estimable LPF and a 'candidate' $\boldsymbol{\beta}$, one can always find infinitely many alternative values of the parameter $\boldsymbol{\beta}$, each of which corresponds to a different value of the this LPF but makes no difference to the $\boldsymbol{y}$-vector.

It emerges from the above discussion that the issue of estimability of an LPF in a linear model is related to a more fundamental question: whether a parameter can be meaningfully identified. Let us formalize this notion.

Definition 3.26. Let $f(\boldsymbol{y};\boldsymbol{\theta})$, $\boldsymbol{\theta} \in \boldsymbol{\Theta}$ be a family of multivariate probability density functions. A measurable parametric function g defined on $\boldsymbol{\Theta}$ is said to be identifiable by distribution, or simply *identifiable*, if for any pair $\boldsymbol{\theta}_1$, $\boldsymbol{\theta}_2$ in $\boldsymbol{\Theta}$, the relation $g(\boldsymbol{\theta}_1) \neq g(\boldsymbol{\theta}_2)$ implies $f(\boldsymbol{y};\boldsymbol{\theta}_1) \neq f(\boldsymbol{y};\boldsymbol{\theta}_2)$ for some $\boldsymbol{y}$. □

The above definition is due to Bunke and Bunke (1974). It essentially says that two distinct values of an identifiable parametric function should always lead to different likelihoods of the observation for some outcome.

Proposition 3.27. *An LPF in the linear model* $(\boldsymbol{y}, \boldsymbol{X\beta}, \sigma^2\boldsymbol{I})$ *is identifiable if and only if it is estimable.*

Proof. Consider the LPF $\boldsymbol{p}'\boldsymbol{\beta}$. It is identifiable if and only if $\boldsymbol{p}'\boldsymbol{\beta}_1 \neq \boldsymbol{p}'\boldsymbol{\beta}_2 \Rightarrow \boldsymbol{X\beta}_1 \neq \boldsymbol{X\beta}_2$ for all $\boldsymbol{\beta}_1$ and $\boldsymbol{\beta}_2$. This condition is equivalent to $\boldsymbol{X\beta} = \boldsymbol{0} \Rightarrow \boldsymbol{p}'\boldsymbol{\beta} = 0$. According to Exercise A.16, the latter condition can be written as $\boldsymbol{p} \in \mathcal{C}(\boldsymbol{X}')$, which is the necessary and sufficient condition for estimability (see Proposition 3.21). □

A consequence of Proposition 3.27 is that a non-estimable LPF in the linear model does not have a linear or nonlinear unbiased estimator (see Exercise 3.3). Non-estimable or non-identifiable LPFs may occur in the linear model when there is some redundancy in the model description in the form of too many parameters (see Remark 3.22). This can be 'rectified', if desired, through a *reparametrization*, which is discussed in Section 3.9. Often it is convenient *not* to reparametrize, particularly when the corresponding $\boldsymbol{X}$ matrix has a special structure. The methods developed in this chapter are perfectly applicable to models with redundancy.

3.6 Best linear unbiased estimation

Suppose $\boldsymbol{p}'\boldsymbol{\beta}$ is an estimable LPF of the linear model $(\boldsymbol{y}, \boldsymbol{X\beta}, \sigma^2\boldsymbol{I})$. Given an LUE of $\boldsymbol{p}'\boldsymbol{\beta}$, we can always construct another LUE by simply adding an LZF to it. Thus, there is a large class of LUEs of any given estimable LPF. We seek to identify a member of this class which has the smallest variance.

Definition 3.28. The *best linear unbiased estimator* (BLUE) of an estimable LPF is defined as the LUE having the smallest variance. □

We shall prove that the BLUE of an estimable LPF not only exists but is also unique. We begin by showing an important connection between BLUEs and LZFs.

Proposition 3.29. *A linear function of the response vector is the BLUE of its expectation if and only if it is uncorrelated with every LZF.* □

Proof. Let $\boldsymbol{l}_1'\boldsymbol{y}$ and $\boldsymbol{l}_2'\boldsymbol{y}$ be two distinct LUEs of the same LPF, and $\boldsymbol{l}_1'\boldsymbol{y}$ be uncorrelated with every LZF. Rewrite $\boldsymbol{l}_2'\boldsymbol{y}$ as

$$\boldsymbol{l}_2'\boldsymbol{y} = \boldsymbol{l}_1'\boldsymbol{y} + (\boldsymbol{l}_2 - \boldsymbol{l}_1)'\boldsymbol{y}.$$

Notice that $(\boldsymbol{l}_2 - \boldsymbol{l}_1)'\boldsymbol{y}$ is a vector LZF and, hence, uncorrelated with $\boldsymbol{l}_1'\boldsymbol{y}$. Therefore,

$$Var(\boldsymbol{l}_2'\boldsymbol{y}) = Var(\boldsymbol{l}_1'\boldsymbol{y}) + Var((\boldsymbol{l}_2 - \boldsymbol{l}_1)'\boldsymbol{y}) > Var(\boldsymbol{l}_1'\boldsymbol{y}).$$

The *strict* inequality follows from the fact that the LZF $(\boldsymbol{l}_2 - \boldsymbol{l}_1)'\boldsymbol{y}$ cannot be identically zero if the two LUEs are distinct. This proves the 'if' part.

In order to prove the 'only if' part, let $\boldsymbol{l}'\boldsymbol{y}$ be an LUE which is *correlated* with the nontrivial LZF, $\boldsymbol{m}'\boldsymbol{y}$. Consider

$$\boldsymbol{l}_1'\boldsymbol{y} = \boldsymbol{l}'\boldsymbol{y} - b\boldsymbol{m}'\boldsymbol{y}, \qquad \text{where} \quad b = Cov(\boldsymbol{l}'\boldsymbol{y}, \boldsymbol{m}'\boldsymbol{y})/Var(\boldsymbol{m}'\boldsymbol{y}).$$

It is easy to see that $Cov(\boldsymbol{l}_1'\boldsymbol{y}, \boldsymbol{m}'\boldsymbol{y}) = 0$. By rewriting the above equation as $\boldsymbol{l}'\boldsymbol{y} = \boldsymbol{l}_1'\boldsymbol{y} + b\boldsymbol{m}'\boldsymbol{y}$, we have

$$Var(\boldsymbol{l}'\boldsymbol{y}) = Var(\boldsymbol{l}_1'\boldsymbol{y}) + Var(b\boldsymbol{m}'\boldsymbol{y}) > Var(\boldsymbol{l}_1'\boldsymbol{y}).$$

Note that $\boldsymbol{l}'\boldsymbol{y}$ and $\boldsymbol{l}_1'\boldsymbol{y}$ are LUEs of the same LPF, so $\boldsymbol{l}'\boldsymbol{y}$ cannot be the BLUE of this LPF. □

Example 3.30. (Trivial example, continued) For the linear model of Example 3.13 it was shown that every LZF is a linear function of y_2 and y_4 (see Example 3.17). Since y_1 and y_3 are both uncorrelated with y_2 and y_4, these must be the respective BLUEs of α_1 and α_2. Thus, the 'natural estimator' mentioned in Example 3.13 is in fact the BLUE. Another LUE of α_1 is $y_1 + y_2$, but it has the additional baggage of the LZF y_2, which inflates its variance. The variance of $y_1 + y_2$ is $2\sigma^2$, while that of the corresponding BLUE (y_1) is only σ^2. □

In less trivial problems, we need to do more work to get the BLUE. It is clear from Proposition 3.29 that if an LPF has a BLUE, then any other LUE of that LPF can be expressed as the sum of two uncorrelated parts: the BLUE and an LZF. Any ordinary LUE has larger variance than that of the BLUE, precisely because of the added LZF component, which carries no information about the LPF. Having understood this, we should be able to improve upon any given LUE by 'trimming the fat.' To accomplish this, we have to subtract a suitable LZF from the given LUE so that the remainder is uncorrelated with *every* LZF. Accounting for every LZF is not very difficult; the task is simplified by the fact that every LZF is of the form $\boldsymbol{m}'(\boldsymbol{I} - \boldsymbol{H})\boldsymbol{y}$ for some vector $\boldsymbol{m}$ (see Proposition 3.14). Thus, decorrelating an LUE from all LZF may be accomplished by decorrelating it with $(\boldsymbol{I} - \boldsymbol{H})\boldsymbol{y}$, using Proposition 2.28.

Proposition 3.31. *If $\boldsymbol{l}'\boldsymbol{y}$ is an LUE of an LPF, then the corresponding BLUE is $\boldsymbol{l}'\boldsymbol{H}\boldsymbol{y}$.*

Proof. Note that one can write $\boldsymbol{l}'\boldsymbol{y} = \boldsymbol{l}'\boldsymbol{H}\boldsymbol{y} + \boldsymbol{l}'(\boldsymbol{I} - \boldsymbol{H})\boldsymbol{y}$. Since $E\boldsymbol{l}'(\boldsymbol{I} - \boldsymbol{H})\boldsymbol{y} = \boldsymbol{0}$, $\boldsymbol{l}'\boldsymbol{H}\boldsymbol{y}$ has the same expectation as $\boldsymbol{l}'\boldsymbol{y}$. Further, $\boldsymbol{l}'\boldsymbol{H}\boldsymbol{y}$ is uncorrelated with any LZF of the form $\boldsymbol{m}'(\boldsymbol{I} - \boldsymbol{H})\boldsymbol{y}$. Therefore, $\boldsymbol{l}'\boldsymbol{H}\boldsymbol{y}$ must be the BLUE of $E(\boldsymbol{l}'\boldsymbol{y})$. □

This proposition gives a constructive proof of the existence of the BLUE of any estimable LPF. Instead of modifying a preliminary estimator, one can also construct the BLUE of a given LPF *directly* using the Gauss-Markov Theorem (see Proposition 3.38).

Remark 3.32. Proposition 3.29 is the linear analogue of Proposition B.10 of general estimation. The BLUE of a single LPF is a linear analogue of the UMVUE, and the LZFs are *linear* estimators of zero.[1] Indeed, when $\boldsymbol{y}$ has the normal distribution, it can be shown that the BLUE of any estimable LPF is its UMVUE and that any LZF is ancillary (Exercise 3.40). In the general case, the uncorrelatedness of the UMVUE and estimators of zero do not provide a direct method of constructing the UMVUE, because it is difficult to characterize the set of all estimators of zero. (We need an unbiased estimator, a complete sufficient statistic and an additional result — Proposition B.11 — for the construction.) In the linear case however, 'zero correlation with LZFs' is an adequate characterization for constructing the BLUE — as we have just demonstrated through Proposition 3.31. □

We now prove that the BLUE of an estimable LPF is unique.

Proposition 3.33. *Every estimable LPF has a unique BLUE.*

Proof. Let $\boldsymbol{l}_1'\boldsymbol{y}$ and $\boldsymbol{l}_2'\boldsymbol{y}$ be distinct BLUEs of the same vector LPF. By writing $\boldsymbol{l}_1'\boldsymbol{y}$ as $\boldsymbol{l}_2'\boldsymbol{y} + (\boldsymbol{l}_1 - \boldsymbol{l}_2)'\boldsymbol{y}$ and using Proposition 3.29, we have $Var(\boldsymbol{l}_1'\boldsymbol{y}) = Var(\boldsymbol{l}_2'\boldsymbol{y}) + Var((\boldsymbol{l}_1 - \boldsymbol{l}_2)'\boldsymbol{y})$. Therefore $(\boldsymbol{l}_1 - \boldsymbol{l}_2)'\boldsymbol{y}$ has zero mean and zero variance. It follows that $E[(\boldsymbol{l}_1 - \boldsymbol{l}_2)'\boldsymbol{y}]^2 = 0$, or $\sigma^2\|\boldsymbol{l}_1 - \boldsymbol{l}_2\|^2 = 0$. Thus, $\boldsymbol{l}_1 = \boldsymbol{l}_2$, which implies $\boldsymbol{l}_1'\boldsymbol{y} = \boldsymbol{l}_2'\boldsymbol{y}$. □

We have already observed (see Remark 3.15) that every LZF is a linear function of the residuals of least squares fit in a linear model. We now formally state this fact along with an equally important characterization of the BLUEs.

Proposition 3.34. *In a linear model, every BLUE is a linear function of the fitted values from the least squares fit, and every LZF is a linear function of the corresponding residuals.*

Proof. Let $\boldsymbol{l}'\boldsymbol{y}$ be a BLUE and $\boldsymbol{p}'\boldsymbol{\beta}$ be its expected value. According to Proposition 3.31, the BLUE of $\boldsymbol{p}'\boldsymbol{\beta}$ is $\boldsymbol{l}'\widehat{\boldsymbol{y}}$, while Proposition 3.33 ensures that $\boldsymbol{l}'\boldsymbol{y}$ is the same as $\boldsymbol{l}'\widehat{\boldsymbol{y}}$, which is a function of the fitted values.

---

[1]See Chapter 11 for a linear version of the fundamental notions of inference.

It follows from Remark 3.15 that every LZF is of the form $\boldsymbol{l}'(\boldsymbol{I} - \boldsymbol{H})\boldsymbol{y}$ or $\boldsymbol{l}'\boldsymbol{e}$ for some $\boldsymbol{l}$. □

Remark 3.35. The class of all vectors $\boldsymbol{l}$ such that $\boldsymbol{l}'\boldsymbol{y}$ is a BLUE is referred to as the *estimation space*. Likewise, the *error space* is the space of vectors $\boldsymbol{m}$ such that $\boldsymbol{m}'\boldsymbol{y}$ is an LZF. Proposition 3.34 implies that the estimation and error spaces of the linear model $(\boldsymbol{y}, \boldsymbol{X\beta}, \sigma^2\boldsymbol{I})$ are $\mathcal{C}(\boldsymbol{X})$ and $\mathcal{C}(\boldsymbol{X})^{\perp}$, respectively. □

Example 3.36. (Age at death, continued) In the age at death example, we had previously found least squares fitted values of the observations as (see page 68)

$$\hat{y}_{ij} = n_j^{-1} \sum_{i=1}^{n_j} y_{ij}, \quad i = 1, \ldots, n_j, \quad j = 1, \ldots, 8.$$

We now use Proposition 3.31 to identify the BLUE of $\tau_1 - \tau_2$. It is easy to see that $y_{11} - y_{12}$ is an LUE of $\tau_1 - \tau_2$. The BLUE would then be $\hat{y}_{11} - \hat{y}_{12}$, obtained by simply substituting every observation in the expression for the LUE by the corresponding fitted value. □

Example 3.37. (Abrasion of denim jeans, continued) By applying the same trick to the data set on the abrasion score of jeans, we obtain the BLUE of $\tau_1 - \tau_2$ as $\hat{y}_{111} - \hat{y}_{211}$, where the fitted values $\hat{y}_{111}$ and $\hat{y}_{211}$ are as defined on page 71. □

As the above examples show, use of Proposition 3.31 to find the BLUE of any specified LPF requires the preliminary step of finding an LUE of the given LPF. We now provide another recipe which, rather than using any preliminary LUE, builds on an LSE of $\boldsymbol{\beta}$. The result says that even if $\widehat{\boldsymbol{\beta}}_{LS}$ is not unique, it provides the BLUEs of the linear model.

Proposition 3.38. (Gauss-Markov Theorem) *If $\boldsymbol{p}'\boldsymbol{\beta}$ is estimable and $\widehat{\boldsymbol{\beta}}_{LS}$ is any LSE of $\boldsymbol{\beta}$, then the BLUE of $\boldsymbol{p}'\boldsymbol{\beta}$ is given by $\boldsymbol{p}'\widehat{\boldsymbol{\beta}}_{LS}$.*

Proof. It is easy to see that an LUE of $\boldsymbol{p}'\boldsymbol{\beta}$ is $\boldsymbol{p}'\boldsymbol{X}^{-}\boldsymbol{y}$. Using this in Proposition 3.31, we have the BLUE of $\boldsymbol{p}'\boldsymbol{\beta}$ given by

$$\boldsymbol{p}'\boldsymbol{X}^{-}\boldsymbol{X}(\boldsymbol{X}'\boldsymbol{X})^{-}\boldsymbol{X}'\boldsymbol{y} = \boldsymbol{p}'(\boldsymbol{X}'\boldsymbol{X})^{-}\boldsymbol{X}'\boldsymbol{y} = \boldsymbol{p}'\widehat{\boldsymbol{\beta}}_{LS},$$

by virtue of (3.4). □

The Gauss-Markov theorem is also called the *principle of substitution*, since the BLUE of any estimable LPF $\boldsymbol{p}'\boldsymbol{\beta}$ is obtained simply by substituting any least squares estimator $\widehat{\boldsymbol{\beta}}_{LS}$ for $\boldsymbol{\beta}$. The following proposition gives a converse to the principle of substitution.

Proposition 3.39. *If $\widehat{\boldsymbol{\beta}}$ is a linear function of $\boldsymbol{y}$ such that for every estimable $\mathbf{p}'\boldsymbol{\beta}$ the BLUE is $\mathbf{p}'\widehat{\boldsymbol{\beta}}$, then $\widehat{\boldsymbol{\beta}}$ must be a least squares estimator of $\boldsymbol{\beta}$.*

Proof. Let $\widehat{\boldsymbol{\beta}} = \boldsymbol{G}\boldsymbol{y}$, which satisfies the condition of the proposition. As $\boldsymbol{X}\boldsymbol{\beta}$ is estimable, $\boldsymbol{X}\boldsymbol{G}\boldsymbol{y}$ is the BLUE of $\boldsymbol{X}\boldsymbol{\beta}$. It follows from Proposition 3.31 that $\widehat{\boldsymbol{y}}$ is the BLUE of $\boldsymbol{X}\boldsymbol{\beta}$. By uniqueness of the BLUE (Proposition 3.33), $\boldsymbol{X}\boldsymbol{G}\boldsymbol{y} = \widehat{\boldsymbol{y}}$ almost surely.

Let $\boldsymbol{F}\boldsymbol{y}$ be any competing estimator of $\boldsymbol{\beta}$. It follows that

$$\begin{aligned}
\|\boldsymbol{y} - \boldsymbol{X}\boldsymbol{F}\boldsymbol{y}\|^2 &= \|\boldsymbol{y} - \boldsymbol{X}\boldsymbol{G}\boldsymbol{y}\|^2 + \|\boldsymbol{X}(\boldsymbol{G} - \boldsymbol{F})\boldsymbol{y}\|^2 + 2(\boldsymbol{y} - \widehat{\boldsymbol{y}})'\boldsymbol{X}(\boldsymbol{G} - \boldsymbol{F})\boldsymbol{y} \\
&= \|\boldsymbol{y} - \boldsymbol{X}\boldsymbol{G}\boldsymbol{y}\|^2 + \|\boldsymbol{X}(\boldsymbol{G} - \boldsymbol{F})\boldsymbol{y}\|^2 + 2\boldsymbol{y}'(\boldsymbol{I} - \boldsymbol{P}_X)\boldsymbol{X}(\boldsymbol{G} - \boldsymbol{F})\boldsymbol{y} \\
&= \|\boldsymbol{y} - \boldsymbol{X}\boldsymbol{G}\boldsymbol{y}\|^2 + \|\boldsymbol{X}(\boldsymbol{G} - \boldsymbol{F})\boldsymbol{y}\|^2 \geq \|\boldsymbol{y}\boldsymbol{X}\boldsymbol{G}\boldsymbol{y}\|^2.
\end{aligned}$$

Thus, $\widehat{\boldsymbol{\beta}}$ is a least squares estimator. □

Remark 3.40. The Gauss-Markov theorem, along with its converse, characterizes the relation between any least squares estimator of $\boldsymbol{\beta}$ with the BLUE of an estimable LPF. On the other hand, it was the vector of least squares fitted values that was identified in Propositions 3.31 and 3.34 as the key to finding the BLUEs. The vectors $\widehat{\boldsymbol{\beta}}_{LS}$ and $\widehat{\boldsymbol{y}}$ are in fact functions of one another:

$$\begin{aligned}
\widehat{\boldsymbol{y}} &= \boldsymbol{X}\widehat{\boldsymbol{\beta}}_{LS}, \\
\widehat{\boldsymbol{\beta}}_{LS} &= (\boldsymbol{X}'\boldsymbol{X})^{-}\boldsymbol{X}'\widehat{\boldsymbol{y}},
\end{aligned}$$

the latter equation being a nonunique representation, equivalent to (3.4). In the special case when $\boldsymbol{X}'\boldsymbol{X}$ is nonsingular, $\widehat{\boldsymbol{\beta}}_{LS}$ is unique and is equal to $(\boldsymbol{X}'\boldsymbol{X})^{-1}\boldsymbol{X}'\widehat{\boldsymbol{y}}$. □

Given the close connection between an LSE of $\boldsymbol{\beta}$ and the BLUEs, we henceforth denote the BLUE of an estimable LPF $\boldsymbol{p}'\boldsymbol{\beta}$ by $\widehat{\boldsymbol{p}'\boldsymbol{\beta}}$ (without the subscript). For any two estimable LPFs $\boldsymbol{p}'\boldsymbol{\beta}$ and $\boldsymbol{q}'\boldsymbol{\beta}$, we can write $\boldsymbol{p}$ and $\boldsymbol{q}$ as $\boldsymbol{X}'(\boldsymbol{X}')^{-}\boldsymbol{p}$ and $\boldsymbol{X}'(\boldsymbol{X}')^{-}\boldsymbol{q}$, respectively. Therefore, we have from (3.14)

$$\begin{aligned}
Cov(\mathbf{p}'\widehat{\boldsymbol{\beta}}, \boldsymbol{q}'\widehat{\boldsymbol{\beta}}) &= Cov(\mathbf{p}'\boldsymbol{X}^{-}\widehat{\boldsymbol{y}}, \boldsymbol{q}'\boldsymbol{X}^{-}\widehat{\boldsymbol{y}}) = \sigma^2\mathbf{p}'\boldsymbol{X}^{-}\boldsymbol{P}_X(\boldsymbol{X}')^{-}\boldsymbol{q} \\
&= \sigma^2\mathbf{p}'(\boldsymbol{X}'\boldsymbol{X})^{-}\boldsymbol{q}, \\
Var(\mathbf{p}'\widehat{\boldsymbol{\beta}}) &= \sigma^2\mathbf{p}'(\boldsymbol{X}'\boldsymbol{X})^{-}\boldsymbol{p}.
\end{aligned}$$

Since $\boldsymbol{p}$ and $\boldsymbol{q}$ are in $\mathcal{C}(\boldsymbol{X}'\boldsymbol{X})$, the above expressions do not depend on the choice of the g-inverse (see Proposition A.10, part (f)).

Example 3.41. (Age at death, continued) We had previously found a class of g-inverses of $\boldsymbol{X}'\boldsymbol{X}$ as (see page 68)

$$(\boldsymbol{X}'\boldsymbol{X})^- = \begin{pmatrix} 0 & 0 & 0 & \cdots & 0 \\ 0 & \frac{1}{n_1} & 0 & \cdots & 0 \\ 0 & 0 & \frac{1}{n_2} & \cdots & 0 \\ \vdots & \vdots & \vdots & \ddots & \vdots \\ 0 & 0 & 0 & \cdots & \frac{1}{n_8} \end{pmatrix} + \begin{pmatrix} 1 \\ -1 \\ -1 \\ \vdots \\ -1 \end{pmatrix} (a:0:0:0:0:0:0:0:0),$$

and the corresponding LSE of $\boldsymbol{\beta}$ as

$$\begin{pmatrix} \hat{\mu} \\ \hat{\tau}_1 \\ \hat{\tau}_2 \\ \vdots \\ \hat{\tau}_8 \end{pmatrix} = \begin{pmatrix} a\sum_{j=1}^{8}\sum_{i=1}^{n_j} y_{ij} \\ n_1^{-1}\sum_{i=1}^{n_1} y_{i1} - a\sum_{j=1}^{8}\sum_{i=1}^{n_j} y_{ij} \\ n_2^{-1}\sum_{i=1}^{n_2} y_{i2} - a\sum_{j=1}^{8}\sum_{i=1}^{n_j} y_{ij} \\ \vdots \\ n_8^{-1}\sum_{i=1}^{n_8} y_{i8} - a\sum_{j=1}^{8}\sum_{i=1}^{n_j} y_{ij} \end{pmatrix}.$$

for any constant a. Though this estimator is not unique, the unique BLUE of $\tau_1 - \tau_2$, obtained from the above LSE via the Gauss-Markov theorem, is

$$\hat{\tau}_1 - \hat{\tau}_2 = \frac{1}{n_1}\sum_{i=1}^{n_1} y_{i1} - \frac{1}{n_2}\sum_{i=1}^{n_2} y_{i2}.$$

Here, $\boldsymbol{p}' = (0:1:-1:0:0:0:0:0:0)$. It also follows that

$$Var(\hat{\tau}_1 - \hat{\tau}_2) = \sigma^2\boldsymbol{p}'(\boldsymbol{X}'\boldsymbol{X})^-\boldsymbol{p} = \frac{\sigma^2}{n_1} + \frac{\sigma^2}{n_2},$$

irrespective of the value of a used in the expression of $(\boldsymbol{X}'\boldsymbol{X})^-$. By choosing $\boldsymbol{q}' = (0:1:0:-1:0:0:0:0:0)$, we obtain the BLUE of $(\tau_1 - \tau_3)$, its variance and its covariance with the first BLUE:

$$\hat{\tau}_1 - \hat{\tau}_3 = \frac{1}{n_1}\sum_{i=1}^{n_1} y_{i1} - \frac{1}{n_3}\sum_{i=1}^{n_3} y_{i3},$$

$$Var(\hat{\tau}_1 - \hat{\tau}_3) = \sigma^2\boldsymbol{q}'(\boldsymbol{X}'\boldsymbol{X})^-\boldsymbol{q} = \frac{\sigma^2}{n_1} + \frac{\sigma^2}{n_3},$$

$$Cov(\hat{\tau}_1 - \hat{\tau}_2, \hat{\tau}_1 - \hat{\tau}_3) = \sigma^2\boldsymbol{p}'(\boldsymbol{X}'\boldsymbol{X})^-\boldsymbol{q} = \frac{\sigma^2}{n_1}.$$

These expressions are uniquely defined, irrespective of the value of a. □

We end this section with yet another optimal property of BLUEs. Suppose $\boldsymbol{A\beta}$ is an estimable vector LPF. Since all the elements of $\boldsymbol{A\beta}$ are estimable, these have their respective BLUEs. We now show that if these BLUEs are arranged as a vector, that vector would be optimal in a stronger sense. Dispersion matrices can be compared with one another through the Löwner order defined in Section A.6 of Appendix A. The next proposition shows that the vector of BLUEs has smaller dispersion matrix than any other vector of LUEs of $\boldsymbol{A\beta}$.

Proposition 3.42. *Let $\boldsymbol{Ly}$ be the vector of BLUEs of the elements of the estimable vector LPF $\boldsymbol{A\beta}$. Then the dispersion matrix of $\boldsymbol{Ly}$ is smaller than that of any other LUE of $A\beta$ in the sense of the Löwner order.*

Proof. Suppose $\boldsymbol{Ty}$ is a vector LUE of $\boldsymbol{A\beta}$ that is distinct from $\boldsymbol{Ly}$. It is clear that $(\boldsymbol{T}-\boldsymbol{L})\boldsymbol{y}$ is a vector of LZFs, which is completely uncorrelated with $\boldsymbol{Ly}$. Therefore,

$$D(\boldsymbol{Ty}) = D(\boldsymbol{Ly} + (\boldsymbol{T}-\boldsymbol{L})\boldsymbol{y}) = D(\boldsymbol{Ly}) + D((\boldsymbol{T}-\boldsymbol{L})\boldsymbol{Y}).$$

Thus, $D(\boldsymbol{Ly}) \leq D(\boldsymbol{Ty})$ in the sense of the Löwner order. □

The Löwner order implies several important algebraic orders. Let $\boldsymbol{Ly}$ be the BLUE and $\boldsymbol{Ty}$ be another LUE of $\boldsymbol{A\beta}$. It follows from Proposition A.21 that $\operatorname{tr}(D(\boldsymbol{Ly})) \leq \operatorname{tr}(D(\boldsymbol{Ty}))$, that is, the total variance of all the components of $\boldsymbol{Ly}$ is less than that of $\boldsymbol{Ty}$. This proposition also implies that $|D(\boldsymbol{Ly})| \leq |D(\boldsymbol{Ty})|$. It can be shown that the volume of an ellipsoidal confidence region of $\boldsymbol{A\beta}$ (see Section 4.3.2) centered at $\boldsymbol{Ty}$ is a monotonically increasing function of $|D(\boldsymbol{Ty})|$. Thus, a confidence region centered at the BLUE is the smallest. It also follows from Proposition A.21 that the extreme eigenvalues of $D(\boldsymbol{Ly})$ are smaller than those of $D(\boldsymbol{Ty})$.

3.7 Maximum likelihood estimation

If the errors in the linear model $(\boldsymbol{y}, \boldsymbol{X\beta}, \sigma^2\boldsymbol{I})$ are assumed to have a multivariate normal distribution, then the log-likelihood of the observation vector $\boldsymbol{y}$ is

$$-\frac{n}{2}\log(2\pi\sigma^2) - \frac{1}{2\sigma^2}(\boldsymbol{y}-\boldsymbol{X\beta})'(\boldsymbol{y}-\boldsymbol{X\beta}).$$

It is clear that MLE of $\boldsymbol{\beta}$ is a minimizer of the quadratic form $(\boldsymbol{y}-\boldsymbol{X\beta})'(\boldsymbol{y}-\boldsymbol{X\beta})$, which is by definition an LSE. After substituting this MLE of $\boldsymbol{\beta}$ into the log-likelihood and maximizing it with respect to σ^2, we obtain the MLE of σ^2 as

$$\widehat{\sigma^2}_{ML} = \frac{1}{n}(\boldsymbol{y} - \boldsymbol{X}\widehat{\boldsymbol{\beta}}_{LS})'(\boldsymbol{y} - \boldsymbol{X}\widehat{\boldsymbol{\beta}}_{LS}).$$

Note that this estimator differs from the unbiased estimator of σ^2 obtained in Section 3.4, by a fraction. Therefore, it is biased. The amount of bias,

$$E\left(\widehat{\sigma^2}_{ML} - \sigma^2\right) = \left(\frac{n-r}{n} - 1\right)\sigma^2$$

(r being the rank of $\boldsymbol{X}$), goes to zero as the sample size n goes to infinity.

An MLE of $\boldsymbol{\beta}$ is an LSE when the errors have the normal distribution. Therefore the condition for its uniqueness is that $\boldsymbol{X}$ should have full column rank. Further, the MLE of any estimable LPF is unique and it coincides with its BLUE (or LSE). If the MLE of $\boldsymbol{\beta}$ is unique, one may use it to obtain the MLE of any *nonlinear* parametric function also.

The multivariate normal distribution is a special case of the general class of spherically symmetric distributions. When the error distribution is spherically symmetric, it can be shown that an MLE of $\boldsymbol{\beta}$ is an LSE (Exercise 3.8).

Although the three estimation strategies considered so far (in Sections 3.1 and 3.6 and the present section) yield the same unbiased estimator of a given estimable LPF, not all is well with this estimator. It is inadmissible with respect to the squared error loss function. It is also sensitive to small changes in the measurements and/or to non-normality of the errors. Other estimation strategies, which take some of these factors into account, are considered briefly in Chapters 5 and 11.

3.8 Error sum of squares and degrees of freedom*

While there are uncountable number of linear functions of the response vector, many of them are related to one another. We have already classified these into LZFs and LUEs. The question that we will try to answer now is: can we have an adequate set of linear functions of each type, so that other functions can be expressed in terms of them?

For the linear model $(\boldsymbol{y}, \boldsymbol{X\beta}, \sigma^2\boldsymbol{I})$, let us define a *generating set of LZFs* as a collection of LZFs of nonzero variance, such that every LZF is almost surely a linear combination of the members of this set. Likewise, a *generating set of BLUEs* is a set of BLUEs such that every BLUE can be written as a linear combination of the members of this set.

We readily get two examples from Proposition 3.34. The set of residuals is a generating set of LZFs, while the set of fitted values is a generating set of the BLUEs. One can construct other examples through linear functions of $\boldsymbol{e}$ and $\widehat{\boldsymbol{y}}$ from which these two vectors can be reconstructed.

The generating sets may have redundancy. Borrowing a notion from the theory of vector spaces, let us define a *basis set of LZFs* as a generating set such that no linear combination of the members of this set is identically zero with probability 1. A *basis set of BLUEs* is a generating set having no linear combination of members almost surely equal to zero for all $\boldsymbol{\beta}$.

The generating and basis sets of BLUEs and LZFs have roots in some fundamental concepts of linear inference. These are discussed in Chapter 11.

As one looks for an orthogonal basis of a vector space, we can also seek to describe LZFs and BLUEs through uncorrelated and standardized representatives. We define a *standardized basis set of LZFs* as a basis set having uncorrelated members, each with variance σ^2. Likewise, a *standardized basis set of BLUEs* is a basis set having uncorrelated members, each with variance σ^2 or zero.

BLUEs with zero variance in a standardized basis set become important in the case of general linear models of the form $(\boldsymbol{y}, \boldsymbol{X\beta}, \sigma^2\boldsymbol{V})$ with $\boldsymbol{V}$ possibly singular (see Sections 11.1.2 and 11.1.3). In the present set-up, every BLUE has a positive variance.

Example 3.43. (Trivial example, continued) For the linear model of Example 3.13, a standardized basis set of LZFs is $\{y_2, y_4\}$, and a standardized basis set of BLUEs is $\{y_1, y_3\}$. These are also generating sets. □

Example 3.44. (Age at death, continued) In Example 3.4 the set of eight distinct fitted values $\{\hat{y}_{11}, \hat{y}_{12}, \ldots, \hat{y}_{18}\}$ (defined on page 68) constitute a basis set of BLUEs, as all fitted values are included in this set. The scaled versions $\{\sqrt{n_1}\hat{y}_{11}, \sqrt{n_2}\hat{y}_{12}, \ldots, \sqrt{n_8}\hat{y}_{18}\}$ would be a standardized basis set. A basis set of LZFs is $\{e_{ij},\ i = 2, \ldots, n_j,\ j = 1, \ldots, 8\}$. □

In the Example 3.44, we have stopped short of identifying a standardized basis set of LZFs. We would now present a construction in the general case, starting with the vector of residuals $\boldsymbol{e} = (\boldsymbol{I} - \boldsymbol{H})\boldsymbol{y}$ that has correlated elements (see (3.15)). The projection matrix $\boldsymbol{I} - \boldsymbol{H}$ can be factored as $\boldsymbol{CC}'$ where $\boldsymbol{C}$ is an $n \times (n-r)$ semi-orthogonal matrix and r is the rank of $\boldsymbol{X}$ (this follows from Proposition A.18(f) of Appendix A). If $\boldsymbol{C}^{-L}$ is any left-inverse of $\boldsymbol{C}$, then $D(\boldsymbol{C}^{-L}\boldsymbol{e}) = \sigma^2\boldsymbol{I}$. Therefore, the $n-r$ elements of the vector $\boldsymbol{C}^{-L}\boldsymbol{e}$ form a standardized basis set of LZFs.

One can similarly construct a standardized basis set of the BLUEs. See Exercise 3.12 for a transformation of $\boldsymbol{y}$ which simultaneously gives a standardized basis set of BLUEs and a standardized basis set of LZFs.

The standardized basis sets have a common property, described below.

Proposition 3.45. *If $\boldsymbol{z}$ is any vector whose elements constitute a standardized basis set of LZFs of the model $(\boldsymbol{y}, \boldsymbol{X\beta}, \sigma^2\boldsymbol{I})$, then*

(a) $\boldsymbol{z}$ has $n-r$ elements, where $r = \rho(\boldsymbol{X})$;
(b) $\boldsymbol{z}'\boldsymbol{z} = \boldsymbol{e}'\boldsymbol{e}$.

Proof. Suppose $\boldsymbol{z}$ has m elements, $\boldsymbol{l}_1'\boldsymbol{y}, \ldots, \boldsymbol{l}_m'\boldsymbol{y}$. Further, let $\boldsymbol{L} = (\boldsymbol{l}_1 \cdots \boldsymbol{l}_m)$. Then $D(\boldsymbol{z}) = \sigma^2\boldsymbol{L}'\boldsymbol{L}$. Since the LZFs contained in the basis set are uncorrelated and have variance σ^2, the columns of $\boldsymbol{L}$ must be orthonormal. Proposition 3.14 implies that $\mathcal{C}(\boldsymbol{L}) \subset \mathcal{C}(\boldsymbol{I} - \boldsymbol{P}_X)$. Therefore,

$$m = \rho(\boldsymbol{L}) \leq \rho(\boldsymbol{I} - \boldsymbol{P}_X) = n-r.$$

If $m < n-r$, we can find a vector $\boldsymbol{l}$ in $\mathcal{C}(\boldsymbol{X})^\perp$ such that $\boldsymbol{L}'\boldsymbol{l} = \boldsymbol{0}$. Then $\boldsymbol{l}'\boldsymbol{y}$ would be a nontrivial LZF uncorrelated with $\boldsymbol{z}$, which is a contradiction. Hence, m must be equal to $n-r$. This proves part (a).

To prove part (b), let $\boldsymbol{e} = \boldsymbol{B}\boldsymbol{z}$. Equating the dispersions of these two vectors, we have $\boldsymbol{I} - \boldsymbol{P}_X = \boldsymbol{B}\boldsymbol{B}'$. Therefore $\rho(\boldsymbol{B}) = \rho(\boldsymbol{B}\boldsymbol{B}') = n-r$, i.e. $\boldsymbol{B}$ has full column rank. It follows that $\boldsymbol{P}_{B'} = \boldsymbol{I}$. Hence,

$$\begin{aligned}\boldsymbol{z}'\boldsymbol{z} &= \boldsymbol{z}'\boldsymbol{P}_{B'}\boldsymbol{z} = \boldsymbol{z}'\boldsymbol{B}'(\boldsymbol{B}\boldsymbol{B}')^-\boldsymbol{B}\boldsymbol{z}\\ &= \boldsymbol{e}'(\boldsymbol{I} - \boldsymbol{P}_X)^-\boldsymbol{e} = \boldsymbol{e}'(\boldsymbol{I} - \boldsymbol{P}_X)\boldsymbol{e} = \boldsymbol{e}'\boldsymbol{e}.\end{aligned}$$ □

Proposition 3.46. *If $\boldsymbol{z}$ is any vector of BLUEs whose elements constitute a standardized basis set, then*

(a) $\boldsymbol{z}$ has r elements, where $r = \rho(\boldsymbol{X})$;
(b) $\boldsymbol{z}'\boldsymbol{z} = \widehat{\boldsymbol{y}}'\widehat{\boldsymbol{y}}$.

Proof. Suppose $\boldsymbol{z}$ has m elements, $\boldsymbol{l}_1'\boldsymbol{y}, \ldots, \boldsymbol{l}_m'\boldsymbol{y}$. Further, let $\boldsymbol{L} = (\boldsymbol{l}_1 \cdots \boldsymbol{l}_m)$. If $Var(\boldsymbol{l}_i'\boldsymbol{y}) = 0$ for any i $(1 \leq i \leq m)$, $\boldsymbol{l}_i'\boldsymbol{l}_i$ must be zero, which is not possible. Therefore, each $\boldsymbol{l}_i'\boldsymbol{y}$ must have variance σ^2. Then $D(\boldsymbol{z}) = \sigma^2\boldsymbol{L}'\boldsymbol{L} = \sigma^2\boldsymbol{I}$, i.e. the columns of $\boldsymbol{L}$ are orthogonal. Proposition 3.29 implies that $Cov(\boldsymbol{L}'\boldsymbol{y}, (\boldsymbol{I} - \boldsymbol{P}_X)\boldsymbol{y}) = \boldsymbol{0}$, i.e. $\mathcal{C}(\boldsymbol{L}) \subset \mathcal{C}(\boldsymbol{X})$. Therefore $m = \rho(\boldsymbol{L}) \leq \rho(\boldsymbol{X}) = r$. If $m < r$, we can find a vector $\boldsymbol{l}$ in $\mathcal{C}(\boldsymbol{X})$ such that $\boldsymbol{L}'\boldsymbol{l} = \boldsymbol{0}$. Then $\boldsymbol{l}'\boldsymbol{y}$ would be a BLUE uncorrelated with $\boldsymbol{z}$, which is a contradiction. This proves part (a).

To prove part (b), let $\widehat{\boldsymbol{y}} = \boldsymbol{Bz}$. Equating the dispersions of these two, we have $\boldsymbol{P}_X = \boldsymbol{BB}'$. Therefore $\rho(\boldsymbol{B}) = \rho(\boldsymbol{BB}') = r$, i.e. $\boldsymbol{B}$ has full column rank. It follows that $\boldsymbol{P}_{B'} = \boldsymbol{I}$. Hence,

$$\boldsymbol{z}'\boldsymbol{z} = \boldsymbol{z}'\boldsymbol{P}_{B'}\boldsymbol{z} = \boldsymbol{z}'\boldsymbol{B}'(\boldsymbol{BB}')^{-}\boldsymbol{Bz} = \widehat{\boldsymbol{y}}'(\boldsymbol{P}_X)^{-}\widehat{\boldsymbol{y}} = \widehat{\boldsymbol{y}}'\boldsymbol{P}_X\widehat{\boldsymbol{y}} = \widehat{\boldsymbol{y}}'\widehat{\boldsymbol{y}}. \qquad \square$$

In view of Proposition 3.45, the unbiased estimator of σ^2 defined in (3.19) can be rewritten as

$$\widehat{\sigma^2} = \frac{\boldsymbol{e}'\boldsymbol{e}}{n-r} = \frac{\boldsymbol{z}'\boldsymbol{z}}{n-r},$$

which is the average of squares of any standardized basis set of LZFs. We have noted earlier (see Remark 3.16) that the LZFs are functions of the model errors alone, and these are the *only* observable linear functions of the model errors. Therefore, an average of squares of a representative set of uncorrelated LZFs, each with variance σ^2, is a natural estimator of the error variance. Proposition 3.45 guarantees that the estimator does not depend on the specific choice of the standardized basis set, and that it takes into account all the linear functions of the model errors that one can get hold of.

The sum of squared values of the residuals, denoted by R_0^2, is referred to as the *residual sum of squares*. This name has another interpretation. It follows from (3.1) that

$$\boldsymbol{e}'\boldsymbol{e} = \|\boldsymbol{y} - \boldsymbol{X}\widehat{\boldsymbol{\beta}}_{LS}\|^2 = \min_{\boldsymbol{\beta}} \|\boldsymbol{y} - \boldsymbol{X\beta}\|^2.$$

Thus, R_0^2 is also the *residual value of the sum of squares* after it has been minimized as much as possible with respect to $\boldsymbol{\beta}$. Proposition 3.45 shows that R_0^2 is in fact a sum of squares of uncorrelated model errors. For this reason, it is also called the *error sum of squares* or *sum of squares due to error* (SSE).

It turns out that the description of R_0^2 as sum of squares of LZFs belonging to any standardized basis set extends easily to the general linear model considered in Chapter 7. However, the interpretation as the sum of squared residuals does not hold in that context. Hence, we prefer to use the phrase 'error sum of squares' instead of 'residual sum of squares', and formally define it as follows.

Definition 3.47. If $\boldsymbol{z}$ is any vector whose elements constitute a standardized basis set of LZFs in the linear model $(\boldsymbol{y}, \boldsymbol{X\beta}, \sigma^2\boldsymbol{V})$, then the *error sum of squares* is defined as $R_0^2 = \boldsymbol{z}'\boldsymbol{z}$. $\square$

Remark 3.48. If $\boldsymbol{z}$ is any vector whose elements constitute a generating set of LZFs, then (see Exercise 3.13)

$$R_0^2 = \boldsymbol{z}'[\sigma^{-2}D(\boldsymbol{z})]^-\boldsymbol{z}, \quad \rho(D(\boldsymbol{z})) = n - r. \qquad \square$$

If we put $\boldsymbol{z} = \boldsymbol{e}$ in the above expressions, then $D(\boldsymbol{z})$ simplifies to $\sigma^2(\boldsymbol{I} - \boldsymbol{P}_X)$ and $\boldsymbol{z}'[\sigma^{-2}D(\boldsymbol{z})]^-\boldsymbol{z}$ simplifies to $\boldsymbol{e}'\boldsymbol{e}$, as expected.

Consider the decomposition of the response vector $\boldsymbol{y}$ into the vector of fitted values and the residual vector:

$$\boldsymbol{y} = \widehat{\boldsymbol{y}} + \boldsymbol{e}.$$

Since $\widehat{\boldsymbol{y}}'\boldsymbol{e} = \boldsymbol{y}'\boldsymbol{H}(\boldsymbol{I} - \boldsymbol{H})\boldsymbol{y} = \boldsymbol{0}$, the sum of squares of the elements of $\boldsymbol{y}$ may be decomposed as

$$\|\boldsymbol{y}\|^2 = \|\widehat{\boldsymbol{y}}\|^2 + \|\boldsymbol{e}\|^2. \tag{3.20}$$

The left-hand side consists of the sum of squares of n uncorrelated observations, each having variance σ^2. Propositions 3.46 and 3.45 show that the terms $\|\widehat{\boldsymbol{y}}\|^2$ and $\|\boldsymbol{e}\|^2$ on the right-hand side account for r BLUEs and $n-r$ LZFs, respectively. These are all uncorrelated and each have variance σ^2. We can refer to the number of summands in each of the three terms as the *degrees of freedom.* The number of uncorrelated observations appearing in the left-hand side is n. The number of uncorrelated BLUEs in $\|\widehat{\boldsymbol{y}}\|^2$, r, is the number of degrees of freedom used for the estimation of the parameters. The number of uncorrelated LZFs in $\|\boldsymbol{e}\|^2$, $n-r$, is referred to as the *error degrees of freedom.* In the case of normally distributed errors, the uncorrelated LZFs and BLUEs have the normal distribution with variance σ^2. In this case the 'degrees of freedom' mentioned above actually indicate the number of squared normal random variables that constitute the sums $\|\boldsymbol{y}\|^2/\sigma^2$, $\|\widehat{\boldsymbol{y}}\|^2/\sigma^2$ and $\|\boldsymbol{e}\|^2/\sigma^2$, which have chi-square distribution. Thus, this notion of 'degrees of freedom' coincides with the 'degrees of freedom' used in the definition of that distribution (see page 34).

A similar decomposition of the dispersion matrix of the response vector follows from Proposition 3.29:

$$D(\boldsymbol{y}) = D(\widehat{\boldsymbol{y}}) + D(\boldsymbol{e}).$$

Equations (3.14) and (3.15) give expressions for the dispersion matrices on the right-hand side. In the case of normal errors, these dispersions can be written as

$$D(\boldsymbol{e}) = D(\boldsymbol{y}|\widehat{\boldsymbol{y}}),$$
$$D(\widehat{\boldsymbol{y}}) = D(\boldsymbol{y}|\boldsymbol{e}).$$

These results follow directly from (2.6). Note that $\boldsymbol{y}$ is an LUE of the vector LPF $\boldsymbol{X\beta}$, but the corresponding BLUE is $\widehat{\boldsymbol{y}}$. The dispersion of the latter is the *remaining* variability of $\boldsymbol{y}$ after the variability of the LZFs has been removed by the conditioning. Similarly, the dispersion of the residual vector corresponds to the remaining variability of $\boldsymbol{y}$ after the effect of the BLUEs are removed. We shall show in Chapter 7 that these interpretations hold even when the model errors are heteroscedastic and correlated.

Even without the assumption of the normal distribution, one can interpret $\widehat{\boldsymbol{y}}$ and $\boldsymbol{e}$ as the BLP of $\boldsymbol{y}$ in terms of $\widehat{\boldsymbol{y}}$ and $\boldsymbol{e}$, respectively (see Proposition 2.25). Consequently, the above dispersions can be written as

$$D(\boldsymbol{e}) = D(\boldsymbol{y} - \widehat{E}(\boldsymbol{y}|\widehat{\boldsymbol{y}})),$$
$$D(\widehat{\boldsymbol{y}}) = D(\boldsymbol{y} - \widehat{E}(\boldsymbol{y}|\boldsymbol{e})),$$

which are the dispersions of the prediction error of BLP of $\boldsymbol{y}$ in terms of $\boldsymbol{e}$ and $\widehat{\boldsymbol{y}}$, respectively.

A geometric view of the decomposition of $\boldsymbol{y}$ into $\widehat{\boldsymbol{y}}$ and $\boldsymbol{e}$ is given in Section 11.4.1.

3.9 Reparametrization*

Consider the model

$$\mathcal{M}_1 = (\boldsymbol{y}, \boldsymbol{X\beta}, \sigma^2\boldsymbol{I}),$$

and suppose $\boldsymbol{Z}$ is any matrix such that $\mathcal{C}(\boldsymbol{Z}) = \mathcal{C}(\boldsymbol{X})$. Then there are matrices $\boldsymbol{T}_1$ and $\boldsymbol{T}_2$ such that $\boldsymbol{X} = \boldsymbol{ZT}_1$ and $\boldsymbol{Z} = \boldsymbol{XT}_2$. If we define a new vector parameter $\boldsymbol{\theta}$ as $\boldsymbol{T}_1\boldsymbol{\beta}$, then the model

$$\mathcal{M}_2 = (\boldsymbol{y}, \boldsymbol{Z\theta}, \sigma^2\boldsymbol{I})$$

is equivalent to $\mathcal{M}_1$ in the sense that for any value of $\boldsymbol{\beta}$ in $\mathcal{M}_1$, leading to a particular distribution of the response $\boldsymbol{y}$, there is a value of $\boldsymbol{\theta}$ in $\mathcal{M}_2$ producing the same distribution, and vice versa. We call the transformation from $\mathcal{M}_1$ to $\mathcal{M}_2$ a *reparametrization.*

Sometimes a reparametrization is done in order to remove a redundancy in the description of the model. In such a case, $\boldsymbol{Z}$ is chosen so that it has r linearly independent columns, where $r = \rho(\boldsymbol{X})$. As a result, each of the r elements of $\boldsymbol{\theta}$ turn out to be estimable (see Exercise 3.16). This is why $\rho(\boldsymbol{X})$ is often referred to as the *effective* number of parameters in the model $(\boldsymbol{y}, \boldsymbol{X\beta}, \sigma^2\boldsymbol{I})$.

Example 3.49. (Abrasion of denim jeans, continued) Consider the model of Example 3.5. It has already been pointed out that $\rho(\boldsymbol{X}) = 5$. In the presence of the first column, one of the next three columns are redundant for spanning their column space, and there is a similar redundancy in the last three columns. Just two linear combinations of each of these sets of three columns should suffice. In particular, we can choose $\boldsymbol{Z} = \boldsymbol{X}\boldsymbol{T}_2$ for the choice of $\boldsymbol{T}_2$ given below, and identify a $\boldsymbol{T}_1$ that would ensure $\boldsymbol{X} = \boldsymbol{Z}\boldsymbol{T}_1$.

$$\boldsymbol{T}_2 = \begin{pmatrix} 1 & 0 & 0 & 0 & 0 \\ 0 & \frac{1}{3} & \frac{1}{3} & 0 & 0 \\ 0 & -\frac{2}{3} & \frac{1}{3} & 0 & 0 \\ 0 & \frac{1}{3} & -\frac{2}{3} & 0 & 0 \\ 0 & 0 & 0 & \frac{1}{3} & \frac{1}{3} \\ 0 & 0 & 0 & -\frac{2}{3} & \frac{1}{3} \\ 0 & 0 & 0 & \frac{1}{3} & -\frac{2}{3} \end{pmatrix}, \qquad \boldsymbol{T}_1 = \begin{pmatrix} 1 & \frac{1}{3} & \frac{1}{3} & \frac{1}{3} & \frac{1}{3} & \frac{1}{3} & \frac{1}{3} \\ 0 & 1 & -1 & 0 & 0 & 0 & 0 \\ 0 & 1 & 0 & -1 & 0 & 0 & 0 \\ 0 & 0 & 0 & 0 & 1 & -1 & 0 \\ 0 & 0 & 0 & 0 & 1 & 0 & -1 \end{pmatrix}.$$

The model $(\boldsymbol{y}, \boldsymbol{X}\boldsymbol{\beta}, \sigma^2\boldsymbol{I})$ is equivalent to the reparametrized model $(\boldsymbol{y}, \boldsymbol{Z}\boldsymbol{\theta}, \sigma^2\boldsymbol{I})$. The parameter $\boldsymbol{\theta}$ can be expressed in terms of $\boldsymbol{\beta}$ as $\boldsymbol{\theta} = \boldsymbol{T}_1\boldsymbol{\beta}$. Specifically,

$$\begin{aligned} \theta_1 &= \mu + (\tau_1 + \tau_2 + \tau_3)/3 + (\beta_1 + \beta_2 + \beta_3)/3, \\ \theta_2 &= \tau_1 - \tau_2, \\ \theta_3 &= \tau_1 - \tau_3, \\ \theta_4 &= \beta_1 - \beta_2, \\ \theta_5 &= \beta_1 - \beta_3. \end{aligned}$$

In the reparametrized model, the entire vector parameter $\boldsymbol{\theta}$ is estimable. This may be contrasted with the original model, where $\boldsymbol{\beta}$ is not estimable.

Note that we could have chosen another matrix $\boldsymbol{Z}$, which would have led to a different reparametrization. For the given choice of $\boldsymbol{Z}$, the above choice of $\boldsymbol{T}_1$ is unique. However, the choice of $\boldsymbol{T}_2$ is not unique. The reader may look for other possible choices of $\boldsymbol{T}_2$ for this $\boldsymbol{Z}$, which satisfy the relation $\boldsymbol{Z} = \boldsymbol{X}\boldsymbol{T}_2$. □

A more general form of reparametrization occurs when $\boldsymbol{\beta}$ is transformed to $\boldsymbol{\theta} = \boldsymbol{T}_1\boldsymbol{\beta} + \boldsymbol{\theta}_0$, where $\boldsymbol{\theta}_0$ is a fixed vector. If $\boldsymbol{Z}$ is a matrix such that $\mathcal{C}(\boldsymbol{Z}) = \mathcal{C}(\boldsymbol{X})$ and $\boldsymbol{T}_1$ and $\boldsymbol{T}_2$ are such that $\boldsymbol{X} = \boldsymbol{Z}\boldsymbol{T}_1$ and $\boldsymbol{Z} = \boldsymbol{X}\boldsymbol{T}_2$, we can rewrite the model equation of $\mathcal{M}_1$ as $\boldsymbol{y} = \boldsymbol{Z}\boldsymbol{T}_1\boldsymbol{\beta} + \boldsymbol{\varepsilon}$, that is,

$$\boldsymbol{y} + \boldsymbol{Z}\boldsymbol{\theta}_0 = \boldsymbol{Z}(\boldsymbol{T}_1\boldsymbol{\beta} + \boldsymbol{\theta}_0) + \boldsymbol{\varepsilon} = \boldsymbol{Z}\boldsymbol{\theta} + \boldsymbol{\varepsilon}.$$

The model $\mathcal{M}_3 = (\boldsymbol{y} + \boldsymbol{Z}\boldsymbol{\theta}_0, \boldsymbol{Z}\boldsymbol{\theta}, \sigma^2\boldsymbol{I})$ can be called a reparametrization of $\mathcal{M}_1$. The parameters of the two models are related as $\boldsymbol{\theta} = \boldsymbol{T}_1\boldsymbol{\beta} + \boldsymbol{\theta}_0$ and

$\boldsymbol{\beta} = \boldsymbol{T}_2(\boldsymbol{\theta} - \boldsymbol{\theta}_0)$. It is easy to see that $\boldsymbol{l}'\boldsymbol{y}$ is an LZF in $\mathcal{M}_1$ if and only if $\boldsymbol{l}'(\boldsymbol{y} + \boldsymbol{Z\theta}_0)$ is an LZF in $\mathcal{M}_3$. Likewise, $\boldsymbol{Ly}$ is a BLUE in $\mathcal{M}_1$ if and only if $\boldsymbol{L}(\boldsymbol{y} + \boldsymbol{Z\theta}_0)$ is a BLUE in $\mathcal{M}_3$. In particular, the BLUEs of $\boldsymbol{X\beta}$ and $\boldsymbol{Z\theta}$ in the respective models are related to one another by the equation

$$\boldsymbol{X}\widehat{\boldsymbol{\beta}} = \boldsymbol{Z}\widehat{\boldsymbol{\theta}} - \boldsymbol{Z\theta}_0.$$

Reparametrization does not alter R_0^2, the degrees of freedom or $\widehat{\sigma^2}$.

3.10 Linear restrictions*

The parameter $\boldsymbol{\beta}$ in the linear model $(\boldsymbol{y}, \boldsymbol{X\beta}, \sigma^2\boldsymbol{I})$ is sometimes subjected to a linear restriction (constraint) of the form $\boldsymbol{A\beta} = \boldsymbol{\xi}$. This restriction may be (a) a fact known from theoretical or experimental considerations, (b) an hypothesis that may have to be tested or (c) an artificially imposed condition to reduce or eliminate redundancy in the description of the model. Let us assume that the restriction is algebraically consistent, i.e. $\boldsymbol{\xi} \in \mathcal{C}(\boldsymbol{A})$. How does the restriction affect estimation?

Example 3.50. (Abrasion of denim jeans, continued) Consider the model of Example 3.5 where we want to take into account the linear restrictions

$$\tau_1 + \tau_2 + \tau_3 = 0$$
$$\text{and } \beta_1 + \beta_2 + \beta_3 = 0.$$

Such a restriction may be imposed in order to eliminate the redundancy of the parameters. A simple way of incorporating this restriction is to define a new set of parameters, $\theta_1, \theta_2, \ldots, \theta_5$ and reparametrize the original model as $(\boldsymbol{y}, \boldsymbol{Z\theta}, \sigma^2\boldsymbol{I})$ in the way we have seen in Example 3.49. Consequently the restriction has no effect on the BLUEs of estimable functions, their dispersions, or the estimator of σ^2. □

Example 3.51. (Abrasion of denim jeans, continued) Suppose we want to impose the restrictions

$$\tau_1 = \tau_2 = \tau_3$$

on the model of Example 3.5. Working with such restrictions is often necessary for testing hypotheses. In order to incorporate this restriction in the model, we may construct a new matrix $\boldsymbol{Z}$ by simply removing the second, third and fourth columns of $\boldsymbol{X}$ which account for the treatment effect. This is *not* a mere reparametrization of the original model, since $\boldsymbol{Z}$ has a smaller rank than $\boldsymbol{X}$. Consequently the restriction has an effect on the BLUEs and other quantities of interest. In particular, the fitted values for the modified model are

$$\tilde{y}_{ijl} = \frac{1}{30} \sum_{i'=1}^{3} \sum_{l'=1}^{10} y_{i'jl'}, \quad i, j = 1, 2, 3, \ l = 1, \ldots, 10,$$

which are different from the fitted values obtained from the original model (see page 71). □

In the above two examples we were able to find an unrestricted model that is equivalent to the original model with the restriction. However, the choice was specifically for the model and the restriction at hand. Given the model $(\boldsymbol{y}, \boldsymbol{X\beta}, \sigma^2 \boldsymbol{I})$ subject to the general restriction $\boldsymbol{A\beta} = \boldsymbol{\xi}$, can we find an equivalent unrestricted model?

A general linear restriction of the form $\boldsymbol{A\beta} = \boldsymbol{\xi}$ can be taken into account by treating $\boldsymbol{\xi}$ as an observation of $\boldsymbol{A\beta}$ with zero error. Therefore, the model $(\boldsymbol{y}, \boldsymbol{X\beta}, \sigma^2 \boldsymbol{I})$ with the restriction $\boldsymbol{A\beta} = \boldsymbol{\xi}$ is equivalent to the unrestricted model $(\boldsymbol{y}_*, \boldsymbol{X}_*\boldsymbol{\beta}, \sigma^2 \boldsymbol{V})$, where

$$\boldsymbol{y}_* = \begin{pmatrix} \boldsymbol{y} \\ \boldsymbol{\xi} \end{pmatrix}, \qquad \boldsymbol{X}_* = \begin{pmatrix} \boldsymbol{X} \\ \boldsymbol{A} \end{pmatrix}, \qquad \boldsymbol{V} = \begin{pmatrix} \boldsymbol{I} & \boldsymbol{0} \\ \boldsymbol{0} & \boldsymbol{0} \end{pmatrix}.$$

The dispersion matrix $\sigma^2 \boldsymbol{V}$ is singular. Singular dispersion matrices are dealt with in Chapter 7, and we shall find other ways of handling linear restrictions before we get there. However, this formulation provides us with an important insight. An LPF $\boldsymbol{p}'\boldsymbol{\beta}$ is estimable in the restricted model if and only if $\boldsymbol{p} \in \mathcal{C}((\boldsymbol{X}_*)')$, i.e. $\boldsymbol{p} \in \mathcal{C}(\boldsymbol{X}' : \boldsymbol{A}')$.[2] On the other hand, $\boldsymbol{p}'\boldsymbol{\beta}$ is estimable in the unrestricted model if and only if $\boldsymbol{p} \in \mathcal{C}(\boldsymbol{X}')$. Thus, every estimable function in the unrestricted model is estimable in the restricted model, but the converse is not necessarily true.

If restrictions can expand the set of estimable functions, what are the functions that become estimable *because of the restrictions*? In the case of Example 3.50, the additional rows of the matrix $\boldsymbol{X}_*$ are $(0 : 1 : 1 : 1 : 0 : 0 : 0)$ and $(0 : 0 : 0 : 0 : 1 : 1 : 1)$. In other words, $\tau_1 + \tau_2 + \tau_3$ and $\beta_1 + \beta_2 + \beta_3$ become estimable after taking the restrictions into account, as these two parameters are 'observed' to be 0. Consequently all the LPFs become estimable. We have seen in Example 3.50 that these restrictions only amount to a reparametrization of the original model. In general, a restricted model is equivalent to a reparametrized model when $\rho(\boldsymbol{X}_*) = \rho(\boldsymbol{X}) + \rho(\boldsymbol{A})$ (Exercise 3.18). We shall refer to such restrictions

[2] This is a consequence of Proposition 3.21. We shall see in Section 7.2.2 that this proposition continues to hold even when the dispersion matrix is singular.

as *model-preserving constraints.* Sometimes the very purpose of imposing the restriction is to make the matrix $\boldsymbol{X}_*$ full column rank, so that all the parameters become estimable.

As another special case, we may have $\rho(\boldsymbol{X}_*) = \rho(\boldsymbol{X})$, in which case the set of estimable functions is the same with or without the restriction. This happens when $\boldsymbol{A\beta}$ is itself estimable in the unrestricted model. (For instance, the LPF $\tau_1 - \tau_2$ of Example 3.51 is estimable.) Estimation under such restrictions is often required for the purpose of conducting tests of hypotheses.

In general, the rank of $\boldsymbol{X}_*$ may be somewhere in between $\rho(\boldsymbol{X})$ and the number of columns of $\boldsymbol{X}$, although the extreme cases are more common. Dasgupta and Das Gupta (2000) show how any algebraically consistent restriction can be decomposed into a model preserving constraint and a restriction involving an estimable function. We shall obtain a similar decomposition in Section 4.2.2.

The model $(\boldsymbol{y}, \boldsymbol{X\beta}, \sigma^2\boldsymbol{I})$ with the restriction $\boldsymbol{A\beta} = \boldsymbol{\xi}$ can also be shown to be equivalent to another unrestricted model with dispersion matrix $\sigma^2\boldsymbol{I}$. We now derive such a model.

When we estimate a vector parameter in the usual linear model, it is implicitly assumed that $\boldsymbol{\beta}$ can be *anywhere* in $\mathbb{R}^p$. The restriction effectively confines $\boldsymbol{\beta}$ to a subset of $\mathbb{R}^p$. Specifically, it follows from Proposition A.23 of Appendix A that the vector $\boldsymbol{\beta}$ satisfies the algebraically consistent restriction $\boldsymbol{A\beta} = \boldsymbol{\xi}$ if and only if it is of the form $\boldsymbol{A}^-\boldsymbol{\xi} + (\boldsymbol{I} - \boldsymbol{A}^-\boldsymbol{A})\boldsymbol{\theta}$, where $\boldsymbol{A}^-$ is a g-inverse of $\boldsymbol{A}$ and $\boldsymbol{\theta}$ is an arbitrary vector. We can ensure that $\boldsymbol{\beta}$ satisfies the restriction using the above form of $\boldsymbol{\beta}$ explicitly in the model equation:

$$\boldsymbol{y} = \boldsymbol{X\beta} + \boldsymbol{\varepsilon} = \boldsymbol{XA}^-\boldsymbol{\xi} + \boldsymbol{X}(\boldsymbol{I} - \boldsymbol{A}^-\boldsymbol{A})\boldsymbol{\theta} + \boldsymbol{\varepsilon}, \qquad E(\boldsymbol{\varepsilon}) = \boldsymbol{0}, \quad D(\boldsymbol{\varepsilon}) = \sigma^2\boldsymbol{I}.$$

Since $\boldsymbol{XA}^-\boldsymbol{\xi}$ is completely known from the restriction, we can transfer it to the left-hand side and write the model equation as

$$\boldsymbol{y} - \boldsymbol{XA}^-\boldsymbol{\xi} = \boldsymbol{X}(\boldsymbol{I} - \boldsymbol{A}^-\boldsymbol{A})\boldsymbol{\theta} + \boldsymbol{\varepsilon}, \qquad E(\boldsymbol{\varepsilon}) = \boldsymbol{0}, \quad D(\boldsymbol{\varepsilon}) = \sigma^2\boldsymbol{I}.$$

Thus, the 'restricted model' is equivalent to the unrestricted model $(\boldsymbol{y} - \boldsymbol{XA}^-\boldsymbol{\xi}, \boldsymbol{X}(\boldsymbol{I} - \boldsymbol{A}^-\boldsymbol{A})\boldsymbol{\theta}, \sigma^2\boldsymbol{I})$, which is under the purview of the discussions of the foregoing sections.

A geometric perspective of the BLUE of $\boldsymbol{X\beta}$ under the restriction $\boldsymbol{A\beta} = \boldsymbol{\xi}$ is given in Section 11.4.2.

Example 3.50. (continued) The restriction may be written as $\boldsymbol{A\beta} = \boldsymbol{\xi}$

where

$$A = \begin{pmatrix} 0 & 1 & 1 & 1 & 0 & 0 & 0 \\ 0 & 0 & 0 & 0 & 1 & 1 & 1 \end{pmatrix} \quad \text{and} \quad \boldsymbol{\xi} = \begin{pmatrix} 0 \\ 0 \end{pmatrix}.$$

We can choose $A^- = \frac{1}{3}A'$, so that the equivalent unrestricted model is $(\boldsymbol{y}, Z\boldsymbol{\theta}, \sigma^2 I)$, where

$$Z = X(I - A^-A) = X \begin{pmatrix} 1 & 0 & 0 & 0 & 0 & 0 & 0 \\ 0 & \frac{2}{3} & -\frac{1}{3} & -\frac{1}{3} & 0 & 0 & 0 \\ 0 & -\frac{1}{3} & \frac{2}{3} & -\frac{1}{3} & 0 & 0 & 0 \\ 0 & -\frac{1}{3} & -\frac{1}{3} & \frac{2}{3} & 0 & 0 & 0 \\ 0 & 0 & 0 & 0 & \frac{2}{3} & -\frac{1}{3} & -\frac{1}{3} \\ 0 & 0 & 0 & 0 & -\frac{1}{3} & \frac{2}{3} & -\frac{1}{3} \\ 0 & 0 & 0 & 0 & -\frac{1}{3} & -\frac{1}{3} & \frac{2}{3} \end{pmatrix}$$

$$= \begin{pmatrix}
\mathbf{1}_{10\times1} & \frac{2}{3}\mathbf{1}_{10\times1} & -\frac{1}{3}\mathbf{1}_{10\times1} & -\frac{1}{3}\mathbf{1}_{10\times1} & \frac{2}{3}\mathbf{1}_{10\times1} & -\frac{1}{3}\mathbf{1}_{10\times1} & -\frac{1}{3}\mathbf{1}_{10\times1} \\
\mathbf{1}_{10\times1} & -\frac{1}{3}\mathbf{1}_{10\times1} & \frac{2}{3}\mathbf{1}_{10\times1} & -\frac{1}{3}\mathbf{1}_{10\times1} & \frac{2}{3}\mathbf{1}_{10\times1} & -\frac{1}{3}\mathbf{1}_{10\times1} & -\frac{1}{3}\mathbf{1}_{10\times1} \\
\mathbf{1}_{10\times1} & -\frac{1}{3}\mathbf{1}_{10\times1} & -\frac{1}{3}\mathbf{1}_{10\times1} & \frac{2}{3}\mathbf{1}_{10\times1} & \frac{2}{3}\mathbf{1}_{10\times1} & -\frac{1}{3}\mathbf{1}_{10\times1} & -\frac{1}{3}\mathbf{1}_{10\times1} \\
\mathbf{1}_{10\times1} & \frac{2}{3}\mathbf{1}_{10\times1} & -\frac{1}{3}\mathbf{1}_{10\times1} & -\frac{1}{3}\mathbf{1}_{10\times1} & -\frac{1}{3}\mathbf{1}_{10\times1} & \frac{2}{3}\mathbf{1}_{10\times1} & -\frac{1}{3}\mathbf{1}_{10\times1} \\
\mathbf{1}_{10\times1} & -\frac{1}{3}\mathbf{1}_{10\times1} & \frac{2}{3}\mathbf{1}_{10\times1} & -\frac{1}{3}\mathbf{1}_{10\times1} & -\frac{1}{3}\mathbf{1}_{10\times1} & \frac{2}{3}\mathbf{1}_{10\times1} & -\frac{1}{3}\mathbf{1}_{10\times1} \\
\mathbf{1}_{10\times1} & -\frac{1}{3}\mathbf{1}_{10\times1} & -\frac{1}{3}\mathbf{1}_{10\times1} & \frac{2}{3}\mathbf{1}_{10\times1} & -\frac{1}{3}\mathbf{1}_{10\times1} & \frac{2}{3}\mathbf{1}_{10\times1} & -\frac{1}{3}\mathbf{1}_{10\times1} \\
\mathbf{1}_{10\times1} & \frac{2}{3}\mathbf{1}_{10\times1} & -\frac{1}{3}\mathbf{1}_{10\times1} & -\frac{1}{3}\mathbf{1}_{10\times1} & -\frac{1}{3}\mathbf{1}_{10\times1} & -\frac{1}{3}\mathbf{1}_{10\times1} & \frac{2}{3}\mathbf{1}_{10\times1} \\
\mathbf{1}_{10\times1} & -\frac{1}{3}\mathbf{1}_{10\times1} & \frac{2}{3}\mathbf{1}_{10\times1} & -\frac{1}{3}\mathbf{1}_{10\times1} & -\frac{1}{3}\mathbf{1}_{10\times1} & -\frac{1}{3}\mathbf{1}_{10\times1} & \frac{2}{3}\mathbf{1}_{10\times1} \\
\mathbf{1}_{10\times1} & -\frac{1}{3}\mathbf{1}_{10\times1} & -\frac{1}{3}\mathbf{1}_{10\times1} & \frac{2}{3}\mathbf{1}_{10\times1} & -\frac{1}{3}\mathbf{1}_{10\times1} & -\frac{1}{3}\mathbf{1}_{10\times1} & \frac{2}{3}\mathbf{1}_{10\times1}
\end{pmatrix}.$$

This matrix is rank deficient, but we can handle that. The form of $(I - A^-A)$ ensures that if $\widehat{\boldsymbol{\theta}}$ is any estimator of $\boldsymbol{\theta}$, the corresponding estimator of $\boldsymbol{\beta}$ is

$$\widehat{\boldsymbol{\beta}} = (I - A^-A)\widehat{\boldsymbol{\theta}} = \begin{pmatrix} 1 & 0 & 0 & 0 & 0 & 0 & 0 \\ 0 & \frac{2}{3} & -\frac{1}{3} & -\frac{1}{3} & 0 & 0 & 0 \\ 0 & -\frac{1}{3} & \frac{2}{3} & -\frac{1}{3} & 0 & 0 & 0 \\ 0 & -\frac{1}{3} & -\frac{1}{3} & \frac{2}{3} & 0 & 0 & 0 \\ 0 & 0 & 0 & 0 & \frac{2}{3} & -\frac{1}{3} & -\frac{1}{3} \\ 0 & 0 & 0 & 0 & -\frac{1}{3} & \frac{2}{3} & -\frac{1}{3} \\ 0 & 0 & 0 & 0 & -\frac{1}{3} & -\frac{1}{3} & \frac{2}{3} \end{pmatrix} \begin{pmatrix} \widehat{\theta}_1 \\ \widehat{\theta}_2 \\ \widehat{\theta}_3 \\ \widehat{\theta}_4 \\ \widehat{\theta}_5 \\ \widehat{\theta}_6 \\ \widehat{\theta}_7 \end{pmatrix},$$

that is,

$$\begin{pmatrix} \widehat{\mu} \\ \widehat{\tau}_1 \\ \widehat{\tau}_2 \\ \widehat{\tau}_3 \\ \widehat{\beta}_1 \\ \widehat{\beta}_2 \\ \widehat{\beta}_3 \end{pmatrix} = \begin{pmatrix} \widehat{\theta}_1 \\ \frac{1}{3}(2\widehat{\theta}_2 - \widehat{\theta}_3 - \widehat{\theta}_4) \\ \frac{1}{3}(-\widehat{\theta}_2 + 2\widehat{\theta}_3 - \widehat{\theta}_4) \\ \frac{1}{3}(-\widehat{\theta}_2 - \widehat{\theta}_3 + 2\widehat{\theta}_4) \\ \frac{1}{3}(2\widehat{\theta}_5 - \widehat{\theta}_6 - \widehat{\theta}_3) \\ \frac{1}{3}(-\widehat{\theta}_5 + 2\widehat{\theta}_6 - \widehat{\theta}_3) \\ \frac{1}{3}(-\widehat{\theta}_5 - \widehat{\theta}_6 + 2\widehat{\theta}_3) \end{pmatrix},$$

which means $\widehat{\tau}_1 + \widehat{\tau}_2 + \widehat{\tau}_3 = 0$ and $\widehat{\beta}_1 + \widehat{\beta}_2 + \widehat{\beta}_3 = 0$. □

Example 3.51. (continued) The restriction is of the form $\boldsymbol{A\beta} = \boldsymbol{\xi}$, where

$$\boldsymbol{A} = \begin{pmatrix} 0 & 1 & -1 & 0 & 0 & 0 & 0 \\ 0 & 1 & 0 & -1 & 0 & 0 & 0 \end{pmatrix} \quad \text{and} \quad \boldsymbol{\xi} = \begin{pmatrix} 0 \\ 0 \end{pmatrix}.$$

We can choose

$$\boldsymbol{A}^- = \begin{pmatrix} 0 & 0 & -1 & 0 & 0 & 0 & 0 \\ 0 & 0 & 0 & -1 & 0 & 0 & 0 \end{pmatrix}',$$

and obtain the equivalent model $(\boldsymbol{y}, \boldsymbol{Z\theta}, \sigma^2 \boldsymbol{I})$, where

$$\boldsymbol{Z} = \boldsymbol{X}(\boldsymbol{I} - \boldsymbol{A}^- \boldsymbol{A})$$

$$= \boldsymbol{X} \begin{pmatrix} 1&0&0&0&0&0&0 \\ 0&1&0&0&0&0&0 \\ 0&1&0&0&0&0&0 \\ 0&1&0&0&0&0&0 \\ 0&0&0&0&1&0&0 \\ 0&0&0&0&0&1&0 \\ 0&0&0&0&0&0&1 \end{pmatrix} = \begin{pmatrix} \mathbf{1}_{10\times1} & \mathbf{1}_{10\times1} & \mathbf{0}_{10\times1} & \mathbf{0}_{10\times1} & \mathbf{1}_{10\times1} & \mathbf{0}_{10\times1} & \mathbf{0}_{10\times1} \\ \mathbf{1}_{10\times1} & \mathbf{1}_{10\times1} & \mathbf{0}_{10\times1} & \mathbf{0}_{10\times1} & \mathbf{1}_{10\times1} & \mathbf{0}_{10\times1} & \mathbf{0}_{10\times1} \\ \mathbf{1}_{10\times1} & \mathbf{1}_{10\times1} & \mathbf{0}_{10\times1} & \mathbf{0}_{10\times1} & \mathbf{1}_{10\times1} & \mathbf{0}_{10\times1} & \mathbf{0}_{10\times1} \\ \mathbf{1}_{10\times1} & \mathbf{1}_{10\times1} & \mathbf{0}_{10\times1} & \mathbf{0}_{10\times1} & \mathbf{0}_{10\times1} & \mathbf{1}_{10\times1} & \mathbf{0}_{10\times1} \\ \mathbf{1}_{10\times1} & \mathbf{1}_{10\times1} & \mathbf{0}_{10\times1} & \mathbf{0}_{10\times1} & \mathbf{0}_{10\times1} & \mathbf{1}_{10\times1} & \mathbf{0}_{10\times1} \\ \mathbf{1}_{10\times1} & \mathbf{1}_{10\times1} & \mathbf{0}_{10\times1} & \mathbf{0}_{10\times1} & \mathbf{0}_{10\times1} & \mathbf{1}_{10\times1} & \mathbf{0}_{10\times1} \\ \mathbf{1}_{10\times1} & \mathbf{1}_{10\times1} & \mathbf{0}_{10\times1} & \mathbf{0}_{10\times1} & \mathbf{0}_{10\times1} & \mathbf{0}_{10\times1} & \mathbf{1}_{10\times1} \\ \mathbf{1}_{10\times1} & \mathbf{1}_{10\times1} & \mathbf{0}_{10\times1} & \mathbf{0}_{10\times1} & \mathbf{0}_{10\times1} & \mathbf{0}_{10\times1} & \mathbf{1}_{10\times1} \\ \mathbf{1}_{10\times1} & \mathbf{1}_{10\times1} & \mathbf{0}_{10\times1} & \mathbf{0}_{10\times1} & \mathbf{0}_{10\times1} & \mathbf{0}_{10\times1} & \mathbf{1}_{10\times1} \end{pmatrix}.$$

In this example the third and the fourth elements of $\boldsymbol{\theta}$ are irrelevant. One can reparametrize by dropping these two elements of $\boldsymbol{\theta}$ and the corresponding columns of $\boldsymbol{Z}$. □

The 'equivalent' model cannot be chosen uniquely, because it depends on the choice of the g-inverse of $\boldsymbol{A}$. As along as a single g-inverse is used in all the computations, the BLUEs of all LPFs that are estimable under the original model, their dispersions and the error sum of squares do not depend on the choice of $\boldsymbol{A}^-$. A possible choice of $\boldsymbol{A}^-$ is $\boldsymbol{A}'(\boldsymbol{A}\boldsymbol{A}')^-$, which leads to the well-defined equivalent model $(\boldsymbol{y} - \boldsymbol{X}\boldsymbol{A}'(\boldsymbol{A}\boldsymbol{A}')^-\boldsymbol{\xi}, \boldsymbol{X}(\boldsymbol{I} - \boldsymbol{P}_{A'})\boldsymbol{\theta}, \sigma^2\boldsymbol{I})$. The vector of fitted values under this model is $\boldsymbol{P}_{X(I-P_{A'})}(\boldsymbol{y} - \boldsymbol{X}\boldsymbol{A}'(\boldsymbol{A}\boldsymbol{A}')^-\boldsymbol{\xi})$. Therefore, the BLUE of $\boldsymbol{X}\boldsymbol{\beta}$ under the restriction $\boldsymbol{A}\boldsymbol{\beta} = \boldsymbol{\xi}$ is

$$\boldsymbol{X}\widehat{\boldsymbol{\beta}}_{rest} = \boldsymbol{X}\boldsymbol{A}'(\boldsymbol{A}\boldsymbol{A}')^-\boldsymbol{\xi} + \boldsymbol{P}_{X(I-P_{A'})}(\boldsymbol{y} - \boldsymbol{X}\boldsymbol{A}'(\boldsymbol{A}\boldsymbol{A}')^-\boldsymbol{\xi}). \tag{3.21}$$

We conclude this section with a formal comparison of the restricted and unrestricted models.

Proposition 3.52. *Let $\boldsymbol{A}\boldsymbol{\beta} = \boldsymbol{\xi}$ be a consistent restriction on the model $(\boldsymbol{y}, \boldsymbol{X}\boldsymbol{\beta}, \sigma^2\boldsymbol{I})$.*

(a) All estimable LPFs of the unrestricted model are estimable under the restricted model.
(b) All LZFs of the unrestricted model are LZFs under the restricted model.
(c) The restriction cannot increase the dispersion of the BLUE of $\boldsymbol{X}\boldsymbol{\beta}$.
(d) The restriction cannot reduce the error sum of squares.

Proof. Part (a) has already been proved via the 'equivalent' model that uses the restriction as additional observations with zero error. We shall use the equivalent model $(\boldsymbol{y} - \boldsymbol{X}\boldsymbol{A}'(\boldsymbol{A}\boldsymbol{A}')^-\boldsymbol{\xi}, \boldsymbol{X}(\boldsymbol{I} - \boldsymbol{P}_{A'})\boldsymbol{\theta}, \sigma^2\boldsymbol{I})$ in order to prove the other parts. For convenience we shall refer to the latter model as $\mathcal{M}_r$ and the original model as $\mathcal{M}$.

Suppose $\boldsymbol{l}'\boldsymbol{y}$ is an LZF in $\mathcal{M}$, so that $\boldsymbol{X}'\boldsymbol{l} = \boldsymbol{0}$. Consequently, $\boldsymbol{l}'\boldsymbol{y} = \boldsymbol{l}'(\boldsymbol{y} - \boldsymbol{X}\boldsymbol{A}'(\boldsymbol{A}\boldsymbol{A}')^-\boldsymbol{\xi})$ and $(\boldsymbol{I} - \boldsymbol{P}_{A'})\boldsymbol{X}'\boldsymbol{l} = \boldsymbol{0}$. Hence, $\boldsymbol{l}'\boldsymbol{y}$ is an LZF of $\mathcal{M}_r$. This proves part (b).

It follows from (3.21) that the dispersion of the BLUE of $\boldsymbol{X}\boldsymbol{\beta}$ under the restriction is $\sigma^2\boldsymbol{P}_{X(I-P_{A'})}$. In contrast, the dispersion of the BLUE of $\boldsymbol{X}\boldsymbol{\beta}$ under $\mathcal{M}$ is $\sigma^2\boldsymbol{P}_X$. Since $\mathcal{C}(\boldsymbol{X}(\boldsymbol{I} - \boldsymbol{P}_{A'})) \subseteq \mathcal{C}(\boldsymbol{X})$, the result of part (c) follows from Proposition A.22(b).

Part (d) follows from the fact that the set of LZFs under $\mathcal{M}_r$ cannot be smaller than that under $\mathcal{M}$, which follows from part (b). □

In the case of model-preserving constraints, the error sum of squares is not affected by the restriction. For other restrictions, the amount of increase is an indication of the validity of the restrictions. We shall examine this quantity in some detail in the next chapter.

3.11 Nuisance parameters*

Often one is interested in a *subset* of the parameters, or linear functions of them. For instance, in Example 3.51, we assumed that the parameters of interest were the differences between the treatment coefficients, $\tau_1 - \tau_2$ and $\tau_1 - \tau_3$. In general, even if the primary interest of analysis is in one set of variables, an additional set of variables may be needed to make the model more realistic. Thus we can write $\boldsymbol{X\beta}$ as $\boldsymbol{X}_1\boldsymbol{\beta}_1 + \boldsymbol{X}_2\boldsymbol{\beta}_2$, where the interest is only on the linear functions of $\boldsymbol{\beta}_1$. The vector $\boldsymbol{\beta}_2$ contains the other parameters in which we have no interest. These parameters are called *nuisance* parameters. They are included in the model usually because the model may be inadequate without them.

In Example 3.51, μ, β_1, β_2 and β_3 may be viewed as nuisance parameters. However, not all linear functions of the parameters of interest (τ_1, τ_2 and τ_3) are estimable. A precise description of the estimable LPFs in such situations is given below.

Proposition 3.53. *In the linear model* $(\boldsymbol{y}, \boldsymbol{X}_1\boldsymbol{\beta}_1 + \boldsymbol{X}_2\boldsymbol{\beta}_2, \sigma^2\boldsymbol{I})$, *the LPF* $\boldsymbol{p}'\boldsymbol{\beta}_1$ *is estimable if and only if* $\boldsymbol{p} \in \mathcal{C}(\boldsymbol{X}_1'(\boldsymbol{I} - \boldsymbol{P}_{X_2}))$.

Proof. Suppose $\boldsymbol{l}'\boldsymbol{y}$ is an LUE of $\boldsymbol{p}'\boldsymbol{\beta}_1$. Then we must have $\boldsymbol{l}'\boldsymbol{X}_1\boldsymbol{\beta}_1 + \boldsymbol{l}'\boldsymbol{X}_2\boldsymbol{\beta}_2 = \boldsymbol{p}'\boldsymbol{\beta}_1$ for all $\boldsymbol{\beta}_1$ and $\boldsymbol{\beta}_2$. Therefore $\boldsymbol{X}_1'\boldsymbol{l} = \boldsymbol{p}$ and $\boldsymbol{X}_2'\boldsymbol{l} = \boldsymbol{0}$. It follows that $\boldsymbol{l} \in \mathcal{C}(\boldsymbol{X}_2)^\perp = \mathcal{C}(\boldsymbol{I}-\boldsymbol{P}_{X_2})$, that is, $\boldsymbol{l}$ is of the form $(\boldsymbol{I}-\boldsymbol{P}_{X_2})\boldsymbol{m}$ for some vector $\boldsymbol{m}$. Consequently $\boldsymbol{p} = \boldsymbol{X}_1'(\boldsymbol{I}-\boldsymbol{P}_{X_2})\boldsymbol{m}$, i.e. $\boldsymbol{p} \in \mathcal{C}(\boldsymbol{X}_1'(\boldsymbol{I}-\boldsymbol{P}_{X_2}))$.

Conversely, if $\boldsymbol{p} \in \mathcal{C}(\boldsymbol{X}_1'(\boldsymbol{I} - \boldsymbol{P}_{X_2}))$, then there is a vector $\boldsymbol{m}$ such that $\boldsymbol{p} = \boldsymbol{X}_1'(\boldsymbol{I} - \boldsymbol{P}_{X_2})\boldsymbol{m}$. Then $\boldsymbol{m}'(\boldsymbol{I} - \boldsymbol{P}_{X_2})\boldsymbol{y}$ is an LUE of $\boldsymbol{p}'\boldsymbol{\beta}_1$. □

Example 3.54. (Abrasion of denim jeans, continued) Suppose $\boldsymbol{\beta}_1 = (\tau_1 : \tau_2 : \tau_3)'$ and $\boldsymbol{\beta}_2 = (\mu : \beta_1 : \beta_2 : \beta_3)'$. Then

$$\boldsymbol{X}_1 = \begin{pmatrix} \boldsymbol{1}_{10\times1} & \boldsymbol{0}_{10\times1} & \boldsymbol{0}_{10\times1} \\ \boldsymbol{0}_{10\times1} & \boldsymbol{1}_{10\times1} & \boldsymbol{0}_{10\times1} \\ \boldsymbol{0}_{10\times1} & \boldsymbol{0}_{10\times1} & \boldsymbol{1}_{10\times1} \\ \boldsymbol{1}_{10\times1} & \boldsymbol{0}_{10\times1} & \boldsymbol{0}_{10\times1} \\ \boldsymbol{0}_{10\times1} & \boldsymbol{1}_{10\times1} & \boldsymbol{0}_{10\times1} \\ \boldsymbol{0}_{10\times1} & \boldsymbol{0}_{10\times1} & \boldsymbol{1}_{10\times1} \\ \boldsymbol{1}_{10\times1} & \boldsymbol{0}_{10\times1} & \boldsymbol{0}_{10\times1} \\ \boldsymbol{0}_{10\times1} & \boldsymbol{1}_{10\times1} & \boldsymbol{0}_{10\times1} \\ \boldsymbol{0}_{10\times1} & \boldsymbol{0}_{10\times1} & \boldsymbol{1}_{10\times1} \end{pmatrix}, \qquad \boldsymbol{X}_2 = \begin{pmatrix} \boldsymbol{1}_{10\times1} & \boldsymbol{1}_{10\times1} & \boldsymbol{0}_{10\times1} & \boldsymbol{0}_{10\times1} \\ \boldsymbol{1}_{10\times1} & \boldsymbol{1}_{10\times1} & \boldsymbol{0}_{10\times1} & \boldsymbol{0}_{10\times1} \\ \boldsymbol{1}_{10\times1} & \boldsymbol{1}_{10\times1} & \boldsymbol{0}_{10\times1} & \boldsymbol{0}_{10\times1} \\ \boldsymbol{1}_{10\times1} & \boldsymbol{0}_{10\times1} & \boldsymbol{1}_{10\times1} & \boldsymbol{0}_{10\times1} \\ \boldsymbol{1}_{10\times1} & \boldsymbol{0}_{10\times1} & \boldsymbol{1}_{10\times1} & \boldsymbol{0}_{10\times1} \\ \boldsymbol{1}_{10\times1} & \boldsymbol{0}_{10\times1} & \boldsymbol{1}_{10\times1} & \boldsymbol{0}_{10\times1} \\ \boldsymbol{1}_{10\times1} & \boldsymbol{0}_{10\times1} & \boldsymbol{0}_{10\times1} & \boldsymbol{1}_{10\times1} \\ \boldsymbol{1}_{10\times1} & \boldsymbol{0}_{10\times1} & \boldsymbol{0}_{10\times1} & \boldsymbol{1}_{10\times1} \\ \boldsymbol{1}_{10\times1} & \boldsymbol{0}_{10\times1} & \boldsymbol{0}_{10\times1} & \boldsymbol{1}_{10\times1} \end{pmatrix}.$$

It follows that

$$X_1'(I - P_{X_2}) = \frac{1}{3}\begin{pmatrix} 2\cdot\mathbf{1}_{10\times1} & -\mathbf{1}_{10\times1} & -\mathbf{1}_{10\times1} \\ -\mathbf{1}_{10\times1} & 2\cdot\mathbf{1}_{10\times1} & -\mathbf{1}_{10\times1} \\ -\mathbf{1}_{10\times1} & -\mathbf{1}_{10\times1} & 2\cdot\mathbf{1}_{10\times1} \\ 2\cdot\mathbf{1}_{10\times1} & -\mathbf{1}_{10\times1} & -\mathbf{1}_{10\times1} \\ -\mathbf{1}_{10\times1} & 2\cdot\mathbf{1}_{10\times1} & -\mathbf{1}_{10\times1} \\ -\mathbf{1}_{10\times1} & -\mathbf{1}_{10\times1} & 2\cdot\mathbf{1}_{10\times1} \\ 2\cdot\mathbf{1}_{10\times1} & -\mathbf{1}_{10\times1} & -\mathbf{1}_{10\times1} \\ -\mathbf{1}_{10\times1} & 2\cdot\mathbf{1}_{10\times1} & -\mathbf{1}_{10\times1} \\ -\mathbf{1}_{10\times1} & -\mathbf{1}_{10\times1} & 2\cdot\mathbf{1}_{10\times1} \end{pmatrix}',$$

so that $\mathcal{C}(X_1'(I - P_{X_2}))$ is the space spanned by the vectors $(2 : -1 : -1)'$ and $(-1 : 2 : -1)'$, or equivalently by the vectors $(1 : -1 : 0)'$ and $(1 : 0 : -1)'$. For $p'\beta_1$ to be estimable, p must be a linear combination of these two vectors. Thus, the only estimable functions of treatment effects are differences such as $\tau_1 - \tau_2$, $\tau_1 - \tau_3$ or linear combinations of these. These functions are generally referred to as contrasts, as they bring out the contrast between different treatment effects (see Proposition 6.3 and the subsequent discussion). □

Once the estimable LPFs are identified, their estimation may proceed in the usual manner. One may then ask if it is possible to construct an equivalent model that only involves β_1, by somehow eliminating the effect of β_2? It is shown in Section 7.10 that an equivalent model is $((I-P_{X_2})y, (I-P_{X_2})X_1\beta_1, \sigma^2(I - P_{X_2}))$. Since the dispersion matrix for this model is singular, we shall return to its analysis only after developing the requisite theory in Chapter 7 (see Proposition 7.45 and Remark 7.46). However, we now briefly visit the special case where X_1 consists of a single column.

Suppose we are interested only in the estimation of the scalar parameter β_1, which happens to be estimable, and regard the rest (including the intercept) as nuisance parameters. In this case X_1 reduces to a vector, which we denote by x_1. As mentioned above, β_1 can be estimated from the vectors $(I - P_{X_2})y$ and $(I - P_{X_2})x_1$. These are residual vectors for the linear models $(y, X_2\beta_2, \sigma^2 I)$ and $(x_1, X_2\beta_2, \sigma^2 I)$. In other words, the residuals $(I - P_{X_2})y$ and $(I - P_{X_2})x_1$ are obtained from linear regression of the response and the first explanatory variable, respectively, on the remaining explanatory variables. The two residual vectors represent sample versions of the variables y^* and x_1^* in Proposition 2.24, which are related by the simplified model (2.18).

Suppose we disregard the correlation among the elements of $(\boldsymbol{I}-\boldsymbol{P}_{X_2})\boldsymbol{y}$, and proceed to obtain the least squares fitted line through the scatter plot of $(\boldsymbol{I}-\boldsymbol{P}_{X_2})\boldsymbol{y}$ vs. $(\boldsymbol{I}-\boldsymbol{P}_{X_2})\boldsymbol{x}_1$. This scatter plot is known as the *added variable plot* or *partial regression plot* for the first explanatory variable in the model $(\boldsymbol{y}, \boldsymbol{X\beta}, \sigma^2\boldsymbol{I})$, and has an important role in regression diagnostics (see Section 5.3.1). It follows that the least squares estimator $\widehat{\beta}_1$ in the model $(\boldsymbol{y}, \boldsymbol{X\beta}, \sigma^2\boldsymbol{I})$ is the slope of the least squares fitted straight line through the said scatter plot, which passes through origin (see Exercise 5.16). This finding makes sense in view of the model (2.18). Further, the sample correlation coefficient between $(\boldsymbol{I}-\boldsymbol{P}_{X_2})\boldsymbol{y}$ and $(\boldsymbol{I}-\boldsymbol{P}_{X_2})\boldsymbol{x}_1$ is equal to the sample partial correlation coefficient between the response and the first explanatory variable, after the linear effects of the other explanatory variables have been corrected for, and is related to $\widehat{\beta}_1$ by a relation similar to (2.19) (see Exercise 3.20). These facts permit one to understand the effect of a particular explanatory variable in multiple linear regression through simple linear regression. However, the latter is an over-simplified model that leads one to a biased estimator of σ^2 (see Exercise 5.16). The bias can be corrected only after taking into account the actual error dispersion matrix, $\sigma^2(\boldsymbol{I}-\boldsymbol{P}_{X_2})$, mentioned above.

3.12 Information matrix and Cramer-Rao bound*

Assuming initially that $\boldsymbol{y} \sim N(\boldsymbol{X\beta}, \sigma^2\boldsymbol{I})$, let us compute the information matrix for $\boldsymbol{\beta}$ and σ^2. Here, $\boldsymbol{\theta} = (\boldsymbol{\beta}' : \sigma^2)'$ and $f_{\boldsymbol{\theta}}(\boldsymbol{y})$ is the density of $N(\boldsymbol{X\beta}, \sigma^2\boldsymbol{I})$. We have

$$\begin{aligned}
\frac{\partial \log f_{\boldsymbol{\theta}}(\boldsymbol{y})}{\partial \boldsymbol{\beta}} &= \frac{1}{\sigma^2}\boldsymbol{X}'(\boldsymbol{y}-\boldsymbol{X\beta}), \\
\frac{\partial \log f_{\boldsymbol{\theta}}(\boldsymbol{y})}{\partial \sigma^2} &= -\frac{n}{2\sigma^2} + \frac{1}{2\sigma^4}\|\boldsymbol{y}-\boldsymbol{X\beta}\|^2, \\
\frac{\partial^2 \log f_{\boldsymbol{\theta}}(\boldsymbol{y})}{\partial \boldsymbol{\beta}\partial \boldsymbol{\beta}'} &= -\frac{1}{\sigma^2}\boldsymbol{X}'\boldsymbol{X}, \\
\frac{\partial^2 \log f_{\boldsymbol{\theta}}(\boldsymbol{y})}{\partial \boldsymbol{\beta}\partial \sigma^2} &= -\frac{1}{\sigma^4}\boldsymbol{X}'(\boldsymbol{y}-\boldsymbol{X\beta}), \\
\frac{\partial^2 \log f_{\boldsymbol{\theta}}(\boldsymbol{y})}{\partial (\sigma^2)^2} &= \frac{n}{2\sigma^4} - \frac{1}{\sigma^6}\|\boldsymbol{y}-\boldsymbol{X\beta}\|^2.
\end{aligned}$$

Consequently

$$\mathcal{I}(\boldsymbol{\theta}) = E\begin{pmatrix} -\dfrac{\partial^2 \log f_\theta(\boldsymbol{y})}{\partial\boldsymbol{\beta}\partial\boldsymbol{\beta}'} & -\dfrac{\partial^2 \log f_\theta(\boldsymbol{y})}{\partial\sigma^2\partial\boldsymbol{\beta}'} \\ -\dfrac{\partial^2 \log f_\theta(\boldsymbol{y})}{\partial\boldsymbol{\beta}\partial\sigma^2} & -\dfrac{\partial^2 \log f_\theta(\boldsymbol{y})}{\partial(\sigma^2)^2} \end{pmatrix} = \begin{pmatrix} \dfrac{1}{\sigma^2}\boldsymbol{X}'\boldsymbol{X} & \boldsymbol{0} \\ \boldsymbol{0} & \dfrac{n}{2\sigma^4} \end{pmatrix}.$$

If $\boldsymbol{A\beta}$ is non-estimable, then it does not have any unbiased estimator (see Exercise 3.3). If $\boldsymbol{A\beta}$ is an estimable LPF, then the Cramer-Rao lower bound for the dispersion of an unbiased estimator of $\boldsymbol{A\beta}$ is $\sigma^2\boldsymbol{A}(\boldsymbol{X}'\boldsymbol{X})^-\boldsymbol{A}'$. The bound is achieved by the BLUE of $\boldsymbol{A\beta}$.

Since the $\mathcal{I}(\boldsymbol{\theta})$ is block diagonal, the information for $\boldsymbol{\beta}$ and σ^2 are decoupled from one another in the sense that the Cramer-Rao bound corresponding to functions of $\boldsymbol{\beta}$ does not depend on the block of the information matrix corresponding to σ^2, and vice-versa. We refer to the two blocks as information of $\boldsymbol{\beta}$ and σ^2, respectively. It is also possible to define the information for the particular LPF $\boldsymbol{p}'\boldsymbol{\beta}$; the expression turns out to be $\sigma^{-2}(\boldsymbol{p}'\boldsymbol{p})^{-2}\boldsymbol{p}'\boldsymbol{X}'(\boldsymbol{I} - \boldsymbol{P}_{X(I-P_p)})\boldsymbol{Xp}$ (see Exercise 3.25).

If $\boldsymbol{x}_i$ is the ith row of $\boldsymbol{X}$, then the information matrix of $\boldsymbol{\beta}$ can be written as $\sum_{i=1}^n \boldsymbol{x}_i\boldsymbol{x}_i'$. Since $\boldsymbol{x}_i\boldsymbol{x}_i'$ is a nonnegative definite matrix, an additional observation cannot reduce the information of $\boldsymbol{\beta}$ in the sense of the Löwner order. For fixed n, the information matrix can be larger for some values of the $\boldsymbol{X}$-matrix than for other values. If one has the option of controlling the $\boldsymbol{X}$-matrix (perhaps under some constraints), then it is desirable — for the purpose of inference — to arrange as large an information matrix as possible. Typically maximization of an increasing function of the eigenvalues of $\boldsymbol{X}'\boldsymbol{X}$ (such as the trace, the determinant or the largest eigenvalue) is chosen as the design criterion. See Chapter 6 for more discussion on this subject.

Example 3.55. (Weighing design — Spring balance) A spring balance is used to weigh three objects of unknown weights β_1, β_2 and β_3. Each object is weighted twice and the average weight is used as the estimate of the weight of that object. The model is $(\boldsymbol{y}, \boldsymbol{X\beta}, \sigma^2\boldsymbol{I})$ with $\boldsymbol{\beta} = (\beta_1 : \beta_2 : \beta_3)'$ and

$$\boldsymbol{X} = \begin{pmatrix} 1\,0\,0 \\ 1\,0\,0 \\ 0\,1\,0 \\ 0\,1\,0 \\ 0\,0\,1 \\ 0\,0\,1 \end{pmatrix}.$$

The elements of the matrix $\boldsymbol{X}$ can only assume binary values. This a characteristic of weighing designs with spring balance. In this case the information matrix for $\boldsymbol{\beta}$ is $2\sigma^{-2}\boldsymbol{I}_{3\times3}$.

Now consider an alternative plan where every *pair* of objects is weighed twice. For this design

$$\boldsymbol{X} = \begin{pmatrix} 1\ 1\ 0 \\ 1\ 1\ 0 \\ 0\ 1\ 1 \\ 0\ 1\ 1 \\ 1\ 0\ 1 \\ 1\ 0\ 1 \end{pmatrix},$$

and the information matrix for $\boldsymbol{\beta}$ is

$$\sigma^{-2}\begin{pmatrix} 4\ 2\ 2 \\ 2\ 4\ 2 \\ 2\ 2\ 4 \end{pmatrix} = 2\sigma^{-2}\boldsymbol{I} + 2\sigma^{-2}\boldsymbol{1}\boldsymbol{1}'.$$

Clearly, this matrix is larger (in the sense of the Löwner order) than the information matrix in the case of the first design. According to the result of Exercise A.26, the BLUEs of β_1, β_2 and β_3 have smaller variance in the case of the second design ($\sigma^2/2$ in the case of the first design, $3\sigma^2/8$ for the second), even though the same number of measurements are used. It can be shown that the second design is not only better than the first, it is the unique design with three weights and six measurements that maximizes the determinant of the information matrix. It follows from (3.22) that the optimality of this design holds even when the error distribution is not normal. □

In order to examine the effect of nuisance parameters, let $\boldsymbol{\beta}$ and $\boldsymbol{X}$ be partitioned as in Section 3.11, and $\boldsymbol{\beta}_2$ be the nuisance parameter. There is a corresponding partition of the information matrix of $\boldsymbol{\beta}$. The diagonal block corresponding to $\boldsymbol{\beta}_1$ is $\sigma^{-2}\boldsymbol{X}_1'\boldsymbol{X}_1$, which is the *same* as what would have been the 'information of $\boldsymbol{\beta}_1$' if $\boldsymbol{\beta}_2$ were not there. However, the corresponding block of a g-inverse of the information matrix very much depends on the other blocks. Thus, the Cramer-Rao lower bound is affected by nuisance parameters. Let $\boldsymbol{t}'(\boldsymbol{I} - \boldsymbol{P}_{X_2})\boldsymbol{X}_1\boldsymbol{\beta}_1$ be an estimable LPF (see Proposition 3.53). Then the Cramer-Rao lower bound for the variance of an unbiased estimator of this LPF is $\sigma^2\boldsymbol{t}'(\boldsymbol{I}-\boldsymbol{P}_{X_2})\boldsymbol{X}(\boldsymbol{X}'\boldsymbol{X})^-\boldsymbol{X}'(\boldsymbol{I}-\boldsymbol{P}_{X_2})\boldsymbol{t}$, which simplifies to $\sigma^2\|\boldsymbol{P}_X(I - \boldsymbol{P}_{X_2})\boldsymbol{t}\|^2$. In the absence of the nuisance parameters the bound would have been $\sigma^2\|\boldsymbol{P}_{X_1}(I-\boldsymbol{P}_{X_2})\boldsymbol{t}\|^2$, which is possibly smaller. A sufficient condition for equality of the two bounds is $\boldsymbol{X}_1'\boldsymbol{X}_2 = \boldsymbol{0}$, that is, the information matrix of $\boldsymbol{\beta}$ is block diagonal. Such segregation of information is desirable in a designed experiment.

Example 3.56. (Abrasion of denim jeans, continued) Consider the model of Example 3.5. Here, the information for $\boldsymbol{\beta}$ is

$$\sigma^{-2}\boldsymbol{X}'\boldsymbol{X} = \sigma^{-2}\begin{pmatrix} 90 & 30 & 30 & 30 & 30 & 30 & 30 \\ 30 & 30 & 0 & 0 & 10 & 10 & 10 \\ 30 & 0 & 30 & 0 & 10 & 10 & 10 \\ 30 & 0 & 0 & 30 & 10 & 10 & 10 \\ 30 & 10 & 10 & 10 & 30 & 0 & 0 \\ 30 & 10 & 10 & 10 & 0 & 30 & 0 \\ 30 & 10 & 10 & 10 & 0 & 0 & 30 \end{pmatrix}.$$

There is no apparent segregation of information. However, the Cramer-Rao lower bound for the variance of an unbiased estimator of $\tau_1 - \tau_2$ is $\sigma^2/15$, which is the same as what it would have been in the absence of the μ, β_1, β_2 and β_3 (nuisance parameters for the purpose of assessing difference in treatment effects). It may be recalled that the bound is achieved by the BLUE.

A reparametrization of the kind described in Example 3.49 would bring out clearly the segregation of information for main and nuisance parameters (see Exercise 3.21). □

Let us now turn to the case of non-normal distributions. Suppose $\boldsymbol{y} = \boldsymbol{X\beta}+\sigma\boldsymbol{u}$, where the n elements of the random vector $\boldsymbol{u}$ are independent and identically distributed with mean 0, variance 1 and density $h(\cdot)$ satisfying $h(-u) = h(u)$ for all u. Suppose further that all the partial derivatives and expected values used in the following derivation exist and the interchanges of derivatives and integrals are permissible. Then

$$\log f_\theta(\boldsymbol{y}) = -\frac{n}{2}\log\sigma^2 + \sum_{i=1}^{n}\log h\left(\frac{y_i - \boldsymbol{x}_i'\boldsymbol{\beta}}{\sigma}\right),$$

where $\boldsymbol{y} = (y_1 : \cdots : y_n)'$ and $\boldsymbol{X} = (\boldsymbol{x}_1 : \cdots : \boldsymbol{x}_n)'$. We have

$$\frac{\partial \log f_\theta(\boldsymbol{y})}{\partial \boldsymbol{\beta}} = -\frac{1}{\sigma}\sum_{i=1}^{n}\boldsymbol{x}_i \cdot \left.\left(\frac{\partial \log h(u)}{\partial u}\right)\right|_{u = (y_i - x_i'\boldsymbol{\beta})/\sigma},$$

$$\frac{\partial \log f_\theta(\boldsymbol{y})}{\partial \sigma^2} = -\frac{n}{2\sigma^2} - \frac{1}{2\sigma^2}\sum_{i=1}^{n}\left.\left(u\frac{\partial \log h(u)}{\partial u}\right)\right|_{u = (y_i - x_i'\boldsymbol{\beta})/\sigma}.$$

Each summand in the right-hand side of the first equation has zero expectation. Therefore,

$$
\begin{aligned}
&E\left[\left(\frac{\partial \log f_\theta(\boldsymbol{y})}{\partial \boldsymbol{\beta}}\right)\left(\frac{\partial \log f_\theta(\boldsymbol{y})}{\partial \boldsymbol{\beta}}\right)'\right] \\
&= \frac{1}{\sigma^2}\sum_{i=1}^{n} \boldsymbol{x}_i\boldsymbol{x}_i' \int_{-\infty}^{\infty} \left(\frac{\partial \log h(u)}{\partial u}\right)^2 \Bigg|_{u\,=\,(y_i - x_i'\boldsymbol{\beta})/\sigma} \cdot \frac{1}{\sigma} h\left(\frac{y_i - \boldsymbol{x}_i'\boldsymbol{\beta}}{\sigma}\right) dy_i \\
&= \frac{1}{\sigma^2}\sum_{i=1}^{n} \boldsymbol{x}_i\boldsymbol{x}_i' \int_{-\infty}^{\infty} \left(\frac{\partial \log h(u)}{\partial u}\right)^2 h(u)du \;=\; \mathcal{I}_\mu \boldsymbol{X}'\boldsymbol{X},
\end{aligned}
$$

where

$$
\mathcal{I}_\mu = \frac{1}{\sigma^2}\int_{-\infty}^{\infty} \left(\frac{\partial \log h(u)}{\partial u}\right)^2 h(u)du.
$$

Further,

$$
\begin{aligned}
&E\left[\left(\frac{\partial \log f_\theta(\boldsymbol{y})}{\partial \boldsymbol{\beta}}\right)\left(\frac{\partial \log f_\theta(\boldsymbol{y})}{\partial \sigma^2}\right)\right] \\
&= \frac{1}{2\sigma^3}\sum_{i=1}^{n} \boldsymbol{x}_i \int_{-\infty}^{\infty} u\left(\frac{\partial \log h(u)}{\partial u}\right)^2 \Bigg|_{u\,=\,(y_i - x_i'\boldsymbol{\beta})/\sigma} \cdot \frac{1}{\sigma} h\left(\frac{y_i - \boldsymbol{x}_i'\boldsymbol{\beta}}{\sigma}\right) dy_i \\
&= \frac{1}{2\sigma^3}\sum_{i=1}^{n} \boldsymbol{x}_i \int_{-\infty}^{\infty} u\left(\frac{\partial \log h(u)}{\partial u}\right)^2 h(u)du \;=\; \boldsymbol{0},
\end{aligned}
$$

as the integrand in the last expression is an odd function of u. Finally,

$$
\begin{aligned}
&E\left[\left(\frac{\partial \log f_\theta(\boldsymbol{y})}{\partial \sigma^2}\right)^2\right] \\
&= \frac{n^2}{4\sigma^4} + \frac{n}{2\sigma^4}\sum_{i=1}^{n} E\left[\left(u\frac{\partial \log h(u)}{\partial u}\right)\Bigg|_{u\,=\,(y_i - x_i'\boldsymbol{\beta})/\sigma}\right] \\
&\quad + \frac{1}{4\sigma^4}\sum_{i=1}^{n}\sum_{j=1}^{n} E\left[\left(u\frac{\partial \log h(u)}{\partial u}\right)\Bigg|_{u\,=\,(y_i - x_i'\boldsymbol{\beta})/\sigma}\right. \\
&\qquad \left.\cdot \left(u\frac{\partial \log h(u)}{\partial u}\right)\Bigg|_{u\,=\,(y_i - x_i'\boldsymbol{\beta})/\sigma}\right]
\end{aligned}
$$

$$
\begin{aligned}
&= \frac{n^2}{4\sigma^4} + \frac{n^2}{2\sigma^4}\int_{-\infty}^{\infty} u\frac{\partial h(u)}{\partial u}du \\
&\quad + \frac{n^2-n}{4\sigma^4}\left(\int_{-\infty}^{\infty} u\frac{\partial h(u)}{\partial u}du\right)^2 + \frac{n}{4\sigma^4}\int_{-\infty}^{\infty}\left(u\frac{\partial \log h(u)}{\partial u}\right)^2 h(u)du \\
&= \frac{n^2}{4\sigma^4} + \frac{n^2}{2\sigma^4}(-1) + \frac{n^2-n}{4\sigma^4}(-1)^2 + \frac{n}{4\sigma^4}\int_{-\infty}^{\infty}\left(u\frac{\partial \log h(u)}{\partial u}\right)^2 h(u)du \\
&= n\mathcal{I}_{\sigma^2},
\end{aligned}
$$

where

$$
\mathcal{I}_{\sigma^2} = \frac{1}{4\sigma^4}\left[\int_{-\infty}^{\infty}\left(u\frac{\partial \log h(u)}{\partial u}\right)^2 h(u)du - 1\right].
$$

Therefore, the information matrix for $\boldsymbol{\theta} = (\boldsymbol{\beta}' : \sigma^2)'$ is

$$
\mathcal{I}(\boldsymbol{\theta}) = \begin{pmatrix} \mathcal{I}_\mu \boldsymbol{X}'\boldsymbol{X} & \mathbf{0} \\ \mathbf{0} & n\mathcal{I}_{\sigma^2} \end{pmatrix}. \tag{3.22}
$$

The information for $\boldsymbol{\beta}$ is $\mathcal{I}_\mu \boldsymbol{X}'\boldsymbol{X}$. Therefore, the design issues (see Section 6.1) can be addressed with reference to the matrix $\boldsymbol{X}'\boldsymbol{X}$ — just as in the normal case.

The scalar $\mathcal{I}_\mu$ is equal to σ^{-2} when the components of $\boldsymbol{y}$ are normally distributed; otherwise it is greater than σ^{-2} (see Exercise 3.26). Thus, the Cramer-Rao lower bound for the dispersion of an unbiased estimator of an estimable LPF is *smaller* in the non-normal case than in the normal case. We have already seen that the dispersion of the BLUE is equal to the 'normal' Cramer-Rao lower bound, irrespective of the error distribution. Since the Cramer-Rao bound in the non-normal case is strictly smaller than the dispersion of the BLUE, there is a potential of achieving lower dispersion than that of the BLUE, by employing another estimator, such as the MLE.

3.13 Collinearity in the linear model

We have seen in Example 3.24 that because of redundancy in the description of the parameters, some linear parametric functions may be non-estimable. In such a case, the matrix $\boldsymbol{X}$ does not have full column rank, and there are some columns of $\boldsymbol{X}$ that are linear combinations of the other columns.

In practice, it is often found that some columns of $\boldsymbol{X}$ are *almost* equal to linear functions of the other columns. This phenomenon is known as *multicollinearity* or simply *collinearity*. This may happen, for instance, due to strong correlation among explanatory variables. An approximate relation among the columns of $\boldsymbol{X}$ may also occur when there is an exact linear relationship among the corresponding explanatory variables, but the variables are measured with some error.

Even if the matrix $\boldsymbol{X}$ has full column rank (so that all LPFs are estimable), the presence of collinearity can make it nearly rank-deficient in the following sense: a small alteration in the elements of $\boldsymbol{X}$ would turn the approximate relation among the columns into an *exact* one, and the perturbed matrix would have smaller rank.

The presence of collinearity can make the variance of certain BLUEs very large compared to the model error variance, σ^2, as demonstrated below.

Example 3.57. Let $\boldsymbol{X} = (\boldsymbol{1} : \boldsymbol{x}_{(1)} : \boldsymbol{x}_{(2)})$, where $\boldsymbol{x}_{(2)} = \boldsymbol{x}_{(1)} + \alpha\boldsymbol{v}$, α is a small number and $\boldsymbol{1}$, $\boldsymbol{x}_{(1)}$ and $\boldsymbol{v}$ are orthogonal vectors with a common norm. It follows that

$$Var(\boldsymbol{p}'\widehat{\boldsymbol{\beta}}) = \sigma^2\boldsymbol{p}'(\boldsymbol{X}'\boldsymbol{X})^{-1}\boldsymbol{p} = \frac{\sigma^2}{\alpha^2\boldsymbol{1}'\boldsymbol{1}}\boldsymbol{p}'\begin{pmatrix}1 & 0 & 0\\ 0 & 1+\alpha^2 & -1\\ 0 & -1 & 1\end{pmatrix}\boldsymbol{p}.$$

In particular, if $\boldsymbol{\beta} = (\beta_0 : \beta_1 : \beta_2)'$, then by choosing $\boldsymbol{p} = (0 : 1 : -1)'$ we have

$$Var(\widehat{\beta}_1 - \widehat{\beta}_2) = \sigma^2 \cdot \frac{1 + 4/\alpha^2}{\boldsymbol{1}'\boldsymbol{1}},$$

which can be very large if α is small. If $\alpha \to 0$, then the variance explodes. Of course, $\beta_1 - \beta_2$ is no longer estimable when $\alpha = 0$.

In contrast, by choosing $\boldsymbol{p} = (0 : 1 : 1)'$ we have

$$Var(\widehat{\beta}_1 + \widehat{\beta}_2) = \sigma^2 \cdot \frac{1}{\boldsymbol{1}'\boldsymbol{1}},$$

which does not depend on α. Thus, the variance of $\widehat{\beta}_1 + \widehat{\beta}_2$ is not affected by collinearity. Note that $\beta_1 + \beta_2$ remains estimable even if $\alpha = 0$. □

This example shows that the variance of certain BLUEs may be very high because of collinearity, while the variance of some other BLUEs may not be affected. It also demonstrates how non-estimability of parameters can be viewed as an extreme form of collinearity.

We now consider the above points in a more general set-up. The presence of collinearity implies that there is a unit vector $\boldsymbol{v}$ such that the linear combination of the columns of $\boldsymbol{X}$ given by $\boldsymbol{Xv}$, is very close to the zero vector. In such a case we have a small value of $\boldsymbol{v}'\boldsymbol{X}'\boldsymbol{Xv}$. According to the expression of the information matrix given on page 109, the information of the LPF $\boldsymbol{v}'\boldsymbol{\beta}$ is proportional to $\boldsymbol{v}'\boldsymbol{X}'\boldsymbol{Xv}$. Thus, a small value of the latter can be interpreted as shortage of information in the direction of $\boldsymbol{v}$. We may refer to such a unit vector as a *direction* of collinearity.

A direction of collinearity can be analysed in terms of contributions of different observed values of the data. To see this, write $\|\boldsymbol{Xv}\|^2$ as

$$\|\boldsymbol{Xv}\|^2 = \boldsymbol{v}'\boldsymbol{X}'\boldsymbol{Xv} = \sum_{i=1}^{n}(\boldsymbol{x}_i'\boldsymbol{v})^2,$$

where $\boldsymbol{x}_1', \boldsymbol{x}_2' \ldots, \boldsymbol{x}_n'$ are the rows of $\boldsymbol{X}$. The ith component of $\boldsymbol{y}$ is an observed value of $\boldsymbol{x}_i'\boldsymbol{\beta}$ (with error). If $\|\boldsymbol{Xv}\|^2$ is small, every $(\boldsymbol{x}_i'\boldsymbol{v})^2$ is small. If this is the case, none of the observations carry much information about $\boldsymbol{v}'\boldsymbol{\beta}$. There is inadequacy of data in this direction. If $(\boldsymbol{x}_i'\boldsymbol{v})^2 = 0$ for all i, the observations do not carry *any* information about $\boldsymbol{v}'\boldsymbol{\beta}$. In this extreme case $\boldsymbol{v}'\boldsymbol{\beta}$ is not estimable.

The vector $\boldsymbol{v}$ can be written as

$$\boldsymbol{v} = \sum_{i=1}^{p}(\boldsymbol{v}'\boldsymbol{v}_i)\boldsymbol{v}_i,$$

where $\sum_{i=1}^{p}\lambda_i\boldsymbol{v}_i\boldsymbol{v}_i'$ is a spectral decomposition of $\boldsymbol{X}'\boldsymbol{X}$, the eigenvalues being in the decreasing order. It follows that

$$\begin{aligned}\|\boldsymbol{Xv}\|^2 &= \boldsymbol{v}'\boldsymbol{X}'\boldsymbol{X}\sum_{i=1}^{p}(\boldsymbol{v}'\boldsymbol{v}_i)\boldsymbol{v}_i\\ &= \boldsymbol{v}'\sum_{i=1}^{p}(\boldsymbol{v}'\boldsymbol{v}_i)\lambda_i\boldsymbol{v}_i = \sum_{i=1}^{p}\lambda_i(\boldsymbol{v}'\boldsymbol{v}_i)^2.\end{aligned}$$

The above expression has the smallest value when $\boldsymbol{v} = \boldsymbol{v}_p$. Therefore, a very small value of λ_p signifies the presence of collinearity. When λ_p is very small, $\boldsymbol{v}_p$ is a direction of collinearity. When $\boldsymbol{X}'\boldsymbol{X}$ has *several* small eigenvalues, the corresponding eigenvectors are directions of collinearity. All unit vectors which are linear combinations of these eigenvectors are also directions of collinearity.

Let $\boldsymbol{X}$ have full column rank, so that all LPFs are estimable. Then

$$Var(\boldsymbol{p}'\widehat{\boldsymbol{\beta}}) = \sigma^2\boldsymbol{p}'(\boldsymbol{X}'\boldsymbol{X})^{-1}\boldsymbol{p} = \sigma^2\sum_{i=1}^{p}\frac{(\boldsymbol{p}'\boldsymbol{v}_i)^2}{\lambda_i}. \tag{3.23}$$

If $\boldsymbol{p}$ is proportional to $\boldsymbol{v}_p$, then the variance of its BLUE is $\boldsymbol{p}'\boldsymbol{p}/\lambda_p$. The presence of collinearity would mean that λ_p is small and therefore, this variance is large. As $\lambda_p \to 0$, the variance goes to infinity. (When $\lambda_p = 0$, we have a rank-deficient $\boldsymbol{X}$ matrix with $\boldsymbol{v}_p \notin \mathcal{C}(\boldsymbol{X}')$, and so $\boldsymbol{p}'\boldsymbol{\beta}$ is not estimable at all.) Similarly, if $\boldsymbol{p}$ has a substantial component $(\boldsymbol{p}'\boldsymbol{v}_i)$ along an eigenvector $(\boldsymbol{v}_i)$ corresponding to *any small eigenvalue* (λ_i) of $\boldsymbol{X}'\boldsymbol{X}$, the variance of $\boldsymbol{p}'\widehat{\boldsymbol{\beta}}$ is large. If $\boldsymbol{p}$ has zero component along all the eigenvectors corresponding to small eigenvalues, then the reciprocals of the smaller eigenvalues do not contribute to the right-hand side of (3.23), and thus $Var(\boldsymbol{p}'\widehat{\boldsymbol{\beta}})$ is not very large.

In summary, all 'estimable' LPFs are not estimable *with equal precision.* Some LPFs can be estimated with greater precision than others. When there is collinearity, there are some LPFs which are estimable but the corresponding BLUEs have very large variance. Non-estimable LPFs can be viewed as extreme cases of LPFs which can be linearly estimated with less precision. When an experiment is designed, one has to choose the matrix $\boldsymbol{X}$ in a way that ensures that the LPFs of interest are estimable with sufficient precision.

If one has a priori knowledge of an approximate relationship among certain columns of $\boldsymbol{X}$, and confines estimation to linear combinations which are orthogonal to these, then collinearity would not have much effect on the inference. This is analogous to the fact, as seen in Example 3.19, that estimable functions can be estimated even if there is one or more exact linear relationship involving the columns of $\boldsymbol{X}$.

3.14 Complements/Exercises

Exercises with solutions given in Appendix C

3.1 The linear model $(\boldsymbol{y}, \boldsymbol{X\beta}, \sigma^2\boldsymbol{I})$ is said to be *saturated* if the error degrees of freedom ($n - \rho(\boldsymbol{X})$, where n is the sample size) is equal to zero. Show that in a saturated model, every linear unbiased estimator is the corresponding BLUE.

3.2 Show that all the components of $\boldsymbol{\beta}$ in the model $(\boldsymbol{y}, \boldsymbol{X\beta}, \sigma^2\boldsymbol{I})$ are estimable if and only if $\boldsymbol{X}$ has full column rank, and that in such a case, every LPF is estimable.

3.3 If there is no linear unbiased estimator of the LPF $\boldsymbol{A\beta}$ in the model $(\boldsymbol{y}, \boldsymbol{X\beta}, \sigma^2\boldsymbol{I})$, show that there is no nonlinear unbiased estimator of $\boldsymbol{A\beta}$.

3.4 Suppose $\boldsymbol{x}_1, \ldots, \boldsymbol{x}_p$ are the columns of the matrix $\boldsymbol{X}$ in the linear model $(\boldsymbol{y}, \boldsymbol{X}\boldsymbol{\beta}, \sigma^2\boldsymbol{I})$. Show that the coefficient of $\boldsymbol{x}_1$ is not estimable if and only if $\boldsymbol{x}_1$ has an exact linear relationship with the other columns of $\boldsymbol{X}$. [This is a case of exact 'collinearity.']

3.5 Show that a vector valued LPF $\boldsymbol{A}\boldsymbol{\beta}$ is estimable if and only if

$$\rho\begin{pmatrix}\boldsymbol{X}\\ \boldsymbol{A}\end{pmatrix} = \rho(\boldsymbol{X}).$$

3.6 Show that the *affine* estimator $\boldsymbol{l}'\boldsymbol{y} + c$ is unbiased for $\boldsymbol{p}'\boldsymbol{\beta}$ if and only if $\boldsymbol{X}'\boldsymbol{l} = \boldsymbol{p}$ and $c = 0$.

3.7 Show that an LUE $(\boldsymbol{l}'\boldsymbol{y})$ of an estimable LPF in the linear model $(\boldsymbol{y}, \boldsymbol{X}\boldsymbol{\beta}, \sigma^2\boldsymbol{I})$ is its BLUE if and only if $\boldsymbol{l} \in \mathcal{C}(\boldsymbol{X})$.

3.8 A multivariate distribution is said to be *spherically symmetric* if its density is of the form

$$f(\boldsymbol{x}) \propto g(\boldsymbol{x}'\boldsymbol{x}),$$

where $g(\cdot)$ is a nonnegative and non-increasing function defined over the positive half of the real line.

(a) Derive the MLE of $\boldsymbol{\beta}$ for the linear model $(\boldsymbol{y}, \boldsymbol{X}\boldsymbol{\beta}, \sigma^2\boldsymbol{I})$, when the errors have a spherically symmetric distribution.

(b) Is the MLE unique?

3.9 The LSE of $\boldsymbol{\beta}$ in the linear model $(\boldsymbol{y}, \boldsymbol{X}\boldsymbol{\beta}, \sigma^2\boldsymbol{I})$, where the p-dimensional vector parameter $\boldsymbol{\beta}$ is estimable, can be written as

$$\widehat{\boldsymbol{\beta}} = \frac{\sum_r |\boldsymbol{X}_r'\boldsymbol{X}_r|\widehat{\boldsymbol{\beta}}_r}{\sum_r |\boldsymbol{X}_r'\boldsymbol{X}_r|},$$

where $\boldsymbol{X}_r$ is a $p \times p$ sub-matrix of $\boldsymbol{X}$, $\boldsymbol{y}_r$ is the corresponding sub-vector of $\boldsymbol{y}$, $\widehat{\boldsymbol{\beta}}_r$ is the LSE from the sub-model $(\boldsymbol{y}_r, \boldsymbol{X}_r\boldsymbol{\beta},\ \sigma^2\boldsymbol{I})$, and the summations are over all such sub-models where $\boldsymbol{\beta}$ is estimable. Interpret this result (due to Subrahmanyam, 1972) and prove it for the special case of simple linear regression.

3.10 Show that $(\boldsymbol{X}'\boldsymbol{X})^-\boldsymbol{X}'$ is a g-inverse of $\boldsymbol{X}$, and $\boldsymbol{X}^-\boldsymbol{X}(\boldsymbol{X}'\boldsymbol{X})^-$ is a g-inverse of $\boldsymbol{X}'\boldsymbol{X}$. Hence, show that $\boldsymbol{X}^-\widehat{\boldsymbol{y}}$ is a least squares estimator of $\boldsymbol{\beta}$ for any choice of $\boldsymbol{X}^-$, and that any least squares estimator can be written as $\boldsymbol{X}^-\widehat{\boldsymbol{y}}$.

3.11 Given the model $(\boldsymbol{y}, \boldsymbol{X}\boldsymbol{\beta}, \sigma^2\boldsymbol{I})$, define a finite set $\mathcal{A}$ of LZFs with the following property: there is no LZF outside $\mathcal{A}$ which has nonzero variance and is uncorrelated with *all* the members of $\mathcal{A}$. Show that $\mathcal{A}$ is a generating set of LZFs.

3.12 Given the model $(\boldsymbol{y}, \boldsymbol{X\beta}, \sigma^2\boldsymbol{I})$ with $\rho(\boldsymbol{X}) = r$, find a transformation matrix $\boldsymbol{L}$ such that the vector $\boldsymbol{Ly}$ has the following properties.

(i) $D(\boldsymbol{Ly}) = \sigma^2\boldsymbol{I}$.

(ii) The first r elements of $\boldsymbol{Ly}$ constitute a standardized basis set of the BLUEs of the given model.

(iii) The last $n-r$ elements of $\boldsymbol{Ly}$ constitute a standardized basis set of the LZFs of the given model.

3.13 Prove the statement of Remark 3.48.

3.14 If $\boldsymbol{z}$ is a vector of BLUEs whose elements constitute a generating set, prove that $D(\boldsymbol{z})$ has rank $\rho(\boldsymbol{X})$.

3.15 Consider the model $(\boldsymbol{y}, \boldsymbol{X\beta}, \sigma^2\boldsymbol{I})$ with normally distributed errors.

(a) Compute the mean squared errors of $\widehat{\sigma^2}$ and $\widehat{\sigma^2}_{ML}$. Which estimator has smaller MSE?

(b) Find c such that cR_0^2 is the estimator of σ^2 having the smallest possible mean squared error. Does the answer coincide with $\widehat{\sigma^2}$ or $\widehat{\sigma^2}_{ML}$?

(c) What is the MSE of cR_0^2 when c has this optimum value?

3.16 Consider the reparametrization of the model $\mathcal{M}_1 = (\boldsymbol{y}, \boldsymbol{X\beta}, \sigma^2\boldsymbol{I})$ as $\mathcal{M}_2 = (\boldsymbol{y}, \boldsymbol{Z\theta}, \sigma^2\boldsymbol{I})$, where $\boldsymbol{Z}$ has full column rank. Express the BLUEs of $\boldsymbol{\theta}$ and $\boldsymbol{X\beta}$ in terms of one another.

3.17 Consider the model of Example 3.19. Identify the BLUEs lost and the LZFs gained *because of* the restriction $\tau_1 = \tau_2 = \tau_3$. What happens to the sets of BLUEs and LZFs when the restrictions $\tau_1 + \tau_2 + \tau_3 = 0$ and $\beta_1 + \beta_2 + \beta_3 = 0$ are introduced?

3.18 If $\rho(\boldsymbol{X}' : \boldsymbol{A}') = \rho(\boldsymbol{X}') + \rho(\boldsymbol{A}')$, show that the restriction $\boldsymbol{A\beta} = \boldsymbol{\xi}$ amounts to a reparametrization of the model $(\boldsymbol{y}, \boldsymbol{X\beta}, \sigma^2\boldsymbol{I})$.

3.19 The Cobb-Douglas model for production function postulates that the production (q) is related to the amount of labour (l) and capital (k) via the equation

$$q = a \cdot l^{\alpha} k^{\beta} \cdot u,$$

where a, α and β are unspecified constants and u is the (positive) model error. A log transformation of both sides of the equation linearizes the model. Economists are sometimes interested in a condition called 'constant returns to scale' (see Poirier, 1995, p. 484), which amounts to $\alpha + \beta = 1$. Suppose n independent observations of the three variables are available, and all the parameters are identifiable.

(a) Derive an unrestricted linear model which is equivalent to the Cobb-Douglas model with the restriction $\alpha + \beta = 1$.

(b) Find an expression for the 'decrease' in the dispersion of the BLUE of $(\log a : \alpha : \beta)'$ because of the restriction $\alpha + \beta = 1$.

3.20 For the model $(\boldsymbol{y}, \boldsymbol{x}_1\beta_1 + \boldsymbol{X}_2\boldsymbol{\beta}_2, \sigma^2\boldsymbol{I})$, suppose $\boldsymbol{X}_2$ includes the intercept column. Show that the sample correlation coefficient between the vectors $(\boldsymbol{I} - \boldsymbol{P}_{X_2})\boldsymbol{y}$ and $(\boldsymbol{I} - \boldsymbol{P}_{X_2})\boldsymbol{x}_1$ is equal to the sample partial correlation coefficient between $\boldsymbol{y}$ and $\boldsymbol{x}_1$, after correcting for the linear effects of $\boldsymbol{X}_2$. Also show that for these vectors, the slope of the least squares fitted line through the origin is related to their sample correlation coefficient through a relation similar to (2.19).

3.21 Compute the information matrix for the five parameters in the reparametrized model of Example 3.49 and show that it is block diagonal. Compare the Cramer-Rao bound for an unbiased estimator of θ_4 with the bound given in Example 3.56.

3.22 Compare the information matrices of $\boldsymbol{\beta}$ for the models of Exercises 3.35 and 3.36, assuming normally distributed errors.

3.23 *Spring balance with bias.* A spring balance with bias is one in which the mean measurement of any weight differs from the 'true' weight by a nonzero constant. Let this constant be β_0, and suppose k objects with weights $\beta_1, \ldots \beta_k$ (in various combinations) are measured in such a balance. There are n measurements. If the errors are uncorrelated and have mean zero and variance σ^2, show that the variance of the BLUE of $\widehat{\beta}_i$ for $i = 1, \ldots, k$ is at least $4\sigma^2/n$. Can all the variances be equal to $4\sigma^2/n$?

3.24 *Chemical balance.* When a chemical balance is used to weigh various combinations of objects having weights $\beta_1, \ldots, \beta_k$, the elements of the matrix $\boldsymbol{X}$ can be 0, 1 or -1. Suppose there are exactly n weighing operations, and there is no bias. Show that the variance of the BLUE of $\widehat{\beta}_i$ for $i = 1, \ldots, k$ is at least σ^2/n. Can all the variances be equal to σ^2/n? What happens when there is a bias in the balance (i.e. an intercept term)?

3.25 Let $\mathcal{I}_\beta$ be the information matrix of $\boldsymbol{\beta}$ in the model $(\boldsymbol{y}, \boldsymbol{X}\boldsymbol{\beta}, \sigma^2\boldsymbol{I})$, given by the top left block of $\mathcal{I}(\boldsymbol{\theta})$ on page 109. Partition $\mathcal{I}_\beta$ as

$$\mathcal{I}_\beta = \begin{pmatrix} \mathcal{I}_{11} & \mathcal{I}_{12} \\ \mathcal{I}_{21} & \mathcal{I}_{22} \end{pmatrix},$$

where $\mathcal{I}_{11}$ is a scalar, and let $\mathcal{I}_{11.2} = \mathcal{I}_{11} - \mathcal{I}_{12}\mathcal{I}_{22}^{-}\mathcal{I}_{21}$. Let β_1 be the first component of $\boldsymbol{\beta}$.

(a) When β_1 is estimable, show that the Cramer-Rao bound on the variance of an unbiased estimator of β_1 is $1/\mathcal{I}_{11.2}$.

(b) When β_1 is non-estimable, show that $\mathcal{I}_{11.2} = 0$.

(c) How do you interpret the results of parts (a) and (b)?

(d) Can the results of parts (a) and (b) and the interpretation of part (c) be extended to a general scalar LPF?

3.26 Let $y = \mu + \sigma u$ where u has zero mean, unit variance, and a completely known and differentiable probability density function $h(\cdot)$ which is symmetric around 0. Assume that the information matrix for $\boldsymbol{\theta} = (\mu : \sigma^2)'$ exists.

(a) Show that the information matrix is $\begin{pmatrix} \mathcal{I}_\mu & 0 \\ 0 & \mathcal{I}_{\sigma^2} \end{pmatrix}$, where

$$\mathcal{I}_\mu = \frac{1}{\sigma^2} \int_{-\infty}^{\infty} \left(\frac{\partial \log h(u)}{\partial u} \right)^2 h(u)du,$$

$$\mathcal{I}_{\sigma^2} = \frac{1}{4\sigma^4} \left[\int_{-\infty}^{\infty} \left(u \frac{\partial \log h(u)}{\partial u} \right)^2 h(u)du - 1 \right].$$

(b) Show that $\sigma^2 \mathcal{I}_\mu \geq 1$.

(c) Show that the result of part (b) holds with equality if and only if h is the density of $N(0, 1)$. Interpret the result.

Additional exercises

3.27 The data object `LAcrime` in the R package `lmreg` contains the monthly total counts of homicides and rapes in the city of Los Angeles from January 1975 to December 1993. The monthly average temperature recorded at the Los Angeles International Airport (in Celsius and Fahrenheit) and the population of the city for these months are also included.[3]

(a) Plot the number of homicides (y) against the temperature in Fahrenheit (x). Does a linear model for y given x look appropriate?

(b) Fit a linear model to the data of part (a) and interpret the coefficients.

[3]The crime data are accessed from the site `https://www.icpsr.umich.edu/icpsrweb/NACJD/studies/6792` (Carlson, 1998). The temperature data for LAX (WMO ID 72295) are accessed from the site `http://www.ncdc.noaa.gov/ghcnm/v2.php` of the National Oceanic and Atmospheric Administration, USA.

3.28 (a) For the Los Angeles crime data of Exercise 3.27, fit another linear model for the number of homicides (y) using the temperature in Celsius (z) as the explanatory variable and interpret the coefficients.

(b) Compare the estimated coefficients obtained in part (a) with those of Exercise 3.27, and examine whether they are consistent with one another. (You can make use of the well-known relation between temperatures expressed in the Celsius and Fahrenheit scales.)

3.29 Estimate the parameters of the two gender-specific models described in Exercise 1.10 for the world record running times data of Table 1.2. What are the standard errors of the estimates? Repeat this computation for the 'grand model' constructed in that exercise, and compare the results with the previous computations.

3.30 Repeat Exercise 3.29 for the model described in Exercise 1.11.

3.31 The data set of Table 3.3, taken from Brownlee (1965), shows the observations from 21 days' operation of a plant for the oxidation of ammonia, which is used for producing nitric acid. The response variable is the

Table 3.3 Stack loss in ammonia oxidation plant (data object `stackloss` of R package `datasets`, Source: Brownlee, 1965)

Air flow	Water temperature	Acid concentration	Stack loss
80	27	89	42
80	27	88	37
75	25	90	37
62	24	87	28
62	22	87	18
62	23	87	18
62	24	93	19
62	24	93	20
58	23	87	15
58	18	80	14
58	18	89	14
58	17	88	13
58	18	82	11
58	19	93	12
50	18	89	8
50	18	86	7
50	19	72	8
50	19	79	8
50	20	80	9
56	20	82	15
70	20	91	15

stack loss defined as the portion of the ingoing ammonia (in parts per 1000) that escapes unabsorbed. The explanatory variables are air flow (rate of operation of plant), cooling water inlet temperature (in °C) and acid concentration (in parts per 1000, minus 500). The data are available as the data object `stackloss` in the R package `datasets`. Using a linear model of stack loss, obtain the least squares estimates of the coefficients of the explanatory variables, along with their standard errors.

3.32 The data object `girlgrowth` in the R package `lmreg` contains the heights of some adolescent girls, aged 7 to 12. Notice from the scatter plot of height against age, given in Figure 1.2, that there are multiple data points at integer ages and that the rate of growth appears to slow down a bit with increasing age. For a better representation of this nonlinear phenomenon, use a linear model with height as the response and age and its square as explanatory variables.

(a) Obtain the least squares estimates of the coefficients of the linear model, their standard errors and the unbiased estimator of the error variance.
(b) Instead of the individual heights, use the average of heights for each age as response (so that thee are just six data points) and repeat the calculations of part (a).
(c) Notice that even though the two sets of estimated coefficients are very similar, the standard errors of the estimates and the estimated error variance obtained in part (b) are much smaller. Does this mean averaging over the response values is a better strategy for estimation? Explain.

3.33 Examine the fitted values and residuals of the model fitted in Exercise 3.30. Do you observe any pattern? Explain.

3.34 Consider the model

$$y_i = \beta_1 + \beta_2 + \beta_3 + \cdots + \beta_i + \varepsilon_i, \quad 1 \le i \le n,$$

with uncorrelated errors having zero mean and variance σ^2.

(a) Obtain explicit expressions for the BLUEs of the parameters and examine the possibility of unbiased estimation of the error variance.
(b) Repeat part (a) when it is known that $\beta_i = \beta_{n-i+1}$, $1 \le i \le n$.

3.35 *Spring balance.* Four items having weights β_1, β_2, β_3 and β_4 are weighed eight times, each item being weighed twice. The measurements follow the model

$$\begin{pmatrix} y_1 \\ y_2 \\ y_3 \\ y_4 \\ y_5 \\ y_6 \\ y_7 \\ y_8 \end{pmatrix} = \begin{pmatrix} 1\,0\,0\,0 \\ 0\,1\,0\,0 \\ 0\,0\,1\,0 \\ 0\,0\,0\,1 \\ 1\,0\,0\,0 \\ 0\,1\,0\,0 \\ 0\,0\,1\,0 \\ 0\,0\,0\,1 \end{pmatrix} \begin{pmatrix} \beta_1 \\ \beta_2 \\ \beta_3 \\ \beta_4 \end{pmatrix} + \begin{pmatrix} \varepsilon_1 \\ \varepsilon_2 \\ \varepsilon_3 \\ \varepsilon_4 \\ \varepsilon_5 \\ \varepsilon_6 \\ \varepsilon_7 \\ \varepsilon_8 \end{pmatrix},$$

with uncorrelated errors having zero mean and variance σ^2. We denote this model by $(\boldsymbol{y}, \boldsymbol{X\beta}, \sigma^2\boldsymbol{I})$.

(a) Show that every LPF of the model is estimable.
(b) When is $\boldsymbol{l}'\boldsymbol{y}$ the BLUE of its expectation?
(c) When is $\boldsymbol{l}'\boldsymbol{y}$ an LZF?
(d) What are the BLUEs of β_j, $j = 1, 2, 3, 4$?
(e) What is the dispersion of the BLUE of $\boldsymbol{\beta}$?
(f) Find an unbiased estimator of σ^2.

3.36 Repeat Exercise 3.35 for the model where three out of four items are measured at a time (instead of only one at a time) and each combination is weighed twice.

3.37 *BLUE from calculus.* Let $\boldsymbol{p}'\boldsymbol{\beta}$ be an estimable LPF in the linear model $(\boldsymbol{y}, \boldsymbol{X\beta}, \sigma^2\boldsymbol{I})$. You have to find the linear estimator $\boldsymbol{l}'\boldsymbol{y}$ that achieves minimum variance (i.e. $\sigma^2\boldsymbol{l}'\boldsymbol{l}$ is as small as possible) while making sure that it satisfies the condition $\boldsymbol{X}'\boldsymbol{l} = \boldsymbol{p}$ for unbiasedness. Formulate this as an optimization problem with Lagrange multipliers, and show that the optimum $\boldsymbol{l}'\boldsymbol{y}$ is $\boldsymbol{p}'(\boldsymbol{X}'\boldsymbol{X})^-\boldsymbol{X}'\boldsymbol{y}$.

3.38 If $\boldsymbol{l}_1'\boldsymbol{y}$ and $\boldsymbol{l}_2'\boldsymbol{y}$ are the BLUEs of the estimable LPFs $\boldsymbol{p}_1'\boldsymbol{\beta}$ and $\boldsymbol{p}_2'\boldsymbol{\beta}$, respectively, prove that $(\boldsymbol{l}_1 + \boldsymbol{l}_2)'\boldsymbol{y}$ is the BLUE of $(\boldsymbol{p}_1 + \boldsymbol{p}_2)'\boldsymbol{\beta}$.

3.39 If $\boldsymbol{X}\widehat{\boldsymbol{\beta}}$ is the BLUE of $\boldsymbol{X\beta}$ and R_0^2 is the error sum of squares for the linear model $(\boldsymbol{y}, \boldsymbol{X\beta}, \sigma^2\boldsymbol{I})$ with normally distributed errors, show that these two statistics are jointly sufficient and complete for the parameters $\boldsymbol{X\beta}$ and σ^2.

3.40 If $\boldsymbol{y}$ in the model $(\boldsymbol{y}, \boldsymbol{X\beta}, \sigma^2\boldsymbol{I})$ has the multivariate normal distribution, show that the BLUE of any estimable LPF is its UMVUE and that any LZF is ancillary for it.

3.41 Consider the linear model for two-way classified data

$$y_{ij} = \mu + \beta_i + \tau_j + \varepsilon_{ij}, \quad 1 \le i \le b,\ 1 \le j \le t,$$

where the errors ε_{ij} have zero mean and are uncorrelated. The parameters $\beta_1, \ldots, \beta_b$ represent the effects of b blocks, while $\tau_1, \ldots, \tau_t$ represent t different treatment effects. Show that a linear function of the treatment parameters, $\sum_{j=1}^{t} c_j \tau_j$ is estimable if and only if $\sum_{j=1}^{t} c_j = 0$. [Functions satisfying this condition are called treatment contrasts; see Proposition 6.3 and the subsequent discussion.]

Chapter 4

Further Inference in the Linear Model

In Chapter 3 we considered point estimation of estimable linear parametric functions (LPFs) in the linear model $(\boldsymbol{y}, \boldsymbol{X\beta}, \sigma^2\boldsymbol{I})$, including scalar LPFs $(\boldsymbol{p}'\boldsymbol{\beta})$ and vector LPFs $(\boldsymbol{A\beta})$. In this chapter we discuss confidence regions for such LPFs, tests of hypotheses, and model-based prediction. In Section 4.1 we derive the distribution theory for the usual estimators of $\boldsymbol{A\beta}$ and σ^2 under the assumption that the errors are independent and normal. (As we shall see in Section 11.5, this assumption can be relaxed somewhat in large samples.) This basic result allows us to test linear hypotheses (Section 4.2) on the parameters and construct confidence regions (Section 4.3) for them. We address the problem of optimal prediction in Section 4.4. In Section 4.5 we discuss the problem of collinearity and examine its effect on confidence regions, prediction, and tests of hypotheses.

4.1 Distribution of the estimators

Consider $\boldsymbol{A\beta}$, a vector of estimable LPFs in the linear model $(\boldsymbol{y}, \boldsymbol{X\beta}, \sigma^2\boldsymbol{I})$ with the $n \times p$ matrix $\boldsymbol{X}$ having rank $\rho(\boldsymbol{X}) = r$. When $\boldsymbol{y}$ is normally distributed, the following result provides the joint distribution of the BLUE $\boldsymbol{A}\widehat{\boldsymbol{\beta}}$ and the natural unbiased estimator $\widehat{\sigma^2}$ defined in (3.19). If the matrix $\boldsymbol{X}$ has independent columns, the g-inverse in this result may be interpreted as the regular inverse.

Proposition 4.1. *If* $\boldsymbol{y} \sim N(\boldsymbol{X\beta}, \sigma^2\boldsymbol{I})$, *then*

(a) $\boldsymbol{A}\widehat{\boldsymbol{\beta}} \sim N(\boldsymbol{A\beta}, \sigma^2\boldsymbol{A}(\boldsymbol{X}'\boldsymbol{X})^-\boldsymbol{A}')$,

(b) $(n-r)\widehat{\sigma^2}/\sigma^2 \sim \chi^2_{n-r}$,

(c) $\boldsymbol{A}\widehat{\boldsymbol{\beta}}$ *and* $\widehat{\sigma^2}$ *are independent.*

Proof. Part (a) follows from the discussion in Section 3.3 and the fact that linear combinations of a multivariate normal random vector has a multivariate normal distribution.

Part (b) follows from the characterization of R_0^2 as the sum of squares of $(n-r)$ uncorrelated LZFs, each with variance σ^2. The LZFs, being linear functions of $\boldsymbol{y}$, themselves have a multivariate normal distribution. Further, the LZFs are independent and have zero mean. Therefore, R_0^2/σ^2 is the sum of squares of $n-r$ independent, *standard normal* random variables, and has the chi-square distribution with $(n-r)$ degrees of freedom, thus proving part (b).

Given that $\boldsymbol{y}$ has a multivariate normal distribution, the BLUEs and LZFs of the model are not only uncorrelated but also independent. Part (c) follows from the fact that $\widehat{\sigma^2}$ is a function of the LZFs only. □

This result can be used to test various hypotheses, as we do in the next section.

4.2 Tests of linear hypotheses

There are many situations that involve testing hypotheses on the components of $\boldsymbol{\beta}$ or more generally on linear functions of $\boldsymbol{\beta}$. For example, we may want to test (a) if a specific coefficient β_j, is zero, (b) if a subset of coefficients are zero, (c) if two coefficients are equal, or (d) if a coefficient is equal to a specified value. All these can be viewed as special cases of testing what is called the *general linear hypothesis*, $\boldsymbol{A\beta} = \boldsymbol{\xi}$ for a given matrix $\boldsymbol{A}$ and vector $\boldsymbol{\xi}$. We start with the first two special cases, which are by far the most common hypotheses that are routinely tested in a regression analysis.

4.2.1 *Significance of regression coefficients*

Let the $n \times 1$ response vector $\boldsymbol{y}$ have the distribution $N(\boldsymbol{X\beta}, \sigma^2\boldsymbol{I})$ with the matrix $\boldsymbol{X}$ being of full rank, i.e. $\rho(\boldsymbol{X}) = p = k+1$, which is the number of β-parameters including the intercept. In this case the matrix $\boldsymbol{X}'\boldsymbol{X}$ is invertible, and all the parameters are estimable. We begin with testing the "significance" of a single parameter, i.e. testing the null hypothesis that a given parameter takes a specified value, which could be zero. If we choose the matrix $\boldsymbol{A}$ in Proposition 4.1 as just the first row of the $p \times p$ identity matrix, then $\boldsymbol{A\beta}$ is equal to the intercept β_0. According to that proposition, the BLUE $\widehat{\beta}_0$ is independent of $\widehat{\sigma^2}$ and has the normal distribution $N\left(\beta_0, \sigma^2(\boldsymbol{X}'\boldsymbol{X})^{11}\right)$, where $(\boldsymbol{X}'\boldsymbol{X})^{ii}$ is the ith diagonal element of the inverse $(\boldsymbol{X}'\boldsymbol{X})^{-1}$. Therefore, the ratio $(\widehat{\beta}_0 - \beta_0)/\sqrt{\sigma^2(\boldsymbol{X}'\boldsymbol{X})^{11}}$ has the standard normal distribution, and is independent of $(n-p)\widehat{\sigma^2}/\sigma^2$, which has the chi-square distribution with $n-p$ degrees of freedom. It follows from Definition 2.7 that the ratio $(\widehat{\beta}_0 - \beta_0)/\sqrt{\widehat{\sigma^2}(\boldsymbol{X}'\boldsymbol{X})^{11}}$ has the student's t-distribution with $n-k$ degrees of freedom. In general, for any j between 0 and k, the corresponding ratio is distributed as follows.

$$\frac{\widehat{\beta}_j - \beta_j}{\sqrt{\widehat{\sigma^2}(\boldsymbol{X}'\boldsymbol{X})^{(j+1)(j+1)}}} \sim t_{n-p}. \tag{4.1}$$

The denominator is the *standard error* of the estimator $\widehat{\beta}_j$. For any j between 0 and k, the above t-statistic can be used to test the null hypothesis

$$\mathcal{H}_0 : \beta_j = 0$$

against any one of the following alternative hypothesis:

$$\mathcal{H}_1 : \beta_j \neq 0,$$
$$\mathcal{H}_2 : \beta_j > 0,$$
$$\mathcal{H}_3 : \beta_j < 0.$$

Specifically, $\mathcal{H}_0$ is rejected in favour of the two-sided alternative $\mathcal{H}_1$ at the specified level α if

$$\frac{|\widehat{\beta}_j|}{\sqrt{\widehat{\sigma^2}(\boldsymbol{X}'\boldsymbol{X})^{(j+1)(j+1)}}} > t_{n-p,\alpha/2}, \tag{4.2}$$

where $t_{n-p,\alpha/2}$ is the $(1-\alpha/2)$ quantile of the null distribution. Similarly, $\mathcal{H}_0$ is rejected in favour of the one-sided hypothesis $\mathcal{H}_2$ (or $\mathcal{H}_3$) if $\widehat{\beta}_j/\sqrt{\widehat{\sigma^2}(\boldsymbol{X}'\boldsymbol{X})^{(j+1)(j+1)}}$ is greater than $t_{n-p,\alpha}$ (or less than $-t_{n-p,\alpha}$).

These decisions on hypothesis testing problems can also be expressed in terms of the p-values. The (two-sided) p-value of the test of $\mathcal{H}_0$ against $\mathcal{H}_1$ for the given data is

$$2P\left[T_{n-p} > \frac{|\widehat{\beta}_j|}{\sqrt{\widehat{\sigma^2}(\boldsymbol{X}'\boldsymbol{X})^{(j+1)(j+1)}}}\right],$$

where T_{n-p} represents a r.v. with the t_{n-p} distribution, and the expression on the other side of the inequality is interpreted as the realized/observed value of the ratio for the data at hand. An unusually small p-value merits rejection of $\mathcal{H}_0$. For example, a two-sided p-value smaller than 0.05 merits rejection at the level 0.05. The (one-sided) p-values of the tests of $\mathcal{H}_0$ against $\mathcal{H}_2$ and $\mathcal{H}_3$ are

$$P\left[T_{n-p} > \widehat{\beta}_j / \sqrt{\widehat{\sigma^2}(\boldsymbol{X}'\boldsymbol{X})^{(j+1)(j+1)}}\right]$$

and

$$P\left[T_{n-p} < \widehat{\beta}_j / \sqrt{\widehat{\sigma^2}(\boldsymbol{X}'\boldsymbol{X})^{(j+1)(j+1)}}\right],$$

respectively. Once again, the thresholds used in these expressions are the realized/observed values for the given data set.

Example 4.2. (Receding galaxies, continued) For the galactic objects data of Table 3.1, where the velocity of the object had been regressed on the distance from Earth, in Example 3.3. The R code for obtaining the estimated regression coefficients was given there. The additional line of code `summary(lmstars)$coef` produces the output

```
              Estimate Std. Error    t value     Pr(>|t|)
(Intercept) -68.15387   89.77970 -0.7591234 4.558360e-01
Distance    465.90284   80.95465  5.7551089 8.653637e-06
```

Evidently, the t-ratios for $\widehat{\beta}_0$ and $\widehat{\beta}_1$ are -0.7591 and 5.755, respectively, and the p-values are 0.4558 and 0.0.000008654, respectively. Therefore, β_1 is statistically significant at the 5% (or even lower) level, but β_0 is not. This means a model without the intercept should be adequate. □

When dealing with several covariates, i.e. $p > 1$, the hypothesis $\beta_j = 0$ postulates that the jth explanatory variable does not contribute to the mean response, even as the other variables might (i.e. the other beta-coefficients are possibly nonzero). As the following example illustrates, it is possible that a particular explanatory variable has insignificant effect on the response, in the presence of the other explanatory variables, although the effect could turn out to be significant when some of those other variables are not present in the model. The opposite situation is also possible.

Example 4.3. (Treatment of leprosy, continued) Table 4.1 shows data from Snedecor and Cochran (1967) on pre- and post-treatment scores on the abundance of leprosy for patients receiving two types of treatments (`treatment` A and `treatment` D) and placebo (`treatment` F). As in Example 1.6, we use the post-treatment score on abundance of leprosy (`post`) as

Table 4.1 Pre- and post-treatment leprosy scores of patients receiving different treatments (data object `leprosy` in R package `lmreg`, source: Senedecor and Cochran, 1967, p. 421)

Treatment	scores		Treatment	scores		Treatment	scores	
type	pre	post	type	pre	post	type	pre	post
A	11	6	D	6	0	F	16	13
A	8	0	D	6	2	F	13	10
A	5	2	D	7	3	F	11	18
A	14	8	D	8	1	F	9	5
A	19	11	D	18	18	F	21	23
A	6	4	D	8	4	F	16	12
A	10	13	D	19	14	F	12	5
A	6	1	D	8	9	F	12	16
A	11	8	D	5	1	F	7	1
A	3	0	D	15	9	F	12	20

the response variable and the usage of drug A (`x1`), usage of drug D (`x2`) and pre-treatment score (`pre`) as explanatory variables. The following R code may be used to read the data, define the new variables and compute estimates as well as their p-values.

```
data(leprosy); attach(leprosy)
x1 <- rep(0,length(treatment)); x1[treatment=="A"] <- 1
x2 <- rep(0,length(treatment)); x2[treatment=="D"] <- 1
summary(lm(post ~ x1 + x2 + pre))$coef; detach(leprosy)
```

It transpires that the fitted regression equation is

```
post = -0.4346712 - 3.446x1 - 3.337x2 + 0.9872pre
```

Further, the p-values of the tests of significance of the coefficients of `x1`, `x2` and `pre` are 0.0793, 0.0835 and 0.00000245, respectively. The effects of the two drugs are insignificant at the 5% level. The positive sign and small p-value of the coefficient of `pre` shows that patients with higher score before treatment would tend to have higher score after it. If this variable is dropped from the model, the fitted equation happens to be

```
post = 12.3 - 7.0x1 - 6.2x2
```

and the p-values for the coefficients of `x1` and `x2` are 0.0157 and 0.0305, respectively. Therefore, if the pre-treatment score is ignored, the two treatments would appear to have a significant effect on the response (i.e. each drug is effective in significantly reducing the mean score) at the 5% level.

This misleading conclusion is rectified when the pre-treatment conditions of patients are factored in, by including the variable `pre` in the model. □

Remark 4.4. It follows from (4.1) and Remark 2.9 that

$$\frac{\widehat{\beta}_j}{\sqrt{\widehat{\sigma^2}(\boldsymbol{X}'\boldsymbol{X})^{(j+1)(j+1)}}} \sim t_{n-p}\left(\frac{\beta_j}{\sigma}\right).$$

This noncentral t-distribution implies that the probability of the event (4.2) is greater than α when the null hypothesis $\beta_j = 0$ does not hold. In fact the probability is higher when β_j is farther away from 0. □

Remark 4.5. One can also test the null hypothesis $\beta_j = \beta_j^*$, where β_j^* is a nonzero number, by replacing the decision rule (4.2) by

$$\frac{|\widehat{\beta}_j - \beta_j^*|}{\sqrt{\widehat{\sigma^2}(\boldsymbol{X}'\boldsymbol{X})^{(j+1)(j+1)}}} > t_{n-p,\alpha/2}.$$

For Galton's family data of Example 1.3, we could use this test for the hypothesis $\beta_1 = 1$, which postulates that, given a certain height of the mother, an extra inch of height of the father translates into an extra inch of height of the first-born son (see Exercise 4.24). □

While the significance of the individual regression coefficients indicate the impact of one explanatory variable at a time (in the presence of other variables), it is also possible to test the impact of *all* the explanatory variables taken together. Suppose we seek a single decision regarding rejection of the null hypothesis

$$\mathcal{H}_0 : \beta_j = 0, \quad j = 1, \ldots, k.$$

The vector of the k parameters can be written as $\boldsymbol{A\beta}$, where $\boldsymbol{A}$ consists of the last k rows of the $p \times p$ identity matrix (where $p = k+1$). Therefore, the hypothesis $\mathcal{H}_0$ can also be written as $\boldsymbol{A\beta} = \boldsymbol{0}$. The alternative hypothesis, $\mathcal{H}_1$, is $\boldsymbol{A\beta} \neq \boldsymbol{0}$. It follows from Proposition 4.1 that the BLUE $\widehat{\boldsymbol{A\beta}}$ has the distribution $N(\boldsymbol{A\beta}, \sigma^2\boldsymbol{A}(\boldsymbol{X}'\boldsymbol{X})^{-1}\boldsymbol{A}')$, and is independent of $\widehat{\sigma^2}$. It follows from Remark 2.12 that $(\boldsymbol{A}\widehat{\boldsymbol{\beta}})'[\sigma^2\boldsymbol{A}(\boldsymbol{X}'\boldsymbol{X})^{-1}\boldsymbol{A}']^{-1}\boldsymbol{A}\widehat{\boldsymbol{\beta}}$ has the chi-square distribution with $k = p-1$ degrees of freedom (with a noncentrality parameter that is 0 under $\mathcal{H}_0$), independently of $(n-p)\widehat{\sigma^2}/\sigma^2$, which is χ^2_{n-p}. Therefore, under $\mathcal{H}_0$, the statistic

$$\frac{n-p}{p-1} \times \frac{(\boldsymbol{A}\widehat{\boldsymbol{\beta}})'[\boldsymbol{A}(\boldsymbol{X}'\boldsymbol{X})^{-1}\boldsymbol{A}')]^{-1}\boldsymbol{A}\widehat{\boldsymbol{\beta}}}{\widehat{\sigma^2}}$$

has the $F_{p-1,n-p}$ distribution, and can be used for testing $\mathcal{H}_0$.

We now provide an alternative derivation of this test statistic. Note that the linear model $(\boldsymbol{y}, \boldsymbol{X\beta}, \sigma^2\boldsymbol{I})$ under the restriction $\boldsymbol{A\beta} = \boldsymbol{0}$ can be written as $(\boldsymbol{y}, \boldsymbol{1}\beta_0, \sigma^2\boldsymbol{I})$. (This actually coincides with the equivalent model $(\boldsymbol{y}, \boldsymbol{X}(\boldsymbol{I} - \boldsymbol{A}^-\boldsymbol{A})\boldsymbol{\theta}, \sigma^2\boldsymbol{I})$ given on page 98, with the choice $\boldsymbol{A}^- = \boldsymbol{A}'$.) The error sum of squares under this model, denoted by R_H^2, is given by

$$R_H^2 = \|(\boldsymbol{I} - \boldsymbol{P}_1)\boldsymbol{y}\|^2 = \|\boldsymbol{y} - \frac{1}{n}\boldsymbol{1}\boldsymbol{1}'\boldsymbol{y}\|^2 = \|\boldsymbol{y} - \bar{y}\boldsymbol{1}\|^2 = \sum_{i=1}^{n}(y_i - \bar{y})^2.$$

In view of Proposition 3.45, this quantity must be the sum of squares of $n-1$ uncorrelated LZFs of the restricted model. On the other hand, the error sum of squares of the unrestricted model, denoted by R_0^2, is the sum of squares of $n-p$ uncorrelated LZFs of that model. According to Proposition 3.52, the latter set of LZFs is included in the set of LZFs of the restricted model. Therefore, a standardized basis set of the larger set of LZFs can be built by augmenting a standardized basis set for the smaller set. We only need $p-1$ additional LZFs. It can be verified that if the full rank matrix $\sigma^{-2}D(\boldsymbol{A}\widehat{\boldsymbol{\beta}}) = \boldsymbol{A}(\boldsymbol{X}'\boldsymbol{X})^{-1}\boldsymbol{A}'$ is factored as $\boldsymbol{C}\boldsymbol{C}'$, then $\boldsymbol{C}^{-1}\boldsymbol{A}\widehat{\boldsymbol{\beta}}$ consists of $p-1$ elements that (i) are uncorrelated, (ii) have variance σ^2, (iii) are uncorrelated with the LZFs of the unrestricted model (since these are BLUEs in that model) and (iv) are LZFs of the unrestricted model. Therefore, the elements of $\boldsymbol{C}^{-1}\boldsymbol{A}\widehat{\boldsymbol{\beta}}$ serve as the additional LZFs that, together with the standardized basis set of LZFs of the unrestricted model, constitute a standardized basis set of LZFs of the restricted model. Hence,

$$R_H^2 - R_0^2 = \|\boldsymbol{C}^{-1}\boldsymbol{A}\widehat{\boldsymbol{\beta}}\|^2 = (\boldsymbol{A}\widehat{\boldsymbol{\beta}})'[\boldsymbol{A}(\boldsymbol{X}'\boldsymbol{X})^{-1}\boldsymbol{A}')]^{-1}\boldsymbol{A}\widehat{\boldsymbol{\beta}}.$$

It follows that the statistic

$$\frac{(R_H^2 - R_0^2)/((p-1)\sigma^2)}{R_0^2/((n-p)\sigma^2)} = \frac{n-p}{p-1} \times \frac{R_H^2 - R_0^2}{R_0^2} \sim F_{p-1,n-p} \qquad (4.3)$$

under $\mathcal{H}_0$, where $F_{p-1,n-p}$ represents the F-distribution with $p-1$ and $n-p$ degrees of freedom (see Definition 2.9). Under the alternative hypothesis, the noncentrality parameter of the distribution is nonzero, which inflates the typical value of the statistic. A level $1-\alpha$ test would be to reject $\mathcal{H}_0$ if

$$\frac{n-p}{p-1} \times \frac{R_H^2 - R_0^2}{R_0^2} > F_{p-1,n-p,\alpha},$$

the threshold for comparison being the $1-\alpha$ quantile of the $F_{p-1,n-p}$ distribution. The p-value of the test is the probability that a random sample from this distribution exceeds the observed value of the ratio $\frac{n-p}{p-1} \times \frac{R_H^2 - R_0^2}{R_0^2}$ calculated from the data.

The quantity R_H^2 is referred to as the *total sum of squares* under the regression model $(\boldsymbol{y}, \boldsymbol{X}\boldsymbol{\beta}, \sigma^2\boldsymbol{I})$, as it represents the sum of squares of the deviations of the response around its mean. It had previously been interpreted as error sum of squares under the restriction $\boldsymbol{A}\boldsymbol{\beta} = \boldsymbol{0}$, that is,

$$\begin{aligned} R_H^2 &= \min_{\boldsymbol{\beta}:\boldsymbol{A}\boldsymbol{\beta}=\boldsymbol{0}} \|\boldsymbol{y} - \boldsymbol{X}\boldsymbol{\beta}\|^2 \\ &= \min_{\substack{\beta_0,\beta_1,\ldots,\beta_k \\ \beta_1=\cdots=\beta_k=0}} \sum_{i=1}^{n} \left(y_i - \beta_0 - \sum_{j=1}^{k} \beta_j x_{ij} \right)^2 = \boldsymbol{y}'\boldsymbol{y} - n\bar{y}^2. \end{aligned}$$

In contrast, R_0^2 is the unrestricted minimum

$$\begin{aligned} R_0^2 &= \min_{\boldsymbol{\beta}} \|\boldsymbol{y} - \boldsymbol{X}\boldsymbol{\beta}\|^2 = \min_{\beta_0,\beta_1,\ldots,\beta_k} \sum_{i=1}^{n} \left(y_i - \beta_0 - \sum_{j=1}^{k} \beta_j x_{ij} \right)^2 \\ &= \boldsymbol{y}'\boldsymbol{y} - \widehat{\boldsymbol{y}}'\widehat{\boldsymbol{y}}, \end{aligned}$$

which must be smaller. Therefore, $R_H - R_0^2$ represents the additional reduction in the sum of squares made possible by the explanatory variables used for regression. For this reason, the difference $R_H^2 - R_0^2$ is called the *regression sum of squares.* Under the null hypothesis, the explanatory variables should have no effect of the mean response, and therefore the difference should be minimal (just the sum of squares of k LZFs having variance σ^2).

The decomposition of the total sum of squares is typically represented through an Analysis of Variance (ANOVA) table shown in Table 4.2. The three quantities shown in the 'Sum of Squares' column, when divided by σ^2, should produce a chi-square distributed statistic with degrees of freedom shown in the column to its right. Under the alternative hypothesis, the chi-square distributions corresponding to the top and bottom rows would

Table 4.2 Analysis of variance table for the hypothesis $\beta_j = 0$, $j = 1, \ldots, k$

Source	Sum of Squares	Degrees of Freedom	Mean Square	F Ratio
Regression	$R_H^2 - R_0^2 = \widehat{\boldsymbol{y}}'\widehat{\boldsymbol{y}} - n\bar{y}^2$	k	$\dfrac{R_H^2 - R_0^2}{k}$	$\frac{n-k-1}{k} \times \frac{R_H^2 - R_0^2}{R_0^2}$
Error	$R_0^2 = \boldsymbol{e}'\boldsymbol{e}$	$n-k-1$	$\dfrac{R_0^2}{n-k-1}$	
Total	$R_H^2 = \boldsymbol{y}'\boldsymbol{y} - n\bar{y}^2$	$n-1$		

be noncentral, while all the three distributions would be central under the null hypothesis. The 'Mean Square' columns represent the ratio of the 'Sum of Squares' to the corresponding degrees of freedom. Under the null hypothesis, the expected value of every 'Mean Square' should be σ^2. Under the alternative hypothesis, the 'Mean Square' in the top row is expected to be considerably larger. The 'F Ratio' reported in the last column is the ratio of the 'Mean Square' in the first and second rows, which is the test statistic with the null distribution $F_{k,n-k-1}$.

The test statistic in (4.3) can be written as $\frac{n-k-1}{k} \times \frac{R^2}{1-R^2}$, where R^2 is the fraction total sum of squares explained by the regressors,

$$R^2 = \frac{R_H^2 - R_0}{R_H^2} = \frac{\widehat{\boldsymbol{y}}'\widehat{\boldsymbol{y}} - n\bar{y}^2}{\boldsymbol{y}'\boldsymbol{y} - n\bar{y}^2}. \tag{4.4}$$

The ratio R^2 is known as the *coefficient of determination*, or simply as the *R-square*. It is the sample version of the square of the multiple correlation coefficient defined in (2.21). This quantity takes values between 0 and 1, and is closer to 1 when much of the variability in $\boldsymbol{y}$ is explained by the explanatory variables, while it is closer to 0 if y depends less on the explanatory variables. This is why R^2 has been traditionally used as an empirical indicator of the degree of fit. A large value of R^2 indicates a strong multiple correlation, i.e. a strong linear dependence of the response on the explanatory variables. The above test can be seen as a formal verification of this dependence.

Example 4.6. (Birth weight of babies, continued) Consider the birth weight data of Example 1.5 (data object `birthwt` in R package `MASS`). The response variable in the model presented on page 6, was the birth weight of a baby (`bwt`), while the predictors were three binary variables indicating whether the mother is a smoker (`smoke`), whether she is black and whether she is non-white and non-black. The null hypothesis of insignificance of the non-intercept coefficients means that none of these binary variables have any effect on the mean birth weight of a baby. In the data set, the racial status is coded as a categorical variable (`race`), which takes the value 2, 3 or 1 depending on whether the mother is white, black or of any other race. By treating this variable as a `factor` (i.e. a categorical variable), we can use the following code to obtain a preliminary analysis.

```
data(birthwt)
lmbw <- lm(bwt ~ smoke + factor(race), data = birthwt)
summary(lmbw)
```

The following output is produced by the code.

```
Coefficients:
               Estimate Std. Error t value Pr(>|t|)
(Intercept)    2880.532     86.293  33.381  < 2e-16 ***
smoke          -427.220    109.008  -3.919 0.000125 ***
factor(race)2   454.618    116.441   3.904 0.000132 ***
factor(race)3     3.476    160.543   0.022 0.982750
---
Signif. codes:  0 *** 0.001 ** 0.01 * 0.05 . 0.1   1

Residual standard error: 688 on 185 degrees of freedom
Multiple R-squared:  0.1235,Adjusted R-squared:  0.1093
F-statistic:  8.69 on 3 and 185 DF,  p-value: 2.007e-05
```

The top part of the output shows the various estimated coefficients, their standard errors, t-statistics for testing their significance and the corresponding p-values. The four rows have direct correspondence with the four coefficients used in the model of page 6. Significance of the coefficients at different levels are coded by stars, double stars and so on. Triple stars mean significance at level 0.001. The `Residual standard error` is $\widehat{\sigma}$, while the associated degrees of freedom are the error degrees of freedom. The multiple R-squared is reported together with adjusted R-squared, which will be defined is Section 5.1.2. The F-statistic and the p-value for testing the significance of all the coefficients other than intercept is reported. However, other aspects of the ANOVA table are missing. These can be obtained through the code `lm1 <- lm(bwt~1,data=birthwt); anova(lm1,lmbw)`, which produces all the ingredients of the ANOVA table, but the format of the output is somewhat different. The requisite form of the table can be obtained by using the command `hanova(lm1,lmbw)`. The ANOVA table turns out to be as follows.

Source	Sum of Squares	Degrees of Freedom	Mean Square	F Ratio
Regression	12341705	3	4113902	8.6905
Error	87575348	185	473380.3	
Total	99917053	188		

The F-statistic has p-value 0.0000201, indicating statistical significance of the three variables as a group at any higher level (e.g. 0.01 or 0.0001).

The regression summary produced by the function `summary` shows the significance of the binary variables created internally to represent the categorical variable `race`. A single F-test for the significance of this variable as a whole may be obtained through the command `anova(lmbw)`, which produces the following output.

```
Analysis of Variance Table
Response: bwt
                Df   Sum Sq Mean Sq F value    Pr(>F)
smoke            1  3573406 3573406  7.5487 0.0065995 **
factor(race)     2  8768299 4384149  9.2614 0.0001468 ***
Residuals      185 87575348  473380
---
Signif. codes:  0 *** 0.001 ** 0.01 * 0.05 . 0.1   1
```

This table does not include the total sum of squares. Indeed, the sum of the three sums of squares is larger than the total sum of squares reported in the ANOVA table. The above table should only be treated as a summary of the tests of significance for various regressors (quantitative as well as categorical). An ANOVA table suitable for the test of significance of `race` in the presence of `smoke` may be found in Example 4.23. □

We now turn to the problem of testing the general hypothesis $\boldsymbol{A\beta} = \boldsymbol{\xi}$, mentioned at the beginning of this section.

4.2.2 *Testability of linear hypotheses**

When the matrix $\boldsymbol{X}$ has linearly dependent columns (i.e. $\boldsymbol{X'X}$ is not invertible), we have to clearly delineate what we can or cannot test statistically.

Example 4.7. (Abrasion of denim jeans, continued) Consider the hypothesis $\tau_1 + \tau_2 + \tau_3 = 0$ in the model of Example 3.5. Following the argument of page 81, it is easy to see that $\tau_1 + \tau_2 + \tau_3$ is not identifiable, that is, one cannot discern one value of $\tau_1 + \tau_2 + \tau_3$ from another on the basis of the observations. Therefore, the hypothesis $\tau_1 + \tau_2 + \tau_3 = 0$ is not statistically testable.

Similarly, the hypothesis $\beta_1 + \beta_2 + \beta_3 = 0$ is not testable.

In contrast, the data gives us information about the estimable LPF $\tau_1 - \tau_2$, which would allow us to test the hypothesis $\tau_1 - \tau_2 = 0$. Likewise, the hypothesis $\tau_2 - \tau_3 = 0$ can also be tested. □

Consider the hypothesis $\boldsymbol{A\beta} = \boldsymbol{\xi}$ where $\boldsymbol{A\beta}$ is a scalar. Following the arguments of the above example, we can formally *define* testability of $\boldsymbol{A\beta} = \boldsymbol{\xi}$ as the same as estimability (or identifiability) of $\boldsymbol{A\beta}$. When $\boldsymbol{A\beta}$ is a vector, it may include estimable as well as non-estimable elements. Therefore, one has to be more careful about the notion of testability.

Definition 4.8. A linear hypothesis $\boldsymbol{A\beta} = \boldsymbol{\xi}$ in the linear model $(\boldsymbol{y}, \boldsymbol{X\beta}, \sigma^2\boldsymbol{I})$ is called *completely testable* if all the elements of the vector $\boldsymbol{A\beta}$ are estimable LPFs. □

According to Remark 3.22, the restriction $\boldsymbol{A\beta} = \boldsymbol{\xi}$ is completely testable if and only if $\mathcal{C}(\boldsymbol{A}') \subseteq \mathcal{C}(\boldsymbol{X}')$.

When the hypothesis $\boldsymbol{A\beta} = \boldsymbol{\xi}$ is not completely testable, a meaningful statistical test may still be possible for certain sub-hypotheses. The hypothesis $\boldsymbol{A\beta} = \boldsymbol{\xi}$ implies that $\boldsymbol{l}'\boldsymbol{A\beta} = \boldsymbol{l}'\boldsymbol{\xi}$ for all $\boldsymbol{l}$. However, if there is an $\boldsymbol{l}$ such that $\boldsymbol{l}'\boldsymbol{A\beta}$ is estimable, we may still be able to test the hypothesis $\boldsymbol{l}'\boldsymbol{A\beta} = \boldsymbol{l}'\boldsymbol{\xi}$. If no such $\boldsymbol{l}$ exists, then no testing is possible.

Definition 4.9. A linear hypothesis $\boldsymbol{A\beta} = \boldsymbol{\xi}$ in the linear model $(\boldsymbol{y}, \boldsymbol{X\beta}, \sigma^2\boldsymbol{I})$ is called *completely untestable* if there is no vector $\boldsymbol{l}$ such that $\boldsymbol{l}'\boldsymbol{A\beta}$ is an estimable LPF. □

Definition 4.10. A linear hypothesis $\boldsymbol{A\beta} = \boldsymbol{\xi}$ in the linear model $(\boldsymbol{y}, \boldsymbol{X\beta}, \sigma^2\boldsymbol{I})$ is called *partially testable* if it is neither completely testable nor completely untestable. □

Example 4.11. (Abrasion of denim jeans, continued) In the model of Example 3.5, the hypothesis

$$\begin{pmatrix} \tau_1 - \tau_2 \\ \tau_1 - \tau_3 \end{pmatrix} = \mathbf{0}$$

is completely testable, the hypothesis

$$\begin{pmatrix} \tau_1 + \tau_2 + \tau_3 \\ \beta_1 + \beta_2 + \beta_3 \end{pmatrix} = \mathbf{0}$$

is completely untestable, and the hypothesis $(\tau_1 : \tau_2 : \tau_3)' = \mathbf{0}$ is partially testable. The third hypothesis implies $\tau_1 - \tau_2 = 0$, which is testable. However, it also implies $\tau_1 + \tau_2 + \tau_3 = 0$, which is untestable. □

The following proposition gives a simple criterion to judge when a linear hypothesis would be completely testable, partially testable or completely untestable.

Proposition 4.12. *The linear hypothesis* $\boldsymbol{A\beta} = \boldsymbol{\xi}$ *in the linear model* $(\boldsymbol{y}, \boldsymbol{X\beta}, \sigma^2\boldsymbol{I})$ *is*

(a) completely testable if and only if $\rho(\boldsymbol{X}' : \boldsymbol{A}') = \rho(\boldsymbol{X}')$;
(b) completely untestable if and only if $\rho(\boldsymbol{X}' : \boldsymbol{A}') = \rho(\boldsymbol{X}') + \rho(\boldsymbol{A}')$;
(c) partially testable if and only if $\rho(\boldsymbol{X}') < \rho(\boldsymbol{X}' : \boldsymbol{A}') < \rho(\boldsymbol{X}') + \rho(\boldsymbol{A}')$.

Proof. Part (a) follows from the fact that $\mathcal{C}(\boldsymbol{A}') \subseteq \mathcal{C}(\boldsymbol{X}')$ if and only if $\rho(\boldsymbol{X}' : \boldsymbol{A}') = \rho(\boldsymbol{X}')$ (see Exercise 3.5). The notion of complete untestability is equivalent to the virtual disjointness of the column spaces of $\boldsymbol{X}'$ and $\boldsymbol{A}'$. Part (b) is a restatement of this condition. Part (c) follows from the other two parts. □

A completely untestable linear restriction is equivalent to a reparametrization of the original model with fewer parameters (see Exercise 3.18).

What would be a meaningful way to test a partially testable hypothesis? We need not draw any conclusion about the untestable part of it. However, we should test for *all* the testable restrictions implied by the original hypothesis. The testable restrictions implied by the hypothesis $\boldsymbol{A\beta} = \boldsymbol{\xi}$ are of the form $\boldsymbol{p}'\boldsymbol{\beta}$ where $\boldsymbol{p} \in \mathcal{C}(\boldsymbol{A}') \cap \mathcal{C}(\boldsymbol{X}')$. The following proposition provides the basis for a test.

Proposition 4.13. *In the linear model* $(\boldsymbol{y}, \boldsymbol{X\beta}, \sigma^2\boldsymbol{I})$, *let* $\mathcal{H}_0 : \ \boldsymbol{A\beta} = \boldsymbol{\xi}$ *be a hypothesis with* $\boldsymbol{\xi} \in \mathcal{C}(\boldsymbol{A})$.

(a) $\mathcal{H}_0$ *is equivalent to the pair of hypotheses* $\mathcal{H}_{01} : \ \boldsymbol{TA\beta} = \boldsymbol{T\xi}$ *and* $\mathcal{H}_{02} : \ (\boldsymbol{I} - \boldsymbol{P}_{X'})\boldsymbol{A}'\boldsymbol{A\beta} = (\boldsymbol{I} - \boldsymbol{P}_{X'})\boldsymbol{A}'\boldsymbol{\xi}$, *where* $\boldsymbol{T}$ *is any matrix such that* $\mathcal{C}(\boldsymbol{A}'\boldsymbol{T}') = \mathcal{C}(\boldsymbol{A}') \cap \mathcal{C}(\boldsymbol{X}')$.
(b) The hypothesis $\mathcal{H}_{01}$ *is completely testable.*
(c) The hypothesis $\mathcal{H}_{02}$ *is completely untestable.*

Proof. It is easy to see that $\mathcal{H}_0$ implies both $\mathcal{H}_{01}$ and $\mathcal{H}_{02}$. The reverse implication is proved if we can show that

$$\mathcal{C}(\boldsymbol{A}') \subseteq \mathcal{C}(\boldsymbol{A}'\boldsymbol{T}') + \mathcal{C}(\boldsymbol{A}'\boldsymbol{A}(\boldsymbol{I} - \boldsymbol{P}_{X'})).$$

Suppose $\boldsymbol{l}$ is a vector which is orthogonal to the right-hand side. Therefore, $(\boldsymbol{I} - \boldsymbol{P}_{X'})\boldsymbol{A}'\boldsymbol{Al} = \boldsymbol{0}$, i.e. $\boldsymbol{A}'\boldsymbol{Al} \in \mathcal{C}(\boldsymbol{X}')$. It follows that $\boldsymbol{A}'\boldsymbol{Al}$ is in $\mathcal{C}(\boldsymbol{A}') \cap \mathcal{C}(\boldsymbol{X}')$, which is equal to $\mathcal{C}(\boldsymbol{A}'\boldsymbol{T}')$, and hence orthogonal to $\boldsymbol{l}$. Consequently $\boldsymbol{Al} = \boldsymbol{0}$. This proves the desired inclusion and part (a).

Part (b) is proved by the fact that $\mathcal{C}(\boldsymbol{A}'\boldsymbol{T}') \subseteq \mathcal{C}(\boldsymbol{X}')$.

In order to prove part (c), let $\boldsymbol{l}$ be such that $\boldsymbol{l}'(\boldsymbol{I} - \boldsymbol{P}_{X'})\boldsymbol{A}'\boldsymbol{A\beta}$ is estimable. The condition of estimability, $\boldsymbol{A}'\boldsymbol{A}(\boldsymbol{I} - \boldsymbol{P}_{X'})\boldsymbol{l} \in \mathcal{C}(\boldsymbol{X}')$, implies that $(\boldsymbol{I} - \boldsymbol{P}_{X'})\boldsymbol{A}'\boldsymbol{A}(\boldsymbol{I} - \boldsymbol{P}_{X'})\boldsymbol{l} = 0$, i.e. $\boldsymbol{A}(\boldsymbol{I} - \boldsymbol{P}_{X'})\boldsymbol{l} = \boldsymbol{0}$. Therefore, $\boldsymbol{l}'(\boldsymbol{I} - \boldsymbol{P}_{X'})\boldsymbol{A}'\boldsymbol{A\beta}$ must be identically zero. □

The decomposition given in Proposition 4.13 is similar to a decomposition due to Dasgupta and Das Gupta (2000) which reduces any linear restriction into two parts: a model-preserving constraint and a restriction that only involves estimable LPFs.

Remark 4.14. The choice of the matrix $\boldsymbol{T}$ in Proposition 4.13 should have no effect on the actual test, because the two versions of $\mathcal{H}_{01}$ corresponding to two distinct choices of $\boldsymbol{T}$ imply one another. It follows from Exercise A.21 of Appendix A that a simple choice of $\boldsymbol{T}$ is $\boldsymbol{X}'\boldsymbol{X}(\boldsymbol{X}'\boldsymbol{X}+\boldsymbol{A}'\boldsymbol{A})^-\boldsymbol{A}'$. □

Example 4.15. (Abrasion of denim jeans, continued) Consider the partially testable hypothesis $(\tau_1 : \tau_2 : \tau_3)' = \boldsymbol{0}$ in the model of Example 3.5. Here,

$$\boldsymbol{A} = \begin{pmatrix} 0\,1\,0\,0\,0\,0\,0 \\ 0\,0\,1\,0\,0\,0\,0 \\ 0\,0\,0\,1\,0\,0\,0 \end{pmatrix}, \quad \boldsymbol{\xi} = \boldsymbol{0}.$$

Given dimensionally compatible matrices and vector $\boldsymbol{X}$, $\boldsymbol{A}$ and $\boldsymbol{\xi}$, the function `hypsplit` of the R package `lmreg` reduces a general hypothesis $\boldsymbol{A\beta} = \boldsymbol{\xi}$ into a pair of completely testable and completely untestable hypotheses, by making use of Proposition 4.13 and Remark 4.14 (not necessarily in a numerically sound way). We now use this function to split $\boldsymbol{A\beta} = \boldsymbol{\xi}$ into $\mathcal{H}_{01}$ and $\mathcal{H}_{02}$, through the following code.

```
data(denim)
attach(denim)
X <- cbind(1,binaries(Denim),binaries(Laundry))
A <- rbind(c(0,1,0,0,0,0,0),c(0,0,1,0,0,0,0),c(0,0,0,1,0,0,0))
xi <- c(0,0,0)
testable <- hypsplit(X,A,xi)[[1]]
untestable <- hypsplit(X,A,xi)[[2]]
testable; untestable
detach(denim)
```

This code produces the output

```
                                                    xi
[1,] 0 0.0000000 -0.7071068  0.7071068 0 0 0  0
[2,] 0 0.8164966 -0.4082483 -0.4082483 0 0 0  0
                                                  xi
[1,] 0 0.5773503 0.5773503 0.5773503 0 0 0  0
```

Thus, subject to a change of scale, the testable part of the hypothesis detected by the code is the pair $\tau_3 - \tau_2 = 0$ and $2\tau_1 - \tau_2 - \tau_3 = 0$, which is equivalent to the pair of testable hypotheses we had identified earlier (see page 132). The untestable part of the hypothesis detected by the code is $\tau_1 + \tau_2 + \tau_3 = 0$, identified earlier by inspection (see page 132).

The reader is encouraged to use the above code for experimenting with other hypotheses such as

```
A <- rbind(c(0,0,0,0,1,-1,0),c(0,0,0,0,1,0,-1))
xi <- c(0,0)
```

which is detected as completely testable, or

```
A <- t(c(0,0,0,0,1,1,1)); xi <- 0
```

which is found to be completely untestable. □

It is easy to see that $\mathcal{H}_{02}$ is trivial when $\mathcal{C}(\boldsymbol{A}') \subseteq \mathcal{C}(\boldsymbol{X}')$ and $\mathcal{H}_{01}$ is trivial when $\rho(\boldsymbol{X}' : \boldsymbol{A}') = \rho(\boldsymbol{X}') + \rho(\boldsymbol{A}')$. Neither hypothesis is trivial when $\boldsymbol{A\beta} = \boldsymbol{\xi}$ is partially testable. One can test $\mathcal{H}_0$ by testing $\mathcal{H}_{01}$, while keeping in mind that the untestable restriction $\mathcal{H}_{02}$ is also implied by the hypothesis. Note that $\mathcal{H}_0$ can be tested directly without formally reducing it to $\mathcal{H}_{01}$ (see Remark 4.22). However, it is important to understand which hypothesis is actually being tested. If there is a mistake in specifying the hypothesis, the restriction $\mathcal{H}_{02}$ may serve as a pointer to it.

4.2.3 *Hypotheses with a single degree of freedom*

Consider the linear model $(\boldsymbol{y}, \boldsymbol{X\beta}, \sigma^2\boldsymbol{I})$ with normal errors and $\rho(\boldsymbol{X}) = r \le p$. We examine the null hypothesis $\mathcal{H}_0 : \boldsymbol{p}'\boldsymbol{\beta} = \xi$. Since $\boldsymbol{p}'\boldsymbol{\beta}$ is a scalar, the question of partial testability does not arise. Thus the hypothesis is completely testable if $\boldsymbol{p}'\boldsymbol{\beta}$ is estimable and completely untestable otherwise. Let us assume that the hypothesis is completely testable. As in the special case of this hypothesis considered in Section 4.2.1 (where $\boldsymbol{p}$ is a column of the $p \times p$ identity matrix), we shall deal with three alternative hypotheses:

$$\mathcal{H}_1 : \boldsymbol{p}'\boldsymbol{\beta} \ne \xi,$$
$$\mathcal{H}_2 : \boldsymbol{p}'\boldsymbol{\beta} > \xi,$$
$$\mathcal{H}_3 : \boldsymbol{p}'\boldsymbol{\beta} < \xi.$$

It follows from Proposition 4.1 and Remark 2.9 that

$$\frac{\boldsymbol{p}'\widehat{\boldsymbol{\beta}} - \xi}{\sqrt{\widehat{\sigma^2}\boldsymbol{p}'(\boldsymbol{X}'\boldsymbol{X})^-\boldsymbol{p}}} \sim t_{n-r}(\boldsymbol{p}'\boldsymbol{\beta} - \xi). \tag{4.5}$$

The noncentrality parameter of the t-distribution depends on $\boldsymbol{\beta}$, the 'true value' of the vector parameter. The noncentrality parameter is zero under $\mathcal{H}_0$, positive under $\mathcal{H}_2$ and negative under $\mathcal{H}_3$. We can test for $\mathcal{H}_0$ against the alternative hypothesis $\mathcal{H}_1$ by rejecting $\mathcal{H}_0$ when the statistic of (4.5) has too large a magnitude. If the intended level of the test is α, then the test amounts to accepting $\mathcal{H}_1$ if

$$\frac{|\boldsymbol{p}'\widehat{\boldsymbol{\beta}} - \xi|}{\sqrt{\widehat{\sigma^2}\boldsymbol{p}'(\boldsymbol{X}'\boldsymbol{X})^{-}\boldsymbol{p}}} > t_{n-r,\alpha/2}, \tag{4.6}$$

and to accept $\mathcal{H}_0$ otherwise. This test coincides with the generalized likelihood ratio test, described in Section 4.2.5 (see Exercise 4.19). A size-α test for the null hypothesis $\mathcal{H}_0$ against the alternative hypothesis $\mathcal{H}_2$ is to accept $\mathcal{H}_2$ when

$$\frac{\boldsymbol{p}'\widehat{\boldsymbol{\beta}} - \xi}{\sqrt{\widehat{\sigma^2}\boldsymbol{p}'(\boldsymbol{X}'\boldsymbol{X})^{-}\boldsymbol{p}}} > t_{n-r,\alpha}, \tag{4.7}$$

and to accept $\mathcal{H}_0$ otherwise. Similarly, a test of the null hypothesis $\mathcal{H}_0$ against the alternative hypothesis $\mathcal{H}_3$ is to accept $\mathcal{H}_3$ when

$$\frac{\boldsymbol{p}'\widehat{\boldsymbol{\beta}} - \xi}{\sqrt{\widehat{\sigma^2}\boldsymbol{p}'(\boldsymbol{X}'\boldsymbol{X})^{-}\boldsymbol{p}}} < -t_{n-r,\alpha},$$

and to accept $\mathcal{H}_0$ otherwise.

The p-values of the three tests are, respectively, the probabilities that a random sample from the t_{n-r} distribution exceeds the ratio $(\boldsymbol{p}'\widehat{\boldsymbol{\beta}} - \xi)/\sqrt{\widehat{\sigma^2}\boldsymbol{p}'(\boldsymbol{X}'\boldsymbol{X})^{-}\boldsymbol{p}}$ in absolute value, exceeds the ratio and is less than it.

The above three tests happen to be *uniformly most powerful unbiased* tests for the respective problems, under the given set-up (see Lehmann and Romano, 2005, Section 5.6).

Example 4.16. (Galton's family data, continued) Recall the height data of Example 1.3, available as the data frame `GaltonFamilies` in the R package `HistData`, and the model used in that example to explain the mature height of a first born son (y) by the heights of his father and mother (x_1 and x_2, respectively). Suppose we wish to test whether the mean height of the first born son is affected more by the father's height than by the mother's height. This hypothesis may be formulated as $\beta_1 > \beta_2$, which is an alternative to the null hypothesis $\beta_1 = \beta_2$. The two hypotheses may be recognized as special cases of $\mathcal{H}_2$ and $\mathcal{H}_0$, respectively, where $\boldsymbol{p} = (0 : 1 : -1)'$ and $\xi = 0$.

The following R code may be used to access the data on the main variables (mature height of child, **childheight**, father's height, **father**, mother's height, **mother**, gender of child, **gender**, and serial order of child, **childNum**), filter them to form the variables y, x_1 and x_2 and carry out the test of hypothesis. It makes use of the function **hyptest** in the R package **lmreg**, designed to carry out test of any linear hypothesis involving a single LPF.

```
library(HistData); attach(GaltonFamilies)
y <- childHeight[gender=="male"&childNum==1]
x1 <- father[gender=="male"&childNum==1]
x2 <- mother[gender=="male"&childNum==1]
lmGF <- lm(y~x1+x2)
p <- c(0,1,-1)
hyptest(lmGF, p, type = "upper")
detach(GaltonFamilies)
```

The point estimate of $\widehat{\beta}_1 - \widehat{\beta}_2$ (i.e. $\boldsymbol{p}'\widehat{\boldsymbol{\beta}}$) turns out to be 0.1967 with standard error 0.0975, while the t-ratio is 2.017 with 176 degrees of freedom. The p-value of the one-sided test is 0.0226. Thus, one can reject $\mathcal{H}_0$ in favour of $\mathcal{H}_2$, indicating significantly stronger effect of the father's height on the first born son's height. □

Example 4.17. (Age at death, continued) In the model of Example 3.4, the hypothesis $\tau_4 - \tau_5 > 1$ means that the age at death of musicians is on the average at least a year more than that of mathematicians and astronomers. This hypothesis is a special case of $\mathcal{H}_2$ (with $\boldsymbol{p} = (0:0:0:0:1:-1:0:0:0)'$ and $\xi = 1$), which is a one-sided alternative to $\mathcal{H}_0$.

An R code for fitting the linear model to the data was given in Example 3.4. The additional lines of code given below may be used to test the null hypothesis $\mathcal{H}_0 : \tau_4 - \tau_5 = 1$ against the alternative $\mathcal{H}_2 : \tau_4 - \tau_5 > 1$.

```
p <- c(0,0,0,1,-1,0,0,0)
hyptest(lmlife, p, xi = 1, type = "upper")
```

The estimated value of the difference $\tau_4 - \tau_5$ turns out to be 6.310 years, with standard error 2.753 years. The t-ratio with 682 degrees of freedom happens to be 1.929, which corresponds to a one-sided p-value of 0.0271. The hypothesis of only one year difference in mean age at death is rejected at the 5% level, confirming that the mean age at death of musicians is at least a year more than mathematicians and astronomers.

However, this 'conclusion' should be made with tongue firmly in cheek. This data set is not a representative sample from a present-day population.

Also, life expectancy is not the same as the average age at death. For these reasons, analysis of this data set only serves the purpose of illustration of various concepts introduced in the previous and the current chapters. No general conclusion should be drawn from these analyses. In particular, while choosing between careers in music and mathematics one need not worry about the prospective impact of that decision on the lifetime. □

4.2.4 *Decomposing the sum of squares**

We now return to the general linear hypothesis $\boldsymbol{A\beta} = \boldsymbol{\xi}$. As we have seen in Section 4.2.2, a partially testable hypothesis can always be reduced to a completely testable hypothesis. We shall henceforth assume that the hypothesis $\boldsymbol{A\beta} = \boldsymbol{\xi}$ is completely testable, i.e. $\mathcal{C}(\boldsymbol{A}') \subseteq \mathcal{C}(\boldsymbol{X}')$. We also assume $\boldsymbol{\xi} \in \mathcal{C}(\boldsymbol{A})$, so that the hypothesis itself has no algebraic inconsistency. Finally, we assume that the error degrees of freedom is positive so that there is at least one LZF available for the estimation of σ^2.

We have already considered in Section 4.2.1 a special case of this hypothesis, where $\boldsymbol{A\beta}$ consisted of the coefficients of the non-constant regressors and $\boldsymbol{\xi}$ was zero. There, we treated the model with restriction as an equivalent model without restrictions, and identified a set of BLUEs of the original model that turn into *additional* LZFs under the restriction. We would now formalize that approach in the general case.

Let us denote the models $(\boldsymbol{y}, \boldsymbol{X\beta}, \sigma^2\boldsymbol{I})$ and $(\boldsymbol{y}-\boldsymbol{XA}^-\boldsymbol{\xi}, \boldsymbol{X}(\boldsymbol{I}-\boldsymbol{A}^-\boldsymbol{A})\boldsymbol{\theta}, \sigma^2\boldsymbol{I})$ by $\mathcal{M}$ and $\mathcal{M}_r$, respectively, where $\boldsymbol{A}^-$ is *any* g-inverse of $\boldsymbol{A}$. It was shown in Section 3.10 that $\mathcal{M}$ with the restriction $\boldsymbol{A\beta} = \boldsymbol{\xi}$ is equivalent to $\mathcal{M}_r$. Recall that the set of LZFs of $\mathcal{M}$ is a subset of the set of LZFs of $\mathcal{M}_r$. We now identify the BLUEs in $\mathcal{M}$ that are LZFs in $\mathcal{M}_r$.

Proposition 4.18. *Let $\boldsymbol{A\beta} = \boldsymbol{\xi}$ be a completely testable and algebraically consistent restriction, and $\widehat{\boldsymbol{A\beta}}$ be the BLUE of $\boldsymbol{A\beta}$ under the model $\mathcal{M}$.*

(a) $\widehat{\boldsymbol{A\beta}} - \boldsymbol{\xi}$ is a vector of LZFs under the model $\mathcal{M}_r$.
(b) $\widehat{\boldsymbol{A\beta}} - \boldsymbol{\xi}$ is uncorrelated with $(\boldsymbol{I} - \boldsymbol{P}_X)\boldsymbol{y}$.
(c) There is no nontrivial LZF of $\mathcal{M}_r$ which is uncorrelated with $\widehat{\boldsymbol{A\beta}} - \boldsymbol{\xi}$ and $(\boldsymbol{I} - \boldsymbol{P}_X)\boldsymbol{y}$.

Proof. Rewrite $\widehat{\boldsymbol{A\beta}} - \boldsymbol{\xi}$ as

$$\begin{aligned}\widehat{\boldsymbol{A\beta}} - \boldsymbol{\xi} &= \boldsymbol{A}(\boldsymbol{X}'\boldsymbol{X})^-\boldsymbol{X}'\boldsymbol{y} - \boldsymbol{AA}^-\boldsymbol{\xi} \\ &= \boldsymbol{A}(\boldsymbol{X}'\boldsymbol{X})^-\boldsymbol{X}'\boldsymbol{y} - \boldsymbol{A}(\boldsymbol{X}'\boldsymbol{X})^-\boldsymbol{X}'\boldsymbol{XA}^-\boldsymbol{\xi} \\ &= \boldsymbol{A}(\boldsymbol{X}'\boldsymbol{X})^-\boldsymbol{X}'(\boldsymbol{y} - \boldsymbol{XA}^-\boldsymbol{\xi}).\end{aligned}$$

Therefore, $A\widehat{\beta} - \xi$ is a linear function in $\mathcal{M}_r$. Its mean (under $\mathcal{M}_r$), obtained by substituting $X(I-A^- A)\theta$ for $(y-XA^-\xi)$ in the last expression, easily simplifies to zero. This proves part (a).

Part (b) follows from the fact that $A\widehat{\beta} - \xi$ and $(I - P_X)y$ are vectors of BLUEs and LZFs in $\mathcal{M}$, respectively.

Part (c) would be proved by contradiction. Let $l'(y - XA^-\xi)$ be an LZF of $\mathcal{M}_r$ which is uncorrelated with $(I - P_X)y$ and $A\widehat{\beta} - \xi$. The first condition of uncorrelatedness implies that $(I - P_X)l = 0$, that is, l is of the form Xm for some vector m. The second condition amounts to $A(X'X)^- X'l = 0$ or $Am = 0$. By putting the twin conditions $Xm = l$ and $Am = 0$ together, we have $X(I - A^- A)m = l$, or $l'(y - XA^-\xi)$ is a BLUE of $\mathcal{M}_r$ (see Exercise 3.7). Since $l'(y - XA^-\xi)$ is a BLUE *and* an LZF of $\mathcal{M}_r$, it must be identically zero with probability one. □

Proposition 4.18 implies that the elements of $(I - P_X)y$ and $A\widehat{\beta} - \xi$ together constitute a generating set of the LZFs of $\mathcal{M}_r$.

Proposition 4.19. *If the SSE of $\mathcal{M}$ is R_0^2, the SSE of $\mathcal{M}_r$ is given by*

$$R_H^2 = R_0^2 + \sigma^2(A\widehat{\beta} - \xi)'[D(A\widehat{\beta})]^-(A\widehat{\beta} - \xi). \tag{4.8}$$

Proof. Consider the rank-factorization of $D(A\widehat{\beta})$, as $\sigma^2 CC'$. Then C has a left-inverse, C^{-L}. The elements of the vector $u_1 = C^{-L}(A\widehat{\beta} - \xi)$ each have variance σ^2, while they are uncorrelated with $(I - P_X)y$ and with each other. Further, the elements of $(I - P_X)y$ constitute a generating set of the LZFs of $\mathcal{M}$. Suppose u_2 is a vector of a corresponding standardized basis set of LZFs. According to Proposition 4.18, a standardized basis set of LZFs of $\mathcal{M}_r$ is given by the elements of u_1 and u_2, each element having variance σ^2. It follows from Proposition 3.45 that

$$\begin{aligned} R_H^2 &= u_2'u_2 + u_1'u_1 = R_0^2 + (A\widehat{\beta} - \xi)'[(C^{-L})'C^{-L}](A\widehat{\beta} - \xi) \\ &= R_0^2 + \sigma^2(A\widehat{\beta} - \xi)'[D(A\widehat{\beta})]^-(A\widehat{\beta} - \xi). \end{aligned}$$

□

Remark 4.20. It is also clear from Proposition 4.18 that the number of additional LZFs that constitute an uncorrelated basis set of LZFs of $\mathcal{M}_r$ is $\rho(D(A\widehat{\beta}))$ or $\rho(A(X'X)^- A')$. Suppose $A = T(X'X)$. Consequently

$$\rho(A(X'X)^- A') = \rho(TX'XT') \le \rho(TX'X) \le \rho(TX').$$

However, $\rho(TX') = \rho((TX')(XT'))$. Hence

$$\rho(D(A\widehat{\beta})) = \rho(TX'X) = \rho(A).$$

Thus, the number of additional LZFs is precisely the number of *linearly independent* restrictions implied by the statement $\boldsymbol{A\beta} = \boldsymbol{\xi}$. The total error degrees of freedom of $\mathcal{M}_r$ is $n - \rho(\boldsymbol{X}) + \rho(\boldsymbol{A})$. □

4.2.5 *GLRT and ANOVA table**

Consider the linear model $(\boldsymbol{y}, \boldsymbol{X\beta}, \sigma^2\boldsymbol{I})$ where $\boldsymbol{y}$ has the multivariate normal distribution, and the testable and algebraically consistent hypothesis $\mathcal{H}_0 : \boldsymbol{A\beta} = \boldsymbol{\xi}$. The generalized likelihood ratio test (GLRT) for $\mathcal{H}_0$ against the general alternative $\mathcal{H}_1 : \boldsymbol{A\beta} \neq \boldsymbol{\xi}$ is given below.

Proposition 4.21. *Under the above set-up, the GLRT at level α is equivalent to rejecting $\mathcal{H}_0$ if*

$$\frac{R_H^2 - R_0^2}{R_0^2} \cdot \frac{n-r}{m} > F_{m,n-r,\alpha}$$

where $r = \rho(\boldsymbol{X})$ and $m = \rho(\boldsymbol{A})$.

Proof. The GLRT statistic is

$$\ell = \frac{\max\limits_{\sigma^2, \boldsymbol{\beta} : \boldsymbol{A\beta} = \boldsymbol{\xi}} (2\pi\sigma^2)^{-\frac{n}{2}} \exp\left[-\frac{1}{2\sigma^2}\|\boldsymbol{y} - \boldsymbol{X\beta}\|^2\right]}{\max\limits_{\sigma^2, \boldsymbol{\beta}} (2\pi\sigma^2)^{-\frac{n}{2}} \exp\left[-\frac{1}{2\sigma^2}\|\boldsymbol{y} - \boldsymbol{X\beta}\|^2\right]}$$

$$= \frac{\max\limits_{\sigma^2, \boldsymbol{\theta}} (2\pi\sigma^2)^{-\frac{n}{2}} \exp\left[-\frac{1}{2\sigma^2}\|\boldsymbol{y} - \boldsymbol{XA}^-\boldsymbol{\xi} - \boldsymbol{X}(\boldsymbol{I} - \boldsymbol{A}^-\boldsymbol{A})\boldsymbol{\theta}\|^2\right]}{\max\limits_{\sigma^2, \boldsymbol{\beta}} (2\pi\sigma^2)^{-\frac{n}{2}} \exp\left[-\frac{1}{2\sigma^2}\|\boldsymbol{y} - \boldsymbol{X\beta}\|^2\right]}.$$

The denominator is maximized with respect to σ^2 when $\sigma^2 = n^{-1}\|\boldsymbol{y} - \boldsymbol{X\beta}\|^2$, while the numerator is maximized by choosing $\sigma^2 = n^{-1}\|\boldsymbol{y} - \boldsymbol{XA}^-\boldsymbol{\xi} - \boldsymbol{X}(\boldsymbol{I} - \boldsymbol{A}^-\boldsymbol{A})\boldsymbol{\theta}\|^2$. Substituting these values in the above expression and simplifying, we have

$$\ell = \left[\frac{\min\limits_{\boldsymbol{\theta}} \|\boldsymbol{y} - \boldsymbol{XA}^-\boldsymbol{\xi} - \boldsymbol{X}(\boldsymbol{I} - \boldsymbol{A}^-\boldsymbol{A})\boldsymbol{\theta}\|^2}{\min\limits_{\boldsymbol{\beta}} \|\boldsymbol{y} - \boldsymbol{X\beta}\|^2}\right]^{-n/2} = (R_H^2/R_0^2)^{-n/2},$$

which is a decreasing function of $(R_H^2 - R_0^2)/R_0^2$. Since the GLRT consists of rejecting $\mathcal{H}_0$ when ℓ is unduly small, it is equivalent to rejecting $\mathcal{H}_0$ when $(R_H^2 - R_0^2)/R_0^2$ is sufficiently large.

In order to find an appropriate critical value for this ratio, notice first from Proposition 4.19 that

$$\frac{R_H^2 - R_0^2}{\sigma^2} = (\boldsymbol{A}\widehat{\boldsymbol{\beta}} - \boldsymbol{\xi})'[D(\boldsymbol{A}\widehat{\boldsymbol{\beta}})]^-(\boldsymbol{A}\widehat{\boldsymbol{\beta}} - \boldsymbol{\xi}),$$

which has the χ_m^2 distribution (see Exercise 2.2). Similarly, Proposition 3.45 implies that

$$\frac{R_0^2}{\sigma^2} \sim \chi_{n-r}^2.$$

Further, these chi-square distributed statistics are sum of squares of different sets of standard normal LZFs which, according to Proposition 4.18, are independent of one another. Therefore, the null distribution of

$$\frac{(R_H^2 - R_0^2)/(m\sigma^2)}{R_0^2/((n-r)\sigma^2)} = \frac{R_H^2 - R_0^2}{R_0^2} \cdot \frac{n-r}{m}$$

is $F_{m,n-r}$ and the statement of the proposition follows. □

Remark 4.22. If $\boldsymbol{A}\boldsymbol{\beta} = \boldsymbol{\xi}$ is a partially testable and algebraically consistent hypothesis, the GLRT of Proposition 4.21 is valid, with

$$m = \rho(\boldsymbol{A}) + \rho(\boldsymbol{X}) - \rho\begin{pmatrix}\boldsymbol{X}\\ \boldsymbol{A}\end{pmatrix}.$$

Proposition 4.19 does not hold in this situation. Rather, R_H^2 should be interpreted as the error sum of squares under the restriction $\boldsymbol{A}\boldsymbol{\beta} = \boldsymbol{\xi}$. If one overlooks the nontestability of the hypothesis, then one may incorrectly use $m = \rho(\boldsymbol{A})$. This would entail a reduction in size and power of the test (see Exercise 4.3). See Peixoto (1986) and von Rosen (1990) for related results. □

The GLRT statistic is intuitively quite meaningful. From Proposition 4.19, the difference $R_H^2 - R_0^2$ coincides with $\sigma^2(\boldsymbol{A}\widehat{\boldsymbol{\beta}} - \boldsymbol{\xi})'[D(\boldsymbol{A}\widehat{\boldsymbol{\beta}})]^-(\boldsymbol{A}\widehat{\boldsymbol{\beta}} - \boldsymbol{\xi})$. This quadratic form accounts for the deviation from the hypothesis $\boldsymbol{A}\boldsymbol{\beta} = \boldsymbol{\xi}$, and should be small if $\mathcal{H}_0$ is indeed true. The other part of R_H^2 is R_0^2, which is present regardless the validity of $\mathcal{H}_0$. The GLRT consists of rejecting $\mathcal{H}_0$ if the quadratic form is too large relative to R_0^2. The decomposition of R_H^2 and the associated degrees of freedom is displayed in the form of the *analysis of variance* (ANOVA) given in Table 4.3. This is a generalization of Table 4.2 presented earlier.

The 'total' sum of squares in this table is in fact the error sum of squares, under the hypothesis $\boldsymbol{A}\boldsymbol{\beta} = \boldsymbol{\xi}$. This 'total' includes the unrestricted sum of squares (R_0^2) and the additional sum of squares arising from the departure

Table 4.3 Analysis of variance table for the hypothesis $\boldsymbol{A\beta} = \boldsymbol{\xi}$

Source	Sum of Squares	Degrees of Freedom	Mean Square	F Ratio
Deviation from $\mathcal{H}_0$	$R_H^2 - R_0^2 = \sigma^2(\boldsymbol{A}\widehat{\boldsymbol{\beta}} - \boldsymbol{\xi})' [D(\boldsymbol{A}\widehat{\boldsymbol{\beta}})]^-(\boldsymbol{A}\widehat{\boldsymbol{\beta}} - \boldsymbol{\xi})$ *	$m = \rho(\boldsymbol{A})$ *	$\frac{R_H^2 - R_0^2}{m}$	$\frac{n-r}{m} \times \frac{R_H^2 - R_0^2}{R_0^2}$
Error	$R_0^2 = \min_{\boldsymbol{\beta}} \Vert\boldsymbol{y} - \boldsymbol{X\beta}\Vert^2$	$n-r = n-\rho(\boldsymbol{X})$	$\frac{R_0^2}{n-r}$	
Total	$R_H^2 = \min_{\boldsymbol{A\beta} = \boldsymbol{\xi}} \Vert\boldsymbol{y} - \boldsymbol{X\beta}\Vert^2$	$n-r+m$		

*These expressions should be bypassed when $\boldsymbol{A\beta} = \boldsymbol{\xi}$ is not testable; see Remark 4.22.

from $\mathcal{H}_0$. The 'departure' here may just be due to statistical fluctuations (since after all, $\boldsymbol{A}\widehat{\boldsymbol{\beta}} - \boldsymbol{\xi}$ need not be identically zero even if $\boldsymbol{A\beta} - \boldsymbol{\xi}$ is) or due to the fact that $\mathcal{H}_0$ is not valid, that is, due to systematic difference between $\boldsymbol{A\beta}$ and $\boldsymbol{\xi}$. The statistical significance test determines whether the 'departure' is large enough to signify the violation of $\mathcal{H}_0$.

The model under restriction can also be viewed as a model nested within the unrestricted model. Thus, the 'total' sum of squares (R_H^2) in the ANOVA table is the error sum of squares under the restricted model, which is larger than that under the unrestricted model (R_0^2). The 'regression' sum of squares is the gap between them, which is higher when the unrestricted model explains the response substantially better.

The ANOVA table can be appreciated better when we interpret all the quantities in terms of LZFs. Recall from the proof of Proposition 4.18 that we can think of a basis set of LZFs of the restricted model as the union of two disjoint subsets: a basis set of LZFs of the unrestricted model and a set of LZFs which would have been BLUEs in the absence of the restrictions. The 'sums of squares' R_0^2 and $R_H^2 - R_0^2$ are in fact the sums of squares of these subsets of LZFs, and the 'degrees of freedom' m and $n - r$ are the numbers of LZFs in these. The *total* 'sum of squares' and 'degree of freedom' correspond to these quantities for the combined set of LZFs. The fourth column of Table 4.3 displays the average squared values of the LZFs of the two subsets and the combined set.

Example 4.23. (Birth weight of babies: subset model) In Example 4.6, the birth weight of a baby was used as response in a linear model, where the explanatory variables were the smoking and racial status of the mother. Let us now test the hypothesis that the racial status has no effect on the birth weight of babies. This means, the coefficients of the two binary variables that represent the racial status are zero. In other words, the smoking status of the mother alone explains the variation in the birth weight. Thus, the null hypothesis amounts to adequacy of a subset of explanatory variables. The R function `anova` is appropriate for testing for a subset model, but the format of the output does not match Table 4.3, as noted in Example 4.6. The function `hanova` of the R package `lmreg`, which brings it to that format, is now used to test the null hypothesis, as follows.

```
data(birthwt)
lmbw <- lm(bwt~smoke+factor(race),data=birthwt)
lm1 <- lm(bwt~smoke,data=birthwt)
hanova(lm1,lmbw)
```

The resulting output is the ANOVA table given below.

```
                          SS  DF        MS   Fratio       pvalue
Departure from H0    8768299   2 4384149.4 9.261369 0.0001467872
Error               87575348 185  473380.3       NA           NA
Total               96343646 187        NA       NA           NA
```

Since the p-value of the test is 0.000147, the null hypothesis that racial status has no effect, is rejected at level 0.01 or even 0.001. □

Example 4.24. (Age at death, continued) In the model described on page 66, the hypothesis $\tau_1 = \tau_2 = \cdots = \tau_8$ means that the age at death of all categories of people have the same mean. This hypothesis can be written as $\boldsymbol{A\beta} = \boldsymbol{0}$, where $\boldsymbol{A\beta} = (\tau_1 - \tau_2 : \cdots : \tau_1 - \tau_8)'$, that is,

$$\boldsymbol{A} = \begin{pmatrix} 0 & 1 & -1 & 0 & 0 & 0 & 0 & 0 & 0 \\ 0 & 1 & 0 & -1 & 0 & 0 & 0 & 0 & 0 \\ 0 & 1 & 0 & 0 & -1 & 0 & 0 & 0 & 0 \\ 0 & 1 & 0 & 0 & 0 & -1 & 0 & 0 & 0 \\ 0 & 1 & 0 & 0 & 0 & 0 & -1 & 0 & 0 \\ 0 & 1 & 0 & 0 & 0 & 0 & 0 & -1 & 0 \\ 0 & 1 & 0 & 0 & 0 & 0 & 0 & 0 & -1 \end{pmatrix}.$$

The restricted or total sum of squares R_H^2 may be computed mechanically as $\|\boldsymbol{y} - \boldsymbol{P}_{X(I-A^-A)}\boldsymbol{y}\|^2$. However, it is easy to see that under the above hypothesis, the mean response of every category is $\mu + \tau_1$, which can be treated as a single constant. The R code given below uses this simple form of the restricted model to augment the computations of Example 3.4 and produces the requisite output.

```
lm1 <- lm(Lifelength~1,data=lifelength)
hanova(lm1,lmlife)
```

The code produces the following ANOVA table.

Source	Sum of Squares	Degrees of Freedom	Mean Square	F Ratio
Deviation from $\mathcal{H}_0$	17025.89	7	2432.27	11.047
Error	150160.1	682	220.18	
Total	167186.0	689		

The p-value for the F-ratio (with 7 and 682 degrees of freedom) is 2.87×10^{-13}. Thus, there is statistically significant (at any reasonable level) heterogeneity in the means of the age of death in different categories.

The R function `hanova` works only when one can write the model under the linear restriction explicitly as a subset model, nested within the unrestricted model. This means, the explanatory variables implied by the restricted model need to be properly identified. Another function `ganova` of the R package `lmreg` produces the requisite ANOVA table without the need for this special formulation. The following R code formats the input data suitably for the function `ganova` (i.e. $\boldsymbol{X}$ as on page 67, $\boldsymbol{A}$ as on page 143 and $\boldsymbol{\xi} = \mathbf{0}$) and uses it to produce an ANOVA table.

```
data(lifelength); attach(lifelength)
X <- cbind(1, binaries(Category))
A <- rbind(c(0,1,-1,0,0,0,0,0,0),c(0,1,0,-1,0,0,0,0,0),
   c(0,1,0,0,-1,0,0,0,0),c(0,1,0,0,0,-1,0,0,0),c(0,1,0,0,0,0,-1,0,0),
   c(0,1,0,0,0,0,0,-1,0),c(0,1,0,0,0,0,0,0,-1))
xi <- rep(0,7)
ganova(Lifelength,X,A,xi); detach(lifelength)
```

The above code produces the same ANOVA table as the earlier one. □

Example 4.25. (Abrasion of denim jeans, continued) Consider the abrasion data of Table 3.2, and the model of Example 3.5. The hypothesis that the treatment effects are homogeneous corresponds to $\tau_1 = \tau_2 = \tau_3$. It has already been identified (see page 132) as a testable linear hypothesis of the form $\boldsymbol{A\beta} = \boldsymbol{\xi}$, where

$$\boldsymbol{A} = \begin{pmatrix} 0 & 1 & -1 & 0 & 0 & 0 & 0 \\ 0 & 1 & 0 & -1 & 0 & 0 & 0 \end{pmatrix}, \qquad \boldsymbol{\xi} = \mathbf{0},$$

as noted in Example 3.51 (page 100). The total sum of squares can be computed as $\|\boldsymbol{y} - \boldsymbol{X}\boldsymbol{A}^{-}\boldsymbol{\xi} - \boldsymbol{P}_{X(I-A^{-}A)}\boldsymbol{y}\|^2$. However, for this specific problem, the simplest way to obtain R^2_H is to compute it as the error sum of squares from the following simpler (one-way) model:

$$y_{ijl} = \mu + \tau_1 + \beta_j + \varepsilon_{ijl}, \quad i,j = 1,2,3, \; l = 1,\ldots,10.$$

The computation of the ANOVA table requires analysis under the above model together with analysis under the unrestricted model, previously done in Example 3.5. The following additional lines of R code makes use of the function `hanova` to obtain the ANOVA table in the requisite format.

```
lmrestr <- lm(Abrasion~Laundrycat)
jeansaov <- anova(lmrestr,lmjeans)
hanova(jeansaov)
```

The above code produces the following ANOVA table.

Source	Sum of Squares	Degrees of Freedom	Mean Square	F Ratio
Deviation from $\mathcal{H}_0$	13.416	2	6.708	37.38
Error	15.255	85	0.1795	
Total	28.671	87		

The p-value for the F-ratio (with 2 and 85 degrees of freedom) is 2.26×10^{-12}. There is statistically significant (at any reasonable level) evidence that the mean effects of the various denim treatments on the abrasion score are different.

Use of the R function `hanova` depends crucially on the fact that the restricted model can be written as a one-way model. Instead, we can use the function `ganova`, after defining $\boldsymbol{X}$ as on page 70, $\boldsymbol{A}$ as on page 144 and $\boldsymbol{\xi} = \boldsymbol{0}$. The following R code accomplishes this task.

```
X <- cbind(1,binaries(Denim),binaries(Laundry))
A <- rbind(c(0,1,-1,0,0,0,0),c(0,1,0,-1,0,0,0))
xi <- c(0,0)
ganova(Abrasion,X,A,xi)
```

The ANOVA table produced by this code is as obtained above.

The R function `ganova` can be used for testing a partially testable hypothesis also. For example, the hypothesis $\tau_1 = \tau_2 = \tau_3 = 0$ may be tested by the above code with the following modification.

```
A <- rbind(c(0,1,0,0,0,0,0),c(0,0,1,0,0,0,0),c(0,0,0,1,0,0,0))
xi <- c(0,0,0)
```

It may be verified that the testable part of this hypothesis is the hypothesis considered earlier, namely $\tau_1 = \tau_2 = \tau_3$ (see Example 4.15). It turns out that the command `ganova(Abrasion,X,A,xi)` produces the same ANOVA table as before. □

In general, whenever one is not sure whether the hypothesis being tested is testable, one can use the function `ganova`, but interpret the findings with care. In particular, the untestable and testable parts of the hypothesis should be delineated by using the function `hypsplit`.

Example 4.26. The hypothesis $\mathcal{H}_0 : \beta_j = 0$ corresponds to the jth explanatory variable being not significant. We can express this hypothesis as $\boldsymbol{A\beta} = \boldsymbol{\xi}$, where $\boldsymbol{A}$ is the jth row of the $p \times p$ identity matrix and $\boldsymbol{\xi} = 0$. In this case $R_H^2 - R_0^2$ has a simpler expression than R_H^2. Let $(\boldsymbol{X}'\boldsymbol{X})^{jj}$ be the jth diagonal element of $(\boldsymbol{X}'\boldsymbol{X})^-$ (since β_j is assumed to be testable, this element does not depend on the g-inverse: see page 87). Then $D(\boldsymbol{A}\widehat{\boldsymbol{\beta}}) = Var(\widehat{\beta}_j) = \sigma^2(\boldsymbol{X}'\boldsymbol{X})^{jj}$. It follows that $R_H^2 - R_0^2 = \widehat{\beta}_j^2/(\boldsymbol{X}'\boldsymbol{X})^{jj}$. This leads to the following ANOVA table.

Source	Sum of Squares	Degrees of Freedom	Mean Square
Deviation from $\mathcal{H}_0$	$R_H^2 - R_0^2 = \widehat{\beta}_j^2/(\boldsymbol{X}'\boldsymbol{X})^{jj}$	1	$R_H^2 - R_0^2$
Error	$R_0^2 = \boldsymbol{e}'\boldsymbol{e}$	$n-p$	$\dfrac{R_0^2}{n-p}$
Total	$R_H^2 = \boldsymbol{e}'\boldsymbol{e} + \widehat{\beta}_j^2/(\boldsymbol{X}'\boldsymbol{X})^{jj}$	$n-k$	

The level-α GLRT is to reject $\mathcal{H}_0$ if

$$(n-p) \cdot \frac{\widehat{\beta}_j^2/(\boldsymbol{X}'\boldsymbol{X})^{jj}}{\boldsymbol{e}'\boldsymbol{e}} > F_{1,n-p,\alpha}.$$

This test is very similar to the test described in (4.6). A direct connection is established in Exercise 4.19. □

4.2.6 *Power of the generalized likelihood ratio test**

Assume once again, that the errors are normal and that the linear hypothesis $\boldsymbol{A\beta} = \boldsymbol{\xi}$ is testable and algebraically consistent. We can calculate the power of the generalized likelihood ratio test using its distribution under the alternative hypothesis. This distribution is provided below.

Proposition 4.27. *Under the above set-up,*

$$\frac{R_H^2 - R_0^2}{R_0^2} \cdot \frac{n-r}{m} \sim F_{m,n-r}(c),$$

where $m = \rho(\boldsymbol{A})$, $c = \sigma^{-2}(\boldsymbol{A\beta} - \boldsymbol{\xi})'[\boldsymbol{A}(\boldsymbol{X}'\boldsymbol{X})^{-}\boldsymbol{A}']^{-}(\boldsymbol{A\beta} - \boldsymbol{\xi})$, and $\boldsymbol{\beta}$ is the 'true' value of the vector parameter.

Proof. Notice that $\boldsymbol{A}\widehat{\boldsymbol{\beta}}$ is a BLUE in the unrestricted model, and $(\boldsymbol{A}\widehat{\boldsymbol{\beta}} - \boldsymbol{\xi}) \sim N(\boldsymbol{A\beta} - \boldsymbol{\xi}, \sigma^2\boldsymbol{A}(\boldsymbol{X}'\boldsymbol{X})^{-}\boldsymbol{A}')$. Rank-factorizing $\sigma^2\boldsymbol{A}(\boldsymbol{X}'\boldsymbol{X})^{-}\boldsymbol{A}'$ as $\boldsymbol{CC}'$, we have $\boldsymbol{C}^{-L}(\boldsymbol{A}\widehat{\boldsymbol{\beta}} - \boldsymbol{\xi}) \sim N(\boldsymbol{C}^{-L}(\boldsymbol{A\beta} - \boldsymbol{\xi}), \boldsymbol{I})$. It is easy to see that $\rho(\boldsymbol{C}) = \rho(\boldsymbol{A}(\boldsymbol{X}'\boldsymbol{X})^{-}\boldsymbol{A}') = \rho(\boldsymbol{A}) = m$. Therefore, by Remark 2.9,

$$(R_H^2 - R_0^2)/\sigma^2 = (\boldsymbol{A}\widehat{\boldsymbol{\beta}} - \boldsymbol{\xi})'(\boldsymbol{C}^{-L})'\boldsymbol{C}^{-L}(\boldsymbol{A}\widehat{\boldsymbol{\beta}} - \boldsymbol{\xi}) \sim \chi_m^2(c).$$

As argued in the proof of Proposition 4.19, the above is independent of R_0^2. The statement of the proposition follows from Remark 2.9. □

Remark 4.28. The value of the noncentrality parameter c does not depend on the choice of the g-inverse of $\boldsymbol{A}(\boldsymbol{X}'\boldsymbol{X})^{-}\boldsymbol{A}'$. To see this, note that $(\boldsymbol{A}\widehat{\boldsymbol{\beta}} - \boldsymbol{A\beta})$ must be almost surely in $\mathcal{C}(\boldsymbol{A}(\boldsymbol{X}'\boldsymbol{X})^{-}\boldsymbol{A}')$, which is identical to $\mathcal{C}(\boldsymbol{A})$. Additionally, the algebraic consistency of the hypothesis (assumed above) ensures that $(\boldsymbol{A\beta} - \boldsymbol{\xi})$ is also in this space. Therefore, $(\boldsymbol{A}\widehat{\boldsymbol{\beta}} - \boldsymbol{\xi})$ must almost surely be in this space too. □

From Propositions 4.21 and 4.27, we find that the power of the generalized likelihood ratio test at level α is $P[F > F_{m,n-r,\alpha}]$, where $F \sim F_{m,n-r}(c)$ and $c = \sigma^{-2}(\boldsymbol{A\beta} - \boldsymbol{\xi})'[\boldsymbol{A}(\boldsymbol{X}'\boldsymbol{X})^{-}\boldsymbol{A}]^{-}(\boldsymbol{A\beta} - \boldsymbol{\xi})$. Given α and any numerical value of c, this probability can be computed from the infinite series expansions of the noncentral F-distribution (see e.g. Abramowitz and Stegun, 2012). The power is a monotonically increasing function of the noncentrality parameter, c.

4.2.7 *Multiple comparisons**

Sometimes one has to test a number of single-degree-of-freedom hypotheses in a linear model. If these are combined to form a hypothesis of the form $\boldsymbol{A\beta} = \boldsymbol{\xi}$, then the rejection of this hypothesis only means that one or more of the single-degree-of-freedom hypotheses are probably incorrect.

One may be interested in checking the validity of these hypotheses on a case-by-case basis, using the test of Section 4.2.3 with a nominal size α. If this is done, and all the hypotheses happen to be true, then the probability of erroneous rejection of *at least one* of the hypotheses is greater than α (since the probability of erroneous rejection of a particular single-degree-of-freedom hypothesis is α). Thus, the nominal size of the tests is misleading. Some adjustment will be needed. We shall mention two sets of tests.

Consider the linear model $(\boldsymbol{y}, \boldsymbol{X\beta}, \sigma^2\boldsymbol{I})$ with n observations and $\rho(\boldsymbol{X}) = r$. Suppose we have to test q testable hypotheses,

$$\mathcal{H}_{0j} : \boldsymbol{a}_j'\boldsymbol{\beta} = \xi_j, \quad \text{against} \quad \mathcal{H}_{1j} : \boldsymbol{a}_j'\boldsymbol{\beta} \neq \xi_j,$$

$j = 1, \ldots, q$. Let $\boldsymbol{A}' = (\boldsymbol{a}_1 : \boldsymbol{a}_2 : \cdots : \boldsymbol{a}_q)$, $\boldsymbol{\xi} = (\xi_1 : \xi_2 : \cdots : \xi_q)'$, and $\rho(\boldsymbol{A}) = m$. The higher-than-nominal probability for false rejection of the usual test stems from the fact that

$$P\left(\bigcup_{j=1}^{q}\left\{\frac{(\boldsymbol{a}_j'\widehat{\boldsymbol{\beta}} - \xi_j)^2}{\widehat{\sigma^2}\boldsymbol{a}_j'(\boldsymbol{X}'\boldsymbol{X})^-\boldsymbol{a}_j} > F_{1,n-r,\alpha}\right\}\middle| \mathcal{H}_{01}, \ldots \mathcal{H}_{0q}\right)$$
$$\geq P\left(\left\{\frac{(\boldsymbol{a}_1'\widehat{\boldsymbol{\beta}} - \xi_1)^2}{\widehat{\sigma^2}\boldsymbol{a}_1'(\boldsymbol{X}'\boldsymbol{X})^-\boldsymbol{a}_1} > F_{1,n-r,\alpha}\right\}\middle| \mathcal{H}_{01}, \ldots \mathcal{H}_{0q}\right) = \alpha.$$

However, using the Bonferroni inequality, we observe that

$$P\left(\bigcup_{j=1}^{q}\left\{\frac{(\boldsymbol{a}_j'\widehat{\boldsymbol{\beta}} - \xi_j)^2}{\widehat{\sigma^2}\boldsymbol{a}_j'(\boldsymbol{X}'\boldsymbol{X})^-\boldsymbol{a}_j} > F_{1,n-r,\frac{\alpha}{q}}\right\}\middle| \mathcal{H}_{01}, \ldots \mathcal{H}_{0q}\right)$$
$$\leq \sum_{j=1}^{q} P\left(\left\{\frac{(\boldsymbol{a}_j'\widehat{\boldsymbol{\beta}} - \xi_j)^2}{\widehat{\sigma^2}\boldsymbol{a}_j'(\boldsymbol{X}'\boldsymbol{X})^-\boldsymbol{a}_j} > F_{1,n-r,\frac{\alpha}{q}}\right\}\middle| \mathcal{H}_{01}, \ldots \mathcal{H}_{0q}\right) = \sum_{j=1}^{q}\frac{\alpha}{q} = \alpha.$$

Thus, a set of conservative tests would be to reject $\mathcal{H}_{0j}$ if

$$\frac{(\boldsymbol{a}_j'\widehat{\boldsymbol{\beta}} - \xi_j)^2}{\widehat{\sigma^2}\boldsymbol{a}_j'(\boldsymbol{X}'\boldsymbol{X})^-\boldsymbol{a}_j} > F_{1,n-r,\frac{\alpha}{q}}, \tag{4.9}$$

for $j = 1, 2, \ldots, q$. The probability of erroneous rejection of at least one of the hypotheses, when all of them actually hold, is at most α. These tests are referred to as *Bonferroni tests.* The above set of multiple tests can have a combined false rejection probability *much* smaller than α, particularly when q is large.

An alternative when dealing with a set of tests, is to consider the GLRT of the combined null hypothesis $\cap_{j=1}^{q}\mathcal{H}_{0j}$ (or $\boldsymbol{A\beta} = \boldsymbol{\xi}$) at level α amounts to rejecting it when

$$(\boldsymbol{A}\widehat{\boldsymbol{\beta}} - \boldsymbol{\xi})'[\boldsymbol{A}(\boldsymbol{X}'\boldsymbol{X})^-\boldsymbol{A}]^-(\boldsymbol{A}\widehat{\boldsymbol{\beta}} - \boldsymbol{\xi}) > mF_{m,n-r,\alpha}\widehat{\sigma^2},$$

where $m = \rho(\boldsymbol{A})$. It follows from a geometric argument (see page 156 of Section 4.3.3 that and Exercise 4.10) the complement of the above event is implied by the simultaneous events

$$(\boldsymbol{a}_j'\widehat{\boldsymbol{\beta}} - \xi_j)^2 \le mF_{m,n-r,\alpha}\widehat{\sigma^2}\boldsymbol{a}_j'(\boldsymbol{X}'\boldsymbol{X})^-\boldsymbol{a}_j, \quad j = 1, \ldots.$$

Therefore, the latter set of simultaneous events must have probability greater than $1 - \alpha$. It transpires that an alternative set of conservative tests would be to reject $\mathcal{H}_{0j}$ if

$$\frac{(\boldsymbol{a}_j'\widehat{\boldsymbol{\beta}} - \xi_j)^2}{\widehat{\sigma^2}\boldsymbol{a}_j'(\boldsymbol{X}'\boldsymbol{X})^-\boldsymbol{a}_j} > mF_{m,n-r,\alpha}, \tag{4.10}$$

for $j = 1, 2, \ldots, q$. These tests are called *Scheffé tests.*

The above procedures for multiple comparisons have their parallels in the construction of simultaneous confidence intervals, discussed in Section 4.3.3. If the components of $\boldsymbol{A}\widehat{\boldsymbol{\beta}}$ are uncorrelated, one can construct a set of tests analogous to the maximum modulus-t confidence intervals introduced in that section. Two other approaches for some special cases are described in Section 6.2.4. We refer the reader to Hocking (2013, Chapter 15), Christensen (2011, Chapter 5) and Hochberg and Tamhane (2009) for more details on these and other methods.

Example 4.29. (Abrasion of denim jeans, continued) The hypothesis of homogeneous mean effects of all denim treatments under the model of page 69 has already been rejected (see page 80). As a follow-up analysis, we consider the statistical significance of all pairs of treatment differences: $\tau_1 - \tau_2$, $\tau_1 - \tau_3$ and $\tau_2 - \tau_3$. These estimable functions can be written as $\boldsymbol{a}_j'\boldsymbol{\beta}$, where $\boldsymbol{a}_1 = (0 : 1 : -1 : 0 : 0 : 0 : 0)'$, $\boldsymbol{a}_2 = (0 : 1 : 0 : -1 : 0 : 0 : 0)'$ and $\boldsymbol{a}_3 = (0 : 0 : 1 : -1 : 0 : 0 : 0)'$. The combined hypothesis is $\boldsymbol{A\beta} = \boldsymbol{\xi}$, with $\boldsymbol{A} = (\boldsymbol{a}_1 : \boldsymbol{a}_2 : \boldsymbol{a}_3)'$ and $\boldsymbol{\xi} = \boldsymbol{0}$ has a subtle difference with the hypothesis considered in Example 3.25. Here, there are $q = 3$ single-degree-of-freedom hypotheses, but $m = \rho(\boldsymbol{A}) = 2$. The third row of $\boldsymbol{A}$ is important for multiple comparisons, though it is redundant for the purpose of testing of treatment heterogeneity. The outcome of the test of treatment heterogeneity would have been exactly the same if we had worked with the current choices of $\boldsymbol{A}$ and $\boldsymbol{\xi}$.

Proceeding with treatment differences, we can compute the ratio $(\boldsymbol{a}_j'\widehat{\boldsymbol{\beta}} - \xi_j)^2/\widehat{\sigma^2}\boldsymbol{a}_j'(\boldsymbol{X}'\boldsymbol{X})^-\boldsymbol{a}_j$, and the corresponding Bonferroni and Scheffé p-values, for $j = 1, \ldots, q$, using the function `multcomp` of the R package `lmreg`, through the following code.

```
data(denim); attach(denim)
X <- cbind(1,binaries(Denim),binaries(Laundry))
A <- rbind(c(0,1,-1,0,0,0,0),c(0,1,0,-1,0,0,0),c(0,0,1,-1,0,0,0))
xi <- c(0,0,0)
\multcomp(Abrasion,X,A,xi); detach(denim)
```

The resulting output is as follows.

```
  V1 V2 V3 V4 V5 V6 V7 xi    Fstat Bonferroni.p    Scheffe.p
1  0  1 -1  0  0  0  0  0 74.58532 8.827362e-13 2.361047e-12
2  0  1  0 -1  0  0  0  0 15.69448 4.628726e-04 7.456978e-04
3  0  0  1 -1  0  0  0  0 21.85238 3.288835e-05 5.983786e-05
```

Thus, the Bonferroni and the Scheffé p-values for all the F-ratios (i.e. for $\tau_1 - \tau_2$, $\tau_1 - \tau_3$ and $\tau_2 - \tau_3$) are smaller than 0.001. Therefore, according to either procedure for multiple comparison, all the pairs of treatment differences are significant at the 0.1% level.

The separate p-values obtained for the three treatment differences may be contrasted with the single p-value of 2.26×10^{-12} obtained in Example 4.25 for the hypothesis of equality of all treatment effects. □

4.2.8 *Nested hypotheses**

Sometimes it is necessary to test hypotheses that are related to each other. For example, given two sets of similar regression data in two groups, we may first check if the regression equations are identical — so that a single model can be used for the two groups. If the answer is negative, then we may ask if the regression surfaces are, at least, parallel — so that the group effect can be taken into account by means of a single added parameter. This is an example of nested hypotheses.

Let $\mathcal{H}_{0j} : \boldsymbol{A}_j\boldsymbol{\beta} = \boldsymbol{\xi}_j$, $j = 1, \ldots, q$ be a series of hypotheses so that for each j, $\mathcal{H}_{0j}$ implies $\mathcal{H}_{0\,j+1}$. We begin by checking $\mathcal{H}_{01}$ using the generalized likelihood ratio test with nominal size α. If this hypotheses is accepted, there is no need to proceed further. If it is rejected, then we can check $\mathcal{H}_{02}$ using another generalized likelihood ratio test with nominal size α. The problem of larger-than-nominal size does not arise here, since $\mathcal{H}_{01}$ implies $\mathcal{H}_{0\,2}$. The (unconditional) probability of incorrect rejection at the second stage cannot be more than the probability of incorrect rejection at the first stage. The tests can thus proceed in a sequential manner, until some hypothesis is accepted or the last hypothesis is rejected.

4.3 Confidence regions

4.3.1 *Confidence interval for a single LPF*

The distribution of a scaled version of an estimated regression coefficient, if estimable, was given in (4.1). Using a similar logic for a general estimable function $\boldsymbol{p}'\boldsymbol{\beta}$, one can use Proposition 4.1 to specify the distribution of its BLUE, $\boldsymbol{p}'\widehat{\boldsymbol{\beta}}$, as

$$\frac{\widehat{\boldsymbol{p}'\boldsymbol{\beta}} - \boldsymbol{p}'\boldsymbol{\beta}}{\sqrt{\widehat{\sigma^2}\boldsymbol{p}'(\boldsymbol{X}'\boldsymbol{X})^-\boldsymbol{p}}} \sim t_{n-r}.$$

It follows that

$$P\left[\frac{\boldsymbol{p}'\widehat{\boldsymbol{\beta}} - \boldsymbol{p}'\boldsymbol{\beta}}{\sqrt{\widehat{\sigma^2}\boldsymbol{p}'(\boldsymbol{X}'\boldsymbol{X})^-\boldsymbol{p}}} \le t_{n-r,\alpha}\right]$$
$$= P\left[\boldsymbol{p}'\boldsymbol{\beta} \ge \boldsymbol{p}'\widehat{\boldsymbol{\beta}} - t_{n-r,\alpha}\sqrt{\widehat{\sigma^2}\boldsymbol{p}'(\boldsymbol{X}'\boldsymbol{X})^-\boldsymbol{p}}\right] = 1-\alpha.$$

This gives a $100(1-\alpha)\%$ lower confidence limit for $\boldsymbol{p}'\boldsymbol{\beta}$, or

$$\left[\boldsymbol{p}'\widehat{\boldsymbol{\beta}} - t_{n-r,\alpha}\sqrt{\widehat{\sigma^2}\boldsymbol{p}'(\boldsymbol{X}'\boldsymbol{X})^-\boldsymbol{p}},\ \infty\right) \tag{4.11}$$

is a $100(1-\alpha)\%$ (one-sided) confidence interval for $\boldsymbol{p}'\boldsymbol{\beta}$. Similar arguments lead to the other one-sided confidence interval (or upper confidence limit)

$$\left(-\infty,\ \boldsymbol{p}'\widehat{\boldsymbol{\beta}} + t_{n-r,\alpha}\sqrt{\widehat{\sigma^2}\boldsymbol{p}'(\boldsymbol{X}'\boldsymbol{X})^-\boldsymbol{p}}\right], \tag{4.12}$$

and the two-sided confidence interval

$$\left[\boldsymbol{p}'\widehat{\boldsymbol{\beta}} - t_{n-r,\alpha/2}\sqrt{\widehat{\sigma^2}\boldsymbol{p}'(\boldsymbol{X}'\boldsymbol{X})^-\boldsymbol{p}},\ \boldsymbol{p}'\widehat{\boldsymbol{\beta}} + t_{n-r,\alpha/2}\sqrt{\widehat{\sigma^2}\boldsymbol{p}'(\boldsymbol{X}'\boldsymbol{X})^-\boldsymbol{p}}\right]. \tag{4.13}$$

If the two-sided confidence interval does not include the value 0, then the null hypothesis of $\boldsymbol{p}'\boldsymbol{\beta} = 0$ can be rejected at the level α in favour of the alternative $\boldsymbol{p}'\boldsymbol{\beta} \ne 0$. If the lower confidence limit is above zero, then the hypothesis $\boldsymbol{p}'\boldsymbol{\beta} = 0$ is rejected in favour of $\boldsymbol{p}'\boldsymbol{\beta} > 0$. If the upper confidence limit is below zero, then the same null hypothesis is rejected in favour of $\boldsymbol{p}'\boldsymbol{\beta} < 0$.

If β_j is estimable, then $\boldsymbol{p}$ may be chosen as the $(j+1)$th column of the $p \times p$ identity matrix, and the above confidence interval simplifies to

$$\left[\widehat{\beta}_j - t_{n-r,\alpha/2}\sqrt{\widehat{\sigma^2}(\boldsymbol{X}'\boldsymbol{X})^{(j+1)(j+1)}},\ \widehat{\beta}_j + t_{n-r,\alpha/2}\sqrt{\widehat{\sigma^2}(\boldsymbol{X}'\boldsymbol{X})^{(j+1)(j+1)}}\right],$$

where $(\boldsymbol{X}'\boldsymbol{X})^{(j+1)(j+1)}$ is the $(j+1)$th diagonal element of $(\boldsymbol{X}'\boldsymbol{X})^-$, which does not depend on the choice of the g-inverse (as we noted on page 87).

Another special case of interest is simple linear regression based on the data $(x_1, y_1), \ldots, (x_n, y_n)$, where the parameter of interest is the mean response $(\beta_0 + \beta_1 x)$ corresponding to some specified value (x) of the explanatory variable. In this case the confidence interval (4.13) simplifies to

$$[\widehat{\beta}_0 + \widehat{\beta}_1 x - a, \widehat{\beta}_0 + \widehat{\beta}_1 x + a], \text{ where } a = t_{n-2,\alpha/2}\widehat{\sigma}\sqrt{\frac{(x-\bar{x})^2}{n(\overline{x^2}-\bar{x}^2)}}, \tag{4.14}$$

where $\bar{x} = \frac{1}{n}\sum_{i=1}^n x_i$ and $\overline{x^2} = \frac{1}{n}\sum_{i=1}^n x_i^2$.

Example 4.30. (Birth weight of babies, continued) Consider the model presented on page 6 for the birth weight (in grams) of a baby expressed in terms of the mother's smoking status and racial status. The coefficient β_1 represents the additional expected weight of the baby in case the mother happens to be a smoker, the racial status being the same. Analysis of the data through the R command `lm(BWT~SMOKE+factor(RACE))$coef` reveals that the BLUE of β_1 is -427.2. Thus, on the average, smoking mothers are expected to have babies that weight 427.2 grams less than other babies.

The function `cisngl` of the R package `lmreg` computes the point estimate together with lower, upper or two-sided confidence limits for a single estimable LPF, depending on whether `type` is set as `"lower"`, `"upper"` or `"both"`, respectively. We now organize the data appropriately for this function and use it to obtain upper and two-sided 95% confidence intervals of β_1.

```
attach(birthwt)
X <- cbind(1,smoke,binaries(race))
p <- c(0,1,0,0,0)
cisngl(bwt,X,p,0.05,type = "upper")
cisngl(bwt,X,p,0.05,type = "both")
is.included(p,t(X)); detach(birthwt)
```

It transpires that a 95% upper confidence limit for β_1 is -247.0. Since this number is smaller than 0, β_1 is significantly negative at the level 0.05. Further, a two-sided confidence interval for β_1 is $[-642.3, -212.2]$. From this analysis one can say with 95% confidence that smoking mothers are expected to have babies weighing 212.2 to 642.3 grams lighter than other newborn babies.

Before looking for a confidence interval, one can check whether the chosen LPF is estimable, using the function `is.included`. □

Example 4.31. (Abrasion of denim jeans, continued) Consider the mean differences in the effects of the denim treatments in the model of Example 3.5. The BLUEs $\widehat{\tau}_1 - \widehat{\tau}_2$, $\widehat{\tau}_1 - \widehat{\tau}_3$ and $\widehat{\tau}_2 - \widehat{\tau}_3$ and their 95% coverage two-sided confidence intervals are obtained through the following R code, similar to the code used in the previous example.

```
data(denim); attach(denim)
X <- cbind(1,binaries(Denim),binaries(Laundry))
p <- c(0,1,-1,0,0,0,0)
cisngl(Abrasion,X,p,0.05,type = "both")
p <- c(0,1,0,-1,0,0,0)
cisngl(Abrasion,X,p,0.05,type = "both")
p <- c(0,0,1,-1,0,0,0)
cisngl(Abrasion,X,p,0.05,type = "both"); detach(denim)
```

The point estimates are computed as 0.9447, 0.4333 and −0.5113, respectively. The confidence intervals for the treatment differences $\tau_1 - \tau_2$, $\tau_1 - \tau_3$ and $\tau_2 - \tau_3$ are obtained as $[0.7272, 1.1622]$, $[0.2159, 0.6508]$ and $[-0.7288, -0.2938]$, respectively.

While any one of the intervals is expected to capture the correct treatment difference with the probability 0.95, the chances of *all* of them capturing the true values of the parameters is less. This issue will be looked into in Section 4.3.3. □

4.3.2 *Confidence region for a vector LPF**

Construction of a confidence region for the vector LPF $\boldsymbol{A\beta}$ is a meaningful task only if $\boldsymbol{A\beta}$ is estimable. Let us assume that it is estimable and $\boldsymbol{y} \sim N(\boldsymbol{X\beta}, \sigma^2\boldsymbol{I})$. It follows from Propositions 4.19 and 4.21 that

$$\frac{(\boldsymbol{A}\widehat{\boldsymbol{\beta}} - \boldsymbol{A\beta})'[\boldsymbol{A}(\boldsymbol{X}'\boldsymbol{X})^-\boldsymbol{A}']^-(\boldsymbol{A}\widehat{\boldsymbol{\beta}} - \boldsymbol{A\beta})}{m\widehat{\sigma^2}} \sim F_{m,n-r}.$$

If $F_{m,n-r,\alpha}$ is the $(1-\alpha)$ quantile of this distribution, we have

$$P\left[(\boldsymbol{A\beta} - \boldsymbol{A}\widehat{\boldsymbol{\beta}})'[\boldsymbol{A}(\boldsymbol{X}'\boldsymbol{X})^-\boldsymbol{A}']^-(\boldsymbol{A\beta} - \boldsymbol{A}\widehat{\boldsymbol{\beta}}) \le m\widehat{\sigma^2}F_{m,n-r,\alpha}\right] = 1 - \alpha.$$

The implied confidence region for $\boldsymbol{A\beta}$ is an m-dimensional ellipsoid given by

$$\Big\{\boldsymbol{A\beta} : (\boldsymbol{A\beta} - \boldsymbol{A}\widehat{\boldsymbol{\beta}})'[\boldsymbol{A}(\boldsymbol{X}'\boldsymbol{X})^-\boldsymbol{A}']^-(\boldsymbol{A\beta} - \boldsymbol{A}\widehat{\boldsymbol{\beta}}) \le m\widehat{\sigma^2}F_{m,n-r,\alpha},$$
$$(\boldsymbol{A\beta} - \boldsymbol{A}\widehat{\boldsymbol{\beta}}) \in \mathcal{C}(\boldsymbol{A}(\boldsymbol{X}'\boldsymbol{X})^-\boldsymbol{A}')\Big\}. \tag{4.15}$$

Example 4.32. (Abrasion of denim jeans, continued) Consider the vector LPF $(\tau_1 - \tau_3 : \tau_2 - \tau_3)'$ in the model of Example 3.5. We write it as $\boldsymbol{A\beta}$, where

$$\boldsymbol{A} = \begin{pmatrix} 0\,1\,0\,-1\,0\,0\,0 \\ 0\,0\,1\,-1\,0\,0\,0 \end{pmatrix}.$$

Here, $m = \rho(\boldsymbol{A}) = 2$, $n - r = 85$, $\widehat{\sigma^2} = 0.1795$, $\boldsymbol{A}\widehat{\boldsymbol{\beta}} = (0.4333 : -0.5113)'$,

$$\boldsymbol{A}(\boldsymbol{X}'\boldsymbol{X})^{-}\boldsymbol{A}' = \begin{pmatrix} \frac{1}{15} & \frac{1}{30} \\ \frac{1}{30} & \frac{1}{15} \end{pmatrix}, \quad [\boldsymbol{A}(\boldsymbol{X}'\boldsymbol{X})^{-}\boldsymbol{A}']^{-1} = \begin{pmatrix} 20 & -10 \\ -10 & 20 \end{pmatrix}.$$

Further, $m\widehat{\sigma^2}F_{m,n-r,\alpha} = 1.1141$. Therefore, the confidence region for the two treatment differences with 95% coverage probability is

$$\begin{pmatrix} \tau_1 - \tau_3 - 0.4333 \\ \tau_3 - \tau_2 + 0.5113 \end{pmatrix}' \begin{pmatrix} 20 & -10 \\ -10 & 20 \end{pmatrix} \begin{pmatrix} \tau_1 - \tau_3 - 0.4333 \\ \tau_3 - \tau_2 + 0.5113 \end{pmatrix} \leq 1.1141.$$

The confidence ellipsoid can be described in terms of three components: the vector $\boldsymbol{A}\widehat{\boldsymbol{\beta}}$ where the ellipse is centered, the central matrix $[\boldsymbol{A}(\boldsymbol{X}'\boldsymbol{X})^{-}\boldsymbol{A}']^{-}$ and the scalar threshold $m\widehat{\sigma^2}F_{m,n-r,\alpha}$ with which the quadratic form is compared. The following R code computes these quantities from specified $\boldsymbol{y}$, $\boldsymbol{X}$, $\boldsymbol{A}$ and α, assuming $\boldsymbol{A\beta}$ to be estimable, using function `confelps` of the R package `lmreg`.

```
data(denim); attach(denim)
X <- cbind(1,binaries(Denim),binaries(Laundry))
A <- rbind(c(0,1,0,-1,0,0,0),c(0,0,1,-1,0,0,0))
confelps(Abrasion, X, A, 0.05); detach(denim)
```

See page 158 for a graph of the confidence region obtained here. □

Suppose $\boldsymbol{\beta}$ is estimable, that is, $\rho(\boldsymbol{X})$ is equal to p, the number of columns of $\boldsymbol{X}$. Then we can find a confidence region of $\boldsymbol{\beta}$ by replacing $\boldsymbol{A}$, $[\boldsymbol{A}(\boldsymbol{X}'\boldsymbol{X})^{-}\boldsymbol{A}']^{-}$ and m in the expression (4.15) by $\boldsymbol{I}$, $\boldsymbol{X}'\boldsymbol{X}$ and p, respectively. Specifically, a confidence region of $\boldsymbol{\beta}$ with confidence coefficient $1-\alpha$ is the p-dimensional ellipsoid

$$\left\{\boldsymbol{\beta} : \|\boldsymbol{X\beta} - \boldsymbol{X}\widehat{\boldsymbol{\beta}}\|^2 \leq p\widehat{\sigma^2}F_{p,n-p,\alpha}\right\}. \tag{4.16}$$

If the assumption of normality of $\boldsymbol{y}$ is not tenable, the above confidence regions may be grossly inaccurate. Alternative confidence regions may be constructed by using resampling techniques (see Sections 9.4–9.5 of Efron and Tibshirani, 1993 and Sections 7.2–7.3 of Shao and Tu, 1996). These methods usually involve considerable computation, but provide satisfactory results for moderate sample sizes.

4.3.3 Simultaneous confidence intervals*

If $\boldsymbol{a}_1', \boldsymbol{a}_2', \ldots, \boldsymbol{a}_q'$ denote the rows of the matrix $\boldsymbol{A}$, then the vector parameter $\boldsymbol{A\beta}$ represents the LPFs $\boldsymbol{a}_1'\boldsymbol{\beta}, \boldsymbol{a}_2'\boldsymbol{\beta}, \ldots, \boldsymbol{a}_q'\boldsymbol{\beta}$, with $m = \rho(\boldsymbol{A}) \leq q$. As an alternative to the ellipsoidal confidence region in the q-dimensional parameter space, one may construct individual confidence intervals for each of the scalar LPFs, $\boldsymbol{a}_1'\boldsymbol{\beta}$, $\boldsymbol{a}_2'\boldsymbol{\beta}, \ldots$, $\boldsymbol{a}_q'\boldsymbol{\beta}$. Viewed in the q-dimensional parameter space, these simultaneous confidence intervals represent a q-dimensional rectangle. Such intervals may be easier to visualize and deal with, compared to the ellipsoidal regions, particularly when q is greater than 3. Since the interest is typically in all the LPFs simultaneously, it is meaningful to assign a *single* coverage probability to the combination of these q confidence intervals, rather than a separate confidence level to each interval. These are referred to as the *simultaneous confidence intervals.* These intervals are designed to simultaneously capture the target parameters with specified probability, somewhat like multiple comparison tests with a specified probability of erroneous rejection of any one of the single-degree-of-freedom hypothesis (see Section 4.2.7).

Let us first examine single confidence intervals of the type described in Section 4.3.1. A two-sided interval for the single LPF $\boldsymbol{a}_j'\boldsymbol{\beta}$ with confidence coefficient $1-\alpha$ is

$$I_j^{(s)} = \left[\boldsymbol{a}_j'\widehat{\boldsymbol{\beta}} - t_{n-r,\frac{\alpha}{2}}\sqrt{\widehat{\sigma^2}\boldsymbol{a}_j'(\boldsymbol{X}'\boldsymbol{X})^-\boldsymbol{a}_j},\ \boldsymbol{a}_j'\widehat{\boldsymbol{\beta}} + t_{n-r,\frac{\alpha}{2}}\sqrt{\widehat{\sigma^2}\boldsymbol{a}_j'(\boldsymbol{X}'\boldsymbol{X})^-\boldsymbol{a}_j}\right],$$

where $r = \rho(\boldsymbol{X})$. Let $\mathcal{E}_j$ denote the event

$$\mathcal{E}_j = \{\boldsymbol{a}_j'\boldsymbol{\beta} \in \boldsymbol{I}_j^{(s)}\}.$$

The coverage probability of $\boldsymbol{I}_j^{(s)}$ is $P(\mathcal{E}_j)$, which is equal to $1-\alpha$ for every j. The coverage probability of the simultaneous confidence intervals $\boldsymbol{I}_1^{(s)}, \ldots, I_q^{(s)}$ is $P(\mathcal{E}_1 \cap \cdots \cap \mathcal{E}_q)$. If $\boldsymbol{a}_j'\widehat{\boldsymbol{\beta}}$, $j = 1, \ldots, q$ were independent, then the coverage probability would have simplified to $(1-\alpha)^q$. These are not, in general, independent (they involve a common $\widehat{\sigma^2}$ for one) and the exact probability becomes difficult to compute. Using the superscript c to denote the complement of a set or event, the Bonferroni inequality gives

$$\begin{aligned} P(\mathcal{E}_1 \cap \cdots \cap \mathcal{E}_q) &= 1 - P(\mathcal{E}_1^c \cup \cdots \cup \mathcal{E}_q^c) \\ &\geq 1 - [P(\mathcal{E}_1^c) + \cdots + P(\mathcal{E}_q^c)] \ = \ 1 - q\alpha, \\ P(\mathcal{E}_1 \cap \cdots \cap \mathcal{E}_q) &\leq P(\mathcal{E}_1) \ = \ 1-\alpha. \end{aligned}$$

The above inequalities can be summarized to produce the following bounds for the coverage probability of the simultaneous confidence intervals:

$$1 - q\alpha \leq P(I_j^{(s)} \text{ includes } \boldsymbol{a}_j'\boldsymbol{\beta} \text{ for all } j) \leq 1-\alpha.$$

It is clear that the combination of the confidence intervals of the single intervals described above, does not have adequate coverage probability. However, if we replace α by α/q, then the resulting simultaneous confident intervals

$$I_j^{(b)} = \left[\boldsymbol{a}_j'\widehat{\boldsymbol{\beta}} - t_{n-r,\frac{\alpha}{2q}}\sqrt{\widehat{\sigma^2}\boldsymbol{a}_j'(\boldsymbol{X}'\boldsymbol{X})^-\boldsymbol{a}_j},\ \boldsymbol{a}_j'\widehat{\boldsymbol{\beta}} + t_{n-r,\frac{\alpha}{2q}}\sqrt{\widehat{\sigma^2}\boldsymbol{a}_j'(\boldsymbol{X}'\boldsymbol{X})^-\boldsymbol{a}_j}\right], \tag{4.17}$$

$j = 1, 2, \ldots, q$, would have coverage probability greater than equal to $1 - q\alpha/q = 1 - \alpha$. These are called *Bonferroni confidence intervals.*

In general, the Bonferroni confidence intervals are conservative in the sense that the actual coverage probability is often much more than the assured minimum coverage probability of $(1 - \alpha)$. In spite of this, the Bonferroni rectangle in the q-dimensional parameter space may not entirely include the ellipsoid discussed in Section 4.3.2. In other words, a vector $\boldsymbol{A\beta}$ may belong to the ellipsoidal confidence region of (4.15), and yet some of its components may lie outside the Bonferroni confidence intervals. Scheffé suggested a set of conservative confidence intervals which avoids this possibility. *Scheffé confidence intervals* can be described geometrically as the smallest q-dimensional rectangle, with faces orthogonal to the parameter axes, which includes the ellipsoid (4.15). Thus, the faces of this rectangle are tangents to the ellipsoid. The algebraic description of Scheffé simultaneous confidence intervals is as follows (see Exercise 4.10).

$$\begin{aligned} I_j^{(sc)} = & \left[\boldsymbol{a}_j'\widehat{\boldsymbol{\beta}} - \sqrt{mF_{m,n-r,\alpha}\boldsymbol{a}_j'(\boldsymbol{X}'\boldsymbol{X})^-\boldsymbol{a}_j\widehat{\sigma^2}},\right. \\ & \left.\boldsymbol{a}_j'\widehat{\boldsymbol{\beta}} + \sqrt{mF_{m,n-r,\alpha}\boldsymbol{a}_j'(\boldsymbol{X}'\boldsymbol{X})^-\boldsymbol{a}_j\widehat{\sigma^2}}\right], \quad j = 1, 2, \ldots, q. \end{aligned} \tag{4.18}$$

The procedures for multiple comparison introduced in Section 4.2.7 have close connection with the confidence intervals described above. Specifically, rejection in any of the multiple comparison tests (4.9) happens if and only if corresponding the Bonferroni confidence interval in (4.17) fails to capture the hypothesized value of the parameter. Likewise, a test described in (4.10) leads to rejection if and only if the hypothesized value lies outside the corresponding Scheffé confidence confidence interval described in (4.18).

Example 4.33. (Abrasion of denim jeans, continued) The function `cisimult` of the R package `lmreg` produces two-sided Bonferroni and Scheffé simultaneous confidence intervals, together with corresponding single confidence intervals, for any vector of estimable functions $\boldsymbol{A\beta}$. These are computed from any given response vector $\boldsymbol{y}$, model matrix $\boldsymbol{X}$, the coefficient matrix $\boldsymbol{A}$ and the non-coverage probability α. This function is used in the following R code to produce the three sets of confidence intervals for the mean differences in the effects of the denim treatments in the model of Example 3.5, with coverage probability 0.95.

```
data(denim); attach(denim)
X <- cbind(1,binaries(Denim),binaries(Laundry))
A <- rbind(c(0,1,-1,0,0,0,0),c(0,1,0,-1,0,0,0),c(0,0,1,-1,0,0,0))
cisimult(Abrasion, X, A, 0.05); detach(denim)
```

The resulting confidence intervals are reported in the following table.

Parameter	Bonferroni SCI	Scheffé SCI	Single CI
$\tau_1 - \tau_2$	$[0.6775, 1.2118]$	$[0.6721, 1.2172]$	$[0.7272, 1.1622]$
$\tau_1 - \tau_3$	$[0.1662, 0.7005]$	$[0.1608, 0.7059]$	$[0.2159, 0.6508]$
$\tau_2 - \tau_3$	$[-0.7785, -0.2442]$	$[-0.7839, -0.2388]$	$[-0.7288, -0.2938]$

The single confidence intervals, previously reported on page 153, are much shorter than the simultaneous ones, as they are not meant to cover all the parameters simultaneously with the stipulated coverage probability. In this example the Bonferroni intervals are shorter than the Scheffé intervals.

Figure 4.1 shows the 95% confidence regions for $\widehat{\tau}_1 - \widehat{\tau}_3$ and $\widehat{\tau}_2 - \widehat{\tau}_3$ implied by these confidence intervals and also the elliptical confidence region obtained on page 154. All the pairs of confidence intervals represent rectangular regions. The Scheffé intervals correspond to the smallest rectangle that encloses the elliptical confidence region. The Bonferroni region, a marginally smaller rectangle has partial overlap with the ellipse. The shortest rectangle, which arises from the single confidence intervals, does not have adequate coverage probability for the pair of parameters. □

A set of simultaneous confidence intervals with *exact* coverage probability can be obtained if the components of $\boldsymbol{A}\widehat{\boldsymbol{\beta}}$ are uncorrelated. In such a case $m = q$, and

$$\max_{1\le j\le m} \frac{|\boldsymbol{a}_j'\widehat{\boldsymbol{\beta}} - \boldsymbol{a}_j'\boldsymbol{\beta}|}{[\sigma^2 \boldsymbol{a}_j'(\boldsymbol{X}'\boldsymbol{X})^- \boldsymbol{a}_j]^{1/2}}$$

has the same distribution as $t_* = \max_{1\le j\le m} |z_j|/s$, where $(n-r)s^2 \sim \chi_{n-r}$, $z_1, \ldots, z_m \sim N(0,1)$ and $s, z_1, \ldots, z_m$ are independent. The joint distribution of $z_1/s, \ldots, z_m/s$ is said to be multivariate t with parameters m and $n-r$, and the distribution of t_* can be derived from it. Let $t_{m,n-r,\alpha}$ be the $1-\alpha$ quantile of the distribution of t_* (see Hahn and Hendrickson,

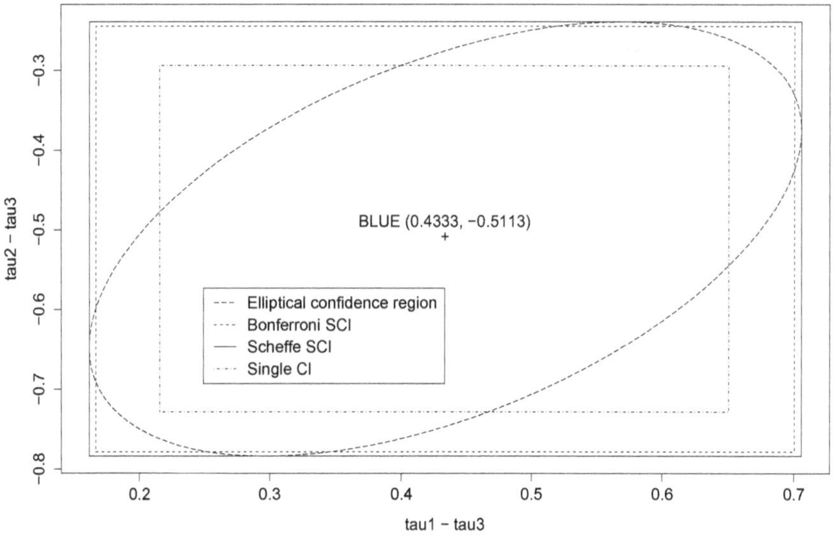

Fig. 4.1 Rectangular and elliptic confidence regions for Examples 4.31–4.33

1971 for a table of these quantiles). Then we have the *maximum modulus-t* confidence intervals

$$I_j^{(t)} = \left[\boldsymbol{a}_j'\widehat{\boldsymbol{\beta}} - t_{m,n-r,\alpha}\sqrt{\widehat{\sigma^2}\boldsymbol{a}_j'(\boldsymbol{X}'\boldsymbol{X})^{-}\boldsymbol{a}_j}, \right.$$
$$\left. \boldsymbol{a}_j'\widehat{\boldsymbol{\beta}} + t_{m,n-r,\alpha}\sqrt{\widehat{\sigma^2}\boldsymbol{a}_j'(\boldsymbol{X}'\boldsymbol{X})^{-}\boldsymbol{a}_j} \right], \quad j = 1, 2, \ldots, m.$$

This confidence interval has coverage probability exactly equal to $1 - \alpha$, only when the of LPFs of interest have uncorrelated BLUEs. Sidak (1968) showed that these confidence intervals are conservative for a general class of correlation pattern of the BLUEs.

Apart from the three simultaneous confidence intervals mentioned here, other useful intervals can be found in some special cases. A few such methods applicable to comparison of groups means are discussed in Section 6.2.4 (see also Miller, 1981, Chapter 2).

4.3.4 *Confidence band for regression surface**

In the context of linear regression analysis we can write the generic model equation for each observation as

$$y = \boldsymbol{x}'\boldsymbol{\beta} + \varepsilon, \tag{4.19}$$

which is another form of (1.1). We wish to specify a neighbourhood of the fitted value $(\boldsymbol{x}'\widehat{\boldsymbol{\beta}})$ which is likely to include the 'true' mean of the response $(\boldsymbol{x}'\boldsymbol{\beta})$ for all reasonable $\boldsymbol{x}$. This region can be called a confidence band for the regression surface.

The problem can be viewed as that of finding simultaneous confidence intervals for infinitely many $\boldsymbol{x}'\boldsymbol{\beta}$s. If we consider only a finite number of estimable LPFs, Scheffé's simultaneous confidence intervals are applicable. A crucial advantage of these intervals is that the distribution involved in the computation depends only on the number of the *linearly independent* LPFs, and *not* on the total number of LPFs (see (4.18) where m is used, but q is not). Thus, if r is the rank of $\boldsymbol{X}$, then simultaneous confidence intervals for r linearly independent LPFs can lead to confidence intervals for any finite number of estimable LPFs. The next proposition shows that this result holds even for infinitely many estimable LPFs.

Proposition 4.34. *Let the response vector $\boldsymbol{y}_{n\times 1}$ have the distribution $N(\boldsymbol{X\beta}, \sigma^2\boldsymbol{I})$ and r be that rank of $\boldsymbol{X}$. Then*

$$P\left[|\boldsymbol{x}'\boldsymbol{\beta}-\boldsymbol{x}'\widehat{\boldsymbol{\beta}}| \le \left\{rF_{r,n-r,\alpha}\boldsymbol{x}'(\boldsymbol{X}'\boldsymbol{X})^-\boldsymbol{x}\widehat{\sigma^2}\right\}^{\frac{1}{2}} \text{ for all } \boldsymbol{x} \in \mathcal{C}(\boldsymbol{X}')\right] = 1-\alpha.$$

Proof. Let $\boldsymbol{l}$ be such that $\boldsymbol{x} = \boldsymbol{X}'\boldsymbol{l}$. Let us define $\boldsymbol{b} = \boldsymbol{P}_X(\boldsymbol{X}\widehat{\boldsymbol{\beta}} - \boldsymbol{X\beta})$ and $\boldsymbol{c} = \boldsymbol{P}_X\boldsymbol{l}$. It follows from the Cauchy-Schwarz inequality that

$$\frac{(\boldsymbol{x}'\widehat{\boldsymbol{\beta}} - \boldsymbol{x}'\boldsymbol{\beta})^2}{\widehat{\sigma^2}\boldsymbol{x}'(\boldsymbol{X}'\boldsymbol{X})^-\boldsymbol{x}} = \frac{(\boldsymbol{l}'\boldsymbol{X}\widehat{\boldsymbol{\beta}} - \boldsymbol{l}'\boldsymbol{X\beta})^2}{\widehat{\sigma^2}\boldsymbol{l}'\boldsymbol{P}_X\boldsymbol{l}} = \frac{(\boldsymbol{c}'\boldsymbol{b})^2}{\widehat{\sigma^2}\boldsymbol{c}'\boldsymbol{c}} \le \frac{\boldsymbol{b}'\boldsymbol{b}}{\widehat{\sigma^2}}.$$

Also, $\boldsymbol{b} \sim N(\boldsymbol{0}, \sigma^2\boldsymbol{P}_X)$, and consequently $\boldsymbol{b}'\boldsymbol{b}/\sigma^2 \sim \chi^2_r$. Since $\boldsymbol{b}$ is independent of $\widehat{\sigma^2}$ (see Proposition 4.1), we have $\boldsymbol{b}'\boldsymbol{b}/(r\widehat{\sigma^2}) \sim F_{r,n-r}$. It follows that

$$P\left[\max_{\boldsymbol{x} \in \mathcal{C}(\boldsymbol{X}')} \frac{(\boldsymbol{x}'\widehat{\boldsymbol{\beta}} - \boldsymbol{x}'\boldsymbol{\beta})^2}{r\widehat{\sigma^2}\boldsymbol{x}'(\boldsymbol{X}'\boldsymbol{X})^-\boldsymbol{x}} \le F_{r,n-r,\alpha}\right] = 1-\alpha. \qquad \square$$

Proposition 4.34 is in fact a consequence of Scheffé's simultaneous confidence intervals in the special case $\boldsymbol{A} = \boldsymbol{X}$.

In the case of simple linear regression, we have the model (4.19) with $\boldsymbol{x} = (1 : x)'$ and $\boldsymbol{\beta} = (\beta_0 : \beta_1)'$. The $100(1-\alpha)\%$ confidence band for the regression line $(\beta_0 + \beta_1 x)$ simplifies to

$$\left[\widehat{\beta}_0 + \widehat{\beta}_1 x - \sqrt{2F_{2,n-2,\alpha}\widehat{\sigma^2}\left(\frac{1}{n} + \frac{(x-\bar{x})^2}{n(\overline{x^2}-\bar{x}^2)}\right)}, \right.$$
$$\left. \widehat{\beta}_0 + \widehat{\beta}_1 x + \sqrt{2F_{2,n-2,\alpha}\widehat{\sigma^2}\left(\frac{1}{n} + \frac{(x-\bar{x})^2}{n(\overline{x^2}-\bar{x}^2)}\right)}\right], \tag{4.20}$$

where $\bar{x}$ and $\overline{x^2}$ are the observed average of x and x^2, respectively (see Exercise 4.13).

Example 4.35. (Receding galaxies, continued) For the galaxies data of Table 3.1, we had already fitted a linear model for the velocity (y) of a galactic object at a given distance from the Earth (x). We now have, from (4.20), the following 95% confidence band for the expected velocity of a star at a distance x.

$$\left[-68.15 + 465.9x - 134.2\sqrt{1 + (x - 0.9114)^2/0.3993},\right.$$
$$\left. -68.15 + 465.9x + 134.2\sqrt{1 + (x - 0.9114)^2/0.3993}\right].$$

The upper and lower parts of the band are plotted in Figure 4.2. The band happens to be narrower in the middle than at the extremes. This is because the width of the band is an increasing function of the gap between x and its mean.

The above computations and the plot are obtained through the following R code.

```
data(stars1)
lmstars <- lm(Velocity~Distance,data = stars1)
x <- stars1[,1]; n <- length(x)
beta <- lmstars$coef
wsig <- summary(lmstars)$sigma
vx <- mean(x^2)-(mean(x))^2
multiplier <- wsig * sqrt(2*qf(0.05,2,n-2,lower.tail = F)/n)
beta; mean(x); vx; multiplier
xseq <- seq(from = min(x), to = max(x), length.out = 200)
hw <- multiplier * sqrt(1 + (xseq - mean(x))^2 / vx)
lcb <- beta[1] + beta[2] * xseq - hw
ucb <- beta[1] + beta[2] * xseq + hw
plot(stars1); lines(xseq,lcb); lines(xseq,ucb)
```

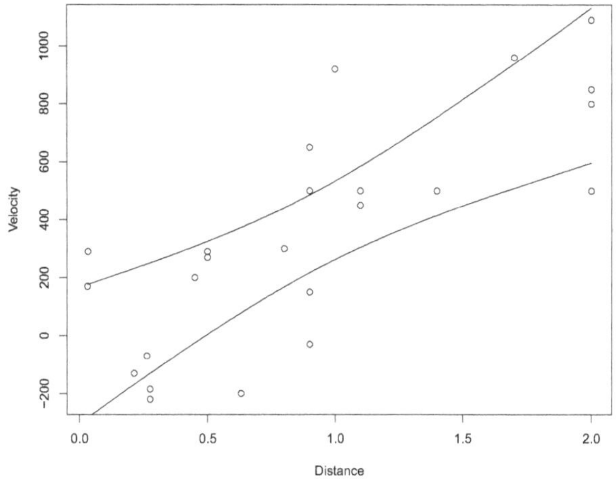

Fig. 4.2 Confidence band for the regression line of Example 4.35

The data for this analysis had been compiled by Edwin Hubble using measurements available at that time. Within a few years of his discovery of an expanding universe, more accurate measurements became available. The new measurements, based on more distant galactic objects with higher velocity, confirmed Hubble's discovery. A regression line based on these data (see Table 4.5 on page 175 and Exercise 4.15) would lie mostly within the confidence band shown in Figure 4.2, but would go marginally above it where the band is the narrowest. We may note that the assumption of errors with zero-means might not have held for Hubble's measurements. □

Further details on confidence band for the regression surface can be found in Miller (1981, Section 3.4.1).

4.4 Prediction in the linear model

Suppose y_0 is an unobserved response, which has to be predicted by making use of the observed response vector $\boldsymbol{y}$. If $g(\boldsymbol{y})$ is a predictor of y_0, then it may be called a good predictor if $E[y_0 - g(\boldsymbol{y})]^2$, the *mean squared error of prediction* (MSEP), is small. It was mentioned in Section 2.3 that the MSEP is minimized when $g(\boldsymbol{y}) = E(y_0|\boldsymbol{y})$. Thus, the regression of y_0 on $\boldsymbol{y}$ is the *best predictor* of y_0. However, the regression may not be known or may not have a simple form.

If we restrict g to be a linear function, then the resulting predictor can be called a linear predictor. The *best linear predictor* (BLP) is the linear function of $\boldsymbol{y}$ which minimizes the MSEP. An expression for $\widehat{E}(y_0|\boldsymbol{y})$, the BLP of y_0 in terms of $\boldsymbol{y}$, is given in Proposition 2.23. The BLP is a linear function of $\boldsymbol{y}$, expressed in terms of the first and the second order moments of y_0 and $\boldsymbol{y}$, which may not be known. The number of moments to be estimated is generally large in comparison to the size of the vector $\boldsymbol{y}$. Therefore, one has to use a model, such as an autoregressive model. This method is not very useful when y_0 has little or no correlation with $\boldsymbol{y}$.

This is where the linear regression model can play a role. Suppose y_0 and $\boldsymbol{y}$ are the responses from the models $(y_0, \boldsymbol{x}_0'\boldsymbol{\beta}, \sigma^2)$ and $(\boldsymbol{y}, \boldsymbol{X\beta}, \sigma^2\boldsymbol{I})$, respectively, where $\boldsymbol{x}_0$ and $\boldsymbol{X}$ are observed values of possibly random explanatory variables. We assume that, given $\boldsymbol{x}_0$ and $\boldsymbol{X}$, y_0 and $\boldsymbol{y}$ are uncorrelated. The links between the two models are the common parameters $\boldsymbol{\beta}$ and σ^2, which are unspecified. Note that the above model for y_0 implies that the BLP of y_0 is $\boldsymbol{x}_0'\boldsymbol{\beta}$, and the mean square prediction error is σ^2. When $\boldsymbol{\beta}$ and σ^2 are unknown, we would have to make use of the fact the $\boldsymbol{y}$ carries some information about them.

4.4.1 *Best linear unbiased predictor*

Suppose we wish to predict y_0 with the linear predictor $\boldsymbol{a}'\boldsymbol{y} + b$. The mean squared prediction error (MSEP) of this predictor can be written as

$$\begin{aligned}E[y_0 - \boldsymbol{a}'\boldsymbol{y} - b]^2 &= E[(y_0 - \boldsymbol{x}_0'\boldsymbol{\beta} + \boldsymbol{x}_0'\boldsymbol{\beta} - \boldsymbol{a}'\boldsymbol{y} - b)^2]\\ &= E[y_0 - \boldsymbol{x}_0'\boldsymbol{\beta}]^2 + E[\boldsymbol{x}_0'\boldsymbol{\beta} - \boldsymbol{a}'\boldsymbol{y} - b]^2,\end{aligned}$$

because y_0 and $\boldsymbol{y}$ are uncorrelated and $E(y_0) = \boldsymbol{x}_0'\boldsymbol{\beta}$. Therefore, minimizing the MSEP with respect to $\boldsymbol{a}$ and b is equivalent to minimizing $E[\boldsymbol{x}_0'\boldsymbol{\beta} - \boldsymbol{a}'\boldsymbol{y} - b]^2$.

At this point we put a crucial restriction on the linear predictor. We require that $\boldsymbol{a}'\boldsymbol{y}+b$ be an *unbiased* predictor of y_0 *for all* $\boldsymbol{\beta}$. Since $E(y_0) = \boldsymbol{x}_0'\boldsymbol{\beta}$, this assumption is equivalent to the condition

$$E(\boldsymbol{a}'\boldsymbol{y} + b) = \boldsymbol{x}_0'\boldsymbol{\beta} \qquad \text{for all } \boldsymbol{\beta}.$$

We would look for the linear unbiased predictor with the smallest MSEP, and call it the *best linear unbiased predictor* (BLUP).

Isn't the BLP itself an unbiased predictor? Of course it is, but it is still not useful as long as it depends on the unknown parameter $\boldsymbol{\beta}$. In order to find a meaningful solution, we put the further condition that $\boldsymbol{a}$ and b should not be functions of $\boldsymbol{\beta}$. This automatically rules out BLP as a candidate for BLUP.

When $\boldsymbol{x}_0 \in \mathcal{C}(\boldsymbol{X}')$, Exercise 3.6 indicates that the condition '$E(\boldsymbol{a}'\boldsymbol{y} + b) = \boldsymbol{x}_0'\boldsymbol{\beta}$ for all $\boldsymbol{\beta}$' holds if and only if $b = 0$ and $\boldsymbol{a}'\boldsymbol{y}$ is an LUE of the estimable LPF $\boldsymbol{x}_0'\boldsymbol{\beta}$. Hence, the solution to the above optimization problem is obtained by choosing b as 0 and $\boldsymbol{a}'\boldsymbol{y}$ as the BLUE of $\boldsymbol{x}_0'\boldsymbol{\beta}$. Thus, the unique BLUP of y_0 is the BLUE of $\boldsymbol{x}_0'\boldsymbol{\beta}$ in the model $(\boldsymbol{y}, \boldsymbol{X\beta}, \sigma^2\boldsymbol{I})$. If $\boldsymbol{x}_0 \notin \mathcal{C}(\boldsymbol{X}')$, it is easy to see that the BLUP does not exist.

The above result depends on the crucial assumption that y_0 and $\boldsymbol{y}$ are conditionally uncorrelated, given $\boldsymbol{x}_0$ and $\boldsymbol{X}$. See Section 7.13 for a generalization to the correlated case.

4.4.2 *Prediction interval*

Suppose a future response y_0 has to be predicted on the basis of past response $\boldsymbol{y}$, the vector of explanatory variables ($\boldsymbol{x}_0$) corresponding to y_0 and the matrix of explanatory variables ($\boldsymbol{X}$) corresponding to $\boldsymbol{y}$. In addition to the best linear unbiased (point) predictor, we want to find an interval which will contain y_0 with a specified probability.

We assume once again that $\boldsymbol{x}_0 \in \mathcal{C}(\boldsymbol{X}')$, i.e. $\boldsymbol{x}_0'\boldsymbol{\beta}$ is an estimable LPF. The prediction error of the BLUP is

$$e_0 = y_0 - \boldsymbol{x}_0'\widehat{\boldsymbol{\beta}} = y_0 - \boldsymbol{x}_0'(\boldsymbol{X}'\boldsymbol{X})^-\boldsymbol{X}'\boldsymbol{y}.$$

The mean of the prediction error is zero, while the variance is

$$Var(e_0) = \sigma^2(1 + \boldsymbol{x}_0'(\boldsymbol{X}'\boldsymbol{X})^-\boldsymbol{x}_0).$$

If y_0 and $\boldsymbol{y}$ (given $\boldsymbol{x}_0$ and $\boldsymbol{X}$) jointly have the normal distribution with appropriate mean and dispersion, then Proposition 4.1 implies that e_0 has the normal distribution with zero mean and the variance given above. Using the argument of Section 4.3 we conclude that the interval

$$[\widehat{y}_0 - a, \widehat{y}_0 + a], \quad \text{where } \widehat{y}_0 = \boldsymbol{x}_0'(\boldsymbol{X}'\boldsymbol{X})^-\boldsymbol{X}'\boldsymbol{y},$$
$$a = t_{n-r,\alpha/2}\sqrt{\widehat{\sigma^2}(1 + \boldsymbol{x}_0'(\boldsymbol{X}'\boldsymbol{X})^-\boldsymbol{x}_0)}, \qquad (4.21)$$

contains the unobserved response y_0 with probability $1 - \alpha$. We call this a $100(1-\alpha)\%$ *prediction interval* for y_0.

In the special case of prediction of y_0 on the basis of a single predictor, let x_0 be the value of that predictor corresponding to y_0 and $x_1, \ldots, x_n$ be its values corresponding to the available data $y_1, \ldots, y_n$. The prediction interval (4.21) simplifies to

$$[\widehat{\beta}_0+\widehat{\beta}_1x_0-a,\widehat{\beta}_0+\widehat{\beta}_1x_0+a], \text{ with } a=t_{n-2,\alpha/2}\sqrt{\widehat{\sigma^2}\left(1+\frac{1}{n}+\frac{(x-\bar{x})^2}{n(\overline{x^2}-\bar{x}^2)}\right)}. \tag{4.22}$$

Note that the prediction interval is wider than the corresponding two-sided *confidence interval* for $\boldsymbol{x}_0'\boldsymbol{\beta}$. The additional width accounts for the error in observing $\boldsymbol{x}_0'\boldsymbol{\beta}$. The difference between the widths of the two intervals can be quite substantial when $\boldsymbol{x}_0'(\boldsymbol{X}'\boldsymbol{X})^-\boldsymbol{x}_0$ is small, which typically happens when the sample size (n) is large. The prediction error of the BLUP is the sum of the estimation error of $\boldsymbol{x}_0'\boldsymbol{\beta}$ (which is $\boldsymbol{x}_0'\widehat{\boldsymbol{\beta}}-\boldsymbol{x}_0'\boldsymbol{\beta}$) and the deviation of the observation from its mean (which is $y_0-\boldsymbol{x}_0'\boldsymbol{\beta}$). We can hope to reduce the estimation error using a lot of data, but we still have to allow for the variability in the observations while constructing the prediction interval. The latter component does not depend on n.

Example 4.36. (Waist circumference) The data set given in Table 4.4, taken from Daniel and Cross (2013, Table 9.3.1), shows the area of lower abdominal adipose tissue in squared centimeters (AT), known to be associated with metabolic disorders considered as risk factors for cardiovascular disease, and waist circumference in centimeters ($waist$) of 109 men. Here, the waist circumference is meant to be an indicator of the extent of adipose tissue. We now regress $\log(AT)$ on $\log(waist)$ and get the estimated coefficients, using the following R code.

```
data(waist)
lmwaist <- lm(log(AT)~log(Waist), data = waist)
summary(lmwaist)$coef
```

The resulting output is given below.

```
                Estimate Std. Error   t value     Pr(>|t|)
(Intercept) -12.460697  0.9820080 -12.68900 4.572668e-23
log(Waist)    3.747567  0.2176302  17.21988 1.287410e-32
```

Thus, the least squares fitted equation is

$$\log(AT) = -12.46 + 3.748\log(waist).$$

The log transformation is used here for better adherence to the assumptions of the linear model; the issue of validation of these assumptions is discussed in Chapter 5, page 221.

Table 4.4 Waist circumference and adipose tissue data (data object `waist` in R package `lmreg`, source: Daniel and Cross, 2013)

waist (cm)	AT (cm^2)	waist (cm)	AT (cm^2)	waist (cm)	AT (cm^2)	waist (cm)	AT (cm^2)
74.75	25.72	86.00	78.89	78.60	58.16	110.00	153.00
72.60	25.89	82.50	64.75	87.80	88.85	112.00	158.00
81.80	42.60	83.50	72.56	86.30	155.00	108.50	183.00
83.95	42.80	88.10	89.31	85.50	70.77	104.00	184.00
74.65	29.84	90.80	78.94	83.70	75.08	111.00	121.00
71.85	21.68	89.40	83.55	77.60	57.05	108.50	159.00
80.90	29.08	102.00	127.00	84.90	99.73	121.00	245.00
83.40	32.98	94.50	121.00	79.80	27.96	109.00	137.00
63.50	11.44	91.00	107.00	108.30	123.00	97.50	165.00
73.20	32.22	103.00	129.00	119.60	90.41	105.50	152.00
71.90	28.32	80.00	74.02	119.90	106.00	98.00	181.00
75.00	43.86	79.00	55.48	96.50	144.00	94.50	80.95
73.10	38.21	83.50	73.13	105.50	121.00	97.00	137.00
79.00	42.48	76.00	50.50	105.00	97.13	105.00	125.00
77.00	30.96	80.50	50.88	107.00	166.00	106.00	241.00
68.85	55.78	86.50	140.00	107.00	87.99	99.00	134.00
75.95	43.78	83.00	96.54	101.00	154.00	91.00	150.00
74.15	33.41	107.10	118.00	97.00	100.00	102.50	198.00
73.80	43.35	94.30	107.00	100.00	123.00	106.00	151.00
75.90	29.31	94.50	123.00	108.00	217.00	109.10	229.00
76.85	36.60	79.70	65.92	100.00	140.00	115.00	253.00
80.90	40.25	79.30	81.29	103.00	109.00	101.00	188.00
79.90	35.43	89.80	111.00	104.00	127.00	100.10	124.00
89.20	60.09	83.80	90.73	106.00	112.00	93.30	62.20
82.00	45.84	85.20	133.00	109.00	192.00	101.80	133.00
92.00	70.40	75.50	41.90	103.50	132.00	107.90	208.00
86.60	83.45	78.40	41.71	110.00	126.00	108.50	208.00
80.50	84.30						

Suppose one wants to find out the typical AT for a man with waist circumference 100 cm. To this end, one can define a new data frame, through the command `newdat = data.frame(Waist = c(100))`. An exponential transformation is necessary to obtain the value of AT corresponding the estimated average of $\log(AT)$. The command `exp(predict(lmwaist,newdat))` produces this point estimate, which happens to be 121.2 cm. One can also get a 95% confidence interval, according to (4.14), as $[112.3, 130.8]$. This computation is achieved through the command

```
exp(predict(lmwaist,newdat,interval = "confidence", level = 0.95))
```

It transpires that if this study is replicated 100 times (starting from collection of data) and similar confidence intervals are computed from each of the data sets, one may expect the value of AT corresponding to the 'true average' $\log(AT)$ to lie in 95 out of these 100 intervals.

Now suppose the objective is to predict the AT for a *particular* man with waist circumference 100 cm. The point prediction is 121.2 cm and a 95% prediction interval, according to (4.22), is $[62.0, 236.9]$. This computation is obtained through the command

```
exp(predict(lmwaist,newdat,interval = "prediction", level = 0.95))
```

Thus, if 95% prediction intervals are obtained from 100 replications of the study with different sets of 109 subjects, and every time the AT of a different man with waist circumference 100 cm is measured and compared with this prediction interval, then one may expect the prediction intervals to successfully capture the measured value of AT 95 times.

As for the present data, one of the two observed responses for individuals having waist circumference 100 cm falls outside the confidence interval, but the prediction interval includes both of these. This is not unexpected, as the confidence interval only accounts for the estimation error of the parameters, and ignores the variation from one individual to another. □

4.4.3 *Simultaneous prediction intervals**

When prediction intervals for a number of future observations have to be specified, we have to be careful about the confidence coefficient associated with all of them together. If $\boldsymbol{x}_{01}, \ldots, \boldsymbol{x}_{0q}$ are the vectors of explanatory variables corresponding to the unobserved response values $y_{01}, \ldots, y_{0q}$, we can provide prediction intervals of the form

$$\Bigg[\boldsymbol{x}_{0,i}'(\boldsymbol{X}'\boldsymbol{X})^-\boldsymbol{X}'\boldsymbol{y} - c\sqrt{\widehat{\sigma^2}(1+\boldsymbol{x}_{0,i}'(\boldsymbol{X}'\boldsymbol{X})^-\boldsymbol{x}_{0,i})},$$
$$\boldsymbol{x}_{0,i}'(\boldsymbol{X}'\boldsymbol{X})^-\boldsymbol{X}'\boldsymbol{y} + c\sqrt{\widehat{\sigma^2}(1+\boldsymbol{x}_{0,i}'(\boldsymbol{X}'\boldsymbol{X})^-\boldsymbol{x}_{0,i})}\Bigg], \quad i = 1, \ldots, q.$$

Use of the Bonferroni inequality leads to the choice $c = t_{n-r,\alpha/2q}$, r being the rank of $\boldsymbol{X}$, in order to ensure coverage probability of at least $(1-\alpha)$. On the other hand, the use of a Scheffé-type argument leads to the choice $c = [qF_{q,n-r,\alpha}]^{1/2}$. Note that, unlike in the case of simultaneous confidence intervals, we cannot use $mF_{m,n-r,\alpha}$ where m is the number of linearly independent vectors out of $\boldsymbol{x}_{01}, \ldots, \boldsymbol{x}_{0q}$ (see Exercise 4.14). Larger the value of q, wider are the simultaneous prediction intervals to allow for uncertainties of all the future observations. (This is the case even when all the $\boldsymbol{x}_{oi}$s are the same, i.e. $m = 1$.) Indeed, both $t_{n-r,\alpha/2q}$ and $qF_{q,n-r,\alpha}$ increase without bound as q increases. When a large and/or uncertain number of future observations have to be predicted, we need a different strategy, discussed next.

4.4.4 *Tolerance interval**

There are two kinds of uncertainties which have to be accounted for in a prediction interval: uncertainty arising from the randomness of the observed sample and that due to the randomness of the future observations. As we have found out, the intervals become very wide when a large number of future observations are 'bracketed' simultaneously, rendering the intervals useless. A more meaningful solution can be found if we set a less ambitious target: that of covering *most* of the future observations — instead of covering them all.

Our revised strategy is to ensure with $100(1-\alpha)\%$ confidence that on the average $100(1-\gamma)\%$ of all the future observations will lie in the specified intervals. These intervals are called *tolerance intervals.* Let us first consider the case where $\boldsymbol{x}_{0i} = \boldsymbol{x}_0$ for $i = 1, \ldots, q$. If $\boldsymbol{\beta}$ and σ^2 are known, we can say with 100% confidence that the interval

$$[\boldsymbol{x}_0'\boldsymbol{\beta} - \sigma z_{\gamma/2}, \boldsymbol{x}_0'\boldsymbol{\beta} + \sigma z_{\gamma/2}]$$

will contain on the average $100(1-\gamma)\%$ of all the future observations, $z_{\gamma/2}$ being the $1-\gamma/2$ quantile of the standard normal distribution. The parameters $\boldsymbol{x}_0'\boldsymbol{\beta}$ and σ are not known, but we can use $100(1-\alpha/2)\%$ confidence intervals of each of these:

$$\left[\widehat{\boldsymbol{x}_0'\boldsymbol{\beta}} - \widehat{\sigma} t_{n-r,\alpha/4}\sqrt{\boldsymbol{x}_0'(\boldsymbol{X}'\boldsymbol{X})^-\boldsymbol{x}_0},\ \widehat{\boldsymbol{x}_0'\boldsymbol{\beta}} + \widehat{\sigma} t_{n-r,\alpha/4}\sqrt{\boldsymbol{x}_0'(\boldsymbol{X}'\boldsymbol{X})^-\boldsymbol{x}_0}\,\right],$$

$$\left[0, \widehat{\sigma}\Big/\sqrt{\chi^2_{n-r,1-\alpha/2}/(n-r)}\,\right]$$

Combining these with the Bonferroni inequality, we have the $100(1-\alpha)\%$ tolerance interval for $100(1-\gamma)\%$ of the future observations:

$$\left[\widehat{\boldsymbol{x}_0'\boldsymbol{\beta}} - \widehat{\sigma}\left(t_{n-r,\alpha/4}\sqrt{\boldsymbol{x}_0'(\boldsymbol{X}'\boldsymbol{X})^-\boldsymbol{x}_0} + z_{\gamma/2}\Big/\sqrt{\chi^2_{n-r,1-\alpha/2}/(n-r)}\right),\right.$$
$$\left.\widehat{\boldsymbol{x}_0'\boldsymbol{\beta}} + \widehat{\sigma}\left(t_{n-r,\alpha/4}\sqrt{\boldsymbol{x}_0'(\boldsymbol{X}'\boldsymbol{X})^-\boldsymbol{x}_0} + z_{\gamma/2}\Big/\sqrt{\chi^2_{n-r,1-\alpha/2}/(n-r)}\right)\right].$$

Note that the size of interval does not depend on q any more, because $100\gamma\%$ of the future observations are allowed to lie outside this tolerance interval.

Let us now turn to the case of $\boldsymbol{x}_{01}, \ldots, \boldsymbol{x}_{0q}$ being possibly different. We only need a minor modification of the above procedure to achieve this end: instead of using a single confidence interval for $\boldsymbol{x}_0'\boldsymbol{\beta}$, we can use the confidence band of $\boldsymbol{x}'\boldsymbol{\beta}$, derived in Section 4.3.4. This procedure leads to the *simultaneous tolerance intervals*

$$\Bigg[\widehat{\boldsymbol{x}_{0i}'\boldsymbol{\beta}} - \widehat{\sigma}\left(\sqrt{rF_{r,n-r,\alpha/2}\boldsymbol{x}_{0i}'(\boldsymbol{X}'\boldsymbol{X})^{-}\boldsymbol{x}_{0i}} + z_{\gamma/2}\Big/\sqrt{\chi^2_{n-r,1-\alpha/2}/(n-r)}\right),$$
$$\widehat{\boldsymbol{x}_{0i}'\boldsymbol{\beta}} + \widehat{\sigma}\left(\sqrt{rF_{r,n-r,\alpha/2}\boldsymbol{x}_{0i}'(\boldsymbol{X}'\boldsymbol{X})^{-}\boldsymbol{x}_{0i}} + z_{\gamma/2}\Big/\sqrt{\chi^2_{n-r,1-\alpha/2}/(n-r)}\right)\Bigg],$$

for $i = 1, \ldots, q$. Note that these intervals contain with probability $1-\alpha$ at least $100(1-\gamma)\%$ of all replications of any combination of $y_{01}, \ldots, y_{0q}$ (on the average). Other simultaneous tolerance intervals can be found in Miller (1981, Section 3.4.2).

Example 4.37. (Receding galaxies, continued) For the galaxies data of Table 3.1, a confidence band for the regression line was obtained in Example 4.35. A set of simultaneous tolerance intervals for 90% of all predicted observations with coverage probability 0.95 ($\alpha = 0.05$, $\gamma = 0.1$) is obtained through the additional lines of code given below.

```
alpha <- 0.05; gam <- 0.1
multiplier <- wsig * qt(alpha/4,n-2,lower.tail = F) / sqrt(n)
addedconst <- qnorm((gam/2),lower.tail = F) * wsig *
  sqrt(((n-2)) / qchisq((alpha/2),(n-2)))
beta; mean(x); vx; multiplier; addedconst
```

The intervals turn out to be

$$\Big[-68.15 + 465.9x - \Big\{123.1\sqrt{1+(x-0.9114)^2/0.3993} + 583.4\Big\},$$
$$-68.15 + 465.9x + \Big\{123.1\sqrt{1+(x-0.9114)^2/0.3993} + 583.4\Big\}\Big].$$

The loci of the upper and lower limits of the tolerance intervals are obtained through the following code.

```
hwtl <- multiplier * sqrt(1 + (xseq - mean(x))^2/vx) + addedconst
ltl <- beta[1] + beta[2] * xseq - hwtl
utl <- beta[1] + beta[2] * xseq + hwtl
plot(stars,ylim=c(-900,1700)); lines(xseq,ltl); lines(xseq,utl)
```

The tolerance intervals are plotted in Figure 4.3. The observed data are shown as dots. All the observed points lie within the band, which is much wider than the confidence band for the regression line shown in Figure 4.2. □

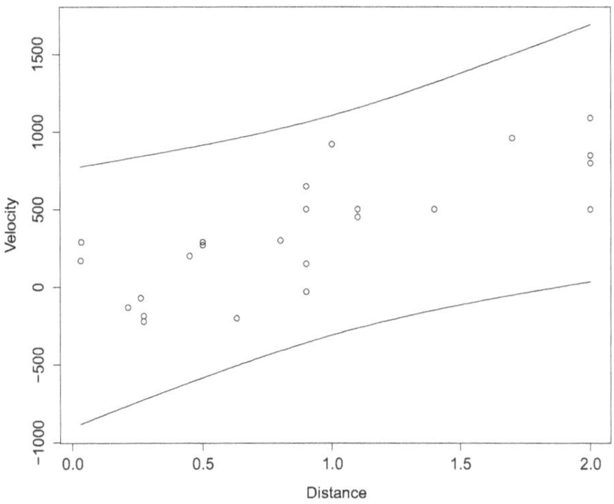

Fig. 4.3 Loci of simultaneous tolerance intervals for Example 4.37

4.5 Consequences of collinearity*

In this chapter we considered problems of testing of hypothesis, interval estimation and prediction, assuming conditional normality of the response given the explanatory variables. Every one of these procedures can be affected by collinearity.

It follows from the discussion of Section 3.13 that the confidence interval of $\boldsymbol{p}'\boldsymbol{\beta}$, described in Section 4.3, would be wide whenever $\boldsymbol{p}$ has a component along an eigenvector of $\boldsymbol{X}'\boldsymbol{X}$ corresponding to one of its small eigenvalues. Likewise, the prediction interval of y_0, described in Section 4.4.2, would be wide whenever $\boldsymbol{x}_0$ has such a component.

In order to study the effect of collinearity on tests of hypothesis, let $\boldsymbol{A\beta} = \boldsymbol{\xi}$ be the testable part of a general hypothesis as per Proposition 4.13. According to Propositions 4.19 and 4.21, the numerator of the F-ratio for the GLRT is proportional to $(\boldsymbol{A}\widehat{\boldsymbol{\beta}} - \boldsymbol{\xi})'[D(\boldsymbol{A}\widehat{\boldsymbol{\beta}})/\sigma^2]^-(\boldsymbol{A}\widehat{\boldsymbol{\beta}} - \boldsymbol{\xi})$. We assume for simplicity that $\boldsymbol{X}'\boldsymbol{X}$ is nonsingular. Even if $\boldsymbol{X}'\boldsymbol{X}$ is singular, the following argument holds with p replaced by $\rho(\boldsymbol{X})$. Note that

$$D(\boldsymbol{A}\widehat{\boldsymbol{\beta}})/\sigma^2 = \boldsymbol{A}(\boldsymbol{X}'\boldsymbol{X})^-\boldsymbol{A}' = \sum_{i=1}^{p} \frac{1}{\lambda_i}(\boldsymbol{A}\boldsymbol{v}_i)(\boldsymbol{A}\boldsymbol{v}_i)',$$

where λ_i and $\boldsymbol{v}_i$, $i = 1, \ldots, p$ are the eigenvalues and eigenvectors of $\boldsymbol{X}'\boldsymbol{X}$.

If $\boldsymbol{l}$ is a vector of unit norm, then

$$\boldsymbol{l}'D(\boldsymbol{A}\widehat{\boldsymbol{\beta}})\boldsymbol{l}/\sigma^2 = \sum_{i=1}^{p} \frac{1}{\lambda_i}(\boldsymbol{l}'\boldsymbol{A}\boldsymbol{v}_i)^2.$$

Suppose there is an $\boldsymbol{l}$ for which $(\boldsymbol{l}'\boldsymbol{A}\boldsymbol{v}_i)^2$ is large while λ_i is small. (This means that the relation $\boldsymbol{l}'\boldsymbol{A}\boldsymbol{\beta} = \boldsymbol{l}'\boldsymbol{\xi}$, implied by the hypothesis $\boldsymbol{A}\boldsymbol{\beta} = \boldsymbol{\xi}$, is such that $\boldsymbol{A}'\boldsymbol{l}$ has a component along an eigenvector corresponding to a small eigenvalue of $\boldsymbol{X}'\boldsymbol{X}$.) In such a case, $\boldsymbol{l}'D(\boldsymbol{A}\widehat{\boldsymbol{\beta}})\boldsymbol{l}/\sigma^2$ is large. Therefore, $D(\boldsymbol{A}\widehat{\boldsymbol{\beta}})/\sigma^2$ must have at least one large eigenvalue.

Recall from Proposition 4.18 that $(\boldsymbol{A}\widehat{\boldsymbol{\beta}} - \boldsymbol{\xi})'[D(\boldsymbol{A}\widehat{\boldsymbol{\beta}})/\sigma^2]^-(\boldsymbol{A}\widehat{\boldsymbol{\beta}} - \boldsymbol{\xi})$ is the sum of squares of a few uncorrelated LZFs (under the restricted model) each having variance 1. These LZFs are all linear functions of $\boldsymbol{A}\widehat{\boldsymbol{\beta}} - \boldsymbol{\xi}$, and are the *additional* LZFs arising from the restriction $\boldsymbol{A}\boldsymbol{\beta} = \boldsymbol{\xi}$. We can construct a set of such LZFs in various ways. Here, we construct it in a way that helps us understand the effect of collinearity. We choose the LZFs as $\boldsymbol{u}_i'(\boldsymbol{A}\widehat{\boldsymbol{\beta}} - \boldsymbol{\xi})$, $i = 1, 2, \ldots, \rho(D(\boldsymbol{A}\widehat{\boldsymbol{\beta}}))$, where the u_i's are unit-norm eigenvectors of $D(\boldsymbol{A}\widehat{\boldsymbol{\beta}})$ corresponding to its nonzero eigenvalues, arranged in decreasing order. Thus, we have

$$\begin{aligned}(\boldsymbol{A}\widehat{\boldsymbol{\beta}} - \boldsymbol{\xi})'&[D(\boldsymbol{A}\widehat{\boldsymbol{\beta}})/\sigma^2]^-(\boldsymbol{A}\widehat{\boldsymbol{\beta}} - \boldsymbol{\xi}) \\ &= \sum_{i=1}^{\rho(D(\boldsymbol{A}\widehat{\boldsymbol{\beta}}))} \frac{\sigma^2(\boldsymbol{u}_i'(\boldsymbol{A}\widehat{\boldsymbol{\beta}} - \boldsymbol{\xi}))^2}{Var(\boldsymbol{u}_i'(\boldsymbol{A}\widehat{\boldsymbol{\beta}} - \boldsymbol{\xi}))} = \sum_{i=1}^{\rho(D(\boldsymbol{A}\widehat{\boldsymbol{\beta}}))} \frac{(\boldsymbol{u}_i'(\boldsymbol{A}\widehat{\boldsymbol{\beta}} - \boldsymbol{\xi}))^2}{\kappa_i}, \qquad (4.23)\end{aligned}$$

where κ_i is the ith ordered eigenvalue of $D(\boldsymbol{A}\widehat{\boldsymbol{\beta}})/\sigma^2$. If some of the κ_i's are large, the above sum would be small.

The hypothesis $\boldsymbol{A}\boldsymbol{\beta} = \boldsymbol{\xi}$ is a combination of several statements of the form $\boldsymbol{p}'\boldsymbol{\beta} = p_0$. We have already argued that whenever *any* of these implied statements is such that $\boldsymbol{p}$ has a component along an eigenvector corresponding to a small eigenvalue of $\boldsymbol{X}'\boldsymbol{X}$, at least one of the κ_i's would be large. Whenever this happens, the last expression of (4.23) is likely to have some small summands. This expression is proportional to the numerator of the F-ratio. The denominator of the F-ratio is not affected by collinearity though, as R_0^2 depends on $\boldsymbol{X}$ only through the projection matrix $\boldsymbol{P}_X$, which is not a function of the eigenvalues of $\boldsymbol{X}'\boldsymbol{X}$.

The impact of collinearity on the GLRT can be easily understood by following the above argument in the special case where $\boldsymbol{A}\boldsymbol{\beta}$ is a single LPF, with $\boldsymbol{A}$ having a substantial component in the 'wrong' direction. In this case the sum of (4.23) consists of a single term with a large denominator, thus making it difficult to reject the null hypotheses. This explains the common experience of regression practitioners: the estimated coefficients of presumably 'important' variables often happen to be statistically insignificant when there is collinearity. (When $\boldsymbol{\xi}$ is a scalar, one can use a t-statistic instead of an F-statistic, as in Section 4.2.3. A simplified form of the above argument would hold in the case of the t-test.)

If $\boldsymbol{A\beta}$ is a vector LPF, the presence of collinearity may make some summands of (4.23) small. The possible rejection of the hypothesis would then depend too much on the other terms. Note that the degrees of freedom for the numerator of the F-ratio is equal to the number of terms of this sum, which remains the same whether or not there is collinearity. Thus, some degrees of freedom of the numerator may be wasted because of collinearity.

In summary, a linear hypothesis can be thought of as a combination of statements. Some of these statements may be difficult to verify statistically because of collinearity. When a single statistic is used to test all these statements simultaneously, precious degrees of freedom are wasted in trying to test the statements which are difficult to verify. The rejection of the hypothesis may then depend unduly on the possible nonconformity of the data with the remaining statements, and may thus become less likely.

In the extreme case of collinearity, a part of $\boldsymbol{A\beta}$ may not be estimable at all. Then there is an $\boldsymbol{l}$ such that $\boldsymbol{A}'\boldsymbol{l}$ is an eigenvector of $\boldsymbol{X}'\boldsymbol{X}$ corresponding to a zero eigenvalue, and $\boldsymbol{l}'\boldsymbol{A\beta} = \boldsymbol{l}'\boldsymbol{\xi}$ is a completely nontestable hypothesis. An oversight of the nontestability leads to reduced chances of rejection of the null hypothesis (see Remark 4.22).

One can also justify the above qualitative statements by analysing the power of the GLRT. The power is an increasing function of the noncentrality parameter c given in Proposition 4.27. This parameter would tend to be small when the hypothesis $\boldsymbol{A\beta} = \boldsymbol{\xi}$ implies some statements of the form $\boldsymbol{p}'\boldsymbol{\beta} = p_0$ where $\|\boldsymbol{Xp}\|$ is small.

4.6 Complements/Exercises

Exercises with solutions given in Appendix C

4.1 Suppose you want to test the hypothesis $\boldsymbol{\beta} = \boldsymbol{\xi}$, where $\boldsymbol{\xi}$ is a *specified* vector. Construct the ANOVA table and describe the GLRT.

4.2 A relatively complex model for the Abrasion of denim jeans data considered in Example 3.5 is

$$y_{ijl} = \mu + \tau_i + \beta_j + \gamma_{ij} + \epsilon_{ijl}, \quad i,j = 1,2,3, \quad l = 1,\ldots,10.$$

This model permits the mean abrasion to be different from merely a linear combination of the wash and laundry effects τ_i and β_j.

(a) How many linearly independent hypotheses can be found that are testable? How many are completely untestable?

(b) Identify which of the following hypotheses are testable, partially testable and completely untestable: (i) $\tau_1 - \bar{\tau} = 0$, (ii) $\beta_1 - \bar{\beta} + \gamma_{21} - \bar{\gamma}_{2\cdot} = 0$, (iii) $\gamma_{11} - \bar{\gamma}_{\cdot 1} - \bar{\gamma}_{1\cdot} + \bar{\gamma}_{\cdot\cdot} = 0$, where $\bar{\tau} = \frac{1}{3}\tau_1 + \tau_2 + \tau_3$, $\bar{\beta} = \frac{1}{3}\beta_1 + \beta_2 + \beta_3$, $\bar{\gamma}_{\cdot 1} = \frac{1}{3}\gamma_{11} + \gamma_{21} + \gamma_{31}$, $\bar{\gamma}_{1\cdot} = \frac{1}{3}\gamma_{11} + \gamma_{12} + \gamma_{13}$ and $\bar{\gamma}_{\cdot\cdot} = \frac{1}{3}\gamma_{\cdot 1} + \gamma_{\cdot 2} + \gamma_{\cdot 3}$.

4.3 Under the set-up of Section 4.2.5, show that if the hypothesis is algebraically consistent but only partially testable, the GLRT of Proposition 4.21 is valid, with $m = \rho(\boldsymbol{A}) + \rho(\boldsymbol{X}) - \rho(\boldsymbol{X}' : \boldsymbol{A}')$. Does the size of the test reduce or increase when one incorrectly uses $m = \rho(\boldsymbol{A})$? What happens to the power of the test?

4.4 *Lack of fit.* Let there be n_i observations of the response (arranged as the $n_i \times 1$ vector $\boldsymbol{y}_i$) for a given combination of the explanatory variables $(\boldsymbol{x}_i)$, $i = 1, \ldots, m$, $n_1 + \cdots + n_m = n$. The plan is to check the adequacy of the model $(\boldsymbol{y}, \boldsymbol{X\beta}, \sigma^2\boldsymbol{I})$ through a formal test of lack-of-fit, assuming normal errors. Here, $\boldsymbol{y} = (\boldsymbol{y}_1' : \cdots : \boldsymbol{y}_m')'$ and

$$\boldsymbol{X}' = (\boldsymbol{x}_1\boldsymbol{1}'_{n_1\times 1} : \cdots : \boldsymbol{x}_m\boldsymbol{1}'_{n_m\times 1}).$$

Assume that $m > r = \rho(\boldsymbol{X})$.

(a) Show that the model $(\boldsymbol{y}, \boldsymbol{X\beta}, \sigma^2\boldsymbol{I})$ is a restricted version of another model, where the response for every given $\boldsymbol{x}_i$ is allowed to have an arbitrary mean.

(b) Obtain the error sum of squares under the unrestricted model (*pure error sum of squares*).

(c) Identify the restriction of part (a) as the hypothesis of adequate fit, and obtain an expression for the sum of squares for deviation from the hypothesis (*lack of fit sum of squares*).

(d) Construct the ANOVA table.

(e) Describe the GLRT for lack of fit.

4.5 Consider the hypothesis $\boldsymbol{\beta} \propto \boldsymbol{b}$, where $\boldsymbol{b}$ is a specified vector. Show that it can be reformulated as a *linear* hypothesis. Construct the ANOVA table and describe the GLRT.

4.6 Consider the model $(\boldsymbol{y}, \boldsymbol{X\beta}, \sigma^2\boldsymbol{I})$ with normally distributed errors. Let $\boldsymbol{A}_{m\times n}(\boldsymbol{u})$ be a matrix whose elements are possibly nonlinear functions of a vector $\boldsymbol{u}_{n\times 1}$.

(a) Show that $E[\boldsymbol{A}(\boldsymbol{X}\widehat{\boldsymbol{\beta}})\boldsymbol{e}] = \boldsymbol{0}$. [Since it is a possibly nonlinear function of $\boldsymbol{y}$, we can call it a *generalized* zero function (GZF).]

(b) Obtain an expression for the dispersion of the GZF of part (a).

(c) Obtain a set of transformed GZFs from those of part (a) such that (i) the transformed GZFs are independently distributed as $N(0, \sigma^2)$, and (ii) the original GZFs can be retrieved from the transformed GZFs via a reverse transformation.

(d) Assuming that $\rho(\boldsymbol{X} : \boldsymbol{A}'(\boldsymbol{X}\widehat{\boldsymbol{\beta}}))$ is a constant with probability 1, how can you scale the transformed GZFs of part (c) so that the distribution of their sum of squares (after scaling) is free of σ^2? Describe this distribution. [See Section 6.3.2 for an application of this construction.]

4.7 Given the linear model $(\boldsymbol{y}, \boldsymbol{X}\boldsymbol{\beta} + \boldsymbol{A}'\boldsymbol{\theta}, \sigma^2\boldsymbol{I})$ with normally distributed errors, obtain the GLRT for the testable hypothesis $\boldsymbol{\theta} = \boldsymbol{0}$. Does the null distribution of the test statistic change if the elements of $\boldsymbol{A}$ are (possibly nonlinear) functions of $\boldsymbol{X}\boldsymbol{\beta}$, and the latter is replaced by $\boldsymbol{X}\widehat{\boldsymbol{\beta}}$ in the statistic? [You can assume that $\rho(\boldsymbol{X} : \boldsymbol{A}'(\boldsymbol{X}\widehat{\boldsymbol{\beta}}))$ is a constant with probability 1.]

4.8 If $\boldsymbol{p}_1'\boldsymbol{\beta}$ and $\boldsymbol{p}_2'\boldsymbol{\beta}$ are estimable LPFs which are not multiples of one another, find the usual $100(1-\alpha)\%$ elliptical confidence region for the vector LPF $(\boldsymbol{p}_1'\boldsymbol{\beta} : \boldsymbol{p}_2'\boldsymbol{\beta} : (\boldsymbol{p}_1 + \boldsymbol{p}_2)'\boldsymbol{\beta})'$, and show that it is the same as the corresponding ellipsoid for $(\boldsymbol{p}_1'\boldsymbol{\beta} : \boldsymbol{p}_2'\boldsymbol{\beta})'$.

4.9 If simultaneous confidence intervals have to be provided for the means of all the observed responses in linear regression (assuming normal errors), which of the three confidence intervals described in Section 4.3.3 should be used? Why?

4.10 (a) Suppose $\boldsymbol{M}$ is a nonnegative definite matrix. Consider the ellipsoidal region $(\boldsymbol{\theta} - \boldsymbol{\theta}_0)'\boldsymbol{M}^-(\boldsymbol{\theta} - \boldsymbol{\theta}_0) \le 1$, $(\boldsymbol{\theta} - \boldsymbol{\theta}_0) \in \mathcal{C}(\boldsymbol{M})$, and the hyperplane $\boldsymbol{a}'\boldsymbol{\theta} = c$. Which values of c will ensure that the intersection of the hyperplane and the ellipsoid contains (i) no point, (ii) exactly one point, (iii) infinitely many points?

(b) Use the result of part (a) to derive Scheffé simultaneous confidence intervals given in (4.18).

4.11 Let $\boldsymbol{p}_1'\boldsymbol{\beta}$ and $\boldsymbol{p}_2'\boldsymbol{\beta}$ be two estimable LPFs in the linear model $(\boldsymbol{y}, \boldsymbol{X}\boldsymbol{\beta}, \sigma^2\boldsymbol{I})$ with normally distributed errors, and suppose $\lambda = \boldsymbol{p}_1'\boldsymbol{\beta}/\boldsymbol{p}_2'\boldsymbol{\beta}$. Find a 95% confidence interval of λ in the following manner.

(a) Find the mean and variance of $a = \boldsymbol{p}_1'\widehat{\boldsymbol{\beta}} - \lambda\boldsymbol{p}_2'\widehat{\boldsymbol{\beta}}$, where λ is the true value of the ratio of the parameters and $\boldsymbol{p}_1'\widehat{\boldsymbol{\beta}}$ and $\boldsymbol{p}_2'\widehat{\boldsymbol{\beta}}$ are BLUEs. Can a be called an LZF?

(b) Determine the distribution of $(a^2/Var(a)) \times (\sigma^2/\widehat{\sigma^2})$, where $\widehat{\sigma^2}$ is the usual estimator of σ^2.

(c) Show that the expression of part (b) is less than a given constant if and only if a quadratic function in λ is negative. Using this fact, obtain a two-sided confidence interval for λ.

[See Exercise 4.12 for an application.]

4.12 *Response surface: continued from Exercise 1.12.* Consider the quadratic regression model

$$y_i = \beta_0 + \beta_1 x_i + \beta_2 x_i^2 + \varepsilon_i, \quad Var(\varepsilon) = \sigma^2, \quad i = 1, \ldots, n.$$

Assuming that $\beta_2 > 0$ and that the errors have the normal distribution, find a 95% confidence interval for the value of the explanatory variable which will minimize the expected response.

4.13 Prove the expression (4.20) for the $100(1-\alpha)\%$ confidence band for the regression line in the special case of simple linear regression. Show that the band is the narrowest where the explanatory variable is equal to its sample average.

4.14 Suppose the response vector of the normal-error linear model $\left(\begin{pmatrix} \boldsymbol{y} \\ \boldsymbol{y}_0 \end{pmatrix}, \begin{pmatrix} \boldsymbol{X} \\ \boldsymbol{X}_0 \end{pmatrix} \boldsymbol{\beta}, \sigma^2 \boldsymbol{I}\right)$ is only partially observed, i.e. $\boldsymbol{y}_0$ is unobserved. The purpose of this exercise is to provide a region where $\boldsymbol{y}_0$ must lie with probability $1-\alpha$.

(a) Show that $\boldsymbol{y}_0$ is contained with probability $1-\alpha$ in the ellipsoidal 'prediction region'

$$(\boldsymbol{y}_0 - \widehat{\boldsymbol{y}}_0)'[\boldsymbol{I} + \boldsymbol{X}_0(\boldsymbol{X}'\boldsymbol{X})^- \boldsymbol{X}_0']^-(\boldsymbol{y}_0 - \widehat{\boldsymbol{y}}_0) \leq qF_{q,n-r,\alpha}\widehat{\sigma^2},$$

where $\widehat{\boldsymbol{y}}_0 = \boldsymbol{X}_0\widehat{\boldsymbol{\beta}}$, $\widehat{\boldsymbol{\beta}}$ is any least squares estimator of $\boldsymbol{\beta}$, n and q are the number of elements of $\boldsymbol{y}$ and $\boldsymbol{y}_0$, respectively, and $r = \rho(\boldsymbol{X})$.

(b) If $\boldsymbol{X}_0 = (\boldsymbol{x}_{01} : \cdots : \boldsymbol{x}_{0q})'$ and $\boldsymbol{y}_0 = (y_{01} : \cdots : y_{0q})'$, then justify the form of the Scheffé prediction intervals given in Section 4.4.3.

Additional exercises

4.15 For the galactic objects data of Table 3.1, it was found in Example 4.2 that the intercept term in a linear model for the velocity of object (with distance as explanatory variable) is statistically insignificant at any reasonable level. Is this finding confirmed by the data given in Table 4.5, which contains similar (but more accurate) information on more distant objects? Does the estimate of the slope change significantly?

Table 4.5 Distance of galactic objects from Earth and their velocities (data object `stars2` in R package `lmreg`, source: Humason, 1936)

Object name	Distance (mpc)*	Velocity (km/s)
Virgo	1.6	890
Pegasus	6.8	3810
Pisces	8.3	4630
Cancer	8.6	4820
Perseus	9.4	5230
Coma	13.4	7500
U.Maj.	21.1	11800
Leo	35.1	19600
NGC 7814	1.8	1000
NGC 7868	10.2	5700
NGC 7869	12.0	6700
NGC 7872	12.5	7000
Gem	43.0	24000
Gem	41.2	23000
Anon 5	34.0	19000
Anon 6	75.3	42000
Anon 7	27.6	15400
Anon 9	69.9	39000
Anon 10	37.6	21000
Anon 11	16.5	9200
Anon 12	22.2	12400

*mpc = million parsec; 1 parsec = 3.26 light years

4.16 The data of Table 4.5 is representative of measurements on several other galactic objects that cemented Hubble's hypothesis that distant objects have proportionately higher velocity (as they should in a universe expanding with constant acceleration). Fit a linear model without intercept for both the data sets (Tables 3.1 and 4.5) and compare the conclusions.

4.17 Consider an agricultural experiment conducted to assess the differential impact of two treatments τ_1 and τ_2, in the presence of a main effect μ and any one of two block effects, β_1 and β_2. The model matrix and the vector parameter are

$$\boldsymbol{X}_{40\times 5} = \begin{pmatrix} \mathbf{1}_{10\times 1} & \mathbf{1}_{10\times 1} & \mathbf{0}_{10\times 1} & \mathbf{1}_{10\times 1} & \mathbf{0}_{10\times 1} \\ \mathbf{1}_{10\times 1} & \mathbf{0}_{10\times 1} & \mathbf{1}_{10\times 1} & \mathbf{1}_{10\times 1} & \mathbf{0}_{10\times 1} \\ \mathbf{1}_{10\times 1} & \mathbf{1}_{10\times 1} & \mathbf{0}_{10\times 1} & \mathbf{0}_{10\times 1} & \mathbf{1}_{10\times 1} \\ \mathbf{1}_{10\times 1} & \mathbf{0}_{10\times 1} & \mathbf{1}_{10\times 1} & \mathbf{0}_{10\times 1} & \mathbf{1}_{10\times 1} \end{pmatrix}, \qquad \boldsymbol{\beta}_{5\times 1} = \begin{pmatrix} \mu \\ \beta_1 \\ \beta_2 \\ \tau_1 \\ \tau_2 \end{pmatrix}.$$

Construct the ANOVA table and describe the GLRT for $\tau_1 = \tau_2$.

4.18 For the Cobb-Douglas model of Exercise 3.19, find an expression for the increase in the error sum of squares because of the restriction $\alpha+\beta = 1$.

4.19 Show that the GLRT of $\mathcal{H}_0 : \beta_j = 0$ against the alternative $\mathcal{H}_1 : \beta_j \neq 0$ described in Example 4.26 is equivalent to the test of (4.2).

4.20 For the Los Angeles crime data of Exercise 3.27, construct the ANOVA table for the hypothesis of no effect of temperature (measured in Fahrenheit) on the monthly number of homicides. Does the answer change when the explanatory variable is chosen as the temperature (measured in Celsius)?

4.21 For the Los Angeles crime data of Exercise 3.27, run a regression of the monthly number of homicides on the temperature and the year. Is the yearly rate of growth of this number, after adjusting for temperature, significant at the 5% level?

4.22 For the Los Angeles crime data of Exercise 3.27, note that the growth in the number of crimes may have been partly due to the growth in population. Using the yearly population available in the data set, define a new response variable called homicide rate, representing the monthly number of homicides per 100,000 persons.

(a) Repeat the regression analysis of Exercise 4.21. Is the yearly rate of growth of the number of homicides per 100,000 persons significant at the 5% level?

(b) Which of the two analyses (part (a) or Exercise 4.21) should be used to determine whether homicide grew over the years? Should the p-values of the regression coefficients obtained in the two analyses be a factor in this decision? Explain.

(c) What percentage of the total variation in the homicide rate is explained by the year and the temperature?

(d) List two variables that are not present in the data set but may potentially explain some part of the remaining variation. [Mention only those variables, for which monthly data during 1975–1993 may already be available somewhere.]

4.23 Consider the model used in Example 4.16 for Galton's data on the mature height of a first born son (y), explained by the heights of his father and mother (x_1 and x_2, respectively). The following is a summary of the regression analysis.

```
> summary(lmGF)
Call:
lm(formula = y ~ x1 + x2)
```

```
Residuals:
    Min      1Q  Median      3Q     Max
-6.0678 -1.2604  0.1227  1.4744  7.8388
Coefficients:
            Estimate Std. Error t value Pr(>|t|)
(Intercept) 19.93652    5.79590   3.440 0.000727 ***
x1           0.47416    0.06299   7.527 2.58e-12 ***
x2           0.27744    0.06778   4.093 6.47e-05 ***
---
Signif. codes:  0 *** 0.001 ** 0.01 * 0.05 . 0.1   1
Residual standard error: 2.127 on 176 degrees of freedom
Multiple R-squared:  0.3159,Adjusted R-squared:  0.3081
F-statistic: 40.63 on 2 and 176 DF,  p-value: 3.111e-15
```

(a) Interpret the estimated regression coefficient of the variable x_1.
(b) What is the estimated average height of a first born son, whose parents are both 70 inches tall?
(c) How will the estimated parameters change if all the heights are expressed in centimeters instead of inches (1 inch = 2.54 cm)?
(d) From the given summary, obtain numerical values of the regression sum of squares, the error sum of squares and the total sum of squares, and the corresponding degrees of freedom.
(e) If one carries out simple linear regression after disregarding the mother's height, i.e. using the father's height as the only predictor, will the multiple R-squared be higher or lower than 0.3159?

4.24 For Galton's family data of Example 4.16, test the hypothesis that, given a certain height of the mother, an extra inch of height of the father translates into an extra inch of height of the first-born son. The alternative hypothesis is the extra height of the first-born son is less than one inch.

4.25 An Australian bank collected data on the total time (in minutes) taken by different branches to process two types of transactions, and the numbers of these two types of transactions (on which the total time was spent). The summary of a regression analysis of the time taken (`Time`) on the numbers of transactions (`T1` and `T2`) is shown below.

```
> summary(lm(Time~T1+T2,data=transact))
Call:
lm(formula = Time ~ T1 + T2, data = transact)
Residuals:
    Min      1Q  Median      3Q     Max
-4652.4  -601.3     2.4   455.7  5607.4
```

```
Coefficients:
             Estimate Std. Error t value Pr(>|t|)
(Intercept) 144.36944  170.54410   0.847    0.398
T1            5.46206    0.43327  12.607   <2e-16 ***
T2            2.03455    0.09434  21.567   <2e-16 ***
---
Signif. codes: 0 *** 0.001 ** 0.01 * 0.05 . 0.1   1
Residual standard error: 1143 on 258 degrees of freedom
Multiple R-squared:  0.9091,    Adjusted R-squared:  0.9083
F-statistic:   1289 on 2 and 258 DF,   p-value: < 2.2e-16
> vcov(summary(lm(Time~T1+T2,data=transact)))
            (Intercept)          T1            T2
(Intercept) 29085.29123 23.58169479 -12.683293995
T1             23.58169  0.18772109  -0.031536343
T2            -12.68329 -0.03153634   0.008899435
```

(a) Interpret the estimated regression coefficient of the variable `T1`.
(b) From the given summary, construct the Analysis of Variance table for this regression.
(c) If the model used here is represented symbolically as `Time` $= \beta_0 + \beta_1$`T1`$+\beta_2$`T2`$+\varepsilon$, what does the hypothesis $\beta_1 = \beta_2$ mean physically?
(d) Test the hypothesis $\beta_1 = \beta_2$ at the level 0.05 using the above summary.

4.26 Using the model of Exercises 1.14–1.15, formulate the hypothesis of 'no change in slope at x_0' as a condition on the parameters of the model. Calculate the p-value of the generalized likelihood ratio test for this hypothesis for the world population data of Table 1.3, assuming normal errors.

4.27 Using the model of Exercises 1.2–1.13, formulate the hypothesis of 'no discontinuity of regression line at x_0' as a condition on the parameters of the model. Calculate the p-value of the generalized likelihood ratio test for this hypothesis for the world population data of Table 1.3, assuming normal errors.

4.28 Suppose you have data from two linear models, $(\boldsymbol{y}_1, \boldsymbol{X}_1\boldsymbol{\beta}_1, \sigma^2\boldsymbol{I})$ and $(\boldsymbol{y}_2, \boldsymbol{X}_2\boldsymbol{\beta}_2, \sigma^2\boldsymbol{I})$. The objective is to test the *equality* of the regression lines, i.e. $\mathcal{H}_0 : \boldsymbol{\beta}_1 = \boldsymbol{\beta}_2$. How will you formulate the testing problem and proceed to solve it?

4.29 Using the world record running times data of Table 1.2 and assuming normality of errors, test the hypothesis of equality of the regressions of the men's and women's log-record times on log-distance, at the level 0.05.

4.30 Suppose, in the preceding problem, that $\boldsymbol{X}_i = (\mathbf{1}_{n\times 1}\ \boldsymbol{Z}_i)$ and $\boldsymbol{\beta}_i' = (1\ \boldsymbol{\theta}_i')$, $i = 1, 2$. The objective is to test the *parallelity* of the regression lines, i.e. $\mathcal{H}_0 : \boldsymbol{\theta}_1 = \boldsymbol{\theta}_2$. How will you formulate the testing problem and proceed to solve it?

4.31 Suppose the restriction of Exercise 1.11(b) is posed as a hypothesis. Compute the p-value of the GLRT statistic for this hypothesis, using the world record running times data of Table 1.2 and assuming normality of errors. Can you conclude at the level 0.05 that the regression lines for the men's and women's data are parallel?

4.32 For the Los Angeles crime data of Exercise 3.27, run a regression of the monthly number of rapes per 100,000 persons on the temperature (measured in Fahrenheit) and the year. Compare the results with those of Exercise 4.22. Observe that the p-value of the regression coefficient of temperature is smaller in the case of rape than in the case of homicides. Does this finding indicate that temperature (measured in Fahrenheit) has a stronger effect on the number of rapes than on the number of homicides? If not, compare the two effects through a suitable test of hypothesis in a suitable model.

4.33 Compute and compare the powers of the tests (4.7) and (4.6) for level 0.05 and values of $\boldsymbol{p}'\boldsymbol{\beta}$ in the range (ξ, ∞).

4.34 Assuming the model of Exercise 1.12 (with normal errors) for the world population data of Table 1.3, find a 95% confidence interval for the yearly rate of growth of population.

4.35 Describe how you can construct a one- or two-sided confidence interval of σ^2, assuming $\boldsymbol{y}$ to be normal and using Proposition 4.1.

4.36 Using the deep abdominal adipose tissue data of Table 4.4, plot the loci of 95% Bonferroni and Scheffé confidence intervals of the mean of $\log(AT)$ for the observed values of $\log(waist)$.

4.37 Using the deep abdominal adipose tissue data of Table 4.4, plot a 95% confidence band for the regression line of $\log(AT)$.

4.38 Assuming the model of Exercise 1.12 (with normal errors) for the world population data of Table 1.3, find a 95% prediction interval for the midyear population of the world in 2001, and compare it with the actual midyear population.

4.39 From the summary given in Exercise 4.25, compute the BLUP of the time taken by a branch to process 3000 transactions of the first type and 5000 transactions of the second type. Construct a prediction interval for the time taken, with 95% coverage probability.

4.40 Consider the simple linear regression model relating the score of a student in the final examination (y) to his/her score in the mid-term examination x, with n observations. The scores are expressed as percentage.

(a) What does the hypothesis $\beta_1 < 1$ mean? Describe a test for the null hypothesis $\beta_1 = 1$ against the alternative hypothesis $\beta_1 < 1$ at the 5% level.

(b) Give explicit expression of a 95% prediction interval for the final examination score of a student whose mid-term score was 40.

(c) Give explicit expression of a 95% confidence interval of the expected final examination score of a student whose mid-term examination score was 40. Explain why it is narrower than the prediction interval of part (b).

(d) The average score in the mid-term examination was 50. Would the prediction interval of part (b) be wider or narrower, if that student's mid-term score had been 70 (instead of 40)? Explain.

4.41 Using the deep abdominal adipose tissue data of Table 4.4, plot the loci of 95% simultaneous tolerance intervals of $\log(AT)$ for 90% of all values of $\log(waist)$ to be observed for a similar group of subjects in future.

4.42 For the data of Table 4.5, obtain a set of simultaneous tolerance intervals for 90% of all predicted velocities (for objects with distance from Earth in the range of the data in Table 4.5) with coverage probability 0.95 ($\alpha = 0.05$, $\gamma = 0.1$).

Chapter 5

Model Building and Diagnostics in Regression

As mentioned in Section 2.3, the regression of y on $x_1, \ldots, x_k$, namely $E(y|x_1, \ldots, x_k)$ represents the 'best' approximation (in the sense of smallest mean squared error) of a random variable y, as a function of other random variables $x_1, \ldots, x_k$. The particular linear model $(\boldsymbol{y}, \boldsymbol{X\beta}, \sigma^2\boldsymbol{I})$ presents us with a simple setup for studying such a regression function and the associated approximation error. Specifically, the model for a single response variable y becomes

$$E(y|x_1, \ldots, x_k) = \beta_0 + \beta_1 x_1 + \cdots + \beta_k x_k,$$
$$Var(y|x_1, \ldots, x_k) = \sigma^2,$$

and the observations on y are regarded as uncorrelated random variables (see (1.7)). While Chapter 3 discussed how the parameters $\boldsymbol{\beta}$ and σ^2 can be estimated, Chapter 4 considered various inferential issues such as testing of hypothesis, construction of confidence intervals and regions, prediction, construction of tolerance and prediction intervals etc., under the additional assumptions that the conditional distribution of y given $x_1, \ldots, x_k$ is normal and that these observations are independent. Such a streamlining of these inference procedures makes the linear model a very popular choice in studying regression problems.

In this chapter we shall refer to y as the response variable and to $x_1, \ldots, x_k$ as explanatory variables or regressors, as is common practice in regression. As already mentioned on page 63, the phrases simple linear regression model and multiple linear regression (or multiple regression) model are used to distinguish between the case of a single explanatory variable ($k = 1$) and multiple explanatory variables ($k > 1$), respectively.

While conducting a multiple regression analysis, often users have a long list of potentially useful explanatory variables. As we shall see, such models may suffer from the inclusion of unnecessary or redundant variables, just as

Table 5.1 Synthetic data set for illustrating importance of diagnostics (data object `anscombeplus` in R package `lmreg`, constructed by expanding the ideas of Anscombe (1973))

x_1	y_1	y_2	y_3	y_4	y_5	x_2	y_6
1	2.886	1.942	–3.136	–5.096	–3.613	7.957	6.818
2	0.052	2.992	–1.531	–4.766	–2.035	7.957	12.707
3	–4.244	3.393	0.035	–3.582	–0.051	7.957	3.676
4	–4.039	2.995	1.660	0.078	1.220	7.957	7.953
5	2.655	4.183	3.195	1.597	2.679	7.957	8.840
6	2.570	4.159	4.897	6.044	4.409	7.957	6.939
7	9.098	4.582	5.596	9.317	5.762	7.957	7.732
8	9.973	5.564	7.533	12.230	7.419	7.957	7.956
9	8.109	5.865	9.746	10.739	8.990	7.957	12.735
10	14.131	7.674	12.070	13.758	25.236	7.957	7.226
11	11.177	10.836	13.753	17.881	11.342	10.603	9.834
12	13.802	11.162	13.923	17.753	13.262	10.603	14.436
13	16.448	12.295	15.660	20.748	14.468	10.603	9.475
14	20.477	13.195	18.495	20.053	16.397	10.603	6.014
15	24.248	16.272	21.305	17.761	17.443	10.603	8.471
16	15.488	17.831	26.370	18.891	19.402	10.603	8.744
17	24.617	22.122	14.651	16.112	21.009	10.603	13.537
18	22.586	25.290	23.290	21.191	22.477	10.603	20.275
19	20.551	28.395	30.35	21.519	23.851	10.603	12.781
20	24.422	34.252	17.207	22.773	25.326	35.000	48.851

they would if we omitted useful variables. In the next section, we discuss how to select appropriate variables from a large set of candidate explanatory variables.

Inference procedures for the simple linear regression model appear rather straightforward. However, one needs to pay attention and exercise some caution while applying this theory to analysing specific data sets, as the following example illustrates.

Example 5.1. (Six data sets with similar regression summary) Table 5.1 contains some fictitious data on eight variables. Consider the following simple linear regression problems.

(a) Response variable is y_1, explanatory variable is x_1.
(b) Response variable is y_2, explanatory variable is x_1.
(c) Response variable is y_3, explanatory variable is x_1.
(d) Response variable is y_4, explanatory variable is x_1.
(e) Response variable is y_5, explanatory variable is x_1.
(f) Response variable is y_6, explanatory variable is x_2.

The following R code would produce the regression summary in these cases.

```
data(anscombeplus)
summary(lm(y1~x1, data = anscombeplus))
summary(lm(y2~x1, data = anscombeplus))
summary(lm(y3~x1, data = anscombeplus))
summary(lm(y4~x1, data = anscombeplus))
summary(lm(y5~x1, data = anscombeplus))
summary(lm(y6~x2, data = anscombeplus))
```

For *each* of these six data sets, the estimated parameter values are found to be the same viz. $\widehat{\beta}_0 = -4.000$, $\widehat{\beta}_1 = 1.500$ with standard errors 1.603 and 0.134, respectively. Also, in each of the six cases, the sample squared multiple correlation coefficient (R^2) is 0.875, and the usual estimate of σ^2 is 3.450^2.

Scatter plots of the data sets are presented in Figure 5.1. These plots bring out the glaring dissimilarities in these data sets, in spite of the commonality of their data analytic summary. From these scatter plots, we see that there is evidently a nonlinear relation between the variables in data set (b). For data set (c), it is difficult to justify the assumption that all observations of y_3 have the same conditional variance given x_1, as the data points for smaller values of x_1 stay closer to the fitted straight line. For data set (d), there appears to be some degree of dependence among the values of y_4 for successively larger values of x_1. For data set (e), there is an outlying observation that makes it difficult to justify the normality of the conditional distribution. For data set (f), the fit is largely determined by the last observation. □

The differences in the data sets of the above example were easy to spot from the scatter plot, since there is only one explanatory variable. However, detecting such unusual occurrences in the case of multiple linear regression can be much more difficult and may be hidden. In this chapter we wish to discuss techniques for detecting violation of assumptions of the linear model (which appears to happen for data sets (b), (c) and (d)), along with possible remedies. We would seek to identify observations with unusual influence on regression analysis, as observed in data sets (e) and (f), and discuss ways of dealing with them. We will also revisit the issue of collinearity in multiple regression, including its detection and some remedial measures. Section 5.2 and subsequent sections of this chapter are devoted to the above topics, collectively known as *regression diagnostics*.

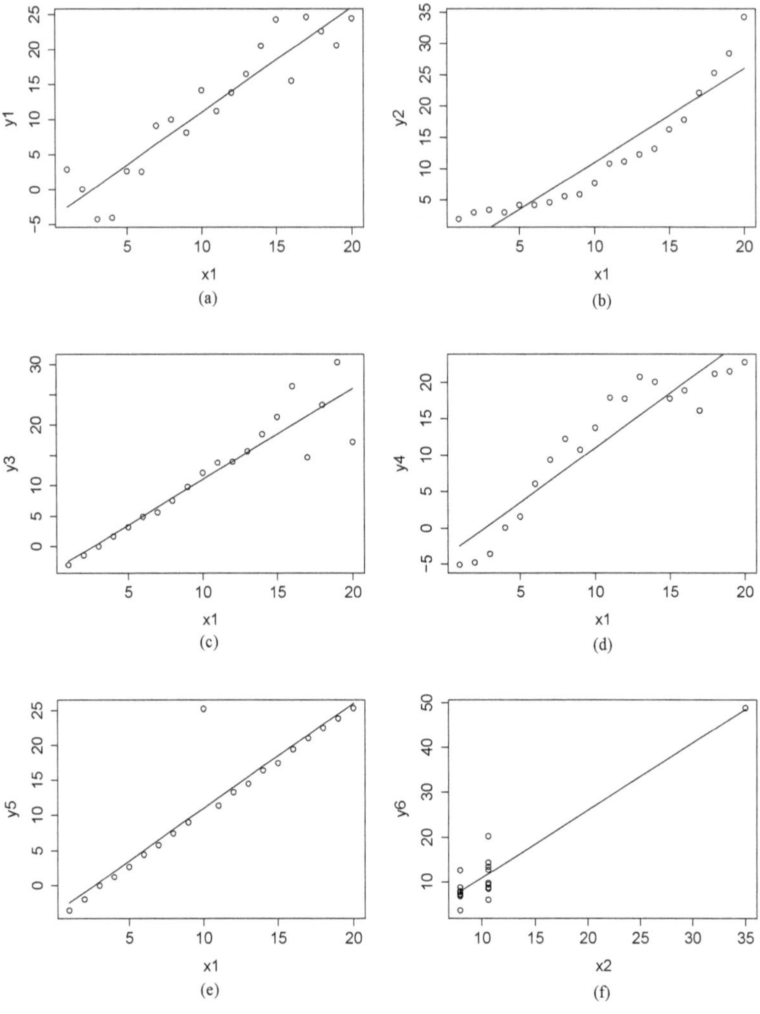

Fig. 5.1 Scatter plots and least squares fitted lines for the data sets (a)–(f)

5.1 Selection of regressors

5.1.1 *Too many and too few regressors*

In order to illustrate the hazard of using too many explanatory variables, let us use the polynomial regression model that was discussed in

Example 1.10. The explanatory variables of this model are powers of a single variable x, i.e. $x_j = x^j$, $j = 1, 2, \ldots, k$. It is a special case of the multiple linear regression model (1.1), which has been discussed earlier.

Example 5.2. We consider the following simple linear regression model

$$y = \beta_0 + \beta_1 x + \varepsilon,$$

with given parameter values $\beta_0 = 0$, $\beta_1 = -2$, and $x \sim N(1, 3^2)$ and $\varepsilon \sim N(0, 1)$ independently of x. We simulate a sample of size $n = 10$ from this model, using the following R code.

```
set.seed(1234)
n <- 10
beta0 <- 0
beta1 <- -2
x <- rnorm(n,mean=1,sd=3); err <- rnorm(n)
y <- beta0 + beta1 * x + err
```

If we use the correct form of the model (a simple linear regression), the fitted equation obtained through the code `lm1 = lm(y~x); summary(lm1)` turns out to be

$$y = -0.1275 - 2.0626x + \varepsilon,$$

where ε is error with mean 0 and variance 1.115^2. The estimated values of the parameters are not far from their correct values, 0 and -2. The coefficient β_1 is highly significant (with p-value 1.8×10^{-7}) while β_0 is not (with p-value 0.727), as expected. The multiple R-square is 0.9717.

We now fit an eighth degree polynomial regression model, with different powers of x up to 8 serving as additional explanatory variables, using the following code.

```
lm2 <- lm(y~poly(x,8,raw=T))
summary(lm2)
```

The fitted equation is

$$\begin{aligned} y = & -4.181 - 7.168x + 0.825x^2 + 2.012x^3 + 0.525x^4 - 0.273x^5 \\ & -0.109x^6 + 0.013x^7 + 0.004x^8 + \varepsilon, \end{aligned}$$

where ε is error with mean 0 and variance 0.147^2. The estimated values of the regression coefficients are far from their correct values, as in our original model all these parameters except β_1 are known to be zero. The p-values of the significance of these coefficients range from 0.097 to 0.746. Even β_1 is

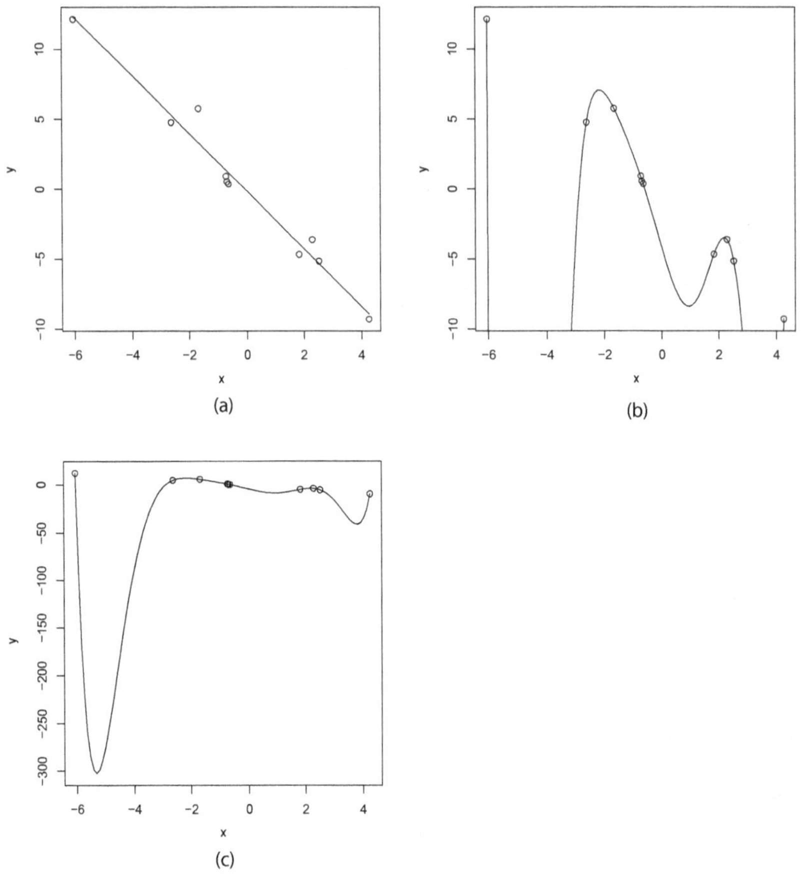

Fig. 5.2 Plots for Example 5.2: scatter plot of y vs. x along with (a) fitted simple regression line, (b) fitted polynomial regression curve and (c) fitted polynomial regression curve (larger scale)

statistically insignificant at any reasonable level. Yet the multiple R-square is 0.9999 — an improvement (from the earlier 0.9717) that one should look at with a great deal of suspicion!

Figure 5.2 shows the fitted regression curves together with the scatter of the observed data. The simple linear regression fit looks appropriate. The fitted polynomial regression curve produces a closer fit at the observed values of x (evidenced by the smaller estimate of the error variance and larger value of multiple R-square). However, this happens at the cost of dramatic departure from the scatter in between the observed values of x. For instance, the predicted value of y for $x = -5$ is less than -250, even though we know from the data generating model that its mean should be 10. The simple linear regression fit produces a predicted value of 10.2 for $x = -5$, which is reasonable. The wild prediction from the polynomial regression model is due to over-fitting of the observed points, which happens because the least squares criterion is insensitive to what happens in between the observed points.

This example shows that having extra variables in the model equation may indeed hurt the analysis. Here, the higher powers of x are nuisance variables, that had no role in the generation of y. Estimation of the coefficients of these terms, the nuisance parameters (β_2, β_3, ..., β_k), cost us a lot. □

In the next example we demonstrate a situation where even a useful variable may create problems.

Example 5.3. A sample of size $n = 10$ is drawn from the simple linear regression model

$$y = \beta_0 + \beta_1 x_1 + \beta_2 x_2 + \varepsilon,$$

where we take $\beta_0 = 20$, $\beta_1 = \beta_2 = -1$, with x_1 the same as the variable x in Example 5.2, $x_2|x_1 \sim N(0.999x_1, 0.05^2)$ and $\varepsilon|x_1, x_2 \sim N(0, 1)$. The data are generated through the following code.

```
set.seed(1234)
n <- 10
beta0 <- 20
beta1 <- -1
beta2 <- -1
x1 <- rnorm(n,mean=1,sd=3)
x2 <- 0.999*x1 + rnorm(n, mean=1, sd=0.05)
err <- rnorm(n)
y <- beta0 + beta1 * x1 + beta2 * x2 + err
```

It can be seen from the process of data generation that x_2 is highly correlated with x_1. Indeed, the sample correlation is 0.99984.

If we regress y on x_1 and x_2, the fitted equation obtained from `summary(lm(y~x1+x2))` turns out to be

$$y = 24.385 + 3.679x_1 - 5.822x_2 + \varepsilon,$$

with $Var(\varepsilon) = 0.560^2$. The multiple R-square is 0.994, which is quite high. However, the estimated values of β_1 and β_2 are rather different from their correct values, -1 and -1. The p-values of the significance of the coefficients β_1 and β_2 are also quite large: 0.333 and 0.145. Thus, the two parameters are not statistically different from 0.

This does not happen just because of the small sample size though. The variable x_2 takes values that are very similar to those of x_1. Therefore, they act as proxies of one another. In other words, while considering the mean of the response y, the combination of x_1 and x_2 may be regarded as a single variable with regression coefficient -2. It makes sense that the sum of the estimated coefficients is -2.143, which is close to -2. Yet the two coefficients are individually insignificant, and their individual values are hardly interpretable.

Regression of y on x_1 alone (obtained from `summary(lm(y~x1))`) leads to the fitted equation

$$y = 18.600 - 2.119x_1 + \varepsilon,$$

with $Var(\varepsilon) = 0.616^2$. The R-square is 0.992, while the p-value of the significance of β_1 is 1.33×10^{-9}. On the other hand, regression of y on x_2 alone (obtained from `summary(lm(y~x2))`) leads to the fitted equation

$$y = 20.715 - 2.129x_2 + \varepsilon,$$

with $Var(\varepsilon) = 0.563^2$. The R-square is 0.9993, while the p-value of the significance of β_2 is 6.45×10^{-10}. The estimated values of β_1 and β_2 in the two cases are close to -2, as expected in the absence of the other variable (see Exercise 5.1). There is no problem with statistical significance, which shows the predictive value of either variable.

Thus, in spite of the omission of an important variable, neither of the fitted simple linear regression models is far from being correct. In a sense, the omission of one of the variables has turned out to be a blessing in disguise! When the two regressors are used together, the effect of each of them turns out to be insignificant in the presence of the other. The multiple regression model cannot be reliably used for any purpose. □

However, omission of some variables can be very costly, as the next example illustrates.

Example 5.4. A sample of size $n = 10$ is drawn from the simple linear regression model

$$y = \beta_0 + \beta_1 x_1 + \beta_2 x_2 + \varepsilon,$$

where $\beta_0 = 20$, $\beta_1 = \beta_2 = -1$, x_1 is equal to x in Example 5.2, $x_2|x_1 \sim N(0.5x_1, 1.5^2)$ and $\varepsilon|x_1, x_2 \sim N(0, 1)$. The data are generated from the following lines of code.

```
set.seed(1234)
n <- 10
beta0 <- 20
beta1 <- -1
beta2 <- -1
x1 <- rnorm(n, mean=1, sd=3)
x2 <- 0.5*x1 + rnorm(n, mean=1, sd=1.5)
err <- rnorm(n)
y <- beta0 + beta1 * x1 + beta2 * x2 + err
```

It can be seen from the process of data generation that x_2 is correlated with x_1, but not as highly as in Example 5.3. The sample correlation is 0.6099.

If we regress y on x_1 and x_2, the fitted equation obtained from `summary(lm(y~x1+x2))` happens to be

$$y = 19.724 - 1.058x_1 - 1.161x_2 + \varepsilon,$$

with $Var(\varepsilon) = 0.560^2$. The multiple R-square is 0.99, which is quite high. The estimated values of β_1 and β_2 are close to their correct values, -1 and -1. The p-values of the significance of the coefficients β_1 and β_2 are 2.99×10^{-6} and 2.44×10^{-5}. Thus, both the parameters are statistically significant at the level 0.01. Both the regressors appear to be useful.

Regression of y on x_1 alone leads to the fitted equation (obtained from `summary(lm(y~x1))`)

$$y = 18.785 - 1.529x_1 + \varepsilon,$$

with $Var(\varepsilon) = 2.01^2$. The R-square is 0.853, while the p-value of the significance of β_1 is 1.35×10^{-4}. Regression of y on x_2 alone leads to the fitted equation (obtained from `summary(lm(y~x2))`)

$$y = 20.607 - 2.130x_2 + \varepsilon,$$

with $Var(\varepsilon) = 2.708^2$. The R-square is 0.700, while the p-value of the significance of β_2 is 1.55×10^{-3}.

It is observed that dropping of either regressor not only reduces the multiple R-square considerably, but also produces grossly inaccurate estimates of the regression coefficients (see Exercise 5.1 for further appreciation of the empirical findings). □

The findings of the above example indicate that there could be a bias in the estimate of β_1 when x_2 is omitted from the model. We now consider these issues systematically from a theoretical perspective.

Consider the model $(\boldsymbol{y}, \boldsymbol{X\beta}, \sigma^2\boldsymbol{I})$. Let the model matrix $\boldsymbol{X}$ and the vector parameter $\boldsymbol{\beta}$ be partitioned as $(\boldsymbol{X}_1 : \boldsymbol{X}_2)$ and $(\boldsymbol{\beta}_1' : \boldsymbol{\beta}_2')'$, respectively, so that $\boldsymbol{X\beta} = \boldsymbol{X}_1\boldsymbol{\beta}_1 + \boldsymbol{X}_2\boldsymbol{\beta}_2$. We wish to consider the prospect of ignoring $\boldsymbol{X}_2$ and working instead with the model $(\boldsymbol{y}, \boldsymbol{X}_1\boldsymbol{\beta}_1, \sigma^2\boldsymbol{I})$. We call it a 'subset model' because it involves only a subset of the explanatory variables.

If the response $\boldsymbol{y}$ follows the subset model, the BLUE of $E(\boldsymbol{y})$ or $\boldsymbol{X}_1\boldsymbol{\beta}_1$ would be $\boldsymbol{X}\widetilde{\boldsymbol{\beta}} = \boldsymbol{P}_{X_1}\boldsymbol{y}$, which may also be interpreted as the BLUE of $\boldsymbol{X\beta}$ under the restriction $\boldsymbol{\beta}_2 = \boldsymbol{0}$. The variance-covariance matrix of this estimator is $\sigma^2\boldsymbol{P}_{X_1}$.

If the subset model is correct but one mistakenly uses the original model (i.e. fails to take into account the restriction $\boldsymbol{\beta}_2 = \boldsymbol{0}$), then the corresponding 'BLUE' of $E(\boldsymbol{y})$ is unbiased but has a larger variance-covariance matrix, $\sigma^2\boldsymbol{P}_X$. Consequently, the variance of the 'BLUE' of every LPF would be unnecessarily large. As we have seen in Example 5.2, larger variance of estimators can lead to insignificance of useful regression coefficients.

However, if $\boldsymbol{y}$ actually follows the original model with $\boldsymbol{\beta}_2 \neq \boldsymbol{0}$, the subset estimator of $E(\boldsymbol{y})$ may be biased. The amount of bias is

$$E(\boldsymbol{X}\widetilde{\boldsymbol{\beta}}) - \boldsymbol{X\beta} = \boldsymbol{P}_{X_1}\boldsymbol{X\beta} - \boldsymbol{X\beta} = -(\boldsymbol{I} - \boldsymbol{P}_{X_1})\boldsymbol{X}_2\boldsymbol{\beta}_2.$$

Clearly, the estimator is unbiased when $\boldsymbol{\beta}_2 = \boldsymbol{0}$. Interestingly, the estimator is unbiased also when $\boldsymbol{\beta}_2 \neq \boldsymbol{0}$ but $(\boldsymbol{I} - \boldsymbol{P}_{X_1})\boldsymbol{X}_2 = \boldsymbol{0}$, i.e. when the columns of $\boldsymbol{X}_2$ are linear combinations of the columns of $\boldsymbol{X}_1$. We have seen a situation similar to this one in Example 5.3.

Let us now compare the two estimators in terms of mean squared error (MSE). The MSE matrix of the subset estimator is

$$E[(\boldsymbol{X}\widetilde{\boldsymbol{\beta}} - \boldsymbol{X\beta})(\boldsymbol{X}\widetilde{\boldsymbol{\beta}} - \boldsymbol{X\beta})'] = \sigma^2\boldsymbol{P}_{X_1} + (\boldsymbol{I} - \boldsymbol{P}_{X_1})\boldsymbol{X}_2\boldsymbol{\beta}_2\boldsymbol{\beta}_2'\boldsymbol{X}_2'(\boldsymbol{I} - \boldsymbol{P}_{X_1}).$$

In contrast, the BLUE from the full model, $\boldsymbol{X}\widehat{\boldsymbol{\beta}}$, is unbiased and has dispersion $\sigma^2\boldsymbol{P}_X$. Therefore, its MSE matrix is

$$E[(\boldsymbol{X}\widehat{\boldsymbol{\beta}} - \boldsymbol{X\beta})(\boldsymbol{X}\widehat{\boldsymbol{\beta}} - \boldsymbol{X\beta})'] = \sigma^2\boldsymbol{P}_X.$$

In order that the subset estimator has lower MSE, we must have

$$E[(\boldsymbol{X}\widehat{\boldsymbol{\beta}} - \boldsymbol{X\beta})(\boldsymbol{X}\widehat{\boldsymbol{\beta}} - \boldsymbol{X\beta})'] \leq E[(\boldsymbol{X}\widetilde{\boldsymbol{\beta}} - \boldsymbol{X\beta})(\boldsymbol{X}\widetilde{\boldsymbol{\beta}} - \boldsymbol{X\beta})']$$

in the sense of the Löwner order. This matrix inequality simplifies to

$$\frac{1}{\sigma^2}(\boldsymbol{I} - \boldsymbol{P}_{X_1})\boldsymbol{X}_2\boldsymbol{\beta}_2\boldsymbol{\beta}_2'\boldsymbol{X}_2'(\boldsymbol{I} - \boldsymbol{P}_{X_1}) \leq \boldsymbol{P}_{(I-P_{X_1})X_2}.$$

This inequality holds if and only if

$$\|(\boldsymbol{I} - \boldsymbol{P}_{X_1})\boldsymbol{X}_2\boldsymbol{\beta}_2\|^2 \leq \sigma^2. \tag{5.1}$$

Since σ^2 and $\boldsymbol{\beta}_2$ are unknown, the inequality cannot be verified in practice. If $\widehat{\boldsymbol{\beta}}_2$ is the BLUE of $\boldsymbol{\beta}_2$ under the full model, the above condition can be alternatively written as

$$\boldsymbol{\beta}_2'[D(\widehat{\boldsymbol{\beta}}_2)]^{-1}\boldsymbol{\beta}_2 \leq 1.$$

This condition would be satisfied if the true value of $\boldsymbol{\beta}_2$ is very small or if the dispersion of $\widehat{\boldsymbol{\beta}}_2$ is very large.

Example 5.5. Consider the data of Example 5.3. Suppose the matrix $\boldsymbol{X}_1$ consists of the intercept term and the values of x_1, and $\boldsymbol{X}_2$ consists of the values of x_2, i.e., the question is whether the variable x_2 should be included in the model. Let us compute the quantity $\|(\boldsymbol{I}-\boldsymbol{P}_{X_1})\boldsymbol{X}_2\boldsymbol{\beta}_2\|^2$, by taking into account the true value of β_2, through the following additional lines of code.

```
X1 <- cbind(1, x1)
sum(((diag(rep(1,n)) - projector(X1)) %*% x2*beta2)^2)
```

The value turns out to be 0.0248. Since $\sigma^2 = 1$, the inequality (5.1) is satisfied. Thus, it makes sense to keep only x_1 in the model. If we drop x_1 and keep x_2 instead, the roles of the two variables are interchanged. The value of $\|(\boldsymbol{I}-\boldsymbol{P}_{X_1})\boldsymbol{X}_2\boldsymbol{\beta}_2\|^2$ happens to be 0.0250, as computed through the following code.

```
X1 <-cbind(1, x2)
sum(((diag(rep(1,n)) - projector(X1)) %*% x1*beta1)^2)
```

Therefore, keeping either one of the variables is better than keeping both of them.

Let us now repeat the above exercise for the data of Example 5.4. When x_2 is used as the candidate variable for selection, we have $\|(\boldsymbol{I}-\boldsymbol{P}_{X_1})\boldsymbol{X}_2\boldsymbol{\beta}_2\|^2 = 6.236$. When the roles of the variables are reversed, $\|(\boldsymbol{I}-\boldsymbol{P}_{X_1})\boldsymbol{X}_2\boldsymbol{\beta}_2\|^2$ is equal to 35.246. Both of these numbers are greater than σ^2, which is equal to 1. Thus, smaller mean squared error of $\boldsymbol{X\beta}$ is achieved by keeping both the variables in the model.

Of course, we are able to verify the inequality (5.1) in the above cases only because the true values of the parameters are known. In practice, neither $\boldsymbol{\beta}$ nor σ^2 would be known, and so the decision to keep or drop a variable has to be based on the data itself. □

We now turn to the estimation of a particular estimable LPF, say $\boldsymbol{A\beta}$. Let us denote the restricted BLUE of $\boldsymbol{A\beta}$ by $\widehat{\boldsymbol{A\beta}}_s$. It is easy to see that

$\widehat{A\beta}_s = C\widehat{X\beta}_s$, where C is a matrix such that $A = CX$. Also, if $\widehat{A\beta}$ is the BLUE of $A\beta$, then $\widehat{A\beta} = C\widehat{X\beta}$. We can compare $\widehat{A\beta}_s$ and $\widehat{A\beta}$ with respect to the quadratic loss function with a nonnegative-definite weight matrix B. Indeed,

$$E[(\widehat{A\beta} - A\beta)'B(\widehat{A\beta} - A\beta)] = E[(\widehat{X\beta} - X\beta)'C'FF'C(\widehat{X\beta} - X\beta)]$$
$$= \mathrm{tr}[F'C(MSE(\widehat{X\beta}))C'F],$$

where $B = FF'$. We can simplify the risk of $\widehat{A\beta}_s$ in a similar manner. Comparing these two expressions, we can conclude that whenever the MSE matrix of $\widehat{X\beta}_s$ is smaller than that of $\widehat{X\beta}$ in the sense of the Löwner order, the risk of $\widehat{A\beta}_s$ is smaller than the risk of $\widehat{A\beta}$ for any estimable $A\beta$ and any nonnegative-definite weight matrix B.

Since the Löwner order of the MSE matrices is a strong condition, one may also look for comparison in a weaker sense. We shall make comparisons in terms of (a) algebraic order of the MSE for an estimable *scalar* LPF and (b) algebraic order of the *trace* of the MSE matrices for $X\beta$.

Let us first consider a scalar LPF $p'\beta$. A necessary and sufficient condition for the MSE of the subset estimator being smaller than the MSE of the BLUE is given in Exercise 5.2. Once again, the subset estimator is found to be more suitable when there is so much collinearity in the model that every column of X_2 is approximately equal to a linear combination of the columns of X_1.

In order to compare the traces of the MSE matrices of the estimators of $X\beta$, note that

$$\mathrm{tr}MSE(\widehat{X\beta}_s) = \mathrm{tr}(\sigma^2 P_{X_1} + (I - P_{X_1})X\beta\beta'X'(I - P_{X_1}))$$
$$= \sigma^2\rho(X_1) + \|(I - P_{X_1})X\beta\|^2. \tag{5.2}$$

Similarly, $\mathrm{tr}MSE(\widehat{X\beta}) = \sigma^2\rho(X)$. It follows that the latter trace is larger if and only if

$$\sigma^2 \geq \frac{\|(I - P_{X_1})X\beta\|^2}{\rho(X) - \rho(X_1)} = \frac{\|(I - P_{X_1})X_2\beta_2\|^2}{\rho(X) - \rho(X_1)}.$$

This condition is generally weaker than (5.1), except when $\rho(X) - \rho(X_1) = 1$ (as in Example 5.5). Note that when X has full column rank, $\rho(X) - \rho(X_1)$ is equal to the number of elements of β_2.

5.1.2 *Some criteria for subset selection*

We have already been using the multiple R-square as a criterion for judging how well a regression model fits the data. The multiple R-square, defined in (4.4), can be written as

$$R^2 = 1 - \frac{\sum_{i=1}^n (y_i - \widehat{y}_i)^2}{\sum_{i=1}^n (y_i - \bar{y})^2}.$$

The sum in the numerator of the last expression is the value of $\sum_{i=1}^n [y_i - (\beta_0 + \beta_1 x_{i1} + \beta_2 x_{i2} + \cdots + \beta_k x_{ik})]^2$, minimized over the regression parameters. The sum in the denominator is the value of $\sum_{i=1}^n (y_i - \beta_0)^2$, minimized over β_0. The latter quantity can also be viewed as the minimized value of $\sum_{i=1}^n [y_i - (\beta_0 + \beta_1 x_{i1} + \beta_2 x_{i2} + \cdots + \beta_k x_{ik})]^2$ with respect to the $k+1$ parameters, subject to the restrictions $\beta_1 = \beta_2 = \cdots = \beta_k = 0$. A restricted minimum cannot be smaller than the unrestricted minimum. Therefore,

$$1 - R^2 = \frac{\min_{\beta_0, \beta_1, \ldots, \beta_k} \sum_{i=1}^n [y_i - (\beta_0 + \beta_1 x_{i1} + \beta_2 x_{i2} + \cdots + \beta_k x_{ik})]^2}{\min_{\beta_0} \sum_{i=1}^n (y_i - \beta_0)^2} \leq 1.$$

Thus, R^2 lies between 0 and 1. It represents the fraction of the sum of squares $\sum_{i=1}^n (y_i - \bar{y})^2$ explained by the explanatory variables.

When subsets of explanatory variables are compared through R^2, the numerator of the above fraction has to be computed according to that subset model (i.e. by excluding some of the available variables). A larger value of R^2 is considered better.

One problem with R^2 is that, when comparing a particular subset with a further subset of it, R^2 always favours the larger subset (Exercise 5.35). Thus, while we can compare two subsets of equal size through R^2 (and prefer the one with larger R^2), we should not trust R^2 while comparing subsets of different sizes.

In order to stop favouring larger subsets, one can put a penalty on the subset size. One way of doing it is to use the *adjusted R-square*, defined as

$$R_a^2 = 1 - \frac{\frac{1}{n-p} \sum_{i=1}^n (y_i - \widehat{y}_i)^2}{\frac{1}{n-1} \sum_{i=1}^n (y_i - \bar{y})^2}.$$

Here, p is the size of the subset, including the intercept. For instance, $p = k + 1$ for the largest possible subset, i.e. the set of all regressors. Note that for every subset model, $\sum_{i=1}^n (y_i - \widehat{y}_i)^2$ has to be computed according to that model and $n - p$ should also be the error degrees of freedom of that model. The denominator is the same for all competing subsets. Thus, comparison of subsets by adjusted R-square amounts to comparing them by $\widehat{\sigma^2}$, the unbiased estimator of σ^2 from that particular subset model. A good subset is one with large R_a^2 or small $\widehat{\sigma^2}$.

The adjusted R-square can sometimes be negative. However, this is not a serious problem, because generally it has a reasonable chance of being negative only for those subsets that cannot explain the response very well anyway (Exercise 5.3).

Another criterion that puts a penalty on subset size is motivated by (5.2). Since $\|(\boldsymbol{I}-\boldsymbol{P}_{X_1})\boldsymbol{y}\|^2-\sigma^2(n-\rho(\boldsymbol{X}_1))$ is an unbiased estimator of $\|(\boldsymbol{I}-\boldsymbol{P}_{X_1})\boldsymbol{X\beta}\|^2$ under the full model (this fact can be verified easily), the trace of the MSE given in (5.2) can be approximated by $\widehat{\sigma^2}C_p$, where

$$C_p=\frac{\|(\boldsymbol{I}-\boldsymbol{P}_{X_1})\boldsymbol{y}\|^2}{\widehat{\sigma^2}}-n+2\rho(\boldsymbol{X}_1)=\frac{\sum_{i=1}^n(y_i-\widehat{y}_i)^2\Big|_{\text{subset model}}}{\widehat{\sigma^2}}-n+2p.$$

Here, p is the size of the subset and $\widehat{\sigma^2}$ is computed from the full model with $k+1$ regression parameters. This quantity is the conceptual predictive criterion of Mallows, popularly known as *Mallows's* C_p. It is used by practitioners not only to compare a subset model with the full model, but also as a criterion for selecting a particular model from a class of competing subset models. A smaller value of C_p is considered to be better. If a subset model of size p happens to be correct for the given response, then the expected value of $\widehat{\sigma^2}C_p$ is $p\sigma^2$ (see Exercise 5.4).

For comparison of subsets of equal size, it can be shown that the criteria of maximizing R^2, maximizing R_a^2 and minimizing C_p produce the same optimizing subset (Exercise 5.35). Also, in the absence of any constraint on the subset size, minimization of C_p produces a subset of smaller size than what is produced by maximization of R_a^2 (Exercise 5.5).

While the above three criteria are meant for linear regression, some general criteria for model selection can also be used. An intuitively appealing criterion for minimization is the cross-validation sum of squares, known in the present context as the prediction sum of squares or *PRESS*. It consists of the sum of squared prediction errors of all the observations, where each observation is predicted through the candidate model from all but that particular observation (see Exercise 5.38 for an expression).

If all the regression parameters are estimable and the form of the error distribution is known, *Akaike's information criterion* (AIC) is to select the subset that minimizes

$$AIC_p=2p-2\log(\widehat{L}_p), \tag{5.3}$$

where $\widehat{L}_p$ is the maximized likelihood. If the error distribution is assumed to be normal, this criterion becomes similar to Mallows's C_p (but not equivalent to it; see Example 5.8 below and Exercise 5.6). Davies et al. (2006) discuss optimality of these two criteria. Another related criterion, namely the *Bayesian Information Criterion* (BIC):

$$BIC_p = p \log n - 2\log(\widehat{L}_p),$$

generally leads to smaller optimal subsets compared to AIC, as it puts a larger penalty ($\log n$ instead of 2) on the subset size. See Hocking (2013) and Ryan (2009) for more details on these and other criteria for subset selection. Selection of erroneously measured variables is considered by Vehkalahti et al. (2007) and Zhang et al. (2017).

Example 5.6. For the data of Example 5.3 the values of the three criteria for the candidate subsets are computed by using the following additional lines of code.

```
M1 <- summary(lm(y~x1))
M2 <- summary(lm(y~x2))
M12 <- summary(lm(y~x1+x2))
M1Cp <- M1$df[2]*(M1$sigma / M12$sigma)^2 - M1$df[2] + M1$df[1]
M2Cp <- M2$df[2]*(M2$sigma / M12$sigma)^2 - M2$df[2] + M2$df[1]
M12Cp <- M12$df[2]*(M12$sigma / M12$sigma)^2 - M12$df[2] + M12$df[1]
c(M1$r.squared, M1$adj.r.squared, M1Cp)
c(M2$r.squared, M2$adj.r.squared, M2Cp)
c(M12$r.squared, M12$adj.r.squared, M12Cp)
```

The corresponding computations for the data of Example 5.4 are obtained through the above code, with the definition of `x2` replaced by `x2 = 0.5*x1 + rnorm(n,mean=1,sd=1.5)`. The values of the three criteria for the candidate subsets for the two examples are as in the table given below.

Data set	Subset	R^2	R_a^2	C_p
	$\{x_1\}$	0.99165	0.99061	3.6872
Example 5.3	$\{x_2\}$	0.99304	0.99217	2.0816
	$\{x_1, x_2\}$	0.99397	0.99224	3.0000
	$\{x_1\}$	0.85320	0.83485	97.120
Example 5.4	$\{x_2\}$	0.73359	0.70029	181.15
	$\{x_1, x_2\}$	0.99004	0.98719	3.0000

It is seen that for both the data sets, multiple R-square is the largest for the full model $\{x_1, x_2\}$, as expected. For the second data set, the full model is clearly the best subset according to both adjusted R-square and Mallows's C_p. For the first data set, Mallows's C_p favours the subset $\{x_2\}$. While adjusted R-square favours the full model, its value for $\{x_2\}$ is only marginally smaller. Therefore, the subset $\{x_2\}$ may be chosen. These empirical decisions for the two data sets are in line with the theoretical findings reported in Example 5.5.

It is interesting to note that unlike R^2 and R_a^2, the measure C_p is not routinely computed in R as part of `summary(lm())`. This is because the computation is impossible without the identification of a 'full model' with respect to which the model under consideration is a 'subset model'. In fact, a given model may have different values of C_p, depending on which model is identified as the 'full model'! □

Example 5.7. (IMF unemployment data) Table 5.2 shows the reported or projected figures of a number of economic variables for a few countries in the year 2015, extracted from IMF World Economic Outlook (2017) available at `http://www.imf.org/external/pubs/ft/weo/2017/01/weodata/weoselgr.aspx`. Suppose one seeks to explain the unemployment rate (UNMP) in terms of the other variables. There are six candidate regressors. The values of the three criteria for the best candidate subset of each size are obtained through the following lines of code.

```
library(leaps)
data(imf2015); attach(imf2015)
xlist = cbind(CAB,DEBT,EXP,GDP,INFL,INV)
leaps(x = xlist, y = UNMP, method = "r2", nbest = 1)
leaps(x = xlist, y = UNMP, method = "adjr2", nbest = 1)
leaps(x = xlist, y = UNMP, method = "Cp", nbest = 1)
detach(imf2015)
```

The best subset of each size, along with the values of the criteria, is given in the following table.

Subset	R^2	R_a^2	C_p
{INV}	0.4099	0.3909	7.130
{GDP, INV}	0.5099	0.4772	3.008
{EXP, GDP, INV}	0.5364	0.4885	3.385
{EXP, GDP, INFL, INV}	0.5637	0.5014	3.715
{DEBT, EXP, GDP, INFL, INV}	0.5696	0.4899	5.356
{CAB, DEBT, EXP, GDP, INFL, INV}	0.5754	0.4774	7.000

It is not surprising that the multiple R-square favours the model that uses the set of all the six regressors. The best subset according to R_a^2 and

Table 5.2 Some country-level figures in 2015 (data object `imf2015` in R package `lmreg`, source: IMF World Economic Outlook, 2017)

Country	Current account balance as % of GDP (CAB)	Govt gross debt as % of GDP (DEBT)	Govt total expenditure as % of GDP (EXP)	GDP per capita, current prices in '000 US$ (GDP)	Inflation, average consumer prices in % (INFL)	Total investment as % of GDP (INV)	Unemployment as % of labor force (UNMP)
Australia	–4.73	37.63	37.27	51.36	1.46	26.30	6.06
Austria	1.85	85.54	51.61	43.75	0.81	23.51	5.75
Belgium	0.44	105.76	53.86	40.52	0.62	23.21	8.49
Canada	–3.40	91.55	40.25	43.35	1.13	23.82	6.90
Cyprus	–2.91	107.53	40.39	23.11	–1.54	13.96	14.89
Czech Rep	0.91	40.31	41.98	17.57	0.34	27.36	5.05
Denmark	9.16	39.55	54.83	53.24	0.45	19.76	6.19
Estonia	2.21	10.05	40.37	17.11	0.07	24.75	6.10
Finland	–0.42	63.66	56.98	42.49	–0.16	21.14	9.38
France	–0.20	96.16	56.98	37.61	0.09	22.36	10.37
Germany	8.33	71.15	43.98	41.20	0.13	19.24	4.61
Greece	0.12	179.35	51.20	17.96	–1.09	9.83	24.90
Iceland	5.47	68.05	42.88	50.47	1.63	19.08	3.99
Ireland	10.24	78.71	29.47	60.90	–0.02	21.76	9.44
Israel	4.35	64.08	39.62	35.74	–0.63	19.95	5.28
Italy	1.62	132.04	50.45	30.03	0.11	17.31	11.91
Japan	3.09	237.97	36.64	34.51	0.79	23.90	3.38
Korea	7.66	37.76	20.92	27.11	0.71	28.92	3.64
Latvia	–0.78	34.84	37.71	13.61	0.21	22.09	9.88
Lithuania	–2.34	42.54	34.41	14.26	–0.68	19.89	9.12
Luxembourg	5.24	22.09	42.12	100.95	0.06	19.63	6.80
Netherlands	8.68	65.12	45.20	44.32	0.22	19.27	6.89
New Zealand	–3.36	29.56	34.23	37.28	0.29	22.75	5.35
Norway	8.66	33.20	47.97	74.26	2.17	28.21	4.37
Portugal	0.07	128.99	48.36	19.23	0.51	15.45	12.44
Singapore	18.11	103.24	18.32	53.63	–0.52	26.77	1.90
Slovak Rep	0.21	52.50	45.27	16.11	–0.34	23.20	11.49
Slovenia	5.18	83.15	44.08	20.75	–0.53	20.06	9.00
Spain	1.37	99.77	43.76	25.72	–0.50	20.06	22.06
Sweden	4.70	42.93	48.92	50.32	0.70	24.21	7.40
Switzerland	11.53	45.80	32.65	81.41	–1.14	23.00	3.18
UK	–4.28	88.96	40.13	43.98	0.05	17.18	5.40
USA	–2.57	105.61	35.28	56.17	0.12	20.35	5.26

C_p have size 4 and 2, respectively, excluding the intercept. Given these contradictory indications, the simpler model (involving only GDP and INV) may be preferred. This is known as the principle of parsimony. While the value of C_p is optimum for this subset, that of R_a^2 is nearly optimum. □

5.1.3 *Methods of subset selection*

Once a criterion has been selected, one can pick the best size-p subset of predictors. In general, this can be done with much less computation than having to evaluate all the $\binom{k}{p}$ possible cases. In order to determine the most appropriate p, the 'best' subsets of different sizes should be compared on the basis of the chosen criterion. Some refer to this task as *best subsets regression.*

The above procedure can be prohibitively lengthy if there is a large number of predictors to choose from. A suboptimal shortcut, which sometimes produces the 'best' subset, is *stepwise regression.* A version of this method is as follows. Choose the predictor variable which has the largest squared correlation coefficient (called current R^2) with the response. Call this $x_{(1)}$. Now choose the next predictor variable which, along with $x_{(1)}$, is the one most closely related to y according to a suitable criterion. Call this variable $x_{(2)}$. Proceed in the same way to choose more variables and stop when the value of the criterion does not improve. This procedure is called forward selection. Backward selection can be done in a similar manner starting with the full set of predictors and dropping one of them at a time. Procedures for simultaneous forward and backward selections are also available. See Rawlings et al. (1998) for further details.

It should be noted that however efficient a stepwise search is, it can miss the subset that optimizes the chosen criterion. Therefore, an exhaustive search through all possible subsets should be made, whenever that is feasible.

Example 5.8. Suppose we leave out the variable GDP from the IMF country level data of Table 5.2, and seek to explain the unemployment rate (UNMP) through the other five variables. Forward stepwise regression, with minimum AIC as the criterion for selection and only the intercept as the starting model, leads one to successively include the variables INV, CAB, INFL and EXP, and stop at the final subset model {INV, CAB, INFL, EXP}. Backward stepwise regression with the same criterion and the full five-regressor model as starting point leads one to exclude DEBT and stop at the same final subset model. The requisite computations are obtained through the following lines of code, which also produce the values of C_p for the different subsets.

```
attach(imf2015)
lm0 <- lm(UNMP ~ 1, data = imf2015)
```

```
summary(step(lm0,scope=UNMP~CAB+DEBT+EXP+INFL+INV,
     direction="forward"))$anova
lm5 <- lm(UNMP ~ CAB+DEBT+EXP+INFL+INV, data = imf2015)
summary(step(lm5, direction = "backward"))$anova
sum((UNMP-mean(UNMP))^2)/((summary(lm5)$sigma)^2)-length(UNMP)+2
                # Cp for intercept only
summary(regsubsets(UNMP~INV+CAB+INFL+EXP+DEBT,data=imf2015,
     method="forward"))$cp
```

These computations are shown in the following table. It transpires that the same final subset would have been obtained by minimizing C_p.

Method	Subset	AIC*	C_p
Forward	{ }	106.89	27.612
	{INV}	91.48	5.585
	{INV, CAB}	91.35	5.421
	{INV, CAB, INFL}	91.28	5.457
	{INV, CAB, INFL, EXP}	90.44	4.942
Backward	{CAB, DEBT, EXP, INFL, INV}	91.31	6.000
	{INV, CAB, INFL, EXP}	90.44	4.942

* up to an added constant

Search over all possible subsets, through the additional lines of code

```
leaps(x=cbind(CAB,DEBT,EXP,INFL,INV),y=UNMP,method="Cp",nbest=1)
leaps(x=cbind(CAB,DEBT,EXP,INFL,INV),y=UNMP,method="adjr2",nbest=1)
```

shows that the set {INV, CAB, INFL, EXP} is indeed the best subset of four regressors according to the C_p and the adjusted R^2 criteria. However, the best subset of three regressors, {EXP, INFL, INV}, has $C_p = 4.912$. This value is smaller than 4.942, the C_p of the 'best' subset obtained through forward or backward selection. Thus, stepwise regression misses the optimal possible subset (according to C_p) in this instance.

The value of AIC for the subset {EXP, INFL, INV}, obtained from the code

```
lm3 <- lm(UNMP ~ EXP+INFL+INV, data = imf2015)
summary(step(lm3, direction = "forward"))$anova
```

happens to be 90.69. It transpires that the best subset according to AIC is still {INV, CAB, INFL, EXP}. This example illustrates that minimizing

C_p is *not* equivalent to minimizing AIC (see Exercise 5.6). It turns out that the above subset of four regressors is also the best one according to R_a^2. In other words, R_a^2 and AIC favour the same subset of size four, while the best subset according to C_p has three regressors. It should be noted that the values of any criterion for these two subsets are not very different, which means the choice is not clear. Since there is no strong reason to favour either subset, one can adopt the principle of parsimony and choose the simpler subset. □

5.1.4 *Selection bias*

If one uses a data set to select a subset model and subsequently estimates the parameters of that model from the same data set, these estimators may be biased.

Example 5.9. Consider the linear regression model with two regressors

$$y = \beta_0 + \beta_1 x_1 + \beta_2 x_2 + \varepsilon,$$

where $\beta_0 = 20$, $\beta_1 = \beta_2 = 1$ and x_1, x_2 and ε are independent sample from the standard normal distribution. Suppose one uses data generated from this model and decides to choose a subset model with only one explanatory variable, through the R^2 criterion. The two variables have equal chance of being selected, because of the symmetry of their roles in the model.

Through the R code given below, we simulate 1000 samples of size 10 from the above multiple regression model, fit each of the two simple linear regression models and split them into two groups depending on whichever model has higher R^2.

```
set.seed(1234)
n <- 10; beta0 <- 20; beta1 <- 1; beta2 <- 1
b1list <- NULL; b2list <- NULL; indlist <- NULL
for (iter in 1:1000) {
  x1 <- rnorm(n); x2 <- rnorm(n); err <- rnorm(n)
  y <- beta0 + beta1 * x1 + beta2 * x2 + err
  b1 <- lm(y~x1)$coef[2]; b2 <- lm(y~x2)$coef[2]
  ind <- 2; if(cor(y,x1)>cor(y,x2)) ind <- 1
  b1list <- c(b1list,b1); b2list <- c(b2list,b2)
  indlist <- c(indlist,ind)
}
```

We then generate box plots of the LSEs $\widehat{\beta}_1$ (coefficient of x_1 in the subset model) and $\widehat{\beta}_2$ (coefficient of x_2 in the subset model) in the two groups, and also box plots of these in the combined sample of both groups, as follows.

```
boxplot(b1list~indlist,names=c("x1 winner","x2 winner"))
abline(h=1,lty=3)
boxplot(b2list~indlist,names=c("x1 winner","x2 winner"))
abline(h=1,lty=3)
boxplot(b1list,names=c("all data sets"))
abline(h=1,lty=3)
boxplot(b2list,names=c("all data sets"))
abline(h=1,lty=3)
```

These box plots are shown in Figure 5.3. It is clear that $\widehat{\beta}_1$ overestimates β_1 on the average in the first group and underestimates it in the second group. Likewise, $\widehat{\beta}_2$ has a negative bias in the first group and positive bias in the second group. Neither estimator is biased in the combined sample.

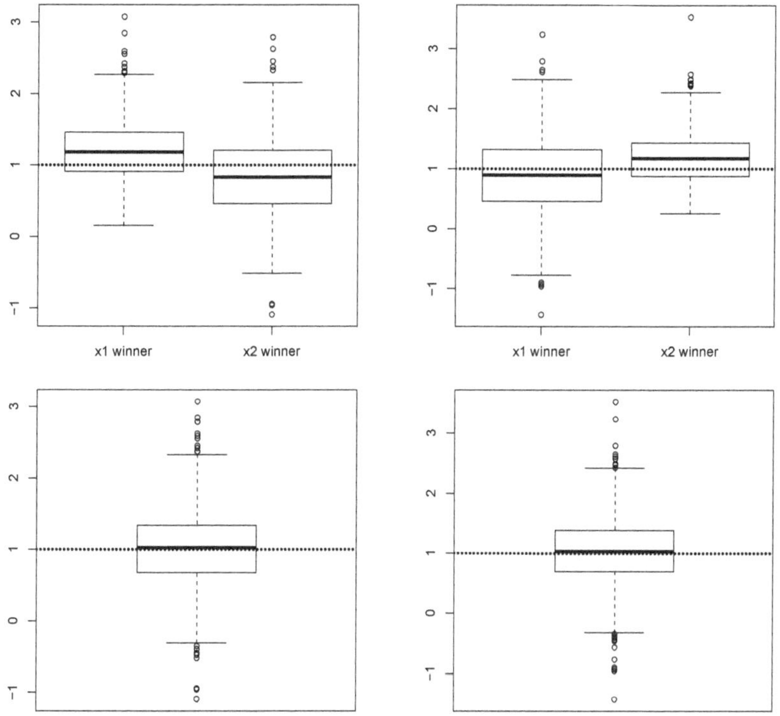

Fig. 5.3 Box plots of $\widehat{\beta}_1$ (left panel) and $\widehat{\beta}_2$ (right panel) obtained from simulation runs segregated by winning predictor (top panel) and all simulation runs (bottom panel), for Example 5.9. Horizontal dotted line in each plot shows the correct value of β_1 and β_2

This remarkable finding can be explained by the fact that the average value of $\widehat{\beta}_1$ in the first group is expected to be $E(\widehat{\beta}_1|R_1^2 > R_2^2)$, where R_1^2 and R_2^2 are the values of R^2 in the two subset models. The inequality $R_1^2 > R_2^2$ corresponds to the event that the simple linear regression model with x_1 as the regressor is the winning subset. Further, through an empirical version of the fact $\beta_1 = \rho\sigma_y/\sigma_x$ observed in Example 2.16, it may be argued that large values of R_1^2 often correspond to large values of $\widehat{\beta}_1^2$. Thus, it makes sense that the above conditional mean is larger than the unconditional mean, β_1, i.e. the estimator $\widehat{\beta}_1$ has a positive bias among the simulation runs where x_1 is the winning variable. □

The bias of the LSE observed in the above example is induced by the preceding selection of a subset on the basis of the same data set. This *selection bias* generally inflates parameter estimates (see Miller, 2002). The bias may be avoided if model building and inference are based on disjoint parts of the data, possibly obtained by splitting it randomly into two parts.

5.2 Leverages and residuals

We begin our discussion of regression diagnostics with the examination of two basic ingredients of the tools needed for it: leverages and residuals.

It follows from (3.8) that the fitted value for the ith observation is

$$\widehat{y}_i = \sum_{j=1}^{n} h_{i,j} y_j,$$

where $h_{i,j}$ is the (i,j)th element of the hat-matrix, $\boldsymbol{H} = \boldsymbol{X}(\boldsymbol{X}'\boldsymbol{X})^-\boldsymbol{X}'$. The $h_{i,j}$s for $j = 1, \ldots, n$ are the weights with which the various components of $\boldsymbol{y}$ are combined to obtain $\widehat{y}_i$. In particular, the diagonal element $h_{i,i}$ is the weight of y_i in the linear combination that gives $\widehat{y}_i$. As already mentioned, this number is called the ith leverage, and the notation is commonly abbreviated as h_i. The larger the leverage of an observation, the larger is its contribution to the corresponding fitted value.

The matrix $\boldsymbol{H}$ is symmetric and idempotent. By equating the ith diagonal elements of the matrices $\boldsymbol{H}$ and $\boldsymbol{H}^2$, we have

$$h_i = \sum_{j+1}^{n} h_{i,j} h_{j,i} = \sum_{j=1}^{n} h_{i,j}^2 \geq h_i^2.$$

Therefore, $h_i - h_i^2 \geq 0$, or $h_i(1 - h_i) \geq 0$. Thus, the leverages are always in the range $[0, 1]$. The leverage of an observation is equal to 0 if and only if this observation is a linear zero function, that is, it is uncorrelated with every BLUE (see Exercise 5.7). The other extreme case, i.e. the leverage being equal to 1, occurs if and only if the observation is a BLUE (see Exercise 5.8).

If the regression model includes the intercept term, the ith leverage can be written as (see Exercise 5.10)

$$h_i = \frac{1}{n} + m_i, \tag{5.4}$$

$$\text{where } m_i = (\boldsymbol{x}_i - \bar{\boldsymbol{x}})'\boldsymbol{S}^-(\boldsymbol{x}_i - \bar{\boldsymbol{x}}), \tag{5.5}$$

and $\bar{\boldsymbol{x}}$ and $\boldsymbol{S}$ are the sample mean vector and the sum of squares and products matrix of the vectors $\boldsymbol{x}_1, \ldots, \boldsymbol{x}_n$, namely

$$\bar{\boldsymbol{x}} = \frac{1}{n}\sum_{i=1}^{n} \boldsymbol{x}_i, \quad \boldsymbol{S} = \sum_{i=1}^{n}(\boldsymbol{x}_i - \bar{\boldsymbol{x}})(\boldsymbol{x}_i - \bar{\boldsymbol{x}})'. \tag{5.6}$$

If the $\boldsymbol{x}_i$'s are regarded as samples from a distribution with mean $\boldsymbol{\mu}$ and variance-covariance matrix $\boldsymbol{\Sigma}$, then the quantity nm_i is the sample version of the squared Mahalanobis distance of the $\boldsymbol{x}_i$ from $\boldsymbol{\mu}$, defined as $(\boldsymbol{x}_i - \boldsymbol{\mu})'\boldsymbol{\Sigma}^-(\boldsymbol{x}_i - \boldsymbol{\mu})$. Thus, the leverage of an observation indicates how far it is located in relation to the center of the data cloud, as far as the explanatory variables are concerned. In particular, observations with extreme values of explanatory variables have high leverage.

In the special case of the simple linear regression model (3.5), where $\boldsymbol{X} = (\boldsymbol{1} : \boldsymbol{x})$, the value of the ith leverage (5.4) simplifies to

$$h_i = \frac{1}{n} + \frac{(x_i - \bar{x})^2}{\sum_{j=1}^{n}(x_j - \bar{x})^2},$$

$\bar{x}$ being the average of the values of the explanatory variable.

One needs a benchmark for identifying observations with high leverage. Note that the trace of the idempotent matrix $\boldsymbol{H}$, or the sum of all leverages, is equal to its rank (see page 607). Hence, when all the $k+1$ regression coefficients are estimable, the average value of a leverage is $(k+1)/n$. A 'rule of thumb' threshold for high leverage cases is twice this average, i.e. $2(k+1)/n$ (see Belsley et al., 2005).

The leverages help us in understanding the residuals. Recall from (3.10) that the residual vector can be written as $\boldsymbol{e} = (\boldsymbol{I} - \boldsymbol{H})\boldsymbol{y}$. It follows from this expression that

$$\begin{aligned} E(\boldsymbol{e}) = (\boldsymbol{I} - \boldsymbol{H})E(\boldsymbol{y}) &= (\boldsymbol{I} - \boldsymbol{H})\boldsymbol{X\beta} = \boldsymbol{X\beta} - \boldsymbol{HX\beta} = \boldsymbol{0}, \\ D(\boldsymbol{e}) = (\boldsymbol{I} - \boldsymbol{H})D(\boldsymbol{y})(\boldsymbol{I} - \boldsymbol{H}) &= (\boldsymbol{I} - \boldsymbol{H})\sigma^2\boldsymbol{I}(\boldsymbol{I} - \boldsymbol{H}) = \sigma^2(\boldsymbol{I} - \boldsymbol{H}). \end{aligned}$$

In particular,

$$E(\boldsymbol{e}_i) = 0, \quad Var(e_i) = (1 - h_i)\sigma^2, \quad Cov(e_j, e_j) = -h_{i,j}\sigma^2.$$

It transpires that the residuals have zero mean and unequal variance, and they are correlated. This is in contrast with the model errors (ε_is), which are uncorrelated and have equal variance (σ^2). All residuals have variance smaller than σ^2. Residuals corresponding to high leverage cases would have particularly small variance.

Consider the extreme example, when $h_i = 1$. In such a case, $E(e_i) = 0$ and $Var(e_i) = 0$. Thus, the residual itself has to be zero. The residual is the difference between the observed and the fitted values of y_i. If the residual is 0, the fitted value coincides with the observed value. In other words, a case with leverage $h_i = 1$ wields so much 'leverage' on the fit that it would force the fitted line or plane right through itself, irrespective of the value of the response vector $\boldsymbol{y}$. When the leverage of a case is high but not equal to 1, the corresponding residual would have relatively small variance, and therefore the fit would be close. As we have seen before, this happens for points having a profile of explanatory variables that is unusually far from the center of the points in the space of explanatory variables. For this reason, very high-leverage points are also referred to as *x-outliers.*

On the other hand, unusually large values of residuals correspond to *y-outliers.* These are points with values of response that are not consistent with the rest of the data — according to the fitted model.

But then, how large is large? The residuals arising from a data set with response measured in centimeters would become ten times larger if the response is expressed instead in millimeters. There has to be some scaling to judge largeness of the residuals. The ideal scaling factor of the residual e_i would be its standard deviation, $\sqrt{(1 - h_i)\sigma^2}$. Since σ is unknown, we can replace it with $\widehat{\sigma}$, the square-root of $\widehat{\sigma^2}$ defined in (3.19). This substitution brings us the *standardized residual*

$$r_i = \frac{e_i}{\widehat{\sigma}\sqrt{1 - h_i}}. \tag{5.7}$$

One can argue that $\widehat{\sigma}$ is not an appropriate substitute of σ in the denominator, because a large residual may inflate the estimator by contributing a large summand in the expression $\widehat{\sigma^2} = \frac{1}{n-k-1}\sum_{i=1}^{n} e_i^2$. An alternatively scaled version, which addresses this concern, is the *studentized residual* (also called *rstudent*)

$$t_i = \frac{e_i}{\widehat{\sigma}_{(-i)}\sqrt{1 - h_i}}, \tag{5.8}$$

where $\widehat{\sigma}_{(-i)}$ is the version of $\widehat{\sigma}$ computed from a reanalysis of the data after the ith case has been left out. Of course, this 'reanalysis' is only notional; algebraic tricks can be used to avoid repeated calculations with one case excluded at a time (see Exercise 9.15 for an explicit expression). Studentized residuals are also referred to as *externally* studentized residuals, to highlight the fact that the standard deviation in the denominator is estimated from cases that are external to the ith case.

Remark 5.10. If one accepts the philosophy of 'externalization', it is logical to extend it to the other terms in the expression (5.8) as well. Specifically, the residual e_i should be replaced by the *deleted residual* $e_{i(-i)} = y_i - \widehat{y}_{i(-i)}$, where $\widehat{y}_{i(-i)}$ is the predicted value of y_i obtained by reanalysing the data after the ith case has been left out. Likewise, and $1-h_i$ should be replaced by $1 - h_{i(-i)}$, the variance of $e_{i(-i)}/\sigma$. The resulting quantity, called the *deleted studentized residual*, turns out to be the same as t_i (Exercise 5.14).

It can be shown that if the model is correct and the errors have normal distribution, t_i has the student's t distribution with $n-k-2$ degrees of freedom (see remark below). This is the reason why t_i is called the studentized residual. Generally both r_i and t_i are regarded as 'large' when they have magnitude greater than 2 (beyond the middle 95% range of the standard normal distribution). When n is much larger than k, the normal approximation is very good. The approximation works better for t_i, as r_i cannot ever have magnitude larger than $\sqrt{n-k-1}$. In fact, it is related to t_i as (see Exercise 9.16)

$$t_i = r_i\sqrt{\frac{n-k-1}{n-k-r_i^2}}. \tag{5.9}$$

This relation shows that t_i has the same sign as r_i, but it has a larger magnitude whenever $r_i^2 > 1$.

Remark 5.11. In the modified model $(\boldsymbol{y}, \boldsymbol{X\beta} + \boldsymbol{u}_i\gamma, \sigma^2\boldsymbol{I})$, where $\boldsymbol{u}_i$ is the ith column of the $n \times n$ identity matrix, the additional parameter γ represents a shift of location of the ith case over and above the presumed linear model. This location-shift model is a way of explaining how a y-outlier appears only in the ith case. By testing for $\gamma = 0$, one can check whether the ith case is really a *location-shift outlier*. The studentized residual t_i turns out to be the student's t-statistic for testing the significance of γ (Exercise 9.17). This fact gives legitimacy to the studentized residual as a flag for y-outlier.

Example 5.12. (Data sets with similar regression summary, continued) For data sets (a), (e) and (f) of Example 5.1, the leverages, standardized residuals and studentized residuals are computed as shown below and reported in Table 5.3.

```
data(anscombeplus)
ma <- lm(y1~x1, data = anscombeplus)
me <- lm(y5~x1, data = anscombeplus)
mf <- lm(y6~x2, data = anscombeplus)
library(MASS)
cbind(hatvalues(ma),hatvalues(me),hatvalues(mf),stdres(ma),
  stdres(me),stdres(mf),studres(ma),studres(me),studres(mf))
```

For each of these data sets, the working threshold for high leverage is $2(k+1)/n = 0.2$. The only case of high leverage happens to be the last case of data set (f). Its status as an x-outlier is corroborated by the plot (f) of Figure 5.1. The tenth case of data set (e) has large values of standardized and studentized residuals, and plot (e) of Figure 5.1 confirms that it is a y-outlier. The eighteenth case of data set (f) is also found to be a y-outlier.

Table 5.3 Leverages and residuals for synthetic data sets (a), (e) and (f)

Leverages for data set			Standardized residuals for data set			Studentized residuals for data set		
(a)	(e)	(f)	(a)	(e)	(f)	(a)	(e)	(f)
0.1857	0.1857	0.0597	1.7301	−0.3575	−0.3341	1.8414	−0.3487	−0.3257
0.1586	0.1586	0.0597	0.3325	−0.3271	1.4262	0.3241	−0.3188	1.4717
0.1346	0.1346	0.0597	−1.4782	−0.1717	−1.2733	−1.5325	−0.1670	−1.2972
0.1135	0.1135	0.0597	−1.8592	−0.2401	0.0052	−2.0101	−0.2337	0.0050
0.0955	0.0955	0.0597	−0.2576	−0.2502	0.2703	−0.2508	−0.2436	0.2633
0.0805	0.0805	0.0597	−0.7346	−0.1786	−0.2979	−0.7248	−0.1737	−0.2902
0.0684	0.0684	0.0597	0.7802	−0.2216	−0.0609	0.7713	−0.2156	−0.0592
0.0594	0.0594	0.0597	0.5896	−0.1736	0.0061	0.5786	−0.1688	0.0059
0.0534	0.0534	0.0597	−0.4145	−0.1519	1.4346	−0.4047	−0.1477	1.4815
0.0504	0.0504	0.0597	0.9312	*4.2347*	−0.2121	0.9276	*67.0977*	−0.2064
0.0504	0.0504	0.0500	−0.3936	−0.3443	−0.6158	−0.3842	−0.3357	−0.6049
0.0534	0.0534	0.0500	−0.0591	−0.2197	0.7528	−0.0575	−0.2138	0.7434
0.0594	0.0594	0.0500	0.2832	−0.3083	−0.7226	0.2758	−0.3004	−0.7126
0.0684	0.0684	0.0500	1.0440	−0.1809	−1.7518	1.0468	−0.1760	−1.8693
0.0805	0.0805	0.0500	1.7373	−0.3194	−1.0211	1.8506	−0.3112	−1.0224
0.0955	0.0955	0.0500	−1.3753	−0.1821	−0.9400	−1.4129	−0.1771	−0.9368
0.1135	0.1135	0.0500	0.9594	−0.1510	0.4854	0.9572	−0.1468	0.4749
0.1346	0.1346	0.0500	−0.1292	−0.1628	*2.4892*	−0.1256	−0.1583	*2.9873*
0.1586	0.1586	0.0500	−1.2482	−0.2049	0.2606	−1.2692	−0.1993	0.2537
0.1857	0.1857	*0.9526*	−0.5071	−0.2163	0.4659	−0.4964	−0.2105	0.4555

All the other cases in the three data sets have standardized and studentized residuals with magnitude smaller than 2. There is no x- or y-outlier in data set (a). □

5.3 Checking for violation of assumptions

Four major assumptions underlying the linear regression model are (a) *linearity* of the regression function, (b) *homoscedasticity* or equal variance of all the observations, (c) *uncorrelatedness* of all the observations and (d) *normality* of the response given the regressor values. These assumptions can be checked, one at a time, either graphically or through a formal statistical test. The advantage of a graphical check is that, in case a plot does not turn out to be as expected, sometimes it helps the user in adopting an appropriate remedial measure.

5.3.1 *Nonlinearity*

In the case of simple linear regression, the scatter plot of the response variable against the explanatory variable can reveal whether there is a nonlinear relation between them. One can also plot the residuals against the regressor. In the case of *multiple* regression, the scatter plot of y against one regressor at a time can be examined. However, the effect of one regressor on the response may be confounded by the effects of other regressors, making it difficult to draw conclusions. Some specialized diagnostic plots, which adjust for the effects of the other variables, are available.

The *component plus residual plot* (also known as the *partial residual plot*) for the jth (non-intercept) regressor is the scatter of the points $(x_{ij}, e_i + \widehat{\beta}_j x_{ij})$ for $i = 1, \ldots, n$. The vertical coordinate of the ith point in this plot can be written as $y_i - \sum_{l \neq j} \widehat{\beta}_l x_{il}$, which is a 'partial' residual that ignores the contribution of the jth regressor.

Another useful diagnostic for detecting nonlinearity is the added variable plot or partial regression plot, already mentioned on page 104 (see also page 52). To construct this plot, y and x_j are regressed separately on all the regressors except x_j. The residuals of the first regression are plotted against the corresponding residuals of the second regression.

The above diagnostic plots for the jth regressor share the following interesting properties: (i) the least squares fitted line through the plot has intercept zero and slope equal to the estimate $\widehat{\beta}_j$; (ii) the sum of squared (vertical) deviations of the points from this line is equal to the error sum of squares, R_0^2 (see Exercises 5.15 and 5.16). Further, the sample correlation between the residuals used in the jth added variable plot is the sample partial correlation between the response and the jth regressor, obtained after adjusting for the linear effects of the remaining regressors (Exercise 3.20).

Example 5.13. (Simulated nonlinear data) A good way to appreciate the working of the diagnostic plots is to examine them for synthetic data arising from a known model with nonlinearity in one of the regressors. We consider a sample of size 20 simulated from the model

$$y = 5 + x_1 + x_2 + 0.1x_3^2 + \varepsilon,$$

where ε is standard normal and independent of the regressors and

$$x_1 \sim N(10, 2^2),\ x_2|x_1 \sim N(20 - x_1, 3^2),\ x_3|x_1, x_2 \sim N(0.5x_1 + 0.5x_2, 3^2).$$

The R code for generating the data is given below, while the generated data are given in Table 5.4.

```
set.seed(4321); n <- 20
x1 <- 10 + 2*rnorm(n)
x2 <- 20 - x1 + 3*rnorm(n)
x3 <- 0.5 * (x1 + x2) + 3*rnorm(n)
y <- 5 + 1 * x1 + 1 * x2 + 0.1 * x3^2 + rnorm(n)
```

Table 5.4 Synthetic data set for demonstrating diagnostic plots for nonlinearity in a single regressor

x_1	x_2	x_3	y	x_1	x_2	x_3	y
9.146	12.304	10.285	36.904	9.866	10.555	10.903	38.038
9.553	10.438	13.545	43.319	10.689	11.298	11.622	39.186
11.435	8.538	11.244	37.087	7.478	15.915	16.121	53.811
11.683	10.097	8.577	34.960	12.279	6.296	15.528	48.451
9.743	9.959	11.995	38.995	7.556	15.001	11.724	42.229
13.219	6.067	9.943	33.753	13.147	4.599	14.028	41.873
9.406	10.738	13.184	41.746	10.147	9.326	12.854	41.199
10.392	10.498	12.972	42.765	7.650	14.606	7.583	33.439
12.481	5.017	9.020	30.850	6.823	13.888	13.441	43.965
8.563	7.315	7.998	27.458	8.505	15.297	12.041	42.373

The scatter plots of y against the individual regressors, the component plus residual plots and the added variable plots of the three regressors are generated by the following code and shown in Figure 5.4.

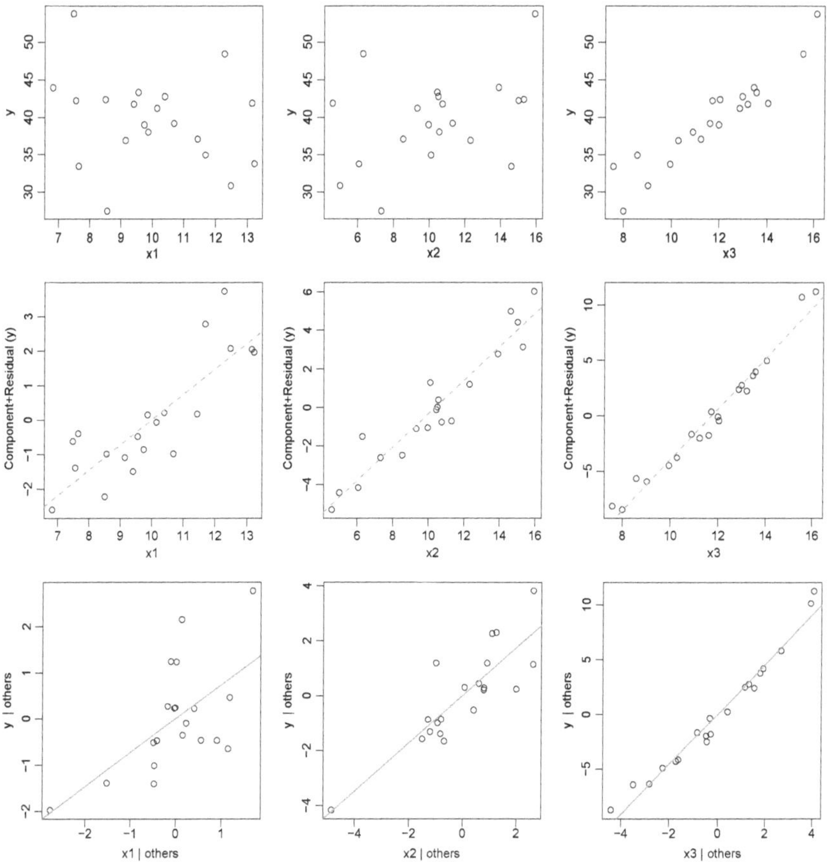

Fig. 5.4 Scatter plot of response against regressors (top row), component plus residual plots of regressors (middle row) and added variable plots of regressors (bottom row) for the data of Example 5.13

```
lm1 <- lm(y~x1+x2+x3)
plot(x1,y); plot(x2,y); plot(x3,y)
library(car)
crPlots(lm1,smooth=F) # Component plus residual plot
avPlots(lm1) # Added variable plot
```

The nonlinear nature of the dependence of the mean response on x_3 is not clear from the third scatter plot in the top row, but a bend in the scatter is visible in the third plots of the next two rows. Thus, for this data set, the component plus residual plot and the added variable plot for the variable x_3 are able to bring out the nonlinearity. □

Unlike the scatter plot that is affected by the confounding of regressors, the component plus residual and the added variable plots exhibit the strength of the linear effect of individual regressors, whenever the linear regression model is correct. However, when the effect of a particular regressor is nonlinear, the functional form may not always come out clearly from either of the plots. While no diagnostic tool is perfect, the two sets of plots give the data analyst a better chance of detecting a nonlinear pattern.

If nonlinearity is detected through any of the above plots, one can use a nonlinear function as an alternative to the linear regression function. However, identifying an appropriate nonlinear relation between the response and the group of explanatory variables can be a very difficult task. After all, linearity can happen in a limited way, but there are unlimited ways for nonlinearity to occur.

One solution to this challenge is to chart a middle course. Instead of looking for a nonlinear function of all explanatory variables, one can look for a nonlinear transformation of one variable at a time. Thus, when we are looking for nonlinearity in the explanatory variable x_1, an alternative model to consider is

$$y = \beta_0 + \beta_1 g(x_1) + \beta_2 x_2 + \cdots + \beta_k x_k + \varepsilon,$$

where g is a nonlinear function. The diagnostic plots mentioned in this section may help us in getting an idea about g. The guiding principle is that one need not get carried away in search for the absolute truth about g. An approximation might do just fine for the working range of x_1.

For example, if any of the three plots for a particular regressor shows a concave pattern and the regressor is positive-valued, one may choose from the following sequence of increasingly concave transformations (referred by practitioners as the *ladder of transformations*) of x: $x^{1/2}$, $\log x$, $-x^{-1/2}$, $-x^{-1}$, $-x^{-2}$, etc. If the observed pattern is convex, one may choose a positive integer power transformation. Power and log transformations are by far the most popular transformations (see Atkinson, 1987). All the power transformations, along with the log transformation (a favourite of econometricians), are combined into a single family of transformations defined as

$$g_\lambda(x) = \begin{cases} \frac{x^\lambda - 1}{\lambda} & \text{if } \lambda \neq 0, \\ \log x & \text{if } \lambda = 0. \end{cases} \tag{5.10}$$

Box and Cox (1964) had proposed this family of transformations for use on the response variable to enhance normality (see Section 5.3.4), while Box and Tidwell (1968) had proposed the use of the family of power transformations on positive valued regressors. For every λ, g_λ is an increasing function. It is convex (i.e. has increasing slope) when $\lambda > 1$, and concave (i.e. has falling slope) when $\lambda < 1$. The function $\log(x)$ happens to be the limit of $(x^\lambda - 1)/\lambda$ as λ goes to 0. The parameter λ controls the degree of convexity/concavity of the transformation, and provides a parametric framework to compare various transformations. The appropriate choice of λ should be the value that maximizes the multiple R-square. This can be easily done, as the model $y = \beta_0 + \beta_1 g_\lambda(x_1) + \beta_2 x_2 + \cdots + \beta_k x_k + \varepsilon$, which we are trying to fit, is still a linear model in $g_\lambda(x_1)$ and other explanatory variables.

One can also bank on the fact that every smooth function has a Taylor series expansion. Therefore, a blind guess with a low degree polynomial (e.g., a quadratic or a cubic function), which may be interpreted as a truncated Taylor series approximation, is generally a good bet as a trial function. When a quadratic term is used, one must not forget to include the linear term also. When a cubic term is used, the quadratic and linear terms should be included, at least initially. This strategy is likely to produce a better fit at the cost of a more complex model. The extra variables may aggravate the problem of collinearity though (see page 254).

Example 5.14. (Simulated nonlinear data, continued) Let us look for an appropriate Box-Tidwell transformation of x_3 in Example 5.13, by experimenting with λ in the model

$$y = \beta_0 + \beta_1 x_1 + \beta_2 x_2 + \beta_3 g_\lambda(x_3) + \varepsilon,$$

where g_λ is the function defined in (5.10). Figure 5.5 (obtained with the R code given below) shows how the value of R-square, obtained by fitting this model to the data of Table 5.4, depends on λ.

```
lambda <- seq(-2,4,.05)
Rsq <- NULL
for (lamb in lambda) {
  tx3 <- (x3^lamb - 1) / lamb
  if (lamb==0) tx3 <- log(x3)
  Rsq <- c(Rsq, summary(lm(y~x1+x2+tx3))$r.sq)
  }
plot(lambda,Rsq,type="l")
```

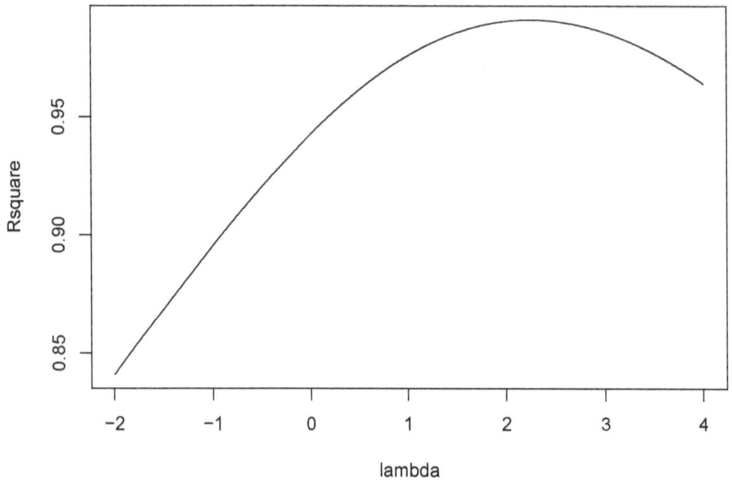

Fig. 5.5 Plot of R-square from the model of Example 5.14 against λ

Evidently the highest value of R-square is achieved when λ is nearly equal to 2 (which is incidentally the appropriate power — as we *know* from the mechanism of data generation, described in Example 5.13). If we use x_3^2 as an additional regressor along with x_1, x_2 and x_3, it turns out that x_3 has a large p-value (0.791). If x_3 is dropped, the coefficients of x_1, x_2 and x_3^2 have p-values smaller than 10^{-4}, and all the component plus residual and the added variable plots show linear patterns. The plots are omitted for brevity. □

The strategy of transforming one regressor at a time may work only if the dependence of y on the regressors can be reasonably approximated by a linear function of transformed regressors. However, it may not succeed where the dependence relation is more complicated. In such a case, one may turn to nonparametric regression methods. A tree-based method (see Breiman et al., 1984) approximates the regression function by a piecewise constant function. One may also seek to approximate it by a smooth function. Kernel, spline, LOESS and projection pursuit regression represent a wide variety of regression functions (see Jones and Sibson, 1987, Härdle, 1990, Hart, 1997, Härdle et al., 2004). These methods generally require lots of data, and the requirement rises steeply with the number of regressors.

5.3.2 *Heteroscedasticity*

The assumption of equal variance of all errors in the linear model is called homoscedasticity. The situation where this assumption is violated, i.e. the errors do not have the same variance, is referred to as heteroscedasticity (also spelled as heteroskedasticity).

While the LSE of the regression parameters and related predictors become biased when nonlinearity is overlooked, they remain unbiased when heteroscedasticity is overlooked (Exercise 5.47). The consequences of ignoring unequal variances of errors lie elsewhere. The following example illustrates what might go wrong.

Example 5.15. (Waist circumference, continued) Consider the problem of predicting the measurement of adipose tissue (AT) by waist circumference ($waist$), from the data given in Table 4.4. Use of the simple linear regression model produces the fitted equation

$$AT = -215.98 + 3.459 waist + 33.06z,$$

where z is error with mean 0 and variance 1. This model may be used to specify a 95% prediction interval of AT for a given value of $waist$. The following code produces the above fit and a scatter plot of the observed data, together with the locus of the upper and lower prediction limits of AT for different values of $waist$, shown in Figure 5.6.

```
data(waist)
attach(waist)
```

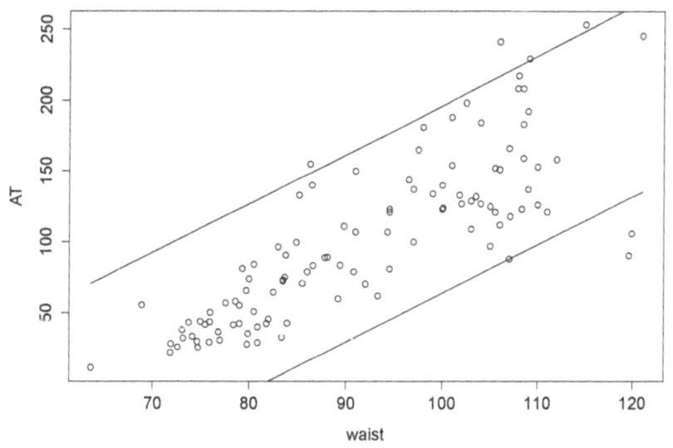

Fig. 5.6 Scatter plot of response AT against regressor $waist$, along with loci of upper and lower 95% prediction limits, for the waist circumference data of Example 5.15

```
summary(lm(AT~Waist))
wrange <- seq(min(Waist), max(Waist), length.out = 101)
newwaist <- data.frame(Waist = wrange)
prednew <- predict(lm(AT~Waist), newwaist, interval = "prediction")
plot(Waist,AT,xlab="waist")
lines(wrange,prednew[,2])
lines(wrange,prednew[,3])
detach(waist)
```

It is observed that the prediction interval is unable to cover 95% of the data when *waist* is large, while the interval is unnecessarily large when *waist* is small. A close examination of the scatter reveals that the observations have a wider spread for larger values of *waist* than for smaller values. This pattern indicates unequal variance of the errors. By ignoring this problem, we get prediction limits that either do not have adequate coverage (for large *waist*) or are unduly wide (for small waist). The locus of prediction limits shown in the figure looks like a straightjacket imposed by the homoscedastic linear model. Ideally the prediction limits should follow the varying spread of the observed cases. □

Like nonlinearity, heteroscedasticity or unequal variances of errors can occur in many ways. Therefore, we try to detect only systematic patterns in variance. For example, the variance may vary with any one of the explanatory variables. If that happens, we may be able to detect it by looking at the residuals. Since the residuals generally have unequal variance (even when model errors have equal variance), we need to look at standardized or studentized residuals. Either of these residuals may be plotted against one explanatory variable at a time, to check if the spread of the residuals changes with the value of the regressor. Ideally the plot should display no pattern. A systematic change in the vertical spread indicates that the error variance may be a function of the corresponding regressor. For example, if the error variance increases with the increase in the value of a particular explanatory variable, then the spread of the plotted residuals would 'fan out'.

While looking for a pattern in the spread of the points, one should not merely examine the envelope of the standardized residuals. It must be remembered that the envelope is *expected* to be wider where there are more data points in that region. After all, the scatter plot of a typical sample from a bivariate normal distribution would have a bulge in the middle, and that has nothing to do with unequal variance.

Table 5.5 Synthetic data set for demonstrating diagnostic plot for heteroscedasticity related to a single regressor

x_1	x_2	y	x_1	x_2	y	x_1	x_2	y
9.118	1.222	10.653	10.071	1.878	10.687	5.739	3.492	8.892
9.271	1.312	13.804	10.673	0.672	13.954	9.623	0.123	14.617
9.378	1.802	11.846	6.441	2.041	11.220	6.276	0.795	12.172
7.165	1.626	11.048	13.001	1.985	12.454	13.996	1.651	15.321
6.776	0.558	11.715	13.946	-0.458	17.661	9.441	1.975	8.728
5.704	2.872	5.433	8.802	-0.154	14.853	8.690	0.676	12.419
9.661	2.478	6.909	17.757	1.423	15.257	12.083	1.029	15.670
15.499	2.155	13.087	16.396	2.548	14.454	3.759	2.479	8.777
10.892	3.545	4.572	15.358	1.527	15.749	9.282	1.727	9.721
15.000	1.502	16.673	9.290	1.595	11.386	8.273	1.895	7.850
6.996	1.187	11.078	12.240	0.339	14.943	9.728	1.003	12.952
5.950	0.856	10.795	14.276	0.166	16.980	13.474	3.123	6.098
7.820	2.291	13.880	10.610	1.475	11.937	13.227	1.084	14.852
11.176	0.943	13.986	7.723	1.987	10.323	13.350	2.286	9.732
3.812	0.601	10.678	11.663	1.104	15.014	10.532	2.038	10.812
8.452	3.099	8.309	6.825	3.817	5.483	11.391	0.532	14.823
12.469	1.587	13.261	8.963	2.731	9.407			

Example 5.16. (Simulated heteroscedastic data) Table 5.5 shows a synthetic data set consisting of a sample of size 50 from the model

$$y = 10 + 0.5x_1 - 2x_2 + \varepsilon,$$

where $x_1 \sim N(10, 3^2)$, $x_2|x_1 \sim N(2, 1)$ and $\varepsilon|x_1, x_2 \sim N(0, x_2^2)$.

Figure 5.7 shows the plots of the studentized residual against the individual regressors. The plot on the left panel does not show any peculiarity, while the plot on the right panel shows that the residuals fan out as x_2 increases. This pattern is a clear indication of heteroscedasticity.

In order to check the nature of dependence of the error variance on x_2, we plot in Figure 5.8 the *squared* values of the studentized residuals against x_2, which should have mean nearly proportional to the error variance. A LOESS smoother (see page 212) run through the plot shows a rising and convex trend. The R code used for generating the data and the plots is given below.

```
set.seed(5678); n <- 50
x1 <- 10 + 3*rnorm(n); x2 <- 2 + rnorm(n)
y <- 10 + 0.5 * x1 - 2 *x2 + x2 * rnorm(n)
lm0 <- lm(y~x1+x2)
library(MASS)
plot(x1,studres(lm0),ylab="Studentized residual")
```

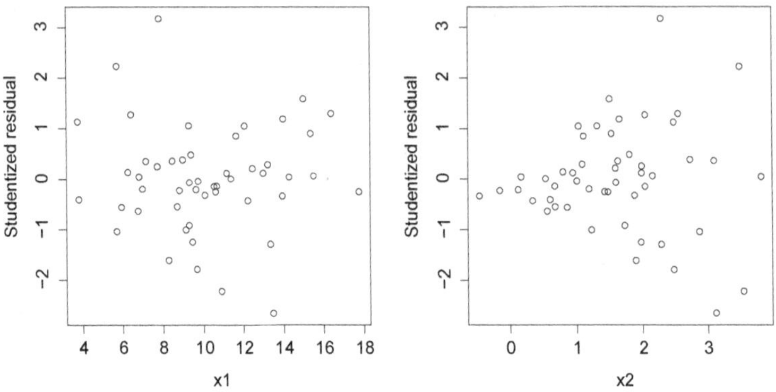

Fig. 5.7 Plot of studentized residual against regressors for the data of Example 5.16

```
plot(x2,studres(lm0),ylab="Studentized residual")
e2 <- studres(lm0)^2
plot(x2,e2,ylab="Studentized residual squared")
lines(sort(x2),loess(e2[order(x2)]~sort(x2),span=2)$fit)
```

The plot indicates that the error variance increases with x_2 at a faster than linear rate. The finding is reasonable, as the errors had indeed been generated with variance proportional to x_2^2. □

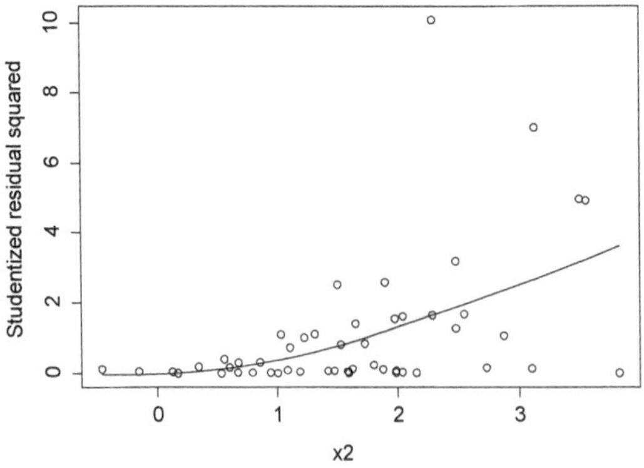

Fig. 5.8 Plot of studentized residual squared against x_2, along with trend curve, for the data of Example 5.16

If the nature of dependence between the error variance and a particular regressor is known, there is a sensible remedial measure. Suppose the error variance is proportional to $g(x)$, x being the said regressor. Instead of the homoscedastic linear model $(\boldsymbol{y}, \boldsymbol{X\beta}, \sigma^2\boldsymbol{I})$, one can use the modified model $(\boldsymbol{y}, \boldsymbol{X\beta}, \sigma^2\boldsymbol{V})$, where $\boldsymbol{V}$ is a known diagonal matrix, the diagonal elements being $g(x)$ evaluated at different values of x in the respective cases. This model will be discussed in Section 7.6. However, as long as the elements of $\boldsymbol{V}$ are positive, we can proceed with a short-cut, by defining $\boldsymbol{T}$ as another diagonal matrix with diagonal elements given by $1/\sqrt{g(x)}$. It follows that the scaled response vector $\boldsymbol{Ty}$ has mean $\boldsymbol{TX\beta}$ and dispersion matrix $\sigma^2\boldsymbol{I}$. Therefore, we can work with the homoscedastic linear model $(\boldsymbol{Ty}, \boldsymbol{TX\beta}, \sigma^2\boldsymbol{I})$, and obtain the least square estimates of $\boldsymbol{\beta}$. This amounts to minimizing the weighted sum of squares

$$\sum_{i=1}^{n} w_i(y_i - \boldsymbol{x}_i'\boldsymbol{\beta})^2,$$

where the weight w_i is equal to $1/g(x_i)$, x_i is the value of the said regressor for the ith case and $\boldsymbol{x}_i$ is the vector of all regressors for the ith case. The minimizer of this criterion is a *weighted least squares* (WLS) estimator of $\boldsymbol{\beta}$ or WLSE. In order to distinguish an LSE without weights from the WLSE, the former is sometimes referred to as an *ordinary least squares* (OLS) estimator or OLSE. In the present situation, the WLSE obtained from the response $\boldsymbol{y}$ is the OLSE obtained from the transformed response $\boldsymbol{Ty}$. (See Sections 7.3.3 and 7.6 for other versions of the WLSE.)

Example 5.17. (Simulated heteroscedastic data, continued) In Example 5.16, we had observed from diagnostic plots that the error variance appears to be a convex and increasing function of x_2. The simplest such function is the square function. Therefore, we obtain WLSE with weights $1/x_2^2$. Figure 5.9 shows the plots of the studentized residual against the individual regressors, obtained after the WLS analysis. Both the plots now show lack of pattern, which justifies the use of WLS. The R code for generating this plot and the WLS and OLS analyses is given below.

```
lm1 <- lm(y~x1+x2,weights = 1/x2^2)
plot(x1,studres(lm1),ylab="Studentized residual")
plot(x2,studres(lm1),ylab="Studentized residual")
summary(lm1)
lm0 <- lm(y~x1+x2)
summary(lm0)
```

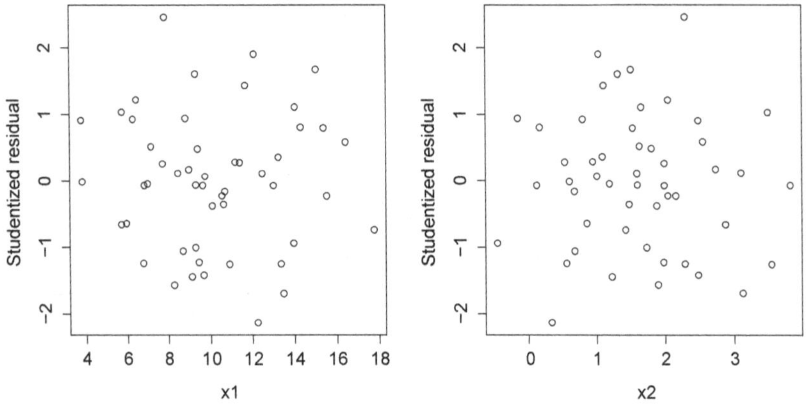

Fig. 5.9 Plot of studentized residual, obtained from WLS analysis, against regressors for the data of Example 5.17

The fitted model from the WLS analysis is

$$y = 9.953 + 0.511x_1 - 2.024x_2 + \varepsilon,$$

with estimated standard deviation of error $0.8617x_2$. This is in contrast with the fitted model from the least squares analysis:

$$y = 10.955 + 0.444x_1 - 2.246x_2 + \varepsilon,$$

with estimated standard deviation of error 1.615. □

As we found out in the above example, WLS amounts to carrying out OLS estimation on a transformed set of variables, though the fitted equation is expressed in terms of the original variables, after a reverse transformation. It needs to be borne in mind that the multiple R^2 from such a scale-transformed model is *not comparable* to the R^2 of the untransformed model. In fact, the R^2 for the transformed variable is not relevant for judging appropriateness of the model expressed in terms of retransformed variables. A reasonable index of fit that can be used across various transformed models is *the squared correlation between the original response and the corresponding (retransformed) fitted value.* Alternatively one can use the following representation of R^2:

$$R^2 = 1 - \frac{\sum_i (y_i - \widehat{y}_i)^2}{\sum_i (y_i - \overline{y})^2}, \tag{5.11}$$

where $\widehat{y}_i$ is the ith retransformed fitted value. Neither of these two versions of R^2, computed from the fitted values of the WLS analysis, can exceed the multiple R^2 computed from the OLS analysis (Exercises 5.17 and 5.18). The utility of the WLS lies in addressing the issue of unequal variance; improvement of R^2 is not the objective.

Another systematic form of heteroscedasticity is brought out by the plot of the standardized or studentized residuals against the *fitted/predicted values.* The fitted values approximate the mean for any given profile of explanatory variables, while the spread of the residuals represents the variance. Any change of the spread from one end of the plot to the other indicates that there is a relation between the variance of the response and its mean. Such a relationship may also be brought out by the scatter of the *observed values* against the *predicted values.* Ideally there should be a uniform scatter of points along the straight line through origin having slope 1. Any systematic pattern in the spread of points around this reference line indicates that the variance may be a function of the mean.

The common remedial measure for this type of heteroscedasticity is to use a transformation. Suppose it is known that $Var(y) \propto g(E(y))$, and we look for an ideal transformation of y, say $t(y)$, such that $Var(t(y))$ would not depend on $E(t(y))$. Assuming t to be differentiable, we can use the Taylor series approximation

$$t(y) \approx t(E(y)) + [y - E(y)]t'(E(y)),$$

and conclude that

$$Var(t(y)) \approx Var(y)[t'(E(y))]^2 \propto g(E(y))[t'(E(y))]^2.$$

If the last expression is a constant, we would expect that the variance of $t(y)$ would be more or less constant also. Therefore, we need to choose the transformation t in such a way that $g(u)[t'(u)]^2$ does not depend on u, i.e. $t'(u) \propto 1/\sqrt{g(u)}$. In other words, the prescription would be to choose

$$t(u) = A \int_B^u \frac{1}{\sqrt{g(v)}} dv$$

for some constants A and B. This transformation is called the *variance stabilizing transformation.* The constants do not matter and may be chosen conveniently.

Example 5.18. (Waist circumference, continued) In Chapter 4, we had analysed the data on waist circumference ($waist$) and measurement of adipose tissue (AT), given in Table 4.4, using the log transformation. We use

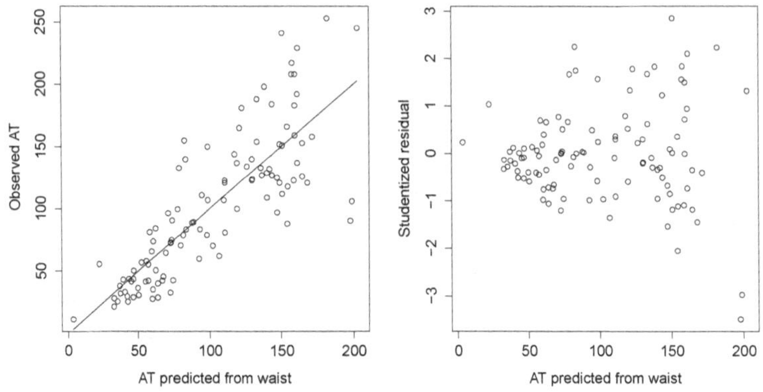

Fig. 5.10 Plots of observed vs. predicted response (left) and the studentized residual vs. predicted response (right) for the waist circumference data of Example 5.18

the two plots mentioned above to examine the need for any transformation in the regression of *AT* on *waist*. In Figure 5.10, the observed vs. predicted response for this regression model (left panel) shows an increase in spread around the diagonal line, while the studentized residual vs. predicted response (right panel) also shows a expanding spread around the zero line.

In an attempt to quantify this behavior, we plot in Figure 5.11 the squared values of the studentized residual against the predicted response, along with a LOESS smoother. The following R code had been used to generate these plots.

```
data(waist); attach(waist)
lm0 <- lm(AT~Waist)
lm0fit <- lm0$fitted.values
plot(lm0fit,AT,xlab="AT predicted from waist",ylab="Observed AT")
lines(sort(lm0fit),sort(lm0fit))
plot(lm0fit,studres(lm0),xlab="AT predicted from waist",
  ylab="Studentized residual")
plot(lm0fit,(studres(lm0))^2,xlab="AT predicted from waist",
  ylab="Studentized residual squared",ylim=c(0,3))
rstsmo<-loess(((studres(lm0))^2)[order(lm0fit)]~sort(lm0fit),span=1.4)
lines(sort(lm0fit),rstsmo$fit)
```

It appears that the variance is a convex and increasing function of the mean. We postulate that the square function will be a reasonable approximation.

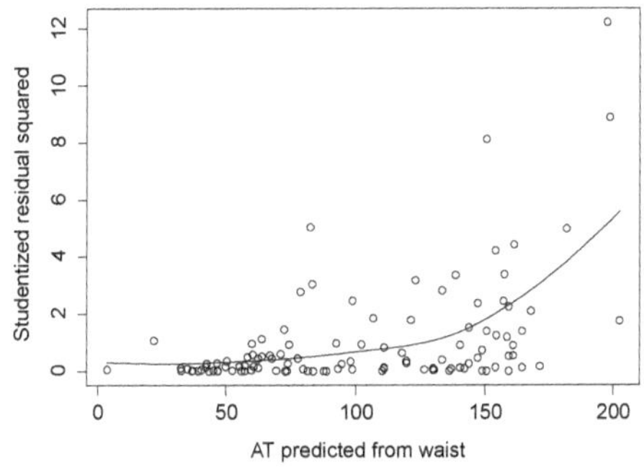

Fig. 5.11 Plot of studentized residual squared against predicted response, along with trend curve, for the waist circumference data of Example 5.18

By identifying $g(v)$ as v^2, we obtain

$$t(y) = A\int_B^y \frac{dv}{\sqrt{g(v)}} = A\int_B^y \frac{dv}{v} = A(\log y - \log B).$$

By arbitrarily choosing $A = B = 1$, we have $t(y) = \log y$. Therefore, we reanalyse the data by replacing the response AT by $\log(AT)$. The resulting plots, shown in the top panel of Figure 5.12, show no unusual pattern. The bottom panel of this figure shows the same plots when the regressor *waist* is also replaced by $\log(waist)$. These plots are very similar to those in the top panel. Thus, the log transformation of the response is useful, while log transformation of the regressor neither helps nor hurts. Expressing $\log(AT)$ as $\beta_0 + \beta_1 \log(waist)$ with additive error is equivalent to approximating AT by $c(waist)^{\beta_1}$ with multiplicative error, where $c = e^{\beta_0}$. We had used log transformations of both the variables in Example 4.36.

The dividend of the strategy to use log-transformed variables can be appreciated from Figure 5.13, which shows the scatter plot of AT against *waist*, along with loci of 95% prediction limits computed from the regression of $\log(AT)$ on $\log(waist)$ after appropriate retransformation. The additional lines of R code used to generate the last two figures are as follows.

```
logAT <- log(AT)
lm1 <- lm(logAT~Waist)
lm1fit <- lm1$fitted.values
plot(lm1fit,logAT,xlab="log(AT) predicted from waist",
 ylab="Observed log(AT)")
lines(range(lm1fit),range(lm1fit))
```

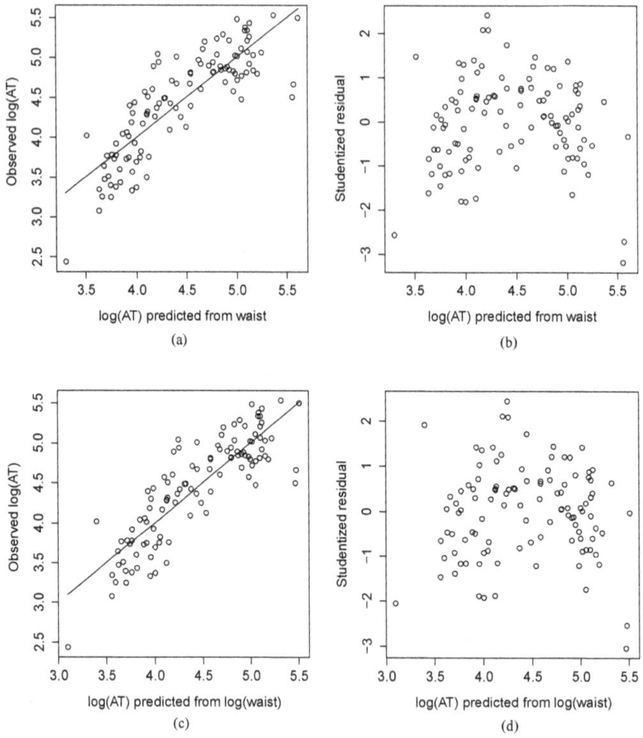

Fig. 5.12 Plots of observed vs. predicted response (left) and the studentized residual vs. predicted response (right) for log(AT) regressed on *waist* (top) and log(*waist*) (bottom) in the waist circumference data of Example 5.18

```
plot(lm1fit,studres(lm1),xlab="log(AT) predicted from waist",
 ylab="Studentized residual")
logwaist <- log(Waist)
lm2 <- lm(logAT~logwaist)
lm2fit <- lm2$fitted.values
plot(lm2fit,logAT,xlab="log(AT) predicted from log(waist)",
 ylab="Observed log(AT)")
lines(range(lm2fit),range(lm2fit))
plot(lm2fit,studres(lm2),xlab="log(AT) predicted from log(waist)",
 ylab="Studentized residual")
logAT <- log(AT)
logwaist <- log(Waist)
wrange <- seq(min(logwaist), max(logwaist), length.out = 101)
newwaist <- data.frame(logwaist = wrange)
```

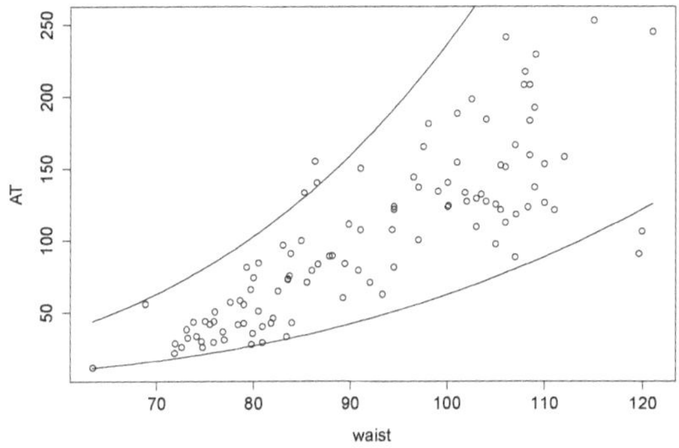

Fig. 5.13 Scatter plot of response AT against regressor *waist*, along with loci of upper and lower 95% prediction limits obtained from model with log-transformed variables, for the waist circumference data of Example 5.18

```
prednew <- predict(lm(logAT~logwaist),newwaist,interval="prediction")
plot(Waist,AT,xlab="waist")
lines(exp(wrange),exp(prednew[,2]))
lines(exp(wrange),exp(prednew[,3]))
detach(waist)
```

In contrast with the 'straight-jacket' observed in Figure 5.6, the latest prediction limits appear to follow the spread of the data points. □

In the above example, a functional relation of the variance of the response with its mean was guessed from the data. Sometimes this functional relationship is known from the underlying model. For example, it is well known that for Poisson count data, the variance is equal to the mean. Using the fact that $g(v) = v$, one can use the variance stabilizing transformation $t(y) = \sqrt{y}$. This would be a natural transformation to use when the response is a count which may have the Poisson distribution. Likewise, for exponentially distributed response y (where the mean is equal to the standard deviation), an appropriate transformation is $t(y) = \log(y)$. For binomial count response y from n trials, the transformation $t(y) = \sin^{-1}(2y/n - 1)$ is appropriate (Exercise 5.48).

When the distribution of the response is known, a better way to handle dependence between the mean and the variance is to use the generalized linear model discussed in Section 5.7. See Section 8.5.2 for a review of systematic yet distribution-free methods of dealing with heteroscedasticity, built on the heuristics discussed in this section.

5.3.3 *Correlated observations*

Like the assumption of equal variance of errors, the assumption of zero correlation across observations can be violated in various ways. We will consider in particular, situations where correlation is induced by the serial order of the observations. This may happen, for instance, when the data are collected serially in time. Hence, this special type of correlation is called *serial correlation.*

As we shall see, the presence of serial correlation can be an opportunity for better prediction rather than a menace. The least squares estimates remain unbiased even when the errors are correlated (Exercise 5.47).

In order to detect the presence of possible serial correlation, one can plot the standardized residual r_i or the studentized residual t_i against the index i, while connecting successive points by straight line segments. This plot is called the *index plot.* Ideally there should be no pattern in the plot. [Though the residuals are *generally* correlated, ideally there should be no *serial* pattern in this correlation.] If successive residuals tend to have similar values, there may be positive serial correlation. Negative serial correlation in residuals — a less common occurrence — is expected to produce a zig-zag pattern in the index plot with frequent changes of sign.

Another useful diagnostic plot is the plot of r_i vs. r_{i-1} or t_i vs. t_{i-1}, with successive points connected by straight line segments. This plot, known as the *lag plot,* generally shows elongation along a line of slope 1 when there is positive serial correlation, and no elongation if there is zero correlation.

In order to understand the patterns to be expected in the index and lag plots, let us consider these plots for a couple of synthetic time series, rather than for actual residuals.

Example 5.19. Consider a synthetic time series generated from the AR(1) model mentioned in (1.13), i.e.

$$x_t = \phi_1 x_{t-1} + \varepsilon_t, \quad t \text{ is an integer,}$$

ε_t being sample from the standard normal distribution. Successive sample values of the series are positively correlated when $\phi_1 > 0$ and uncorrelated when $\phi_1 = 0$. Figure 5.14 shows the index and lag plots for samples of size 50 generated from this model, for $\phi_1 = 0.7$ (top panel) and $\phi_1 = 0$ (bottom panel), respectively, obtained from the following R code.

```
set.seed(987) #456
n <- 50
phi <- 0.7
```

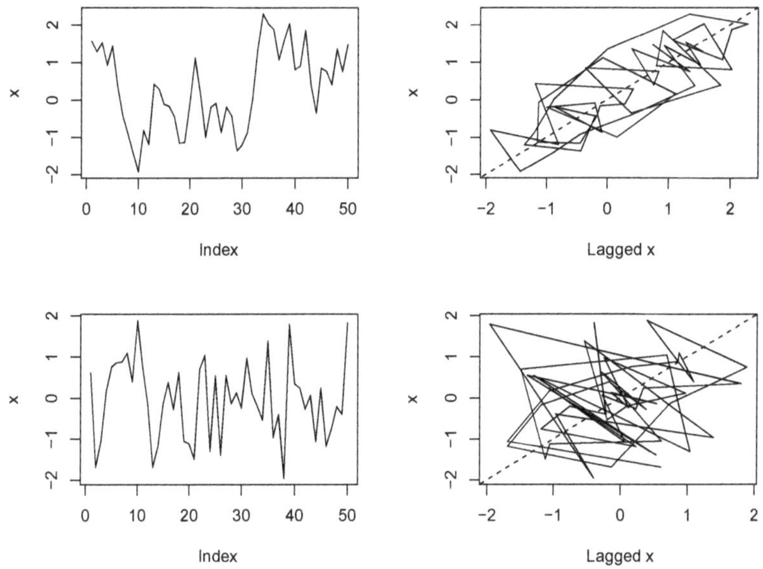

Fig. 5.14 Index plot (left) lag plot (right) for time series generated from the model of Example 5.19 with $\phi_1 = 0.7$ (top panel) and $\phi_1 = 0$ (bottom panel)

```
z <- rnorm(n) * sqrt(1 - phi^2)
x <- array(dim=n)
x[1] <- rnorm(1)
for (i in 2:n) x[i] <- phi * x[i-1] + z[i]
plot(x,type="l", ylab = "x")
plot(x[1:(n-1)], x[2:n], xlab = "Lagged x", ylab = "x", type="l")
lines(c(-4,4),c(-4,4),lty=2)
phi <- 0
z <- rnorm(n) * sqrt(1 - phi^2)
x[1] <- rnorm(1)
for (i in 2:n) x[i] <- phi * x[i-1] + z[i]
plot(x,type="l", ylab = "x")
plot(x[1:(n-1)], x[2:n], xlab = "Lagged x", ylab = "x", type="l")
lines(c(-4,4),c(-4,4),lty=2)
```

The index plot has less fluctuation for $\phi_1 = 0.7$, and the lag plot is elongated along a line of slope 1 (shown in dashed line). These patterns would be accentuated for higher values of ϕ_1. □

A formal test for no serial correlation is the *Durbin-Watson test*, which is based on the statistic

$$DW = \frac{\sum_{i=2}^{n}(e_i - e_{i-1})^2}{\sum_{i=1}^{n} e_i^2}.$$

It can be shown that $0 \le DW \le 4$ (Exercise 5.50). Small values of DW corresponds to highly positive correlation of successive observations, while large values of DW (close to 4) indicates highly negative correlation.

If serial correlation among the residuals is detected, one has to modify the model. The natural modification in this situation is to replace the 'uncorrelated errors' in the model (1.1) by errors with a stipulated structure of serial correlation. The simplest such structure is the AR(1) model described by (1.13). Thus, a linear regression model with serial correlation is

$$\begin{aligned} y_t &= \beta_0 + \beta_1 x_{t1} + \beta_2 x_{t2} + \cdots + \beta_k x_{tk} + \varepsilon_t, \\ \varepsilon_t &= \phi_1 \varepsilon_{t-1} + \delta_t \end{aligned} \tag{5.12}$$

where δ_t are uncorrelated errors with zero mean and common variance σ^2.

For the model (5.12), a two-stage process of least squares estimation may be carried out. In the first stage, one would obtain the OLSE of the regression parameters (which happen to be unbiased) from the data set with n observations, and compute the residuals. Then the residuals would be regarded as substitutes for the model errors, and therefore following the approximate model

$$e_t = \phi_1 e_{t-1} + \delta_t. \tag{5.13}$$

The least squares estimate of ϕ_1, which minimizes $\sum_{t=2}^{n}(e_t - \phi_1 e_{t-1})^2$, is $\sum_t e_t e_{t-1} / \sum_t e_t^2$. The estimate of ϕ_1 paves the way for the second stage of estimation. Note that if ϕ_1 had been *known*, then the errors in the modified model

$$\begin{aligned} y_t - \phi_1 y_{t-1} = (1-\phi_1)\beta_0 + \beta_1(x_{t1} - \phi_1 x_{(t-1)1}) + \beta_2(x_{t2} - \phi_1 x_{(t-1)2}) + \\ \cdots + \beta_k(x_{tk} - \phi_1 x_{(t-1)k}) + (\varepsilon_t - \phi_1 \varepsilon_{t-1}), \qquad t = 2, \ldots, n, \end{aligned}$$

would be $\delta_2, \ldots, \delta_n$, which are uncorrelated. Therefore, the OLSE of $\boldsymbol{\beta}$ from this model would be appropriate. Since ϕ_1 is not known, one can plug its estimate into the modified model before estimating $\boldsymbol{\beta}$ from it. This method can be generalized for more complex models of serial correlation (see Section 8.4.1). Alternatively one can assume the normal distribution and look for MLE of all the parameters. The MLE in the special case of (5.12) is discussed in Example 8.20.

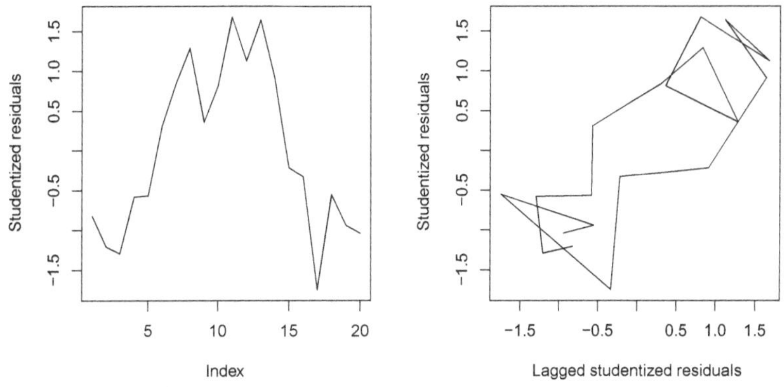

Fig. 5.15 Index plot (left) lag plot (right) of studentized residuals for data set (d) of Example 5.1

Example 5.20. For data set (d) of Example 5.1, the index and lag plots of studentized residuals given in Figure 5.15 show slow movement and diagonal elongation, respectively, indicating the presence of serial correlation. The Durbin-Watson test statistic is 0.4428, with p-value 8.02×10^{-07}, which formally confirms the presence of serial correlation. The R code that led to the figure and these findings is as follows.

```
data(anscombeplus)
attach(anscombeplus)
n <- length(x1)
md <- lm(y4~x1)
par(mfrow=c(1,2))
library(MASS)
sres <- studres(md)
plot(sres,type="l", ylab = "Studentized residuals")
plot(sres[1:(n-1)], sres[2:n], xlab = "Lagged studentized residuals",
 ylab = "Studentized residuals", type="l")
library(lmtest)
dwtest(lm(y4~x1))
```

The first stage of the two stage least squares estimation yields the fitted model

$$y_t = -4.000 + 1.500x_t + \varepsilon_t,$$

with $R^2 = 0.875$ and $Var(\varepsilon_t) = 3.450^2$, while fitting of the AR(1) model (5.13) to the residuals (by the least squares method) yields the estimate of

ϕ_1 as 0.776. The second stage least squares estimation with transformed data yields the fitted model

$$(y_t - 0.776y_{t-1}) = 0.405 + 1.100(x_t - 0.776x_{t-1}) + \delta_t,$$

with $R^2 = 0.301$ and $Var(\delta_t) = 2.171^2$. The following R code was used for these analyses.

```
summary(md)
res <- md$resid
phi1 <-  ar(res, order.max = 1, method="ols")$ar[1]; phi1
ty4 <- y4[-1] - phi1 * y4[-n]
tx1 <- x1[-1] - phi1 * x1[-n]
tmd <- lm(ty4~tx1)
summary(tmd)
```

Note that the two values of R^2 are not comparable, as the responses are different. The error variance in the second stage is less.

In order to appreciate the utility of the second stage of least squares estimation, let us consider the problem of predicting the last observed value of the response from the first 19 observations. By repeating this analysis for the truncated data set, and using the value $x_{20} = 20$, we obtain (at the first stage) the point prediction of y_{20} as 26.736 and a 95% prediction interval as (18.687, 34.785). The actual value of y_{20} (not used in this analysis) is 22.773. The R code given below was used to obtain these numbers.

```
y <- y4[-n]; x <- x1[-n]
xpred <- x1[n]
md <- lm(y~x)
newx <- data.frame(x = xpred)
predict(md, newx, interval = "prediction"); y4[n]
```

At the second stage, we have the point prediction of $y_{20} - \phi_1 y_{19}$ as 16.577, obtained from the R code

```
res <- md$resid
phi1 <-  ar(res, order.max = 1, method="ols")$ar[1]
ty <- y[-1] - phi1 * y[-(n-1)]
tx <- x[-1] - phi1 * x[-(n-1)]
txpred <- x1[n] - phi1 * x1[n-1]
tmd <- lm(ty~tx)
newtx <- data.frame(tx = txpred)
predty <- predict(tmd, newtx, interval = "prediction"); predty[1]
```

Using the observed value of y_{19} and the estimated value of ϕ_1, we obtain the prediction of y_{20} (with the help of the additional line of code `phi1 * y4[n-1] + predty`). The point prediction happens to be 22.939, which is much closer to the truth than the point prediction obtained at the first stage. Further, the associated 95% prediction interval is (17.653, 28.226), which is considerably narrower than the interval obtained at the end of the first stage of least squares estimation. □

All predictions rely on correlation or some other form of association. Prediction through a regression model is generally based on association of the response with the regressors. Prediction of a univariate time series utilizes the association of the future sample with past values of the same series. The linear regression model with autocorrelated errors is a combination of regression and time series models, where the autocorrelation of the response is attributed partially to autocorrelation of the errors in the regression model. In the above example, the improved prediction from the second stage of least squares was made possible by the additional information harnessed from the correlation between the successive error terms in the model.

5.3.4 *Non-normality*

The assumption of normality is not crucial for the derivation of the least squares estimator (or the BLUE). But it becomes important when we construct confidence intervals or prediction intervals or conduct test of hypothesis. The distributional results used there depend crucially on the assumption of normality of the model errors.

Since the residuals are proxies of the model errors, we can use them to look for violation of the assumption of normality. We have already seen that, unlike the actual model errors, the residuals have unequal variances. Therefore, a scaled version of the residual (e.g. the studentized or the standardized residual) should be used. An advantage of using them is that they are adjusted for σ^2 also. Therefore, if the sample size is not too small, their distribution should be similar/comparable to the standard normal distribution, i.e. $N(0,1)$. The most common tool for checking this fact graphically is the *QQ plot* for the normal distribution, also known as the *normal plot.* The name 'QQ plot' originates from quantiles. The quantiles of the sample are plotted against those of the theoretical distribution. Specifically, the ith smallest studentized residual, which is the $\frac{i}{n}$th sample quantile, is plotted against the $\frac{i}{n}$th quantile of the standard normal distribution (i.e. the value

z such that $P(Z \leq z) = \frac{i}{n}$). (In another version of the normal plot, one plots on the horizontal axis the expected value of the ith smallest value in a sample of size n from $N(0,1)$.) The ideal shape of the normal plot should be a straight line with slope 1, passing through the origin. In practice, an approximate straight line with any slope or intercept is deemed acceptable, as linear functions of normal random variables are normal too.

Certain types of departure of the normal plot from the ideal straight line can be easily interpreted. An S-shaped plot indicates a distribution with heavier tails than the normal distribution. An inverse S-shaped plot indicates a distribution with lighter tails. If the plot intersects the vertical axis much below the origin, the distribution may be left-skewed. The opposite behavior is suggestive of a right-skewed distribution. Deviation of the normal plot from the ideal straight line may also be because of the presence of y-outliers, or the violation of other model assumptions (e.g., the assumption of homoscedasticity).

Two formal tests of the assumption of the normal distribution are the *Shapiro-Wilk test* and the one-sample *Kolmogorov-Smirnov test*. The Shapiro-Wilk test is based on the matching of order statistics of the sample at hand with the order statistics of the normal distribution, while the Kolmogorov-Smirnov test is based on the divergence of the empirical distribution of the data from the normal distribution function.

Example 5.21. (Waist circumference, continued) Consider once again the data on waist circumference (*waist*) and measurement of adipose tissue (*AT*), given in Table 4.4. In Example 4.36, we had obtained prediction intervals of *AT* by regressing log(*AT*) on log(*waist*). Figure 5.16 shows the QQ plots of this regression (panel (a)), along with the regression of *AT* on *waist* (panel (b)). The latter plot shows noticeable departure from the ideal straight line. The R code for generating these plots and carrying out formal tests of normality is given below.

```
data(waist)
attach(waist)
logAT <- log(AT)
logwaist <- log(Waist)
lm1 <- lm(logAT~logwaist)
library(MASS)
qqnorm(studres(lm1))
qqline(studres(lm1))
lm0 <- lm(AT~Waist,data=waist)
qqnorm(studres(lm0))
```

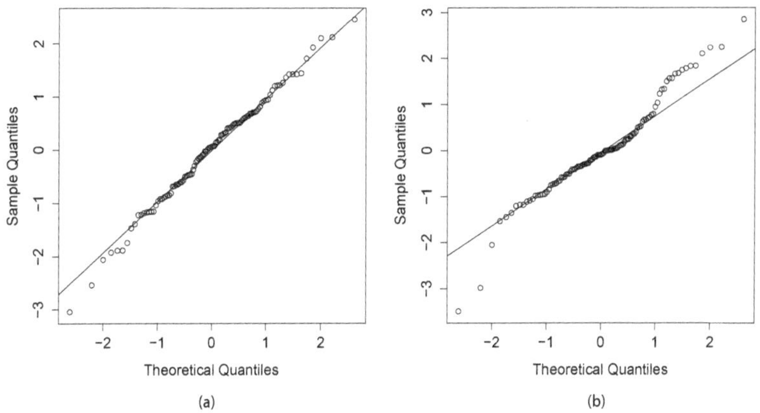

Fig. 5.16 Normal plots of studentized residuals from regressions of log(AT) on log($waist$) (left) and AT on $waist$ (right), for Example 5.21

```
qqline(studres(lm0))
shapiro.test(studres(lm1))
ks.test(studres(lm1), pnorm)
shapiro.test(studres(lm0))
ks.test(studres(lm0), pnorm)
```

For the regression of log(AT) on log($waist$), the Shapiro-Wilk test and the one-sample Kolmogorov-Smirnov tests have p-values 0.7966 and 0.9324, respectively, indicating no violation of the assumption of normality. For the regression of AT on $waist$, the two tests have p-values 0.0031 and 0.1836, respectively. The Shapiro-Wilk test indicates that the assumption of normal distribution is violated. The Kolmogorov-Smirnov test is not designed specifically for the normal distribution, and is known to have less power. □

One of the ways of dealing with non-normality of the model errors (or of the response) is to transform the response. Some commonly used transformations are the power and log transformations. These are special cases of the Box-Cox family of transformations (5.10), which we rewrite as

$$y^{(\lambda)} = \begin{cases} \frac{y^\lambda - 1}{\lambda} & \text{if } \lambda \neq 0, \\ \log y & \text{if } \lambda = 0. \end{cases} \tag{5.14}$$

to indicate explicitly the dependence of the response on the parameter λ. When we had used this transformation on an explanatory variable, the parameter λ was chosen to ensure best R-square. Here, the response itself is being transformed. R-square for one choice of λ is not even comparable with the R-square for another choice. Assuming that the transformed response would be normally distributed for a specific choice of λ (and therefore not normal for other choices), we select that λ which maximizes the normal likelihood (see Section 3.7) computed with $y^{(\lambda)}$ as the response. We have already seen that the MLE of the regression parameters and the error variance can be obtained explicitly. By substituting these estimates in the log-likelihood, we get a more complicated function of the single parameter λ, which may be called the log-likelihood profile of λ. The recommended value of λ is the one which maximizes this profile.

If the response is transformed to achieve normality, the fitted or predicted values need to be reverse transformed for comparability of the observed response.

We have already seen that the response variable is sometimes transformed to reduce heteroscedasticity. If the Box-Cox transformation is used for this purpose, there may not be a magic value of λ that meets this objective while also ensuring normality. Ruppert and Aldershof (1989) suggested a method to improve homogeneity of the variance along with symmetry of the distribution.

Example 5.22. (Waist circumference, continued) Let us proceed with the regression of *AT* on *waist* and see where the Box-Cox transformation leads us. The top left panel of Figure 5.17, obtained from the additional line of code `boxcox(lm0,lambda = seq(-2, 2, 1/10), plotit = TRUE)`, shows the plot of log-likelihood profile against the parameter λ. The log-likelihood is maximized at about $\lambda = 1/3$. Using the transformation (5.14) with this value of λ is equivalent to using the power transformation $AT^{1/3}$, which may affect the linearity of the response in the regressor. Hence, we check the scatter plot of $AT^{1/3}$ vs. *waist* in the top right panel of Figure 5.17, obtained through the R code

```
tat <- (AT)^(1/3)
plot(Waist,tat,xlab = "Waist circumference",
 ylab = "Adipose tissue^(1/3)")
```

The scatter shows a concave pattern. Therefore, we bring in a quadratic term, using the R code

```
Waistsq <- Waist^2
lm2 <- lm(tat~Waist+Waistsq)
summary(lm2)
```

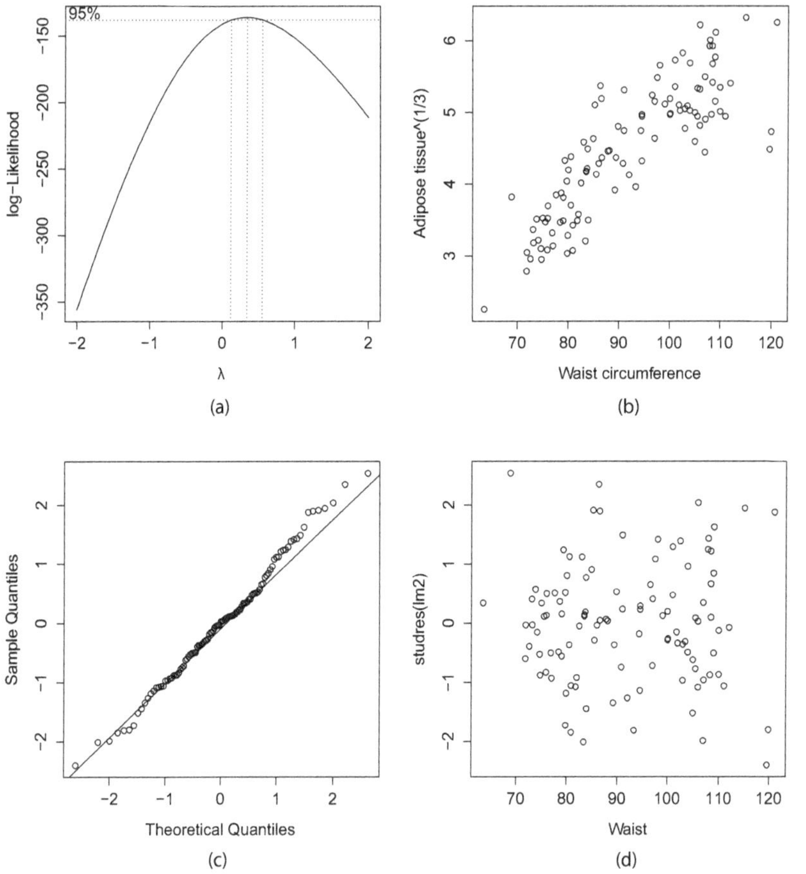

Fig. 5.17 Plots for Example 5.22: (a) log-likelihood profile of λ for regression of AT on *waist*, (b) scatter plot of $AT^{1/3}$ vs. *waist* (top right), (c) normal plot of studentized residuals from (5.15) and (d) scatter plot of studentized residuals from (5.15) vs. *waist*

The fitted model turns out to be

$$AT^{1/3} = -10.14 + 0.2634 waist - 0.00111 waist^2 + 0.4586 z, \qquad (5.15)$$

where z is error with mean 0 and variance 1. The bottom left panel of Figure 5.17, obtained from the additional line of code `qqnorm(studres(lm2)); qqline(studres(lm2))`, shows the normal probability plot of studentized residuals from this regression. The plot shows improved adherence to the assumption of normality. The Shapiro-Wilk test and the one-sample Kolmogorov-Smirnov tests, carried out through the R code `shapiro.test(studres(lm2)); ks.test(studres(lm2),pnorm)`, have p-values 0.7286 and 0.9420, respectively, indicating no violation of the assumption of normality. Finally, we check if this alternative model would have the problem of heteroscedasticity. The plot of the studentized residuals against *waist*, obtained through the code `plot(Waist,studres(lm2))` and shown in the bottom right panel of Figure 5.17, indicates no such problem, as the spread of the residuals is quite uniform.

The correlation of AT with the (reverse transformed) fitted values from this model is 0.829, as compared to 0.787 obtained from the regression of $\log(AT)$ on $\log(waist)$. These calculations are obtained through the R code `cor((lm2$fitted.values)^3,AT); cor(exp(lm1$fitted.values),AT)`. Thus the alternative model (5.15) may be preferred. □

If all the assumptions of the linear model — except normality — appear to hold, one can adopt an alternate approach. Since the question becomes one about the distributional assumption of the estimators/predictors as well as the related test statistics, one can use the bootstrap technique to find a more appropriate distribution. A model-based version of the bootstrap is to generate data from the fitted model, with additive errors obtained as a simple random sample drawn with replacement from the pool of residuals. If this process is repeated many times and a statistic of interest (e.g. an estimator) is computed from each resample, the empirical distribution of these numbers is generally used as the bootstrap distribution of the statistic. This is in contrast with model-free bootstrap, where one repeatedly draws a simple random sample with replacement from the index set of cases, and selects the corresponding data points (including response and regressors). Whichever way the resampling is done, every bootstrap sample would lead to a set of new estimates and correspondingly fitted model. Appropriate quantiles of these estimates may be used to construct confidence intervals of the parameter estimates. As for prediction interval, a bootstrap point prediction may be generated by adding the bootstrap fitted value with a further sample from the original set of residuals, and then suitable quantiles of the set of point predictions may be used to form prediction intervals.

Example 5.23. Consider data set (e) of Example 5.1. The corresponding scatter plot of Figure 5.1 shows that the fit is not too bad, though there is misfit for a single observation. The normal plot for this analysis, based on studentized residuals, appears in panel (a) of Figure 5.18. The plot is dominated by a single large residual. The vertical scale of the plot is

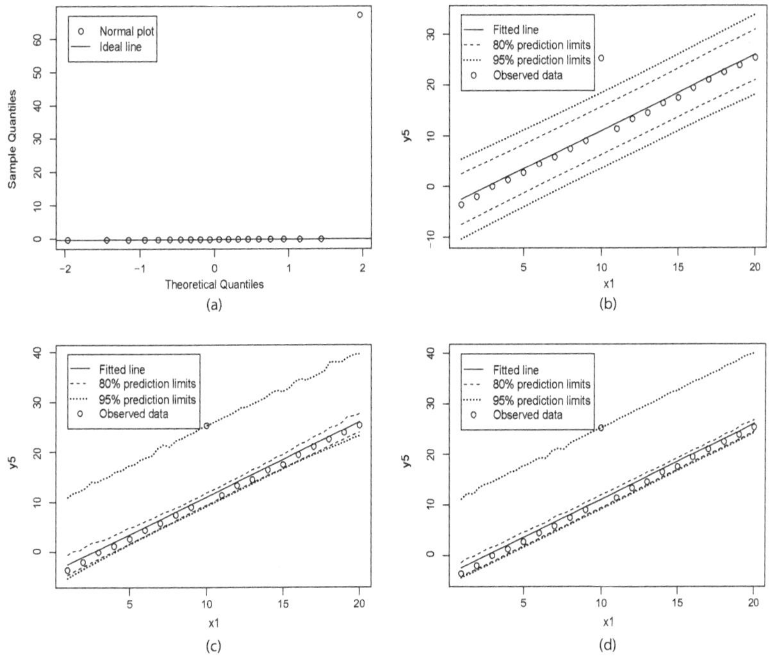

Fig. 5.18 Plots for Example 5.23: (a) normal plot of studentized residuals, (b) fitted line and 80% and 95% prediction limits assuming normal distribution, (c) fitted line and 80% and 95% prediction limits from model-based bootstrap and (d) fitted line and 80% and 95% prediction limits from model-free bootstrap

adjusted to accommodate this point, because of which the ideal line looks almost horizontal. The p-value of the Shapiro-Wilks and the Kolmogorov-Smirnov tests are 2.85×10^{-9} and 2.57×10^{-5}, respectively. The assumption of normality is clearly violated. The ill-effect of this violation is visible from the prediction limits plotted in panel (b) of Figure 5.18. The R code for generating the two plots and carrying out the tests are given below.

```
library(MASS)
data(anscombeplus)
attach(anscombeplus)
me <- lm(y5~x1, data = anscombeplus)
par(mfrow=c(2,2))
qqnorm(studres(me), main = "")
qqline(studres(me))
legend(-1.9,65,c("Normal plot","Ideal line"),lty=c(0,1),pch=c(1,NA))
```

```
shapiro.test(studres(me))
ks.test(studres(me), pnorm)
# Prediction limits
xset <- seq(min(x1), max(x1), length.out = 50)
newdat <- data.frame(x1 = xset)
pred <- predict(me, newdat, interval = "prediction", level = 0.8)
pred2 <- predict(me, newdat, interval = "prediction")
matplot(xset,cbind(pred,pred2[,2:3]),type="l",lty=c(1,2,2,3,3),
 col=c(1,1,1,1,1), xlab="x1", ylab="y5")
points(x1,y5)
legend(1,33,c("Fitted line","80% prediction limits","95% prediction
 limits","Observed data"),lty=c(1,2,3,0),pch=c(NA,NA,NA,1))
```

The (symmetric) limits given in the plot of panel (b) are too wide on the lower side and too narrow on the upper side. Even the 95% prediction limits utterly fail to include the y-outlier found in the data. If we believe that this data point came from the right tail of the underlying error distribution, then these prediction limits are certainly off the mark. Model-based and model-free bootstrap procedures described above lead to the prediction limits shown in panels (c) and (d), respectively, of Figure 5.18. The 95% prediction limits are highly asymmetric, and extend up to the y-outlier. The 80% prediction limits, which are much narrower than the 80% 'normal' prediction limits of panel (b), are still able to cover 80% of the observed data. The bootstrap prediction limits make much more sense, as they are in line with the observed scatter of points on the two sides of the fitted line.

The R code for generating the two types of bootstrap prediction intervals is as follows.

```
# Model based bootstrap
respool = me$res
set.seed(1234); nboot <- 1000; predlist <- NULL
uplim1 <- NULL; lowlim1 <- NULL; uplim2 <- NULL; lowlim2 <- NULL
newdat <- data.frame(x1 = xset)
for (i in 1:nboot) {
  yb <- predict(me, interval = "none")
   + sample(respool, size = length(y5), replace = T)
  mboot <- lm(yb~x1)
  bootfit <- predict(mboot, newdat, interval = "none")
  predlist <- rbind(predlist, bootfit
   + sample(respool, size = length(xset), replace = T))
}
for (j in 1:length(xset)) {
  uplim1  <- c(uplim1, quantile(predlist[,j],probs = 0.9))
```

```
  lowlim1 <- c(lowlim1,quantile(predlist[,j],probs = 0.1))
  uplim2  <- c(uplim2, quantile(predlist[,j],probs = 0.975))
  lowlim2 <- c(lowlim2,quantile(predlist[,j],probs = 0.025))
}
matplot(xset, cbind(pred[,1],uplim1,lowlim1,uplim2,lowlim2),
 type="l", lty=c(1,2,2,3,3), col=c(1,1,1,1,1), xlab="x1", ylab="y5")
points(x1,y5)
legend(1,39,c("Fitted line","80% prediction limits","95% prediction
 limits","Observed data"),lty=c(1,2,3,0),pch=c(NA,NA,NA,1))

# Model-free bootstrap
set.seed(1234); nboot <- 1000; predlist <- NULL
uplim1 <- NULL; lowlim1 <- NULL; uplim2 <- NULL; lowlim2 <- NULL
newdat <- data.frame(xb = xset)
for (i in 1:nboot) {
  ib <- sample((1:length(y5)), size = length(y5), replace = T)
  xb <- x1[ib]; yb <- y5[ib]; mboot <- lm(yb~xb)
  bootfit <- predict(mboot, newdat, interval = "none")
  predlist <- rbind(predlist, bootfit
   + sample(respool, size = length(xset), replace = T))
}
for (j in 1:length(xset)) {
  uplim1  <- c(uplim1, quantile(predlist[,j],probs = 0.9))
  lowlim1 <- c(lowlim1,quantile(predlist[,j],probs = 0.1))
  uplim2  <- c(uplim2, quantile(predlist[,j],probs = 0.975))
  lowlim2 <- c(lowlim2,quantile(predlist[,j],probs = 0.025))
}
matplot(xset, cbind(pred[,1], uplim1, lowlim1, uplim2, lowlim2),
 type="l", lty=c(1,2,2,3,3), col=c(1,1,1,1,1), xlab="x1", ylab="y5")
points(x1,y5)
legend(1,39,c("Fitted line","80% prediction limits","95% prediction
 limits","Observed data"),lty=c(1,2,3,0),pch=c(NA,NA,NA,1))
detach(anscombeplus)
```
□

Resampling methods for the linear model, including bootstrap, are discussed in detail by Efron and Tibshirani (1993) and Shao and Tu (1996).

5.4 Casewise diagnostics

A few observations sometimes stand out from the others because of their unusual values. As we have seen in Section 5.2, outlying observations in the space of explanatory variables, also known as x-outliers, have a strong leverage on the outcome of the analysis. On the other hand, y-outliers generally have an overly large impact on the least squares estimation of the conditional mean response, besides being poorly fitted themselves. We have already seen some examples of x- and y-outliers in Example 5.12.

An observation may influence a least squares regression analysis in myriad ways, even if it is not clearly identifiable as an x- or y-outlier. We now look at some indicators of case influence on different aspects of analysis. Many of these measures are obtained by studying the effect of deleting an observation, and are collectively called *deletion diagnostics.* (There are other measures; see e.g. Chatterjee and Hadi, 1988, Section 4.2.4 for measures based on empirical influence functions.) These measures generally simplify to expressions in terms of leverages and residuals. We discuss a few common measures below; see Chatterjee and Hadi (2012) and Belsley, Kuh and Welsch (2005) for some other measures.

5.4.1 *Diagnostics for parameter estimates*

A measure of influence of the ith observation on β_j is

$$DFBETAS_{ij} = \frac{\widehat{\beta}_j - \widehat{\beta}_{j(-i)}}{\sqrt{\widehat{\sigma^2}_{(-i)}(\boldsymbol{X}'\boldsymbol{X})^{(j+1)(j+1)}}}, \quad j = 0, 1, \ldots, k, \ i = 1, 2, \ldots, n, \tag{5.16}$$

where $(\boldsymbol{X}'\boldsymbol{X})^{(j+1)(j+1)}$ is the diagonal element of the matrix $(\boldsymbol{X}'\boldsymbol{X})^{-1}$ corresponding to the coefficient β_j, and $\widehat{\beta}_{j(-i)}$ and $\widehat{\sigma^2}_{(-i)}$ are the modified estimates of β_j and σ^2, respectively, when the ith observation is dropped from the data. It is easy to see that this diagnostic is obtained by evaluating the scaled difference $(\widehat{\beta}_j - \beta_j)/Var(\widehat{\beta}_j)$ at $\beta_j = \widehat{\beta}_{j(-i)}$ and $\sigma^2 = \widehat{\sigma^2}_{(-i)}$. Since $(\widehat{\beta}_j - \beta_j)/Var(\widehat{\beta}_j)$ has the standard normal distribution under the linear model with normal error, the hypothesis that the true value of the jth regression coefficient is β_j would be rejected at level 0.05 if this ratio is larger than 2 or so. Thus, it would appear that the appropriate threshold of $|DFBETAS_{ij}|$ for identifying an unusual case should be about 2. However, the threshold is needed as a simple rule of thumb for indicative purpose, rather than for a formal test of hypothesis at any level. In analysis of large data sets, it is very uncommon to find any $|DFBETAS_{ij}|$ larger than 2. The reason can be understood by considering the special case of mean estimation, i.e. where there is no regressor. In this case the expression for $DFBETAS_{ij}$ simplifies to $\sqrt{n}e_i/[(n-1)\hat{\sigma}_{(-i)}]$. The multiplier $\sqrt{n}/(n-1)$, which is of the order of $1/\sqrt{n}$, makes the diagnostic very small for large n. A similar logic applies to multiple regression, though the algebra is not so clean. From these considerations, Belsley et al. (2005) argue that a size-adjusted threshold for $|DFBETAS_{ij}|$ should be proportional to $1/\sqrt{n}$, and they suggest the heuristic threshold $2/\sqrt{n}$.

5.4.2 *Diagnostics for fit*

The studentized residual r_i and the standardized residual t_i (see Section 5.2) may be regarded as diagnostics for fit. A deletion diagnostic for fit is the scaled change in the fitted value of the ith observation when it is deleted, i.e.

$$DFFITS_i = \frac{\widehat{y}_i - \widehat{y}_{i(-i)}}{\sqrt{\widehat{\sigma^2}_{(-i)} h_i}} = \left(\frac{h_i}{1-h_i}\right)^{1/2} t_i, \tag{5.17}$$

where $\widehat{y}_{i(-i)}$ is $E(y_i)$ evaluated at $\beta_j = \widehat{\beta}_{j(-i)}$ for $j = 1, 2, \ldots, k$. The last expression in (5.17) is obtained after some algebraic manipulation (see Exercise 5.20). Since the average value of the leverages is $(k+1)/n$, the typical value of $\sqrt{h_i(1-h_i)}$ for large n is about $\sqrt{(k+1)/n}$. The threshold generally used for indicating large values of $|DFFITS_i|$ is $2\sqrt{(k+1)/n}$.

Another diagnostic for the overall fit is a scaled measure of the change in $\widehat{\boldsymbol{\beta}}$ as a whole due to the dropping of y_i, known as *Cook's squared distance* (commonly referred to as *Cook's distance*):

$$COOKD_i = \frac{1}{k+1}(\widehat{\boldsymbol{\beta}} - \widehat{\boldsymbol{\beta}}_{(-i)})'[\widehat{\sigma^2}(\boldsymbol{X}'\boldsymbol{X})^{-1}]^{-1}(\widehat{\boldsymbol{\beta}} - \widehat{\boldsymbol{\beta}}_{(-i)}). \tag{5.18}$$

It may be observed that when the $n \times k$ matrix $\boldsymbol{X}$ has rank k, $COOKD_i$ is algebraically identical to the F-statistic for testing $\boldsymbol{\beta} = \boldsymbol{\beta}_0$, given in Table 4.3, when $\boldsymbol{\beta}_0 = \widehat{\boldsymbol{\beta}}_{(-i)}$. Every F-statistic is a ratio of two estimate variances. When the degrees of freedom are large, the median of an F-statistic is around 1. Cook and Weisberg (1994) recommended the simple threshold of 1 for indicating large values of $COOKD_i$, regardless of the sample size or the number of regressors. In view of the fact that (see Exercise 5.21)

$$COOKD_i = \frac{(\widehat{\boldsymbol{y}} - \widehat{\boldsymbol{y}}_{(-i)})'(\widehat{\boldsymbol{y}} - \widehat{\boldsymbol{y}}_{(-i)})}{(k+1)\widehat{\sigma^2}} = \frac{1}{k+1}\left(\frac{h_i}{1-h_i}\right) r_i^2, \tag{5.19}$$

i.e. $COOKD_i$ is a variation of $DFFITS_i^2$ with t_i replaced by r_i and an extra factor of $1/(k+1)$, others have advocated a threshold of $4/n$ (see Fox, 1991).

5.4.3 *Precision diagnostics*

A diagnostic for the influence of y_i on the precision of $\widehat{\boldsymbol{\beta}}$ is

$$COVRATIO_i = \frac{|\widehat{\sigma^2}_{(-i)}(\boldsymbol{X}'\boldsymbol{X})^{-1}_{(-i)}|}{|\widehat{\sigma^2}(\boldsymbol{X}'\boldsymbol{X})^{-1}|}, \tag{5.20}$$

where $(\boldsymbol{X}'\boldsymbol{X})^{-1}_{(-i)}$ is $(\boldsymbol{X}'\boldsymbol{X})^{-1}$ with the ith row of $\boldsymbol{X}$ deleted. It may be shown that the volume of any confidence ellipsoid of $\boldsymbol{\beta}$, having the form (4.16), is proportional to the square-root of the determinant, $|\widehat{\sigma^2}(\boldsymbol{X}'\boldsymbol{X})^{-1}|$. The diagnostic $COVRATIO_i$ is simply the fractional change of the squared volume resulting from the dropping of the ith observation. When the ratio is greater than 1, the precision of the point estimator suffers from dropping of the ith observation. When the ratio is less than 1, the precision improves after the deletion.

It can be shown after some algebra that (Exercise 9.18)

$$COVRATIO_i = \left(\frac{\widehat{\sigma^2}_{(-i)}}{\widehat{\sigma^2}}\right)^{k+1} \frac{1}{1-h_i} = \frac{1}{\left(1+\frac{t_i^2-1}{n-k-1}\right)^{k+1}(1-h_i)}. \tag{5.21}$$

The ratio is small when t_i^2 is large but h_i is small, and large when t_i^2 is small but h_i is large. If we use the thresholds 0 and 2 for t_i^2 and $1/n$ and $2(k+1)/n$ for h_i (see Section 5.2), and assume that n is much larger than k, then the upper threshold for the diagnostic becomes $[1-1/(n-k-1)]^{-k-1}(1-2(k+1)/n)^{-1}$, which may be approximated by $(1+3(k+1)/n)$, and the lower threshold is $[1+3/(n-k-1)]^{-k-1}(1-1/n)^{-1}$, which is approximately $(1-3(k+1)/n)$. Using these approximations, Belsley et al. (2005) recommended the cutoff $1 \pm 3(k+1)/n$ for $COVRATIO_i$.

Example 5.24. (IMF unemployment data, continued) For the country level unemployment data of Table 5.2, we had identified in Example 5.7 the predictors GDP and INV as a suitable subset model for regression of the response variable, UNMP. Table 5.6 shows the values of $DFBETA$ of the three regression coefficients, $DFFIT$, $COOKD$ and $COVRATIO$ for the different countries, obtained through the following lines of code.

```
data(imf2015); row.names(imf2015)=imf2015$Country
head(imf2015)
lm2 <- lm(UNMP~GDP+INV, data = imf2015)
influence.measures(lm2)
```

Table 5.6 Casewise diagnostics for IMF unemployment data

Country	DFBETAS			DFFITS	Cook's distance	COVRATIO
	β_0	β_1	β_2			
Australia	–0.1246	0.0396	0.1330	0.1907	0.0124	1.149
Austria	0.0098	–0.0026	–0.0143	–0.0334	0.0004	1.148
Belgium	–0.0193	–0.0052	0.0367	0.0910	0.0028	1.123
Canada	–0.0146	0.0019	0.0208	0.0426	0.0006	1.149
Cyprus	0.0201	–0.0046	–0.0168	0.0211	0.0002	*1.293*
Czech Republic	0.0375	0.0544	–0.0651	–0.0862	0.0026	*1.312*
Denmark	–0.0480	–0.0792	0.0592	–0.1377	0.0065	1.130
Estonia	0.0305	0.1059	–0.0848	–0.1472	0.0074	1.214
Finland	0.0145	0.0089	–0.0066	0.0629	0.0014	1.128
France	–0.0012	–0.0228	0.0344	0.1407	0.0067	1.078
Germany	–0.1747	–0.0444	0.1469	–0.2937	0.0278	0.941
Greece	*1.5731*	–0.2710	*–1.3968*	*1.5897*	*0.7210*	0.891
Iceland	–0.1660	–0.1693	0.1841	–0.3441	0.0381	0.952
Ireland	–0.0121	0.1752	–0.0229	0.2418	0.0196	1.084
Israel	–0.1217	0.0299	0.0731	–0.2298	0.0173	0.992
Italy	0.0067	–0.0016	–0.0052	0.0080	0.0000	1.185
Japan	0.0591	0.0705	–0.1179	–0.2155	0.0155	1.054
Korea	0.0174	0.0125	–0.0245	–0.0284	0.0003	*1.331*
Latvia	0.0020	–0.0103	0.0032	0.0127	0.0001	1.215
Lithuania	–0.0852	0.1364	0.0151	–0.1807	0.0111	1.160
Luxembourg	0.0127	*0.5345*	–0.1821	0.5649	0.1080	*1.601*
Netherlands	–0.0785	–0.0400	0.0725	–0.1427	0.0069	1.104
New Zealand	0.0097	0.0208	–0.0361	–0.1086	0.0040	1.109
Norway	*–0.3763*	0.3127	0.3043	0.5362	0.0947	1.174
Portugal	–0.1457	0.0623	0.1090	–0.1615	0.0089	1.227
Singapore	0.0842	–0.0304	–0.0868	–0.1226	0.0052	1.196
Slovak Republic	–0.0024	–0.1894	0.0995	0.2463	0.0205	1.139
Slovenia	–0.0548	0.0741	0.0129	–0.1135	0.0044	1.152
Spain	*0.4754*	*–0.4950*	–0.1588	*0.9374*	*0.1880*	*0.277*
Sweden	–0.0572	0.0403	0.0618	0.1324	0.0060	1.124
Switzerland	0.0167	–0.0632	0.0011	–0.0714	0.0018	*1.316*
United Kingdom	–0.3296	–0.1216	0.3262	–0.4388	0.0610	0.926
United States	–0.0354	–0.1048	0.0534	–0.1616	0.0089	1.122

The diagnostic values exceeding thresholds are marked in *italics*. There is no instance of Cook's distance exceeding 1, and the threshold $4/n$ is used instead. The most noteworthy cases are those of Greece and Spain, where the fit as well as the multiple parameter estimates are overly influenced. These are the countries with excessively high unemployment (see Table 5.2). A single paramcter estimates has notable change with the deletion of either Luxemburg or Norway. COVRATIO is large for many countries. Interestingly, this diagnostic is much smaller than 1 in the case of Spain. Thus, the deletion of Spain from the data set would improve precision of the estimates considerably. □

5.4.4 *Spotting unusual cases graphically*

Identifying influential observations from a tabular display like Table 5.6 can be a difficult task, even if there are rule-of-thumb thresholds for assistance. The problem can be particularly acute for large data sets. Therefore, a graphical display of the diagnostics against the observation index, along with the threshold, may be used to identify unusual observations. In the case of DFBETAS, the diagnostics for the different parameters can be displayed in the same plot, using different plotting symbols.

The ideal tool for a visual assessment of the x- and y-outliers is the scatter plot of standardized (or studentized) residuals against the leverages. The x-outliers would appear on the right side of the plot, while y-outliers would flock to the top and the bottom part, just as one expects to find them in a scatter plot of response against regressor in the case of a single regressor.

Another interesting plot in this regard is that of Cook's distance against $h_i/(1-h_i)$. The high leverage points appear on the right end of the plot. The points influential to the overall fit appear at the top. Since the slope of the line joining the ith point with the origin is $r_i^2/(k+1)$ (see (5.19)), the y-outliers appear as points with high slope.

Example 5.25. (IMF unemployment data, continued) We demonstrate in Figure 5.19 the above plots for the country level unemployment data of Table 5.2, where the response is unemployment rate (UNMP) and the predictors are per capita GDP (GDP) and investment (INV). The requisite R code is given below.

```
data(imf2015); cases <- imf2015[,1]
lm2 <- lm(UNMP~GDP+INV, data = imf2015)
im2 <- influence.measures(lm2)
p <- summary(lm2)$df[1]
n <- sum(summary(lm2)$df[1:2])
thresh <- 2/sqrt(n)  # threshold for dfbetas
hihi <- which(hatvalues(lm2)>2*p/n) # cases with hi leverage
hiri <- which(abs(stdres(lm2))>2)    # cases with high std resid
hicd <- which((im2[[1]])[,(p+3)]>thresh^2) # cases with high CookD
mark <- sort(unique(c(hihi,hiri,hicd))) # cases w high lev/stdres/CD
starlab = which(rowSums(sign(abs(dfbetas(lm2))-thresh) + 1) / 2 > 0)
          # cases with high dfbetas
```

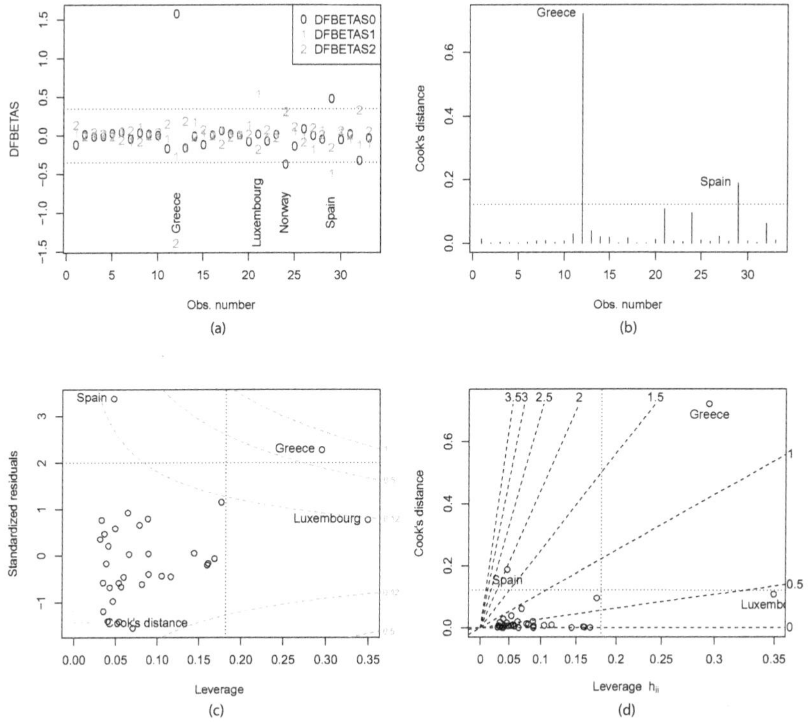

Fig. 5.19 Plots for Example 5.25: (a) index plot of DFBETAS, (b) index plot of Cook's distance as vertical lines, (c) scatter plot of standardized residual against leverage (with some contours of constant Cook's distance) and (d) scatter plot of Cook's distance against leverage (overlaid on some radial lines of specific slopes)

```
matplot(dfbetas(lm2), xlab = "Obs. number", ylab = "DFBETAS",
 pch = c("0","1","2"), col = c(1,2,4))
abline(h=thresh, lty=3); abline(h=-thresh, lty=3)
legend("topright",c("DFBETAS0","DFBETAS1","DFBETAS2"),lty=c(0,0,0),
 pch = c("0","1","2"), col = c(1,2,4))
text(starlab, rep(-1,length(starlab)), cases[starlab], srt = 90)
plot(lm2, which=4, caption="", sub.caption="", id.n=0)
abline(h = thresh^2, lty = 3)
text(hicd, (im2[[1]])[hicd,(p+3)], cases[hicd], pos=2)
cdlim <- round(thresh^2, digits=2)
plot(lm2, which=5, cook.levels=c(cdlim,0.5,1), add.smooth=F,
 caption="", sub.caption="", id.n=0)
abline(h=2, lty=3); abline(h=-2, lty=3)
```

```
abline(v = 2*p/n, lty = 3)
text(hatvalues(lm2)[mark], stdres(lm2)[mark], cases[mark], pos=2)
plot(lm2, which=6, add.smooth=F, caption="", sub.caption="", id.n=0)
abline(h = 4/n, lty = 3)
abline(v = (2*p/n)/(1 - (2*p/n)), lty = 3)
text(hatvalues(lm2)[mark]/(1-hatvalues(lm2)[mark]),
     (im2[[1]])[mark,(p+3)],cases[mark],pos=1)
```

Panel (a) shows the scatter plots of $DFBETA$ against observation number for the intercept and the coefficients of GDP and INV, represented by symbols 0, 1 and 2, respectively. The common thresholds, $\pm 2/\sqrt{n}$, are represented by the two dotted lines. The two large DFBETAs for each of Greece and Spain and the single large DFBETAS for each of Luxemburg and Norway can be spotted easily.

Panel (b) shows the plot of the Cook's distance against the index number. The threshold $4/n$ is shown in dotted lines. The countries with large values of the diagnostic (Greece and Spain) are visible as tall vertical lines. Greece has by far the tallest line.

Panel (c) shows the scatter plot of the standardized residual against the leverage. The threshold $2(k+1)/n$ for high leverage is shown as a dotted vertical line. The thresholds of ± 2 for standardized residuals are shown as dotted horizontal lines. These lines reveal that Greece is an x- as wells as y-outlier, Spain is a y-outlier and Luxemburg is an x-outlier. Greece and Spain have the highest unemployment rate, so there is no surprise about their being y-outliers. The x-outlier status of Luxemberg may be traced to its unusually high GDP, while that of Greece may be traced to its combination of low GDP and unusually low level of investment (see Table 5.2). This plot also shows contours of fixed values of Cook's distance in dashed lines, the values being 1, 0.5 and $4/n$ (or 0.12). Greece has the highest Cook's distance (between 0.5 and 1), followed by Spain (between 0.12 and 0.5) and Luxemburg and Norway (just under 0.12).

Panel (d) shows the scatter plot of Cook's distance against $h_i/(1-h_i)$, overlaid on a grid of radial lines representing different slopes. The horizontal axis is marked by the value of the leverage h_i, which explains the non-uniform spacing of the axis labels. The label against each grid line is proportional to $|r_i|$ (or the square root of the slope). The country with the highest slope is Spain, and its standardized residual has magnitude of about 4. Luxemburg with highest leverage appears to the right, while Greece with highest Cook's distance appears at the top. □

5.4.5 *Dealing with discordant observations*

When an influential observation is identified, it is understood that one or more aspects of the analysis is sensitive to that observation. It is often found that the list of influential observations (according to the measures discussed above) are dominated by a handful of observations that influence almost every aspect of the analysis. As we have seen in Example 5.25, occurrence of an influential observation can sometimes be attributed to unusual values of one or more variables for that observation. These values should be scrutinized and checked for correctness. Rousseeuw and Leroy (2003, p. 26) gave an example showing how diagnostics can lead to detection of data error.

Once the correctness of the data has been ascertained, one has to deal with the influential observations. If the cases with high influence happen to be x-outliers, it transpires that the regression fit would be different in the absence the outliers. If the region in the x-space represented by the outliers is not important for the analysis, one may contemplate an alternative analysis after leaving aside the outliers. If the said region is crucial for the analysis, it would not be prudent to throw away the available data. However, the fact of overly large influence of certain observations on the outcome of the analysis should be reported.

If any x-outlier is kept out of the analysis, care should be taken to ensure that the fitted model is not used to make prediction in the (outlying) region of the x-space represented by the omitted data point.

The occurrence of y-outliers generally obscures the pattern of dependence of the response on the regressors. A better inference of the regression model may be possible once these outliers are kept out of the way. If this is done, one can always factor in the occurrence of y-outliers through appropriate modeling of the error, as we did through bootstrap in Section 5.3.4.

One of the strategies of keeping x- or y-outliers out of the way is to carry out the analysis after dropping the discordant observations. A better strategy is to use a method of analysis that is less sensitive to outliers. A number of *robust regression* techniques are available. The *least absolute deviation* (LAD) estimator of regression coefficients seeks to represent the conditional median, rather than the conditional mean, as a linear function of the regressors. Since the median is resistant to outliers, the LAD regression estimator is insensitive to y-outliers. The *M-estimator* minimizes a weighted sum of squared residuals, the weights being a concave and increasing function of the squared residuals. The weight function makes it resistant to y-outliers, but not to x-outliers. With appropriate choice of the weight function, this estimator is MLE under some non-normal distribution, but has reasonable efficiency when the error distribution is actually normal. The *least trimmed squares* (LTS) estimator minimizes the of squared residuals after disregarding the largest few terms, thus allowing insensitivity to y-outliers. A special case of LTS estimator is the *least median of squares* estimator, which is highly resistant to both x- and y-outliers. The *S-estimator* minimizes a robust estimator of the scale of the residuals, and is designed to be resistant to both x- and y-outliers. For more information on robust and rank-based methods, we refer the interested reader to Rousseeuw and Leroy (2003), Boldin, Simonova and Tyurin (1997), Hettmansperger and McKean (1998) and Rao and Toutenburg (1999).

5.5 Collinearity

Consider a regression problem where all the p regression parameters, including the intercept and the coefficients of the k regressors ($p = k+1$), are estimable. As mentioned in Section 3.13, the phenomenon of collinearity (also known as multicollinearity) refers to the existence of a linear combination of the columns of the matrix $\boldsymbol{X}$ that is very small, so that $\boldsymbol{X}$ is nearly rank deficient. Collinearity makes the estimates of some regression coefficients highly susceptible to errors in observations and may lead to large standard errors of some of these estimates. It may also result in the statistical insignificance of the estimates of some 'important' regression coefficients, and/or 'wrong' signs of some estimated coefficients (see Section 4.5). The next example gives a visualization of collinearity and illustrates this issues.

Example 5.26. We simulate a sample of size 25 from the model described in Example 3.57 with $\beta_0 = 10$, $\beta_1 = 2$, $\beta_2 = 1$ and $\sigma^2 = 1$ in two cases: (a) $\alpha = 0.01$ and (b) $\alpha = 1$. The three-dimensional scatter plot of the fitted values against the two regressors and the least squares fitted regression plane in both the cases are shown in Figure 5.20. These are generated through the R code is given at the end of this paragraph. When $\alpha = 0.01$ (top panel), the fitted values lie almost on a straight line. The fitted plane appears to be perched precariously on a thin fence. There is lack of information away from the fence, which means the estimated location of the plane in that region would have a high standard error. These problems are not there when $\alpha = 1$ (bottom panel).

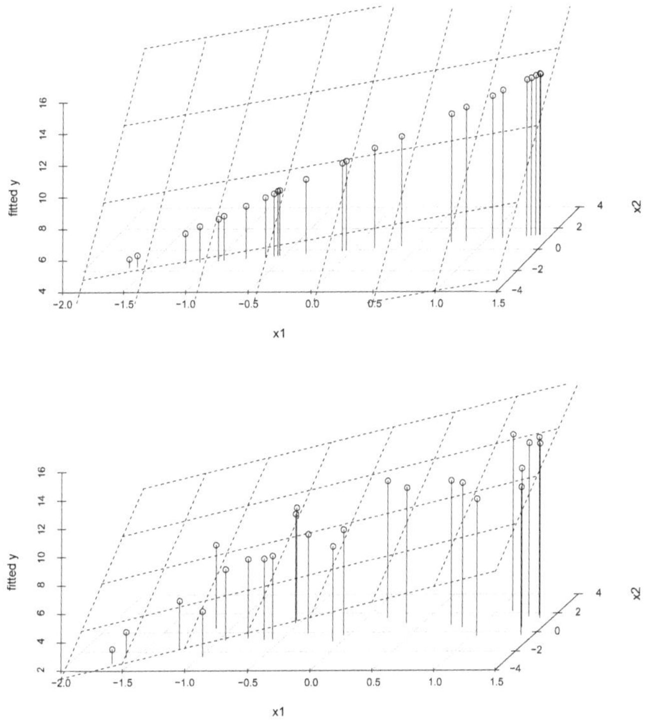

Fig. 5.20 Three-dimensional scatter plots for the data of Example 5.26 together with fitted regression plane for $\alpha = 0.01$ (top) and $\alpha = 1$ (bottom)

```
library(scatterplot3d)
set.seed(8504); n <- 25
x1 <- 10 * runif(n); x1 <-  x1 - mean(x1) # x1 orthogonal with 1
x1 <- x1 * sqrt(n) / sqrt(sum(x1^2))      # x1 has squared norm n
v <- 5* rnorm(n); v <- v - mean(v)        # v orthogonal with 1
v <- v - x1 * (sum(v*x1) / sum(x1^2))     # v orthogonal with x1
v <- v * sqrt(n) / sqrt(sum(v^2))         # v has squared norm n
err <- rnorm(n)
par(mfrow=c(2,1))                         # two plots in one column
alpha <- 0.01
x2 <- x1 + alpha * v
y <- 10 + 2 * x1 + 1 * x2 + err
lm1 <- lm(y~x1+x2)
s3d <- scatterplot3d(x1, x2, lm1$fit, ylim=c(-4,4), y.margin.add=0.2,
     xlab = "x1", ylab = "x2", zlab = "fitted y",
```

```
    angle = 60, pch=1, type="h", box = F)
s3d$plane3d(lm1)
alpha <- 1
x2 <- x1 + alpha * v
y <- 10 + 2 * x1 + 1 * x2 + err
lm2 <- lm(y~x1+x2)
s3d <- scatterplot3d(x1, x2, lm2$fit, ylim=c(-4,4), y.margin.add=0.2,
    xlab = "x1", ylab = "x2", zlab = "fitted y",
    angle = 60, pch=1, type="h", box = F)
s3d$plane3d(lm2)
```

It can be checked through the additional command `summary(lm2)` that for $\alpha = 1$, the estimated values of β_1 and β_2 are 2.144 and 1.008, respectively, which are close to the correct values (2 and 1, respectively). The p-values of significance of both the coefficients are smaller than 10^{-3}. However, when $\alpha = 0.01$, the estimates (obtained through the command `summary(lm1)`) are 1.381 and 1.771, respectively, which are away from the correct values (2 and 1, respectively). The p-values of significance of both the coefficients are high. The reader is encouraged to run this simulation repeatedly by setting the seed for random number generation at different values. These are likely to produce wildly fluctuating estimates of the parameters (which would almost always be insignificant), and very different fitted planes. □

5.5.1 *Indicators of collinearity*

Since linear dependence among regressors is the main issue in collinearity, one can check the pairwise correlations of regressors for any large value. While a high correlation indicates linear dependence of two regressors, absence of any large correlation does not guarantee absence of linear dependence. For example, it can be easily verified that if the variables x_1, x_2 and x_3 have the innocuous looking correlation matrix

$$\begin{pmatrix} 1 & 0.5 & 0.5 \\ 0.5 & 1 & -0.5 \\ 0.5 & -0.5 & 1 \end{pmatrix},$$

then the variance of $x_1 - x_2 - x_3$ is zero. In other words, each variable is a perfectly linear combination of the other two, even though no pairwise correlation is larger than 0.5 in magnitude. Thus, pairwise correlations are not adequate indicators of collinearity when there are more than two regressors. Instead, the extent of linear dependence of a regressor on all the others is measured by its sample multiple correlation coefficient with them.

Suppose R_j is the multiple correlation coefficient for the jth regressor based on all the other regressors. A set of widely accepted measures of collinearity are the *variance inflation factors* (VIFs),

$$VIF_j = \frac{1}{1-R_j^2}, \qquad j = 1, \ldots, k.$$

The name is justified by the fact that if all the regressors are linearly transformed to have zero sample mean and unit sample standard deviation, then $\sigma^2 VIF_j$ is the variance of the least squares estimator of the jth regression coefficient, for $j = 1, \ldots, k$. Thus, VIF_j is the factor by which σ^2 has to be inflated to obtain the variance of the jth estimated regression coefficient. The VIFs are determined entirely by the $\boldsymbol{X}$ matrix. The reciprocal of the VIF is called the tolerance of the variable concerned.

The VIFs are attractive measures of collinearity, as they directly quantify the main ill-effect of collinearity, namely, inflated variance. The normalization of the regressors somewhat alters the original regression problem though. The VIFs give no indication of the inflation factor applicable to the coefficients of the unadjusted regressors. The scaling part of the normalization is easily justified, as our assessment of the extent of collinearity should not be cluttered by the chosen scale of measurement of the variables. Mean-correction of the regressors is a more complicated matter. If the regression analysis is conducted for the purpose of prediction, then mean-correction would pose no problem, as the mean-corrected and/or scaled variables would produce exactly the same predictions and prediction error variances as the original variables. However, if the regression analysis is conducted in order to estimate the effects of the regressors, then the coefficients of the adjusted and the unadjusted variable can be very different. In such a case, VIFs would give a misleadingly diminished account of the effect of collinearity. This is because the act of mean correction completely eliminates collinearity involving the constant (intercept) term.

This distortion may be averted by computing the variance inflation after adjustment for scale but no adjustment for mean (see Belsley, 1991). The *intercept augmented VIFs* (referred to as uncentered VIFs by Belsley) may be defined as

$$IVIF_j = \sigma^{-2} Var(\widehat{\beta}_j) \|\boldsymbol{x}_{(j+1)}\|^2, \quad j = 0, 1, \ldots, k, \tag{5.22}$$

where $\boldsymbol{x}_{(j)}$ is the jth column of $\boldsymbol{X}$. The factor σ^{-2} ensures that $IVIF_j$ depends only on the matrix $\boldsymbol{X}$, while the factor $\|\boldsymbol{x}_{(j+1)}\|^2$ ensures that this measure is not altered by a change in scale of the corresponding variable (see Exercise 3.22). All the variance inflation factors are greater than or equal to 1, and a very large value indicates that the variance of the BLUE of the corresponding parameter is inflated. VIFs running into two or more digits are generally considered large (see e.g. Kutner et al., 2004). Likewise, IVIFs running into three digits may be used to flag collinearity. This threshold comes from an upper bound (see Exercise 5.23) of IVIF by the square of condition number, introduced below, for which a threshold of 30 is recommended (see next page).

Example 5.27. (IMF unemployment data, continued) For the country level unemployment data of Table 5.2, let us consider regression of the unemployment rate (UNMP) on all the predictors. The VIFs and IVIFs are computed through the functions `vif` and `ivif` of the R packages `car` and `lmreg`, respectively, as shown in the R code given below, and the computed values are reported in the following table.

```
data(imf2015)
lm6 <- lm(UNMP~CAB+DEBT+EXP+GDP+INFL+INV, data = imf2015)
library(car)
vif(lm6)
ivif(lm6)
```

	Intercept	CAB	DEBT	EXP	GDP	INFL	INV
VIF	-	1.457	1.299	1.408	1.434	1.805	2.270
IVIF	161.845	1.896	4.857	32.327	7.198	1.889	67.627

The VIFs happen to be rather small. The IVIF for the intercept is more than 100 and other IVIFs are not too large (though larger than the corresponding VIF). The IVIFs represent the status of collinearity better, since we do have a problem of collinearity here. The problem is manifested in the fact that the seven regression parameters happen to be insignificant at level 0.1, even though a simple linear regression of UNMP on each of the six regressors leads to a significant slope at the level 0.05. □

There may be several approximately linear relationships among the regressors. The VIFs and IVIFs cannot discern this complex situation from the simpler case of a single approximately linear relationship. These are brought out through a singular value decomposition (SVD; see Section A.5 of Appendix A) of $\boldsymbol{X}_s$, the matrix obtained by scaling the columns of $\boldsymbol{X}$ to ensure $\boldsymbol{X}_s'\boldsymbol{X}_s = 1$. Suppose an SVD of $\boldsymbol{X}_s$ is of the form $\sum_{i=1}^{p} \sigma_i \boldsymbol{u}_i \boldsymbol{v}_i'$, where $\sigma_1 > \sigma_2 > \cdots > \sigma_p$, and the $\boldsymbol{u}_i$'s and $\boldsymbol{v}_i$'s are two sets of orthogonal

Table 5.7 Condition indices and singular vectors

Condition	Element of singular vector corresponding to			
index	Intercept	Regressor 1		Regressor k
$\kappa_1 = 1$	$v_{1,1}$	$v_{2,1}$	$\cdots$	$v_{p,1}$
$\kappa_2 = \sigma_1/\sigma_2$	$v_{1,2}$	$v_{2,2}$	$\cdots$	$v_{p,2}$
$\vdots$	$\vdots$	$\vdots$	$\ddots$	$\vdots$
$\kappa_p = \sigma_1/\sigma_p$	$v_{1,p}$	$v_{2,p}$	$\cdots$	$v_{p,p}$

unit vectors. Since $\boldsymbol{X}_s\boldsymbol{v}_i = \sigma_i\boldsymbol{u}_i$, each small singular value represents the magnitude of a linear combination of the scaled regressors which is approximately equal to zero. In this context smallness of a singular value is judged relative to σ_1. The ith *condition index* $\boldsymbol{X}_s$ is defined as $\kappa_i = \sigma_1/\sigma_i$. Since $\lambda_i = \sigma_i^2$ is the ith largest eigenvector of $\boldsymbol{X}_s'\boldsymbol{X}_s$ (with eigenvector $\boldsymbol{v}_i$), the ith condition index can also be written as $\kappa_i = (\lambda_1/\lambda_i)^{1/2}$.

In order to identify the multiple dimensions of collinearity, one may use Table 5.7. In this table v_{ij} is the ith element of $\boldsymbol{v}_j$, $i, j = 1, \ldots, p$. Since $\|\boldsymbol{X}_s\boldsymbol{v}_i\| = \sigma_i$, the bottom rows corresponding to high condition indices describe the independent linear combinations that are nearly zero. Belseley et al. (1980) suggest 30 as a rule-of-thumb threshold for flagging large condition indices.

The *condition number* κ of $\boldsymbol{X}_s$ is its largest condition index. The number κ is large if and only if at least one of the IVIFs is large (Exercise 5.23).

There are further connections between the IVIFs and the condition indices. It can be shown that (Exercise 5.22)

$$IVIF_j = \sum_{i=1}^{p} \frac{v_{i(j+1)}^2}{\lambda_i}, \quad j = 0, \ldots, k.$$

This decomposition shows how small eigenvalues of $\boldsymbol{X}_s'\boldsymbol{X}_s$ can inflate the variance of certain regressors. If the different summands are expressed as fractions of the sum, we have the variance proportions

$$\pi_{ij} = v_{ij}^2/(\lambda_i IVIF_{j-1}), \qquad i, j = 1, \ldots, p.$$

Note that π_{ij} represents the fraction of $IVIF_{j-1}$ which may be attributed to the ith largest eigenvalue. Belsley et al. (2005) proposed a matrix arrangement of the π_{ij}'s, called the *variance proportions table.* They suggest 0.5 as a working threshold for identifying large value of π_{ij}. They also suggest that if κ_i is large and π_{ij} is larger than this threshold, the $(j-1)$th variable may be said to have be affected by the ith collinear relationship,

Table 5.8 Variance proportions and IVIF

Condition index	Variance decomposition proportion for Intercept	Regressor 1		Regressor k
$\kappa_1 = 1$	$\pi_{1,1}$	$\pi_{2,1}$	$\cdots$	$\pi_{p,1}$
$\kappa_2 = \sigma_1/\sigma_2$	$\pi_{1,2}$	$\pi_{2,2}$	$\cdots$	$\pi_{p,2}$
$\vdots$	$\vdots$	$\vdots$	$\ddots$	$\vdots$
$\kappa_p = \sigma_1/\sigma_p$	$\pi_{1,p}$	$\pi_{2,p}$	$\cdots$	$\pi_{p,p}$
	Intercept-augmented Variance Inflation Factors			
	VIF_0	VIF_1	$\cdots$	VIF_k

i.e. $\boldsymbol{X}_s\boldsymbol{v}_i \approx \boldsymbol{0}$. This conclusion makes sense only if $IVIF_{j-1}$ is large. For this reason, it is important to tabulate the IVIFs alongside the variance proportions, to form Table 5.8.

To summarize, the linear combinations of collinearity may be identified from the table of condition indices and singular vectors, reported earlier, while the VP table with IVIFs identifies the regressor estimates affected by collinearity and also the specific linear combinations affecting them. The two tables are somewhat complementary to one another.

Example 5.28. (IMF unemployment data, continued) For the country level unemployment data of Table 5.2, we consider once again regression of the unemployment rate (UNMP) on all the predictors. Table 5.9 exhibits the condition numbers and the corresponding singular vectors. It is seen that there is only one condition number greater than 30. The corresponding right singular vector, appearing in the last row of the table, shows the linear combination of regressors that has the smallest magnitude.

Table 5.9 Condition indices and singular vectors for IMF unemployment data

Condition index	element of singular vector corresponding to Intercept	CAB	DEBT	EXP	GDP	INFL	INV
1.000	–0.444	–0.265	–0.390	–0.435	–0.424	–0.133	–0.441
2.251	–0.071	–0.143	–0.188	–0.039	0.046	0.967	0.025
2.533	0.143	–0.902	0.300	0.221	–0.140	–0.051	0.064
4.614	–0.158	0.241	0.803	–0.144	–0.400	0.199	–0.227
6.739	–0.245	–0.164	0.250	–0.234	0.797	–0.031	–0.400
10.959	0.115	–0.101	0.109	–0.784	0.044	–0.034	0.589
34.037	0.824	0.013	–0.065	–0.264	–0.046	0.054	–0.492

Table 5.10 Variance proportions table for IMF unemployment data

Condition	Variance decomposition proportions for						
index	Intercept	CAB	DEBT	EXP	GDP	INFL	INV
1.000	0.000	0.008	0.006	0.001	0.005	0.002	0.001
2.251	0.000	0.011	0.008	0.000	0.000	0.513	0.000
2.533	0.000	0.563	0.024	0.002	0.004	0.002	0.000
4.614	0.001	0.133	0.578	0.003	0.097	0.091	0.003
6.739	0.003	0.131	0.120	0.016	0.819	0.005	0.022
10.959	0.002	0.131	0.061	0.467	0.007	0.015	0.126
34.037	0.993	0.023	0.204	0.511	0.069	0.372	0.848
	Intercept-augmented Variance Inflation Factors						
	161.845	1.896	4.857	32.327	7.198	1.889	67.627

Table 5.10 shows the VP table for this data set. For the largest condition number (34.037), several VP numbers appearing in the last row are larger than 0.5, but we need not worry about all of them. The largest IVIF is seen to be 161.845, which corresponds to the intercept term. Two other VPs greater than 0.5, appearing in the row of the largest condition index, are in the columns of EXP and INV. These variance proportions represent parts of IVIFs that are only moderately large (32.327 and 67.627, respectively).

These two tables may be generated by using the following R code, which makes use of the functions `cisv` and `colldiag` of the R packages `lmreg` and `perturb`, respectively.

```
data(imf2015)
lm6 <- lm(UNMP~CAB+DEBT+EXP+GDP+INFL+INV, data = imf2015)
cisv(lm6) # Table of condition indices and singular vectors
library(perturb)
colldiag(lm6); ivif(lm6) # VP table and IVIF
```

The reason for the estimation of the intercept being affected by collinearity may be appreciated from the numbers reported in Table 5.2. Several variables, most notably EXP and INV, have little variations compared to their respective means. The coefficient of variation for these two variables are 0.217 and 0.189 (the other coefficients of variation being greater than 0.5). Since these two variables have a hidden constant part, they act as proxies of the intercept term. Thus, there is some confusion about pinpointing the exclusive effect of the intercept term. This is why there is collinearity involving the intercept.

The coefficients of variation of all the variables can be computed simultaneously in R by invoking `library(matrixStats)` and running the code `colSds(model.matrix(lm6))/colMeans(model.matrix(lm6))`. □

Sometime a single observation has a major impact on collinearity in a regression analysis. Sengupta and Bhimasankaram (1997) have provided diagnostics for detecting this influence.

5.5.2 *Strategies for collinear data*

Before one looks for a way of dealing with collinearity, it is important to check whether collinearity really causes any problem for the intended analysis. As noted in Section 3.13, collinearity is essentially dearth of information in certain areas of the space of explanatory variables. There can yet be adequate information in other areas. We have seen in Example 3.57 that estimation of some functions can be unaffected when there is an approximate (or even exact) linear relationship involving the columns of $\boldsymbol{X}$. In general, estimation of regression coefficients with low VIFs do not suffer much from collinearity. Further, prediction of a new response, when the observation is not an x-outlier, is also generally unaffected by collinearity.

Collinearity involving the intercept may be avoided wherever possible. We have seen in Example 5.28 that variables with small coefficient of variation tend to be involved in such linear relations. Origin of measurement (i.e. location of 'zero' on the scale of the regressor) has a bearing on the extent of collinearity. For example, if the origin of measurement of a regressor is shifted to its sample mean, the mean-corrected regressor would be orthogonal to the intercept. The condition indices and IVIFs are likely to be smaller as a result of this transformation. However, this improvement is only cosmetic. Once the fitted model is expressed in terms of the original variables, the estimated coefficient of the re-transformed regressor, its standard error and other aspects of the analysis would be the same as what they had been without the transformation. Therefore, 'temporary' relocation of origin does not serve any purpose. A relocation of origin may be considered if the regression equation can be meaningfully expressed in terms of the transformed variable, so that the transformed variable is regarded as a replacement of the original one. For example, if the calendar year is a regressor, it may be replaced by the number of years since a certain landmark date.

The lack of information in certain areas in the space of regressors, which is the essential problem of collinearity, may be overcome through additional information. One can collect more data only if one can design or control at least some of the values of the explanatory variables which are involved in the approximately linear relationships. Another strategy is to use a prior in a Bayesian formulation of the problem (see Broemeling, 1984).

Sometimes the problem of collinearity is aggravated when several derived variables are included in the equation. This is typically true for polynomial transformations. In market research also, one often starts to build a regression model with a laundry list of regressors that might have some linkage with the response. Care should be taken while selecting candidate variables. Every new variable included in the model should have a potential purpose.

It is also possible to carry out a smarter analysis of the available data in a collinear situation, by subjecting the estimator to some reasonable conditions. This principle, known as *regularization*, compels one to look beyond unbiased estimators. We deal with the relevant techniques in the next section. Yet anther approach that combines subset selection with regularization is the *lasso*, for which the reader is referred to Hastie et al., (2015). Methods for high dimensional data that permit reasonable inference in the presence of covariates were also proposed by Li and Lu (2018) and Cattaneo et al. (2018).

5.6 Biased estimators with smaller dispersion*

One of the popular strategies of dealing with collinear data is dimension reduction. This can be done via subset selection or principal components regression. The other common strategy is to keep all the regressors but somehow regularize the estimation process to avoid nonsensical estimates (see Exercise 5.54 for an example of wild estimates and perils of subset selection for prediction with collinear data). Principal components, ridge and shrinkage regression fall into this category of methods. We have already discussed subset selection in Section 5.1. The other three methods are discussed in this section. All of these estimators have smaller dispersion compared to the BLUE, but this comes at the cost of some bias. The subset estimator is a special case of BLUE with linear restrictions. The principal components estimator is a subset estimator in a reparametrized model. The ridge estimator is a form of Bayes estimator (see Section 11.3.1).

We continue to work under the assumption that the matrix $\boldsymbol{X}$ in the linear model $(\boldsymbol{y}, \boldsymbol{X\beta}, \sigma^2\boldsymbol{I})$ considered here has full column rank, $p = k+1$, k being the number of regressors.

5.6.1 *Principal components estimator*

The point of departure of principal components regression is the fact that the dispersion matrix $\sigma^2(\boldsymbol{X}'\boldsymbol{X})^{-1}$ has very large eigenvalues, which are reciprocals of the small eigenvalues of $\boldsymbol{X}'\boldsymbol{X}$. Let $\boldsymbol{U\Lambda U}'$ be a spectral decomposition of $\boldsymbol{X}'\boldsymbol{X}$. We can arrange the eigenvalues of $\boldsymbol{X}'\boldsymbol{X}$ in the decreasing order, and partition the matrices $\boldsymbol{U}$ and $\boldsymbol{\Lambda}$ suitably so that

$$\boldsymbol{U\Lambda U}' = (\boldsymbol{U}_1 : \boldsymbol{U}_2)\begin{pmatrix}\boldsymbol{\Lambda}_1 & \boldsymbol{0}\\ \boldsymbol{0} & \boldsymbol{\Lambda}_2\end{pmatrix}\begin{pmatrix}\boldsymbol{U}_1'\\ \boldsymbol{U}_2'\end{pmatrix} = \boldsymbol{U}_1\boldsymbol{\Lambda}_1\boldsymbol{U}_1' + \boldsymbol{U}_2\boldsymbol{\Lambda}_2\boldsymbol{U}_2',$$

where the diagonal elements of $\boldsymbol{\Lambda}_2$ are small. Rewrite the model equation as

$$\boldsymbol{y} = \boldsymbol{X\beta} + \boldsymbol{\varepsilon} = \boldsymbol{X}(\boldsymbol{U}_1\boldsymbol{U}_1' + \boldsymbol{U}_2\boldsymbol{U}_2')\boldsymbol{\beta} + \boldsymbol{\varepsilon} = \boldsymbol{Z}_1\boldsymbol{\gamma}_1 + \boldsymbol{Z}_2\boldsymbol{\gamma}_2 + \boldsymbol{\varepsilon} = \boldsymbol{Z\gamma} + \boldsymbol{\varepsilon},$$

where $\boldsymbol{Z}_i = \boldsymbol{XU}_i$ and $\boldsymbol{\gamma}_i = \boldsymbol{U}_i'\boldsymbol{\beta}$ for $i = 1, 2$, $\boldsymbol{Z} = \boldsymbol{XU} = (\boldsymbol{Z}_1 : \boldsymbol{Z}_2)$ and $\boldsymbol{\gamma} = (\boldsymbol{\gamma}_1' : \boldsymbol{\gamma}_2')' = \boldsymbol{U}'\boldsymbol{\beta}$. Note that $(\boldsymbol{y}, \boldsymbol{Z\gamma}, \sigma^2\boldsymbol{I})$ is a reparametrization of the original model. An important aspect of the reparametrized model is that the dispersion of the BLUE of $\boldsymbol{\gamma}$ is $\sigma^2(\boldsymbol{Z}'\boldsymbol{Z})^{-1} = \sigma^2\boldsymbol{\Lambda}^{-1}$. The dispersion matrix is diagonal, and the lower right block of this matrix, $\sigma^2\boldsymbol{\Lambda}_2^{-1}$, has large diagonal elements that correspond to those elements of the vector parameter $\boldsymbol{\gamma}$ which cannot be estimated with good precision.

In principal components regression, $\boldsymbol{\gamma}$ is estimated by its BLUE under the restriction $\boldsymbol{\gamma}_2 = \boldsymbol{0}$. It is easy to see that this estimator is

$$\widehat{\boldsymbol{\gamma}}_{pc} = \begin{pmatrix}\boldsymbol{\Lambda}_1^{-1}\boldsymbol{Z}_1'\boldsymbol{y}\\ \boldsymbol{0}\end{pmatrix}.$$

Using the transformation $\boldsymbol{\gamma} = \boldsymbol{U}'\boldsymbol{\beta}$ (i.e. $\boldsymbol{\beta} = \boldsymbol{U\gamma}$), we can write the *principal components estimator* of $\boldsymbol{\beta}$ as

$$\widehat{\boldsymbol{\beta}}_{pc} = \boldsymbol{U}\widehat{\boldsymbol{\gamma}}_{pc} = \boldsymbol{U}_1\boldsymbol{\Lambda}_1^{-1}\boldsymbol{Z}_1'\boldsymbol{y} = (\boldsymbol{U}_1\boldsymbol{\Lambda}_1^{-1}\boldsymbol{U}_1')\boldsymbol{X}'\boldsymbol{y}.$$

Thus, $\widehat{\boldsymbol{\beta}}_{pc}$ is obtained by reverse transformation of a subset estimator in a reparametrized model. Therefore, comparison of the mean squared errors of this estimator and the BLUE can proceed along the lines of the analysis of the subset estimator. It can be shown that the MSEs of $\widehat{\boldsymbol{\beta}}_{pc}$ and $\widehat{\boldsymbol{\beta}}$ (the BLUE of $\widehat{\boldsymbol{\beta}}$) are

$$\begin{aligned} MSE(\widehat{\boldsymbol{\beta}}_{pc}) &= \sigma^2\boldsymbol{U}_1\boldsymbol{\Lambda}_1^{-1}\boldsymbol{U}_1' + \boldsymbol{U}_2\boldsymbol{\gamma}_2\boldsymbol{\gamma}_2'\boldsymbol{U}_2'\\ MSE(\widehat{\boldsymbol{\beta}}) &= \sigma^2(\boldsymbol{U}_1\boldsymbol{\Lambda}_1^{-1}\boldsymbol{U}_1' + \boldsymbol{U}_2\boldsymbol{\Lambda}_2^{-1}\boldsymbol{U}_2'). \end{aligned}$$

Therefore,

$$MSE(\widehat{\boldsymbol{\beta}}) - MSE(\widehat{\boldsymbol{\beta}}_{pc}) = \sigma^2\boldsymbol{U}_2\boldsymbol{\Lambda}_2^{-1}\boldsymbol{U}_2' - \boldsymbol{U}_2\boldsymbol{\gamma}_2\boldsymbol{\gamma}_2'\boldsymbol{U}_2'.$$

This quantity is nonnegative definite if and only if $\sigma^2\boldsymbol{\Lambda}_2^{-1} - \boldsymbol{\gamma}_2\boldsymbol{\gamma}_2'$ is nonnegative definite. The latter condition is equivalent to the inequality

$$\sigma^2 \geq \boldsymbol{\gamma}_2'\boldsymbol{\Lambda}_2\boldsymbol{\gamma}_2 = \boldsymbol{\beta}'\boldsymbol{U}_2\boldsymbol{\Lambda}_2\boldsymbol{U}_2'\boldsymbol{\beta}. \tag{5.23}$$

This condition is satisfied if $\boldsymbol{\Lambda}_2$ has sufficiently small diagonal elements.

The difference between the traces of the MSEs of the two estimators of $\boldsymbol{X\beta}$ corresponding to $\widehat{\boldsymbol{\beta}}$ and $\widehat{\boldsymbol{\beta}}_{pc}$ are

$$\begin{aligned}\text{tr}(MSE(\boldsymbol{X}\widehat{\boldsymbol{\beta}}) - MSE(\boldsymbol{X}\widehat{\boldsymbol{\beta}}_{pc}) &= \sigma^2\text{tr}(\boldsymbol{Z}_2\boldsymbol{\Lambda}_2^{-1}\boldsymbol{Z}_2') - \|\boldsymbol{Z}_2\boldsymbol{\gamma}_2\|^2\\ &= \sigma^2\text{tr}(\boldsymbol{\Lambda}_2^{-1}\boldsymbol{Z}_2'\boldsymbol{Z}_2) - \boldsymbol{\gamma}_2'\boldsymbol{Z}_2'\boldsymbol{Z}_2\boldsymbol{\gamma}_2\\ &= \sigma^2\rho(\boldsymbol{U}_2) - \boldsymbol{\beta}'\boldsymbol{U}_2\boldsymbol{\Lambda}_2\boldsymbol{U}_2'\boldsymbol{\beta}.\end{aligned}$$

In the above, $\rho(\boldsymbol{U}_2)$ is the number of elements of $\boldsymbol{\Lambda}_2$, which is equal to the number of discarded 'variables'. The difference between the MSEs is nonnegative if and only if

$$\sigma^2 \geq \boldsymbol{\beta}'\boldsymbol{U}_2\boldsymbol{\Lambda}_2\boldsymbol{U}_2'\boldsymbol{\beta}/\rho(\boldsymbol{U}_2).$$

This condition is evidently weaker than (5.23).

An important qualitative difference between the subset and the principal components methods is the following. There is a clear hierarchy among the (linearly transformed) variables of the model $(\boldsymbol{y}, \boldsymbol{Z\gamma}, \sigma^2\boldsymbol{I})$ in terms of the variance of the estimators of the corresponding coefficients, which happen to be uncorrelated. Thus, one can choose a cut-off for the eigenvalues, and obtain a reasonable 'subset' right away. However, search for a suitable subset is not easy, as there is no hierarchy among the untransformed variables.

A drawback of the principal components method is that the discarded components may not necessarily be poor as explanatory variables. It may be possible to find a discarded variable having more correlation with the response than a retained variable. Another drawback is that even though the effective number of variables is reduced, the remaining transformed variables are usually linear functions of all the original variables. If the cost of collecting data on some variables is high, the principal components method does not provide any savings in cost. Nevertheless, this method serves as an important tool for dimension reduction. It may also be used to get an idea of the approximate size of the subset model that one might look for.

5.6.2 *Ridge estimator*

Hoerl and Kennard (1970a, b) suggested a simple solution to the problem of large eigenvalues of $(\boldsymbol{X}'\boldsymbol{X})^{-1}$: replace $(\boldsymbol{X}'\boldsymbol{X})^{-1}$ in the expression of the BLUE by $(\boldsymbol{X}'\boldsymbol{X}+r\boldsymbol{I})^{-1}$, where r is a positive number. The effect of this alteration is to increase the diagonal elements of the matrix $\boldsymbol{X}'\boldsymbol{X}$ by a constant amount. Since the change takes place only along the main diagonal of this matrix (like the rise of a steep mountain ridge from an ordinary landscape), the corresponding estimator is called the *ridge estimator*. It is formally defined as

$$\widehat{\boldsymbol{\beta}}_r = (\boldsymbol{X}'\boldsymbol{X}+r\boldsymbol{I})^{-1}\boldsymbol{X}'\boldsymbol{y}. \tag{5.24}$$

This estimator exists even if $\boldsymbol{X}$ does not have full column rank. The limit of this estimator as r goes to zero is just the least squares estimator.

It is easy to see that the bias of the ridge estimator is $-r(\boldsymbol{X}'\boldsymbol{X}+r\boldsymbol{I})^{-1}\boldsymbol{\beta}$, the magnitude of which increases linearly with r. The dispersion of the ridge estimator is

$$D(\widehat{\boldsymbol{\beta}}_r) = \sigma^2(\boldsymbol{X}'\boldsymbol{X}+r\boldsymbol{I})^{-1}\boldsymbol{X}'\boldsymbol{X}(\boldsymbol{X}'\boldsymbol{X}+r\boldsymbol{I})^{-1},$$

which is a decreasing function of r, in the sense of the Löwner order (Exercise 5.25). Therefore, the constant r controls the trade-off between bias and dispersion of the ridge estimator. Such a trade-off also exists in the case of the subset and principal components estimators discussed earlier, but the choice is limited by the number of candidate models. In this case the number of choices is infinite because r can be any positive number.

The difference between the mean squared errors of the BLUE and the ridge estimator of $\boldsymbol{\beta}$ is

$$\begin{aligned}
&MSE(\widehat{\boldsymbol{\beta}}) - MSE(\widehat{\boldsymbol{\beta}}_r)\\
&= \sigma^2[(\boldsymbol{X}'\boldsymbol{X})^{-1} - (\boldsymbol{X}'\boldsymbol{X}+r\boldsymbol{I})^{-1}\boldsymbol{X}'\boldsymbol{X}(\boldsymbol{X}'\boldsymbol{X}+r\boldsymbol{I})^{-1}]\\
&\qquad -r^2(\boldsymbol{X}'\boldsymbol{X}+r\boldsymbol{I})^{-1}\boldsymbol{\beta}\boldsymbol{\beta}'(\boldsymbol{X}'\boldsymbol{X}+r\boldsymbol{I})^{-1}\\
&= \sigma^2(\boldsymbol{X}'\boldsymbol{X}+r\boldsymbol{I})^{-1}\\
&\qquad \cdot[(\boldsymbol{X}'\boldsymbol{X}+r\boldsymbol{I})(\boldsymbol{X}'\boldsymbol{X})^{-1}(\boldsymbol{X}'\boldsymbol{X}+r\boldsymbol{I})-\boldsymbol{X}'\boldsymbol{X}-r^2\sigma^{-2}\boldsymbol{\beta}\boldsymbol{\beta}'](\boldsymbol{X}'\boldsymbol{X}+r\boldsymbol{I})^{-1}\\
&= r\sigma^2(\boldsymbol{X}'\boldsymbol{X}+r\boldsymbol{I})^{-1}[(2\boldsymbol{I}+r(\boldsymbol{X}'\boldsymbol{X})^{-1})-r\sigma^{-2}\boldsymbol{\beta}\boldsymbol{\beta}'](\boldsymbol{X}'\boldsymbol{X}+r\boldsymbol{I})^{-1}.
\end{aligned} \tag{5.25}$$

The above difference is nonnegative definite if and only if the matrix in the square bracket is nonnegative definite, which is equivalent to the condition

$$\sigma^2 \ge \boldsymbol{\beta}'(2r^{-1}\boldsymbol{I}+(\boldsymbol{X}'\boldsymbol{X})^{-1})^{-1}\boldsymbol{\beta} = \|\boldsymbol{X}\boldsymbol{\beta}\|^2 \cdot \frac{\boldsymbol{\beta}'(2r^{-1}\boldsymbol{I}+(\boldsymbol{X}'\boldsymbol{X})^{-1})^{-1}\boldsymbol{\beta}}{\boldsymbol{\beta}'\boldsymbol{X}'\boldsymbol{X}\boldsymbol{\beta}}.$$

The maximum value of the ratio given in the last expression is the largest eigenvalue of the matrix $(2r^{-1}\boldsymbol{X}'\boldsymbol{X}+\boldsymbol{I})^{-1}$, which is equal to $(2\lambda/r+1)^{-1}$, where λ is the *minimum* eigenvalue of $\boldsymbol{X}'\boldsymbol{X}$. It follows that the ridge estimator has smaller MSE matrix than the least squares estimator (in the sense of the Löwner order) for *all* $\boldsymbol{\beta}$ whenever

$$r^{-1} > (\|\boldsymbol{X\beta}\|^2/\sigma^2 - 1)/(2\lambda). \tag{5.26}$$

The condition is satisfied for any choice of r in the special case $\|\boldsymbol{X\beta}\|^2 < \sigma^2$ (Exercise 5.27(a)). This case is not interesting, because it happens when the systematic part of the model is very weak in comparison to the error (Exercise 5.27(d)). Usually we have $\|\boldsymbol{X\beta}\|^2 > \sigma^2$, and the above condition is satisfied if r is chosen to be a small positive number. There is always a range of values of r for which the ridge estimator is better than the LSE. Unfortunately the ratio $\|\boldsymbol{X\beta}\|^2/\sigma^2$ is not known in practice. As a result, one has to choose r on the basis of the data (see Judge et al., 1985). Note that the above comparison of mean squared error matrices holds only when r is a constant. If r is chosen on the basis of the data, the ridge estimator is no longer a linear estimator, and the above analysis does not hold.

The ridge estimator (5.24) can also be interpreted as a restricted least squares estimator. It can be shown that the sum of squares $\|\boldsymbol{y}-\boldsymbol{X\beta}\|^2$ is minimized subject to the quadratic restriction $\|\boldsymbol{\beta}\|^2 \le b^2$ by an estimator of the form $\widehat{\boldsymbol{\beta}}_r = (\boldsymbol{X}'\boldsymbol{X}+r\boldsymbol{I})^{-1}\boldsymbol{X}'\boldsymbol{y}$, where r is such that $\|\widehat{\boldsymbol{\beta}}_r\|^2 = b^2$ (see Exercise 5.26). Note that this estimator for any fixed b is not linear, because r depends on $\boldsymbol{y}$.

5.6.3 *Shrinkage estimator*

The trade-off between reduced variance and increased bias can also be achieved by simply multiplying the BLUE by a constant. The resulting estimator,

$$\boldsymbol{X}\widehat{\boldsymbol{\beta}}_s = s\boldsymbol{X}\widehat{\boldsymbol{\beta}},$$

where $\boldsymbol{X}\widehat{\boldsymbol{\beta}}$ is the BLUE of $\boldsymbol{X\beta}$, is called the *shrinkage estimator* (Mayer and Willke, 1973). The name 'shrinkage' is derived from the fact that s is chosen to be a positive number less than 1. This choice ensures that the dispersion of the shrinkage estimator is less than that of the BLUE, in the sense of the Löwner order.

Let $\widehat{\boldsymbol{\beta}}$ and $\widehat{\boldsymbol{\beta}}_s$ be the least squares and shrinkage estimators of $\boldsymbol{\beta}$. It is easy to see that

$$MSE(\widehat{\boldsymbol{\beta}}) - MSE(\widehat{\boldsymbol{\beta}}_s) = (1-s^2)\sigma^2(\boldsymbol{X}'\boldsymbol{X})^{-1} - (1-s)^2\boldsymbol{\beta}\boldsymbol{\beta}'. \tag{5.27}$$

The difference is positive definite if and only if

$$s > \frac{\|\boldsymbol{X\beta}\|^2/\sigma^2 - 1}{\|\boldsymbol{X\beta}\|^2/\sigma^2 + 1}. \tag{5.28}$$

Barring the pathological case $\|\boldsymbol{X\beta}\|^2 < \sigma^2$ (Exercise 5.27), the above condition is satisfied when s is marginally smaller than 1. There is always a range of values of s for which the shrinkage estimator would have a smaller MSE matrix than the least squares estimator. However, this range is not known because $\boldsymbol{\beta}$ and σ^2 are unknown. If s is chosen on the basis of the data, then the resulting estimator is no longer linear. The James-Stein estimator

$$\left(1 - \frac{cr\widehat{\sigma^2}}{\|\boldsymbol{X}\widehat{\boldsymbol{\beta}}\|^2}\right)\boldsymbol{X}\widehat{\boldsymbol{\beta}}, \quad c = \frac{(n-r)(r-2)}{(n-r+2)r},$$

defined for $r = \rho(\boldsymbol{X}) > 2$, is such an estimator. This nonlinear estimator is *known* to have smaller trace of mean squared error than the least squares estimator, provided $\boldsymbol{y}$ has the normal distribution (see Gruber, 1998, p. 197).

The shrinkage estimator is not the only estimator having a magnitude smaller than the BLUE. It can be shown that the ridge (Exercise 5.26, part (d)) and the principal components (Exercise 5.24) estimators also have smaller magnitude than the corresponding BLUE.

The shrinkage estimator is a convex combination of the least squares estimator, $\widehat{\boldsymbol{\beta}}$ and the trivial estimator, $\boldsymbol{0}$. If there is a prior guess of $\boldsymbol{\beta}$, (say, $\boldsymbol{\beta}_0$), it may be wiser to choose a convex combination of the least squares estimator and $\boldsymbol{\beta}_0$. This estimator can be formally written as

$$\widehat{\boldsymbol{\beta}}_{s,\beta_0} = (1-s)\boldsymbol{\beta}_0 + s\widehat{\boldsymbol{\beta}} = \widehat{\boldsymbol{\beta}_0} + (1-s)(\boldsymbol{\beta}_0 - \widehat{\boldsymbol{\beta}}).$$

The act of moving $\widehat{\boldsymbol{\beta}}$ towards $\boldsymbol{\beta}_0$ is called *shrinkage towards* $\boldsymbol{\beta}_0$. This turns out to be a good strategy when the prior guess $\boldsymbol{\beta}_0$ is reasonably good (Exercise 5.28).

5.7 Generalized linear model

Suppose the response in a regression problem is thought to have the normal distribution. This distribution has two parameters: mean and variance. The linear model assumes that a linear function of the regressors controls the mean, while the variance remains unaffected by the regressors. If the data indicates that these assumptions may not hold, we often try to make adjustments so that the assumptions can be justified. We have discussed in Section 5.3 several adjustments of this kind, such as transforming the regressors or the response, using weights and so on.

There may be an inherent contradiction in the assumptions when the response has some other distribution. For example, if the response is a count having the Poisson distribution, then its mean and variance happen to be the same parameter. It is impossible that the mean would be a linear combination of the regressors, while the variance would not depend on them! If the response is binary (taking the values 1 with probability π and 0 with probability $1-\pi$), then its mean and variance are π and $\pi(1-\pi)$, respectively. If the response has the exponential distribution, the standard deviation is equal to the mean. In all these cases, the mean and the variance are so inter-connected that it is impossible to make separate assumptions about them. Regression modelling in these situations has to take into account the peculiarities of these distributions. On the other hand, a linear combination of regressors is such a convenient way of aggregating their effects that one would like to retain this aspect in the model. A generalized linear model is built on these two principles.

Suppose the response y has the probability density function (or the probability mass function — in case it is discrete) f, which can be written as

$$f(y;\theta,\phi) = \exp\left[\frac{y\theta - \boldsymbol{b}(\theta)}{a(\phi)} + c(y,\phi)\right], \tag{5.29}$$

where $a(\cdot)$, $b(\cdot)$ and $c(\cdot)$ are known functions and θ and ϕ are parameters. A distribution that adheres to this specification is said to belong to the location-scale exponential family, with θ as the canonical parameter. Using the identities

$$E\left[\frac{\partial \log f(y;\theta,\phi)}{\partial\theta}\right]=0,\ E\left[\frac{\partial^2 \log f(y;\theta,\phi)}{\partial\theta^2}\right]+E\left[\left\{\frac{\partial \log f(y;\theta,\phi)}{\partial\theta}\right\}^2\right]=0,$$

we have

$$\begin{aligned} E(y) &= b'(\theta), \\ Var(y) &= b''(\theta)a(\phi). \end{aligned}$$

The *generalized linear model* (GLM) presumes that the conditional distribution of y given the regressors $x_1,\ldots,x_k$ is of the form (5.29) with the canonical parameter θ controlled by the regressors implicitly through the relation

$$\eta(b'(\theta)) = \eta(E[y|x_1,\ldots,x_k]) = \beta_0 + \sum_{j=1}^{k}\beta_j x_j, \tag{5.30}$$

where $\eta(\cdot)$ is a known function called the *link function*. In case $\eta(\cdot)$ is chosen such that $\eta(b'(\theta)) = \theta$, i.e. θ is equal to the linear combination in (5.30), this choice of $\eta(\cdot)$ is called the *canonical* link function.

Example 5.29. Suppose y has the normal distribution $N(\mu, \sigma^2)$. Its density can be written as

$$f(y; \mu, \sigma^2) = \exp\left[\frac{y\mu - \mu^2/2}{\sigma^2} - \frac{y^2}{2\sigma^2} - \frac{1}{2}\log(2\pi\sigma^2)\right],$$

which is of the form (5.29) with $\theta = \mu$, $b(\theta) = \theta^2/2$, $\phi = \sigma^2$, $a(\phi) = \phi$ and $c(y, \phi) = -\frac{1}{2}[y^2/\sigma^2 + \log(2\pi\sigma^2)]$. Therefore, $b'(\theta) = \theta$, which means the canonical link function is $\eta(x) = x$. With this link function, $E(y|x_1, \ldots, x_k) = \beta_0 + \sum_{j=1}^k \beta_j x_j$ and $Var(y|x_1, \ldots, x_k) = b''(\theta)a(\phi) = \sigma^2$. It follows that the GLM with canonical link function for normally distributed response is the well-known linear regression model. □

Example 5.30. (Loglinear model) Suppose y is Poisson with mean λ. Its probability mass function can be written as

$$f(y; \lambda) = \frac{e^{-\lambda}\lambda^y}{y!} = \exp\left[y \log \lambda - \lambda - \log y!\right],$$

which is of the form (5.29) with $\theta = \log \lambda$, $b(\theta) = \lambda = e^\theta$ and $c(y) = -\log y!$. There is no ϕ in this case. It follows that, $b'(\theta) = e^\theta = \lambda$, which means the canonical link function is

$$\eta(\lambda) = \log \lambda.$$

Therefore the GLM with canonical link function for Poisson response is

$$\log\left(E(y|x_1, \ldots, x_k)\right) = \beta_0 + \sum_{j=1}^k \beta_j x_j.$$

This regression model is known as the *loglinear model*. Under this model,

$$Var(y|x_1, \ldots, x_k) = \exp\left[\beta_0 + \sum_{j=1}^k \beta_j x_j\right].$$

According to the loglinear model, the log of the conditional mean of y is a linear function of the regressors. In particular, e^{β_i} is the factor of change in the mean of y when x_i increases by one unit, provided the other regressors remain the same. □

As seen in Example 5.29, the linear model (1.8), is a special case of the GLM with the ink function in (5.30) chosen as the identity function. While the GLM permits different choices of the link function, *some* form of this function has to be assumed. Further, the GLM requires a distributional assumption on the response, which is not necessary for the linear model (1.8). In this sense the GLM is more restrictive (i.e. less generalized) than the linear model!

5.7.1 *Maximum likelihood estimation*

Since the GLM comes with an assumption of the response distribution, parameters in this model can be estimated through the method of maximum likelihood. Suppose y_i is the response in the ith case and $x_{i1},\ldots,x_{ik}$ are the corresponding explanatory variables for $i=1,\ldots,n$ independent observations. The log-likelihood of the data under the model (5.29)–(5.30) is

$$\ell=\sum_{i=1}^{n}\frac{y_i\theta_i-b(\theta_i)}{a(\phi)}+\sum_{i=1}^{n}c(y_i,\phi)=\sum_{i=1}^{n}l_i+\sum_{i=1}^{n}c(y_i,\phi), \tag{5.31}$$

where $\theta_i=g(\boldsymbol{x}_i'\boldsymbol{\beta})$, $g(\cdot)$ is the inverse of $\eta(b'(\cdot))$, $\boldsymbol{x}_i=(1:x_{i1}:\cdots:x_{ik})'$ and $\boldsymbol{\beta}=(\beta_0:\beta_1:\cdots:\beta_k)'$. The MLE of $\boldsymbol{\beta}$ may be obtained by maximizing ℓ. If there is a parameter ϕ present in the model, it can be shown that the information matrix, when partitioned into parts corresponding to $\boldsymbol{\beta}$ and ϕ, is block diagonal. Thus, the estimation problem of $\boldsymbol{\beta}$ is decoupled from that of ϕ, and so one can obtain the MLE of $\boldsymbol{\beta}$ by maximizing $\sum_{i=1}^{n}l_i$ in (5.31).

A Newton-Raphson iterative scheme to obtain the MLE is to update the estimate at the tth stage of iteration as

$$\boldsymbol{\beta}^{(t+1)}=\boldsymbol{\beta}^{(t)}-\boldsymbol{H}^{-1}\left(\boldsymbol{\beta}^{(t)}\right)\boldsymbol{s}\left(\boldsymbol{\beta}^{(t)}\right), \tag{5.32}$$

where $\boldsymbol{s}(\cdot)$ and $\boldsymbol{H}(\cdot)$ are the gradient (score) vector and the Hessian matrix, respectively (see Section B.2 of Appendix B):

$$\begin{aligned}\boldsymbol{s}(\boldsymbol{\beta})&=\frac{\partial l}{\partial\boldsymbol{\beta}}=\frac{1}{a(\phi)}\sum_{i=1}^{n}\left[y_i-b'(g(\boldsymbol{x}_i'\boldsymbol{\beta}))\right]g'(\boldsymbol{x}_i'\boldsymbol{\beta})\boldsymbol{x}_i,\\ \boldsymbol{H}(\boldsymbol{\beta})&=\frac{\partial^2 l}{\partial\boldsymbol{\beta}\partial\boldsymbol{\beta}'}=-\frac{1}{a(\phi)}\sum_{i=1}^{n}b''(g(\boldsymbol{x}_i'\boldsymbol{\beta}))\{g'(\boldsymbol{x}_i'\boldsymbol{\beta})\}^2\boldsymbol{x}_i\boldsymbol{x}_i'\\ &\quad+\frac{1}{a(\phi)}\sum_{i=1}^{n}\left[\{y_i-b'(g(\boldsymbol{x}_i'\boldsymbol{\beta}))\}g''(\boldsymbol{x}_i'\boldsymbol{\beta})\right]\boldsymbol{x}_i\boldsymbol{x}_i'.\end{aligned}$$

Note that the expected value of the second sum is zero. By making use of this fact, one can use a simpler iterative method called *Fisher's scoring*, where $-\boldsymbol{H}(\cdot)$ is replaced by its expectation, or the Fisher information

$$\boldsymbol{I}(\boldsymbol{\beta}) = \frac{1}{a(\phi)} \sum_{i=1}^{n} b''(g(\boldsymbol{x}_i'\boldsymbol{\beta}))\{g'(\boldsymbol{x}_i'\boldsymbol{\beta})\}^2 \boldsymbol{x}_i \boldsymbol{x}_i'.$$

The iterative step in this method is

$$\boldsymbol{\beta}^{(t+1)} = \boldsymbol{\beta}^{(t)} + \boldsymbol{I}^{-1}\left(\boldsymbol{\beta}^{(t)}\right) \boldsymbol{s}\left(\boldsymbol{\beta}^{(t)}\right). \tag{5.33}$$

In the special case of canonical link function, $g(\cdot)$ is the identity function, and therefore the Hessian reduces to

$$\boldsymbol{H}(\boldsymbol{\beta}) = -\frac{1}{a(\phi)} \sum_{i=1}^{n} b''(\boldsymbol{x}_i'\boldsymbol{\beta}) \boldsymbol{x}_i \boldsymbol{x}_i'.$$

Therefore, in this case, Newton-Raphson iterations (5.32) and Fisher's scoring iterations (5.33) both simplify to the common form

$$\boldsymbol{\beta}^{(t+1)} = \boldsymbol{\beta}^{(t)} + \left[\sum_{i=1}^{n} b''(\boldsymbol{x}_i'\boldsymbol{\beta}) \boldsymbol{x}_i \boldsymbol{x}_i'\right]^{-1} \left[\sum_{i=1}^{n} [y_i - b'(\boldsymbol{x}_i'\boldsymbol{\beta})]\, \boldsymbol{x}_i\right]\Bigg|_{\boldsymbol{\beta}=\boldsymbol{\beta}^{(t)}}.$$

Suppose

$$\boldsymbol{X} = \begin{pmatrix} \boldsymbol{x}_1 \\ \boldsymbol{x}_2 \\ \vdots \\ \boldsymbol{x}_n \end{pmatrix}, \qquad \boldsymbol{V}(\boldsymbol{\beta}) = \begin{pmatrix} b''(\boldsymbol{x}_1'\boldsymbol{\beta}) & 0 & \cdots & 0 \\ 0 & b''(\boldsymbol{x}_2'\boldsymbol{\beta}) & \cdots & 0 \\ \vdots & \vdots & \ddots & \vdots \\ 0 & 0 & \cdots & b''(\boldsymbol{x}_n'\boldsymbol{\beta}) \end{pmatrix}^{-1}.$$

Then the above updating equation can be written as

$$\begin{aligned}
&\boldsymbol{\beta}^{(t+1)} \\
&= \boldsymbol{\beta}^{(t)} + \left[\boldsymbol{X}'\boldsymbol{V}^{-1}\left(\boldsymbol{\beta}^{(t)}\right)\boldsymbol{X}\right]^{-1} \left[\sum_{i=1}^{n} \left[y_i - b'(\boldsymbol{x}_i'\boldsymbol{\beta}^{(t)})\right] \boldsymbol{x}_i\right] \\
&= \left[\boldsymbol{X}'\boldsymbol{V}^{-1}\left(\boldsymbol{\beta}^{(t)}\right)\boldsymbol{X}\right]^{-1} \left[\boldsymbol{X}'\boldsymbol{V}^{-1}\left(\boldsymbol{\beta}^{(t)}\right)\boldsymbol{X}\boldsymbol{\beta}^{(t)} + \sum_{i=1}^{n} \left[y_i - b'(\boldsymbol{x}_i'\boldsymbol{\beta}^{(t)})\right] \boldsymbol{x}_i\right] \\
&= \left[\boldsymbol{X}'\boldsymbol{V}^{-1}\left(\boldsymbol{\beta}^{(t)}\right)\boldsymbol{X}\right]^{-1} \boldsymbol{X}'\boldsymbol{V}^{-1}\left(\boldsymbol{\beta}^{(t)}\right) \widetilde{\boldsymbol{y}}\left(\boldsymbol{\beta}^{(t)}\right)
\end{aligned}$$

where

$$\widetilde{\boldsymbol{y}}(\boldsymbol{\beta}) = \left(\boldsymbol{x}_1'\boldsymbol{\beta} + \frac{y_1 - b'(\boldsymbol{x}_1'\boldsymbol{\beta})}{b''(\boldsymbol{x}_1'\boldsymbol{\beta})} : \cdots : \boldsymbol{x}_n'\boldsymbol{\beta} + \frac{y_n - b'(\boldsymbol{x}_n'\boldsymbol{\beta})}{b''(\boldsymbol{x}_n'\boldsymbol{\beta})}\right)'.$$

The final version of the updating equation has the form of a WLSE. Since $b'(\boldsymbol{x}_i'\boldsymbol{\beta})$ is the conditional mean of y_i, the ith element of $\widetilde{\boldsymbol{y}}(\boldsymbol{\beta})$ may be interpreted as a linear approximation of $b'^{-1}(y_i)$ obtained through a Taylor series expansion at the point $b'(\boldsymbol{x}_i'\boldsymbol{\beta})$. Thus, every step of the iteration amounts to computing a WLSE from a linearized version of the data.

The MLE $\widehat{\boldsymbol{\beta}}$ is obtained through convergence of the above numerical optimization. Under certain regularity conditions (see Borokov, 1999), the distribution of $\sqrt{n}(\widehat{\boldsymbol{\beta}} - \boldsymbol{\beta})$ converges to a multivariate normal distribution with zero mean and dispersion matrix $n\boldsymbol{I}^{-1}(\boldsymbol{\beta})$. A consistent estimate of the dispersion of $\widehat{\boldsymbol{\beta}}$ is $\boldsymbol{I}^{-1}(\widehat{\boldsymbol{\beta}})$, which is obtained as a byproduct of the iterative procedure. This matrix can be used to test for the significance of regression parameters or to construct confidence intervals.

5.7.2 *Logistic regression*

Consider a binary response y with $P(y=1) = \pi$, $P(y=0) = 1-\pi$. Its probability mass function can be written as

$$f(y;\pi) = \pi^y(1-\pi)^{1-y} = \exp\left[y\log\left(\frac{\pi}{1-\pi}\right) + \log(1-\pi)\right],$$

which is of the form (5.29) with $\theta = \log\left(\frac{\pi}{1-\pi}\right)$, $b(\theta) = -\log(1-\pi) = \log(1+e^\theta)$ and $c(y) = 0$. There is no ϕ in this special case, and so $a(\phi) = 1$. It follows that, $b'(\theta) = e^\theta/(1+e^\theta)$, which means the canonical link function is

$$\eta(\pi) = \log\left(\frac{\pi}{1-\pi}\right).$$

This function is also called the logit link. It follows that the GLM with canonical link function for binary response is

$$\log\left(\frac{E(y|x_1,\ldots,x_k)}{1-E(y|x_1,\ldots,x_k)}\right) = \beta_0 + \sum_{j=1}^{k}\beta_j x_j, \tag{5.34}$$

which can be alternatively written as

$$E(y|x_1,\ldots,x_k) = \frac{\exp(\beta_0 + \sum_{j=1}^k \beta_j x_j)}{1+\exp(\beta_0 + \sum_{j=1}^k \beta_j x_j)}. \tag{5.35}$$

These two equations are equivalent descriptions of the logistic regression model. Under this model,

$$Var(y|x_1,\ldots,x_k) = b''(\theta)a(\phi) = \frac{\exp\left(\beta_0 + \sum_{j=1}^k \beta_j x_j\right)}{\left[1+\exp\left(\beta_0 + \sum_{j=1}^k \beta_j x_j\right)\right]^2}.$$

The conditional mean of y is also the conditional probability that y is equal to one. For all values of $\boldsymbol{x}'\boldsymbol{\beta}$, the right-hand side of (5.35) is a number between 0 and 1, which is an appropriate description of a probability. Further, the right-hand side is an increasing function of $\boldsymbol{x}'\boldsymbol{\beta}$. The right-hand side is close to one when $\boldsymbol{x}'\boldsymbol{\beta}$ is a large positive number and close to zero when $\boldsymbol{x}'\boldsymbol{\beta}$ is a large negative number. This type of function is known as a *sigmoid* function.

The ratio $\pi/(1-\pi)$ is called the *odds* of the event $y = 1$. The model (5.34) can be written as

$$\log\left(\frac{P(y=1|x_1,\ldots,x_k)}{P(y=0|x_1,\ldots,x_k)}\right) = \beta_0 + \sum_{j=1}^{k}\beta_j x_j,$$

which says that the log of the conditional odds of $y = 1$ is a linear function of the regressors. In particular, β_j is the amount of increase in log-odds of $y = 1$ when x_j increases by one unit, while the other regressors are unchanged. The corresponding change in the odds of $y = 1$ is by the factor e^{β_j}. This factor can also be interpreted as the odds ratio for $x_j + 1$ and x_j when the other regressors are held fixed. The interpretability of the regression coefficients makes the logistic regression model an attractive option for binary response.

A related regression model for binary response is the *probit regression model*, where the link function is the inverse of the standard normal distribution function $\Phi(\cdot)$. Under this model, the binary response y has conditional mean and variance given by

$$E(y|x_1,\ldots,x_k) = \Phi\left(\beta_0 + \sum_{j=1}^{k}\beta_j x_j\right),$$

$$Var(y|x_1,\ldots,x_k) = \Phi\left(\beta_0 + \sum_{j=1}^{k}\beta_j x_j\right)\left[1 - \Phi\left(\beta_0 + \sum_{j=1}^{k}\beta_j x_j\right)\right].$$

Even though the link function $\Phi^{-1}(\cdot)$ is not the canonical link for binary response, this model is popular because of its simplicity and interpretability. A key interpretation is given by postulating that there is an unobserved random variable or *latent variable* z, having the standard normal distribution, such that for the given values of the regressors,

$$y = \begin{cases} 1 & \text{if } z \le \beta_0 + \sum_{j=1}^{k}\beta_j x_j, \\ 0 & \text{otherwise.} \end{cases}$$

It can be easily verified that the variable y synthesized in this manner would follow the probit regression model.

It should be noted that the logistic regression model can also be postulated to arise from a latent variable formulation, where the latent variable z has the logistic distribution, i.e. $P(z \leq u) = e^u/(1+e^u)$.

Turning to estimation under the logistic regression model, we observe that the log-likelihood (5.31) in the case of logistic regression reduces to

$$\ell = \sum_{i=1}^{n} \left[y_i \boldsymbol{x}_i'\boldsymbol{\beta} - \log(1+\exp(\boldsymbol{x}_i'\boldsymbol{\beta}))\right].$$

The MLE may be obtained by maximizing ℓ through the series of iterations

$$\boldsymbol{\beta}^{(t+1)} = \left[\boldsymbol{X}'\boldsymbol{V}^{-1}\left(\boldsymbol{\beta}^{(t)}\right)\boldsymbol{X}\right]^{-1}\boldsymbol{X}'\boldsymbol{V}^{-1}\left(\boldsymbol{\beta}^{(t)}\right)\widetilde{\boldsymbol{y}}\left(\boldsymbol{\beta}^{(t)}\right),$$

where

$$\boldsymbol{V}(\boldsymbol{\beta}) = \begin{pmatrix} \frac{\exp(\boldsymbol{x}_1'\boldsymbol{\beta})}{[1+\exp(\boldsymbol{x}_1'\boldsymbol{\beta})]^2} & \cdots & 0 \\ \vdots & \ddots & \vdots \\ 0 & \cdots & \frac{\exp(\boldsymbol{x}_n'\boldsymbol{\beta})}{[1+\exp(\boldsymbol{x}_n'\boldsymbol{\beta})]^2} \end{pmatrix}^{-1},$$

and

$$\widetilde{\boldsymbol{y}}(\boldsymbol{\beta}) = \begin{pmatrix} \boldsymbol{x}_1'\boldsymbol{\beta} + y_1\exp(-\boldsymbol{x}_1'\boldsymbol{\beta})[1+\exp(\boldsymbol{x}_1'\boldsymbol{\beta})]^2 - [1+\exp(\boldsymbol{x}_1'\boldsymbol{\beta})] \\ \vdots \\ \boldsymbol{x}_n'\boldsymbol{\beta} + y_n\exp(-\boldsymbol{x}_n'\boldsymbol{\beta})[1+\exp(\boldsymbol{x}_n'\boldsymbol{\beta})]^2 - [1+\exp(\boldsymbol{x}_n'\boldsymbol{\beta})] \end{pmatrix}.$$

The estimated (asymptotic) dispersion matrix of $\widehat{\boldsymbol{\beta}}$ is $[X'\boldsymbol{V}^{-1}(\widehat{\boldsymbol{\beta}})\boldsymbol{X}]^{-1}$.

Example 5.31. (O-ring distress in space shuttles) Table 5.11 shows data relating to thermal distress in rubber O-rings used to seal adjacent sections of the body of booster rockets used in the first 23 flights of the space shuttle programme. For each mission, there were two booster rockets and three O-rings in each rocket. The last six columns correspond to the six O-rings of a particular mission, numbered serially. Evidence of some distress is recorded as 1, while absence of such evidence is recorded as zero. The ambient temperature at the time of launch (in °F) and pressure rating (in psi) of the rings are suspected to have some effect on the propensity of distress. These data had been considered by a technical team on the eve of the catastrophic flight of the shuttle *Challenger*, which was the 24th mission of the programme. The accident had later been linked to the thermal failure of a particular O-ring. All the earlier missions had taken place at

Table 5.11 O-ring thermal distress data on space shuttle flights prior to *Challenger* accident (data frame `orings` of R package `DPpackage`)

Flight number	Temperature (°F)	Pressure (psi)	Whether there was thermal distress in					
			Ring 1	Ring 2	Ring 3	Ring 4	Ring 5	Ring 6
1	66	50	0	0	0	0	0	0
2	70	50	1	0	0	0	0	0
3	69	50	0	0	0	0	0	0
4	68	50	0	0	0	0	0	0
5	67	50	0	0	0	0	0	0
6	72	50	0	0	0	0	0	0
7	73	100	0	0	0	0	0	0
8	70	100	0	0	0	0	0	0
9	57	200	1	0	0	0	0	0
10	63	200	1	0	0	0	0	0
11	70	200	1	0	0	0	0	0
12	78	200	0	0	0	0	0	0
13	67	200	0	0	0	0	0	0
14	53	200	1	1	0	0	0	0
15	67	200	0	0	0	0	0	0
16	75	200	0	0	0	0	0	0
17	70	200	0	0	0	0	0	0
18	81	200	0	0	0	0	0	0
19	76	200	0	0	0	0	0	0
20	79	200	0	0	0	0	0	0
21	75	200	0	0	0	0	0	0
22	76	200	0	0	0	0	0	0
23	58	200	1	0	0	0	0	0

much higher atmospheric temperature than the temperature (31°F) that had been forecast for the morning of the fateful launch. The night before, the technical team had tried to evaluate the prospect of thermal failure of O-rings and debated about whether to proceed with the launch.

A linkage between the probability of thermal distress and the explanatory variables (temperature and pressure) is now explored through logistic regression analysis of the data. By pooling all the O-rings of all the flights, we have data on 138 cases. After a preliminary analysis under the logistic regression model, the effect of pressure was found to be insignificant (p-value 0.76065). Subsequently, the occurrence of thermal distress (y) was regressed on temperature (x) alone. The fitted model (with MLE found through Fisher's scoring iterations) was

$$\log\left(\frac{P(y=1|x)}{P(y=0|x)}\right) = 8.817 - 0.1795x.$$

The p-values of the intercept and the effect of temperature were 0.0145 and 0.0021, respectively. Thus, there is a significant effect of temperature. Specifically, for every degree Fahrenheit rise in temperature, the odds of O-ring distress would reduce by an estimated factor of $e^{-0.1795}$ or 0.8357. Thus, had the mission been postponed till the temperature rose, there would have been substantial reduction of risk.

The R code given below was used to invoke the data and obtain the fitted models.

```
library(DPpackage)
data(orings)
analysis <- glm(ThermalDistress~Temperature+Pressure,
 data = orings, family = binomial(link = "logit"))
summary(analysis)
analysis <- glm(ThermalDistress~Temperature,
 data = orings, family = binomial(link = "logit"))
summary(analysis)
```

If the fitted probability is extrapolated to the unusually low temperature of the morning of the launch (31°F), using the following R code, one obtains the graph shown in Figure 5.21.

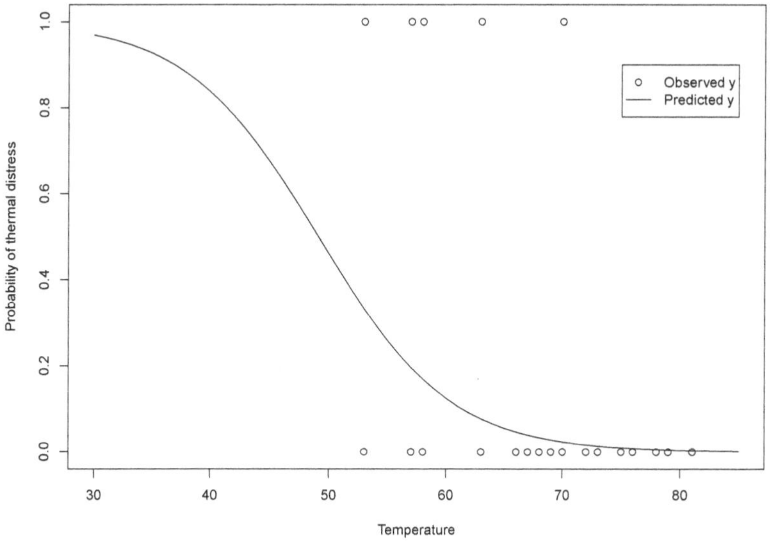

Fig. 5.21 Observed and predicted thermal distress in O-rings at different temperatures

```
attach(orings)
plot(Temperature,ThermalDistress,xlim=c(30,85),
    ylab="Probability of thermal distress")
tempgrid <- data.frame(Temperature = 30:85)
predprob <- predict(analysis, newdata = tempgrid,
 type = "response")
lines(30:85,predprob)
legend(75,0.9,c("Observed y","Predicted y"),lty=c(NA,1),pch=c(1,NA))
detach(orings)
```

Thus, according to a logistic regression analysis, the risk taken by the technical team (which did not include a statistician) had been unnecessarily high. See Dalal et al. (1987) for a more elaborate analysis of the pre-accident data. □

See McCullagh and Nelder (1989) or Dobson and Barnett (2018) for more information on the generalized linear model and inference related to it.

5.8 Complements/Exercises

Exercises with solutions given in Appendix C

5.1 For the models of Examples 5.3 and 5.4, obtain the theoretical expressions for the regression of y on x_1 and relate them with the empirical findings reported in those examples.

5.2 Consider the BLUE $\widehat{\boldsymbol{p}'\boldsymbol{\beta}}$ of a single estimable LPF $\boldsymbol{p}'\boldsymbol{\beta}$ in the linear model $(\boldsymbol{y}, \boldsymbol{X\beta}, \sigma^2\boldsymbol{I})$, and the corresponding 'subset estimator' $\widehat{\boldsymbol{p}'\boldsymbol{\beta}}_s$ obtained from the model $(\boldsymbol{y}, \boldsymbol{X}_1\boldsymbol{\beta}_1, \sigma^2\boldsymbol{I})$. Assume that $\boldsymbol{\beta}_2$ is estimable, its BLUE under the full model is $\widehat{\boldsymbol{\beta}}_2$, and the dispersion matrix of this BLUE is positive definite.

(a) If $\boldsymbol{p}_1$ and $\boldsymbol{p}_2$ are sub-vectors of $\boldsymbol{p}$ such that $\boldsymbol{p}'\boldsymbol{\beta} = \boldsymbol{p}_1'\boldsymbol{\beta}_1 + \boldsymbol{p}_2'\boldsymbol{\beta}_2$, show that $\boldsymbol{p}_1'\boldsymbol{\beta}_1$ is estimable in both the models.

(b) Show that $D(\widehat{\boldsymbol{\beta}}_2) = \sigma^2[\boldsymbol{X}_2'(\boldsymbol{I} - \boldsymbol{P}_{X_1})\boldsymbol{X}_2]^{-1}$.

(c) Show that $Cov(\widehat{\boldsymbol{p}'\boldsymbol{\beta}}, \widehat{\boldsymbol{\beta}}_2) = [\boldsymbol{p}_2' - \boldsymbol{p}_1'(\boldsymbol{X}_1'\boldsymbol{X}_1)^-\boldsymbol{X}_1'\boldsymbol{X}_2]D(\widehat{\boldsymbol{\beta}}_2)$.

(d) Using (7.18), show that the subset estimator $\widehat{\boldsymbol{p}'\boldsymbol{\beta}}_s$ has smaller MSE than the BLUE $\widehat{\boldsymbol{p}'\boldsymbol{\beta}}$ if and only if
$$\sigma^2 \geq (\boldsymbol{q}'\boldsymbol{\beta}_2)^2/[\boldsymbol{q}'(\boldsymbol{X}_2'(\boldsymbol{I} - \boldsymbol{P}_{X_1})\boldsymbol{X}_2)^{-1}\boldsymbol{q}].$$

(e) Explain how the vector $\boldsymbol{q} = \boldsymbol{p}_2 - \boldsymbol{X}_2'\boldsymbol{X}_1(\boldsymbol{X}_1'\boldsymbol{X}_1)^-\boldsymbol{p}_1$ can be interpreted as the prediction error for $\boldsymbol{p}_2$ in a suitable model. Interpret the matrix $\boldsymbol{X}_2'(\boldsymbol{I} - \boldsymbol{P}_{X_1})\boldsymbol{X}_2$ in terms of this model.

5.3 Assuming normal distribution of model errors, derive an expression for the probability that adjusted R-square for a subset model is negative. By analysing this expression, explain why the probability should be small unless $\|(\boldsymbol{I} - \boldsymbol{P}_1)X\beta\|^2/\sigma^2$ is small.

5.4 Show that if a subset model of size p happens to be correct for the given response, then the expected value of $\widehat{\sigma^2}C_p$ is $p\sigma^2$. [For this reason, some books (e.g., Gujarati and Sangeetha, 2007) recommend the choice of a subset that has value of C_p closest to p.]

5.5 Show that the R_a^2 criterion cannot give smaller 'best' subset than Mallows's C_p.

5.6 Consider AIC for variable selection in multiple linear regression with normal errors, where all the regression parameters are estimable under the full model.

(a) Show that AIC for any given subset of regressors simplifies to

$$AIC_p = n\log\left(\frac{1}{n}\sum_{i=1}^{n}(y_i - \widehat{y}_i)^2 \Big|_{\text{subset model}}\right) + 2p + n + n\log(2\pi).$$

(b) Suppose the likelihood in AIC (5.3) is maximized with the error variance σ^2 held fixed, and then σ^2 is replaced by the unbiased estimate $\widehat{\sigma^2}$ obtained from the full model (irrespective of the candidate subset for which AIC_p is computed). Show that using this modified version of AIC is equivalent to using Mallows's C_p. [Sometimes this 'equivalence' is described without mention of the modification (see, e.g. the abstract of Boisbunon et al., 2014), which can be misleading.]

5.7 Show that the leverage of an observation in the linear model $(\boldsymbol{y}, \boldsymbol{X\beta}, \sigma^2\boldsymbol{I})$ is equal to 0 if and only if this observation is a linear zero function.

5.8 Show that the leverage of an observation in the linear model $(\boldsymbol{y}, \boldsymbol{X\beta}, \sigma^2\boldsymbol{I})$ is equal to 1 if and only if this observation is itself the BLUE of its expected value.

5.9 Consider the linear model with homoscedastic errors. Show that if the leverage of the ith observation is 1, the model (or a possibly reparametrized version of it) is of the form $(\boldsymbol{y}, \boldsymbol{Z\beta} + \boldsymbol{u}_i\gamma + \sigma^2\boldsymbol{I})$, where $\boldsymbol{u}_i$ is the ith column of the identity matrix of appropriate size, or it. Also show that in such a case, the ith row of the design matrix is not a linear combination of the other rows.

5.10 Show that if the intercept term in the linear regression model is not excluded, the ith leverage can be written as in (5.4).

5.11 Consider the linear model $(\boldsymbol{y}, \boldsymbol{X\beta}, \sigma^2\boldsymbol{I})$ having n observations and k components of the parameter $\boldsymbol{\beta}$. If h_i and e_i are the ith leverage and ith residual, respectively, show that

$$0 \le h_i + e_i^2/\boldsymbol{e}'\boldsymbol{e} \le 1.$$

(Thus, fitted values of observations with leverage close to 1 cannot be very different from the observed value of the response.)

5.12 Show that in the linear model, the inclusion of a new observation does not increase the leverage of the existing observations.

5.13 Prove that if a row or the negative of it occurs r times in the model matrix, then the corresponding leverage is less than or equal to $1/r$.

5.14 (a) Show that the ith deleted residual $e_{i(-i)}$ described in Remark 5.10 is a constant multiple of the ith residual e_i.
(b) Show that the ith deleted studentized residual described in Remark 5.10 is the same as the ith studentized residual t_i, defined in (5.8).

5.15 Consider the component plus residual plot for the last variable in the model $(\boldsymbol{y}, \boldsymbol{X\beta}, \sigma^2\boldsymbol{I})$, i.e. the plot of $\boldsymbol{e} + \widehat{\beta}_k\boldsymbol{x}_k$ vs. $\boldsymbol{x}_k$, where $\boldsymbol{e}$ is the residual vector, $\boldsymbol{x}_k$ is the last column of $\boldsymbol{X}$ and $\widehat{\beta}_k$ is the least squares estimator of the last regressor. Assume that the model contains an intercept.

(a) Show that the least squares fitted line through the scatter of this plot has intercept 0 and slope equal to $\widehat{\beta}_k$.
(b) Show that the least squares residuals for the scatter of this plot are equal to the corresponding residuals of the given model.
(c) Are the usual estimators of σ^2 obtained from the models $(\boldsymbol{e} + \widehat{\beta}_k\boldsymbol{x}_k, \boldsymbol{x}_k\beta_k, \sigma^2\boldsymbol{I})$ and $(\boldsymbol{y}, \boldsymbol{X\beta}, \sigma^2\boldsymbol{I})$ identical? Explain.

5.16 Consider the added variable plot for the last variable in the model $(\boldsymbol{y}, \boldsymbol{X\beta}, \sigma^2\boldsymbol{I})$, i.e. the plot of $\boldsymbol{y}_{res}$ vs. $\boldsymbol{x}_{k,res}$, where $\boldsymbol{X} = (\boldsymbol{X}_{(k-1)} : \boldsymbol{x}_k)$, $\boldsymbol{\beta} = (\boldsymbol{\beta}'_{(k-1)} : \beta_k)'$, $\boldsymbol{y}_{res} = (\boldsymbol{I} - \boldsymbol{P}_{X_{(k-1)}})\boldsymbol{y}$ and $\boldsymbol{x}_{k,res} = (\boldsymbol{I} - \boldsymbol{P}_{X_{(k-1)}})\boldsymbol{x}_k$. Assume that the model contains an intercept.

(a) Show that the least squares fitted line through the scatter of this plot has intercept 0 and slope equal to $\widehat{\beta}_k$, the BLUE of β_k.
(b) Show that the least squares residuals for the scatter of this plot are equal to the corresponding residuals of the given model.
(c) Are the usual estimators of σ^2 obtained from the models $(\boldsymbol{y}_{res}, \boldsymbol{x}_{k,res}\beta_k, \sigma^2\boldsymbol{I})$ and $(\boldsymbol{y}, \boldsymbol{X\beta}, \sigma^2\boldsymbol{I})$ identical? Explain.

5.17 For the linear model $(\boldsymbol{y}, \boldsymbol{X\beta}, \sigma^2\boldsymbol{V})$, where $\boldsymbol{V}$ is a diagonal matrix with positive diagonal elements $1/w_1, \ldots, 1/w_n$, show that fitted values of $\boldsymbol{y}$ corresponding to the weighted least squares estimator of $\boldsymbol{\beta}$ (obtained by minimizing $\sum_{i=1}^n w_i(y_i - \boldsymbol{x}_i'\boldsymbol{\beta})^2$) cannot have larger sample correlation with $\boldsymbol{y}$ than the fitted values corresponding to the OLSE.

5.18 Can the fitted values obtained from the WLS analysis of Exercise 5.17 produce a larger value of the R^2 defined in (5.11) than the fitted values obtained from the OLS analysis?

5.19 The Durbin-Watson test mentioned in Section 5.3.3 is in fact an adaptation (to residuals of a linear model) of the original test

$$DW = \frac{\sum_{i=1}^{n-1}(\varepsilon_{i+1} - \varepsilon_i)^2}{\sum_{i=1}^n \varepsilon_i^2}$$

defined for successive samples of a time series $\varepsilon_1, \ldots, \varepsilon_n$.

(a) Suppose the time series follows the model (1.13) with $p = 1$ (i.e. the AR(1) model) with the AR parameter ϕ_1 $(-1 < \phi_1 < 1)$, and the statistic converges in probability to the ratio of the respective expected values of the numerator and denominator. Find this limit. What happens when $\phi_1 = 0$?

(b) Let the statistic DW be computed from the least squares residuals of the model (5.12). Assuming that all the leverages are smaller than c/n for some positive constant c, show that the result of part (a) continues to hold. [Thus, the Durbin-Watson statistic can be used to detect serial correlation among the model errors.]

5.20 Verify the simplified expression of $DFFITS_i$ given in (5.17).

5.21 Verify the simplified expression of $COOKD_i$ given in (5.19).

5.22 Suppose $\boldsymbol{X} = (\boldsymbol{x}_{(0)} : \cdots : \boldsymbol{x}_{(k)})$ where $\boldsymbol{x}_{(0)} = \boldsymbol{1}$, $\boldsymbol{D}$ is a diagonal matrix with $\|\boldsymbol{x}_{(j+1)}\|$ in the jth diagonal position and $\boldsymbol{X}_s = \boldsymbol{XD}^{-1}$, that is, the columns of $\boldsymbol{X}_s$ have unit norm and are proportional to the columns of $\boldsymbol{X}$. Let $\boldsymbol{X}$ have full column rank.

(a) Show that $IVIF_j$ is the $(j+1)$th diagonal element of the matrix $(\boldsymbol{X}_s'\boldsymbol{X}_s)^{-1}$.

(b) Show that $IVIF_j \geq 1$ for $j = 0, \ldots, k$.

(c) If $p = k + 1$, $\lambda_1 \geq \cdots \geq \lambda_p$ are the eigenvalues of $\boldsymbol{X}_s'\boldsymbol{X}_s$ and $\boldsymbol{v}_1, \ldots, \boldsymbol{v}_p$ are the corresponding eigenvectors, show that

$$IVIF_j = \sum_{i=1}^p \frac{v_{i(j+1)}^2}{\lambda_i}, \quad j = 0, \ldots, k,$$

v_{ij} being the ith element of $\boldsymbol{v}_j$, $i, j = 1, \ldots, p$.

5.23 (a) Show that $\pi_{1j} \le 1/IVIF_{j-1}$, that is, if $IVIF_{j-1}$ is large then π_{1j} is small (other variance proportions can be large).

(b) Show that

$$IVIF_j \le \kappa^2 \le (k+1)\sum_{j=1}^{k+1} IVIF_j.$$

[Thus, κ is large if and only if at least one of the variance inflation factors is large.]

5.24 If the matrix $\boldsymbol{X}$ in the linear model $(\boldsymbol{y}, \boldsymbol{X\beta}, \sigma^2\boldsymbol{I})$ has full column rank, show that the principal components estimator of $\boldsymbol{\beta}$ has smaller magnitude than the least squares estimator.

5.25 Let $\boldsymbol{D}_r$ be the dispersion matrix of the ridge estimator $(\boldsymbol{X}'\boldsymbol{X} + r\boldsymbol{I})^{-1}\boldsymbol{X}'\boldsymbol{y}$ in the linear model $(\boldsymbol{y}, \boldsymbol{X\beta}, \sigma^2\boldsymbol{I})$, r being a positive number. Show that $\boldsymbol{D}_{r_1} > \boldsymbol{D}_{r_2}$ in the sense of the Löwner order whenever $0 \le r_1 < r_2$.

5.26 Consider the linear model $(\boldsymbol{y}, \boldsymbol{X\beta}, \sigma^2\boldsymbol{I})$ where the matrix $\boldsymbol{X}$ has full column rank. Let b be a positive number which is smaller than $\|(\boldsymbol{X}'\boldsymbol{X})^{-1}\boldsymbol{X}'\boldsymbol{y}\|$. The purpose of this exercise is to find an estimator of $\boldsymbol{\beta}$ which minimizes $\|\boldsymbol{y} - \boldsymbol{X\beta}\|^2$ subject to the restriction $\|\boldsymbol{\beta}\| \le b^2$.

(a) Show that subject to the restriction $\|\boldsymbol{\beta}\| = b^2$, the sum of squares $\|\boldsymbol{y} - \boldsymbol{X\beta}\|^2$ is minimized by the estimator $\widehat{\boldsymbol{\beta}}_r = (\boldsymbol{X}'\boldsymbol{X} + r\boldsymbol{I})^{-1}\boldsymbol{X}'\boldsymbol{y}$, where r is such that $\|\widehat{\boldsymbol{\beta}}_r\|^2 = b^2$.

(b) Show that $\|\boldsymbol{y} - \boldsymbol{X}\widehat{\boldsymbol{\beta}}_r\|^2$ is an increasing function of r.

(c) Show that r is a decreasing function of b.

(d) Show that the estimator described in part (a) indeed minimizes $\|\boldsymbol{y} - \boldsymbol{X\beta}\|^2$ subject to the restriction $\boldsymbol{\beta}'\boldsymbol{\beta} \le b^2$.

5.27 Let the matrix $\boldsymbol{X}$ in the linear model $(\boldsymbol{y}, \boldsymbol{X\beta}, \sigma^2\boldsymbol{I})$ have full column rank.

(a) Find a necessary and sufficient condition on $\boldsymbol{\beta}$ and σ^2 so that the ridge estimator $\widehat{\boldsymbol{\beta}}_r$ has smaller MSE matrix than the BLUE, in the sense of the Löwner order, for *any* $r > 0$.

(b) Find a necessary and sufficient condition on $\boldsymbol{\beta}$ and σ^2 so that the shrinkage estimator $\widehat{\boldsymbol{\beta}}_s$ has smaller MSE matrix than the BLUE, in the sense of the Löwner order, for *any* $s \in (0, 1)$.

(c) Find a necessary and sufficient condition on $\boldsymbol{\beta}$ and σ^2 so that the trivial estimator $\boldsymbol{0}$ has smaller MSE matrix than the BLUE, in the sense of the Löwner order.

(d) Comment on the results of parts (a)–(c).

5.28 Find the necessary and sufficient condition for the estimator $\widehat{\boldsymbol{\beta}}_{s,\beta_0} = \widehat{\boldsymbol{\beta}}+(1-s)(\boldsymbol{\beta}_0-\widehat{\boldsymbol{\beta}})$ in the model $(\boldsymbol{y}, \boldsymbol{X\beta}, \sigma^2\boldsymbol{I})$ (where $\boldsymbol{X}$ has full column rank) to have a smaller mean square error matrix than the least squares estimator, $\widehat{\boldsymbol{\beta}}$. Find a condition on $\boldsymbol{\beta}$ and σ^2 that would ensure this dominance for *all* values of s.

5.29 Consider the BLUE ($\widehat{\boldsymbol{A\beta}}$) and the shrinkage estimator ($\widehat{\boldsymbol{A\beta}}_s = s\widehat{\boldsymbol{A\beta}}$) of an estimable LPF $\boldsymbol{A\beta}$ in the model $(\boldsymbol{y}, \boldsymbol{X\beta}, \sigma^2\boldsymbol{V})$.

(a) Find a necessary and sufficient condition for $MSE(\boldsymbol{X}\widehat{\boldsymbol{\beta}}) \geq MSE(\boldsymbol{X}\widehat{\boldsymbol{\beta}}_s)$ in the sense of the Löwner order.

(b) Find a necessary and sufficient condition for the above order to hold for *all* values of s.

(c) Find a necessary and sufficient condition for the dominance of $MSE(\widehat{\boldsymbol{A\beta}}_s)$ by $MSE(\widehat{\boldsymbol{A\beta}})$ for all estimable $\boldsymbol{A\beta}$.

(d) Simplify the above conditions for the case $\boldsymbol{V} = \boldsymbol{I}$.

5.30 Suppose there is a single binary predictor x for a binary response y. Show that the logistic and the probit regression models of y given x are reparametrizations of one another. Would the likelihood ratio test for the significance of the coefficient of x would be the same under either model? What about the test based on normal approximation of the estimated coefficient of x?

Additional exercises

5.31 Simulate 50 data points from the model $y = 2 + 4x - x^2 + \varepsilon$, where $x \sim N(2,1)$ and $\varepsilon|x \sim N(0,1)$. Fit the simple linear regression model $y = \beta_0 + \beta_1 x + \varepsilon$ to your data, and comment on the nature of fit.

5.32 Fit the fourth degree polynomial regression model $y = \beta_0 + \beta_1 x + \beta_2 x^2 + \beta_3 x^3 + \beta_4 x^4 + \varepsilon$ to the data generated in Problem 5.31. Is the fit adequate? Comment on the significance of the regression coefficients.

5.33 Fit the fourth degree polynomial regression model $y = \beta_0 + \beta_1 x + \beta_2 x^2 + \beta_3 x^3 + \beta_4 x^4 + \varepsilon$ to the data generated in Problem 5.31, by including successively higher order terms sequentially, while checking for the significance of the coefficient of the latest term at each step.

5.34 Consider the model $(\boldsymbol{y}, \boldsymbol{X\beta}, \sigma^2\boldsymbol{I})$ where $\boldsymbol{\beta} = (\beta_0 : \beta_1 : \beta_2 : \beta_3)'$, and

$$\boldsymbol{X}' = \begin{pmatrix} \boldsymbol{x}_0' \\ \boldsymbol{x}_1' \\ \boldsymbol{x}_2' \\ \boldsymbol{x}_3' \end{pmatrix} = \begin{pmatrix} 1 & 1 & 1 & 1 & 1 & 1 & 1 & 1 \\ 1 & 1 & 1 & 1 & -1 & -1 & -1 & -1 \\ 1 & 1 & -1 & 1 & 1 & 1 & -1 & -1 \\ 1 & -1 & 1 & -1 & 1 & -1 & 1 & -1 \end{pmatrix}.$$

The objective of this study is to determine whether the subset model consisting only of $\boldsymbol{x}_0$ and $\boldsymbol{x}_1$ will be more suitable than the full model for the purpose of estimating certain LPFs.

(a) Will the 'subset estimator' of $\beta_3 - \beta_0 - \beta_1 - \beta_2$ have smaller MSE than the BLUE from the full model, if the true parameter values are such that $\beta_2 = \beta_3$?

(b) Will the 'subset estimator' of $\beta_1 - \beta_0 - \beta_2 - \beta_3$ have smaller MSE than the BLUE from the full model, if the true parameter values are such that $\beta_2 = \beta_3$?

(c) Can you give an intuitive explanation of the discrepancy in the answers to parts (a) and (b)?

5.35 Consider the linear model $(\boldsymbol{y}, \boldsymbol{X\beta}, \sigma^2\boldsymbol{I})$ with explanatory variables $\boldsymbol{x}_1, \ldots, \boldsymbol{x}_k$. Let A and B be the index sets of two different subsets of explanatory variables. Let $\mathcal{M}_A$ and $\mathcal{M}_B$ be the subset models corresponding to A and B, respectively.

(a) If $A \subset B$, show that the sample squared multiple correlation coefficient R^2 (see (4.4)) of $\mathcal{M}_B$ is at least as large as that for $\mathcal{M}_A$. [Thus, R^2 is not very useful as a criterion for comparing nested subsets.]

(b) Show that, when comparison is made between subsets of equal size, the criteria R^2, R_a^2 and C_p are equivalent. [Hint: Show that each of the three criteria is a monotone function of $\widehat{\sigma^2}$.]

5.36 For the data generated in Problem 5.31, determine, using the adjusted R-square criterion, the most appropriate subset of explanatory variables among the power terms x, x^2, x^3 and x^4. Does the Mallows's C_p criterion lead to a different 'best' subset?

5.37 The data set `mtcars` is a part of the `datasets` package built in R. The data consists of the gas mileage (`mpg`) of 32 types of cars having different values of ten explanatory variables. Find a suitable linear model for the gas mileage, with regressors chosen from the ten available candidates, using best subset regression, according to the Mallows's C_p criterion. Does the adjusted R-square criterion lead to a different 'best' subset?

5.38 Express the PRESS criterion, defined on page 194, in terms of residuals and leverages in the candidate linear model.

5.39 Examine the leverages, standardized residuals and studentized residuals for the regression of unemployment rate (UNMP) on the variables EXP, INFL and INV of the IMF unemployment data provided in Table 5.2 and identify x- and y-outliers, if any.

5.40 For the growth data analysed in Exercise 3.32, compare the plots of the studentized residuals against age, when the height is regressed on age alone and when the square of age is brought in as an additional regressor. Can a model with a single regressor (i.e. a transformed version of age) work equally well?

5.41 For the running time data analysed through the model of Exercise 3.33, examine the plot of the studentized residuals against running distance and comment on it. Bring in suitable nonlinear terms, if necessary, for a more appropriate analysis.

5.42 For the data set `mtcars` of Exercise 5.37, use the subset model with four regressors having smallest Mallows's C_p to generate added variable plots of all the regressors. A nonlinear and decreasing pattern should be noticeable in the added variable plot of `hp`. Replace it with a new variable `ihp`, defined as the reciprocal of `hp`, and search again for the best subset model according to Mallows's Cp. Is this model of `mpg` simpler than the 'best' models found in Exercise 5.37? Is it better in terms of adjusted R-square?

5.43 For the 'best' model for `mpg` found in Exercise 5.42, plot the leverages of the 32 cases. Identify the cases with leverage larger than $2(k+1)/n$. Mark these cases on the scatter plot of the two explanatory variables. Do they appear to be far out from the center of the data?

5.44 The data set `sleep1` is a part of the `alr3` package in R. It contains data on 62 species of animals, in respect of variables described in Weisberg (2005, p. 86). Variables of present interest are the total sleep in hours per day (`TS`), which may depend on body weight in kg (`BodyWt`), brain weight in g (`BrainWt`), gestational period in days (`GP`), maximum life span in years (`Life`), danger index (`D`, score of 1 to 5), predation index (`P`, score 1 to 5) and sleep exposure index (`SE`, score 1 to 5). For the present analysis, the three scores may be regarded as real valued variables, and all cases with missing data may be omitted.

(a) Find a suitable linear model for `TS`, with explanatory variables to be chosen from the seven available candidates, according to the Mallows's C_p criterion.

(b) Notice that the `BodyWt` and `BrainWt` data have some very large values (as the chosen animals have drastically different size), which indicates a skewed distribution. Verify that the log transformation of these variables are just about the ideal Box-Cox transformation for enhanced normality.

(c) Replace the variables `BodyWt` and `BrainWt` with their respective log transformations, and repeat the analysis of part (a). What can you conclude from the findings?

5.45 For the `sleep1` data of Exercise 5.44, address the issue of non-linearity in a revised analysis, as follows.

(a) While using all the candidate explanatory variables considered in part (c) of Exercise 5.44, check for nonlinearity in the variables using appropriate diagnostic plots. If you identify any nonlinearity, use a quadratic term to model it, and run best subsets regression again with the Mallow's C_p criterion. Comment on your findings.
(b) Look at the regression summary for the best model identified in part (a). Are all the regression coefficients significant at the 5% level?
(c) Should the regression coefficients of the 'best' subset model be significant?

5.46 Check whether the model mentioned in Example 1.8 for the drug price data of Table 1.1 is adequate. If not, derive a suitable alternative model.
5.47 For the linear model $(\boldsymbol{y}, \boldsymbol{X\beta}, \sigma^2\boldsymbol{V})$, show that the LSE of any estimable linear function of $\boldsymbol{\beta}$ is unbiased. Also show that if y_0 is a random outcome with mean $\boldsymbol{x}_0'\boldsymbol{\beta}$ that is estimable under the above model, then the LSE of $\boldsymbol{x}_0'\boldsymbol{\beta}$ is a linear unbiased predictor of y_0 (though not necessarily the best one).
5.48 By studying the relation between the variance and the mean, find an appropriate variance stabilizing transformation for the response when the response distribution is known to be (a) Poisson, (b) binomial with n trials, (c) exponential and (d) sum of m independent and identical exponentials.
5.49 Fit a suitable linear regression model to the data set (c) of Example 5.1.
5.50 Verify that the Durbin-Watson test statistic has value in between 0 and 4.
5.51 The data set `wblake1` in the `alr3` package in R contains data on `Age` at capture (in years), `Length` at capture (in mm) and `Scale` radius (in mm) of a sample of 439 smallmouth bass fish captured in West Bearskin Lake, Minnesota in 1991. The purpose of this exercise is to build a suitable model for predicting `Length` by `Age`.

(a) Examine the issue of nonlinearity and include either a quadratic term or a suitable power transformation, if necessary, to tackle it.

(b) Examine the issue of heteroscedasticity and take a suitable corrective action, if necessary, to tackle it.
(c) Examine the issue of non-normality and make a suitable power transformation, if necessary, to tackle it.
(d) Reanalyse the data to determine whether the linear model assumptions can be assumed to hold after all the corrective actions are taken.
(e) Obtain a prediction interval for `Length` of a 5 year old fish, so that the coverage probability is 95%. Is the interval symmetric with respect to the predicted value?

5.52 Violation of the four underlying assumptions of the linear model has been dealt with in Section 5.3. Examine whether any of these violations can make the OLSE biased.

5.53 For the `sleep1` data of Exercise 5.44, carry out the following computations of casewise diagnostics for the regression of `TS` on log of `BrainWt`, `GP`, `D`, `P`, square of `P` and `SE`.

(a) Identify the cases with high values of $DFFITS_i$ and $COVRATIO_i$.
(b) Plot the $DFBETAS_{ij}$ against case indices and identify the cases with values of these.
(c) Plot the standardized residuals against leverages, with the contour of Cook's distance equal to $4/n$ overlaid on it, and identify the cases of extreme values of these.

5.54 *Perils of collinearity.* For the data generated in Example 5.3, observe and explain the output generated by the following lines of additional code.

```
M12 <- lm(y~x1+x2); M1 <- lm(y~x1); M2 <- lm(y~x2)
xnew1 <- data.frame(x1 = c(min(x1),median(x1),max(x1)),
                    x2 = c(min(x2),median(x2),max(x2)))
predict(M12,newdat=xnew1,interval="prediction")
predict(M1,newdat=xnew1,interval="prediction")
predict(M2,newdat=xnew1,interval="prediction")
xnew2 <- data.frame(x1 = c(min(x1),max(x1)),
                    x2 = c(max(x2),min(x2)))
predict(M12,newdat=xnew2,interval="prediction")
predict(M1,newdat=xnew2,interval="prediction")
predict(M2,newdat=xnew2,interval="prediction")
```

5.55 For the world population data of Table 1.3, calculate the condition number κ and the intercept-augmented variance inflation factors. Explain why the IVIFs for the two parameters are the same.

5.56 For the world population data of Table 1.3, consider replacing the variable 'year' by the 'number of years since 1980'.

(a) Calculate the least squares estimates of the parameters of the model with 'year' as the regressor and also of the model with 'number of years since 1980' as the regressor. Compare the findings.

(b) Calculate the dispersion of the vector of estimated parameters for the two models of part (a). Compare the findings.

(c) Calculate $\widehat{\sigma^2}$ for the two models of part (a). Compare the findings.

(d) Repeat Exercise 5.55 for the model with 'number of years since 1980' as the regressor. Explain the findings.

5.57 For the `sleep1` data of Exercise 5.44, carry out carry out collinearity analysis as in Example 5.28, for the regression of `TS` on log of `BrainWt`, `GP`, `D`, `P`, square of `P` and `SE`.

5.58 Specify precisely the GLM, where the response has the exponential distribution, and the predictors are linked to the mean response by the canonical link function. Suggest a good reason why, instead of using this link function, one might prefer to use the log function as link (a common choice in the field of Survival Analysis). Write down the log-likelihood of the regression parameters under the GLM with the latter link function, assuming there are n paired observations on the response and a scalar predictor. Explain how you can maximize it for estimating these parameters.

5.59 For data on birth weight of babies was considered in Example 1.5, suppose babies weighing less than 2500 grams are considered underweight. Use the binary indicator of whether a baby is underweight (`low`) as response, and the three binary variables used in Example 4.6 as explanatory variables, to fit a logistic regression model. Do all the variables have a significant effect on the response?

Chapter 6

Analysis of Variance

One of the invariables in our life, it has been observed, is variability itself. All human beings do not have the same height. Yield of wheat per acre of land is not the same everywhere. Even the microchips, for which we desire very low tolerances, vary in their performance characteristics, due to factors beyond the manufacturer's control.

In trying to understand this omnipresent variability, we might ask what factors cause this variability. For instance, individual heights vary possibly because of our parents heights and other genetic factors, our sex, dietary and exercise habits and so on. Similarly the yield (per acre) of a wheat crop may vary depending on what variety of wheat it is, the soil type, the amount of irrigation, the amount and type of fertilizer used and so on. We might achieve a better understanding of such variability in a given context and possibly help control it, if we are able to list most of the major causes for the variation and split the total variation into parts, each of which is attributable to a given cause. Since we cannot possibly list *all* the causes, we expect that at the end of such an exercise, there will be a component that might be called the residual (left-over, unexplained, or error) variation. Achieving such a decomposition of the total variability into assignable causes, is the grand goal of the statistical tool called the *analysis of variance* (ANOVA). The systematic and efficient conduct of an experiment which permits us to identify these components, is the subject of *design of experiments.*

In this chapter we consider linear models for experiments where the explanatory variables are not necessarily given/observed factors, but are chosen from a finite set of values by careful design. For instance, in an agricultural yield experiment, one may be allowed to choose the amount of water, or fertilizer applied. When the model matrix $\boldsymbol{X}$ of the linear model $(\boldsymbol{y}, \boldsymbol{X\beta}, \sigma^2\boldsymbol{I})$ is thus designed, we call it the *design matrix.*

We have already come across a rudimentary ANOVA in Table 4.2, where the variation present in the response is measured by the sum of squared deviations from the mean. The total sum of squares was decomposed into regression sum of squares and error sum of squares in Example 4.6. In the case of designed experiments, the matrix $\boldsymbol{X}$ usually has a simple structure. Depending on the model, which determines the design matrix, it is often possible to further decompose the regression sum of squares into components which are attributable to different identifiable sources of variation. This chapter deals with such decompositions for different practically important yet simple models, and testing whether any of the factors (sources of variation) contribute significantly to the total variation. Some of the factors under study may be of primary interest to the experimenter (for example, which variety of wheat gives the most yield?). However in order to control the error (or the unexplained part), the other factors and their effects are also brought into the model. These effects correspond to what may be called nuisance parameters. For conducting tests of linear hypotheses we shall assume the normality of $\boldsymbol{y}$.

Much of the initial development in experimental designs came from agricultural research, going back to Fisher (1926). The different factors whose effects are being studied, are called *treatments*, as for example the different varieties of wheat or different manufacturing processes, from which we want to choose. The basic unit of material on which these treatments are applied, is called an *experimental unit.* For instance, a plot of land where various types of wheat can be grown, or a batch of steel produced by the manufacturing process, is an experimental unit. Finally a measure of the effectiveness of the treatment on the experimental unit is referred to as the *yield*, as for instance the amount of wheat per plot, or the tensile strength of steel produced by the manufacturing process. In the jargon of a linear model, each experimental unit corresponds to an observation or case, the yield is the value of the response and treatments are explanatory variables.

Without going too deeply into the principles of experimental designs, we aim to provide a flavour of optimal designs in the next section. In subsequent sections we show how the analysis of some basic designs helps answer some important questions. The treatment developed here relies on the ideas discussed in Chapters 3 and 4 that emphasize linear zero functions, and the reader will find that it differs somewhat from what is found in other books on design of experiments.

6.1 Optimal designs

In order to draw inference on some parameters of a linear model such as the treatment effects, an objective function may be identified so that optimizing this function over all possible designs would enhance the quality of inference. If there is only one parameter of interest, an obvious criterion is to minimize its variance or the inverse of the (Fisher) information. If the interest is in all the parameters, a real-valued function of the information matrix is chosen as the objective function. Some popular criteria for optimal design are as follows.

A-optimality: Minimize the average (or sum) of the variances of the parameter estimates (this corresponds to minimizing the sum of reciprocals of the positive eigenvalues of the information matrix).

D-optimality: Minimize the product of the variances of the parameter estimates (this corresponds to minimizing the product of reciprocals of the positive eigenvalues of the information matrix).

E-optimality: Minimize the maximum (extreme) variance of the parameter estimates (this corresponds to minimizing the reciprocal of the smallest positive eigenvalue of the information matrix).

Note that these objective functions are monotonically non-increasing functions of the eigenvalues of the information matrix. If an information matrix is larger than another one in the sense of the Löwner order, then it follows from Proposition A.21 that the design corresponding to the first information matrix is better with respect to each of the above criteria.

Usually an optimal design has to be selected subject to some constraints. There are limits on the number of observations because of cost and other considerations. Another typical constraint is that some elements of the matrix $\boldsymbol{X}$ can only assume finitely many values. We have already come across such a problem in Example 3.56, where the elements of $\boldsymbol{X}$ can be either 0 or 1. In general, the task of finding an optimal design in the discrete case suffers from the handicap that derivatives cannot be used. See Shah and Sinha (1989) for a detailed discussion of optimal designs.

Example 6.1. Suppose the means of t populations $(\mu_1, \ldots, \mu_t)$ are to be estimated using a total of n observations from these, and the variance of any of these observations is σ^2. Let the number of observations allocated to population i be n_i, $i = 1, \ldots, t$, so that $\sum_{i=1}^t n_i = n$. Let us find the A-, D- and E-optimal designs assuming that all the means are estimable, i.e. $n_i \geq 1$ for $i = 1, \ldots, t$.

By arranging the observations as a vector, we can use a linear model where the matrix $\boldsymbol{X}$ consist of 0s and 1s. There is exactly one 1 in each row of $\boldsymbol{X}$ and exactly n_i 1s in the column corresponding to μ_i. The information matrix is diagonal. The reciprocals of its diagonal elements (or eigenvalues) are $\sigma^2/n_1, \ldots, \sigma^2/n_t$. Because of the well-known order between the arithmetic and geometric means of positive numbers, we have

$$\max_{1\le i\le t} \frac{\sigma^2}{n_i} \ge t^{-1}\left(\frac{\sigma^2}{n_1} + \cdots + \frac{\sigma^2}{n_t}\right) \ge \left(\prod_{i=1}^{t} \frac{\sigma^2}{n_i}\right)^{1/t} \ge \frac{\sigma^2}{n/t}.$$

Any one of the inequalities holds with equality if and only if $n_1 = \cdots = n_t = n/t$, in which case *all* the inequalities hold with equality. This is only possible if n is a multiple of t. It is clear that the design which allocates equal number of observations to each population is at once E-, A- and D-optimal. Such a design is called a *balanced* design.

The design of Example 3.56 had indeed been a balanced one. □

The model discussed in the next section is a variation of the model of Example 6.1, but the design is not assumed to be balanced.

6.2 One-way classified data

6.2.1 *The model*

Suppose we are asked to compare t types of treatments and are given n experimental units on which to conduct the experiment. One of the simple ways to do this, is to select integers $n_1, n_2, \ldots, n_t$ such that $n_1 + n_2 + \cdots + n_t = n$ and apply treatment i on n_i units, $i = 1, \ldots, t$ (different treatments being applied to different sets of units). If the units are known to be homogeneous, that is, if there is no factor (other than the treatment itself) which may cause some of them to have a different mean response than others, then the allocation of the units to the t groups may be done at random. This design is called *completely randomized design* (CRD). Clearly we would want $n_i \ge 2$ for each i, so that each treatment is replicated, providing a measure of internal variability. If no other prior information is available, it might well be best to subdivide n into t approximately equal parts and apply each of these treatments to an equal number of units (see Example 6.1).

Let y_{ij} denote the yield of the jth experimental unit which received the ith treatment, $j = 1, \ldots, n_i$, $i = 1, \ldots, t$. The yield may be modelled as

$$\begin{aligned} y_{ij} &= \mu + \tau_i + \varepsilon_{ij},\ j = 1, \ldots, n_i,\ \ i = 1, \ldots, t, \\ E(\varepsilon_{ij}) &= 0, \\ Cov(\varepsilon_{ij}, \varepsilon_{i'j'}) &= \begin{cases} \sigma^2 & \text{if } i = i' \text{ and } j = j', \\ 0 & \text{otherwise.} \end{cases} \end{aligned} \tag{6.1}$$

The parameter μ represents the baseline response that might be present in all the units, and $\tau_1, \ldots, \tau_t$ are the additive effects of the t different treatments. We refer to these parameters as the *baseline effect* and *treatment effects*, respectively. The matrix-vector form of the model is

$$\boldsymbol{y}_{n\times 1} = \boldsymbol{X}_{n\times(t+1)}\boldsymbol{\beta}_{(t+1)\times 1} + \boldsymbol{\varepsilon}_{n\times 1}, \quad E(\boldsymbol{\varepsilon}) = \boldsymbol{0}, \quad D(\boldsymbol{\varepsilon}) = \sigma^2\boldsymbol{I},$$

where

$$\boldsymbol{y} = (y_{11} : \cdots : y_{1n_1} : y_{21} : \cdots : y_{2n_2} : \cdots\cdots : y_{t1} : \cdots : y_{tn_t})',$$

$$\boldsymbol{X} = \begin{pmatrix} \boldsymbol{1}_{n_1\times 1} & \boldsymbol{1}_{n_1\times 1} & \boldsymbol{0}_{n_1\times 1} & \cdots & \boldsymbol{0}_{n_1\times 1} \\ \boldsymbol{1}_{n_2\times 1} & \boldsymbol{0}_{n_2\times 1} & \boldsymbol{1}_{n_2\times 1} & \cdots & \boldsymbol{0}_{n_2\times 1} \\ \vdots & \vdots & & \ddots & \vdots \\ \boldsymbol{1}_{n_t\times 1} & \boldsymbol{0}_{n_t\times 1} & \boldsymbol{0}_{n_t\times 1} & \cdots & \boldsymbol{1}_{n_t\times 1} \end{pmatrix}, \qquad \boldsymbol{\beta} = \begin{pmatrix} \mu \\ \tau_1 \\ \vdots \\ \tau_t \end{pmatrix},$$

$$\boldsymbol{\varepsilon} = (\varepsilon_{11} : \cdots : \varepsilon_{1n_1} : \varepsilon_{21} : \cdots : \varepsilon_{2n_2} : \cdots\cdots : \varepsilon_{t1} : \cdots : \varepsilon_{tn_t})'.$$

The model can be reparametrized by defining $\mu_i = \mu + \tau_i$, $i = 1, \ldots, t$, so that the new parameters $\mu_1, \ldots, \mu_t$ are estimable. This reparametrization highlights the crucial fact that one-way classified data model (6.1) may arise not only from CRD, but also from other problems such as comparison of population means of t samples, considered in Example 6.1. It may even arise in observational studies such as the age at death data considered in Example 3.4. We shall proceed with estimation without this reparametrization.

Example 6.2. (Energy absorbance of test machines) The Charpy test uses a swinging pendulum to measure the resistance of a steel or other material to brittle fracture. Charpy V-notch impact machines are used for this purpose. The machines have to be tested themselves against specimens of known toughness, for the sake of standardization. The data set in Table 6.1 consists of absorbed energies (in foot-pounds) for four machines (Tinius1, Tinius2, Satec and Tokyo) from tests with a total of 100 specimens.

Equating the machines (represented by the variable `Machine` in the data object `splett2`) with treatments, we can generate the design matrix $\boldsymbol{X}$ using the following R code.

Table 6.1 Energy absorbed by four machines for Charpy V-notch testing (data object `splett2` in R package `lmreg`, source: Dataplot webpage of the National Institute of Standards and Technology (NIST), USA at `https://www.itl.nist.gov/div898/software/dataplot/data/SPLETT2.DAT`)

Energy absorbed by Machine 1 (Tinius1)	Energy absorbed by Machine 2 (Tinius2)	Energy absorbed by Machine 3 (Satec)	Energy absorbed by Machine 4 (Tokyo)
67.4	69.0	73.0	67.6
65.5	66.2	78.9	64.2
72.0	70.0	75.0	65.9
73.6	68.5	72.3	65.9
65.2	66.0	72.4	68.2
67.0	67.5	74.1	71.1
66.3	68.5	72.0	67.6
67.9	66.5	72.0	71.6
65.8	73.0	70.9	72.8
69.9	69.0	74.5	68.2
64.5	69.0	72.0	67.6
66.0	74.5	72.5	67.1
66.8	68.0	72.4	67.1
67.0	68.5	74.0	68.2
69.9	67.5	75.0	65.4
70.1	70.0	70.9	66.5
69.7	69.0	70.9	67.6
68.3	72.5	76.6	67.1
67.0	68.0	74.2	71.1
68.2	69.0	69.5	67.1
65.0	69.0	68.8	65.4
66.6	71.0	68.5	67.6
65.4	68.0	70.1	67.6
68.1	75.0	73.0	70.5
	67.0	70.9	70.5

```
data(splett2)
X <- cbind(1, binaries(splett2$Machine))
X
```

The matrix $\boldsymbol{X}$ produced by this code (not shown here) has the neat structure described on page 285, but that is because the cases happen to be ordered conveniently, with all cases for a particular treatment appearing together. If this order is not maintained in the data file, the design matrix $\boldsymbol{X}$ produced by the above command would be a permuted version of the structured matrix. That would still be appropriate for the response vector. □

6.2.2 *Estimation of model parameters*

Note that the first column of the matrix $\boldsymbol{X}$ is the sum of the remaining columns, the latter being linearly independent. Therefore, $\rho(\boldsymbol{X}) = t$. It is clear that not all linear parametric functions of this model are estimable. In fact, none of the individual parameters of the model is estimable.

Comparison of the treatments under the model (6.1) amounts to comparing the treatment effects $\tau_1, \ldots, \tau_t$ associated with the treatments. Let us first find out which linear functions of the treatment effects are estimable.

Proposition 6.3. *For a linear function $\sum_{j=1}^t c_j\tau_j$ of the treatment effects in the linear model* (6.1)*, the following statements are equivalent.*

(i) The LPF $\sum_{j=1}^t c_j\tau_j$ is estimable.
(ii) The LPF $\sum_{j=1}^t c_j\tau_j$ is a linear combination of the treatment differences, $\tau_2 - \tau_1, \ldots, \tau_t - \tau_1$.
(iii) The coefficient vector $\mathbf{c} = (c_1 : \cdots : c_t)'$ satisfies the condition $\mathbf{c}'\mathbf{1} = 0$.

Proof. The LPF $\sum_{j=1}^t c_j\tau_j$ can be written as $\boldsymbol{p}'\boldsymbol{\beta}$, where $\boldsymbol{p}' = (0 : \boldsymbol{c}')$. As already noted, $\rho(\boldsymbol{X}) = t$. Thus, there can be at most t linearly independent choices of the $(t+1) \times 1$ vector $\boldsymbol{p}$ such that $\boldsymbol{p}'\boldsymbol{\beta}$ is estimable. Note that $\mu + \tau_1$ is estimable (y_{11} being an LUE of it) and it can be written as $\boldsymbol{p}'\boldsymbol{\beta}$ with $\boldsymbol{p}' = (1 : 1 : 0 \cdots : 0)$, which is *not* of the form $(0 : \boldsymbol{c}')$. Thus, there may be at most $t-1$ linearly independent choices of $(0 : \boldsymbol{c}')$ such that $\sum_{j=1}^t c_j\tau_j$ is estimable. If we can identify any one set of $t-1$ vectors $\mathbf{c}$ such that this LPF is estimable, then all vectors corresponding to estimable linear combinations of the treatment effects would be linear functions of them. We argue that the coefficient vectors corresponding to the $t-1$ LPFs listed in statement (ii) constitute a requisite set. They are linearly independent, because they are obtained by subtracting the first column of the $t \times t$ identity matrix from each of the remaining columns. They are also estimable ($y_{12} - y_{11}, \ldots, y_{1t} - y_{11}$ being respective LUEs). This proves that statement (i) implies statement (ii). The reverse implication is obvious.

Each of the $t-1$ linearly independent vectors identified above are orthogonal to the $t \times 1$ vector $\mathbf{1}$. Therefore, they span the space of all vectors that are orthogonal to $\mathbf{1}_{t\times 1}$. This proves that statement (ii) is equivalent to statement (iii). □

An LPF $\sum_{j=1}^t c_j\tau_j$ with the restriction $\boldsymbol{c}'\mathbf{1} = \sum_{j=1}^t c_j = 0$ is called a *treatment contrast*. The significance of this name follows from their characterization as linear functions of differences (or contrasts) between pairs of treatment effects.

Treatment contrasts are not the only linear parametric functions of $\boldsymbol{\beta}$ which are estimable. It is obvious that $\mu + \tau_j$ is estimable for $j = 1, \ldots, t$.

In order to find the BLUE of $\boldsymbol{X\beta}$, write $\boldsymbol{X}$ as $(\boldsymbol{1} : \boldsymbol{X}_1)$ and observe

$$\boldsymbol{P}_X = \boldsymbol{P}_{X_1} = \boldsymbol{X}_1(\boldsymbol{X}_1'\boldsymbol{X}_1)^-\boldsymbol{X}_1'$$

$$= \boldsymbol{X}_1 \begin{pmatrix} n_1 & 0 & \cdots & 0 \\ 0 & n_2 & \cdots & 0 \\ \vdots & \vdots & \ddots & \vdots \\ 0 & 0 & \cdots & n_t \end{pmatrix}^{-1} \boldsymbol{X}_1' \quad = \begin{pmatrix} \boldsymbol{P}_{1_{n_1}} & 0 & \cdots & 0 \\ 0 & \boldsymbol{P}_{1_{n_2}} & \cdots & 0 \\ \vdots & \vdots & \ddots & \vdots \\ 0 & 0 & \cdots & \boldsymbol{P}_{1_{n_t}} \end{pmatrix}.$$

It follows that

$$\widehat{\boldsymbol{y}} = \begin{pmatrix} \overline{y}_{1\cdot}\boldsymbol{1}_{n_1} \\ \vdots \\ \overline{y}_{t\cdot}\boldsymbol{1}_{n_t} \end{pmatrix}, \quad \text{where } \overline{y}_{i\cdot} = \frac{y_{i\cdot}}{n_i},\ y_{i\cdot} = \sum_{j=1}^{n_i} y_{ij},\ i = 1, \ldots, t. \tag{6.2}$$

In other words, for any i and j, the fitted value of the yield y_{ij} is the average of the yield in the ith treatment group, $\overline{y}_{i\cdot}$. The corresponding residual is $y_{ij} - \overline{y}_{i\cdot}$, the deviation from the group mean. It follows that the error sum of squares and the usual unbiased estimator of σ^2 are

$$R_0^2 = \boldsymbol{e}'\boldsymbol{e} = \sum_{i=1}^{t}\sum_{j=1}^{n_i}(y_{ij} - \overline{y}_{i\cdot})^2, \tag{6.3}$$

$$\widehat{\sigma^2} = R_0^2/(n-t). \tag{6.4}$$

The dispersion matrix of the vector of fitted values is

$$D(\widehat{\boldsymbol{X\beta}}) = \sigma^2\boldsymbol{P}_X = \sigma^2 \begin{pmatrix} \boldsymbol{P}_{1_{n_1}} & 0 & \cdots & 0 \\ 0 & \boldsymbol{P}_{1_{n_2}} & \cdots & 0 \\ \vdots & \vdots & \ddots & \vdots \\ 0 & 0 & \cdots & \boldsymbol{P}_{1_{n_t}} \end{pmatrix}. \tag{6.5}$$

Let $\boldsymbol{\tau} = (\tau_1 : \cdots : \tau_t)'$. The BLUE of a treatment contrast $\boldsymbol{c}'\boldsymbol{\tau}$ can be obtained from the formulae given in Chapter 3. However, there is a simpler way of obtaining the BLUE of any contrast and its variance from those of the fitted values. From the definition of a treatment contrast it follows that $\boldsymbol{c}'\boldsymbol{\tau} = \boldsymbol{c}'(\mu\boldsymbol{1} + \boldsymbol{\tau})$. The vector $\mu\boldsymbol{1} + \boldsymbol{\tau}$ is completely estimable, as its

ith element is the expected value of y_{i1}. Therefore, the BLUE of the ith element of $\mu\mathbf{1} + \boldsymbol{\tau}$ is $\overline{y}_{i\cdot}$. Consequently the BLUE of $\mathbf{c}'\boldsymbol{\tau}$ is

$$\widehat{\mathbf{c}'\boldsymbol{\tau}} = \sum_{i=1}^{t} c_i \overline{y}_{i\cdot}. \tag{6.6}$$

Further, (6.5) implies that

$$Var(\widehat{\mathbf{c}'\boldsymbol{\tau}}) = Var\left(\sum_{i=1}^{t} c_i \overline{y}_{i\cdot}\right) = \sum_{i=1}^{t} c_i^2 Var(\overline{y}_{i\cdot}) = \sigma^2 \sum_{i=1}^{t} \frac{c_i^2}{n_i}. \tag{6.7}$$

For instance, the BLUE of the contrast $\tau_1 - \tau_2$ is $\overline{y}_{1\cdot} - \overline{y}_{2\cdot}$, and its variance is $\sigma^2/n_1 + \sigma^2/n_2$. An extension of the above arguments shows that the covariance between the BLUEs of the contrasts $\sum_{i=1}^{t} c_{1i}\tau_i$ and $\sum_{i=1}^{t} c_{2i}\tau_i$ is

$$Cov\left(\sum_{i=1}^{t} \widehat{c_{1i}\tau_i}, \sum_{i=1}^{t} \widehat{c_{2i}\tau_i}\right) = \sigma^2 \sum_{i=1}^{t} \frac{c_{1i}c_{2i}}{n_i}.$$

Example 6.4. (Energy absorbance of test machines, continued) Consider the energy absorbance data of Table 6.1. The BLUEs of the six treatment differences (with standard errors in parentheses), computed from (6.6) and (6.7) are reported in the following table.

Contrast	BLUE (standard error)
Tinius1 – Tinius2	−1.5747 (0.6576)
Tinius1 – Satec	−4.9427 (0.6576)
Tinius1 – Tokyo	−0.3467 (0.6576)
Tinius2 – Satec	−3.3680 (0.6509)
Tinius2 – Tokyo	1.2280 (0.6509)
Satec – Tokyo	4.5960 (0.6509)

The R code used to produce the above contrasts and standard errors is given below.

```
data(splett2)
n <- dim(splett2)[1]; nt <- length(unique(splett2$Machine))
ws <- summary(lm(Energy~factor(Machine), data=splett2))$sig^2
library(data.table)
dt <- data.table(splett2)
grps <- dt[,list(mean=mean(Energy), ng=length(Energy)), by=Machine]
mnames <- c("Tinius1","Tinius2","Satec","Tokyo")
cname <- NULL; meandiff <- NULL; sterr <- NULL
```

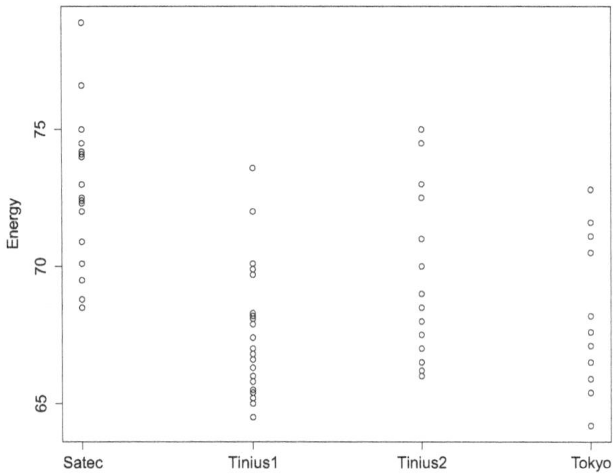

Fig. 6.1 Dot plot of the absorbed energy for various machines in Example 6.2

```
for (i in 1:(nt-1)) {
  for (j in (i+1):nt) {
    meandiff <- c(meandiff, grps$mean[i] - grps$mean[j])
    sterr <- c(sterr, sqrt(ws/grps$ng[i] + ws/grps$ng[j]))
    cname <- c(cname, paste(mnames[i], "-", mnames[j], sep = " "))
  }
}
as.data.frame(cbind(meandiff, sterr), row.names = cname)
```

A visual display of the data, obtained through the additional line of code `stripchart(Energy~mnames[Machine], data=splett2, vertical=T, pch=1)` and shown in Figure 6.1, may be used to cross-check the signs of the BLUEs. □

Let $\overline{y}_{..} = n^{-1}y_{..}$, where $y_{..}$ is the sum of all the observations. Since

$$\overline{y}_{..} = \sum_{i=1}^{t} \frac{n_i}{n}\overline{y}_{i\cdot},$$

that is, $\overline{y}_{..}$ is a linear combination of the fitted values, it must be the BLUE of its expectation, which is $\mu + \sum_{i=1}^{t}(n_i/n)\tau_i$. Sometimes the redundancy of the parameters of (6.1) is sought to be removed by introducing the 'side-condition' $\sum_{i=1}^{t}(n_i/n)\tau_i = 0$. This restriction is a model-preserving constraint (see page 98), so it does not affect the BLUEs of estimable functions. Under this restriction, all the parameters of the model are estimable, and $\bar{y}_{..}$ is the BLUE of the baseline mean yield (μ). Its variance works out to be σ^2/n.

6.2.3 *Analysis of variance*

The main hypothesis of interest here is that of 'no difference in treatment effects',

$$\mathcal{H}_0 : \tau_1 = \tau_2 = \cdots = \tau_t.$$

This hypothesis can be rephrased as

$$\mathcal{H}_0 : \begin{pmatrix} \tau_1 - \tau_2 \\ \tau_1 - \tau_3 \\ \vdots \\ \tau_1 - \tau_t \end{pmatrix} = \mathbf{0},$$

or as $\boldsymbol{A\beta} = \mathbf{0}$ where

$$\boldsymbol{A}_{(t-1)\times(t+1)} = \begin{pmatrix} 0 & 1 & -1 & 0 & \cdots & 0 \\ 0 & 1 & 0 & -1 & \cdots & 0 \\ \vdots & \vdots & \vdots & \ddots & \ddots & \vdots \\ 0 & 1 & 0 & \cdots & 0 & -1 \end{pmatrix}.$$

The error sum of squares under the hypothesis (R_H^2) is very easy to calculate, since the restriction $\boldsymbol{A\beta} = \mathbf{0}$ reduces (6.1) to a model with common mean of all the observations. Therefore,

$$R_H^2 = \min_{\boldsymbol{\beta}:\, \boldsymbol{A\beta} = \mathbf{0}} \|\boldsymbol{y} - \boldsymbol{X\beta}\|^2 = \min_{\mu,\, \tau_1} \sum_{i=1}^{t}\sum_{j=1}^{n_i}(y_{ij} - \mu - \tau_1)^2$$

$$= \min_{\theta} \sum_{i=1}^{t}\sum_{j=1}^{n_i}(y_{ij} - \theta)^2 = \sum_{i=1}^{t}\sum_{j=1}^{n_i}(y_{ij} - \bar{y}_{..})^2. \qquad (6.8)$$

Thus, R_H^2 is the sum of squared deviations from the grand mean of all the observations. We can also find an interpretable expression for $R_H^2 - R_0^2$, as follows.

$$R_H^2 = \sum_{i=1}^{t}\sum_{j=1}^{n_i}(y_{ij} - \bar{y}_{..})^2 = \sum_{i=1}^{t}\sum_{j=1}^{n_i}(y_{ij} - \bar{y}_{i.} + \bar{y}_{i.} - \bar{y}_{..})^2$$

$$= \sum_{i=1}^{t}\sum_{j=1}^{n_i}(y_{ij} - \bar{y}_{i.})^2 + \sum_{i=1}^{t}\sum_{j=1}^{n_i}(\bar{y}_{i.} - \bar{y}_{..})^2, \qquad (6.9)$$

since the cross terms, when summed over j, reduce to zero. Comparing the first term of the last expression with (6.3), we find that it is equal to R_0^2. Therefore,

$$R_H^2 - R_0^2 = \sum_{i=1}^{t}\sum_{j=1}^{n_i}(\overline{y}_{i\cdot} - \overline{y}_{\cdot\cdot})^2. \tag{6.10}$$

The summands of the right-hand side are squared deviations of group means from the grand mean. Each of these deviations is a BLUE under the alternative hypothesis, $\boldsymbol{A\beta} \neq \boldsymbol{0}$. These BLUEs turn into LZFs under $\mathcal{H}_0$. The above sum is called the *between-groups sum of squares*, as it captures the variation across group means. The expression for R_0^2 is called the *within-group sum of squares*, for obvious reasons. The sum of these two, R_H^2, is the *total sum of squares.* The between-groups sum of squares represents the departure from the null hypothesis of equal group means. Thus, it makes intuitive sense that a large value of this quantity, relative to the within-group sum of squares, would lead to rejection of the null hypothesis. The generalized likelihood ratio test (GLRT) for $\mathcal{H}_0$, under the assumption of normality of the errors reduces to this criterion. It follows from the discussion of Section 4.2.5 that the GLRT rejects $\mathcal{H}_0$ when

$$\frac{R_H^2 - R_0^2}{R_0^2} \cdot \frac{n-t}{t-1} > F_{t-1,n-t,\alpha},$$

where $F_{t-1,n-t,\alpha}$ is the $(1-\alpha)$ quantile of the $F_{t-1,n-t}$ distribution.

The analysis of variance for the model (6.1) is given in Table 6.2. The GLRT statistic is obtained from this table as the ratio of the mean squares, MS_g/MS_w.

Table 6.2 ANOVA for model (6.1) of one-way classified data

Source	Sum of Squares	Degrees of Freedom	Mean Square
Between groups	$R_H^2 - R_0^2 = \sum_{i=1}^{t} n_i(\overline{y}_{i\cdot} - \overline{y}_{\cdot\cdot})^2$	$t-1$	$MS_g = \dfrac{R_H^2 - R_0^2}{t-1}$
Within groups	$R_0^2 = \sum_{i=1}^{t}\sum_{j=1}^{n_i}(y_{ij} - \overline{y}_{i\cdot})^2$	$n-t$	$MS_w = \dfrac{R_0^2}{n-t}$
Total	$R_H^2 = \sum_{i=1}^{t}\sum_{j=1}^{n_i}(y_{ij} - \overline{y}_{\cdot\cdot})^2$	$n-1$	

The ANOVA reported in Table 6.2 corresponds to the decomposition of a projection matrix into two projection matrices:

$$(\boldsymbol{I} - \boldsymbol{P}_{1_n}) = (\boldsymbol{P}_X - \boldsymbol{P}_{1_n}) + (\boldsymbol{I} - \boldsymbol{P}_X). \tag{6.11}$$

Sum of squares of the response vector projected by these three matrices are the total sum of squares, the between groups sum of squares and the within group sum of squares, respectively. The corresponding degrees of freedom are the ranks of the respective matrices.

Example 6.5. (Energy absorbance of test machines, continued) The ANOVA table for testing homogeneity of the Charpy V-notch impact machines (see page 286) is given in the following table.

Source	Sum of Squares	Degrees of Freedom	Mean Square
Between groups	$R_H^2 - R_0^2 = 378.30$	3	$MS_g = 126.1$
Within groups	$R_0^2 = 503.04$	95	$MS_w = 5.295$
Total	$R_H^2 = 881.34$	98	

This table is obtained by the following R code, where the function `aov` can be used interchangeably with `lm`.

```
aov1 <- aov(Energy~factor(Machine), data = splett2)
anova(aov1); colSums(anova(aov1))[1:2]
```

The F-ratio is found to be 23.814, and the corresponding p-value is 1.406×10^{-11}. The hypothesis of mean homogeneity of treatment effects is strongly rejected.

The following code can be used to compute the sums of squares (and the corresponding degrees of freedom) as squared norms of the response vector projected by the three projection matrices of (6.11).

```
X1 <- binaries(splett2$Machine); n <- dim(X1)[1]
one <- rep(1,n); I <- diag(one)
PX <- projector(X1); P1 <- projector(one)
y <- splett2$Energy
t(y)%*%(PX - P1)%*%y
t(y)%*%(I - PX)%*%y
```

```
t(y)%*%(I - P1)%*%y
qr(PX-P1)$rank; qr(I-PX)$rank; qr(I-P1)$rank
```

The computations of the projection matrices (which work even if the rows of the data set are permuted) will be useful later. □

6.2.4 *Multiple comparisons of group means*

When the null hypothesis of 'equal group means' is rejected, we need to further investigate which of the treatments are better than others. The multiple comparison techniques described in Section 4.2.7, namely Bonferroni, Scheffé and maximum modulus-t methods, can be used for this purpose. Apart from these general methods, there are some methods designed specifically for one-way classified data. We describe here two such methods.

If $\tau_i = \tau_j$, then $\bar{y}_{i\cdot} - \bar{y}_{j\cdot}$ has the $N(0, \sigma^2(n_i^{-1} + n_j^{-1}))$ distribution, and $(\bar{y}_{i\cdot} - \bar{y}_{j\cdot})/[\widehat{\sigma^2}(n_i^{-1} + n_j^{-1})]^{1/2}$ has the t-distribution with $n - t$ degrees of freedom.[1] In the absence of other comparisons, the hypothesis $\tau_i = \tau_j$ should be rejected at the level α when $|\bar{y}_{i\cdot} - \bar{y}_{j\cdot}|$ is larger than

$$LSD_{ij} = t_{n-t,\alpha/2}\sqrt{\widehat{\sigma^2}(n_i^{-1} + n_j^{-1})}.$$

One can use this criterion simultaneously for the differences of several pairs of group means — provided the hypothesis of 'equal group means' has been rejected. If all the group means are equal, then the probability of erroneous rejection of the hypothesis $\tau_1 = \cdots = \tau_t$ through the level-α GLRT is exactly equal to α. Hence, the probability of erroneous rejection of this hypothesis, followed by the rejection of any one of the hypotheses of the type $\tau_i = \tau_j$ is at most α. The very fact that the GLRT precedes the multiple comparisons, protects the level of the latter. This critical value of LSD_{ij} is called Fisher's *protected least significant difference* (PLSD), when it is used in this manner.

Tukey suggested a procedure which can be used without carrying out the GLRT, in the special case $n_1 = \cdots = n_t$. Under the hypothesis of equal group means, the mean-adjusted and scaled group averages $(\bar{y}_1 - \tau_1)/\sqrt{\widehat{\sigma^2}/n_1}, \ldots, (\bar{y}_t - \tau_1)/\sqrt{\widehat{\sigma^2}/n_t}$ have the multivariate t-distribution with parameters t and $n - t$ (see page 157). The null distribution of the range

[1] This is the only section of the book where the notation 't' is used both as the quantile of a distribution and as the number of treatments. The quantile always appears with a subscript.

of these ratios,

$$\max_{1\le i\le t} \frac{\bar{y}_i}{\sqrt{\widehat{\sigma^2}/n_1}} - \min_{1\le i\le t} \frac{\bar{y}_i}{\sqrt{\widehat{\sigma^2}/n_1}},$$

is called the *studentized range distribution* with parameters t and $n-t$. If $q_{t,n-t,\alpha}$ is the $1-\alpha$ quantile of this distribution, then the hypotheses $\tau_i = \tau_j$, $i,j = 1,\ldots,t$, $i \neq j$, can be tested simultaneously at the level α by checking if $|\bar{y}_{i\cdot} - \bar{y}_{j\cdot}|$ is larger than

$$HSD = q_{t,n-t,\alpha}\sqrt{\widehat{\sigma^2}/n_1}.$$

This critical value of HSD is called Tukey's *honestly significant difference* (HSD). Tables of percentage points of the studentized range distribution are given by Harter (1960). When $n_1,\ldots,n_t$ are unequal, this procedure needs modification. The Tukey-Kramer method is to use the HSD as the cut-off for $|\bar{y}_{i\cdot} - \bar{y}_{j\cdot}|$, with $1/n_1$ replaced by $(1/n_i + 1/n_j)/2$. See Miller (1981, Chapter 2), Hochberg and Tamhane (2009) and Shaffer (1995) for more information on these and other multiple comparison methods for one-way classified data.

Benjamini and Hochberg (1995) and Benjamini and Yekutieli (2001) proposed multiple comparison procedures that control the expected proportion of falsely rejected hypotheses (which they call 'false discovery rate'), rather than the probability of false rejection of every hypothesis. This results in a less conservative procedure that would nevertheless be adequate, if one agrees with the criterion.

Example 6.6. (Energy absorbance of test machines, continued) The adjusted p-values (by four different methods) for testing homogeneity of pairwise group means for the Charpy V-notch impact machines (see page 286) are obtained through the additional lines of code given below.

```
library(DescTools)
fMachine <- factor(splett2$Machine, labels = mnames)
aov1 <- aov(Energy ~ fMachine, data = splett2)
PostHocTest(aov1, method = "lsd")
PostHocTest(aov1, method = "bonferroni")
PostHocTest(aov1, method = "scheffe")
PostHocTest(aov1, method = "hsd")
```

The output is summarized in the following table.

Contrast	p-value according to			
	LSD	Bonferroni	Scheffé	Tukey
Tinius1 – Tinius2	0.0186	0.112	0.132	0.0850
Tinius1 – Satec	3.10×10^{-11}	1.86×10^{-10}	1.1×10^{-9}	6.50×10^{-10}
Tinius1 – Tokyo	0.599	1.000	0.964	0.952
Tinius2 – Satec	1.270×10^{-6}	7.62×10^{-6}	2.87×10^{-5}	7.50×10^{-6}
Tinius2 – Tokyo	0.0622	0.373	0.319	0.241
Satec – Tokyo	2.70×10^{-10}	1.62×10^{-9}	9.27×10^{-9}	2.08×10^{-9}

Fisher's LSD, which is the most powerful procedure, is applicable in this case only because the hypothesis of homogeneity of all means has been rejected. The other procedures lead to similar conclusions (significance of the second, the fourth and the sixth contrasts). Interestingly, the first contrast is significant at the 5% level only if Fisher's LSD is used. The analysis shows that the rejection of the hypothesis of mean heterogeneity (see Example 6.5) has been mostly due to the mean of the Satec standing apart from the means of the other three machines. Figure 6.1 gives qualitative support to this finding. □

6.3 Two-way classified data

As we mentioned earlier in this chapter, our main interest is often in checking if the treatments have equal effects and in the event that they are not all the same, to pick the best among them. In any such study however, we cannot ignore other major factors that contribute significantly to the total variability, since if we do, this contribution will become part of the residual or error sum of squares. *Error control* should be part of any good design. To this end, we might separate the experimental units into groups, called *blocks* which are homogeneous with respect to all non-treatment factors and replicate the complete set of t treatments inside each block. For instance, in an agricultural experiment where we wish to find which variety of wheat is best, the effect of different levels of soil-fertility on the experimental units can be an important source of variability. We can divide the available experimental units into blocks so that soil-fertility within each block is nearly equal. This is known as *blocking*.

6.3.1 Single observation per cell

Let us first consider the simple case where we have $n = t \times b$ experimental units and these are divided into b blocks of t units each. We then randomly assign the t treatments, one to each unit inside the block, so that each block represents a complete replication of the treatments. This type of design is called a *randomized block design* (RBD) with one observation per cell, a cell representing a combination of treatment and block. Let y_{ij} denote the yield on the ith treatment in the jth block, $i = 1, \ldots, t$, $j = 1, \ldots, b$. We may assume the simple additive effects model

$$\begin{aligned} y_{ij} &= \mu + \tau_i + \beta_j + \varepsilon_{ij}, \quad i = 1, \ldots, t, \; j = 1, \ldots, b, \\ E(\varepsilon_{ij}) &= 0, \\ Cov(\varepsilon_{ij}, \varepsilon_{i'j'}) &= \begin{cases} \sigma^2 & \text{if } i = i' \text{ and } j = j', \\ 0 & \text{otherwise,} \end{cases} \end{aligned} \tag{6.12}$$

where μ represents the baseline effect, τ_i the effect of the ith treatment and β_j the effect of the jth block.

The matrix-vector form of the model is

$$\boldsymbol{y}_{n\times 1} = \boldsymbol{X}_{n\times(t+b+1)}\boldsymbol{\beta}_{(t+b+1)\times 1} + \boldsymbol{\varepsilon}_{n\times 1}, \quad E(\boldsymbol{\varepsilon}) = \boldsymbol{0}, \quad D(\boldsymbol{\varepsilon}) = \sigma^2\boldsymbol{I},$$

where

$$\begin{aligned} \boldsymbol{y} &= (y_{11} : \cdots : y_{1b} : y_{21} : \cdots : y_{2b} : \cdots\cdots : y_{t1} : \cdots : y_{tb})', \\ \boldsymbol{X} &= (\boldsymbol{1}_{n\times 1} : \boldsymbol{I}_{t\times t} \otimes \boldsymbol{1}_{b\times 1} : \boldsymbol{1}_{t\times 1} \otimes \boldsymbol{I}_{b\times b}), \\ &= \begin{pmatrix} \boldsymbol{1}_{b\times 1} & \boldsymbol{1}_{b\times 1} & \boldsymbol{0}_{b\times 1} & \cdots & \boldsymbol{0}_{b\times 1} & \boldsymbol{I}_{b\times b} \\ \boldsymbol{1}_{b\times 1} & \boldsymbol{0}_{b\times 1} & \boldsymbol{1}_{b\times 1} & \cdots & \boldsymbol{0}_{b\times 1} & \boldsymbol{I}_{b\times b} \\ \vdots & \vdots & \vdots & \ddots & \vdots & \vdots \\ \boldsymbol{1}_{b\times 1} & \boldsymbol{0}_{b\times 1} & \boldsymbol{0}_{b\times 1} & \cdots & \boldsymbol{1}_{b\times 1} & \boldsymbol{I}_{b\times b} \end{pmatrix} \\ \boldsymbol{\beta} &= (\mu : \tau_1 : \cdots : \tau_t : \beta_1 : \cdots : \beta_b)', \\ \boldsymbol{\varepsilon} &= (\varepsilon_{11} : \cdots : \varepsilon_{1b} : \varepsilon_{21} : \cdots : \varepsilon_{2b} : \cdots\cdots : \varepsilon_{t1} : \cdots : \varepsilon_{tb})'. \end{aligned}$$

In the above, the notation '$\otimes$' signifies the Kronecker product.

The first column of $\boldsymbol{X}$ is equal to the sum of the next t columns and also to the sum of the last b columns. It can be verified that the last $t + b - 1$ columns of $\boldsymbol{X}$ are linearly independent. Thus, $\rho(\boldsymbol{X}) = t + b - 1$.

Example 6.7. Table 6.3 shows part of a larger data set from a designed experiment (Wilkie, 1962). The response is the position of highest speed of air blown down the space between a roughened rod and a smoothed

Table 6.3 Air speed experiment data (data object **airspeed** in R package **lmreg**, source: Wilkie, 1962)

Rib height (i)	4.8	4.9	5.0	5.1	5.2	5.3
	Reynolds number (j)					
0.010 inch	–0.024	–0.023	0.001	0.008	0.029	0.023
0.015 inch	0.033	0.028	0.045	0.057	0.074	0.080
0.020 inch	0.037	0.079	0.079	0.095	0.101	0.111

pipe surrounding it. This position is defined as the distance in inches from the center of the rod, in excess of 1.4 inches. The height of ribs on the roughened rod can have three different values. For each height category, one measurement is taken for six different Reynolds numbers.

Let the rib height be regarded as treatment and the Reynolds number as block. Note that each combination of treatment and block appears only once. The following code uses the function `yX` of the R package `lmreg` to produce the $\boldsymbol{y}$ vector and the $\boldsymbol{X}$ matrix defined in the foregoing discussion.

```
data(airspeed)
yX(airspeed$Posmaxspeed, airspeed$Reynolds, airspeed$Ribht)
```

The output is omitted for brevity; the reader may verify that the data are in the requisite format. □

Sometimes it is assumed that $\sum_{i=1}^{t}\tau_i = 0$ and $\sum_{j=1}^{b}\beta_j = 0$. If these restrictions are imposed, then the baseline effect μ can be interpreted as the overall mean effect. These are model-preserving constraints which make all the parameters estimable. However, we shall not need any such restriction for our analysis.

As indicated earlier, our main interest is in treatment effects. Let $\boldsymbol{c} = (c_1 : \cdots : c_t)'$ and $\boldsymbol{\tau} = (\tau_1 : \cdots : \tau_t)'$. According to Exercise 3.41, $\boldsymbol{c}'\boldsymbol{\tau}$ is estimable if and only if $\boldsymbol{c}'\boldsymbol{1} = 0$. Thus, treatment contrasts turn out to be the only estimable linear functions of the treatment parameters — as in the case of CRD.

In order to find the BLUE of $\boldsymbol{X\beta}$, let us determine $\boldsymbol{P}_X$. Since

$$\begin{aligned}\mathcal{C}(\boldsymbol{X}) &= \mathcal{C}(\boldsymbol{1}_{n\times 1} : \boldsymbol{I}_{t\times t} \otimes \boldsymbol{1}_{b\times 1} : \boldsymbol{1}_{t\times 1} \otimes \boldsymbol{I}_{b\times b}) \\ &= \mathcal{C}(\boldsymbol{1}_{n\times 1} : (\boldsymbol{I} - t^{-1}\boldsymbol{1}\boldsymbol{1}') \otimes \boldsymbol{1} : \boldsymbol{1} \otimes (\boldsymbol{I} - b^{-1}\boldsymbol{1}\boldsymbol{1}')),\end{aligned} \tag{6.13}$$

and the three sets of columns of the last matrix are orthogonal, we have[2]

$$\begin{aligned} \boldsymbol{P}_X &= \boldsymbol{P}_{1_{n\times 1}} + \boldsymbol{P}_{(I-t^{-1}11')\otimes 1} + \boldsymbol{P}_{1\otimes(I-b^{-1}11')} \\ &= n^{-1}\mathbf{1}\mathbf{1}' + (\boldsymbol{I} - t^{-1}\mathbf{1}\mathbf{1}') \otimes (b^{-1}\mathbf{1}\mathbf{1}') + (t^{-1}\mathbf{1}\mathbf{1}') \otimes (\boldsymbol{I} - b^{-1}\mathbf{1}\mathbf{1}'). \quad (6.14) \end{aligned}$$

The above decomposition of $\boldsymbol{P}_X$ implies

$$\boldsymbol{X}\widehat{\boldsymbol{\beta}} = \boldsymbol{P}_X\boldsymbol{y} = \overline{y}_{..}\mathbf{1}_{n\times 1} + \begin{pmatrix} \overline{y}_{1.} - \overline{y}_{..} \\ \vdots \\ \overline{y}_{t.} - \overline{y}_{..} \end{pmatrix} \otimes \mathbf{1}_{b\times 1} + \mathbf{1}_{t\times 1} \otimes \begin{pmatrix} \overline{y}_{.1} - \overline{y}_{..} \\ \vdots \\ \overline{y}_{.b} - \overline{y}_{..} \end{pmatrix}, \quad (6.15)$$

where 'dot' in the subscript indicates averaging over the corresponding index. In particular, fitted value and residual for y_{ij} are

$$\widehat{y}_{ij} = \overline{y}_{..} + (\overline{y}_{i.} - \overline{y}_{..}) + (\overline{y}_{.j} - \overline{y}_{..}) \ = \ \overline{y}_{i.} + \overline{y}_{.j} - \overline{y}_{..}, \quad (6.16)$$

$$e_{ij} = y_{ij} - \overline{y}_{i.} - \overline{y}_{.j} + \overline{y}_{..}. \quad (6.17)$$

The three terms in the first expression of $\widehat{y}_{ij}$ are the BLUEs of the following estimable functions: the grand mean $\left(\mu + t^{-1}\sum_{i=1}^t \tau_i + b^{-1}\sum_{j=1}^b \beta_j\right)$, the deviation of the ith treatment effect from the mean treatment effect $\left(\tau_i - t^{-1}\sum_{j=1}^t \tau_j\right)$ and the deviation of the jth block effect from the mean block effect $\left(\beta_j - b^{-1}\sum_{i=1}^b \beta_i\right)$, respectively. Under the model preserving constraints $\sum_{i=1}^t \tau_i = 0$ and $\sum_{j=1}^b \beta_j = 0$, these three terms are the BLUEs of μ, τ_i and β_j, respectively.

It follows from the expression of $\boldsymbol{P}_X$ that

$$D(\boldsymbol{X}\widehat{\boldsymbol{\beta}}) = \sigma^2[n^{-1}\mathbf{1}\mathbf{1}' + (\boldsymbol{I} - t^{-1}\mathbf{1}\mathbf{1}') \otimes (b^{-1}\mathbf{1}\mathbf{1}') + (t^{-1}\mathbf{1}\mathbf{1}') \otimes (\boldsymbol{I} - b^{-1}\mathbf{1}\mathbf{1}')]. \quad (6.18)$$

The error sum of squares and the usual unbiased estimator of σ^2 are (see (6.17))

$$R_0^2 = \sum_{i=1}^t \sum_{j=1}^b (y_{ij} - \overline{y}_{i.} - \overline{y}_{.j} + \overline{y}_{..})^2, \quad (6.19)$$

$$\widehat{\sigma^2} = R_0^2/(n - t - b + 1). \quad (6.20)$$

[2]Here as well as in some of the other designs to follow, decomposition of the projection matrix as the sum of several projection matrices plays a crucial role in arriving at the analysis of variance. The algebra of this decomposition may initially appear to be involved, but the compact representation opens the door for analysis of more complicated designs. The benefits are sure to outweigh the effort needed to get used to this approach. This decomposition also corresponds to a reparametrization; see Exercise 6.2.

In view of (6.17), we can decompose the total sum of squares as

$$\begin{aligned} S_t &= \sum_{i=1}^{t}\sum_{j=1}^{b}(y_{ij} - \overline{y}_{..})^2 \\ &= \sum_{i=1}^{t}\sum_{j=1}^{b}[e_{ij} + (\overline{y}_{i.} - \overline{y}_{..}) + (\overline{y}_{.j} - \overline{y}_{..})]^2 \\ &= \sum_{i=1}^{t}\sum_{j=1}^{b} e_{ij}^2 + \sum_{i=1}^{t}\sum_{j=1}^{b}(\overline{y}_{i.} - \overline{y}_{..})^2 + \sum_{i=1}^{t}\sum_{j=1}^{b}(\overline{y}_{.j} - \overline{y}_{..})^2. \end{aligned}$$

The last step follows from the fact that each of the cross-terms, when summed over either i or j, become zero. The first of the three sums in the last expression is immediately recognized as R_0^2; we denote the second and the third sums by S_τ and S_β, respectively. The sum

$$S_\tau = \sum_{i=1}^{t}\sum_{j=1}^{b}(\overline{y}_{i.} - \overline{y}_{..})^2 = b\sum_{i=1}^{t}(\overline{y}_{i.} - \overline{y}_{..})^2$$

can be called the sum of squares due to difference between treatments, as it measures the total squared departure of treatment-specific mean responses from the overall mean response. Likewise, the sum

$$S_\beta = \sum_{i=1}^{t}\sum_{j=1}^{b}(\overline{y}_{.j} - \overline{y}_{..})^2 = t\sum_{j=1}^{b}(\overline{y}_{.j} - \overline{y}_{..})^2$$

can be called the sum of squares due to difference between blocks.

As in the case of CRD, an important hypothesis of interest is that of 'no difference in treatment effects',

$$\mathcal{H}_0 : \tau_1 = \tau_2 = \cdots = \tau_t.$$

The hypothesis can be written as $\boldsymbol{A\beta} = \mathbf{0}$, where

$$\boldsymbol{A}_{(t-1)\times(t+b+1)} = \begin{pmatrix} 0 & 1 & -1 & 0 \cdots & 0 & 0 \cdots & 0 \\ 0 & 0 & 1 & -1 \cdots & 0 & 0 \cdots & 0 \\ \vdots & \vdots & \vdots & \ddots \quad \ddots & \vdots & \vdots \ddots & \vdots \\ 0 & 0 & 0 \cdots & 1 & -1 & 0 \cdots & 0 \end{pmatrix}.$$

Under $\mathcal{H}_0$, (6.12) reduces to a model with only block effect and no treatment effect. This is a version of (6.1), with blocks assuming the roles of treatments. Therefore, the error sum of squares under $\mathcal{H}_0$ is (see (6.3))

$$R_H^2 = \sum_{i=1}^{t}\sum_{j=1}^{b}(y_{ij} - \overline{y}_{.j})^2, \tag{6.21}$$

which implies

$$R_H^2 - R_0^2 = \sum_{i=1}^{t}\sum_{j=1}^{b}[e_{ij} + (\overline{y}_{i\cdot} - \overline{y}_{\cdot\cdot})]^2 - R_0^2 = S_\tau.$$

Once again, the cross-terms vanish because $\sum_{j=1}^{b} e_{ij} = 0$ for $i = 1, \ldots, t$. Thus, the sum of squares $\boldsymbol{S}_\tau$ accounts for departure from $\mathcal{H}_0$. Note that the deviation of the ith treatment effect from the mean $(\overline{y}_{i\cdot} - \overline{y}_{\cdot\cdot})$ is a BLUE of (6.12) which turns into an LZF under $\mathcal{H}_0$, for $i = 1, \ldots, t$. All of these are linear functions of $\boldsymbol{A}\widehat{\boldsymbol{\beta}}$. Thus, the number of degrees of freedom associated with the sum of squares S_τ is equal to the number of linearly independent LZFs (under $\mathcal{H}_0$) contained in $\boldsymbol{A}\widehat{\boldsymbol{\beta}}$, which is equal to $\rho(\boldsymbol{A})$, i.e. $t-1$. By symmetry of the block and treatment effects in the model (6.12), the degrees of freedom associated with S_β is $b-1$. The degrees of freedom associated with the error sum of squares is $n - \rho(\boldsymbol{X}) = n - t - b + 1 = (b-1)(t-1)$. Thus, we have the detailed analysis of variance given in Table 6.4.

The GLRT statistic for $\mathcal{H}_0$ is given by MS_τ/MS_e, which simplifies to $(b-1)S_\tau/R_0^2$. This statistic has the $F_{(t-1),(b-1)(t-1)}$ distribution under $\mathcal{H}_0$. By analogy, the GLRT for the hypothesis of 'no difference in block effects' is $(t-1)S_\beta/R_0^2$, and has the $F_{(b-1),(b-1)(t-1)}$ distribution under this null hypothesis. When two-way classified data arises from a RBD, this test can be used to determine whether heterogeneity due to the non-treatment factors has been accounted for by 'blocking'.

Table 6.4 ANOVA for model (6.12) of two-way classified data

Source	Sum of Squares	Degrees of Freedom	Mean Square
Between treatments	$S_\tau = b\sum_{i=1}^{t}(\overline{y}_{i\cdot} - \overline{y}_{\cdot\cdot})^2$	$t-1$	$MS_\tau = \frac{S_\tau}{t-1}$
Between blocks	$S_\beta = t\sum_{j=1}^{b}(\overline{y}_{\cdot j} - \overline{y}_{\cdot\cdot})^2$	$b-1$	$MS_\beta = \frac{S_\beta}{b-1}$
Error	$R_0^2 = \sum_{i=1}^{t}\sum_{j=1}^{b}(y_{ij} - \overline{y}_{i\cdot} - \overline{y}_{\cdot j} + \overline{y}_{\cdot\cdot})^2$	$(b-1)(t-1)$	$MS_e = \frac{R_0^2}{(b-1)(t-1)}$
Total	$S_t = \sum_{i=1}^{t}\sum_{j=1}^{b}(y_{ij} - \overline{y}_{\cdot\cdot})^2$	$n-1$	

The decomposition of projection matrices given in (6.14) leads us to another decomposition:

$$\begin{aligned} \boldsymbol{P}_t &= \boldsymbol{P}_\tau + \boldsymbol{P}_\beta + \boldsymbol{P}_e, \qquad (6.22)\\ \text{where } \boldsymbol{P}_\tau &= (\boldsymbol{I} - t^{-1}\mathbf{1}\mathbf{1}') \otimes (b^{-1}\mathbf{1}\mathbf{1}'),\\ \boldsymbol{P}_\beta &= (t^{-1}\mathbf{1}\mathbf{1}') \otimes (\boldsymbol{I} - b^{-1}\mathbf{1}\mathbf{1}'),\\ \boldsymbol{P}_e &= \boldsymbol{I} - \boldsymbol{P}_X,\\ \boldsymbol{P}_t &= \boldsymbol{I} - \boldsymbol{P}_1. \end{aligned}$$

The ranks of these four projection matrices are the degrees of freedom given in the four rows of Table 6.4, while the sums of squares in those rows are the squared norms of the response vector projected by these matrices.

Example 6.8. (Birth of aeroplane) The Wright brothers, credited with the first controlled flight of a heavier-than-air self-propelled aeroplane, had designed their craft based on a home-made wind tunnel experiment. Their measurements of air pressure on 16 types of wings (numbered 1 through 17 with number 14 missing) at 14 different angles, are shown in Table 6.5. We would test whether the variation in the pressure is significantly explained by the variation in angle or wing type, using the two-way classified data model (6.12), after ignoring wing type 13 (for which there are a couple of missing data). The ANOVA table, including the F-ratios of the tests of homogeneity 'between angles' and the 'between wind types' are obtained through the R code given below.

```
data(Wright)
wright <- Wright[Wright$Wing!=13,]
wrightfit <- aov(Pressure~factor(Angle)+factor(Wing),data=wright)
anova(wrightfit)                 # ANOVA table
colSums(anova(wrightfit))[1:2]   # bottom row of ANOVA table
```

The result is displayed in the following table.

Source	Sum of Squares	Degrees of Freedom	Mean Square	F ratio
Between angles	32061	13	2466.23	$\frac{2466.23}{32.93} = 74.89$
Between wing types	7003.7	14	500.26	$\frac{500.26}{32.93} = 15.19$
Error	5993.8	182	32.93	
Total	45058	209		

Table 6.5 Wright brothers' 1901 wind tunnel data on pressure (in psi) over different types of wings at different angles (data object `Wright` in R package `lmreg`, source: Dataplot webpage of the National Institute of Standards and Technology (NIST), USA at `ftp://ftp.nist.gov/pub/dataplot/other/reference/WRIGHT11.DAT`)

Wing	Angle (degrees)													
type	0	2.5	5	7.5	10	12.5	15	17.5	20	25	30	35	40	45
1	0	2	4	8	11	15	19	23	27	34	38	37	29	27
2	0	5	11	17	22	27	31	32	33	33	31	30	28	27
3	0	7	13	20	27	30	32	33	33	32	32	32	32	32
4	7	11	15	18	22	27	32	37	42	49	57	58	47	35
5	6	8	12	16	19	24	28	33	39	47	54	55	40	33
6	5	8	11	15	19	22	27	32	36	44	49	50	38	30
7	8	17	25	31	38	52	61	63	60	50	46	45	43	41
8	8	17	23	29	39	49	55	56	52	47	44	42	41	39
9	8	15	22	27	39	46	50	51	48	44	41	40	40	38
10	7	18	26	33	36	36	38	39	41	44	41	39	39	38
11	7	16	25	32	37	37	38	41	42	41	39	38	38	37
12	6	13	22	32	39	44	46	45	44	41	39	38	38	36
13	8	15	22	27	29	30	32	34	35	36	37			30
15	4	8	12	16	19	24	29	36	40	49	56	52	38	30
16	4	6	10	14	19	22	28	33	37	47	52	48	34	29
17	4	6	9	13	17	21	26	31	35	44	49	45	32	29

The p-values for both the F-ratios are smaller than 2.2×10^{-16}, which is the limit of precision available for this computation. Thus, there is significant heterogeneity among the mean effects of angle and the wing type. A greater part of the variation is explained by the variation in angle. Thus, there is much to be gained in terms of the lift generated by the air pressure, if the angle is chosen optimally. This data based decision had given the Wright brothers an edge over other aspiring developers of a flying machine.

For this data set, the following code computes the sums of squares of the ANOVA table (along with the corresponding degrees of freedom) through projections of the response vector by different projection matrices, by utilizing the function `yX` for constructing the response vector and the design matrix.

```
trment <- wright$Angle; block <- wright$Wing
wrightyX <- yX(wright$Pressure,trment,block)
y <- wrightyX[[1]]; X <- wrightyX[[2]]; n = length(y)
nt = length(unique(trment));  T <- X[,2:(nt+1)]
nb = length(unique(block));  B <- X[,(nt+2):(nt+nb+1)]
one <- rep(1,n); I <- diag(one); P1 = projector(one)
Ptau <- projector(T) - P1
```

```
Pbeta <- projector(B) - P1
Pt <- I - P1
Pe <- Pt - Ptau - Pbeta
t(y)%*%Ptau%*%y; t(y)%*%Pbeta%*%y; t(y)%*%Pe%*%y; t(y)%*%Pt%*%y
qr(Ptau)$rank; qr(Pbeta)$rank; qr(Pe)$rank; qr(Pt)$rank
```

The resulting values coincide with the four corresponding sums of squares reported in the foregoing table. □

6.3.2 *Interaction in two-way classified data*

Suppose within-block heterogeneity has been removed by appropriate 'blocking'. The model (6.12) implies that the block and treatment effects are additive. An implication of this model is that a 'good' block is good for all varieties of treatment, and a good treatment would result in the same incremental improvement of mean response in all the blocks. This assumption may not always hold in practice. For instance, a fertilizer may be very good for the yield of a crop when it is grown on a particular type of soil, but not as good when a different soil type is used. This kind of departure from the additive model (6.12) is known as *interaction* effect between the block and treatment effects.

The effect of interaction can be taken into account by introducing an *interaction term* in (6.12). The resulting model is

$$\begin{aligned} y_{ij} &= \mu + \tau_i + \beta_j + \gamma_{ij} + \varepsilon_{ij},\ i = 1, \ldots, t,\ j = 1, \ldots, b, \\ E(\varepsilon_{ij}) &= 0, \\ Cov(\varepsilon_{ij}, \varepsilon_{i'j'}) &= \begin{cases} \sigma^2 & \text{if } i = i' \text{ and } j = j', \\ 0 & \text{otherwise,} \end{cases} \end{aligned} \tag{6.23}$$

where γ_{ij} represents the interaction effect, and the other parameters are as in (6.12). The design matrix corresponding to this model has rank n. There are effectively n parameters, one for each observation. The model (6.23) is called a *saturated* model.

The model (6.23) is not an adequate vehicle for testing if an interaction is present. This is because there are so many parameters affecting the mean response that after estimating these parameters one no longer has the degrees of freedom to estimate σ^2. As a result, one cannot test for the significance of any parametric function in such a model.

A simpler model which incorporates a limited type of interaction is

$$
\begin{aligned}
y_{ij} &= \mu + \tau_i + \beta_j + \lambda(\tau_i - \bar{\tau})(\beta_j - \bar{\beta}) + \varepsilon_{ij}, \\
&\qquad i = 1, \ldots, t, \; j = 1, \ldots, b, \\
E(\varepsilon_{ij}) &= 0, \\
Cov(\varepsilon_{ij}, \varepsilon_{i'j'}) &= \begin{cases} \sigma^2 & \text{if } i = i' \text{ and } j = j', \\ 0 & \text{otherwise,} \end{cases}
\end{aligned}
\tag{6.24}
$$

where $\bar{\tau} = t^{-1}\sum_{i=1}^{t} \tau_i$, $\bar{\beta} = b^{-1}\sum_{j=1}^{b} \beta_j$, λ represents the extent of interaction, and the other parameters are as in (6.12). The interaction term has a more prominent effect when the treatment and block effects (τ_i and β_j) are both far from their respective averages. The model reduces to (6.12) when $\lambda = 0$. Thus, the hypothesis $\lambda = 0$ signifies absence of interaction (i.e. additivity of the block and treatment effects). Even though the model (6.24) is nonlinear in the parameters, Tukey (1949) showed that a simple test for this hypothesis can be derived in the following manner.

If we assume for the moment that $\mu, \tau_1, \ldots, \tau_t, \beta_1, \ldots, \beta_b$ are *known*, then (6.24) can be rewritten as

$$
\begin{aligned}
y_{ij} - \mu - \tau_i - \beta_j &= \lambda(\tau_i - \bar{\tau})(\beta_j - \bar{\beta}) + \varepsilon_{ij}, \\
&\qquad i = 1, \ldots, t, \; j = 1, \ldots, b, \\
E(\varepsilon_{ij}) &= 0, \\
Cov(\varepsilon_{ij}, \varepsilon_{i'j'}) &= \begin{cases} \sigma^2 & \text{if } i = i' \text{ and } j = j', \\ 0 & \text{otherwise,} \end{cases}
\end{aligned}
\tag{6.25}
$$

which is a linear model, with transformed response $y_{ij} - \mu - \tau_i - \beta_j$, $i = 1, \ldots, t$, $j = 1, \ldots, b$. The parameter λ is estimable, and its BLUE is easily seen to be

$$
\widehat{\lambda} = \frac{\sum_{i=1}^{t}\sum_{j=1}^{b}(y_{ij} - \mu - \tau_i - \beta_j)(\tau_i - \bar{\tau})(\beta_j - \bar{\beta})}{\sum_{i=1}^{t}\sum_{j=1}^{b}(\tau_i - \bar{\tau})^2(\beta_j - \bar{\beta})^2}. \tag{6.26}
$$

By calculating $R_H^2 - R_0^2$ for this model, it turns out that the sum of squares due to deviation from the hypothesis $\lambda = 0$ is (see Exercise 6.4)

$$
S_\lambda = \frac{\left(\sum_{i=1}^{t}\sum_{j=1}^{b}(y_{ij} - \mu - \tau_i - \beta_j)(\tau_i - \bar{\tau})(\beta_j - \bar{\beta})\right)^2}{\sum_{i=1}^{t}\sum_{j=1}^{b}(\tau_i - \bar{\tau})^2(\beta_j - \bar{\beta})^2}. \tag{6.27}
$$

Since $\mu, \tau_1, \ldots, \tau_t, \beta_1, \ldots, \beta_b$ are *unknown*, we can replace these in the above expression by their respective estimators, and reject the hypothesis of no interaction if the above quantity is significantly different from 0. We shall now derive the null distribution of the resulting statistic under the usual assumption of multivariate normality of the errors.

When $\lambda = 0$, (6.25) reduces to (6.12). According to this model, the BLUEs of $\mu + \tau_i + \beta_j$, $(\tau_i - \bar{\tau})$ and $(\beta_j - \bar{\beta})$ are $\widehat{y}_{ij}$, $\overline{y}_{i\cdot} - \overline{y}_{\cdot\cdot}$ and $\overline{y}_{\cdot j} - \overline{y}_{\cdot\cdot}$, respectively (see the discussion following (6.16)). Substituting these BLUEs in the expression for S_λ, we have the statistic

$$\widehat{S}_\lambda = \frac{\left(\sum_{i=1}^t \sum_{j=1}^b e_{ij}(\overline{y}_{i\cdot} - \overline{y}_{\cdot\cdot})(\overline{y}_{\cdot j} - \overline{y}_{\cdot\cdot})\right)^2}{\sum_{i=1}^t \sum_{j=1}^b (\overline{y}_{i\cdot} - \overline{y}_{\cdot\cdot})^2(\overline{y}_{\cdot j} - \overline{y}_{\cdot\cdot})^2}. \tag{6.28}$$

To find the distribution of $\widehat{S}_\lambda$, note that it can be written as

$$\widehat{S}_\lambda = \frac{\left(\sum_{i=1}^t \sum_{j=1}^b a_i b_j e_{ij}\right)^2}{\sum_{i=1}^t \sum_{j=1}^b a_i^2 b_j^2},$$

where $a_i = \overline{y}_{i\cdot} - \overline{y}_{\cdot\cdot}$ and $b_j = \overline{y}_{\cdot j} - \overline{y}_{\cdot\cdot}$, $i = 1, \ldots, t$, $j = 1, \ldots, b$. For fixed a_i and b_j, the numerator is the square of an LZF of (6.12), and the variance of this LZF is σ^2 times the denominator (see Exercise 6.26). Therefore, for fixed a_i and b_j, $\widehat{S}_\lambda/\sigma^2$ has the χ_1^2 distribution, under the assumption of multivariate normality of the model errors. Since $\overline{y}_{i\cdot} - \overline{y}_{\cdot\cdot}$ and $\overline{y}_{\cdot j} - \overline{y}_{\cdot\cdot}$ are BLUEs of the model (6.12) for $i = 1, \ldots, t$, $j = 1, \ldots, b$ these are independent of the LZFs. Therefore, the conditional distribution of $\widehat{S}_\lambda/\sigma^2$ given the BLUEs is χ_1^2. Since the conditional distribution does not depend on the BLUEs, the unconditional distribution must also be χ_1^2.

In order to construct a test statistic, we have to use an estimator of σ^2 which is independent of $\widehat{S}_\lambda$. The latter is the square of an LZF having variance σ^2. Therefore, one can form a standardized basis set of LZFs by augmenting this LZF with $n - t - b$ other LZFs which are independent of the first one. Since the sum of squares of all the $n - t - b + 1$ LZFs is the error sum of squares for (6.23) (see Definition 3.47), the sum of squares of the additional $n - t - b$ LZFs is $R_0^2 - \widehat{S}_\lambda$, which must be independent of $\widehat{S}_\lambda$. It follows that $(n - t - b)\widehat{S}_\lambda/(R_0^2 - \widehat{S}_\lambda)$ has the $F_{1,n-t-b}$ distribution under the hypothesis of $\lambda = 0$. The test which rejects the hypothesis of no interaction (that is, the hypothesis of additivity of block and treatment effects) for large values of $(n - t - b)\widehat{S}_\lambda/(R_0^2 - \widehat{S}_\lambda)$ is known as *Tukey's one-degree of freedom test for nonadditivity.*

The analysis of variance for the model (6.24) is given in Table 6.6. Strictly speaking, $\widehat{S}_\lambda$ is not a sum of squares, but the sum of squares of some 'generalized zero functions' of (6.12), which are nonlinear functions of the response (see Exercise 4.6). The test statistic for the hypothesis of

Table 6.6 ANOVA for model (6.24) of two-way classified data with limited interaction

Source	Sum of Squares	Degrees of Freedom	Mean Square
Between treatments	$S_\tau = b\sum_{i=1}^{t}(\overline{y}_{i\cdot} - \overline{y}_{\cdot\cdot})^2$	$t-1$	$MS_\tau = \dfrac{S_\tau}{t-1}$
Between blocks	$S_\beta = t\sum_{j=1}^{b}(\overline{y}_{\cdot j} - \overline{y}_{\cdot\cdot})^2$	$b-1$	$MS_\beta = \dfrac{S_\beta}{b-1}$
Non-additivity	$\widehat{S}_\lambda = \dfrac{\left(\sum_{i=1}^{t}\sum_{j=1}^{b} e_{ij}(\overline{y}_{i\cdot}-\overline{y}_{\cdot\cdot})(\overline{y}_{\cdot j}-\overline{y}_{\cdot\cdot})\right)^2}{\sum_{i=1}^{t}\sum_{j=1}^{b}(\overline{y}_{i\cdot}-\overline{y}_{\cdot\cdot})^2(\overline{y}_{\cdot j}-\overline{y}_{\cdot\cdot})^2}$	1	$MS_\lambda = \widehat{S}_\lambda$
Error	$R_0^2 - \widehat{S}_\lambda$	$n-t-b$	$MS_e = \dfrac{R_0^2 - \widehat{S}_\lambda}{n-t-b}$
Total	$S_t = \sum_{i=1}^{t}\sum_{j=1}^{b}(y_{ij} - \overline{y}_{\cdot\cdot})^2$	$n-1$	

additivity is the ratio of the mean squares, MS_λ/MS_e. It is a special case of a more general class of tests (see Exercise 6.33).

Ignoring interaction can produce reasonable point estimates but unduly wide confidence intervals of treatment contrasts (see Exercise 6.32). See Scheffé (1959, pp. 134–136) for other effects of ignored interaction in two-way classified data with one observation per cell.

One has to be careful about the interpretation of statistical findings when there is interaction. For instance, if the contrast $\tau_1 - \tau_2$ is found to be significantly positive, it only means that the effect of treatment 1 is likely to be more than that of treatment 2 *when averaged over the b blocks*. It does not necessarily mean that this order holds in every block. As another example, consider the case where the hypothesis of 'no treatment difference' is accepted but the hypothesis of 'no interaction' is rejected. This can happen in a situation where there are differences among the treatments, but those differences somewhat offset one another when averaged over the various blocks.

Example 6.9. (Birth of aeroplane, continued) For the Wright brothers' pressure data given in Table 6.5, the first two rows of Table 6.6, as also the last row, would be as obtained in Example 6.8. In order to generate the third and fourth rows and the F-ratios, we use the following code.

```
wrightfit <- lm(Pressure~factor(Angle)+factor(Wing), data=wright)
errors <- wrightfit$res
yangle <- lm(Pressure~factor(Angle), data=wright)$fit
ywing <- lm(Pressure~factor(Wing), data=wright)$fit
ybar <- lm(Pressure~1, data=wright)$fit
Tukey.num <- (sum(errors*(yangle-ybar)*(ywing-ybar)))^2
Tukey.den <- sum(((yangle-ybar)^2)*((ywing-ybar)^2))
Tukey.ss <- Tukey.num/Tukey.den
ResSS <- sum(errors^2) - Tukey.ss
Resdf <- anova(wrightfit)$Df[3] - 1
ResMS <- ResSS/Resdf # error MS
Tukey.ss; c(ResSS,Resdf,ResMS)
anova(wrightfit)$Mean[1:2] / ResMS # F ratio: treatment & block
Tukey.ss / ResMS # F ratio for nonadditivity
pf((Tukey.ss / ResMS), 1, Resdf, lower.tail=F) # p: nonadditivity
```

The ANOVA Table 6.6 takes the following form, after incorporation of the F-ratios of the three tests.

Source	Sum of Squares	Degrees of Freedom	Mean Square	F ratio
Between angles	32061	13	2466.23	$\frac{2466.23}{33.11} = 74.48$
Between wing types	7003.7	14	500.26	$\frac{500.26}{33.11} = 15.11$
Non-additivity	0.4828	1	0.48	$\frac{0.48}{33.11} = 0.015$
Error	5993.3	181	33.11	
Total	45058	209		

The p-values for the first two F-ratios are smaller than 2.2×10^{-16}, as before. The p-value for the F-ratio for nonadditivity is 0.904. Thus, with the limited data, there is no evidence of interaction. In other words, the model (6.1) should be adequate. □

The model (6.24) represents a very specific type of interaction. Broader interaction between treatment and block effects makes it more difficult to allocate variance to various sources, as clearly as in Table 6.6. Multiple observations per cell provide a way out, as we shall see in the next section.

6.3.3 Multiple observations per cell: balanced data

In Section 6.3.2 we could handle interaction only to a limited extent, as we did not have adequate degrees of freedom to assess all possible types of interaction. This inadequacy is removed if there are multiple observations for every combination of block and treatment. We first consider the case of *balanced data*, when there are equal number of observations for each combination. Thus, we have the following extension of (6.23).

$$\begin{aligned} y_{ijk} &= \mu+\tau_i+\beta_j+\gamma_{ij}+\varepsilon_{ijk},\ i=1,\ldots,t,\ j=1,\ldots,b,\\ &\qquad\qquad\qquad\qquad k=1,\ldots,m,\\ E(\varepsilon_{ijk}) &= 0, \\ Cov(\varepsilon_{ijk},\varepsilon_{i'j'k'}) &= \begin{cases}\sigma^2 & \text{if } i=i',\ j=j' \text{ and } k=k',\\ 0 & \text{otherwise.}\end{cases} \end{aligned} \tag{6.29}$$

The model can be written in the matrix-vector form as

$$\boldsymbol{y}_{n\times 1} = \boldsymbol{X}_{n\times(t+1)(b+1)}\boldsymbol{\beta}_{(t+1)(b+1)\times 1} + \boldsymbol{\varepsilon}_{n\times 1},\quad E(\boldsymbol{\varepsilon}) = \boldsymbol{0},\ \boldsymbol{D}(\boldsymbol{\varepsilon}) = \sigma^2\boldsymbol{I},$$

where $n = tbm$ and

$$\begin{aligned} \boldsymbol{y} &= (((y_{111} : \cdots : y_{11m}) : \cdots : (y_{1b1} : \cdots : y_{1bm})) : \cdots \\ &\qquad \cdots : ((y_{t11} : \cdots : y_{t1m}) : \cdots : (y_{tb1} : \cdots : y_{tbm})))', \\ \boldsymbol{X} &= (\boldsymbol{1}_{t\times 1}\otimes\boldsymbol{1}_{b\times 1} : \boldsymbol{I}_{t\times t}\otimes\boldsymbol{1}_{b\times 1} : \boldsymbol{1}_{t\times 1}\otimes\boldsymbol{I}_{b\times b} : \boldsymbol{I}_{t\times t}\otimes\boldsymbol{I}_{b\times b})\otimes\boldsymbol{1}_{m\times 1}, \\ \boldsymbol{\beta} &= (\mu : (\tau_1 : \cdots : \tau_t) : (\beta_1 : \cdots : \beta_b) : \\ &\qquad (\gamma_{11} : \cdots : \gamma_{1b}) : \cdots : (\gamma_{t1} : \cdots : \gamma_{tb}))', \\ \boldsymbol{\varepsilon} &= (((\varepsilon_{111} : \cdots : \varepsilon_{11m}) : \cdots : (\varepsilon_{1b1} : \cdots : \varepsilon_{1bm})) : \cdots \\ &\qquad \cdots : ((\varepsilon_{t11} : \cdots : \varepsilon_{t1m}) : \cdots : (\varepsilon_{tb1} : \cdots : \varepsilon_{tbm})))'. \end{aligned}$$

Example 6.10. Table 6.7 gives the survival times (in 10 hour units) of groups of four animals randomly allocated to three poisons and four

Table 6.7 Survival times of animals exposed to poison and treatment (data object `poison` in R package `lmreg`, source: Box and Cox, 1964)

Poison I				Poison II				Poison III			
Treatment				Treatment				Treatment			
A	B	C	D	A	B	C	D	A	B	C	D
3.1	8.2	4.3	4.5	3.6	9.2	4.4	5.6	2.2	3.0	2.3	3.0
4.5	11	4.5	7.1	2.9	6.1	3.5	10.2	2.1	3.7	2.5	3.6
4.6	8.8	6.3	6.6	4.0	4.9	3.1	7.1	1.8	3.8	2.4	3.1
4.3	7.2	7.6	6.2	2.3	12.4	4.0	3.8	2.3	2.9	2.2	3.3

treatments. The data, which appear in Box and Cox (1964), arise from an experiment that was part of an investigation to study the effects of certain toxic agents. There is no blocking, and both the factors are of interest. The following code uses the function `yXm` of the R package `lmreg` to produce the $\boldsymbol{y}$ vector and $\boldsymbol{X}$ matrix defined above.

```
data(poison)
yXm(poison$Survtime,poison$Treatment,poison$Poison)
```

The output is omitted for brevity; it may be verified that it corresponds to a reordered version of the original data and is in the requisite format. □

Note from the definition of $\boldsymbol{X}$ that

$$\begin{aligned}&\mathcal{C}(\boldsymbol{X})\\&=\mathcal{C}((\mathbf{1}_{t\times1}\otimes\mathbf{1}_{b\times1}:\boldsymbol{I}_{t\times t}\otimes\mathbf{1}_{b\times1}:\mathbf{1}_{t\times1}\otimes\boldsymbol{I}_{b\times b}:\boldsymbol{I}_{t\times t}\otimes\boldsymbol{I}_{b\times b})\otimes\mathbf{1}_{m\times1})\\&=\mathcal{C}((\mathbf{1}_{t\times1}\otimes\mathbf{1}_{b\times1}:(\boldsymbol{I}-\boldsymbol{P}_{\mathbf{1}_{t\times1}})\otimes\mathbf{1}_{b\times1}:\mathbf{1}_{t\times1}\otimes(\boldsymbol{I}-\boldsymbol{P}_{\mathbf{1}_{b\times1}}):\\&\qquad(\boldsymbol{I}-\boldsymbol{P}_{\mathbf{1}_{t\times1}})\otimes(\boldsymbol{I}-\boldsymbol{P}_{\mathbf{1}_{b\times1}}))\otimes\mathbf{1}_{m\times1}).\end{aligned}$$

The columns in the four partitions of the last matrix are orthogonal to one another. Therefore,

$$\boldsymbol{P}_X=\boldsymbol{P}_\mu+\boldsymbol{P}_\tau+\boldsymbol{P}_\beta+\boldsymbol{P}_\gamma, \tag{6.30}$$

where

$$\begin{aligned}\boldsymbol{P}_\mu&=\boldsymbol{P}_{\mathbf{1}_{t\times1}}\otimes\boldsymbol{P}_{\mathbf{1}_{b\times1}}\otimes\boldsymbol{P}_{\mathbf{1}_{m\times1}},\\\boldsymbol{P}_\tau&=(\boldsymbol{I}-\boldsymbol{P}_{\mathbf{1}_{t\times1}})\otimes\boldsymbol{P}_{\mathbf{1}_{b\times1}}\otimes\boldsymbol{P}_{\mathbf{1}_{m\times1}},\\\boldsymbol{P}_\beta&=\boldsymbol{P}_{\mathbf{1}_{t\times1}}\otimes(\boldsymbol{I}-\boldsymbol{P}_{\mathbf{1}_{b\times1}})\otimes\boldsymbol{P}_{\mathbf{1}_{m\times1}},\\\boldsymbol{P}_\gamma&=(\boldsymbol{I}-\boldsymbol{P}_{\mathbf{1}_{t\times1}})\otimes(\boldsymbol{I}-\boldsymbol{P}_{\mathbf{1}_{b\times1}})\otimes\boldsymbol{P}_{\mathbf{1}_{m\times1}}.\end{aligned}$$

Therefore, the BLUE of $\boldsymbol{X\beta}$ is

$$\boldsymbol{X}\widehat{\boldsymbol{\beta}}=\boldsymbol{P}_\mu\boldsymbol{y}+\boldsymbol{P}_\tau\boldsymbol{y}+\boldsymbol{P}_\beta\boldsymbol{y}+\boldsymbol{P}_\gamma\boldsymbol{y}. \tag{6.31}$$

In particular, the fitted value of y_{ijk} and the corresponding residual are

$$\widehat{y}_{ijk}=\bar{y}_{\cdots}+(\bar{y}_{i\cdot\cdot}-\bar{y}_{\cdots})+(\bar{y}_{\cdot j\cdot}-\bar{y}_{\cdots})+(\bar{y}_{ij\cdot}-\bar{y}_{i\cdot\cdot}-\bar{y}_{\cdot j\cdot}+\bar{y}_{\cdots})=\bar{y}_{ij\cdot} \tag{6.32}$$

$$e_{ijk}=y_{ijk}-\bar{y}_{ij\cdot}, \tag{6.33}$$

where 'dot' in the subscript indicates averaging over the corresponding index. The four terms in the middle expression of (6.32) are the respective BLUEs of the following estimable parametric functions (see Exercise 6.7):

(a) the grand mean, $\mu+\bar{\tau}+\bar{\beta}+\bar{\gamma}_{\cdot\cdot}$;

(b) the deviation of the ith treatment effect from the average treatment effect (averaged over all the blocks), $\tau_i - \bar{\tau} + \bar{\gamma}_{i\cdot} - \bar{\gamma}_{\cdot\cdot}$;

(c) the deviation of the jth block effect from the average block effect (averaged over all the treatments), $\beta_j - \bar{\beta} + \bar{\gamma}_{\cdot j} - \bar{\gamma}_{\cdot\cdot}$;

(d) the deviation of the ijth interaction effect from the average interaction effects of the ith treatment and the jth block, $\gamma_{ij} - \bar{\gamma}_{i\cdot} - \bar{\gamma}_{\cdot j} + \bar{\gamma}_{\cdot\cdot}$.

Under the model-preserving 'side-conditions' $\bar{\tau} = 0$, $\bar{\beta} = 0$, $\bar{\gamma}_{i\cdot} = 0$, $i = 1, \ldots, t$ and $\bar{\gamma}_{\cdot j} = 0$, $j = 1, \ldots, b$, the above four parametric functions simplify to μ, τ_i, β_j and γ_{ij}, respectively.

The dispersion of $\boldsymbol{X}\widehat{\boldsymbol{\beta}}$ is $\sigma^2 \boldsymbol{P}_X$, where $\boldsymbol{P}_X$ is given in (6.30). Since the four components of this projection matrix are orthogonal, the four parts of $\widehat{y}_{ijk}$ are uncorrelated. The error sum of squares and the usual unbiased estimator of σ^2 are (see Exercise 6.7)

$$R_0^2 = \sum_{i=1}^{t} \sum_{j=1}^{b} \sum_{k=1}^{m} (y_{ijk} - \bar{y}_{ij\cdot})^2, \tag{6.34}$$

$$\widehat{\sigma^2} = R_0^2/(n - tb) = R_0^2/[tb(m-1)]. \tag{6.35}$$

Using the decomposition

$$\boldsymbol{y} = \boldsymbol{P}_\mu \boldsymbol{y} + \boldsymbol{P}_\tau \boldsymbol{y} + \boldsymbol{P}_\beta \boldsymbol{y} + \boldsymbol{P}_\gamma \boldsymbol{y} + (\boldsymbol{I} - \boldsymbol{P}_X)\boldsymbol{y},$$

we can define the sum of squares,

$$S_\tau = \|\boldsymbol{P}_\tau \boldsymbol{y}\|^2 = \sum_{i=1}^{t} \sum_{j=1}^{b} \sum_{k=1}^{m} (\bar{y}_{i\cdot\cdot} - \bar{y}_{\cdot\cdot\cdot})^2 = bm \sum_{i=1}^{t} (\bar{y}_{i\cdot\cdot} - \bar{y}_{\cdot\cdot\cdot})^2,$$

$$S_\beta = \|\boldsymbol{P}_\beta \boldsymbol{y}\|^2 = \sum_{i=1}^{t} \sum_{j=1}^{b} \sum_{k=1}^{m} (\bar{y}_{\cdot j\cdot} - \bar{y}_{\cdot\cdot\cdot})^2 = tm \sum_{j=1}^{b} (\bar{y}_{\cdot j\cdot} - \bar{y}_{\cdot\cdot\cdot})^2,$$

$$S_\gamma = \|\boldsymbol{P}_\gamma \boldsymbol{y}\|^2 = \sum_{i=1}^{t} \sum_{j=1}^{b} \sum_{k=1}^{m} (\bar{y}_{ij\cdot} - \bar{y}_{i\cdot\cdot} - \bar{y}_{\cdot j\cdot} + \bar{y}_{\cdot\cdot\cdot})^2$$

$$= m \sum_{i=1}^{t} \sum_{j=1}^{b} (\bar{y}_{ij\cdot} - \bar{y}_{i\cdot\cdot} - \bar{y}_{\cdot j\cdot} + \bar{y}_{\cdot\cdot\cdot})^2,$$

$$R_0^2 = \|(\boldsymbol{I} - \boldsymbol{P}_X)\boldsymbol{y}\|^2 = \sum_{i=1}^{t} \sum_{j=1}^{b} \sum_{k=1}^{m} (y_{ijk} - \bar{y}_{ij\cdot})^2,$$

$$S_t = \|(\boldsymbol{I} - \boldsymbol{P}_\mu)\boldsymbol{y}\|^2 = \sum_{i=1}^{t} \sum_{j=1}^{b} \sum_{k=1}^{m} (y_{ijk} - \bar{y}_{\cdot\cdot\cdot})^2.$$

Table 6.8 ANOVA for model (6.29) of balanced two-way classified data with interaction

Source	Sum of Squares	Degrees of Freedom	Mean Square
Between treatments	$S_\tau = \|\|\boldsymbol{P}_\tau \boldsymbol{y}\|\|^2$	$t-1$	$MS_\tau = \dfrac{S_\tau}{t-1}$
Between blocks	$S_\beta = \|\|\boldsymbol{P}_\beta \boldsymbol{y}\|\|^2$	$b-1$	$MS_\beta = \dfrac{S_\beta}{b-1}$
Interaction	$S_\gamma = \|\|\boldsymbol{P}_\gamma \boldsymbol{y}\|\|^2$	$(t-1)\cdot(b-1)$	$MS_\gamma = \dfrac{S_\gamma}{(t-1)(b-1)}$
Error	$R_0^2 = \|\|(\boldsymbol{I} - \boldsymbol{P}_X)\boldsymbol{y}\|\|^2$	$n - tb$	$MS_e = \dfrac{R_0^2}{n-tb}$
Total	$S_t = \|\|(\boldsymbol{I} - \boldsymbol{P}_\mu)\boldsymbol{y}\|\|^2$	$n-1$	

Thus, we have the analysis of variance of model (6.29), given in Table 6.8.

The mean squares in the last column of Table 6.8 can be used to test several hypotheses, assuming that the errors have the multivariate normal distribution. The GLRT for the hypothesis of 'no treatment effect' consists of rejecting the hypothesis when the statistic MS_τ/MS_e is too large. The null distribution of this statistic is $F_{t-1,n-tb}$. The GLRT for the hypothesis of 'no block effect' can be obtained similarly. The GLRT for the hypothesis of 'no interaction effect' is to reject the null hypothesis when MS_γ/MS_e is too large, the null distribution of the statistic being $F_{(t-1)(b-1),n-tb}$. Tests for the significance of specific contrasts or interaction effects can also be obtained from the general theory (see Exercises 6.36 and 6.37).

If the hypothesis of no interaction cannot be rejected, then one may test the hypotheses of 'no block effect' and 'no treatment effect' using a reduced model with no interaction. This model, given below, is obtained by eliminating the γ_{ij}s from (6.29).

$$
\begin{aligned}
y_{ijk} &= \mu + \tau_i + \beta_j + \varepsilon_{ijk},\ i = 1,\ldots,t,\ j = 1,\ldots,b,\\
&\qquad\qquad\qquad k = 1,\ldots,m,\\
E(\varepsilon_{ijk}) &= 0, \qquad\qquad\qquad\qquad\qquad\qquad\qquad (6.36)\\
Cov(\varepsilon_{ijk},\varepsilon_{i'j'k'}) &= \begin{cases} \sigma^2 & \text{if } i=i',\ j=j' \text{ and } k=k',\\ 0 & \text{otherwise.}\end{cases}
\end{aligned}
$$

The resulting analysis of variance is similar to Table 6.8, except that all the BLUEs corresponding to the interaction effects become LZFs. Therefore,

S_γ has to be added to R_0^2 in order to obtain the error sum of squares of the simplified model, and the corresponding number of degrees of freedom is $n - bt + (t-1)(b-1) = n - b - t + 1$. The hypotheses of 'no treatment effect' or 'no block effect' can be tested on the basis of this table.

Example 6.11. (Abrasion of denim jeans, continued) We revisit the data given in Table 3.2, under the general model (6.29). For these data, we construct Table 6.8 using the code given below.

```
data(denim)
jeansaov <- aov(Abrasion~factor(Denim)+factor(Laundry)
                +factor(Denim)*factor(Laundry), data = denim)
anova(jeansaov)
colSums(anova(jeansaov))[1:2]
```

The resulting table (with F-ratios's included in the last column) is as follows.

Source	Sum of Squares	Degrees of Freedom	Mean Square	F ratio
Between denim treatments	13.4163	2	6.7082	39.0194
Between laundry cycles	4.2714	2	2.1357	12.4227
Interaction	1.3296	4	0.3324	1.9335
Error	13.9254	81	0.1719	
Total	32.9428	89		

The p-values corresponding to the three F-ratios are 1.358×10^{-12}, 1.97×10^{-05} and 0.1127, respectively. Clearly, there is strong evidence of heterogeneity of denim treatment effects and Laundry cycles, but no significant interaction (even at 10% level).

The sums of squares reported above, along with the corresponding degrees of freedom, can also be obtained as on page 311 (through the projection matrices defined on page 310), using the code given below.

```
jeansyXm <- yXm(denim$Abrasion,denim$Denim,denim$Laundry)
y <- jeansyXm[[1]]; X <- jeansyXm[[2]]; n = length(y)
nt = length(unique(denim$Denim))
nb = length(unique(denim$Laundry))
```

```
T <- X[,2:(nt+1)]
B <- X[,(nt+2):(nt+nb+1)]
G <- X[,(nt+nb+2):dim(X)[2]]
one <- rep(1,n)
I <- diag(one)
P1 = projector(one)
Pt <- I - P1
Ptau <- projector(T) - P1
Pbeta <- projector(B) - P1
Pe <- I - projector(G)
Pgamma <- Pt - Ptau - Pbeta - Pe
t(y)%*%Ptau%*%y; qr(Ptau)$rank
t(y)%*%Pbeta%*%y; qr(Pbeta)$rank
t(y)%*%Pgamma%*%y; qr(Pgamma)$rank
t(y)%*%Pe%*%y; qr(Pe)$rank
t(y)%*%Pt%*%y; qr(Pt)$rank
```

The sums of squares produced by this code coincide with those reported in the ANOVA table.

Since the interaction term appears to be unnecessary for this data set, one can use the simpler model (6.36), which is essentially the same as the model presented in Example 3.5. The simplified ANOVA table for this model is obtained through the above code after dropping the interaction term `factor(Denim)*factor(Laundry)` from the `aov` function. (The corresponding changes in the projection matrices are that `Pgamma` should be ignored and `Pe` should be redefined as `Pt - Ptau - Pbeta`.) The resulting table is as follows.

Source	Sum of Squares	Degrees of Freedom	Mean Square	F ratio
Between denim treatments	13.4163	2	6.7082	37.377
Between laundry cycles	4.2714	2	2.1357	11.900
Error	15.2551	85	0.1795	
Total	32.9428	89		

The p-values for the two F-ratios are 2.26×10^{-12} and 2.78×10^{-05}, respectively, indicating strong heterogeneity in the mean effects of denim treatments as well as laundry cycles. □

6.3.4 Unbalanced data

If a two-way classified design occurs with an unequal number of observations per cell, then the data are said to be *unbalanced*. Such a model is given by

$$\begin{aligned}
y_{ijk} &= \mu+\tau_i+\beta_j+\gamma_{ij}+\varepsilon_{ijk},\ i=1,\ldots,t,\ j=1,\ldots,b,\\
&\qquad\qquad\qquad\qquad k=1,\ldots,m_{ij},\\
E(\varepsilon_{ijk}) &= 0, \qquad\qquad\qquad\qquad\qquad\qquad\qquad\qquad (6.37)\\
Cov(\varepsilon_{ijk},\varepsilon_{i'j'k'}) &= \begin{cases}\sigma^2 & \text{if } i=i',\ j=j' \text{ and } k=k',\\ 0 & \text{otherwise.}\end{cases}
\end{aligned}$$

The total number of observations is $n=\sum_{i=1}^t\sum_{j=1}^b m_{ij}$. The matrix-vector form of the model is

$$\boldsymbol{y}_{n\times1}=\boldsymbol{X}_{n\times(t+1)(b+1)}\boldsymbol{\beta}_{(t+1)(b+1)\times1}+\boldsymbol{\varepsilon}_{n\times1},\quad E(\boldsymbol{\varepsilon})=\boldsymbol{0},\ \boldsymbol{D}(\boldsymbol{\varepsilon})=\sigma^2\boldsymbol{I},$$

where

$$\begin{aligned}
\boldsymbol{y} &= (((y_{111}:\cdots:y_{11m_{11}}):\cdots:(y_{1b1}:\cdots:y_{1bm_{1b}})):\cdots\\
&\qquad\cdots:((y_{t11}:\cdots:y_{t1m_{t1}}):\cdots:(y_{tb1}:\cdots:y_{tbm_{tb}})))',\\
\boldsymbol{X} &= \begin{pmatrix}\boldsymbol{1}_{m_{11}\times1} & \boldsymbol{0}_{m_{11}\times1} & \cdots & \boldsymbol{0}_{m_{11}\times1}\\ \boldsymbol{0}_{m_{12}\times1} & \boldsymbol{1}_{m_{12}\times1} & \cdots & \boldsymbol{0}_{m_{12}\times1}\\ \vdots & \vdots & \ddots & \vdots\\ \boldsymbol{0}_{m_{tb}\times1} & \boldsymbol{0}_{m_{tb}\times1} & \cdots & \boldsymbol{1}_{m_{tb}\times1}\end{pmatrix}_{n\times tb}\\
&\qquad\cdot(\boldsymbol{1}_{t\times1}\otimes\boldsymbol{1}_{b\times1}:\boldsymbol{I}_{t\times t}\otimes\boldsymbol{1}_{b\times1}:\boldsymbol{1}_{t\times1}\otimes\boldsymbol{I}_{b\times b}:\boldsymbol{I}_{t\times t}\otimes\boldsymbol{I}_{b\times b}),\\
\boldsymbol{\beta} &= (\mu:(\tau_1:\cdots:\tau_t):(\beta_1:\cdots:\beta_b):\\
&\qquad(\gamma_{11}:\cdots:\gamma_{1b}):\cdots:(\gamma_{t1}:\cdots:\gamma_{tb}))',\\
\boldsymbol{\varepsilon} &= (((\varepsilon_{111}:\cdots:\varepsilon_{11m_{11}}):\cdots:(\varepsilon_{1b1}:\cdots:\varepsilon_{1bm_{1b}})):\cdots\\
&\qquad\cdots:((\varepsilon_{t11}:\cdots:\varepsilon_{t1m_{t1}}):\cdots:(\varepsilon_{tb1}:\cdots:\varepsilon_{tbm_{tb}})))'.
\end{aligned}$$

The function `yXm` of the R package `lmreg` can be used, as in Example 6.10, to generate the $\boldsymbol{X}$ matrix in the above form and to permute the $\boldsymbol{y}$ vector accordingly.

The key to the analysis of variance in the case of balanced data had been the decomposition of the vector of fitted values, given in (6.31). The four components of the decomposition represented sets of BLUEs which are not only attributable to various effects (grand mean, difference in treatment effects, difference in block effects and interaction), but these were also uncorrelated to one another. One of the last three terms turn into LZFs under the hypothesis of 'no difference in treatment effects', 'no difference in block effects' or 'no interaction effect', respectively.

In the case of unbalanced data one can still identify BLUEs that signify difference in treatment effects, following the general principles. These BLUEs turn into LZFs under the hypothesis of 'no difference in treatment effects'. A GLRT for this hypothesis can also be obtained. Similar analysis is also possible for the block and interaction effects. *However, the sets of BLUEs for the various effects are in general correlated. As a result, it is not possible to conduct a detailed analysis of variance of the type described in Table 6.8.* One can take at most one effect at a time and form a limited ANOVA table similar to Table 4.3. We refer the reader to Hocking (2013, Chapter 14) and Searle (2016) for more details on the subject.

Even if the data are unbalanced, a detailed analysis of variance is possible if $m_{ij} = m_i n_j$ for some m_i and n_j, $i = 1, \ldots, t$, $j = 1, \ldots, b$ (see Exercise 6.9).

Sometimes unbalanced data occur from missing observations in an experiment which is designed as balanced. If the number of missing observations is not too large, then tractable solutions can be found by exploiting the structure of the original design. We outline here two methods of analysis, but defer proofs to Chapter 9. The tests of hypotheses obtained from both the methods work even when the missing observations render some potentially estimable parameters non-estimable. One only has to be careful about what is being tested (see Section 4.2.2) and keep track of the degrees of freedom.

The first technique is called *missing plot substitution*. The missing values of the responses are treated as parameters, and the parameters are estimated by minimizing the error sum of squares with respect to these additional parameters. Parameter estimates under any restriction are obtained by minimizing the sum of squares under that restriction. The idea is that these sums of squares would have explicit expressions, owing to the designed nature of the experiment, and be amenable to easy minimization. The GLRT for a linear hypothesis is obtained by replacing the restricted and unrestricted sums of squares by their respectively minimized values. The name of this technique arises from the substitution of the missing values with their estimators. The degrees of freedom for the restricted and unrestricted sums of squares are obtained from the unbalanced model in the usual manner. A proof of validity of this technique in a more general set-up is given in Section 9.2.5. See Exercise 6.10 for the step-by-step construction of a test procedure in the special case of two-way classified data.

The second technique is based on the fact that, for the purpose of inference, a missing observation can be treated as an available observation in a model having an extra parameter. Specifically, if the last l out of n observations of the balanced-data model $(\boldsymbol{y}, \boldsymbol{X\beta}, \sigma^2\boldsymbol{I})$ are missing, then the truncated (unbalanced-data) set-up is equivalent to the modified model $(\boldsymbol{y}, \boldsymbol{X\beta} + \boldsymbol{Z\eta}, \sigma^2\boldsymbol{I})$, where $\boldsymbol{Z}$ is an $n \times l$ matrix obtained from the last l columns of the $n \times n$ identity matrix, and the missing elements of $\boldsymbol{y}$ can be substituted by an arbitrary set of numbers. The proof of this equivalence (originally due to Bartlett, 1937a) is given in Section 9.5. The model $(\boldsymbol{y}, \boldsymbol{X\beta} + \boldsymbol{Z\eta}, \sigma^2\boldsymbol{I})$ is a special case of the *analysis of covariance* model which is discussed in Section 6.6. The construction of a test procedure in this special case is outlined in Exercises 6.14, 6.15 and 6.17. See Dodge (1985) for more details on this topic.

6.4 Multiple treatment/block factors

So far we have made a clear distinction between treatment and block effects by stating that blocks are formed by putting together experimental units having homogeneity with respect to all non-treatment factors. Sometimes the blocks represent a second kind of treatment. In other words, every experimental unit is subject to a combination of two treatments, each treatment being chosen from a finite number of possibilities. In such a case, one may be interested in knowing which (if any) of the treatments makes a significant contribution to the variance of the response, and whether there is any interaction. In the case of balanced data, analysis of variance gives a clear answer to this question. When the data are unbalanced, the comparison of the treatment effects can be viewed as a problem of model selection. One has to determine whether the three sets of parameters corresponding to treatment 1, treatment 2 and interaction deserve to be present in the model. See Christensen (2011, Chapter 7) for a discussion of some interesting scenarios that may arise in this regard.

When there are two or more treatment factors, the non-treatment factors may be controlled by blocking. This leads to the general p-way classification model with $p > 2$. This model may also arise when there are more than one block factors. In particular, when homogeneity among experimental units is sought to be ensured through blocking by two factors, the resulting set-up is called a *row-column design* (see Exercise 6.11). The analysis of balanced p-way classified data is similar to the analysis described in Section 6.3.3.

6.5 Nested models

Suppose various groups of experimental units are subjected to a number of treatments. We have seen how heterogeneity within treatment classes due to non-treatment factors is removed by blocking. Sometimes the treatment classes have within-group heterogeneity due to treatment-related factors. For instance, each treatment may be a type of drug while the experimental units subjected to a particular drug may receive different doses of it. The dose levels for one drug can be completely different from those of another. So there is no question of 'blocking' by doses, or of using the two-way classification model. The dose levels being specific to a given treatment, their effects are 'nested' within the treatment effects. Assuming that the treatment and nested effects (i.e. the effects of groups and subgroups) are additive and that there is no other effect, this set-up can be described by the *nested classification model*

$$\begin{aligned} y_{ijk} &= \mu + \tau_i + \gamma_{ij} + \varepsilon_{ijk},\ k = 1,\ldots,m_{ij},\ j = 1,\ldots,b_i, \\ &\qquad\qquad\qquad\qquad i = 1,\ldots,t, \\ E(\varepsilon_{ijk}) &= 0, \\ Cov(\varepsilon_{ijk}, \varepsilon_{i'j'k'}) &= \begin{cases} \sigma^2 & \text{if } i = i',\ j = j' \text{ and } k = k', \\ 0 & \text{otherwise.} \end{cases} \end{aligned} \tag{6.38}$$

The total number of observations is $n = \sum_{i=1}^t \sum_{j=1}^{b_i} m_{ij}$. In this model $\gamma_{i1}, \ldots, \gamma_{ib_i}$ are the effects of the factor (with b_i possible levels) nested in treatment i, $i = 1, \ldots, t$. The matrix-vector form of the model is

$$\boldsymbol{y} = \boldsymbol{X\beta} + \boldsymbol{\varepsilon},\quad E(\boldsymbol{\varepsilon}) = \boldsymbol{0},\quad \boldsymbol{D}(\boldsymbol{\varepsilon}) = \sigma^2\boldsymbol{I},$$

where

$$\begin{aligned} \boldsymbol{y}_{n\times 1} &= (((y_{111} : \cdots : y_{11m_{11}}) : \cdots : (y_{1b_11} : \cdots : y_{1b_1m_{1b_1}})) : \cdots \\ &\qquad \cdots : ((y_{t11} : \cdots : y_{t1m_{t1}}) : \cdots : (y_{tb_t1} : \cdots : y_{tb_tm_{tb_t}})))', \end{aligned}$$

$$\boldsymbol{X}_{n\times\left(1+t+\sum_{i=1}^t b_i\right)} = \begin{pmatrix} \boldsymbol{1} & \boldsymbol{a}_1 & \boldsymbol{0} & \cdots & \boldsymbol{0} & \boldsymbol{A}_1 & \boldsymbol{0} & \cdots & \boldsymbol{0} \\ \boldsymbol{1} & \boldsymbol{0} & \boldsymbol{a}_2 & \cdots & \boldsymbol{0} & \boldsymbol{0} & \boldsymbol{A}_2 & \cdots & \boldsymbol{0} \\ \vdots & \vdots & \vdots & \ddots & \vdots & \vdots & \vdots & \ddots & \vdots \\ \boldsymbol{1} & \boldsymbol{0} & \boldsymbol{0} & \cdots & \boldsymbol{a}_t & \boldsymbol{0} & \boldsymbol{0} & \cdots & \boldsymbol{A}_t \end{pmatrix},$$

$$\boldsymbol{a}_i = \begin{pmatrix} \boldsymbol{1}_{m_{i1}} \\ \boldsymbol{1}_{m_{i2}} \\ \vdots \\ \boldsymbol{1}_{m_{ib_i}} \end{pmatrix},\quad \boldsymbol{A}_i = \begin{pmatrix} \boldsymbol{1}_{m_{i1}} & \boldsymbol{0}_{m_{i1}} & \cdots & \boldsymbol{0}_{m_{i1}} \\ \boldsymbol{0}_{m_{i2}} & \boldsymbol{1}_{m_{i2}} & \cdots & \boldsymbol{0}_{m_{i2}} \\ \vdots & \vdots & \ddots & \vdots \\ \boldsymbol{0}_{m_{ib_i}} & \boldsymbol{0}_{m_{ib_i}} & \cdots & \boldsymbol{1}_{m_{ib_i}} \end{pmatrix},$$

Table 6.9 Beta angles (in degrees) in three types of kink bands of different orders in Himalayan rocks (data object **kinks** in R package **lmreg**, source: personal communication with Dr. Sayandeep Banerjee of Banaras Hindu University)

Conjugate kink band			Dextral kink band			Sinistral kink band			
order 1	order 2	order 3	order 1	order 2	order 3	order 1	order 2	order 3	order 4
51	47	62	40	43	25	41	28	65	64
57	53	63	34	46	44	50	35	58	60
49	46	56	39	50	45	48	47	62	63
48	49	55	60	47	48	43	49	54	64
65	52	66	44	40	47	52	38	59	58
54	40	67	60	47	39	47	41	62	60
53	46	64	55	41	39	45	32	50	60
52	51	68	58	43	42	53	50	60	58
51	50	64	68	50	39	49	39	55	59
54	47	53			16	51		52	
	50	58			61	40			

$$\begin{aligned}\boldsymbol{\beta}_{(1+t+\sum_{i=1}^{t} b_i)\times 1} &= (\mu : (\tau_1 : \cdots : \tau_t) : (\gamma_{11} : \cdots : \gamma_{1b_1}) : \cdots \\ &\quad \cdots : (\gamma_{t1} : \cdots : \gamma_{tb_t}))', \\ \boldsymbol{\varepsilon}_{n\times 1} &= (((\varepsilon_{111} : \cdots : \varepsilon_{11m_{11}}) : \cdots : (\varepsilon_{1b_11} : \cdots : \varepsilon_{1b_1m_{1b_1}})) : \cdots \\ &\quad \cdots : ((\varepsilon_{t11} : \cdots : \varepsilon_{t1m_{t1}}) : \cdots : (\varepsilon_{tb_t1} : \cdots : \varepsilon_{tb_tm_{tb_t}})))'.\end{aligned}$$

Example 6.12. (Kink bands in rocks) Kink bands are folding patterns in sedimentary rocks that provide clue to the formation of those rocks. Table 6.9 shows measurements of an angular dimension (beta angle) found in Daling phyllite in the Darjeeling-Sikkim Himalayas. Three types of kink bands are represented, and each type has sub-categories depending on whether the measurement is from a main fold or sub-fold of a higher order. The third category has four sub-categories, while the first two have only three sub-categories. We would deal with the issue of group and subgroup heterogeneity in Example 6.13. The following code processes data on the response, the group and the subgroup variables (`beta`, `type` and `order`, respectively) to produce the matrix $\boldsymbol{X}$ in the form described above and the vector $\boldsymbol{y}$ in conformity with $\boldsymbol{X}$, using the R function `yXn` of the package `lmreg`.

```
data(kinks)
yXn(kinks$beta,kinks$type,kinks$order)
```

□

The model (6.38) implies that there are $\sum_{i=1}^{t} b_i$ subgroups of response, with homogeneity of mean within every subgroup. Therefore, it follows from (6.2) that the fitted values are

$$\widehat{y}_{ijk} = \bar{y}_{ij\cdot},$$

with usual notations. This can be decomposed as

$$\widehat{y}_{ijk} = \bar{y}_{\cdots} + (\bar{y}_{i\cdot\cdot} - \bar{y}_{\cdots}) + (\bar{y}_{ij\cdot} - \bar{y}_{i\cdot\cdot}). \tag{6.39}$$

The three terms on the right-hand side are the BLUEs of the grand mean $\left(\mu + \sum_{i=1}^t \tau_i/t + \sum_{i=1}\sum_{j=1}^{b_i}\gamma_{ij}/\sum_{i=1}^t b_i\right)$, the deviation of the ith group mean from the grand mean $\left(\tau_i + \sum_{j=1}^{b_i}\gamma_{ij}/b_i - \sum_{i=1}^t \tau_i/t - \sum_{i=1}^t\sum_{j=1}^{b_i}\gamma_{ij}/\sum_{i=1}^t b_i\right)$, and the deviation of the ijth subgroup mean from the ith group mean $\left(\gamma_{ij} - \sum_{j=1}^{b_i}\gamma_{ij}/b_i\right)$, respectively. The model-preserving constraints $\sum_{j=1}^{b_i}\gamma_{ij} = 0$, $i = 1, \ldots, t$ and $\sum_{i=1}^t \tau_i = 0$ make all the parameters estimable. Under these restrictions, the three terms of the right-hand side of (6.39) are the BLUEs of μ, τ_i and γ_{ij}, respectively.

The expression (6.39) of fitted value leads to the following decomposition of the deviation from the grand mean:

$$y_{ijk} - \bar{y}_{\cdots} = (\bar{y}_{i\cdot\cdot} - \bar{y}_{\cdots}) + (\bar{y}_{ij\cdot} - \bar{y}_{i\cdot\cdot}) + e_{ijk}, \tag{6.40}$$

where e_{ijk} is the residual for the observation y_{ijk}. It is clear that the BLUEs $(\bar{y}_{i\cdot\cdot} - \bar{y}_{\cdots})$ and $(\bar{y}_{ij\cdot} - \bar{y}_{i\cdot\cdot})$ are uncorrelated with the residual e_{ijk}. We shall argue that the two BLUEs are uncorrelated with one another. To see this, consider the restriction $\gamma_{i1} = \cdots = \gamma_{ib_i} = b_i^{-1}\sum_{j=1}^{b_i}\gamma_{ij}$, which means that all the subgroups within the ith group have equal mean. Under this restriction, $\bar{y}_{i\cdot\cdot} - \bar{y}_{\cdots}$ continues to be a BLUE (according to the one-way classification model), while $\bar{y}_{ij\cdot} - \bar{y}_{i\cdot\cdot}$ turns into an LZF. Therefore, the two linear functions are uncorrelated. Thus, the three terms in the decomposition (6.40) are uncorrelated. The sums of squares of these terms lead to the analysis of variance given in Table 6.10.

The null hypothesis of no significant effect of any subgroup can be tested by the GLRT statistic MS_γ/MS_e, which has the F distribution with $\sum_{i=1}^t b_i - t$ and $n - \sum_{i=1}^t b_i$ degrees of freedom under the null hypothesis. If this hypothesis is rejected, one can look for the groups where the subgroup effect is significant, using techniques of multiple comparisons (see Section 6.2.4). For a fixed group i, the GLRT statistic for the null hypothesis of no subgroup effect is

$$\frac{\sum_{j=1}^{b_i}(\bar{y}_{ij\cdot} - \bar{y}_{i\cdot\cdot})^2}{b_i - 1}\Bigg/ MS_e,$$

Table 6.10 ANOVA for model (6.38) of nested classification

Source	Sum of Squares	Degrees of Freedom	Mean Square
Between groups	$S_\tau = \sum_{i=1}^{t}\sum_{j=1}^{b_i} m_{ij}(\bar{y}_{i\cdot\cdot} - \bar{y}_{\cdot\cdot\cdot})^2$	$t-1$	$MS_\tau = \dfrac{S_\tau}{t-1}$
Between subgroups	$S_\gamma = \sum_{i=1}^{t}\sum_{j=1}^{b_i} m_{ij}(\bar{y}_{ij\cdot} - \bar{y}_{i\cdot\cdot})^2$	$\sum_{i=1}^{t} b_i - t$	$MS_\gamma = \dfrac{S_\gamma}{\sum_{i=1} b_i - t}$
Error	$R_0^2 = \sum_{i=1}^{t}\sum_{j=1}^{b_i}\sum_{k=1}^{m_{ij}} e_{ijk}^2$	$n - \sum_{i=1}^{t} b_i$	$MS_e = \dfrac{R_0^2}{n - \sum_{i=1}^{t} b_i}$
Total	$S_t = \sum_{i=1}^{t}\sum_{j=1}^{b_i}\sum_{k=1}^{m_{ij}} (y_{ijk} - \bar{y}_{\cdot\cdot\cdot})^2$	$n-1$	

which has an F distribution with $b_i - 1$ and $n - \sum_{i=1}^{t} b_i$ degrees of freedom, under the null hypothesis. If this hypothesis is tested for several (or all) groups simultaneously, one has to be careful about the levels of the tests.

The GLRT statistic for the hypothesis of no group effect is

$$\frac{S_\tau + S_\gamma}{\sum_{i=1}^{t} b_i - 1} \Bigg/ MS_e,$$

which has the F distribution with $\sum_{i=1}^{t} b_i - 1$ and $n - \sum_{i=1}^{t} b_i$ degrees of freedom under the null hypothesis.

Apart from the model (6.38), there are nested classification models for more than one main factor. See Hocking (2013, Chapter 11) for more details.

Example 6.13. (Kink bands in rocks, continued) For the kink bands data of Table 6.9, we would like to test whether there is homogeneity across the categories and subcategories. The elements of Table 6.10 for this problem are obtained through the code given below.

```
data(kinks); n <- dim(kinks)[[1]]
m0 <- aov(beta~1, data = kinks)
m1 <- aov(beta~factor(type), data = kinks)
subgroups <- n * kinks$type + kinks$order
m2 <- aov(beta~factor(subgroups), data = kinks)
anova(m0,m1,m2)
```

After putting the different parts of the output in appropriate places, we have the following ANOVA table.

Source	Sum of Squares	Degrees of Freedom	Mean Square	F ratio
Between groups	1336.8	2	$\frac{1336.8}{2}$	14.48
Between subgroups	4067.1	7	$\frac{4067.1}{7}$	12.58
Error	4155.1	90	$\frac{4155.1}{90}$	
Total	9559.0	99		

The p-values corresponding to the two F-ratios are 3.53×10^{-6} and 3.75×10^{-11}. The group and the subgroup effects are both significant.

In order to obtain the sums of squares of the above table (along with the corresponding degrees of freedom) through projection matrices, one can make use of the following code, which utilizes the function `yXn`.

```
kinksyXn <- yXn(kinks$beta, kinks$type, kinks$order)
y <- kinksyXn[[1]]; X <- kinksyXn[[2]]; n = length(y)
nt = length(unique(kinks$type))
T <- X[,2:(nt+1)]
one <- rep(1,n); I <- diag(one); P1 = projector(one)
Pt <- I - P1
Pgroup <- projector(T) - P1
Pe <- I - projector(X[,-(1:(nt+1))])
Psubgroup <- Pt - Pgroup - Pe
sum((Pgroup%*%y)^2); sum((Psubgroup%*%y)^2)
sum((Pe%*%y)^2); sum((Pt%*%y)^2)
qr(Pgroup)$rank; qr(Psubgroup)$rank; qr(Pe)$rank; qr(Pt)$rank
```

The resulting sums of squares and degrees of freedom coincide with those reported in the ANOVA table. □

6.6 Analysis of covariance

6.6.1 *The model*

In Section 6.3 we had used the method of blocking in order to account for the nonuniformity of the experimental units and to reduce the experimental error, so that treatment comparisons can be made more precise. There are many experiments where, for each experimental unit, one has supplementary or concomitant variables (also called covariates) which might influence the response. In such a case, comparison of treatment effects can be meaningful only after accounting for the effects of the concomitant variables.

The effects of designed factors and concomitant variables are combined in the analysis of covariance (ANCOVA) model,

$$\boldsymbol{y} = \boldsymbol{X\beta} + \boldsymbol{Z\eta} + \boldsymbol{\varepsilon}, \quad E(\boldsymbol{\varepsilon}) = \boldsymbol{0}, \quad D(\boldsymbol{\varepsilon}) = \sigma^2 \boldsymbol{I}, \tag{6.41}$$

where the elements of the matrix $\boldsymbol{X}$ represent the designed part of the experiment such as block/treatment levels, the elements of $\boldsymbol{\beta}$ are the corresponding effects, the columns of the matrix $\boldsymbol{Z}$ contain values of the respective covariates and $\boldsymbol{\eta}$ represents the effect of these covariates on the mean response.

The model (6.41) is a generalization of the model of Example 1.6 of Chapter 1. For given $\boldsymbol{\eta}$, it can be written as

$$\boldsymbol{y} - \boldsymbol{Z\eta} = \boldsymbol{X\beta} + \boldsymbol{\varepsilon},$$

which is essentially the linear model for a designed experiment. For given $\boldsymbol{\beta}$, (6.41) can be written as

$$\boldsymbol{y} - \boldsymbol{X\beta} = \boldsymbol{Z\eta} + \boldsymbol{\varepsilon},$$

which is a linear model with explanatory variables that do not come from a design.

6.6.2 *Uses of the model*

It has already been mentioned that the model (6.41) can be used to reduce experimental error. Example 1.6 is a case in point. In this example the pre-treatment leprosy abundance score is used as the concomitant variable. If this variable is excluded, then the model reduces to that of a designed experiment, but the variation in the pre-treatment score across the subjects would make the treatment comparisons more imprecise. Inclusion of this variable means that the error variance represents the *conditional* variance of the post-treatment score for any treatment, *given the pre-treatment score.* This should be smaller than the unconditional variance.

In order to reduce the error variance, it is important that the concomitant variables influence the response considerably (that is, the conditional variance is much smaller than the unconditional variance). Identification of appropriate concomitant variables is, therefore, an important task. Care should be taken that the concomitant variables do not influence or are not influenced by the treatments or the blocks. If this precaution is not taken, the design is no longer randomized with respect to the concomitant variables, and there may be some bias in the estimators.

The model (6.41) is also used in *observational* studies where the objective is to study the effects of some binary variables, but there are some additional variables having possible effect on the response. For instance, in a comparison of heights of children from two different schools, Greenberg, (1953) took into account the age of the children in order to make the comparison meaningful. Omission of these additional variables may not only inflate the error variance, but also introduce bias in the estimators (see Section 5.1.1). In contrast to the case of randomized experiments, the bias due to omitted variables in observational studies in general cannot be removed by randomization. See Cochran (1957) for a discussion on the finer points of this subject.

Sometimes the analysis of covariance model is used to achieve a deeper understanding of treatment effects. If the difference between two treatments is significant, but it becomes insignificant after taking into account an explanatory variable, then this explanatory variable may be responsible for the difference in these treatment effects.

If parallel regression lines are to be fitted to two or more groups of data, the model used for this purpose is essentially (6.41) (see Exercise 1.11).

It was pointed out in Section 6.3.4 that the analysis of covariance model can be used to carry out analysis of variance when some observations are missing. This follows from the fact that deletion of an observation is equivalent to inclusion of an additional explanatory variable in the model (see Section 9.5 for a proof of this equivalence). The effects of these concocted variables corresponding to all the missing observations assume the role of η in (6.41).

6.6.3 *Estimation of parameters*

We have seen in the foregoing sections how the special structure of the matrix $\boldsymbol{X}$ leads to neat expressions of various BLUEs — when there is no covariate. Presence of covariates changes the scenario altogether, as the matrix $\boldsymbol{Z}$ does not have a special structure. What we intend to do here is to exploit the structure of $\boldsymbol{X}$ by estimating $\boldsymbol{\eta}$ and $\boldsymbol{\beta}$ successively.

Let us first consider the estimation of the estimable functions of $\boldsymbol{\eta}$. For this purpose $\boldsymbol{\beta}$ is a vector of nuisance parameters. It follows from Proposition 3.53 that the estimable functions of $\boldsymbol{\eta}$ are of the form

$L(I - P_X)Z\eta$. It is shown in Remark 7.46 that the BLUE of $L(I - P_X)Z\eta$ is obtained by replacing η with a solution of the reduced normal equation

$$Z'(I - P_X)Z\eta = Z'(I - P_X)y.$$

Let us denote such a solution by $\widehat{\eta}$. It also follows from Remark 7.46 that

$$D((I - P_X)Z\widehat{\eta}) = \sigma^2 P_{(I-P_X)Z}.$$

Let us use the notation

$$\begin{pmatrix} R_{0\beta}^2 & r' \\ r & R \end{pmatrix} = \begin{pmatrix} y' \\ Z' \end{pmatrix} (I - P_X)\,(y\ Z)\,. \tag{6.42}$$

The reduced normal equation for η can be written simply as $R\eta = r$, so that the substitution estimator is

$$\widehat{\eta} = R^- r. \tag{6.43}$$

Note that the normal equation for the simultaneous estimation of the estimable linear functions of β and η is

$$\begin{pmatrix} X'X & X'Z \\ Z'X & Z'Z \end{pmatrix} \begin{pmatrix} \beta \\ \eta \end{pmatrix} = \begin{pmatrix} X'y \\ Z'y \end{pmatrix}.$$

Using the first of these equations and substituting $\eta = \widehat{\eta}$, we have the solution for β,

$$\widehat{\beta} = (X'X)^-[X'y - X'Z\widehat{\eta}]. \tag{6.44}$$

The BLUE of any estimable function of the form $A\beta$ is given by $A\widehat{\beta}$, where $\widehat{\beta}$ is as in (6.44) and $\widehat{\eta}$ is as in (6.43).

Remark 6.14. The expression of $\widehat{\beta}$ can be interpreted in the following manner. Write (6.41) as

$$\begin{aligned} y = X\beta + Z\eta + \varepsilon &= X\beta + P_X Z\eta + (I - P_X)Z\eta + \varepsilon \\ &= X\beta_0 + (I - P_X)Z\eta + \varepsilon, \end{aligned} \tag{6.45}$$

where $\beta_0 = \beta + (X'X)^- X'Z\eta$. Let z_j be the jth column of Z (that is, the column containing the values of the jth concomitant variable), $j = 1, \ldots, q$. Then we can write

$$\beta = \beta_0 - \sum_{j=1}^{q} \eta_j \widehat{\alpha}_j,$$

where η_j is the jth element of η and $\widehat{\alpha}_j$ is a least squares estimator of α_j from the model $(z_j, X\alpha_j, \sigma^2 I)$ (that is, a model where the jth covariate plays the role of response). This is only an interpretation. As we condition

$\boldsymbol{y}$ on $\boldsymbol{Z}$, $\boldsymbol{\alpha}_j$ need not be treated as random. Replacing $\boldsymbol{\beta}_0$ and $\boldsymbol{\eta}$ by their respective least squares estimators ($\widehat{\boldsymbol{\beta}}_0 = (\boldsymbol{X}'\boldsymbol{X})^-\boldsymbol{X}'\boldsymbol{y}$ and $\widehat{\boldsymbol{\eta}}$ as in (6.43)), we have

$$\widehat{\boldsymbol{\beta}} = \widehat{\boldsymbol{\beta}}_0 - \sum_{j=1}^{q} \widehat{\eta}_j \widehat{\boldsymbol{\alpha}}_j.$$

This expression is equivalent to (6.44), as (6.45) is only a reparametrization of (6.41). □

Example 6.15. (Treatment of leprosy, continued) A model for the post-treatment leprosy abundance score, explained through the antibiotic used for treatment and the pre-treatment score, had been presented on page 7. Here, we use the one-way classified data model with covariate:

$$y_{ij} = \mu + \tau_i + \eta z_{ij} + \varepsilon_{ij}, \quad j = 1, \ldots, n_i, \; i = 1, \ldots, 3,$$

with uncorrelated errors ε_{ij} having mean zero and variance σ^2. There are three treatments: antibiotics A, B and F (placebo) with effects τ_1, τ_2 and τ_3, respectively. The parameter η is the effect of z_{ij}, the pre-treatment score of the patient having post-treatment score y_{ij}. In the matrix-vector form, this model is a special case of (6.41), where $\boldsymbol{\beta} = (\mu : \tau_1 : \tau_2 : \tau_3)'$, the matrix $\boldsymbol{X}$ is as in Section 6.2.1 with $t = 3$, and $\boldsymbol{Z}$ is the single vector consisting of the z_{ij}s arranged in the same order as the y_{ij}s in the response vector $\boldsymbol{y}$. The structure of the matrix $\boldsymbol{P}_X$ ensures that $\boldsymbol{P}_X\boldsymbol{y}$ and $\boldsymbol{P}_X\boldsymbol{Z}$ comprise of only the group means (e.g. $\overline{y}_{i\cdot}$ appears in place of y_{ij} and $\overline{z}_{i\cdot}$ in place of z_{ij}). Specifically, (6.42) simplifies to

$$R_{0\beta}^2 = \boldsymbol{y}'(\boldsymbol{I} - \boldsymbol{P}_X)\boldsymbol{y} = \sum_{j=1}^{t}\sum_{j=1}^{n_i}(y_{ij} - \overline{y}_{i\cdot})^2 = 995.1,$$

$$\boldsymbol{r} = \boldsymbol{Z}'(\boldsymbol{I} - \boldsymbol{P}_X)\boldsymbol{y} = \sum_{j=1}^{t}\sum_{j=1}^{n_i}(z_{ij} - \overline{z}_{i\cdot})(y_{ij} - \overline{y}_{i\cdot}) = 585.4,$$

$$\boldsymbol{R} = \boldsymbol{Z}'(\boldsymbol{I} - \boldsymbol{P}_X)\boldsymbol{Z} = \sum_{j=1}^{t}\sum_{j=1}^{n_i}(z_{ij} - \overline{z}_{i\cdot})^2 = 593,$$

and

$$\widehat{\eta} = \frac{\boldsymbol{r}}{\boldsymbol{R}} = \frac{\sum_{j=1}^{t}\sum_{j=1}^{n_i}(z_{ij} - \overline{z}_{i\cdot})(y_{ij} - \overline{y}_{i\cdot})}{\sum_{j=1}^{t}\sum_{j=1}^{n_i}(z_{ij} - \overline{z}_{i\cdot})^2} = 0.9872.$$

The R code used for the above computations is as follows.

```
data(leprosy)
z <- leprosy$pre; y <- leprosy$post; treat <- leprosy$treatment
n <- length(y); one <- rep(1,n)
X <- cbind(one,binaries(treat))
IH <- diag(one) - projector(X)
R02 <- t(y)%*%IH%*%y; r <- t(z)%*%IH%*%y
R <- t(z)%*%IH%*%z; eta <- r/R
c(R02,r,R,eta)
```

It follows from (6.44) that for estimation of $\boldsymbol{\beta}$ (or its functions), one can use the one-way ANOVA results, with the response y_{ij} replaced by $y_{ij} - 0.9872z_{ij}$. For example, the BLUE of $\tau_i - \tau_j$ is $(\overline{y}_{i\cdot} - \overline{y}_{j\cdot}) - 0.9872(\overline{z}_{i\cdot} - \overline{z}_{j\cdot})$. In particular, the contrasts between the effects of antibiotics A and F and B and F are $\widehat{\tau}_1 - \widehat{\tau}_3 = -3.446$ and $\widehat{\tau}_2 - \widehat{\tau}_3 = -3.337$, respectively, as obtained by the following code.

```
beta <- lsfit(binaries(treat),(y - z*eta))$coef
beta[2]-beta[4]; beta[3]-beta[4]
```

In the absence of adjustment for the pre-treatment score, these contrasts would have been estimated (by replacing `(y - z*eta)` with `y` in the above code) as -7 and -6.2, respectively. In other words, the treatment effects would appear to be unduly large. □

6.6.4 *Tests of hypotheses*

We shall now assume that the conditional distribution of $\boldsymbol{y}$ given $\boldsymbol{Z}$ is normal. Let us first consider the hypothesis $\boldsymbol{\eta} = \boldsymbol{0}$, which essentially means that the covariates may be ignored. The error sum of squares under the hypothesis is obviously $R_H^2 = \boldsymbol{y}'(\boldsymbol{I} - \boldsymbol{P}_X)\boldsymbol{y}$ with $n - \rho(\boldsymbol{X})$ degrees of freedom. The error sum of squares for the model (6.41) is

$$R_0^2 = \boldsymbol{y}'(\boldsymbol{I} - \boldsymbol{P}_{(X:Z)})\boldsymbol{y} = \boldsymbol{y}'(\boldsymbol{I} - \boldsymbol{P}_X - \boldsymbol{P}_{(I-P_X)Z})\boldsymbol{y},$$

which follows from Proposition A.14(b). In view of (6.42), we can write

$$R_0^2 = R_{0\beta}^2 - \boldsymbol{r}'\boldsymbol{R}^-\boldsymbol{r} = R_H^2 - \boldsymbol{r}'\boldsymbol{R}^-\boldsymbol{r}.$$

The associated degrees of freedom is $n - \rho(\boldsymbol{X} : \boldsymbol{Z})$. It follows that the GLRT for the hypothesis $\boldsymbol{\eta} = \boldsymbol{0}$ is to reject the null hypothesis when the ratio $[(n - \rho(\boldsymbol{X} : \boldsymbol{Z}))(\boldsymbol{r}'\boldsymbol{R}^-\boldsymbol{r})/[(\rho(\boldsymbol{X} : \boldsymbol{Z}) - \rho(\boldsymbol{X}))R_0^2]$ is too large. The null distribution of the statistic is $F_{\rho(X:Z)-\rho(X),n-\rho(X:Z)}$.

We now turn to the main problem of testing a general linear hypothesis of the form $\boldsymbol{A\beta} = \boldsymbol{0}$. Tests for the hypotheses such as no treatment effect, no block effect, no interaction and no nested effect are all special cases of this problem. It follows along the lines of the discussion of Section 3.10 that the model (6.41) is equivalent to

$$\boldsymbol{y} = \boldsymbol{X}(\boldsymbol{I} - \boldsymbol{P}_{A'})\boldsymbol{\theta} + \boldsymbol{Z}\boldsymbol{\eta} + \boldsymbol{\varepsilon}, \quad E(\boldsymbol{\varepsilon}) = \boldsymbol{0}, \quad D(\boldsymbol{\varepsilon}) = \sigma^2\boldsymbol{I}. \tag{6.46}$$

We have already seen that the error sum of squares for the model (6.41) can be written as

$$R_0^2 = R_{0\beta}^2 - \boldsymbol{r}'\boldsymbol{R}^-\boldsymbol{r}, \tag{6.47}$$

where the terms on the right-hand side are given by (6.42). Similarly, the error sum of squares for the model (6.46) is

$$R_H^2 = R_{H\beta}^2 - \boldsymbol{r}'_H\boldsymbol{R}_H^-\boldsymbol{r}_H, \tag{6.48}$$

where the terms on the right-hand side are given by

$$\begin{pmatrix} R_{H\beta}^2 & \boldsymbol{r}'_H \\ \boldsymbol{r}_H & \boldsymbol{R}_H \end{pmatrix} = \begin{pmatrix} \boldsymbol{y}' \\ \boldsymbol{Z}' \end{pmatrix} (\boldsymbol{I} - \boldsymbol{P}_{X(I-P_{A'})}) \,(\boldsymbol{y}\ \boldsymbol{Z})\,. \tag{6.49}$$

The degrees of freedom associated with R_0^2 and R_H^2 are $n - \rho(\boldsymbol{X} : \boldsymbol{Z})$ and $n - \rho(\boldsymbol{X}(\boldsymbol{I} - \boldsymbol{P}_{A'}) : \boldsymbol{Z})$, respectively. Thus, the GLRT of the hypothesis $\boldsymbol{A\beta} = \boldsymbol{0}$ is to reject the null hypothesis for large values of the statistic

$$\frac{R_H^2 - R_0^2}{R_0^2} \cdot \frac{n - \rho(\boldsymbol{X} : \boldsymbol{Z})}{\rho(\boldsymbol{X} : \boldsymbol{Z}) - \rho(\boldsymbol{X}(\boldsymbol{I} - \boldsymbol{P}_{A'}) : \boldsymbol{Z})}, \tag{6.50}$$

which has the null distribution $F_{\rho(X:Z)-\rho(X(I-P_{A'}):Z),n-\rho(X:Z)}$. If the concomitant variables are independent of the various effects, then $\mathcal{C}(\boldsymbol{Z})$ and $\mathcal{C}(\boldsymbol{X})$ are virtually disjoint. In such a case, $\rho(\boldsymbol{X} : \boldsymbol{Z}) = \rho(\boldsymbol{X}) + \rho(\boldsymbol{Z})$ and $\rho(\boldsymbol{X}(\boldsymbol{I}-\boldsymbol{P}_{A'}) : \boldsymbol{Z}) = \rho(\boldsymbol{X}(\boldsymbol{I}-\boldsymbol{P}_{A'}))+\rho(\boldsymbol{Z})$. Consequently, the test statistic of (6.50) simplifies to

$$\frac{R_H^2 - R_0^2}{R_0^2} \cdot \frac{n - \rho(\boldsymbol{X}) - \rho(\boldsymbol{Z})}{\rho(\boldsymbol{X}) - \rho(\boldsymbol{X}(\boldsymbol{I} - \boldsymbol{P}_{A'}))},$$

and its null distribution is $F_{\rho(X)-\rho(X(I-P_{A'})),n-\rho(X)-\rho(Z)}$.

When an ANCOVA model arises from covariates inserted in lieu of missing observations (see Section 6.3.4), the assumption $\rho(\boldsymbol{X} : \boldsymbol{Z}) = \rho(\boldsymbol{X}) + \rho(\boldsymbol{Z})$ means that no parameter becomes non-estimable *because of* the missing observations.

Example 6.16. (Treatment of leprosy, continued) Continuing with the model and the computations of Example 6.15, let us consider the hypothesis of homogeneity of treatment effects, in the presence of the pre-treatment score as covariate. The adjusted value of R_0^2, obtained from (6.47), is

$$R_0^2 = 995.1 - 995.1^2/593 = 417.2,$$

with $n - \rho(\boldsymbol{X} : \boldsymbol{Z}) = 30 - 3 - 1 = 26$ degree of freedom. Under the hypothesis of mean heterogeneity, all the group means are replaced by the grand mean, that is,

$$R_{H\beta}^2 = \boldsymbol{y}'(\boldsymbol{I} - \boldsymbol{P}_X)\boldsymbol{y} = \sum_{j=1}^{t}\sum_{j=1}^{n_i}(y_{ij} - \overline{y}_{..})^2 = 1288.7,$$

$$\boldsymbol{r}_H = \boldsymbol{Z}'(\boldsymbol{I} - \boldsymbol{P}_X)\boldsymbol{y} = \sum_{j=1}^{t}\sum_{j=1}^{n_i}(z_{ij} - \overline{z}_{..})(y_{ij} - \overline{y}_{..}) = 731.2,$$

$$\boldsymbol{R}_H = \boldsymbol{Z}'(\boldsymbol{I} - \boldsymbol{P}_X)\boldsymbol{Z} = \sum_{j=1}^{t}\sum_{j=1}^{n_i}(z_{ij} - \overline{z}_{..})^2 = 665.9,$$

so that the adjusted value of the total (restricted) sum of squares is

$$R_H^2 = 1288.7 - 731.2^2/665.9 = 485.8,$$

with $n - \rho(\boldsymbol{X}(\boldsymbol{I} - \boldsymbol{P}_{A'}) : \boldsymbol{Z}) = 30 - 1 - 1 = 28$ degrees of freedom. These computations are obtained through the code given below, which builds on the code given in Example 6.15.

```
R02 <- t(y)%*%IH%*%y; dR02 <- n - qr(X)$rank
R0a2 <- R02 - (r^2)/R; dR0a2 <- n - qr(cbind(X,z))$rank
IH0 <- diag(one) - projector(one)
RH2 <- t(y)%*%IH0%*%y; dRH2 <- n - 1
rH <- t(z)%*%IH0%*%y
RH <- t(z)%*%IH0%*%z
RHa2 <- RH2 - (rH^2)/RH; dRHa2 <- n - qr(cbind(1,z))$rank
c(R0a2,dR0a2,RH2,dRH2,rH,RH,RHa2,dRHa2)
```

The F-ratio is

$$\frac{485.8 - 417.2}{417.2} \times \frac{26}{28 - 26} = 2.136,$$

with 2 and 26 degrees of freedom, and the associated p-value is 0.138, as obtained from the following additional code

```
Fadj <- ((RHa2-R0a2)/R0a2) * dR0a2/(dRHa2-dR0a2)
Fadj; pf(Fadj,(dRHa2-dR0a2),dR0a2,lower.tail=F)
```

The null hypothesis of treatment homogeneity cannot be rejected even at the 10% level.

If the covariate had not been adjusted for, the F-ratio would have been

$$\frac{1288.7 - 995.1}{995.1} \times \frac{27}{29-27} = 3.98,$$

with 2 and 27 degrees of freedom, and the corresponding p-value would have been 0.0305 (obtained by replacing `RHa2`, `R0a2`, `dR0a2` and `dRHa2` in the above code by the unadjusted values `RH2`, `R02`, `dR02` and `dRH2`, respectively), leading to the rejection of the hypothesis of treatment homogeneity at the 5% level. The decision would have been faulty.

The adjusted and unadjusted F-tests of treatment homogeneity could have been carried out directly through the following code.

```
lm1a <- lm(post~factor(treatment)+pre,data=leprosy)
lm0a <- lm(post~pre,data=leprosy)
lm1 <- lm(post~factor(treatment),data=leprosy)
lm0 <- lm(post~1,data=leprosy)
anova(lm0a,lm1a); anova(lm0,lm1)
```

This code produces the same values of the F-ratios and the corresponding p-values. □

6.6.5 *ANCOVA table and adjustment for covariates**

Recall that in the absence of covariates, the ANOVA table can be used to compute the GLRT statistics for the common hypothesis testing problems. Can there be a similar table for the computation of (6.50)? The key to the computation lies with the matrices defined in (6.42) and (6.49). Indeed, the top left elements of these two matrices can be obtained from a suitable analysis of variance table. These are the sum of squares $R_{0\beta}^2$ and $R_{H\beta}^2$, respectively, with no adjustment for covariates. If we can compute $R_{0\beta}^2$ and $R_{H\beta}^2$ from a table, we should also be able to derive the other elements of the matrices of (6.42) and (6.49) from an expanded table. It is clear from the structure of the matrices that the remaining diagonal elements are obtained from an 'ANOVA' table where $\boldsymbol{y}$ is replaced by a column of $\boldsymbol{Z}$. Likewise, the off-diagonal elements are obtained by replacing every sum of squares in the ANOVA table by a *sum of squares and products*, where the factors in each product correspond to the response or some of the covariates.

We illustrate this method with an extended version of the balanced two-way classification model with interaction (considered in Section 6.3.3), where covariates are also included. The model is

$$
\begin{aligned}
y_{ijk} &= \mu+\tau_i+\beta_j+\gamma_{ij}+\textstyle\sum_{l=1}^{q} c_{ijkl}\eta_l+\varepsilon_{ijk},\\
&\qquad\qquad i=1,\ldots,t,\quad j=1,\ldots,b,\quad k=1,\ldots,m,\\
E(\varepsilon_{ijk}) &= 0, \qquad\qquad (6.51)\\
Cov(\varepsilon_{ijk},\varepsilon_{i'j'k'}) &= \begin{cases}\sigma^2 & \text{if } i=i',\ j=j' \text{ and } k=k',\\ 0 & \text{otherwise.}\end{cases}
\end{aligned}
$$

The matrix-vector form of the model is

$$\boldsymbol{y}=\boldsymbol{X\beta}+\boldsymbol{Z\eta}+\boldsymbol{\varepsilon},\quad E(\boldsymbol{\varepsilon})=\boldsymbol{0},\ \boldsymbol{D}(\boldsymbol{\varepsilon})=\sigma^2\boldsymbol{I},$$

where $\boldsymbol{y}$, $\boldsymbol{X}$, $\boldsymbol{\beta}$ and $\boldsymbol{\varepsilon}$ are as in Section 6.3.3, $\boldsymbol{\eta}=(\eta_1:\cdots:\eta_q)'$, $\boldsymbol{Z}=(\boldsymbol{z}_1:\cdots:\boldsymbol{z}_q)$ and

$$
\begin{aligned}
\boldsymbol{z}_j = (((c_{111j}:\cdots:c_{11mj}):\cdots:(c_{1b1j}:\cdots:c_{1bmj})):\cdots\\
\cdots:((c_{t11j}:\cdots:c_{t1mj}):\cdots:(c_{tb1j}:\cdots:c_{tbmj})))',
\end{aligned}
$$

for $j=1,\ldots,q$.

Using the projection matrices of (6.30), we form the ANCOVA table of model (6.51), given in Table 6.11.

Note that the middle column of the ANCOVA table contains matrices of dimension $(q+1)\times(q+1)$. Alternatively scalar values could have been reported in separate columns of the table for the different elements of the matrices. The matrix representation is used for brevity.

For any $(q+1)\times(q+1)$ nonnegative definite matrix

$$\begin{pmatrix} s_{1\times 1} & \boldsymbol{s}'_{1\times q}\\ \boldsymbol{s}_{q\times 1} & \boldsymbol{S}_{q\times q}\end{pmatrix},\ \text{let } g\begin{pmatrix} s & \boldsymbol{s}'\\ \boldsymbol{s} & \boldsymbol{S}\end{pmatrix}$$

Table 6.11 ANCOVA for model (6.51) of balanced two-way classified data with interaction and covariates

Source	Sum of Squares and products	Degrees of Freedom
Between treatments	$\boldsymbol{S}_\tau=(\boldsymbol{y}:\boldsymbol{Z})'\boldsymbol{P}_\tau(\boldsymbol{y}:\boldsymbol{Z})$	$t-1$
Between blocks	$\boldsymbol{S}_\beta=(\boldsymbol{y}:\boldsymbol{Z})'\boldsymbol{P}_\beta(\boldsymbol{y}:\boldsymbol{Z})$	$b-1$
Interaction	$\boldsymbol{S}_\gamma=(\boldsymbol{y}:\boldsymbol{Z})'\boldsymbol{P}_\gamma(\boldsymbol{y}:\boldsymbol{Z})$	$(t-1)(b-1)$
Error	$\boldsymbol{S}_e=(\boldsymbol{y}:\boldsymbol{Z})'(\boldsymbol{I}-\boldsymbol{P}_X)(\boldsymbol{y}:\boldsymbol{Z})$	$n-tb$
Total	$\boldsymbol{S}_t=(\boldsymbol{y}:\boldsymbol{Z})'(\boldsymbol{I}-\boldsymbol{P}_\mu)(\boldsymbol{y}:\boldsymbol{Z})$	$n-1$

denote the number $s - \boldsymbol{s}'\boldsymbol{S}^{-}\boldsymbol{s}$. We shall use this notation to describe the tests of the following hypotheses.

$$\begin{aligned}
\mathcal{H}_\tau &: \text{There is no treatment effect,}\\
\mathcal{H}_\beta &: \text{There is no block effect,}\\
\mathcal{H}_\gamma &: \text{There is no interaction effect,}\\
\mathcal{H}_{\tau\gamma} &: \text{There is no treatment or interaction effect,}\\
\mathcal{H}_{\beta\gamma} &: \text{There is no block or interaction effect,}\\
\mathcal{H}_a &: \text{All the effects are present.}
\end{aligned}$$

The matrix of (6.49) for the six hypotheses are $\boldsymbol{S}_\tau+\boldsymbol{S}_e$, $\boldsymbol{S}_\beta+\boldsymbol{S}_e$, $\boldsymbol{S}_\gamma+\boldsymbol{S}_e$, $\boldsymbol{S}_t - \boldsymbol{S}_\beta$, $\boldsymbol{S}_t - \boldsymbol{S}_\tau$ and $\boldsymbol{S}_e$, respectively. The corresponding corrected sum of squares, after eliminating the effect of the covariates, are $g(\boldsymbol{S}_\tau + \boldsymbol{S}_e)$, $g(\boldsymbol{S}_\beta + \boldsymbol{S}_e)$, $g(\boldsymbol{S}_\gamma + \boldsymbol{S}_e)$, $g(\boldsymbol{S}_t - \boldsymbol{S}_\beta)$, $g(\boldsymbol{S}_t - \boldsymbol{S}_\tau)$ and $g(\boldsymbol{S}_e)$, respectively. A careful examination of $\rho(\boldsymbol{X}(\boldsymbol{I} - \boldsymbol{P}_{A'}))$ of (6.50) for the various hypotheses leads to the GLRT statistics listed in Table 6.12. In this table c denotes $\rho(\boldsymbol{Z})$, and it is assumed that $\rho(\boldsymbol{X} : \boldsymbol{Z}) = \rho(\boldsymbol{X}) + \rho(\boldsymbol{Z})$. (We remind the reader that for covariates inserted in lieu of missing observations, as in Section 6.3.4, the assumption $\rho(\boldsymbol{X} : \boldsymbol{Z}) = \rho(\boldsymbol{X}) + \rho(\boldsymbol{Z})$ is equivalent to

Table 6.12 List of GLRT statistics for various hypotheses for the ANCOVA model (6.51)

Null hypothesis	Alternative hypothesis	GLRT statistic
$\mathcal{H}_\tau$	$\mathcal{H}_a$	$\dfrac{g(\boldsymbol{S}_\tau + \boldsymbol{S}_e) - g(\boldsymbol{S}_e)}{g(\boldsymbol{S}_e)} \cdot \dfrac{n - tb - c}{t-1}$
$\mathcal{H}_\beta$	$\mathcal{H}_a$	$\dfrac{g(\boldsymbol{S}_\beta + \boldsymbol{S}_e) - g(\boldsymbol{S}_e)}{g(\boldsymbol{S}_e)} \cdot \dfrac{n - tb - c}{b-1}$
$\mathcal{H}_\gamma$	$\mathcal{H}_a$	$\dfrac{g(\boldsymbol{S}_\gamma + \boldsymbol{S}_e) - g(\boldsymbol{S}_e)}{g(\boldsymbol{S}_e)} \cdot \dfrac{n - tb - c}{(t-1)(b-1)}$
$\mathcal{H}_{\tau\gamma}$	$\mathcal{H}_\gamma$	$\dfrac{g(\boldsymbol{S}_t - \boldsymbol{S}_\beta) - g(\boldsymbol{S}_\gamma + \boldsymbol{S}_e)}{g(\boldsymbol{S}_\gamma + \boldsymbol{S}_e)} \cdot \dfrac{n-t-b+1-c}{t-1}$
$\mathcal{H}_{\beta\gamma}$	$\mathcal{H}_\gamma$	$\dfrac{g(\boldsymbol{S}_t - \boldsymbol{S}_\tau) - g(\boldsymbol{S}_\gamma + \boldsymbol{S}_e)}{g(\boldsymbol{S}_\gamma + \boldsymbol{S}_e)} \cdot \dfrac{n-t-b+1-c}{b-1}$
$\mathcal{H}_{\tau\gamma}$	$\mathcal{H}_a$	$\dfrac{g(\boldsymbol{S}_t - \boldsymbol{S}_\beta) - g(\boldsymbol{S}_e)}{g(\boldsymbol{S}_e)} \cdot \dfrac{n - tb - c}{b(t-1)}$
$\mathcal{H}_{\beta\gamma}$	$\mathcal{H}_a$	$\dfrac{g(\boldsymbol{S}_t - \boldsymbol{S}_\tau) - g(\boldsymbol{S}_e)}{g(\boldsymbol{S}_e)} \cdot \dfrac{n - tb - c}{t(b-1)}$

assuming that no parameter becomes non-estimable because of the missing observations.) The null hypothesis is rejected if one finds too large a value of the F-ratio, with the degrees of freedom clear from the context.

6.7 Complements/Exercises

Exercises with solutions given in Appendix C

6.1 For the model (6.1), find the expected value of the between-groups mean of squares (MS_g).

6.2 Identify the reparametrization of (6.12) which corresponds to the second partition of $\mathcal{C}(\boldsymbol{X})$ given in (6.13).

6.3 Is it possible to obtain simultaneous confidence intervals *with exact confidence coefficient* for all pairs of treatment differences, in respect of model (6.12) for two-way classified data with one observation per cell, using any of the methods described in Sections 4.3.3 and 6.2.4? Explain.

6.4 Derive the BLUE of λ and the sum of squares due to deviation from the hypothesis $\lambda = 0$, for the model (6.25).

6.5 How can Tukey's one-degree-of-freedom test for interaction be generalized to the case of balanced data with multiple observations per cell?

6.6 Show that, in the absence of any side-condition, no linear function of the treatment effects of the model (6.29) is estimable.

6.7 In the case of two-way classified data with multiple observations per cell, obtain a simple expression for $(\boldsymbol{I} - \boldsymbol{P}_{\boldsymbol{X}})$, where $\boldsymbol{X}$ is the design matrix. Hence, show that the four terms of (6.32) are indeed the BLUEs identified thereafter, and justify the expression of the error sum of squares given in (6.34).

6.8 We wish to test the hypothesis $\gamma_{ij} = 0$ for all i, j (i.e. no interaction), for the linear model (6.29). Find the testable part of this hypothesis and interpret the result. What is the untestable part of the hypothesis?

6.9 Consider the model (6.37) for two-way classified data with interaction and unequal number of observations per cell, and assume that $m_{ij} = m_i n_j$ for some m_i and n_j, $i = 1, \ldots, t$, $j = 1, \ldots, b$. Split the index k into two indices k_1 and k_2, and rewrite the model as follows:

$$y_{ik_1jk_2} = \mu + \tau_i + \beta_j + \gamma_{ij} + \varepsilon_{ik_1jk_2}, \quad k_1 = 1, \ldots, m_i,$$
$$k_2 = 1, \ldots, n_j, \quad i = 1, \ldots, t, \quad j = 1, \ldots, b,$$

and the errors have the usual properties. Rearrange the observations in such a way that k_2 changes faster than j, which changes faster than

k_1, followed by i. Verify that the model can be written in the form $(\boldsymbol{y}, \boldsymbol{X\beta}, \sigma^2\boldsymbol{I})$ such that

$$\boldsymbol{X} = (\boldsymbol{a} \otimes \boldsymbol{b} : \boldsymbol{A} \otimes \boldsymbol{b} : \boldsymbol{a} \otimes \boldsymbol{B} : \boldsymbol{A} \otimes \boldsymbol{B}),$$

where

$$\boldsymbol{A} = \begin{pmatrix} \boldsymbol{1}_{m_1\times 1} & \boldsymbol{0}_{m_1\times 1} & \cdots & \boldsymbol{0}_{m_1\times 1} \\ \boldsymbol{0}_{m_2\times 1} & \boldsymbol{1}_{m_2\times 1} & \cdots & \boldsymbol{0}_{m_2\times 1} \\ \vdots & \vdots & \ddots & \vdots \\ \boldsymbol{0}_{m_t\times 1} & \boldsymbol{0}_{m_t\times 1} & \cdots & \boldsymbol{1}_{m_t\times 1} \end{pmatrix}, \quad \boldsymbol{a} = \boldsymbol{A1}_{t\times 1},$$

$$\boldsymbol{B} = \begin{pmatrix} \boldsymbol{1}_{n_1\times 1} & \boldsymbol{0}_{n_1\times 1} & \cdots & \boldsymbol{0}_{n_1\times 1} \\ \boldsymbol{0}_{n_2\times 1} & \boldsymbol{1}_{n_2\times 1} & \cdots & \boldsymbol{0}_{n_2\times 1} \\ \vdots & \vdots & \ddots & \vdots \\ \boldsymbol{0}_{n_b\times 1} & \boldsymbol{0}_{n_b\times 1} & \cdots & \boldsymbol{1}_{n_b\times 1} \end{pmatrix}, \quad \boldsymbol{b} = \boldsymbol{B1}_{b\times 1}.$$

Hence, obtain a decomposition of the fitted values similar to (6.31) and analysis of variance in the form of Table 6.8.

6.10 Suppose the observation y_{kl} in the model (6.12) is missing. Derive the GLRT for the hypothesis of 'no difference in treatment effects' using the missing plot technique, in the following manner.

(a) Obtain the value of y_{kl} which minimizes the error sum of squares R_0^2 given in (6.20). Call it y_a.
(b) Obtain the value of y_{kl} which minimizes the restricted sum of squares R_H^2 given in (6.21). Call it y_b.
(c) Derive the test statistics with appropriate degrees of freedom.

6.11 *Three-way classified data from row-column design.* Describe a linear model with three-way classified data with a single observation per cell and no interaction, the classification being according to two types of block factors (with b and h levels, respectively) and a treatment effect (t levels). Describe the ANOVA table.

6.12 *Latin square design.* Consider a design where there are two block factors and one treatment factor, all three effects having b levels. There are a total of b^2 observations, one each from every combination of block levels. If the two block factors are arranged in rows and columns, then there is exactly one treatment allocated to each row and one to each column. This is called a $b \times b$ latin square design. The model equation is

$$y_{ijk} = \mu+\tau_i+\beta_j+\gamma_k+\varepsilon_{ijk}, \qquad j = 1,\ldots,b, \ k = 1,\ldots,b,$$

$$i = \begin{cases} j+k-1 & \text{if } j+k-1 \le b, \\ j+k-1-b & \text{otherwise,} \end{cases}$$

with $E(\varepsilon_{ijk}) = 0$ for all i, j, k and

$$Cov(\varepsilon_{ijk}, \varepsilon_{i'j'k'}) = \begin{cases} \sigma^2 & \text{if } i = i',\ j = j' \text{ and } k = k', \\ 0 & \text{otherwise.} \end{cases}$$

(a) Show that the model can be represented as $(\boldsymbol{y}, \boldsymbol{X\beta}, \sigma^2\boldsymbol{I})$ with

$$\boldsymbol{X} = (\boldsymbol{1}_{b\times 1} \otimes \boldsymbol{1}_{b\times 1} : \boldsymbol{Z}_{b^2\times b} : \boldsymbol{I}_{b\times b} \otimes \boldsymbol{1}_{b\times 1} : \boldsymbol{1}_{b\times 1} \otimes \boldsymbol{I}_{b\times b}),$$

where $\boldsymbol{Z}' = (\boldsymbol{J}_b^0 : \boldsymbol{J}_b^1 : \cdots : \boldsymbol{J}_b^{b-1})'$ and the matrix $\boldsymbol{J}_b$ is obtained from $\boldsymbol{I}_{b\times b}$ by removing the first column and appending it after the last column.

(b) Show that

$$\begin{aligned} \mathcal{C}(\boldsymbol{X}) = \mathcal{C}\big(&\boldsymbol{1}_{b\times 1} \otimes \boldsymbol{1}_{b\times 1} : \boldsymbol{Z} - b^{-1}\boldsymbol{1}_{b\times 1} \otimes \boldsymbol{1}_{b\times 1}\boldsymbol{1}'_{b\times 1} \\ &: (\boldsymbol{I}_{b\times b} - b^{-1}\boldsymbol{1}_{b\times 1}\boldsymbol{1}'_{b\times 1}) \otimes \boldsymbol{1}_{b\times 1} \\ &: \boldsymbol{1}_{b\times 1} \otimes (\boldsymbol{I}_{b\times b} - b^{-1}\boldsymbol{1}_{b\times 1}\boldsymbol{1}'_{b\times 1})\big), \end{aligned}$$

and the column spaces of the four partitions are pairwise orthogonal.

(c) Obtain a suitable decomposition of $\boldsymbol{P}_X$ and the ANOVA.

6.13 *RBD with nested effects.* A set of t drugs, each having d dose levels, are administered to subjects divided into b blocks. Each dose level of every drug is applied to m subjects of every block, while the allocation is completely random. The response is a measure of degree of relief caused by the drug. Write down a suitable nested model for this set-up and derive the ANOVA table.

6.14 Consider the model (6.41) where $\boldsymbol{X\beta}$ is as in (6.12), $\boldsymbol{\eta}$ is an estimable scalar parameter (written as η) and $\boldsymbol{Z}$ is a known vector (written as $\boldsymbol{z}$). Find the BLUEs of η and $\boldsymbol{X\beta}$, and the fitted values. Give simple expressions for $Var(\widehat{\eta})$ and $D(\boldsymbol{X}\widehat{\boldsymbol{\beta}})$.

6.15 Given the ANCOVA model of Exercise 6.14, how can you test the hypothesis of 'no difference in treatment effects'?

6.16 Describe the ANCOVA table for the model of Exercise 6.14.

6.17 Suppose the vector $\boldsymbol{z}$ of the ANCOVA model of Exercise 6.14 has the element 1 at the location corresponding to y_{kl} and 0 everywhere else. Describe explicitly the GLRT for the hypothesis of 'no difference in treatment effects'.

6.18 Show that the test of Exercise 6.17 does not depend on the value of y_{kl}, and explain the result.

6.19 Prove the equivalence of the tests derived in Exercises 6.10 and 6.17, in the following manner.

(a) Show that the value of the uncorrected R_0^2 at $y_{kl} = y_a$, obtained in Exercise 6.10 is the same as the value of the corrected (for covariate) R_0^2, obtained in Exercise 6.17, at $y_{kl} = y_a$.
(b) Show that the value of the uncorrected R_H^2 at $y_{kl} = y_b$, obtained in Exercise 6.10 is the same as the value of the corrected (for covariate) R_H^2, obtained in Exercise 6.17, at $y_{kl} = y_a$.
(c) Hence, show that test derived from the missing plot technique is the same as the test derived by using analysis of covariance.

Additional exercises

6.20 *Spring balance.* A spring balance with no bias is used to weigh two objects of unknown weights β_1 and β_2. The objects can be weighed individually or together, but the maximum number of measurements that can be taken is 6. The measurement errors are independent and identically distributed with mean 0 and variance σ^2. Find the D-optimal design subject to the condition that each weight should be estimable.

6.21 Find the A- and E-optimal designs for the problem of Exercise 6.20.

6.22 Table 6.13 gives data, taken from Gutsell (1951), on measured hemoglobin content in the blood of brown trout that were randomly allocated to four troughs. The fish in the four troughs received food containing various concentrations of sulfamerazine, 35 days prior to measurement. Assuming that the response (hemoglobin content) follows the model (6.1) with normal errors, test the hypothesis that sulfamerazine has no effect on hemoglobin content of trout blood, using this data.

6.23 For the brown trout hemoglobin data of Table 6.13, determine which of the six pairs of group means have a significant difference at the level

Table 6.13 Brown trout hemoglobin data (data object `trout` in R package `lmreg`, source: Gutsell, 1951)

Sulfamerazine content (grams per 100 pounds of fish)	Hemoglobin in Brown Trout blood (grams per 100 ml of blood)									
0	6.7	7.8	5.5	8.4	7.0	7.8	8.6	7.4	5.8	7.0
5	9.9	8.4	10.4	9.3	10.7	11.9	7.1	6.4	8.6	10.6
10	10.4	8.1	10.6	8.7	10.7	9.1	8.8	8.1	7.8	8.0
15	9.3	9.3	7.2	7.8	9.3	10.2	8.7	8.6	9.3	7.2

0.95, using Tukey's HSD and assuming that the response (hemoglobin content) follows the model (6.1) with normal errors. Compare the results with those obtained from the Bonferroni and Scheffé methods, and comment. Can the maximum modulus-t or Fisher's PLSD methods be used for this problem?

6.24 *Testing for heterogeneity of variances.* The hypothesis of equality of group means is often tested through one-way ANOVA, while assuming equality of the within-group variances. The purpose of this problem is to test the latter assumption. Given a random sample y_{ij}, $j = 1, \ldots, n_i$, $i = 1, \ldots, t$ from $N(\mu_i, \sigma_i^2)$, find the generalized likelihood ratio test for the null hypothesis $\sigma_1^2 = \cdots = \sigma_t^2$. You may assume that $\min_{1 \le i \le t} n_i$ is large and use the asymptotic null distribution of the GLRT given on page 633. [Bartlett (1937b) proposed a scaled and modified version of this test where the MLEs of the variances are replaced by their respective unbiased estimators.]

6.25 Consider the model (6.1) for one-way classified data. The following data summary are available for groups $i = 1, \ldots, t$: sample size (n_i), sum of y-values (a_i) and sum of squares of y-values (b_i).

(a) Describe the ANOVA table and a test for the hypothesis of no difference among group means.

(b) If b_1 is missing, can you still carry out the test of the hypothesis stated in part (a)? Justify your answer.

(c) If a_1 is missing, can you still carry out the test of the hypothesis stated in part (a)? Justify your answer.

6.26 Derive the variance of the LZF $\sum_{i=1}^t \sum_{j=1}^b a_i b_j e_{ij}$ in the model (6.12).

6.27 Using the log-record times for the data of Table 1.2, and treating the running distances as blocks, test for the significance of the gender effect — under a suitable ANOVA model.

6.28 Derive the BLUE of the treatment contrast $\boldsymbol{c}'\boldsymbol{\tau}$ in the model (6.12), and its variance.

6.29 For the air speed data of Table 6.3, use a two-way classification model with no interaction to obtain the ANOVA table and test for (a) no difference in effects of rib height (b) no difference in effects of Reynolds numbers.

6.30 Show that the estimator obtained in Exercise 6.28 remains unbiased and its variance remains the same even if there is interaction of the type described in (6.24). Is it the BLUE of $\boldsymbol{c}'\boldsymbol{\tau}$ in (6.24)?

6.31 For the air speed experiment data of Table 6.3, test for interaction as per model (6.24).

6.32 Show that the estimator of σ^2 given in (6.20) is an overestimate when the true model is (6.24), i.e. when interaction is present. Comment on the appropriateness of confidence intervals of treatment contrasts computed from the model (6.12) when the correct model is (6.24).

6.33 Show that Tukey's one degree of freedom test for nonadditivity is a special case of the test described in Exercise 4.7.

6.34 For the survival time data of Table 6.7, construct the ANOVA table for the two-way classification model with interaction, and carry out the GLRT for 'no difference in effects of poisons', 'no difference in treatment effects' and 'no interaction effect'. What does interaction mean in this case?

6.35 For the survival time data of Table 6.7, construct the ANOVA table for the two-way classification model without interaction, and carry out the GLRT for 'no treatment difference'.

6.36 Given the model (6.29) and assuming that the model errors are independent and have normal distribution, find a t-statistic for the hypothesis of 'no difference in average effects of the first and second treatments'. Is this the same as the hypothesis $\tau_1 = \tau_2$?

6.37 Given the model (6.29) with independent and normally distributed errors, suppose we have to test if there is significant interaction between the first treatment and second block. Formulate this problem as a testable hypothesis involving the model parameters, and find a t-statistic for testing it.

6.38 Table 6.14 shows measurements of absorbance of light at a particular wavelength for positive control samples in an enzyme-linked immunosorbent assay (ELISA) test for human immunodeficiency virus (HIV), which is believed to cause the acquired immunodeficiency syndrome (AIDS). The data are taken from Hoaglin et al. (1991). The materials for the test come in lots, and each lot contains enough material for three runs. Every run consists of measurements of three control samples. The purpose of the experiment is to test for significance of between-lot differences and run-to-run difference within a lot. Obtain an ANOVA table as per the model (6.38) and carry out the GLRT for these two problems.

6.39 Given the set-up of Exercise 6.13, how will you test the following hypotheses?

(a) The dose levels of none of the drugs have different effects.

Table 6.14 Light absorbance for positive control samples in an ELISA test for HIV (data object `hiv` in R package `lmreg`, source: Hoaglin et al., 1991)

	Run 1	Run 2	Run 3	Run 4	Run 5
Lot *A*	1.053	0.881	0.896	0.971	0.984
	1.708	0.788	1.038	1.234	0.986
	0.977	0.788	0.963	1.089	1.067
Lot *B*	0.996	1.019	1.120	1.327	1.079
	1.129	1.088	1.054	1.361	1.120
	1.016	1.280	1.235	1.233	0.959
Lot *C*	1.229	1.118	1.053	1.140	0.963
	1.027	1.066	1.082	1.172	1.064
	1.109	1.146	1.113	0.966	1.086
Lot *D*	0.985	0.847	1.033	0.988	1.308
	0.894	0.799	0.943	1.169	1.498
	1.019	0.918	1.089	1.106	1.271
Lot *E*	1.128	0.990	0.929	0.873	0.930
	1.141	0.801	0.950	0.871	0.968
	1.144	0.416	0.899	0.786	0.844

(b) The t drugs do not have different effects.

(c) The various dose levels of Drug 1 do not have different effects.

6.40 The data set of Table 6.15, taken from Williams (1959), consists of the maximum compressive strength parallel to the grain (y) and moisture content (z) of 10 hoop trees for five temperature categories. Using y

Table 6.15 Compressive strength and moisture content of wood in hoop trees (data object `hoop` in R package `lmreg`, source: Williams, 1959)

Tree	Temperature in Celsius									
	−20		0		20		40		60	
	y	z	y	z	y	z	y	z	y	z
1	13.14	42.1	12.46	41.1	9.43	43.1	7.63	41.4	6.34	39.1
2	15.90	41.0	14.11	39.4	11.30	40.3	9.56	38.6	7.27	36.7
3	13.39	41.1	12.32	40.2	9.65	40.6	7.90	41.7	6.41	39.7
4	15.51	41.0	13.68	39.8	10.33	40.4	8.27	39.8	7.06	39.3
5	15.53	41.0	13.16	41.2	10.29	39.7	8.67	39.0	6.68	39.0
6	15.26	42.0	13.64	40.0	10.35	40.3	8.67	40.9	6.62	41.2
7	15.06	40.4	13.25	39.0	10.56	34.9	8.10	40.1	6.15	41.4
8	15.21	39.3	13.54	38.8	10.46	37.5	8.30	40.6	6.09	41.8
9	16.90	39.2	15.23	38.5	11.94	38.5	9.34	39.4	6.26	41.7
10	15.45	37.7	14.06	35.7	10.74	36.7	7.75	38.9	6.29	38.2

as response and z as a covariate, describe the ANCOVA table and test for the hypothesis that the five temperature categories do not have different effects. How will the conclusions change if the covariate is ignored? Carry out a test for the significance of the covariate effect.

6.41 For the Wright brothers' wind tunnel experiment data of Table 6.5, revise the analysis of Example 6.8 to include the data on all types of wing (including type 13), using ANCOVA to account for the two missing values.

6.42 The data set of Table 6.16, taken from Pearce (1983, p. 284), shows aggregate weight (in pounds) of apple produced in a plot in four years following one of six treatments, together with average crop volume (in bushels) in four years in that plot prior to treatment, the plots being arranged in four randomized blocks coded as 1 to 4. The treatments consist of one of five types of permanent cropping under the apple tree (coded as 1 to 5), or no cropping at all (0).

(a) Using the post-treatment weight as response, test for the hypothesis that the six under-the-tree cropping regimes do not have different effects.

(b) Repeat the above analysis, while using pre-treatment volume as a covariate, and compare the conclusions.

(c) Which of the agricultural regimes have a positive impact on the yield?

Table 6.16 Apple yield with cropping under tree (data object `appletree` in R package `lmreg`, source: Pearce, 1983, p. 284)

Treat-ment	Block 1		Block 2		Block 3		Block 4	
	Weight (pound)	Volume (bushel)	Weight (pound)	Volume (bushel)	Weight (pound)	Volume (bushel)	Weight (pound)	Volume (bushel)
1	8.2	287	9.4	290	7.7	254	8.5	307
2	8.2	271	6.0	209	9.1	243	10.1	348
3	6.8	234	7.0	210	9.7	286	9.9	371
4	5.7	189	5.5	205	10.2	312	10.3	375
5	6.1	210	7.0	276	8.7	279	8.1	344
0	7.6	222	10.1	301	9.0	238	10.5	357

Chapter 7

General Linear Model

In this chapter we discuss the 'general' case of the linear model, $(\boldsymbol{y}, \boldsymbol{X\beta}, \sigma^2\boldsymbol{V})$, where $\boldsymbol{V}$ is not necessarily the identity matrix. In contrast to the homoscedastic model, this general choice for $\boldsymbol{V}$ allows the observations to be correlated as well as to have different variances. Although we allowed $\boldsymbol{X}$ to be rank deficient in the preceding chapters, here for the first time, we also allow the dispersion matrix $\boldsymbol{V}$ to be rank-deficient i.e. singular. We refer to the linear model with a singular dispersion matrix as the *singular linear model*.

A careful review of the literature on such a singular linear model shows that this case has been treated by most authors as if it is an entirely different object, compared to the model with nonsingular dispersion matrix (see e.g. Gross, 2004, Kala and Pordzik, 2009, and the references therein). Besides the obvious differences such as the non-invertibility of $\boldsymbol{V}$, there are other subtle differences between the two situations, which we highlight in Section 7.2. Such differences have made the singular linear model a happy hunting ground for researchers equipped with the artillery of linear algebra. However the heavy use of algebra as well as the apprehension that intuition may sometimes fail us in this context, has had the effect of turning practitioners away from the singular linear model. One of the primary goals of this chapter is to demonstrate that the singular linear model can be dealt with, using exactly the same fundamental principles that were used for the nonsingular case that has been discussed so far. One can continue to use most of the results obtained in Chapter 3 for the latter case, essentially unmindful of the fact that the model is singular.

In Section 7.1 we discuss why the singular model is important, and provide some examples. After dealing briefly with the nuances of the singular model in Section 7.2, we extend the results of Chapter 3 to the general linear model — including the singular case — in Sections 7.3–7.10. The approach adopted here reinforces the strong commonality in the analyses of the general linear model and the more common homoscedastic linear model. As in Chapter 4, we assume that the errors are normally distributed while deriving tests of hypotheses, confidence sets, and prediction and tolerance intervals in Sections 7.11, 7.12 and 7.13, respectively. This assumption can be relaxed when the sample size is large, as we shall see in Section 11.5.

7.1 Why study the singular model?

Recall that, as observed on page 98, the usual model with linear restrictions can be expressed in terms of an equivalent unrestricted model — making it possible to apply the standard techniques to the restricted model. However, such an equivalent model is expressed in terms of a transformed set of explanatory variables as well as parameters. It is then necessary to use the reverse transform, to make inferences on the original parameters. An alternative to this strategy is to treat the restrictions as a set of *observations with zero error*, as we did on page 97. Thus, the model $(\boldsymbol{y}, \boldsymbol{X\beta}, \sigma^2\boldsymbol{I})$ under the restriction $\boldsymbol{A\beta} = \boldsymbol{\xi}$ is represented by the augmented model equation

$$\begin{pmatrix} \boldsymbol{y} \\ \boldsymbol{\xi} \end{pmatrix} = \begin{pmatrix} \boldsymbol{X} \\ \boldsymbol{A} \end{pmatrix} \boldsymbol{\beta} + \begin{pmatrix} \boldsymbol{\varepsilon} \\ \boldsymbol{0} \end{pmatrix}, \qquad E(\boldsymbol{\varepsilon}) = \boldsymbol{0}, \quad D(\boldsymbol{\varepsilon}) = \sigma^2\boldsymbol{I}.$$

This is equivalent to the unrestricted model $(\boldsymbol{y}_*, \boldsymbol{X}_*\boldsymbol{\beta}, \sigma^2\boldsymbol{V})$, with

$$\boldsymbol{y}_* = \begin{pmatrix} \boldsymbol{y} \\ \boldsymbol{\xi} \end{pmatrix}, \qquad \boldsymbol{X}_* = \begin{pmatrix} \boldsymbol{X} \\ \boldsymbol{A} \end{pmatrix}, \qquad \boldsymbol{V} = \begin{pmatrix} \boldsymbol{I} & \boldsymbol{0} \\ \boldsymbol{0} & \boldsymbol{0} \end{pmatrix}.$$

This is clearly a singular model, since $\boldsymbol{V}$ is a singular matrix. The most attractive feature of this model is that its parameters are identical to those in the original (unrestricted) model.

A similar dispersion structure may also arise *naturally* when a subset of measurements come error-free or nearly so. This may happen because of sophisticated measurement of certain physical variables. More commonly, some measurements may have much smaller variance than others and a model with singular $\boldsymbol{V}$ may serve as a limiting special case of a model with *nearly* rank-deficient $\boldsymbol{V}$. In an econometric context, Buser (1977) gives an example where the dispersion matrix of a set of investment returns involving 'risk-free' mutual funds, may be singular.

If one or more linear combinations of the response is constrained to have a specified value, the dispersion matrix becomes singular. For instance, if the response consists of a few proportions whose sum must be equal to one, then the sum of the model errors has zero variance (see also Example 7.11). Scott et al. (1990) shows how such constraints on the response occur when the *generalized linear model* of Example 1.14 is used (see also Sengupta, 1995). As indicated in Section 5.7.1, estimation in such models typically involves an iterative procedure with a new linear model appearing at every stage of the iteration. Methodology for the singular linear model can be useful for such problems.

The dispersion matrix can also be singular when the elements of $\boldsymbol{y}$ are not measured directly, but are *derived* from other measurements. Rowley (1977) and Bich (1990) provide examples of this phenomenon in the fields of Economics and Metrology, respectively.

Analysis of models with nuisance parameters can lead to singular dispersion matrices. We shall see in Section 7.10 that when the only objects of interest in the model $(\boldsymbol{y}, \boldsymbol{X}_1\boldsymbol{\beta}_1 + \boldsymbol{X}_2\boldsymbol{\beta}_2, \sigma^2\boldsymbol{I})$ are the estimable linear functions of $\boldsymbol{\beta}_1$, we can work with the reduced model $((\boldsymbol{I} - \boldsymbol{P}_{X_2})\boldsymbol{y}, (\boldsymbol{I} - \boldsymbol{P}_{X_2})\boldsymbol{X}_1\boldsymbol{\beta}_1, \sigma^2(\boldsymbol{I} - \boldsymbol{P}_{X_2}))$, which does not involve the nuisance parameters. The dispersion matrix of this reduced model is singular.

Kempthorne (1976) and Zyskind (1975) show that in finite population sampling, the response obtained from certain sampling schemes can be represented as a linear model (corresponding to a completely randomized design) whose covariance structure is singular. Similar singularity of the error dispersion occurs in randomized block designs and some other designs in this context.

Examples of a singular error dispersion matrix abound in the literature of state-space models, particularly in the area of automatic control (see Kohn and Ansley, 1983, Shaked and Soroka, 1987 and Bekir, 1988 for examples). It is shown in Section 9.1.6 how the minimum mean squared error linear predictor in a state-space model can be computed by means of best linear unbiased estimation in a special linear model, which may be singular.

While some of the examples cited above can be handled by specialized techniques on a case-by-case basis, the general linear model with possibly singular dispersion matrix provides an appropriate and unified framework for the discussion of all such situations.

7.2 Special considerations with singular models

Before developing the theory, it would be a good idea to examine some of the 'peculiarities' of a singular model. Some readers may want to skip this section at the first reading, but it should be noted that in dealing with singular models, Proposition 3.14 regarding the LUEs and LZFs has to be replaced by the more general Proposition 7.3.

7.2.1 *Checking for model consistency**

A fundamental difference between the linear models with singular and nonsingular $\boldsymbol{V}$ is that unlike the latter, the singular model conveys an almost deterministic message about the response. According to the singular linear model, certain linear combinations of $\boldsymbol{y}$ have zero variance, i.e. these are constant with probability 1.

To see this, note that the model error vector must lie in $\mathcal{C}(\boldsymbol{V})$ with probability 1, while the mean of the response must lie in $\mathcal{C}(\boldsymbol{X})$. Therefore, we must have $\boldsymbol{y} \in \mathcal{C}(\boldsymbol{X} : \boldsymbol{V})$ with probability 1. Other equivalent forms of this condition are: (a) $(\boldsymbol{I} - \boldsymbol{P}_{X:V})\boldsymbol{y} = \boldsymbol{0}$ with probability 1, (b) $(\boldsymbol{I} - \boldsymbol{P}_V)\boldsymbol{y} \in \mathcal{C}((\boldsymbol{I} - \boldsymbol{P}_V)\boldsymbol{X})$ with probability 1 and (c) $(\boldsymbol{I} - \boldsymbol{P}_X)\boldsymbol{y} \in \mathcal{C}((\boldsymbol{I} - \boldsymbol{P}_X)\boldsymbol{V})$ with probability 1. If $\boldsymbol{V}$ is of full rank, these conditions are automatically satisfied. When $\boldsymbol{V}$ is singular, the conditions sometimes follow readily from the formulation of the model. However, it is a good idea to check if one of these conditions is met, before proceeding with inference.

To understand the issue of model consistency when $\boldsymbol{V}$ is singular, consider first the case of a *nearly* singular dispersion matrix, i.e. when $\boldsymbol{V}$ has a determinant (and at least one eigenvalue) very close to zero. In such a case, there is a linear function $\boldsymbol{l}'\boldsymbol{y}$ which is *close* to its mean, $\boldsymbol{l}'\boldsymbol{X}\boldsymbol{\beta}$. If the observed value of $\boldsymbol{l}'\boldsymbol{y}$ is far from $\boldsymbol{l}'\boldsymbol{X}\boldsymbol{\beta}$ for every choice of $\boldsymbol{l}$, then we would have to suspect that the model is bad. If this happens in the extreme case when $\boldsymbol{V}$ is perfectly singular, the 'suspicion' would turn into disbelief, and we would conclude that the model is *inconsistent* with the data.

Example 7.1. Consider the model $(\boldsymbol{y}, \boldsymbol{X\beta}, \sigma^2\boldsymbol{V})$ with

$$\boldsymbol{y} = \begin{pmatrix} 1 \\ 2 \\ 3 \\ 4 \end{pmatrix}, \quad \boldsymbol{X} = \begin{pmatrix} 1 & 1 & 0 \\ 1 & 1 & 0 \\ 1 & 0 & 1 \\ 1 & 0 & 1 \end{pmatrix}, \quad \boldsymbol{\beta} = \begin{pmatrix} \beta_0 \\ \beta_1 \\ \beta_2 \end{pmatrix}, \quad \boldsymbol{V} = \begin{pmatrix} 1 & 0 & 0 & 0 \\ 0 & 1 & 0 & 0 \\ 0 & 0 & \alpha & 0 \\ 0 & 0 & 0 & \alpha \end{pmatrix},$$

and σ^2 *known* to be 1. If α is very small, say $\alpha = 0.0001$ (making $\boldsymbol{V}$ nearly singular), we expect that the last two observations (3 and 4) to be known with a high degree of precision. The model stipulates that these observations are noisy measurements of a common entity $(\beta_0 + \beta_2)$, and they should not be far from one another. From Chebyshev's inequality,

$$P[|y_3 - y_4| \geq 1] \leq \frac{Var(y_3 - y_4)}{1^2} = 2\alpha = 0.0002,$$

which makes the observed values of 3 and 4, quite improbable. This fact casts some doubt on the appropriateness of the model. Had α been larger, say 0.4, the observed values would have been more plausible and we would not be as concerned about the issue. In the extreme case $\alpha = 0$ (when $\boldsymbol{V}$ is singular), the model postulates that y_3 and y_4 should be *identical* with probability 1, while in reality they are not. In such a case, the model is *inconsistent* with the data.

In the latter case ($\alpha = 0$),

$$(\boldsymbol{I} - \boldsymbol{P}_V)\boldsymbol{y} = \begin{pmatrix} 0 \\ 0 \\ 3 \\ 4 \end{pmatrix}, \qquad (\boldsymbol{I} - \boldsymbol{P}_V)\boldsymbol{X} = \begin{pmatrix} 0 & 0 & 0 \\ 0 & 0 & 0 \\ 1 & 0 & 1 \\ 1 & 0 & 1 \end{pmatrix},$$

and the condition $(\boldsymbol{I} - \boldsymbol{P}_V)\boldsymbol{y} \in \mathcal{C}((\boldsymbol{I} - \boldsymbol{P}_V)\boldsymbol{X})$ is not satisfied. The reader may verify that neither of the equivalent conditions $\boldsymbol{y} \in \mathcal{C}(\boldsymbol{X} : \boldsymbol{V})$ and $(\boldsymbol{I} - \boldsymbol{P}_X)\boldsymbol{y} \in \mathcal{C}((\boldsymbol{I} - \boldsymbol{P}_X)\boldsymbol{V})$ is satisfied. □

There is no reason why a properly formulated singular model will turn out to be inconsistent. Inconsistency often results from overlooking facts, either in model formulation or in measurement.

7.2.2 LUE, LZF, estimability and identifiability*

Consider the model $(\boldsymbol{y}, \boldsymbol{X\beta}, \sigma^2\boldsymbol{V})$ where $\boldsymbol{V}$ is singular. Then as we saw earlier, there is a constant vector $\boldsymbol{d}$ such that $(\boldsymbol{I} - \boldsymbol{P}_V)\boldsymbol{y} = \boldsymbol{d}$ with probability 1. Consequently $(\boldsymbol{I} - \boldsymbol{P}_d)(\boldsymbol{I} - \boldsymbol{P}_V)\boldsymbol{y}$ is zero with probability 1. The vector $\boldsymbol{d}$ may not be known before the data are gathered. If the singularity of $\boldsymbol{V}$ arises from incorporating a linear restriction, then $\boldsymbol{d}$ is known. If the singularity arises from zero measurement error, then $\boldsymbol{d}$ is not known until the measurements are actually recorded. Whichever the case may be, the fact that matters in the following discussion is that there is such a vector $\boldsymbol{d}$ and it is nonrandom.

Let $\boldsymbol{p} = \boldsymbol{X}'\boldsymbol{l}$, so that $\boldsymbol{l}'\boldsymbol{y}$ is an LUE of $\boldsymbol{p}'\boldsymbol{\beta}$. Note that $\boldsymbol{k}'\boldsymbol{y}$ is also an LUE of $\boldsymbol{p}'\boldsymbol{\beta}$ when $\boldsymbol{k} = \boldsymbol{l} + (\boldsymbol{I} - \boldsymbol{P}_V)(\boldsymbol{I} - \boldsymbol{P}_d)\boldsymbol{m}$ for an arbitrary $\boldsymbol{m}$. However, $\boldsymbol{X}'\boldsymbol{k}$ is not necessarily equal to $\boldsymbol{p}$. This shows that Proposition 3.14(a) does not hold when $\boldsymbol{V}$ is singular.

Likewise, if $\boldsymbol{l}$ is a vector in $\mathcal{C}(\boldsymbol{X})^{\perp}$, then $\boldsymbol{l}'\boldsymbol{y}$ is an LZF. The linear function $\boldsymbol{k}'\boldsymbol{y}$ is also an LZF when $\boldsymbol{k} = \boldsymbol{l}+(\boldsymbol{I}-\boldsymbol{P}_d)(\boldsymbol{I}-\boldsymbol{P}_V)\boldsymbol{m}$ for an arbitrary $\boldsymbol{m}$. However, $\boldsymbol{X}'\boldsymbol{k}$ is not necessarily equal to $\boldsymbol{0}$. Thus, the characterization of LZFs given in Proposition 3.14(b) is not quite appropriate when $\boldsymbol{V}$ is singular.

Example 7.2. Consider the model $(\boldsymbol{y}, \boldsymbol{X\beta}, \sigma^2\boldsymbol{V})$ where $\boldsymbol{y}$ and $\boldsymbol{X}$ are as in Example 7.1, and $\boldsymbol{V}$ is a diagonal matrix with diagonal elements 1, 0, 1 and 0, respectively. It is easy to see that

$$\boldsymbol{d} = \begin{pmatrix} 0 \\ 2 \\ 0 \\ 4 \end{pmatrix}, \qquad (\boldsymbol{I}-\boldsymbol{P}_d)(\boldsymbol{I}-\boldsymbol{P}_V) = \begin{pmatrix} 0 & 0 & 0 & 0 \\ 0 & 0.8 & 0 & -0.4 \\ 0 & 0 & 0 & 0 \\ 0 & -0.4 & 0 & 0.2 \end{pmatrix}.$$

If we choose $\boldsymbol{l}_1 = (1:0:0:0)'$ and $\boldsymbol{m}_1 = (0:0:0:1)'$, then $\boldsymbol{k}_1 = (1: -0.4:0:0.2)'$ and $\boldsymbol{X}'\boldsymbol{l}_1 = \boldsymbol{p} = (1:1:0)'$ but $\boldsymbol{X}'\boldsymbol{k}_1 = (2:1:1)'$. Thus, $\boldsymbol{k}_1'\boldsymbol{y}$ is an LUE of $\boldsymbol{p}'\boldsymbol{\beta}$ and yet $\boldsymbol{X}'\boldsymbol{k}_1 \neq \boldsymbol{p}$.

If we choose $\boldsymbol{l}_2 = (1:-1:0:0)'$ and $\boldsymbol{m}_2 = (0:0:0:1)'$, then $\boldsymbol{k}_2 = (1:-1.4:0:0.2)'$ and $\boldsymbol{X}'\boldsymbol{l}_2 = \boldsymbol{0}$ but $\boldsymbol{X}'\boldsymbol{k}_2 = (-0.2:-0.4:0.2)'$. Clearly $\boldsymbol{k}_2'\boldsymbol{y}$ is an LZF even though $\boldsymbol{X}'\boldsymbol{k}_2 \neq \boldsymbol{0}$. □

Thus, Proposition 3.14 is no longer valid in the case of a singular linear model. Another difficulty arises from the fact that $\boldsymbol{\beta}$ is no longer a free parameter: it must satisfy the constraint $(\boldsymbol{I}-\boldsymbol{P}_V)\boldsymbol{\beta} = \boldsymbol{d}$, and the definitions of LUE and LZF have to be interpreted in the light of this constraint. This constraint also affects the definition of estimability. According to Definition 3.20, we should call $\boldsymbol{p}'\boldsymbol{\beta}$ an estimable function whenever there is a linear function $\boldsymbol{l}'\boldsymbol{y}$ such that $E(\boldsymbol{l}'\boldsymbol{y}) = \boldsymbol{p}'\boldsymbol{\beta}$ for all $\boldsymbol{\beta}$ *that satisfies the above constraint.* We shall revisit this definition. We shall also have to reexamine the issue of identifiability.

The first clue to resolving this confusion comes from the following fact. Although the vector $\boldsymbol{k}_1$ in Example 7.2 violates Proposition 3.14, the offending LUE $\boldsymbol{k}_1'\boldsymbol{y}$ is identical to the compliant LUE $\boldsymbol{l}_1'\boldsymbol{y}$, with probability 1. Thus, $\boldsymbol{k}_1'\boldsymbol{y}$ is not a different LUE of $\boldsymbol{p}'\boldsymbol{\beta}$, but just an equivalent form of $\boldsymbol{l}_1'\boldsymbol{y}$. Likewise, $\boldsymbol{k}_2'\boldsymbol{y}$ is just another representation of the LZF $\boldsymbol{l}_2'\boldsymbol{y}$. Therefore, we need only a minor modification of Proposition 3.14, which is given below.

Proposition 7.3. (Rao, 1973a) *Consider the model $(\boldsymbol{y}, \boldsymbol{X\beta}, \sigma^2\boldsymbol{V})$ where $\boldsymbol{V}$ may be singular.*

(a) $\boldsymbol{k}'\boldsymbol{y}$ is an LUE of $\boldsymbol{p}'\boldsymbol{\beta}$ if and only if there is a vector $\boldsymbol{l}$ such that $\boldsymbol{X}'\boldsymbol{l} = \boldsymbol{p}$ and $\boldsymbol{k}'\boldsymbol{y} = \boldsymbol{l}'\boldsymbol{y}$ with probability 1.

(b) $\boldsymbol{k}'\boldsymbol{y}$ *is an LZF if and only if there is a vector* $\boldsymbol{l}$ *such that* $\boldsymbol{X}'\boldsymbol{l} = \boldsymbol{0}$ *and* $\boldsymbol{k}'\boldsymbol{y} = \boldsymbol{l}'\boldsymbol{y}$ *with probability 1.*

Proof. The sufficiency in part (a) is obvious. In order to prove the necessity, let $\boldsymbol{k}'\boldsymbol{y}$ be an LUE of $\boldsymbol{p}'\boldsymbol{\beta}$. It follows that $\boldsymbol{k}'\boldsymbol{X}\boldsymbol{\beta} = \boldsymbol{p}'\boldsymbol{\beta}$ for all $\boldsymbol{\beta}$ satisfying the condition $(\boldsymbol{I} - \boldsymbol{P}_V)\boldsymbol{X}\boldsymbol{\beta} = \boldsymbol{d}$.

Choose an arbitrary $\boldsymbol{\beta}_1$ so that $(\boldsymbol{I}-\boldsymbol{P}_d)(\boldsymbol{I}-\boldsymbol{P}_V)\boldsymbol{X}\boldsymbol{\beta}_1 = \boldsymbol{0}$. It follows that $(\boldsymbol{I} - \boldsymbol{P}_V)\boldsymbol{X}\boldsymbol{\beta}_1 \in \mathcal{C}(\boldsymbol{d})$. Therefore, we must either have $(\boldsymbol{I} - \boldsymbol{P}_V)\boldsymbol{X}\boldsymbol{\beta}_1\alpha = \boldsymbol{d}$ for some constant $\alpha \neq 0$, or $(\boldsymbol{I} - \boldsymbol{P}_V)\boldsymbol{X}\boldsymbol{\beta}_1 = \boldsymbol{0}$. In the former case, the choice $\boldsymbol{\beta} = \boldsymbol{\beta}_1\alpha$ satisfies the condition $(\boldsymbol{I} - \boldsymbol{P}_V)\boldsymbol{X}\boldsymbol{\beta} = \boldsymbol{d}$, so it must also satisfy $\boldsymbol{k}'\boldsymbol{X}\boldsymbol{\beta} = \boldsymbol{p}'\boldsymbol{\beta}$, and therefore $(\boldsymbol{X}'\boldsymbol{k} - \boldsymbol{p})'\boldsymbol{\beta}_1 = \boldsymbol{0}$. In the latter case, for every solution $\boldsymbol{\beta}_0$ to the equation $(\boldsymbol{I} - \boldsymbol{P}_V)\boldsymbol{X}\boldsymbol{\beta} = \boldsymbol{d}$, the vector $\boldsymbol{\beta}_0 + \boldsymbol{\beta}_1$ is also a solution. Therefore, $\boldsymbol{\beta}_0$ and $\boldsymbol{\beta}_0 + \boldsymbol{\beta}_1$ both satisfy the equation $(\boldsymbol{X}'\boldsymbol{k} - \boldsymbol{p})'\boldsymbol{\beta} = \boldsymbol{0}$. It follows that $(\boldsymbol{X}'\boldsymbol{k} - \boldsymbol{p})'\boldsymbol{\beta}_1 = \boldsymbol{0}$. We conclude from the analysis of the two cases that the equation $(\boldsymbol{X}'\boldsymbol{k} - \boldsymbol{p})'\boldsymbol{\beta} = \boldsymbol{0}$ holds whenever $(\boldsymbol{I}-\boldsymbol{P}_d)(\boldsymbol{I}-\boldsymbol{P}_V)\boldsymbol{X}\boldsymbol{\beta} = \boldsymbol{0}$, i.e. $(\boldsymbol{X}'\boldsymbol{k}-\boldsymbol{p}) \in \mathcal{C}(\boldsymbol{X}'(\boldsymbol{I}-\boldsymbol{P}_V)(\boldsymbol{I}-\boldsymbol{P}_d))$. Therefore, there is an $\boldsymbol{m}$ such that $(\boldsymbol{X}'\boldsymbol{k} - \boldsymbol{p}) = \boldsymbol{X}'(\boldsymbol{I} - \boldsymbol{P}_V)(\boldsymbol{I} - \boldsymbol{P}_d)\boldsymbol{m}$. Let $\boldsymbol{l} = \boldsymbol{k} - (\boldsymbol{I} - \boldsymbol{P}_V)(\boldsymbol{I} - \boldsymbol{P}_d)\boldsymbol{m}$. Clearly $\boldsymbol{X}'\boldsymbol{l} = \boldsymbol{p}$. Also, $\boldsymbol{k}'\boldsymbol{y} - \boldsymbol{l}'\boldsymbol{y} = \boldsymbol{m}'(\boldsymbol{I} - \boldsymbol{P}_d)(\boldsymbol{I} - \boldsymbol{P}_V)\boldsymbol{y} = 0$ with probability 1.

This proves part (a). The proof of part (b) follows from part (a) by putting $\boldsymbol{p} = \boldsymbol{0}$. □

We now turn to the questions of estimability and identifiability in the singular case. The results stated earlier in Proposition 3.21 and Proposition 3.27 for the case $\boldsymbol{V} = \boldsymbol{I}$, continue to hold. So we restate these results and give proofs for the general case of possibly singular $\boldsymbol{V}$. Consider the linear model $(\boldsymbol{y}, \boldsymbol{X}\boldsymbol{\beta}, \sigma^2\boldsymbol{V})$ where $\boldsymbol{V}$ may be singular, and let $\boldsymbol{d}$ be a constant vector such that $(\boldsymbol{I} - \boldsymbol{P}_V)\boldsymbol{y} = \boldsymbol{d}$ with probability 1.

Proposition 7.4. (Restatement of Proposition 3.21) *A necessary and sufficient condition for the estimability of an LPF* $\boldsymbol{p}'\boldsymbol{\beta}$ *in the general linear model* $(\boldsymbol{y}, \boldsymbol{X}\boldsymbol{\beta}, \sigma^2\boldsymbol{V})$ *is that* $\boldsymbol{p} \in \mathcal{C}(\boldsymbol{X}')$.

Proof. Suppose $\boldsymbol{p}'\boldsymbol{\beta}$ is an estimable function, i.e. there is a linear estimator $\boldsymbol{k}'\boldsymbol{y}$ of $\boldsymbol{p}'\boldsymbol{\beta}$ such that $E(\boldsymbol{k}'\boldsymbol{y}) = \boldsymbol{p}'\boldsymbol{\beta}$ for all $\boldsymbol{\beta}$ satisfying the condition $(\boldsymbol{I} - \boldsymbol{P}_V)\boldsymbol{X}\boldsymbol{\beta} = \boldsymbol{d}$. Let $\boldsymbol{\beta}_0$ be a choice of $\boldsymbol{\beta}$ which satisfies the condition $(\boldsymbol{I} - \boldsymbol{P}_V)\boldsymbol{X}\boldsymbol{\beta} = \boldsymbol{d}$. Then $\boldsymbol{\beta}_1 = \boldsymbol{\beta}_0 + (\boldsymbol{I} - \boldsymbol{P}_{X'})\boldsymbol{p}$ is another such choice. Therefore, $\boldsymbol{k}'\boldsymbol{X}\boldsymbol{\beta}_i = \boldsymbol{p}'\boldsymbol{\beta}_i$, $i = 0, 1$. It follows that

$$\boldsymbol{p}'\boldsymbol{\beta}_0 = \boldsymbol{k}'\boldsymbol{X}\boldsymbol{\beta}_0 = \boldsymbol{k}'\boldsymbol{X}\boldsymbol{\beta}_1 = \boldsymbol{p}'\boldsymbol{\beta}_1 = \boldsymbol{p}'\boldsymbol{\beta}_0 + \|(\boldsymbol{I} - \boldsymbol{P}_{X'})\boldsymbol{p}\|^2.$$

Therefore, $\|(\boldsymbol{I}-\boldsymbol{P}_{X'})\boldsymbol{p}\|^2 = 0$ and $\boldsymbol{p}$ must be in $\mathcal{C}(\boldsymbol{X}')$. The sufficiency of this condition is obvious. □

It transpires from the above proposition that the following is an equivalent but simpler definition of estimability, which involves *all values of* $\boldsymbol{\beta}$ rather that *all possible values of* $\boldsymbol{\beta}$.

Definition 7.5. An LPF $\boldsymbol{p}'\boldsymbol{\beta}$ is called estimable if there is a linear estimator $\boldsymbol{l}'\boldsymbol{y}$ of $\boldsymbol{p}'\boldsymbol{\beta}$ such that $E(\boldsymbol{l}'\boldsymbol{y}) = \boldsymbol{p}'\boldsymbol{\beta}$ for *all* $\boldsymbol{\beta}$. □

The following result shows that the characterization given in Proposition 3.27 for identifiability, continues to hold in the singular case.

Proposition 7.6. (Restatement of Proposition 3.27) *An LPF in the model* $(\boldsymbol{y}, \boldsymbol{X\beta}, \sigma^2\boldsymbol{V})$ *is identifiable if and only if it is estimable.*

Proof. The LPF $\boldsymbol{p}'\boldsymbol{\beta}$ is identifiable if and only if $\boldsymbol{p}'\boldsymbol{\beta}_1 \neq \boldsymbol{p}'\boldsymbol{\beta}_2 \Rightarrow \boldsymbol{X\beta}_1 \neq \boldsymbol{X\beta}_2$. The latter condition is equivalent to $\boldsymbol{X}(\boldsymbol{\beta}_1 - \boldsymbol{\beta}_2) = \boldsymbol{0} \Rightarrow \boldsymbol{p}'(\boldsymbol{\beta}_1 - \boldsymbol{\beta}_2) = 0$, i.e. $\boldsymbol{p} \in \mathcal{C}(\boldsymbol{X}')$. According to Proposition 7.4, this condition characterizes estimability also. □

We have seen that the building blocks for inference in the linear model are estimable LPFs, LUEs and LZFs and that their definitions do not involve the dispersion matrix $\boldsymbol{V}$. As the above discussion shows, these basic building blocks remain essentially the same even when $\boldsymbol{V}$ is singular, though we may have (a) a set of LZFs which are identically zero with probability 1, and (b) a set of BLUEs with variance zero. These LZFs may be added to the other LZFs and LUES (those characterized by Proposition 3.14) to give them a different appearance. However the notions as well as the conditions for estimability and identifiability remain exactly the same.

Baksalary et al. (1992) examine in detail, the effects of the linear restriction on $\boldsymbol{\beta}$ implied by the singularity of $\boldsymbol{V}$, on various aspects of linear estimation in the linear model. These results are similar in spirit to Proposition 7.3.

7.3 Best linear unbiased estimation

7.3.1 *BLUE, fitted values and residuals*

The main message from the previous section is that one may continue to use LUEs and LZFs in the general case of possibly singular $\boldsymbol{V}$, simply by appealing to Proposition 7.3 in place of Proposition 3.14. In particular, the characterization of LZFs as linear functions of $(\boldsymbol{I} - \boldsymbol{P}_X)\boldsymbol{y}$ continues to hold (see Remark 3.15). Since the proofs of Propositions 3.29 and 3.33 do not involve the form of the dispersion matrix of $\boldsymbol{y}$, these results continue to hold in the general case (a fact for which Baksalary, 2004, provides a fresh proof) and lead to the following representation of the BLUE of an estimable LPF.

Proposition 7.7. *Consider the vector LPF $\boldsymbol{LX\beta}$ which is estimable in the model $(\boldsymbol{y}, \boldsymbol{X\beta}, \sigma^2\boldsymbol{V})$. The BLUE $\widehat{\boldsymbol{LX\beta}}$ of this LPF is given by*

$$\boldsymbol{L}[\boldsymbol{I} - \boldsymbol{V}(\boldsymbol{I} - \boldsymbol{P}_X)\{(\boldsymbol{I} - \boldsymbol{P}_X)\boldsymbol{V}(\boldsymbol{I} - \boldsymbol{P}_X)\}^-(\boldsymbol{I} - \boldsymbol{P}_X)]\boldsymbol{y}.$$

Further, the BLUE is unique.

Proof. Note that $\boldsymbol{Ly}$ is an LUE of $\boldsymbol{LX\beta}$, and the corresponding BLUE has to be uncorrelated with $(\boldsymbol{I}-\boldsymbol{P}_X)\boldsymbol{y}$, so that it is uncorrelated with *all* LZFs. By decorrelating $\boldsymbol{u} = \boldsymbol{Ly}$ from $\boldsymbol{v} = (\boldsymbol{I} - \boldsymbol{P}_X)\boldsymbol{y}$ as per Proposition 2.28, we find the expression given in the proposition. Since the mean of this quantity is $E(\boldsymbol{u}) = \boldsymbol{LX\beta}$, it must be the (unique) BLUE of $\boldsymbol{LX\beta}$. □

Remark 7.8. Note that $\mathcal{C}((\boldsymbol{I}-\boldsymbol{P}_X)\boldsymbol{V}) = \mathcal{C}(Cov((\boldsymbol{I}-\boldsymbol{P}_X)\boldsymbol{y}, \boldsymbol{y}))$ and $\mathcal{C}((\boldsymbol{I}-\boldsymbol{P}_X)\boldsymbol{V}(\boldsymbol{I} - \boldsymbol{P}_X)) = \mathcal{C}(D((\boldsymbol{I} - \boldsymbol{P}_X)\boldsymbol{y}))$. It follows from Proposition 2.13 that $(\boldsymbol{I} - \boldsymbol{P}_X)\boldsymbol{y}$ is contained in $\mathcal{C}((\boldsymbol{I} - \boldsymbol{P}_X)\boldsymbol{V}(\boldsymbol{I} - \boldsymbol{P}_X))$, and $\mathcal{C}((\boldsymbol{I} - \boldsymbol{P}_X)\boldsymbol{V})$ is a subset of the latter. It follows from part (f) of Proposition A.10 that the expression of BLUE given in Proposition 7.7 does not depend on the choice of the g-inverse. □

Remark 7.9. Since any estimable vector LPF $\boldsymbol{A\beta}$ can be written as $\boldsymbol{AX}^-\boldsymbol{X\beta}$, its BLUE is

$$\widehat{\boldsymbol{A\beta}} = \boldsymbol{AX}^-[\boldsymbol{I} - \boldsymbol{V}(\boldsymbol{I} - \boldsymbol{P}_X)\{(\boldsymbol{I} - \boldsymbol{P}_X)\boldsymbol{V}(\boldsymbol{I} - \boldsymbol{P}_X)\}^-(\boldsymbol{I} - \boldsymbol{P}_X)]\boldsymbol{y}.$$

According to Remark 7.16 (to follow), the above expression does not depend on the choice of $\boldsymbol{X}^-$. □

Remark 7.10. When $\boldsymbol{V} = \boldsymbol{I}$, the expression for $\widehat{\boldsymbol{A\beta}}$ simplifies to $\boldsymbol{AX}^-\boldsymbol{P}_X\boldsymbol{y}$ or $\boldsymbol{A}(\boldsymbol{X}'\boldsymbol{X})^-\boldsymbol{X}'\boldsymbol{y}$, as in the Gauss-Markov theorem (Proposition 3.38). □

Example 7.11. (Centered data) Sometimes in linear regression the response as well as the explanatory variables are 'centered' by subtracting the respective sample means from the observed values of these variables. The operation of centering a vector $\boldsymbol{u}_{n\times 1}$ amounts to replacing it with $(\boldsymbol{I} - \boldsymbol{P}_{\boldsymbol{1}_{n\times 1}})\boldsymbol{u}$. Suppose we begin with a regular homoscedastic model

$(\boldsymbol{y}, \boldsymbol{X\beta}, \sigma^2\boldsymbol{I})$, and obtain $\boldsymbol{y}_c$ and $\boldsymbol{X}_c$ after centering $\boldsymbol{y}$ and $\boldsymbol{X}$, respectively. As $D(\boldsymbol{y}_c) = \sigma^2(\boldsymbol{I} - \boldsymbol{P}_1)$, a homoscedastic model is inappropriate for $\boldsymbol{y}_c$, and we use the model $(\boldsymbol{y}_c, \boldsymbol{X}_c\boldsymbol{\beta}, \sigma^2(\boldsymbol{I} - \boldsymbol{P}_1))$. Putting $\boldsymbol{V} = \boldsymbol{I} - \boldsymbol{P}_1$ in the expression of BLUE in Proposition 7.7 and using the fact $(\boldsymbol{I} - \boldsymbol{P}_1)(\boldsymbol{I} - \boldsymbol{P}_{X_c}) = \boldsymbol{I} - \boldsymbol{P}_1 - \boldsymbol{P}_{X_c}$ to simplify it, we have

$$\widehat{\boldsymbol{LX\beta}} = \boldsymbol{L}[\boldsymbol{I} - (\boldsymbol{I} - \boldsymbol{P}_1 - \boldsymbol{P}_{X_c})(\boldsymbol{I} - \boldsymbol{P}_1 - \boldsymbol{P}_{X_c})^-(\boldsymbol{I} - \boldsymbol{P}_{X_c})]\boldsymbol{y}_c = \boldsymbol{L}\boldsymbol{P}_{X_c}\boldsymbol{y}_c.$$

Thus, the estimator is the same as what it should be if $\boldsymbol{V}$ were equal to $\boldsymbol{I}$. This is not just a coincidence, as we shall see in Section 8.1.1. □

The vector of fitted values, obtained by substituting $\boldsymbol{L} = \boldsymbol{I}$ in Proposition 7.7, is

$$\widehat{\boldsymbol{y}} = [\boldsymbol{I} - \boldsymbol{V}(\boldsymbol{I} - \boldsymbol{P}_X)\{(\boldsymbol{I} - \boldsymbol{P}_X)\boldsymbol{V}(\boldsymbol{I} - \boldsymbol{P}_X)\}^-(\boldsymbol{I} - \boldsymbol{P}_X)]\boldsymbol{y}. \tag{7.1}$$

Hence $\widehat{\boldsymbol{A\beta}} = \boldsymbol{AX}^-\widehat{\boldsymbol{y}}$. Therefore, we can formally define the following estimator of $\boldsymbol{\beta}$:

$$\widehat{\boldsymbol{\beta}} = \boldsymbol{X}^-\widehat{\boldsymbol{y}} = \boldsymbol{X}^-[\boldsymbol{I} - \boldsymbol{V}(\boldsymbol{I} - \boldsymbol{P}_X)\{(\boldsymbol{I} - \boldsymbol{P}_X)\boldsymbol{V}(\boldsymbol{I} - \boldsymbol{P}_X)\}^-(\boldsymbol{I} - \boldsymbol{P}_X)]\boldsymbol{y}, \tag{7.2}$$

where $\boldsymbol{X}^-$ is an arbitrary g-inverse of $\boldsymbol{X}$. Accordingly, the estimator is not uniquely defined in general. It is uniquely defined if and only if $\boldsymbol{X}$ has full column rank, in which case it is the BLUE of $\boldsymbol{\beta}$ (Exercise 7.29). Even if $\boldsymbol{X}$ is rank deficient, $\widehat{\boldsymbol{\beta}}$ can be used as a plug-in estimator. In particular, the (unique) BLUE of any estimable LPF $\boldsymbol{A\beta}$ is identical to $\boldsymbol{A}\widehat{\boldsymbol{\beta}}$.

The residual vector $\boldsymbol{e}$ corresponding to $\widehat{\boldsymbol{y}}$ in (7.1) is given by

$$\boldsymbol{e} = \boldsymbol{y} - \widehat{\boldsymbol{y}} = \boldsymbol{V}(\boldsymbol{I} - \boldsymbol{P}_X)\{(\boldsymbol{I} - \boldsymbol{P}_X)\boldsymbol{V}(\boldsymbol{I} - \boldsymbol{P}_X)\}^-(\boldsymbol{I} - \boldsymbol{P}_X)\boldsymbol{y}. \tag{7.3}$$

A geometric view of the BLUE of $\boldsymbol{X\beta}$ in the possibly singular linear model is given in Section 11.4.3.

Example 7.12. Consider the model $(\boldsymbol{y}, \boldsymbol{X\beta}, \sigma^2\boldsymbol{V})$ with

$$\boldsymbol{X} = \begin{pmatrix} 1 & 1 & 0 \\ 1 & 1 & 0 \\ 1 & 0 & 1 \\ 1 & 0 & 1 \end{pmatrix}, \qquad \boldsymbol{V} = \begin{pmatrix} 1 & \frac{1}{2} & 1 & \frac{1}{2} \\ \frac{1}{2} & 1 & \frac{1}{2} & 1 \\ 1 & \frac{1}{2} & 1 & \frac{1}{2} \\ \frac{1}{2} & 1 & \frac{1}{2} & 1 \end{pmatrix}.$$

For the purpose of discussion, we define the orthogonal unit vectors

$$\boldsymbol{u}_1 = \frac{1}{2}\begin{pmatrix} 1 \\ 1 \\ -1 \\ -1 \end{pmatrix}, \quad \boldsymbol{u}_2 = \frac{1}{2}\begin{pmatrix} 1 \\ 1 \\ 1 \\ 1 \end{pmatrix}, \quad \boldsymbol{u}_3 = \frac{1}{2}\begin{pmatrix} 1 \\ -1 \\ 1 \\ -1 \end{pmatrix}, \quad \boldsymbol{u}_4 = \frac{1}{2}\begin{pmatrix} 1 \\ -1 \\ -1 \\ 1 \end{pmatrix}.$$

It is easy to see that $\mathcal{C}(\boldsymbol{X}) = \mathcal{C}(\boldsymbol{u}_1 : \boldsymbol{u}_2)$ and $\boldsymbol{V} = 3\boldsymbol{u}_2\boldsymbol{u}_2' + \boldsymbol{u}_3\boldsymbol{u}_3'$. Thus, there is a *partial* overlap between the column spaces of $\boldsymbol{X}$ and $\boldsymbol{V}$.

Note that $(\boldsymbol{I} - \boldsymbol{P}_X) = \boldsymbol{u}_3\boldsymbol{u}_3' + \boldsymbol{u}_4\boldsymbol{u}_4'$. Hence, $\boldsymbol{V}(\boldsymbol{I} - \boldsymbol{P}_X) = (\boldsymbol{I} - \boldsymbol{P}_X)\boldsymbol{V} = \boldsymbol{u}_3\boldsymbol{u}_3'$. A g-inverse of $(\boldsymbol{I} - \boldsymbol{P}_X)\boldsymbol{V}(\boldsymbol{I} - \boldsymbol{P}_X)$ is also $\boldsymbol{u}_3\boldsymbol{u}_3'$. Calculations made on the basis of (7.3) show that

$$\boldsymbol{e} = \boldsymbol{u}_3\boldsymbol{u}_3'\boldsymbol{y} = \frac{1}{4}\begin{pmatrix} y_1 - y_2 + y_3 - y_4 \\ -y_1 + y_2 - y_3 + y_4 \\ y_1 - y_2 + y_3 - y_4 \\ -y_1 + y_2 - y_3 + y_4 \end{pmatrix}; \ \widehat{\boldsymbol{y}} = \frac{1}{4}\begin{pmatrix} 3y_1 + y_2 - y_3 + y_4 \\ y_1 + 3y_2 + y_3 - y_4 \\ -y_1 + y_2 + 3y_3 + y_4 \\ y_1 - y_2 + y_3 + 3y_4 \end{pmatrix}.$$

□

One does not necessarily have to use the form of the BLUE given in Proposition 7.7 for computational purposes. We shall examine several other ways of obtaining the BLUE in Section 7.7. As we shall see however, the explicit expression given here is a very useful theoretical device. Our derivation makes use of the principle of decorrelation, described in Proposition 2.28. While the idea of decorrelation in the context of linear models goes back many years (see, for instance, Rao, 1965) and this algebraic expression itself appears occasionally in the literature (see Albert, 1973 and Searle, 1994), it was Bhimasankaram and Sengupta (1996) who gave a statistical derivation.

Although the BLUE is unique, it does not have a unique representation when $\boldsymbol{V}$ is singular. This is because of the fact that an arbitrary LZF with zero dispersion can be added to a BLUE, producing 'another' BLUE. As pointed out in Section 7.2.2, the two estimators would have identical values with probability 1.

Linear statistics with zero dispersion have generated much interest among theoreticians. Rao (1973a) characterizes all possible representations of $\boldsymbol{l}$ such that $\boldsymbol{l}'\boldsymbol{y}$ is the BLUE of its expectation. Rao (1979) and Harville (1981) consider the class of *virtually linear* estimators having the form $a((\boldsymbol{I} - \boldsymbol{P}_V)\boldsymbol{y}) + \boldsymbol{y}'\boldsymbol{b}((\boldsymbol{I} - \boldsymbol{P}_V)\boldsymbol{y})$ and show that the BLUE is the minimum variance unbiased estimator in the wider class of estimators where $a(\cdot)$ and $\boldsymbol{b}(\cdot)$ are allowed to be nonlinear functions. Schönfeld and Werner (1987) consider estimators of the form $a(\boldsymbol{\beta}) + \boldsymbol{y}'\boldsymbol{b}(\boldsymbol{\beta})$ which are identical to linear estimators with probability 1, and show that the minimum variance unbiased estimators in this class have the same dispersion as that of the corresponding BLUE. All these results make the 'best' linear unbiased estimator look better than ever before. However, there remains a question about the practical utility of these extended classes of estimators.

7.3.2 *Dispersions*

It follows from (7.1) that

$$D(\widehat{\boldsymbol{y}}) = \sigma^2[\boldsymbol{V} - \boldsymbol{V}(\boldsymbol{I}-\boldsymbol{P}_X)\{(\boldsymbol{I}-\boldsymbol{P}_X)\boldsymbol{V}(\boldsymbol{I}-\boldsymbol{P}_X)\}^-(\boldsymbol{I}-\boldsymbol{P}_X)\boldsymbol{V}], \tag{7.4}$$

$$D(\boldsymbol{e}) = \sigma^2\boldsymbol{V}(\boldsymbol{I}-\boldsymbol{P}_X)\{(\boldsymbol{I}-\boldsymbol{P}_X)\boldsymbol{V}(\boldsymbol{I}-\boldsymbol{P}_X)\}^-(\boldsymbol{I}-\boldsymbol{P}_X)\boldsymbol{V}. \tag{7.5}$$

The sum of these two components add up to the total dispersion, $\sigma^2\boldsymbol{V}$, just as $\widehat{\boldsymbol{y}}$ and $\boldsymbol{e}$ add up to $\boldsymbol{y}$. In the case of normal errors, $D(\widehat{\boldsymbol{y}}) = D(\boldsymbol{y}|\boldsymbol{e})$ and $D(\boldsymbol{e}) = D(\boldsymbol{y}|\widehat{\boldsymbol{y}})$. As in the homoscedastic case, the BLUEs are linear functions of $\widehat{\boldsymbol{y}}$ and the LZFs are linear functions of $\boldsymbol{e}$ with probability 1 (see Exercise 7.1). Their variances and covariances can be expressed in terms of $D(\widehat{\boldsymbol{y}})$ and $D(\boldsymbol{e})$. In particular, the dispersion of the BLUE of $\boldsymbol{A\beta}$ (if it is estimable) is

$$\begin{aligned} D(\boldsymbol{A}\widehat{\boldsymbol{\beta}}) &= D(\boldsymbol{AX}^-\widehat{\boldsymbol{y}}) \\ &= \sigma^2\boldsymbol{AX}^-[\boldsymbol{V} - \boldsymbol{V}(\boldsymbol{I}-\boldsymbol{P}_X)\{(\boldsymbol{I}-\boldsymbol{P}_X)\boldsymbol{V}(\boldsymbol{I}-\boldsymbol{P}_X)\}^-(\boldsymbol{I}-\boldsymbol{P}_X)\boldsymbol{V}](\boldsymbol{AX}^-)'. \end{aligned}$$

According to Remark 7.8 and Proposition 7.15 (which is to follow), the above expression does not depend on the choice of $\{(\boldsymbol{I}-\boldsymbol{P}_X)\boldsymbol{V}(\boldsymbol{I}-\boldsymbol{P}_X)\}^-$ and $\boldsymbol{X}^-$.

Example 7.13. (Centered data, continued) For the centered model $(\boldsymbol{y}_c, \boldsymbol{X}_c\boldsymbol{\beta}, \sigma^2(\boldsymbol{I} - \boldsymbol{P}_1))$ of Example 7.11, we have

$$\begin{aligned} D(\widehat{\boldsymbol{y}}_c) &= \sigma^2\boldsymbol{P}_{X_c}, \\ D(\boldsymbol{e}) &= \sigma^2(\boldsymbol{I} - \boldsymbol{P}_1 - \boldsymbol{P}_{X_c}). \end{aligned}$$

If one ignores the singularity of the dispersion matrix and erroneously uses the homoscedastic model $(\boldsymbol{y}_c, \boldsymbol{X}_c\boldsymbol{\beta}, \sigma^2\boldsymbol{I})$, then the resulting value of $D(\boldsymbol{e})$ would be $\sigma^2(\boldsymbol{I} - \boldsymbol{P}_{X_c})$, which is obviously too large. □

Example 7.14. Consider the model of Example 7.12 along with the orthogonal vectors $\boldsymbol{u}_1$, $\boldsymbol{u}_2$, $\boldsymbol{u}_3$ and $\boldsymbol{u}_4$ defined there. It follows from the simplifications $(\boldsymbol{I} - \boldsymbol{P}_X) = \boldsymbol{u}_3\boldsymbol{u}_3' + \boldsymbol{u}_4\boldsymbol{u}_4'$, $\boldsymbol{V}(\boldsymbol{I} - \boldsymbol{P}_X) = \boldsymbol{u}_3\boldsymbol{u}_3'$ and $(\boldsymbol{I}-\boldsymbol{P}_X)\boldsymbol{V}(\boldsymbol{I}-\boldsymbol{P}_X) = \boldsymbol{u}_3\boldsymbol{u}_3'$ that $D(\widehat{\boldsymbol{y}}) = 3\sigma^2\boldsymbol{u}_2\boldsymbol{u}_2'$ and $D(\boldsymbol{e}) = \sigma^2\boldsymbol{u}_3\boldsymbol{u}_3'$.

Further, since $\boldsymbol{u}_1'\boldsymbol{u}_2 = 0$, we have $var(\boldsymbol{u}_1'\widehat{\boldsymbol{y}}) = 0$. Also, $E(\boldsymbol{u}_1'\widehat{\boldsymbol{y}}) = \boldsymbol{u}_1'\boldsymbol{X\beta} = \beta_1 - \beta_2$, which means the BLUE $\boldsymbol{u}_1'\widehat{\boldsymbol{y}}$ of the estimable parameter $\beta_1 - \beta_2$ has variance 0. (In contrast, the BLUE $\boldsymbol{u}_2'\widehat{\boldsymbol{y}}$ of another estimable parameter $2\beta_0 + \beta_1 + \beta_2$ has nonzero variance, $3\sigma^2$.) The existence of estimable parameters that can be known exactly (i.e. estimated unbiasedly with zero variance) is made possible by the singularity of the dispersion matrix of the model errors. □

We now characterize the column spaces spanned by the respective dispersion matrices of $\widehat{\boldsymbol{y}}$ and $\boldsymbol{e}$.

Proposition 7.15. *For the linear model* $(\boldsymbol{y}, \boldsymbol{X\beta}, \sigma^2\boldsymbol{V})$,

(a) $\mathcal{C}(D(\widehat{\boldsymbol{y}})) = \mathcal{C}(\boldsymbol{X}) \cap \mathcal{C}(\boldsymbol{V})$.
(b) $\mathcal{C}(D(\boldsymbol{e})) = \mathcal{C}(\boldsymbol{V}(\boldsymbol{I} - \boldsymbol{P}_X))$.

Proof. The expression of $D(\widehat{\boldsymbol{y}})$ in (7.4) directly implies that $\mathcal{C}(D(\widehat{\boldsymbol{y}})) \subseteq \mathcal{C}(\boldsymbol{V})$. Further, $(\boldsymbol{I} - \boldsymbol{P}_X)D(\widehat{\boldsymbol{y}})$ is easily seen to be identically zero. Consequently $\mathcal{C}(D(\widehat{\boldsymbol{y}})) \subseteq \mathcal{C}(\boldsymbol{X})$ and indeed, $\mathcal{C}(D(\widehat{\boldsymbol{y}})) \subseteq \mathcal{C}(\boldsymbol{X}) \cap \mathcal{C}(\boldsymbol{V})$.

Now let $\boldsymbol{l} \in \mathcal{C}(D(\widehat{\boldsymbol{y}}))^{\perp}$, so that $[\boldsymbol{V} - \boldsymbol{V}(\boldsymbol{I}-\boldsymbol{P}_X)\{(\boldsymbol{I}-\boldsymbol{P}_X)\boldsymbol{V}(\boldsymbol{I}-\boldsymbol{P}_X)\}^-(\boldsymbol{I}-\boldsymbol{P}_X)\boldsymbol{V}]\boldsymbol{l} = 0$. We shall show that $\boldsymbol{l} \in [\mathcal{C}(\boldsymbol{X}) \cap \mathcal{C}(\boldsymbol{V})]^{\perp}$. To prove this, take a vector $\boldsymbol{m}$ from $\mathcal{C}(\boldsymbol{X}) \cap \mathcal{C}(\boldsymbol{V})$. Write $\boldsymbol{m}$ as $\boldsymbol{V}\boldsymbol{l}_1$ and then as $\boldsymbol{X}\boldsymbol{l}_2$, so that

$$\begin{aligned}\boldsymbol{l}'\boldsymbol{m} = \boldsymbol{l}'\boldsymbol{V}\boldsymbol{l}_1 &= \boldsymbol{l}'\boldsymbol{V}(\boldsymbol{I}-\boldsymbol{P}_X)\{(\boldsymbol{I}-\boldsymbol{P}_X)\boldsymbol{V}(\boldsymbol{I}-\boldsymbol{P}_X)\}^-(\boldsymbol{I}-\boldsymbol{P}_X)\boldsymbol{V}\boldsymbol{l}_1\\ &= \boldsymbol{l}'\boldsymbol{V}(\boldsymbol{I}-\boldsymbol{P}_X)\{(\boldsymbol{I}-\boldsymbol{P}_X)\boldsymbol{V}(\boldsymbol{I}-\boldsymbol{P}_X)\}^-(\boldsymbol{I}-\boldsymbol{P}_X)\boldsymbol{X}\boldsymbol{l}_2 = 0.\end{aligned}$$

Therefore, $\mathcal{C}(D(\widehat{\boldsymbol{y}}))^{\perp} \subseteq [\mathcal{C}(\boldsymbol{X}) \cap \mathcal{C}(\boldsymbol{V})]^{\perp}$. This proves part (a).

The expression of $D(\boldsymbol{e})$ given in (7.5) implies that $\mathcal{C}(D(\boldsymbol{e})) \subseteq \mathcal{C}(\boldsymbol{V}(\boldsymbol{I} - \boldsymbol{P}_X)$. The reverse inclusion viz. $\mathcal{C}(\boldsymbol{V}(\boldsymbol{I} - \boldsymbol{P}_X) \subseteq \mathcal{C}(D(\boldsymbol{e}))$, follows from the fact that $D(\boldsymbol{e})(\boldsymbol{I} - \boldsymbol{P}_X) = \sigma^2\boldsymbol{V}(\boldsymbol{I} - \boldsymbol{P}_X)$. This proves part (b). □

Remark 7.16. Since $E(\widehat{\boldsymbol{y}}) = \boldsymbol{X\beta}$, by virtue of part (a) of Proposition 2.13 and Proposition 7.15, we have

$$\begin{aligned}&\widehat{\boldsymbol{y}} \in \mathcal{C}(\boldsymbol{X}),\\ &\boldsymbol{e} \in \mathcal{C}(\boldsymbol{V}(\boldsymbol{I} - \boldsymbol{P}_X))\end{aligned}$$

almost surely. □

It also follows from Propositions 2.13 and 7.15 that

$$(\boldsymbol{X}\widehat{\boldsymbol{\beta}} - \boldsymbol{X\beta}) \in \mathcal{C}(\boldsymbol{X}) \cap \mathcal{C}(\boldsymbol{V}).$$

This result has a nice interpretation. A consequence of best linear unbiased estimation is that we approximate the unknown decomposition $\boldsymbol{y} = \boldsymbol{X\beta} + \boldsymbol{\varepsilon}$ by $\boldsymbol{y} = \boldsymbol{X}\widehat{\boldsymbol{\beta}} + \boldsymbol{e}$. The error in this decomposition, $(\boldsymbol{X}\widehat{\boldsymbol{\beta}} - \boldsymbol{X\beta})$, must be a vector that has wrongly been put in the systematic part, $\boldsymbol{X\beta}$, although it should have been part of the error. Such a 'mixup' can occur if and only if this vector simultaneously belongs to the column space of the systematic part, $\mathcal{C}(\boldsymbol{X})$, and the space where $\boldsymbol{\varepsilon}$ belongs, $\mathcal{C}(\boldsymbol{V})$. If $\mathcal{C}(\boldsymbol{X})$ and $\mathcal{C}(\boldsymbol{V})$ are virtually disjoint, then there would be no scope of such an error. Indeed, in such a case $\boldsymbol{X}\widehat{\boldsymbol{\beta}} = \boldsymbol{X\beta}$ with probability 1.

A geometric interpretation of the decomposition of $\boldsymbol{y}$ into components belonging to various subspaces is discussed in Chapter 11.

7.3.3 *The nonsingular case*

Proposition 7.17. *If $\boldsymbol{V}$ is positive definite and $\boldsymbol{A\beta}$ is an estimable LPF, then the BLUE of $\boldsymbol{A\beta}$ is*

$$\widehat{\boldsymbol{A\beta}} = \boldsymbol{A}(\boldsymbol{X}'\boldsymbol{V}^{-1}\boldsymbol{X})^{-}\boldsymbol{X}'\boldsymbol{V}^{-1}\boldsymbol{y},$$

and its dispersion matrix is

$$D(\widehat{\boldsymbol{A\beta}}) = \sigma^2\boldsymbol{A}(\boldsymbol{X}'\boldsymbol{V}^{-1}\boldsymbol{X})^{-}\boldsymbol{A}'.$$

Proof. Let $\boldsymbol{CC}'$ be a rank-factorization of $\boldsymbol{V}$. Since the column spaces of $\boldsymbol{I} - \boldsymbol{P}_{\!X}$ and $\boldsymbol{X}$ are orthogonal complements of one another, the column spaces of $\boldsymbol{C}'(\boldsymbol{I} - \boldsymbol{P}_{\!X})$ and $\boldsymbol{C}^{-1}\boldsymbol{X}$ must be orthogonal complements of one another. Therefore, we can rewrite (7.1) as

$$\begin{aligned}
\widehat{\boldsymbol{y}} &= \boldsymbol{C}[\boldsymbol{I} - \boldsymbol{C}'(\boldsymbol{I} - \boldsymbol{P}_{\!X})\{(\boldsymbol{I} - \boldsymbol{P}_{\!X})\boldsymbol{CC}'(\boldsymbol{I} - \boldsymbol{P}_{\!X})\}^{-}(\boldsymbol{I} - \boldsymbol{P}_{\!X})\boldsymbol{C}]\boldsymbol{C}^{-1}\boldsymbol{y} \\
&= \boldsymbol{C}[\boldsymbol{I} - \boldsymbol{P}_{C'(I-P_X)}]\boldsymbol{C}^{-1}\boldsymbol{y} \;=\; \boldsymbol{CP}_{C^{-1}X}\boldsymbol{C}^{-1}\boldsymbol{y} \\
&= \boldsymbol{CC}^{-1}\boldsymbol{X}[\boldsymbol{X}'(\boldsymbol{C}^{-1})'\boldsymbol{C}^{-1}\boldsymbol{X}]^{-}\boldsymbol{X}'(\boldsymbol{C}^{-1})'\boldsymbol{C}^{-1}\boldsymbol{y} \\
&= \boldsymbol{X}[\boldsymbol{X}'\boldsymbol{V}^{-1}\boldsymbol{X}]^{-}\boldsymbol{X}'\boldsymbol{V}^{-1}\boldsymbol{y}.
\end{aligned}$$

According to Remark 7.9, $\widehat{\boldsymbol{A\beta}} = \boldsymbol{AX}^{-}\widehat{\boldsymbol{y}}$ and the assertions follow. □

The above proposition implies that

$$\begin{aligned}
D(\widehat{\boldsymbol{y}}) &= \sigma^2\boldsymbol{X}(\boldsymbol{X}'\boldsymbol{V}^{-1}\boldsymbol{X})^{-}\boldsymbol{X}', \\
\text{and } D(\boldsymbol{e}) &= \sigma^2[\boldsymbol{V} - \boldsymbol{X}(\boldsymbol{X}'\boldsymbol{V}^{-1}\boldsymbol{X})^{-}\boldsymbol{X}'].
\end{aligned}$$

Remark 7.18. If $\boldsymbol{V}$ is nonsingular and $\boldsymbol{X}$ has full column rank, then $\boldsymbol{\beta}$ is estimable. Putting $\boldsymbol{A} = \boldsymbol{I}$ in Proposition 7.17, we have the BLUE of $\boldsymbol{\beta}$ given by

$$\widehat{\boldsymbol{\beta}} = (\boldsymbol{X}'\boldsymbol{V}^{-1}\boldsymbol{X})^{-1}\boldsymbol{X}'\boldsymbol{V}^{-1}\boldsymbol{y}.$$

This widely used expression was first obtained by Aitken (1935), and is sometimes referred to as the *Aitken estimator*. The dispersion of this estimator is

$$D(\widehat{\boldsymbol{\beta}}) = \sigma^2(\boldsymbol{X}'\boldsymbol{V}^{-1}\boldsymbol{X})^{-1}.$$

The Aitken estimator belongs to the genre of weighted least squares estimators, discussed in Section 7.6. The WLSE used in Section 5.3.2 had been a special case of the Aitken estimator, where $\boldsymbol{V}$ is a diagonal matrix. It further simplifies to $\widehat{\boldsymbol{\beta}}_{LS} = (\boldsymbol{X}'\boldsymbol{X})^{-1}\boldsymbol{X}'\boldsymbol{y}$ when $\boldsymbol{V} = \boldsymbol{I}$. □

7.4 Estimation of error variance

In order to obtain a reasonable estimator of σ^2, we have to utilize the LZFs. We begin by extending Proposition 3.45 to the general linear model $(\boldsymbol{y}, \boldsymbol{X\beta}, \sigma^2\boldsymbol{V})$. The definitions of a generating set, a basis set and a standardized basis set of LZFs given in Section 3.8 remain the same.

Proposition 7.19. *If $\boldsymbol{z}$ is any vector whose elements constitute a standardized basis set of LZFs of the model $(\boldsymbol{y}, \boldsymbol{X\beta}, \sigma^2\boldsymbol{V})$, then*

(a) $\boldsymbol{z}$ has $\rho(\boldsymbol{V} : \boldsymbol{X}) - \rho(\boldsymbol{X})$ elements;
(b) the value of $\boldsymbol{z}'\boldsymbol{z}$ does not depend on the choice of the standardized basis set.

Proof. Let m be the number of elements of $\boldsymbol{z}$. Since $\boldsymbol{z}$ and $\boldsymbol{e}$ are both basis sets, there are $n \times m$ matrices $\boldsymbol{C}$ and $\boldsymbol{B}$ such that $\boldsymbol{e} = \boldsymbol{Cz}$ and $\boldsymbol{z} = \boldsymbol{B}'\boldsymbol{e}$. Therefore,

$$m = \rho(D(\boldsymbol{z})) = \rho(\boldsymbol{B}'D(\boldsymbol{e})\boldsymbol{B}) \leq \rho(D(\boldsymbol{e})) = \rho(\boldsymbol{C}D(\boldsymbol{z})\boldsymbol{C}') = \rho(\boldsymbol{C}) \leq m.$$

It follows from the above and Proposition 7.15 that $m = \rho(D(\boldsymbol{e})) = \rho(\boldsymbol{V}(\boldsymbol{I} - \boldsymbol{P}_{\boldsymbol{X}}))$. The last expression is equal to $\rho(\boldsymbol{V} : \boldsymbol{X}) - \rho(\boldsymbol{X})$ (by Proposition A.14). This proves part (a).

In order to prove part (b), note that $D(\boldsymbol{e}) = D(\boldsymbol{Cz}) = \sigma^2\boldsymbol{CC}'$. Also,

$$\sigma^2\boldsymbol{I} = D(\boldsymbol{z}) = D(\boldsymbol{B}'\boldsymbol{e}) = D(\boldsymbol{B}'\boldsymbol{Cz}) = \sigma^2(\boldsymbol{B}'\boldsymbol{C})(\boldsymbol{C}'\boldsymbol{B}).$$

$\boldsymbol{B}'\boldsymbol{C}$ must be an orthogonal matrix, which means that $\boldsymbol{C}'\boldsymbol{BB}'\boldsymbol{C} = \boldsymbol{I}$. Consequently $\boldsymbol{CC}'\boldsymbol{BB}'\boldsymbol{CC}' = \boldsymbol{CC}'$, which means $\boldsymbol{BB}'$ must be a g-inverse of $\boldsymbol{CC}'$. It follows that

$$\boldsymbol{z}'\boldsymbol{z} = \boldsymbol{e}'\boldsymbol{BB}'\boldsymbol{e} = \boldsymbol{e}'(\boldsymbol{CC}')^-\boldsymbol{e} = \sigma^2\boldsymbol{e}'[D(\boldsymbol{e})]^-\boldsymbol{e},$$

which does not depend on the choice of the standardized basis set $\boldsymbol{z}$. □

The above proposition implies that we can continue to use Definition 3.47 of the error sum of squares (R_0^2) in the case of general linear models. (However, R_0^2 would *not* be equal to the sum of squared residuals, $\boldsymbol{e}'\boldsymbol{e}$, in the general case.) Further, a natural unbiased estimator of σ^2 is

$$\widehat{\sigma^2} = \frac{R_0^2}{\rho(\boldsymbol{V} : \boldsymbol{X}) - \rho(\boldsymbol{X})} = \frac{\boldsymbol{e}'[\sigma^{-2}D(\boldsymbol{e})]^-\boldsymbol{e}}{\rho(\boldsymbol{V} : \boldsymbol{X}) - \rho(\boldsymbol{X})}. \tag{7.6}$$

Remark 7.20. If $\boldsymbol{z}$ is any vector of LZFs whose elements constitute a generating set, then $R_0^2 = \boldsymbol{z}'[\sigma^{-2}D(\boldsymbol{z})]^-\boldsymbol{z}$, $\rho(D(\boldsymbol{z})) = \rho(\boldsymbol{V} : \boldsymbol{X}) - \rho(\boldsymbol{X})$ and $\widehat{\sigma^2} = \boldsymbol{z}'[\sigma^{-2}D(\boldsymbol{z})]^-\boldsymbol{z}/\rho(D(\boldsymbol{z}))$ (Exercise 7.6). This is an extension of the statement of Remark 3.48 to the general linear model. □

We have already seen the special case obtained by putting $z = e$ in the above statement. An alternative expression may be obtained by choosing $z = (I - P_X)y$:

$$R_0^2 = y'(I - P_X)\{(I - P_X)V(I - P_X)\}^-(I - P_X)y. \qquad (7.7)$$

According to Proposition 7.19, the number of elements in a standardized basis set of LZFs must be $\rho(V : X) - \rho(X)$. This is the number of *error degrees of freedom* of the general linear model.

Example 7.21. For the model of Example 7.12, it has been noted that $(I - P_X) = u_3u_3' + u_4u_4'$, and a g-inverse of $(I - P_X)V(I - P_X)$ is u_3u_3'. Hence,

$$\widehat{\sigma^2} = \frac{y'(u_3u_3' + u_4u_4')u_3u_3'(u_3u_3' + u_4u_4')y}{3-2} = \|u_3'y\|^2,$$

which simplifies to $(y_1 - y_2 + y_3 - y_4)^2/4$. □

In order to simplify the expression of $\widehat{\sigma^2}$, we may try to write R_0^2 as $e'Me$ for a suitable matrix M. The following result gives a general description of M.

Proposition 7.22. *If M is an arbitrary g-inverse of $V + XUX'$, where U is any matrix of appropriate order, then $R_0^2 = e'Me$.*

Proof. See Exercise 7.7. □

Note that there is no condition whatsoever on the matrix U. (For instance, we need not have $\mathcal{C}(V + XUX') = \mathcal{C}(X : V)$ — a condition we use for another purpose in Section 7.7.1.) The choice $M = V^-$ has a special significance, as we shall see in Section 7.5. This choice leads to the following simple form of the above unbiased estimator of σ^2:

$$\widehat{\sigma^2} = e'V^-e/[\rho(V : X) - \rho(X)]. \qquad (7.8)$$

The expression reduces to $e'V^{-1}e/[n - \rho(X)]$ when V is nonsingular.

Example 7.23. (Centered data, continued) For the centered model $(y_c, X_c\beta, \sigma^2(I - P_1))$ of Example 7.11, we have $e = (I - P_{X_c})y_c$, $V = I - P_1$ and $\rho(V : X_c) = \rho(V) = n - 1$. Hence,

$$\widehat{\sigma^2} = \frac{\|(I - P_1 - P_{X_c})(I - P_{X_c})y_c\|^2}{n - 1 - \rho(X_c)} = \frac{\|(I - P_{X_c})y_c\|^2}{n - \rho(X_c) - 1}.$$

If one ignores the singularity of the dispersion matrix and erroneously uses the homoscedastic model $(y_c, X_c\beta, \sigma^2 I)$, then the resulting value of $\widehat{\sigma^2}$ would be $\|(I - P_{X_c})y_c\|^2/(n - \rho(X_c))$, which underestimates σ^2. □

We may wish to obtain a decomposition of $\boldsymbol{y}'\boldsymbol{y}$ in terms of BLUEs and LZFs as given in Section 3.8. This can be done only after some essential questions regarding basis sets of BLUEs are answered. These questions are raised and answered in Section 11.1.2 and the decomposition given in Section 11.1.3.

7.5 Maximum likelihood estimation

Let $\boldsymbol{y} \sim N(\boldsymbol{X\beta}, \sigma^2\boldsymbol{V})$, and $\boldsymbol{CC}'$ be a rank-factorization of $\boldsymbol{V}$. Then the joint likelihood of the observation vector is (see Section 2.1.4)

$$(2\pi\sigma^2)^{-\rho(V)/2}|\boldsymbol{C}'\boldsymbol{C}|^{-1/2}\exp[-\tfrac{1}{2\sigma^2}(\boldsymbol{y}-\boldsymbol{X\beta})'\boldsymbol{V}^-(\boldsymbol{y}-\boldsymbol{X\beta})],$$

with the restriction $(\boldsymbol{I}-\boldsymbol{P}_{V})\boldsymbol{X\beta} = (\boldsymbol{I}-\boldsymbol{P}_{V})\boldsymbol{y}$, which ensures that the quadratic function in the exponent of the likelihood does not depend on the choice of the g-inverse $\boldsymbol{V}$. Following the derivation in the homoscedastic case, the MLEs can be shown to be

$$\widehat{\boldsymbol{\beta}}_{ML} = \arg\min_{\boldsymbol{\beta}}[(\boldsymbol{y}-\boldsymbol{X\beta})'\boldsymbol{V}^-(\boldsymbol{y}-\boldsymbol{X\beta})],$$

$$\widehat{\sigma^2}_{ML} = \frac{1}{\rho(\boldsymbol{V})}\min_{\boldsymbol{\beta}}[(\boldsymbol{y}-\boldsymbol{X\beta})'\boldsymbol{V}^-(\boldsymbol{y}-\boldsymbol{X\beta})].$$

If $\boldsymbol{\beta}_0$ represents the *true* value of $\boldsymbol{\beta}$, then $\boldsymbol{y}-\boldsymbol{X\beta}_0$ has to lie in $\mathcal{C}(\boldsymbol{V})$ with probability 1. When the quadratic function is minimized with respect to $\boldsymbol{\beta}$, the choice must be restricted to the set of values which satisfy the condition $(\boldsymbol{y}-\boldsymbol{X\beta}) \in \mathcal{C}(\boldsymbol{V})$.

Proposition 7.24. *If $\boldsymbol{y} \sim N(\boldsymbol{X\beta}, \sigma^2\boldsymbol{V})$, then the MLE of $\boldsymbol{X\beta}$ is given by $\boldsymbol{X}\widehat{\boldsymbol{\beta}}_{ML} = \widehat{\boldsymbol{y}}$, defined in (7.1).*

Proof. It follows from the preceding discussion that the MLE of $\boldsymbol{X\beta}$ is the vector $\boldsymbol{u}$ which minimizes $(\boldsymbol{y}-\boldsymbol{u})'\boldsymbol{V}^-(\boldsymbol{y}-\boldsymbol{u})$ subject to the conditions $(\boldsymbol{y}-\boldsymbol{u}) \in \mathcal{C}(\boldsymbol{V})$ and $\boldsymbol{u} \in \mathcal{C}(\boldsymbol{X})$.

The quadratic function can be written as $(\widehat{\boldsymbol{y}}-\boldsymbol{u}+\boldsymbol{e})'\boldsymbol{V}^-(\widehat{\boldsymbol{y}}-\boldsymbol{u}+\boldsymbol{e})$, where $\widehat{\boldsymbol{y}}$ and $\boldsymbol{e}$ are as defined in Section 7.3.1. Minimizing this with respect to $\boldsymbol{u}$ is equivalent to minimizing $(\boldsymbol{d}+\boldsymbol{e})'\boldsymbol{V}^-(\boldsymbol{d}+\boldsymbol{e})$ with respect to $\boldsymbol{d}$, where $\boldsymbol{d} = \widehat{\boldsymbol{y}}-\boldsymbol{u}$. Since $\boldsymbol{e} \in \mathcal{C}(\boldsymbol{V})$ and $\widehat{\boldsymbol{y}} \in \mathcal{C}(\boldsymbol{X})$, the twin conditions $(\boldsymbol{y}-\boldsymbol{u}) \in \mathcal{C}(\boldsymbol{V})$ and $\boldsymbol{u} \in \mathcal{C}(\boldsymbol{X})$ are equivalent to $\boldsymbol{d} \in \mathcal{C}(\boldsymbol{V})$ and $\boldsymbol{d} \in \mathcal{C}(\boldsymbol{X})$. Thus we have the equivalent minimization problem

$$\min_{\boldsymbol{d}\in\mathcal{C}(\boldsymbol{X})\cap\mathcal{C}(\boldsymbol{V})}(\boldsymbol{d}+\boldsymbol{e})'\boldsymbol{V}^-(\boldsymbol{d}+\boldsymbol{e}).$$

Suppose $\boldsymbol{D} = \boldsymbol{V} - \boldsymbol{V}(\boldsymbol{I} - \boldsymbol{P}_X)\{(\boldsymbol{I} - \boldsymbol{P}_X)\boldsymbol{V}(\boldsymbol{I} - \boldsymbol{P}_X)\}^-(\boldsymbol{I} - \boldsymbol{P}_X)\boldsymbol{V}$. Proposition 7.15 indicates that $\mathcal{C}(\boldsymbol{D}) = \mathcal{C}(\boldsymbol{X}) \cap \mathcal{C}(\boldsymbol{V})$. Therefore, the minimizer of the above quadratic function must be of the form $\boldsymbol{Dl}$ for some $\boldsymbol{l}$, and the minimization problem becomes

$$\min_{\boldsymbol{l}} (\boldsymbol{Dl} + \boldsymbol{e})'\boldsymbol{V}^-(\boldsymbol{Dl} + \boldsymbol{e}).$$

It is easy to see from Proposition 7.15 that $\boldsymbol{e} \in \mathcal{C}(\boldsymbol{V}(\boldsymbol{I} - \boldsymbol{P}_X))$ with probability 1. It follows that $\boldsymbol{DV}^-\boldsymbol{e} = \boldsymbol{0}$ with probability 1. After combining this with the fact that $\boldsymbol{DV}^-\boldsymbol{D} = \boldsymbol{D}$, the above quadratic function simplifies almost surely to $\boldsymbol{l}'\boldsymbol{Dl} + \boldsymbol{e}'\boldsymbol{V}^-\boldsymbol{e}$, which is minimized if and only if $\boldsymbol{Dl} = \boldsymbol{0}$. Since $\boldsymbol{u} = \widehat{\boldsymbol{y}} - \boldsymbol{d} = \widehat{\boldsymbol{y}} - \boldsymbol{Dl}$, the uniquely optimal choice of $\boldsymbol{u}$ is $\widehat{\boldsymbol{y}}$. □

Proposition 7.24 immediately leads to the following two results.

Proposition 7.25. *The MLE of any estimable LPF is unique and it coincides with the corresponding BLUE. If $\boldsymbol{\beta}$ is not entirely estimable, the MLE of $\boldsymbol{\beta}$ is not unique, and is given by $\boldsymbol{X}^-\widehat{\boldsymbol{y}}$ for any choice of $\boldsymbol{X}^-$. The MLE of a non-estimable LPF, $\mathbf{p}'\boldsymbol{\beta}$ is of the form $\mathbf{p}'\boldsymbol{X}^-\widehat{\boldsymbol{y}}$, which is not uniquely defined.* □

Proposition 7.26. *The MLE of σ^2 is $\widehat{\sigma^2}_{ML} = \boldsymbol{e}'\boldsymbol{V}^-\boldsymbol{e}/\rho(\boldsymbol{V})$.* □

It is clear from the discussion at the end of Section 7.4 and Proposition 7.26 that the MLE of σ^2 is biased and underestimates σ^2. It also transpires from this discussion that the minimized value of the quadratic function $(\boldsymbol{y} - \boldsymbol{X\beta})'\boldsymbol{V}^-(\boldsymbol{y} - \boldsymbol{X\beta})$ subject to the restriction $(\boldsymbol{y} - \boldsymbol{X\beta}) \in \mathcal{C}(\boldsymbol{V})$ is R_0^2.

By an argument similar to that used in Remark 3.9, it can be shown that if $\boldsymbol{y}$ given $\boldsymbol{X}$ has the distribution $N(\boldsymbol{X\beta}, \sigma^2\boldsymbol{V})$, then $\widehat{\boldsymbol{y}}$ and $\widehat{\sigma^2}$ are the UMVUEs of $\boldsymbol{X\beta}$ and σ^2, respectively. Other optimal properties of $\widehat{\sigma^2}$ are discussed in Chapter 8 (see Section 8.2.3 and Exercise 8.22).

7.6 Weighted least squares estimation

Suppose we want to estimate $\boldsymbol{\beta}$ by the vector which minimizes $(\boldsymbol{y} - \boldsymbol{X\beta})'\boldsymbol{M}(\boldsymbol{y} - \boldsymbol{X\beta})$, where $\boldsymbol{M}$ is a symmetric and nonnegative definite 'weight' matrix. Setting the derivative (*gradient*) of the above quadratic function with respect to $\boldsymbol{\beta}$ equal to zero, we have

$$-2\boldsymbol{X}'\boldsymbol{M}(\boldsymbol{y} - \boldsymbol{X\beta}) = \boldsymbol{0}, \qquad \text{or} \quad (\boldsymbol{X}'\boldsymbol{MX})\boldsymbol{\beta} = \boldsymbol{X}'\boldsymbol{My}.$$

Thus, the general solution is of the form $(\boldsymbol{X}'\boldsymbol{M}\boldsymbol{X})^-\boldsymbol{X}'\boldsymbol{M}\boldsymbol{y}$. The matrix of second derivatives (Hessian), $2\boldsymbol{X}'\boldsymbol{M}\boldsymbol{X}$, is nonnegative definite, confirming that this corresponds to a *minimum.* We refer to this method of estimation as the *weighted least squares* (WLS) method, and the vector $(\boldsymbol{X}'\boldsymbol{M}\boldsymbol{X})^-\boldsymbol{X}'\boldsymbol{M}\boldsymbol{y}$ as a *weighted least squares estimator* (WLSE) of $\boldsymbol{\beta}$.

A WLSE of $\boldsymbol{\beta}$ depends on the choice of $\boldsymbol{M}$. In Section 5.3.2 we had considered a WLSE, where $\boldsymbol{M}$ is a diagonal matrix. In general, a WLSE may not be unique. However, the minimized value of the quadratic function,

$$\min_{\boldsymbol{\beta}}(\boldsymbol{y}-\boldsymbol{X}\boldsymbol{\beta})'\boldsymbol{M}(\boldsymbol{y}-\boldsymbol{X}\boldsymbol{\beta}) = \boldsymbol{y}'\boldsymbol{M}\boldsymbol{y} - \boldsymbol{y}'\boldsymbol{M}\boldsymbol{X}(\boldsymbol{X}'\boldsymbol{M}\boldsymbol{X})^-\boldsymbol{X}'\boldsymbol{M}\boldsymbol{y},$$

is unique. This expression can be used to obtain the following unbiased estimator of σ^2 (see Exercise 7.32):

$$\widehat{\sigma^2}_{WLS} = \frac{\boldsymbol{y}'\boldsymbol{M}\boldsymbol{y} - \boldsymbol{y}'\boldsymbol{M}\boldsymbol{X}(\boldsymbol{X}'\boldsymbol{M}\boldsymbol{X})^-\boldsymbol{X}'\boldsymbol{M}\boldsymbol{y}}{\operatorname{tr}(\boldsymbol{M}\boldsymbol{V} - \boldsymbol{M}\boldsymbol{X}(\boldsymbol{X}'\boldsymbol{M}\boldsymbol{X})^-\boldsymbol{X}'\boldsymbol{M}\boldsymbol{V})}. \tag{7.9}$$

Remark 7.27. In the previous section we found that the problem of maximizing the normal likelihood with respect to $\boldsymbol{\beta}$ is equivalent to minimizing $(\boldsymbol{y}-\boldsymbol{X}\boldsymbol{\beta})\boldsymbol{V}^-(\boldsymbol{y}-\boldsymbol{X}\boldsymbol{\beta})$ subject to a linear constraint. The constraint $(\boldsymbol{y}-\boldsymbol{X}\boldsymbol{\beta}) \in \mathcal{C}(\boldsymbol{V})$ is automatically satisfied if $\mathcal{C}(\boldsymbol{X}) \subseteq \mathcal{C}(\boldsymbol{V})$, and in particular, when $\boldsymbol{V}$ is positive definite. In such a case the normal MLE of $\boldsymbol{X}\boldsymbol{\beta}$ (which is also the BLUE) is a special case of the WLSE corresponding to the choice, $\boldsymbol{M} = \boldsymbol{V}^-$. This equivalence of the BLUE and WLSE holds even if the error distribution is not normal (see also Exercise 7.2). □

An important question is: is there a choice of $\boldsymbol{M}$ such that the WLSE is the same as the BLUE in the general case? Rao (1973b) shows that the WLSE coincides with the BLUE, and the estimator given in (7.9) is the usual unbiased estimator of σ^2, if and only if $\boldsymbol{M}$ is a symmetric g-inverse of $\boldsymbol{W} = \boldsymbol{V} + \boldsymbol{X}\boldsymbol{U}\boldsymbol{X}'$, where $\boldsymbol{U}$ is any symmetric matrix such that $\mathcal{C}(\boldsymbol{W}) = \mathcal{C}(\boldsymbol{V} : \boldsymbol{X})$. We prove the sufficiency of this form of $\boldsymbol{M}$ in Section 7.7.1, with the additional restriction that $\boldsymbol{U}$ is a nonnegative definite matrix. Note that when $\boldsymbol{M} = \boldsymbol{W}^-$, the quadratic function does not depend on the choice of the g-inverse, because $(\boldsymbol{y}-\boldsymbol{X}\boldsymbol{\beta})$ is almost surely in $\mathcal{C}(\boldsymbol{W})$. In the special case of nonsingular $\boldsymbol{V}$, the choice $\boldsymbol{U} = \boldsymbol{0}$ and $\boldsymbol{M} = \boldsymbol{V}^{-1}$ produces the Aitken estimator of Section 7.3.3, which coincides with the BLUE.

It may appear from the above discussion that the singular model can be dealt with, very much like the nonsingular case, simply by replacing $\boldsymbol{V}$ with $\boldsymbol{W}$. However, this is not true. Although the expression for the BLUE obtained by such a substitution is correct, the resulting dispersion matrix is too large. See Proposition 7.30(b) for the correct dispersion in this case.

Example 7.28. Consider once again the model of Example 7.12 along with the orthogonal vectors $\boldsymbol{u}_1$, $\boldsymbol{u}_2$, $\boldsymbol{u}_3$ and $\boldsymbol{u}_4$ defined there. In order to use the WLS approach, we have to find a suitable $\boldsymbol{U}$ such that $\boldsymbol{W} = \boldsymbol{V} + \boldsymbol{XUX}'$ satisfies $\mathcal{C}(\boldsymbol{W}) = \mathcal{C}(\boldsymbol{X} : \boldsymbol{V}) = \mathcal{C}(\boldsymbol{u}_1 : \boldsymbol{u}_2 : \boldsymbol{u}_3)$. We choose $\boldsymbol{W} = \boldsymbol{u}_1\boldsymbol{u}_1' + 3\boldsymbol{u}_2\boldsymbol{u}_2' + \boldsymbol{u}_3\boldsymbol{u}_3'$, which has the requisite form with $\boldsymbol{U} = \frac{1}{4}(0 : 1 : -1)'(0 : 1 : -1)$. It follows that $\boldsymbol{W}^-$ may be chosen as $\boldsymbol{u}_1\boldsymbol{u}_1' + \frac{1}{3}\boldsymbol{u}_2\boldsymbol{u}_2' + \boldsymbol{u}_3\boldsymbol{u}_3'$, and that

$$\boldsymbol{X}'\boldsymbol{W}^-\boldsymbol{X} = (\boldsymbol{X}'\boldsymbol{u}_1)(\boldsymbol{X}'\boldsymbol{u}_1)' + \frac{1}{3}(\boldsymbol{X}'\boldsymbol{u}_2)(\boldsymbol{X}'\boldsymbol{u}_2)' = 2\boldsymbol{v}_1\boldsymbol{v}_1' + 2\boldsymbol{v}_2\boldsymbol{v}_2',$$

where

$$\boldsymbol{v}_1 = \frac{1}{\sqrt{2}}\begin{pmatrix} 0 \\ 1 \\ -1 \end{pmatrix}, \qquad \boldsymbol{v}_2 = \frac{1}{\sqrt{6}}\begin{pmatrix} 2 \\ 1 \\ 1 \end{pmatrix},$$

and $\boldsymbol{v}_1$ and $\boldsymbol{v}_2$ are orthogonal unit vectors. Thus, we can write

$$(\boldsymbol{X}'\boldsymbol{W}^-\boldsymbol{X})^- = \frac{1}{2}\boldsymbol{v}_1\boldsymbol{v}_1' + \frac{1}{2}\boldsymbol{v}_2\boldsymbol{v}_2', \quad \boldsymbol{X}'\boldsymbol{W}^-\boldsymbol{y} = \sqrt{2}(\boldsymbol{u}_1'\boldsymbol{y})\boldsymbol{v}_1 + \sqrt{\frac{2}{3}}(\boldsymbol{u}_2'\boldsymbol{y})\boldsymbol{v}_2,$$

which lead to

$$\boldsymbol{X}(\boldsymbol{X}'\boldsymbol{W}^-\boldsymbol{X})^-\boldsymbol{X}'\boldsymbol{W}^-\boldsymbol{y} = \frac{\boldsymbol{u}_1'\boldsymbol{y}}{\sqrt{2}}\boldsymbol{X}\boldsymbol{v}_1 + \frac{\boldsymbol{u}_2'\boldsymbol{y}}{\sqrt{6}}\boldsymbol{X}\boldsymbol{v}_2 = (\boldsymbol{u}_1\boldsymbol{u}_1' + \boldsymbol{u}_2\boldsymbol{u}_2')\boldsymbol{y}.$$

This is the WLSE $\widehat{\boldsymbol{y}}$. The value of $\widehat{\boldsymbol{y}}$ obtained in Example 7.12 was $(\boldsymbol{I} - \boldsymbol{u}_3\boldsymbol{u}_3')\boldsymbol{y}$, which is the same as $(\boldsymbol{u}_1\boldsymbol{u}_1' + \boldsymbol{u}_2\boldsymbol{u}_2' + \boldsymbol{u}_4\boldsymbol{u}_4')\boldsymbol{y}$. The apparent difference between the two expressions, $\boldsymbol{u}_4\boldsymbol{u}_4'\boldsymbol{y}$, is in fact zero, as $\boldsymbol{y} \in \mathcal{C}(\boldsymbol{X} : \boldsymbol{V}) = \mathcal{C}(\boldsymbol{u}_1 : \boldsymbol{u}_2 : \boldsymbol{u}_3)$ with probability 1. The equivalence of the two expressions is a confirmation of Proposition 7.30, to be proved later.

For a comparison, consider the model $(\boldsymbol{y}, \boldsymbol{X\beta}, \sigma^2\boldsymbol{W})$ where $\boldsymbol{W}$ is as defined above. The value of $\widehat{\boldsymbol{y}}$ turns out to be the same as above. However,

$$\boldsymbol{W}(\boldsymbol{I} - \boldsymbol{P}_{\!X}) = (\boldsymbol{I} - \boldsymbol{P}_{\!X})\boldsymbol{W} = \boldsymbol{u}_3\boldsymbol{u}_3'$$

which leads to

$$\begin{aligned} D(\widehat{\boldsymbol{y}}) &= \sigma^2[\boldsymbol{W} - \boldsymbol{W}(\boldsymbol{I} - \boldsymbol{P}_{\!X})\{(\boldsymbol{I} - \boldsymbol{P}_{\!X})\boldsymbol{W}(\boldsymbol{I} - \boldsymbol{P}_{\!X})\}^-(\boldsymbol{I} - \boldsymbol{P}_{\!X})\boldsymbol{W}] \\ &= \sigma^2(\boldsymbol{u}_1\boldsymbol{u}_1' + 3\boldsymbol{u}_2\boldsymbol{u}_2'). \end{aligned}$$

This is larger than the expression $D(\widehat{\boldsymbol{y}}) = 3\sigma^2\boldsymbol{u}_2\boldsymbol{u}_2'$ obtained for the actual model in Example 7.14. □

7.7 Some recipes for obtaining the BLUE*

In this section we outline the major methods of obtaining the BLUE, its dispersion and the estimator of error variance, which are available in the literature. Since these methods are generally justified through algebraic arguments, we had shunned them at the beginning, and opted instead for the characterization of BLUE through LZFs (Proposition 3.29) and the principle of decorrelation (Proposition 2.28) as the basis of our derivations, for clearer insight. We now introduce these alternative methods, using statistical arguments as much as possible to explain them.

7.7.1 *'Unified theory' of least squares estimation*

We have observed in Remark 7.27 that a BLUE can be computed through the weighted least squares method when $\mathcal{C}(\boldsymbol{X}) \subseteq \mathcal{C}(\boldsymbol{V})$. This condition may not always hold, but we can try to ensure it by expanding the column space of $\boldsymbol{V}$. This we do by introducing more error into the model!

Let $\mathcal{M}$ denote the model $(\boldsymbol{y}, \boldsymbol{X}\boldsymbol{\beta}, \sigma^2\boldsymbol{V})$. Suppose $\boldsymbol{y}_* = \boldsymbol{y} + \boldsymbol{X}\boldsymbol{\gamma}$, where the random vector $\boldsymbol{\gamma}$ is uncorrelated with $\boldsymbol{y}$, has zero mean and $D(\boldsymbol{\gamma}) = \sigma^2\boldsymbol{U}$. Clearly $D(\boldsymbol{y}_*) = \sigma^2(\boldsymbol{V} + \boldsymbol{X}\boldsymbol{U}\boldsymbol{X}')$. Let us denote the matrix $\boldsymbol{V} + \boldsymbol{X}\boldsymbol{U}\boldsymbol{X}'$ by $\boldsymbol{W}$, and the model $(\boldsymbol{y}_*, \boldsymbol{X}\boldsymbol{\beta}, \sigma^2\boldsymbol{W})$ by $\mathcal{M}^*$.

Proposition 7.29. *Let the models $\mathcal{M}$ and $\mathcal{M}^*$ be as defined above.*

(a) The estimable LPFs in the models $\mathcal{M}$ and $\mathcal{M}^*$ are identical.
(b) The set of LZFs in the models $\mathcal{M}$ and $\mathcal{M}^*$ are identical.
(c) $\boldsymbol{l}'\boldsymbol{y}$ is the BLUE of $\mathbf{p}'\boldsymbol{\beta}$ in the model $\mathcal{M}$ if and only if $\boldsymbol{l}'\boldsymbol{y}_*$ is the BLUE of $\mathbf{p}'\boldsymbol{\beta}$ in the model $\mathcal{M}^*$.

Proof. Part (a) follows from the fact that the systematic parts of the two models are identical. Part (b) is a consequence of Remark 3.15 and the fact that $(\boldsymbol{I} - \boldsymbol{P}_{\boldsymbol{X}})\boldsymbol{X}\boldsymbol{\gamma} = \boldsymbol{0}$ almost surely. Part (c) follows from the fact that $Cov(\boldsymbol{l}'\boldsymbol{y}_*, \boldsymbol{k}'\boldsymbol{y}) = Cov(\boldsymbol{l}'\boldsymbol{y}, \boldsymbol{k}'\boldsymbol{y})$ where $\boldsymbol{k}'\boldsymbol{y}$ is an LZF in either model. □

Proposition 7.29 establishes a kind of equivalence between the models $\mathcal{M}$ and $\mathcal{M}^*$. In order to be able to use the weighted least squares method for the computation of BLUE in the latter model, we have to ensure that the sufficient condition $\mathcal{C}(\boldsymbol{X}) \subseteq \mathcal{C}(\boldsymbol{W})$ (mentioned in Remark 7.27) holds. We have to choose the matrix $\boldsymbol{U}$ in model $\mathcal{M}^*$ such that $\mathcal{C}(\boldsymbol{W}) = \mathcal{C}(\boldsymbol{V} : \boldsymbol{X})$.

(This is indeed the 'best case scenario', as in general $\mathcal{C}(\boldsymbol{W}) \subseteq \mathcal{C}(\boldsymbol{V} : \boldsymbol{X})$; see Exercise 7.8.) This choice will produce an appropriate BLUE through weighted least squares, but we should expect the dispersion obtained from $\mathcal{M}^*$ to be unduly large, as that model contains additional error. The next proposition gives a formal statement of the results.

Proposition 7.30. *Given the model $(\boldsymbol{y}, \boldsymbol{X\beta}, \sigma^2\boldsymbol{V})$, suppose $\boldsymbol{U}$ is a symmetric and nonnegative definite matrix such that the matrix $\boldsymbol{W} = \boldsymbol{V} + \boldsymbol{XUX}'$ satisfies the condition $\mathcal{C}(\boldsymbol{W}) = \mathcal{C}(\boldsymbol{V} : \boldsymbol{X})$. Then*

(a) *The BLUE of $\boldsymbol{X\beta}$ is*
$$\widehat{\boldsymbol{X\beta}} = \boldsymbol{X}\widehat{\boldsymbol{\beta}}_{WLS} = \boldsymbol{X}(\boldsymbol{X}'\boldsymbol{W}^-\boldsymbol{X})^-\boldsymbol{X}'\boldsymbol{W}^-\boldsymbol{y},$$
$\widehat{\boldsymbol{\beta}}_{WLS}$ being a WLSE which minimizes $(\boldsymbol{y} - \boldsymbol{X\beta})'\boldsymbol{W}^-(\boldsymbol{y} - \boldsymbol{X\beta})$.

(b) *The dispersion of $\boldsymbol{X}\widehat{\boldsymbol{\beta}}$ is*
$$D(\boldsymbol{X}\widehat{\boldsymbol{\beta}}) = \sigma^2\boldsymbol{X}[(\boldsymbol{X}'\boldsymbol{W}^-\boldsymbol{X})^- - \boldsymbol{U}]\boldsymbol{X}'.$$

(c) *The error sum of squares can be written as the minimized value of the quadratic form,*
$$R_0^2 = (\boldsymbol{y} - \boldsymbol{X}\widehat{\boldsymbol{\beta}}_{WLS})'\boldsymbol{W}^-(\boldsymbol{y} - \boldsymbol{X}\widehat{\boldsymbol{\beta}}_{WLS}).$$

(d) *The natural unbiased estimator of σ^2 that is a multiple of the error sum of squares is given by $\widehat{\sigma^2} = R_0^2/[\rho(\boldsymbol{W}) - \rho(\boldsymbol{X})]$.*

Proof. The condition $\boldsymbol{W} = \boldsymbol{V} + \boldsymbol{XUX}'$ ensures $\mathcal{C}(\boldsymbol{X}) \subseteq \mathcal{C}(\boldsymbol{W})$. According to Remark 7.27, the BLUE of $\boldsymbol{X\beta}$ in the model $\mathcal{M}^*$ is $\boldsymbol{X}(\boldsymbol{X}'\boldsymbol{W}^-\boldsymbol{X})^-\boldsymbol{X}'\boldsymbol{W}^-\boldsymbol{y}_*$, which must be unique. The result of part (a) follows from part (c) of Proposition 7.29.

Let us rewrite the BLUE under the models $\mathcal{M}$ and $\mathcal{M}^*$ as $\boldsymbol{Cy}$ and $\boldsymbol{Cy}_*$, respectively, where $\boldsymbol{C} = \boldsymbol{X}(\boldsymbol{X}'\boldsymbol{W}^-\boldsymbol{X})^-\boldsymbol{X}'\boldsymbol{W}^-$. Then we have
$$D(\boldsymbol{Cy}_*) = D(\boldsymbol{Cy} + \boldsymbol{C\gamma}) = D(\boldsymbol{Cy}) + D(\boldsymbol{CX\gamma}) = D(\boldsymbol{Cy}) + D(\boldsymbol{X\gamma}).$$
Therefore,
$$D(\boldsymbol{X}\widehat{\boldsymbol{\beta}}) = D(\boldsymbol{Cy}_*) - D(\boldsymbol{X\gamma}) = \sigma^2\boldsymbol{X}(\boldsymbol{X}'\boldsymbol{W}^-\boldsymbol{X})^-\boldsymbol{X}' - \sigma^2\boldsymbol{XUX}'.$$
This proves part (b).

As the Definition 3.47 of error sum of squares continues to hold in the case of the general linear model, parts (c) and (d) follow from the identity of the LZFs under the models $\mathcal{M}$ and $\mathcal{M}^*$ as established in Proposition 7.29(b). □

Example 7.31. For the model of Examples 7.12 and 7.28, it has been shown that by choosing $\boldsymbol{U} = \frac{1}{4}(0 : 1 : -1)'(0 : 1 : -1)$, we obtain the appropriate BLUE of $X\beta$ by the weighted least squares method. However the dispersion of the BLUE of $X\beta$ computed from the model $\mathcal{M}^*$ is inappropriate. According to Proposition 7.30, we need to adjust the latter dispersion by subtracting $\sigma^2 XUX'$ from it. In the present case, this adjustment amounts to subtracting $\sigma^2 u_1 u_1'$ from $\sigma^2(u_1 u_1' + 3u_2 u_2')$. The correct dispersion matrix is $3\sigma^2 u_2 u_2'$, which coincides with the expression computed directly in Example 7.14. The expression of R_0^2 obtained from Proposition 7.30 is

$$R_0^2 = e'W^- e = y' u_3 u_3' [u_1 u_1' + \tfrac{1}{3} u_2 u_2' + u_3 u_3'] u_3 u_3' y = (u_3' y)^2,$$

which simplifies to $(y_1 - y_2 + y_3 - y_4)^2/4$. Since $\rho(W) - \rho(X) = 1$, $\widehat{\sigma^2}$ is also equal to this expression, as found in Example 7.21. □

As a direct consequence of Proposition 7.30, we have the following result.

Proposition 7.32. *If the matrix W is as described in Proposition 7.30, then the dispersion of the BLUE can be written as*

$$D(\widehat{y}) = Cov(\widehat{y}, y) = \sigma^2 X(X'W^- X)^- X'W^- V,$$

which must be a symmetric matrix. If $\mathcal{C}(X) \subseteq \mathcal{C}(V)$, then

$$D(\widehat{y}) = \sigma^2 X(X'V^- X)^- X'V^- V = \sigma^2 X(X'V^- X)^- X'. \quad \square$$

Remark 7.33. Since matrices of the form $W = V + XUX'$ are so useful when $\mathcal{C}(W) = \mathcal{C}(V : X)$, equivalent forms of this condition are important. It can be shown that two equivalent conditions are $\mathcal{C}(X) \subseteq \mathcal{C}(W)$ and $\rho(W) = \rho(V : X)$ (see Exercise 7.9). □

Proposition 7.30 can be strengthened by dropping the condition of nonnegative definiteness of U (Exercise 7.12). From a practical point of view, not much is lost by forcing U to be symmetric and nonnegative definite. Nevertheless, considerable research has been done with the aim of relaxing these conditions. See Baksalary and Mathew (1990) and the references therein for a collection of sufficient conditions for the equivalence of the BLUE with a WLSE.

7.7.2 *The inverse partitioned matrix approach*

Suppose we wish to find the BLUE of $X\beta$ and the residual vector simultaneously. Let the BLUE of $X\beta$ be $L'y$. By Proposition 3.29, $Cov((I - P_X)y, L'y) = (I - P_X)VL = 0$. Thus $\mathcal{C}(VL) \subset \mathcal{C}(X)$, i.e.

there is a matrix $\boldsymbol{T}$ such that $\boldsymbol{VL} + \boldsymbol{XT} = \mathbf{0}$. Combining this with the unbiasedness condition, $\boldsymbol{L}'\boldsymbol{X} = \boldsymbol{X}$, we have

$$\begin{pmatrix} \boldsymbol{V} & \boldsymbol{X} \\ \boldsymbol{X}' & \mathbf{0} \end{pmatrix} \begin{pmatrix} \boldsymbol{L} \\ \boldsymbol{T} \end{pmatrix} = \begin{pmatrix} \mathbf{0} \\ \boldsymbol{X}' \end{pmatrix}. \tag{7.10}$$

The task of finding the BLUE of $\boldsymbol{X\beta}$ and the residual vector amounts to finding a decomposition $\boldsymbol{y} = \widehat{\boldsymbol{y}} + \boldsymbol{e}$, such that the summands should satisfy the conditions given in Remark 7.16. Therefore, we can write the decomposition as $\boldsymbol{y} = \boldsymbol{Xu} + \boldsymbol{Vv}$ where $\boldsymbol{v} \in \mathcal{C}(\boldsymbol{I} - \boldsymbol{P}_X)$, i.e. $\boldsymbol{X}'\boldsymbol{v} = \mathbf{0}$. The last two equations can be written in a combined form as

$$\begin{pmatrix} \boldsymbol{V} & \boldsymbol{X} \\ \boldsymbol{X}' & \mathbf{0} \end{pmatrix} \begin{pmatrix} \boldsymbol{v} \\ \boldsymbol{u} \end{pmatrix} = \begin{pmatrix} \boldsymbol{y} \\ \mathbf{0} \end{pmatrix}. \tag{7.11}$$

Combining (7.10) and (7.11), we have the matrix equation

$$\begin{pmatrix} \boldsymbol{V} & \boldsymbol{X} \\ \boldsymbol{X}' & \mathbf{0} \end{pmatrix} \begin{pmatrix} \boldsymbol{L} & \boldsymbol{v} \\ \boldsymbol{T} & \boldsymbol{u} \end{pmatrix} = \begin{pmatrix} \mathbf{0} & \boldsymbol{y} \\ \boldsymbol{X}' & \mathbf{0} \end{pmatrix}. \tag{7.12}$$

After solving the above equation we should have the BLUE of $\boldsymbol{X\beta}$ as $\boldsymbol{L}'\boldsymbol{y}$ or $\boldsymbol{Xu}$, and the residual vector as $\boldsymbol{Vv}$.

Proposition 7.34. (Rao, 1973c) *Suppose a g-inverse of the first matrix of (7.12) is given by*

$$\begin{pmatrix} \boldsymbol{V} & \boldsymbol{X} \\ \boldsymbol{X}' & \mathbf{0} \end{pmatrix}^{-} = \begin{pmatrix} \boldsymbol{C}_1 & \boldsymbol{C}_2 \\ \boldsymbol{C}_3 & -\boldsymbol{C}_4 \end{pmatrix}.$$

Then

(a) The BLUE of $\boldsymbol{X\beta}$ is $\boldsymbol{X}\widehat{\boldsymbol{\beta}} = \boldsymbol{XC}_2'\boldsymbol{y} = \boldsymbol{XC}_3\boldsymbol{y}$.
(b) The dispersion of $\boldsymbol{X}\widehat{\boldsymbol{\beta}}$ is $D(\boldsymbol{X}\widehat{\boldsymbol{\beta}}) = \sigma^2\boldsymbol{XC}_4\boldsymbol{X}'$.
(c) The residual vector corresponding to the BLUE is $\boldsymbol{e} = \boldsymbol{VC}_1\boldsymbol{y}$.
(d) The error sum of squares is given by $R_0^2 = \boldsymbol{y}'\boldsymbol{C}_1\boldsymbol{y}$, while its multiple that is an unbiased estimator of σ^2 is $\widehat{\sigma^2} = R_0^2/[\rho(\boldsymbol{V} : \boldsymbol{X}) - \rho(\boldsymbol{X})]$.

Proof. It follows from the discussion preceding this proposition that the system of equations (7.12) is consistent. A possible set of solutions is given by

$$\begin{pmatrix} \boldsymbol{L} & \boldsymbol{v} \\ \boldsymbol{T} & \boldsymbol{u} \end{pmatrix} = \begin{pmatrix} \boldsymbol{C}_1 & \boldsymbol{C}_2 \\ \boldsymbol{C}_3 & -\boldsymbol{C}_4 \end{pmatrix} \begin{pmatrix} \mathbf{0} & \boldsymbol{y} \\ \boldsymbol{X}' & \mathbf{0} \end{pmatrix}.$$

Part (a) follows immediately from the representations of the BLUE given by $\boldsymbol{L}'\boldsymbol{y}$ and $\boldsymbol{Xu}$.

Using the conditions $\boldsymbol{VL} + \boldsymbol{XT} = \mathbf{0}$ and $\boldsymbol{L}'\boldsymbol{X} = \boldsymbol{X}$, we have

$$D(\boldsymbol{X}\widehat{\boldsymbol{\beta}}) = \sigma^2\boldsymbol{L}'\boldsymbol{VL} = -\sigma^2\boldsymbol{L}'\boldsymbol{XT} = \sigma^2\boldsymbol{L}'\boldsymbol{XC}_4\boldsymbol{X}' = \sigma^2\boldsymbol{XC}_4\boldsymbol{X}'.$$

This proves part (b).

Part (c) follows from the representations of the residual vector given by $\boldsymbol{e} = \boldsymbol{Vv}$.

In order to prove part (d), we simplify the numerator of (7.8) as follows, using the conditions $\boldsymbol{X}'\boldsymbol{v} = \mathbf{0}$, $\boldsymbol{e} = \boldsymbol{Vv}$ and $\widehat{\boldsymbol{y}} = \boldsymbol{Xu}$.

$$R_0^2 = \boldsymbol{e}'\boldsymbol{V}^-\boldsymbol{e} = \boldsymbol{e}'\boldsymbol{V}^-\boldsymbol{Vv} = \boldsymbol{e}'\boldsymbol{v} = \boldsymbol{y}'\boldsymbol{v} - \boldsymbol{u}'\boldsymbol{X}'\boldsymbol{v} = \boldsymbol{y}'\boldsymbol{v} = \boldsymbol{y}'\boldsymbol{C}_1\boldsymbol{y}.$$

This leads immediately to the expression for $\widehat{\sigma^2}$. □

Example 7.35. For the model of Example 7.12, let

$$\begin{pmatrix} \boldsymbol{V} & \boldsymbol{X} \\ \boldsymbol{X}' & \mathbf{0} \end{pmatrix}^+ = \begin{pmatrix} \boldsymbol{C}_1 & \boldsymbol{C}_2 \\ \boldsymbol{C}_3 & -\boldsymbol{C}_4 \end{pmatrix}.$$

It can be shown after some computation that

$$\boldsymbol{C}_1 = \frac{1}{4}\begin{pmatrix} 1 & -1 & 1 & -1 \\ -1 & 1 & -1 & 1 \\ 1 & -1 & 1 & -1 \\ -1 & 1 & -1 & 1 \end{pmatrix}, \quad \boldsymbol{C}_2 = \frac{1}{6}\begin{pmatrix} 1 & 2 & -1 \\ 1 & 2 & -1 \\ 1 & -1 & 2 \\ 1 & -1 & 2 \end{pmatrix},$$

$$\boldsymbol{C}_3 = \frac{1}{6}\begin{pmatrix} 1 & 1 & 1 & 1 \\ 2 & 2 & -1 & -1 \\ -1 & -1 & 2 & 2 \end{pmatrix}, \quad \boldsymbol{C}_4 = \frac{1}{12}\begin{pmatrix} 4 & 2 & 2 \\ 2 & 1 & 1 \\ 2 & 1 & 1 \end{pmatrix}.$$

Using part (a) of Proposition 7.34, we have

$$\widehat{\boldsymbol{y}} = \left(\frac{y_1 + y_2}{2} : \frac{y_1 + y_2}{2} : \frac{y_3 + y_4}{2} : \frac{y_3 + y_4}{2}\right)',$$

which is almost surely the same as the expression obtained in Example 7.12 in view of the fact that $\boldsymbol{u}_4'\boldsymbol{y} = 0$ with probability 1. The other parts of Proposition 7.34 lead to values of $D(\boldsymbol{X}\widehat{\boldsymbol{\beta}})$, $\boldsymbol{e}$ and $\widehat{\sigma^2}$ that are identical to those obtained in Examples 7.14, 7.12 and 7.21, respectively. □

7.7.3 *A constrained least squares approach*

Since the error vector in the linear model $(\boldsymbol{y}, \boldsymbol{X\beta}, \sigma^2\boldsymbol{V})$ is contained in $\mathcal{C}(\boldsymbol{V})$ almost surely, we can write the observation vector as

$$\boldsymbol{y} = \boldsymbol{X\beta} + \boldsymbol{Fu}, \tag{7.13}$$

where $\boldsymbol{FF}'$ is a rank-factorization of $\boldsymbol{V}$. Note that

$$\|\boldsymbol{u}\|^2 = \|\boldsymbol{F}^{-L}(\boldsymbol{y} - \boldsymbol{X\beta})\|^2 = (\boldsymbol{y} - \boldsymbol{X\beta})'\boldsymbol{V}^-(\boldsymbol{y} - \boldsymbol{X\beta}).$$

We proved in Section 7.5 that the BLUE of $\boldsymbol{X\beta}$ uniquely minimizes the right-hand side of the above equation subject to the constraint $(\boldsymbol{y}-\boldsymbol{X\beta}) \in \mathcal{C}(\boldsymbol{V})$. As $\mathcal{C}(\boldsymbol{V}) = \mathcal{C}(\boldsymbol{F})$, the constraint is equivalent to (7.13) for some $\boldsymbol{\beta}$ and $\boldsymbol{u}$. The minimization problem can be solved without invoking normality of $\boldsymbol{y}$, as long as the response vector satisfies the constraint $\boldsymbol{y} \in \mathcal{C}(\boldsymbol{V} : \boldsymbol{X})$ for consistency. Therefore, we have the following result.

Proposition 7.36. *Let $\boldsymbol{FF}'$ be a rank-factorization of $\boldsymbol{V}$ in the linear model $(\boldsymbol{y}, \boldsymbol{X\beta}, \sigma^2\boldsymbol{V})$, and let $\widehat{\boldsymbol{\beta}}$ and $\widehat{\boldsymbol{u}}$ be a choice of $\boldsymbol{\beta}$ and $\boldsymbol{u}$ which minimizes $\|\boldsymbol{u}\|^2$ subject to the constraint (7.13). Then the BLUE of $\boldsymbol{X\beta}$ is $\boldsymbol{X}\widehat{\boldsymbol{\beta}}$ which is unique, and the corresponding residual vector is $\boldsymbol{F}\widehat{\boldsymbol{u}}$.* □

The importance of Proposition 7.36 is that the formulation given here lends itself to a numerically stable computational procedure for obtaining the quantities of interest. Kourouklis and Paige (1981) outline a procedure for obtaining the BLUE of $\boldsymbol{X\beta}$, its dispersion, and an uncorrelated basis set of LZFs (see Exercise 7.11).

The idea of obtaining the BLUE in the general linear model as the solution of a constrained quadratic optimization problem is quite old. Goldman and Zelen (1964), the first authors to formally consider the general linear model with possibly singular covariance matrix, show that the BLUE can be obtained by minimizing $(\boldsymbol{y} - \boldsymbol{X\beta})'\boldsymbol{V}^-(\boldsymbol{y} - \boldsymbol{X\beta})$ with respect to $\boldsymbol{\beta}$ subject to a linear constraint on $\boldsymbol{\beta}$. The constraint is equivalent to $(\boldsymbol{I} - \boldsymbol{P}_V)\boldsymbol{X\beta} = (\boldsymbol{I} - \boldsymbol{P}_V)\boldsymbol{y}$, which becomes important only when the dispersion matrix is singular.

7.8 Information matrix and Cramer-Rao bound*

If $\boldsymbol{y} \sim N(\boldsymbol{X\beta}, \sigma^2\boldsymbol{V})$ and $\boldsymbol{V}$ is nonsingular, then it is easily seen, via a derivation similar to that of Section 3.12, that the information matrix for the vector parameter $\boldsymbol{\theta} = (\boldsymbol{\beta}' : \sigma^2)'$ is

$$\mathcal{I}(\boldsymbol{\theta}) = \begin{pmatrix} \frac{1}{\sigma^2}\boldsymbol{X}'\boldsymbol{V}^{-1}\boldsymbol{X} & \boldsymbol{0} \\ \boldsymbol{0} & \frac{n}{2\sigma^2} \end{pmatrix}.$$

Consequently the Cramer-Rao lower bound for the dispersion of an unbiased estimator of the estimable function $\boldsymbol{A\beta}$ is $\sigma^2\boldsymbol{A}(\boldsymbol{X}'\boldsymbol{V}^{-1}\boldsymbol{X})^-\boldsymbol{A}'$.

When $\boldsymbol{V}$ is singular, this argument does not hold. To see this, it is enough to consider the special case $\boldsymbol{V} = \boldsymbol{0}$. As the distribution is degenerate, the partial derivatives used in the definition of the information matrix do not exist. Consequently the information matrix does not exist. However, the BLUE of every estimable function has zero variance. Therefore, the Cramer-Rao lower bound for every estimable LPF exists and is equal to 0.

The Cramer-Rao lower bound can be generally determined when $\boldsymbol{V}$ is singular, even though the information matrix may not exist.

Example 7.37. Let $\boldsymbol{y} \sim (\boldsymbol{X}_*\boldsymbol{\eta}, \sigma^2\boldsymbol{V}_*)$, where $\boldsymbol{y}$, $\boldsymbol{X}_*$, $\boldsymbol{\eta}$ and $\boldsymbol{V}_*$ have the following forms with conformable partitions:

$$\boldsymbol{y} = \begin{pmatrix} \boldsymbol{y}_1 \\ \boldsymbol{y}_2 \\ \boldsymbol{y}_3 \\ \boldsymbol{y}_4 \end{pmatrix}, \quad \boldsymbol{X}_* = \begin{pmatrix} \boldsymbol{I} & \boldsymbol{0} \\ \boldsymbol{0} & \boldsymbol{I} \\ \boldsymbol{0} & \boldsymbol{0} \\ \boldsymbol{0} & \boldsymbol{0} \end{pmatrix}, \quad \boldsymbol{\eta} = \begin{pmatrix} \boldsymbol{\eta}_1 \\ \boldsymbol{\eta}_2 \end{pmatrix}, \quad \boldsymbol{V}_* = \begin{pmatrix} \boldsymbol{I} & \boldsymbol{0} & \boldsymbol{0} & \boldsymbol{0} \\ \boldsymbol{0} & \boldsymbol{0} & \boldsymbol{0} & \boldsymbol{0} \\ \boldsymbol{0} & \boldsymbol{0} & \boldsymbol{I} & \boldsymbol{0} \\ \boldsymbol{0} & \boldsymbol{0} & \boldsymbol{0} & \boldsymbol{0} \end{pmatrix}.$$

Evidently $\boldsymbol{\eta}_2$ can be unbiasedly estimated by $\boldsymbol{y}_2$, which has dispersion $\boldsymbol{0}$. Note that $\boldsymbol{y}_1$, $\boldsymbol{y}_2$, $\boldsymbol{y}_3$ and $\boldsymbol{y}_4$ are independent and the distribution of $\boldsymbol{y}_2$ and $\boldsymbol{y}_4$ do not involve $\boldsymbol{\eta}_1$ and σ^2. Hence, we can ignore the distributions of $\boldsymbol{y}_2$ and $\boldsymbol{y}_4$ for computing the information matrix for $(\boldsymbol{\eta}_1' : \sigma^2)'$, which happens to be

$$\begin{pmatrix} \sigma^{-2}\boldsymbol{I} & \boldsymbol{0} \\ \boldsymbol{0} & \rho(\boldsymbol{V}_*)/(2\sigma^4) \end{pmatrix}.$$

Every estimable LPF in the model $(\boldsymbol{y}, \boldsymbol{X}_*\boldsymbol{\eta}, \sigma^2\boldsymbol{V}_*)$ can be expressed as $\boldsymbol{A}_1\boldsymbol{\eta}_1 + \boldsymbol{A}_2\boldsymbol{\eta}_2$. The statistic $\boldsymbol{t}(\boldsymbol{y})$ is an unbiased estimator of this LPF if and only if $\boldsymbol{t}(\boldsymbol{y}) - \boldsymbol{A}_2\boldsymbol{y}_2$ is an unbiased estimator of $\boldsymbol{A}_1\boldsymbol{\eta}_1$. As $\boldsymbol{t}(\boldsymbol{y})$ and $\boldsymbol{t}(\boldsymbol{y}) - \boldsymbol{A}_2\boldsymbol{y}_2$ have the same dispersion matrix, the same lower bound should work for both. The Cramer-Rao lower bound for an unbiased estimator of $\boldsymbol{A}_1\boldsymbol{\eta}_1$ is $\sigma^2\boldsymbol{A}_1\boldsymbol{A}_1'$. This bound holds for any unbiased estimator of $\boldsymbol{A}_1\boldsymbol{\eta}_1 + \boldsymbol{A}_2\boldsymbol{\eta}_2$ also. The lower bound for the variance of unbiased estimators of σ^2 is $2\sigma^4/\rho(\boldsymbol{V}_*)$. □

The simple model of Example 7.37 has all the essential features of a singular linear model. It is shown in Section 11.1.3 that every general linear model can be reduced to this simple form. We use this decomposition to derive the Cramer-Rao lower bound in the general case.

Proposition 7.38. *If* $\boldsymbol{y} \sim N(\boldsymbol{X\beta}, \sigma^2\boldsymbol{V})$, *then the Cramer-Rao lower bound for the dispersion of an unbiased estimator of the estimable LPF*

$A\beta$ is

$$\sigma^2 AX^-[V - V(I - P_X)\{(I - P_X)V(I - P_X)\}^-(I - P_X)V](AX^-)',$$

which does not depend on the choice of the g-inverses. The lower bound for the variance of an unbiased estimator of σ^2 is $2\sigma^4/\rho(V)$.

Proof. According to Proposition 11.16, there is a nonsingular matrix $L = (L_1' : L_2' : L_3' : L_4')'$ such that $Ly \sim N(X_*\eta, \sigma^2 V_*)$, where X_* and V_* are as in Example 7.37 and

$$\eta = \begin{pmatrix} \eta_1 \\ \eta_2 \end{pmatrix} = \begin{pmatrix} L_1X \\ L_2X \end{pmatrix} \beta.$$

Further, every BLUE is almost surely a linear function of L_1y and L_2y. Therefore, there is a matrix $(K_1 : K_2)$ such that the BLUE of $X\beta$ is almost surely equal to $K_1L_1y + K_2L_2y$. Equating the expected values of these, we have $X\beta = K_1\eta_1 + K_2\eta_2$. Equating the dispersions, we have $D(X\widehat{\beta}) = \sigma^2 K_1K_1'$. Using the argument given in Example 7.37 leads one to the conclusion that the Cramer-Rao lower bound for the dispersion of any unbiased estimator of $A\beta$ (or $AX^-K_1\eta_1 + AX^-K_2\eta_2$) is

$$\sigma^2(AX^-K_1)(AX^-K_1)' = (AX^-)D(X\widehat{\beta})(AX^-)',$$

which simplifies to the given expression (see Section 7.3.2). Invariance under the choice of g-inverses was shown in Section 7.3.2. The lower bound corresponding to σ^2 is similarly found to be $2\sigma^4/\rho(V_*)$, which simplifies to $2\sigma^4/\rho(V)$. □

The lower bound for the dispersion of an unbiased (not necessarily linear) estimator of $A\beta$ coincides with the dispersion of its BLUE, which is the UMVUE in the normal case. Thus, the UMVUE of every estimable LPF achieves the Cramer-Rao lower bound.

Remark 7.39. When $y \sim N(X\beta, \sigma^2 V)$ with $\mathcal{C}(X) \subseteq \mathcal{C}(V)$, it can be shown that the information matrix for $\theta = (\beta' : \sigma^2)'$ exists and is equal to

$$\begin{pmatrix} \sigma^{-2}X'V^-X & 0 \\ 0 & \rho(V)/(2\sigma^4) \end{pmatrix}.$$

The Cramer-Rao lower bound for the dispersion of an unbiased estimator of the estimable LPF $A\beta$ is $\sigma^2 A(X'V^-X)^-A'$. Neither the information matrix nor the lower bound depends on the choice of the g-inverses (see Exercise 7.13). □

7.9 Effect of linear restrictions

7.9.1 *Linear restrictions in the general linear model*

Consider the linear model $\mathcal{M} = (\boldsymbol{y}, \boldsymbol{X\beta}, \sigma^2\boldsymbol{V})$. If we impose the (algebraically consistent) linear restriction $\boldsymbol{A\beta} = \boldsymbol{\xi}$ on $\mathcal{M}$, then the restricted model is equivalent to the unrestricted model $\mathcal{M}_r = (\boldsymbol{y} - \boldsymbol{XA}^-\boldsymbol{\xi}, \boldsymbol{X}(\boldsymbol{I} - \boldsymbol{A}^-\boldsymbol{A})\boldsymbol{\theta}, \sigma^2\boldsymbol{V})$. This statement may be justified along the lines of the arguments in the homoscedastic case (see Section 3.10). As mentioned there, the parameters in the two models are related by the equation

$$\boldsymbol{X\beta} = \boldsymbol{XA}'(\boldsymbol{AA}')^-\boldsymbol{\xi} + \boldsymbol{X}(\boldsymbol{I} - \boldsymbol{P}_{\boldsymbol{A}'})\boldsymbol{\theta}. \tag{7.14}$$

Recall from Section 7.2.1 that the response in a singular model must satisfy a consistency condition. The consistency condition of $\mathcal{M}_r$ is

$$(\boldsymbol{I} - \boldsymbol{P}_{\boldsymbol{V}})(\boldsymbol{y} - \boldsymbol{XA}^-\boldsymbol{\xi}) \in \mathcal{C}((\boldsymbol{I} - \boldsymbol{P}_{\boldsymbol{V}})\boldsymbol{X}(\boldsymbol{I} - \boldsymbol{A}^-\boldsymbol{A})). \tag{7.15}$$

It is a good idea to check this condition before proceeding with any analysis of the restricted model.

The restricted model given above depends on the choice of $\boldsymbol{A}^-$. The specific choice $\boldsymbol{A}^- = \boldsymbol{A}'(\boldsymbol{AA}')^-$ leads to the well-defined model $(\boldsymbol{y} - \boldsymbol{XA}'(\boldsymbol{AA}')^-\boldsymbol{\xi}, \boldsymbol{X}(\boldsymbol{I} - \boldsymbol{P}_{\boldsymbol{A}'})\boldsymbol{\theta}, \sigma^2\boldsymbol{V})$. The BLUE of $\boldsymbol{X\beta}$ under the restriction can be computed by using the decomposition (7.14). The first part is a known constant, while the second is estimable in $\mathcal{M}_r$, and has a unique BLUE. Adding these two, we have the BLUE of $\boldsymbol{X\beta}$.

The model $\mathcal{M}$ subject to the restriction $\boldsymbol{A\beta} = \boldsymbol{\xi}$ is also equivalent to the model $\mathcal{M}_R$ defined as

$$\mathcal{M}_R = \left(\begin{pmatrix}\boldsymbol{y}\\ \boldsymbol{\xi}\end{pmatrix}, \begin{pmatrix}\boldsymbol{X}\\ \boldsymbol{A}\end{pmatrix}\boldsymbol{\beta}, \sigma^2\begin{pmatrix}\boldsymbol{V} & \boldsymbol{0}\\ \boldsymbol{0} & \boldsymbol{0}\end{pmatrix}\right).$$

The consistency condition of $\mathcal{M}_R$ simplifies to

$$\begin{pmatrix}(\boldsymbol{I} - \boldsymbol{P}_{\boldsymbol{V}})\boldsymbol{y}\\ \boldsymbol{\xi}\end{pmatrix} \in \mathcal{C}\begin{pmatrix}(\boldsymbol{I} - \boldsymbol{P}_{\boldsymbol{V}})\boldsymbol{X}\\ \boldsymbol{A}\end{pmatrix}. \tag{7.16}$$

Propositions 3.52 and 4.18 had brought out the effect of the restrictions on the model $(\boldsymbol{y}, \boldsymbol{X\beta}, \sigma^2\boldsymbol{I})$. We shall now show that these two propositions hold for the model $(\boldsymbol{y}, \boldsymbol{X\beta}, \sigma^2\boldsymbol{V})$ as well. We shall use $\mathcal{M}_R$ to simplify the proofs. Note that we were unable to use $\mathcal{M}_R$ in Chapters 3 and 4 because of the singularity of its dispersion matrix.

Proposition 7.40. (Restatement of Proposition 3.52) *Let $\boldsymbol{A\beta} = \boldsymbol{\xi}$ be a consistent restriction on the model $(\boldsymbol{y}, \boldsymbol{X\beta}, \sigma^2\boldsymbol{V})$. Then*

(a) *All estimable LPFs of the unrestricted model are estimable under the restricted model.*
(b) *All LZFs of the unrestricted model are LZFs under the restricted model.*
(c) *The restriction cannot increase the dispersion of the BLUE of $\boldsymbol{X\beta}$.*
(d) *The restriction cannot reduce the error sum of squares.*

Proof. Part (a) follows directly from Proposition 7.4 and the structures of the model matrices of $\mathcal{M}$ and $\mathcal{M}_R$.

To prove part (b), let $\boldsymbol{l}'\boldsymbol{y}$ be an LZF in $\mathcal{M}$. Then there must be a vector $\boldsymbol{k}$ such that $\boldsymbol{l}'\boldsymbol{y} = \boldsymbol{k}'y$ and $\boldsymbol{X}'\boldsymbol{k} = \boldsymbol{0}$. Therefore, $(\boldsymbol{X}'\,\boldsymbol{A}')(\boldsymbol{k}'\,\boldsymbol{0}')' = \boldsymbol{0}$, i.e. $\boldsymbol{l}'\boldsymbol{y} = (\boldsymbol{k}'\,\boldsymbol{0}')(\boldsymbol{y}'\,\boldsymbol{\xi}')'$ is an LZF in $\mathcal{M}_R$.

Part (b) implies that one can construct a basis set of LZFs of $\mathcal{M}_R$ by expanding a basis set of LZFs of $\mathcal{M}$. Therefore, the BLUE of $\boldsymbol{X\beta}$ under $\mathcal{M}_R$ can be obtained by decorrelation of $\boldsymbol{y}$ (an unbiased estimator of $\boldsymbol{X\beta}$) with this larger basis set. The result of Exercise 2.12 implies that the dispersion of the BLUE of $\boldsymbol{X\beta}$ under $\mathcal{M}_R$ would be larger than that of the unrestricted BLUE. This proves part (c).

Part (d) is a straightforward consequence of part (b). □

We now impose the restriction $\mathcal{C}(\boldsymbol{A}') \subseteq \mathcal{C}(\boldsymbol{X}')$, i.e. $\boldsymbol{A\beta} = \boldsymbol{\xi}$ is a completely testable restriction. We prove the statement of Proposition 4.18 with $\mathcal{M}_r$ replaced by $\mathcal{M}_R$, defined above.

Proposition 7.41. (Restatement of Proposition 4.18) *Let $\boldsymbol{A\beta} = \boldsymbol{\xi}$ be a completely testable and algebraically consistent restriction, and $\widehat{\boldsymbol{A\beta}}$ be the BLUE of $\boldsymbol{A\beta}$ under the model $\mathcal{M}$.*

(a) *$\widehat{\boldsymbol{A\beta}} - \boldsymbol{\xi}$ is a vector of LZFs under the model $\mathcal{M}_R$.*
(b) *$\widehat{\boldsymbol{A\beta}} - \boldsymbol{\xi}$ is uncorrelated with $(\boldsymbol{I} - \boldsymbol{P}_X)\boldsymbol{y}$.*
(c) *There is no nontrivial LZF of $\mathcal{M}_R$ which is uncorrelated with $\widehat{\boldsymbol{A\beta}} - \boldsymbol{\xi}$ and $(\boldsymbol{I} - \boldsymbol{P}_X)\boldsymbol{y}$.*

Proof. Note that $\widehat{\boldsymbol{A\beta}} - \boldsymbol{\xi}$ is a linear function of $(\boldsymbol{y}' : \boldsymbol{\xi}')'$. Part (a) is proved directly by computing the expectation of $\widehat{\boldsymbol{A\beta}} - \boldsymbol{\xi}$.

Part (b) follows from the fact that $\widehat{\boldsymbol{A\beta}}$ and $(\boldsymbol{I} - \boldsymbol{P}_X)\boldsymbol{y}$ are BLUEs and LZFs in $\mathcal{M}$, respectively.

In order to prove part (c) by contradiction, let $\boldsymbol{l}_1'\boldsymbol{y} + \boldsymbol{l}_2'\boldsymbol{\xi}$ be an LZF of $\mathcal{M}_R$ which is uncorrelated with both $\widehat{\boldsymbol{A\beta}} - \boldsymbol{\xi}$ and $(\boldsymbol{I} - \boldsymbol{P}_X)\boldsymbol{y}$. The condition $Cov((\boldsymbol{I} - \boldsymbol{P}_X)\boldsymbol{y}, (\boldsymbol{l}_1'\boldsymbol{y} + \boldsymbol{l}_2'\boldsymbol{\xi})) = \boldsymbol{0}$ is equivalent to $\boldsymbol{V}\boldsymbol{l}_1 = \boldsymbol{X}\boldsymbol{m}$ for some vector $\boldsymbol{m}$. In view of this, the condition $Cov((\widehat{\boldsymbol{A\beta}} - \boldsymbol{\xi}), (\boldsymbol{l}_1'\boldsymbol{y} + \boldsymbol{l}_2'\boldsymbol{\xi})) = \boldsymbol{0}$ is equivalent to

$$\boldsymbol{A}\boldsymbol{X}^{-}[\boldsymbol{V} - \boldsymbol{V}(\boldsymbol{I} - \boldsymbol{P}_X)\{(\boldsymbol{I} - \boldsymbol{P}_X)\boldsymbol{V}(\boldsymbol{I} - \boldsymbol{P}_X)\}^{-}(\boldsymbol{I} - \boldsymbol{P}_X)\boldsymbol{V}]\boldsymbol{l}_1 = \boldsymbol{A}\boldsymbol{m} = \boldsymbol{0}.$$

Suppose $\boldsymbol{k}_1'\boldsymbol{y} + \boldsymbol{k}_2'\boldsymbol{\xi}$ is another LZF of $\mathcal{M}_R$, and assume without loss of generality that $\boldsymbol{X}'\boldsymbol{k}_1 + \boldsymbol{A}'\boldsymbol{k}_2 = \boldsymbol{0}$ (see Proposition 7.3). It follows that

$$Cov((\boldsymbol{l}_1'\boldsymbol{y} + \boldsymbol{l}_2'\boldsymbol{\xi}), (\boldsymbol{k}_1'\boldsymbol{y} + \boldsymbol{k}_2'\boldsymbol{\xi})) = \boldsymbol{l}_1'\boldsymbol{V}\boldsymbol{k}_1 = \boldsymbol{m}'\boldsymbol{X}'\boldsymbol{k}_1 + \boldsymbol{m}'\boldsymbol{A}'\boldsymbol{k}_2 = \boldsymbol{0}.$$

Since the $\boldsymbol{l}_1'\boldsymbol{y} + \boldsymbol{l}_2'\boldsymbol{\xi}$ is uncorrelated with *every* LZF of $\mathcal{M}_2$, it must be uncorrelated with itself, i.e. it must be identically zero with probability one. □

Proposition 7.41 establishes that the elements of $\boldsymbol{e}$ and $\boldsymbol{A}\widehat{\boldsymbol{\beta}} - \boldsymbol{\xi}$ constitute a basis set of the LZFs of $\mathcal{M}_R$. Denoting the SSE in this model by R_H^2, we have from Remark 3.48

$$\begin{aligned}
R_H^2 &= \sigma^2 \begin{pmatrix} \boldsymbol{e} \\ \boldsymbol{A}\widehat{\boldsymbol{\beta}} - \boldsymbol{\xi} \end{pmatrix}' \left[D \begin{pmatrix} \boldsymbol{e} \\ \boldsymbol{A}\widehat{\boldsymbol{\beta}} - \boldsymbol{\xi} \end{pmatrix} \right]^{-} \begin{pmatrix} \boldsymbol{e} \\ \boldsymbol{A}\widehat{\boldsymbol{\beta}} - \boldsymbol{\xi} \end{pmatrix} \\
&= \sigma^2 \begin{pmatrix} \boldsymbol{e} \\ \boldsymbol{A}\widehat{\boldsymbol{\beta}} - \boldsymbol{\xi} \end{pmatrix}' \begin{pmatrix} D(\boldsymbol{e}) & \boldsymbol{0} \\ \boldsymbol{0} & D(\boldsymbol{A}\widehat{\boldsymbol{\beta}} - \boldsymbol{\xi}) \end{pmatrix}^{-} \begin{pmatrix} \boldsymbol{e} \\ \boldsymbol{A}\widehat{\boldsymbol{\beta}} - \boldsymbol{\xi} \end{pmatrix} \\
&= \sigma^2 \begin{pmatrix} \boldsymbol{e} \\ \boldsymbol{A}\widehat{\boldsymbol{\beta}} - \boldsymbol{\xi} \end{pmatrix}' \begin{pmatrix} [D(\boldsymbol{e})]^{-} & \boldsymbol{0} \\ \boldsymbol{0} & [D(\boldsymbol{A}\widehat{\boldsymbol{\beta}} - \boldsymbol{\xi})]^{-} \end{pmatrix} \begin{pmatrix} \boldsymbol{e} \\ \boldsymbol{A}\widehat{\boldsymbol{\beta}} - \boldsymbol{\xi} \end{pmatrix} \\
&= R_0^2 + (\boldsymbol{A}\widehat{\boldsymbol{\beta}} - \boldsymbol{\xi})'[\sigma^{-2}D(\boldsymbol{A}\widehat{\boldsymbol{\beta}} - \boldsymbol{\xi})]^{-}(\boldsymbol{A}\widehat{\boldsymbol{\beta}} - \boldsymbol{\xi}), \qquad (7.17)
\end{aligned}$$

which is a restatement of Proposition 4.19 in the general case. The number of *additional* LZFs in an uncorrelated basis of $\mathcal{M}_R$ is $\rho(D(\boldsymbol{A}\widehat{\boldsymbol{\beta}} - \boldsymbol{\xi}))$.

The computations for the 'equivalent' model described above can also be performed by using any one of the methods described in Section 7.7. Baksalary and Pordzik (1989) develop an inverse partitioned matrix method specifically for models with linear restrictions, where the restrictions are explicitly split into completely testable and completely untestable parts.

Remark 7.42. Rao (1978) shows that when $\boldsymbol{V}$ is singular, there is no matrix $\boldsymbol{M}$ such that the minimized value of $(\boldsymbol{y} - \boldsymbol{X}\boldsymbol{\beta})'\boldsymbol{M}(\boldsymbol{y} - \boldsymbol{X}\boldsymbol{\beta})$ subject to a linear restriction produces the appropriate R_H^2 for *all* completely testable restrictions. This result exposes an important limitation of the WLSE approach to analysing the linear model in the singular case (see Sections 7.6 and 7.7.1). □

7.9.2 *Improved estimation through restrictions*

Part (c) of Proposition 7.40 shows that the dispersion of the BLUE of $\boldsymbol{X\beta}$ is generally reduced when a linear restriction is introduced. Sometimes a linear restriction is imposed on the parameters, without definite knowledge about its validity, with the purpose of reducing dispersion. For example, some elements of $\boldsymbol{\beta}$ may be set equal to zero, which amounts to using a subset model, considered in Section 5.1. In such a case, there is a possibility that the restriction may result in a bias in the estimator of $\boldsymbol{X\beta}$. We now examine, in the spirit of Section 5.1.1, the trade-off between the increased bias and the reduced dispersion of the 'restricted' BLUE under the unrestricted model $\mathcal{M}$, by comparing the mean squared error matrices of the two estimators.

We begin with the assumption that the restriction $\boldsymbol{A\beta} = \boldsymbol{\xi}$ is testable (if it is not, we can work with the testable part of it). It follows from Proposition 7.41 that the BLUE of $\boldsymbol{X\beta}$ under the restriction can be written as

$$\boldsymbol{X}\widehat{\boldsymbol{\beta}}_R = \boldsymbol{X}\widehat{\boldsymbol{\beta}} - \boldsymbol{C}\boldsymbol{D}^{-}(\boldsymbol{A}\widehat{\boldsymbol{\beta}} - \boldsymbol{\xi}),$$

where $\boldsymbol{X}\widehat{\boldsymbol{\beta}}$ is the unrestricted BLUE of $\boldsymbol{X\beta}$, $\boldsymbol{A}\widehat{\boldsymbol{\beta}}$ is the unrestricted BLUE of $\boldsymbol{A\beta}$, $\boldsymbol{C} = Cov(\boldsymbol{X}\widehat{\boldsymbol{\beta}}, \boldsymbol{A}\widehat{\boldsymbol{\beta}})$ and $\boldsymbol{D} = D(\boldsymbol{A}\widehat{\boldsymbol{\beta}})$. We also assume that $\boldsymbol{D}$ is nonsingular. Consequently the bias and the dispersion of the restricted BLUE are:

$$\begin{aligned} E(\boldsymbol{X}\widehat{\boldsymbol{\beta}}_R) - \boldsymbol{X\beta} &= -\boldsymbol{C}\boldsymbol{D}^{-1}(\boldsymbol{A\beta} - \boldsymbol{\xi}), \\ D(\boldsymbol{X}\widehat{\boldsymbol{\beta}}_R) &= D(\boldsymbol{X}\widehat{\boldsymbol{\beta}}) - \boldsymbol{C}\boldsymbol{D}^{-1}\boldsymbol{C}'. \end{aligned}$$

Let us denote the mean squared error matrix of a vector estimator by $MSE(\cdot)$. We have

$$\begin{aligned} &MSE(\boldsymbol{X}\widehat{\boldsymbol{\beta}}) - MSE(\boldsymbol{X}\widehat{\boldsymbol{\beta}}_R) \\ &= D(\boldsymbol{X}\widehat{\boldsymbol{\beta}}) - D(\boldsymbol{X}\widehat{\boldsymbol{\beta}}_R) - (E(\boldsymbol{X}\widehat{\boldsymbol{\beta}}_R) - \boldsymbol{X\beta})(E(\boldsymbol{X}\widehat{\boldsymbol{\beta}}_R) - \boldsymbol{X\beta})' \\ &= \boldsymbol{C}\boldsymbol{D}^{-1}\boldsymbol{C}' - \boldsymbol{C}\boldsymbol{D}^{-1}(\boldsymbol{A\beta} - \boldsymbol{\xi})(\boldsymbol{A\beta} - \boldsymbol{\xi})'\boldsymbol{D}^{-1}\boldsymbol{C}' \\ &= \boldsymbol{C}\boldsymbol{D}^{-1}[\boldsymbol{D} - (\boldsymbol{A\beta} - \boldsymbol{\xi})(\boldsymbol{A\beta} - \boldsymbol{\xi})']\boldsymbol{D}^{-1}\boldsymbol{C}'. \end{aligned} \tag{7.18}$$

A necessary and sufficient condition for $MSE(\boldsymbol{X}\widehat{\boldsymbol{\beta}}_R) \leq MSE(\boldsymbol{X}\widehat{\boldsymbol{\beta}})$ in the sense of the Löwner partial order is that the matrix $\boldsymbol{D} - (\boldsymbol{A\beta} - \boldsymbol{\xi})(\boldsymbol{A\beta} - \boldsymbol{\xi})'$ is nonnegative definite. The latter condition is equivalent to the scalar inequality (Exercise 7.16)

$$(\boldsymbol{A\beta} - \boldsymbol{\xi})'\boldsymbol{D}^{-1}(\boldsymbol{A\beta} - \boldsymbol{\xi}) \leq 1. \tag{7.19}$$

If the above condition holds, then for any estimable function with nonsingular dispersion the restricted 'BLUE' will have smaller MSE matrix. This result implies that imposing a restriction may be a good idea when $\boldsymbol{\xi}$ is close to the true value of $\boldsymbol{A\beta}$ (i.e. the restriction is almost true) or when $\boldsymbol{D}$ is large (i.e. estimation error of $\boldsymbol{A}\widehat{\boldsymbol{\beta}}$ is large).

See Rao and Toutenburg (1999) for other criteria for comparing the estimators, and for the implications of misspecified linear restrictions.

7.9.3 *Stochastic restrictions**

Suppose the linear model $(\boldsymbol{y}, \boldsymbol{X\beta}, \sigma^2\boldsymbol{V})$ is subject to a somewhat uncertain linear restriction. The restriction is

$$\boldsymbol{A\beta} = \boldsymbol{\xi} + \boldsymbol{\delta}, \tag{7.20}$$

where $\boldsymbol{A}$ and $\boldsymbol{\xi}$ are known, $\boldsymbol{\delta}$ is a random vector with zero mean and dispersion $\tau^2\boldsymbol{W}$, and $\boldsymbol{\delta}$ is uncorrelated with $\boldsymbol{y}$. The stochastic restriction may have resulted from prior information or an independent study. In order that the restrictions are consistent, we must have $\boldsymbol{\xi} \in \mathcal{C}(\boldsymbol{A} : \boldsymbol{W})$. The case $\boldsymbol{W} = \boldsymbol{0}$ corresponds to a deterministic restriction, which was considered earlier.

We can treat $\boldsymbol{\xi}$ as a set of additional observations, and consider the model

$$\begin{pmatrix}\boldsymbol{y}\\ \boldsymbol{\xi}\end{pmatrix} = \begin{pmatrix}\boldsymbol{X}\\ \boldsymbol{A}\end{pmatrix}\boldsymbol{\beta} + \begin{pmatrix}\boldsymbol{\varepsilon}\\ -\boldsymbol{\delta}\end{pmatrix}; \quad E\begin{pmatrix}\boldsymbol{\varepsilon}\\ -\boldsymbol{\delta}\end{pmatrix} = \boldsymbol{0}, \quad D\begin{pmatrix}\boldsymbol{\varepsilon}\\ -\boldsymbol{\delta}\end{pmatrix} = \begin{pmatrix}\sigma^2\boldsymbol{V} & \boldsymbol{0}\\ \boldsymbol{0} & \tau^2\boldsymbol{W}\end{pmatrix}.$$

If $\tau^2 = \sigma^2$, this model fits into the framework of this chapter. Otherwise, the methods outlined in Section 8.3 may be used.

We shall now assume that $\tau^2 = \sigma^2$ and $\mathcal{C}(\boldsymbol{A}') \subseteq \mathcal{C}(\boldsymbol{X}')$, and examine the effect of these restrictions on the BLUE and its dispersion.

Proposition 7.43. *Suppose the unrestricted and restricted models, $\mathcal{M}$ and $\mathcal{M}_R$, respectively, are defined as*

$$\mathcal{M} = (\boldsymbol{y}, \boldsymbol{X\beta}, \sigma^2\boldsymbol{V}); \quad \mathcal{M}_R = \left(\begin{pmatrix}\boldsymbol{y}\\ \boldsymbol{\xi}\end{pmatrix}, \begin{pmatrix}\boldsymbol{X}\\ \boldsymbol{A}\end{pmatrix}\boldsymbol{\beta}, \sigma^2\begin{pmatrix}\boldsymbol{V} & \boldsymbol{0}\\ \boldsymbol{0} & \boldsymbol{W}\end{pmatrix}\right),$$

such that $\mathcal{C}(\boldsymbol{A}') \subseteq \mathcal{C}(\boldsymbol{X}')$. Let $\boldsymbol{X}\widehat{\boldsymbol{\beta}}$ and $\boldsymbol{X}\widehat{\boldsymbol{\beta}}_R$ be the BLUEs of $\boldsymbol{X\beta}$ under the models $\mathcal{M}$ and $\mathcal{M}_R$, respectively, and $\widehat{\boldsymbol{\beta}}$ be as defined in (7.2).

(a) All estimable LPFs of $\mathcal{M}$ are estimable under $\mathcal{M}_R$.
(b) All LZFs of $\mathcal{M}$ are LZFs under $\mathcal{M}_R$.
(c) $\boldsymbol{A}\widehat{\boldsymbol{\beta}} - \boldsymbol{\xi}$ is a vector of LZFs under the model $\mathcal{M}_R$.

(d) $A\widehat{\beta} - \xi$ *is uncorrelated with* $(I - P_X)y$.

(e) *There is no nontrivial LZF of* $\mathcal{M}_R$ *which is uncorrelated with* $A\widehat{\beta} - \xi$ *and* $(I - P_X)y$.

(f) *The BLUEs of* $X\beta$ *under the two models are related as follows:*

$$X\widehat{\beta}_R = X\widehat{\beta} - D(X\widehat{\beta})(AX^-)'[D(A\widehat{\beta}) + \sigma^2 W]^-(A\widehat{\beta} - \xi),$$

where $D(X\widehat{\beta})$ *is as given in (7.4), and*

$$D(A\widehat{\beta}) = AX^- D(X\widehat{\beta})(AX^-)'.$$

(g) *The respective dispersions of the BLUEs of* $X\beta$ *under the two models are related as follows:*

$$\begin{aligned} D(X\widehat{\beta}_R) &= D(X\widehat{\beta}) \\ &\quad - D(X\widehat{\beta})(AX^-)'[D(A\widehat{\beta}) + \sigma^2 W]^- AX^- D(X\widehat{\beta}). \end{aligned}$$

(h) *The error sum of squares under* $\mathcal{M}_R$ *is given by*

$$R_{0R}^2 = R_0^2 + (A\widehat{\beta} - \xi)'[\sigma^{-2} D(A\widehat{\beta}) + W]^-(A\widehat{\beta} - \xi),$$

and the associated number of degrees of freedom is $\rho(V : X) - \rho(X) + \rho(D(A\widehat{\beta}) + \sigma^2 W)$.

Proof. Proofs of parts (a) and (b) are similar to the proofs of Proposition 7.40(a) and (b) (where W was the null matrix).

Parts (c), (d) and (e) are proved along the lines of the proof of Proposition 7.41. Specifically for part (e), let $l_1'y + l_2'\xi$ be an LZF of $\mathcal{M}_R$ which is uncorrelated with $A\widehat{\beta} - \xi$ and $(I - P_X)y$. These two conditions are equivalent to $Vl_1 = Xm$ and $Wl_2 = Am$ for some vector m. Let $k_1'y + k_2'\xi$ be another LZF of $\mathcal{M}_R$, and assume without loss of generality that $X'k_1 + A'k_2 = 0$ (see Proposition 7.3). Then

$$\begin{aligned} Cov(l_1'y + l_2'\xi, k_1'y + k_2'\xi) &= \sigma^2[k_1'Vl_1 + k_2'Wl_2] \\ &= \sigma^2(k_1'X + k_2'A)m = 0. \end{aligned}$$

It follows that $l_1'y + l_2'\xi$ is uncorrelated with *every* LZF of $\mathcal{M}_2$, and therefore it must be identically zero.

Parts (b)–(e) imply that the uncorrelated vectors $(I - P_X)y$ and $A\widehat{\beta} - \xi$ together constitute a basis set of LZFs of $\mathcal{M}_R$. Part (f) follows immediately via the principle of decorrelation (Proposition 2.28).

Part (g) follows from part (f) by expressing $X\widehat{\beta}$ as the sum of $X\widehat{\beta}_R$ and an uncorrelated term.

Part (h) is an immediate consequence of Remark 3.48 and the description of a basis set of LZFs of $\mathcal{M}_R$ given above. □

Note that all the above results are generalizations of the case of non-stochastic restrictions ($\boldsymbol{W} = \boldsymbol{0}$). When $\boldsymbol{X}$ and $\boldsymbol{V}$ have full column rank and $\boldsymbol{A}$ has full row rank, the expression for the restricted BLUE simplifies to

$$\boldsymbol{X}\widehat{\boldsymbol{\beta}}_R = \boldsymbol{X}\widehat{\boldsymbol{\beta}} - (\boldsymbol{X}'\boldsymbol{V}^{-1}\boldsymbol{X})^{-1}\boldsymbol{A}'[\boldsymbol{A}(\boldsymbol{X}'\boldsymbol{V}^{-1}\boldsymbol{X})^{-1}\boldsymbol{A}' + \boldsymbol{W}]^{-1}(\boldsymbol{A}\widehat{\boldsymbol{\beta}} - \boldsymbol{\xi}).$$

7.9.4 *Inequality constraints**

Deterministic constraints of the form $\boldsymbol{A\beta} \leq \boldsymbol{\xi}$ (where the vector inequality represents inequality of the corresponding components) are quite common in econometric literature. For instance, some components of $\boldsymbol{\beta}$ may be known to be nonnegative.

Inequality constraints make it difficult to work with LUEs, because these estimators may not satisfy the constraints. Judge and Takayama (1966) consider the least squares estimator under inequality constraints, which coincides with the MLE in the case of independent and normally distributed errors. This led them to a quadratic programming problem which can be solved by a version of the simplex algorithm. Liew (1976) presents another solution to this problem, and shows how the dispersion matrix of the estimator can be computed. Werner (1990) presents an expression of the estimator that minimizes $(\boldsymbol{y} - \boldsymbol{X\beta})'\boldsymbol{V}^{-}(\boldsymbol{y} - \boldsymbol{X\beta})$ subject to a set of inequality constraints in terms of various projectors and generalized inverses, assuming that $\boldsymbol{V}$ is nonsingular. Werner and Yapar (1996) extend this geometric approach to the case of possibly singular $\boldsymbol{V}$. The estimator is nonlinear and does not have a neat form except in some special cases.

The inequality constrained MLE of $\boldsymbol{X\beta}$ in the normal case with possibly singular error dispersion matrix can be described as follows. Suppose there are m inequality constraints, involving estimable LPFs only. There are 2^m possible subsets of these inequalities which can be converted to 'equality constraints'. For a given set of equality constraints, we can compute the BLUE of $\boldsymbol{X\beta}$ subject to these linear restrictions as well as the consistency condition $\boldsymbol{y} - \boldsymbol{X\beta} \in \mathcal{C}(\boldsymbol{V})$. Some of these 2^m 'BLUE's satisfy all the inequalities. The desired solution is given by that 'BLUE' which corresponds to the smallest value of $(\boldsymbol{y} - \boldsymbol{X\beta})'\boldsymbol{V}^{-}(\boldsymbol{y} - \boldsymbol{X\beta})$ and satisfies all the inequalities.

The next example demonstrates how a simple form of the inequality constrained least squares estimator is available in some special cases.

Example 7.44. Consider the model $(\boldsymbol{y}, \boldsymbol{X\beta}, \sigma^2\boldsymbol{V})$ (with $\boldsymbol{V}$ possibly singular) subject to the constraint $\beta_1 \leq b$. Assume that β_1 is estimable, and that the singularity of $\boldsymbol{V}$ does not make β_1 equal to a constant with probability 1. The appropriate minimization problem is

$$\min_{\substack{\boldsymbol{\beta}:\ \beta_1 \le b \\ (\boldsymbol{y}-\boldsymbol{X\beta}) \in \mathcal{C}(\boldsymbol{V})}} (\boldsymbol{y}-\boldsymbol{X\beta})'\boldsymbol{V}^-(\boldsymbol{y}-\boldsymbol{X\beta}).$$

Partition $\boldsymbol{X}$ and $\boldsymbol{\beta}$ as $(\boldsymbol{x}_1 : \boldsymbol{X}_2)$ and $(\beta_1 : \boldsymbol{\beta}_2')'$, respectively. Let $\boldsymbol{z}(\beta_1) = \boldsymbol{y} - \boldsymbol{x}_1\beta_1$. If we ignore the inequality constraint, then the above problem can be solved by

(a) minimizing $(\boldsymbol{z}(\beta_1)-\boldsymbol{X}_2\boldsymbol{\beta}_2)'\boldsymbol{V}^-(\boldsymbol{z}(\beta_1)-\boldsymbol{X}_2\boldsymbol{\beta}_2)$ subject to the constraint $(\boldsymbol{z}(\beta_1)-\boldsymbol{X}_2\boldsymbol{\beta}_2) \in \mathcal{C}(\boldsymbol{V})$ for every feasible value of β_1, and then
(b) minimizing the resulting function with respect to β_1.

The solution to the first problem is given by the BLUE of $\boldsymbol{X}_2\boldsymbol{\beta}_2$ in the model $(\boldsymbol{z}(\beta_1), \boldsymbol{X}_2\boldsymbol{\beta}_2, \sigma^2\boldsymbol{V})$. An expression for this BLUE can be obtained by using (7.1). Therefore, the function of β_1 which has to be minimized with respect to β_1 in the second step is quadratic in β_1. [It is easy to see that this 'function' is free of β_1 whenever β_1 is not estimable.] The constraint $\beta_1 \le b$ can be incorporated in the second step. The constraint $(\boldsymbol{y}-\boldsymbol{X\beta}) \in \mathcal{C}(\boldsymbol{V})$ is automatically satisfied because of the constraint $(\boldsymbol{z}(\beta_1)-\boldsymbol{X}_2\boldsymbol{\beta}_2) \in \mathcal{C}(\boldsymbol{V})$ used in the first step. If the minimizer of the quadratic function in the second step automatically satisfies the constraint $\beta_1 \le b$, then the overall solution with the inequality constraint, coincides with the unconstrained solution. Otherwise, the quadratic function in β_1 has the minimum feasible value at $\beta_1 = b$ and the remaining part of the solution is given by the BLUE of $\boldsymbol{X}_2\boldsymbol{\beta}_2$ in the model $(\boldsymbol{z}(\beta_1), \boldsymbol{X}_2\boldsymbol{\beta}_2, \sigma^2\boldsymbol{V})$. Thus, the solution to the original problem is

$$\boldsymbol{X}\widehat{\boldsymbol{\beta}}_{constrained} = \begin{cases} \text{BLUE of } \boldsymbol{X\beta} \text{ in } (\boldsymbol{y}, \boldsymbol{X\beta}, \sigma^2\boldsymbol{V}), & \text{if } \widehat{\beta}_1 \le b, \\ \\ \text{BLUE of } \boldsymbol{X\beta} \text{ in } (\boldsymbol{y}, \boldsymbol{X\beta}, \sigma^2\boldsymbol{V}) & \\ \text{subject to } \beta_1 = b, & \text{otherwise.} \end{cases}$$

The estimator is obviously not linear in $\boldsymbol{y}$. □

The simple estimator in the above example is sometimes referred to as the two-step estimator. The result can be extended to an inequality constraint involving any single estimable LPF (Exercise 7.18). Extension to *multiple* inequality constraints is similar (see Werner, 1990). Nevertheless, data analysts working with prior knowledge of the signs of some coefficients are sometimes tempted to conduct a two-step analysis where *all* the estimated coefficients with wrong sign in the first step are constrained to be zero in the second step. Lovell (1970) shows that this procedure (in the special case $\boldsymbol{V} = \boldsymbol{I}$) can lead to bias and inefficiency. A limited simulation study by Liew (1976) indicates that even the optimally constrained estimators generally tend to be biased.

7.10 Model with nuisance parameters

Consider the model $\mathcal{M} = (\boldsymbol{y}, \boldsymbol{X\beta}, \sigma^2\boldsymbol{V})$ where $\boldsymbol{X} = (\boldsymbol{X}_1 : \boldsymbol{X}_2)$ and $\boldsymbol{\beta} = (\boldsymbol{\beta}_1' : \boldsymbol{\beta}_2')'$ so that $\boldsymbol{X\beta} = \boldsymbol{X}_1\boldsymbol{\beta}_1 + \boldsymbol{X}_2\boldsymbol{\beta}_2$. If one is interested only in the estimable linear functions of $\boldsymbol{\beta}_1$, then $\boldsymbol{\beta}_2$ is a vector of nuisance parameters. Proposition 3.53 regarding the estimability of such functions still holds, although with a slightly modified proof (Exercise 7.19). Carrying the idea of this proposition further, we can pre-multiply the model equation by $(\boldsymbol{I}-\boldsymbol{P}_{X_2})$, which leads us to the 'reduced' model $\mathcal{M}^* = ((\boldsymbol{I}-\boldsymbol{P}_{X_2})\boldsymbol{y}, (\boldsymbol{I}-\boldsymbol{P}_{X_2})\boldsymbol{X}_1\boldsymbol{\beta}_1, \sigma^2(\boldsymbol{I}-\boldsymbol{P}_{X_2})\boldsymbol{V}(\boldsymbol{I}-\boldsymbol{P}_{X_2}))$. This model is free of the nuisance parameters. The following proposition proves that this model is equivalent to $\mathcal{M}$ for the purpose of inference.

Proposition 7.45. *Let the models $\mathcal{M}$ and $\mathcal{M}^*$ be as defined above. Then*

(a) The set of LZFs in $\mathcal{M}^*$ coincides with that in $\mathcal{M}$.
(b) $\boldsymbol{p}'\boldsymbol{\beta}_1$ is estimable in $\mathcal{M}^*$ if and only if it is estimable in $\mathcal{M}$.
(c) The set of BLUEs in $\mathcal{M}^*$ coincides with the set of BLUEs of estimable linear functions of $\boldsymbol{\beta}_1$ in $\mathcal{M}$.
(d) The dispersion of $(\boldsymbol{I}-\boldsymbol{P}_{X_2})\boldsymbol{X}_1\boldsymbol{\beta}_1$ under the models $\mathcal{M}^*$ and $\mathcal{M}$ are identical.
(e) The SSE under the models $\mathcal{M}^*$ and $\mathcal{M}$ are identical.
(f) The error degrees of freedom under the models $\mathcal{M}^*$ and $\mathcal{M}$ are identical.

Proof. A vector of a basis set of LZFs of $\mathcal{M}^*$ is

$$(\boldsymbol{I}-\boldsymbol{P}_{(I-P_{X_2})X_1})(\boldsymbol{I}-\boldsymbol{P}_{X_2})\boldsymbol{y} = (\boldsymbol{I}-\boldsymbol{P}_X+\boldsymbol{P}_{X_2})(\boldsymbol{I}-\boldsymbol{P}_{X_2})\boldsymbol{y} = (\boldsymbol{I}-\boldsymbol{P}_X)\boldsymbol{y},$$

by virtue of the result of Proposition A.14(b). This proves part (a).

Part (b) follows from the estimability condition in $\mathcal{M}$, $(\boldsymbol{p}' : \boldsymbol{0})' \in \mathcal{C}(\boldsymbol{X}_1 : \boldsymbol{X}_2)'$, which was shown in Proposition 3.53 to be equivalent to $\boldsymbol{p} \in \mathcal{C}(\boldsymbol{X}_1'(\boldsymbol{I}-\boldsymbol{P}_{X_2}))$.

Let $\boldsymbol{l}'\boldsymbol{y}$ be the BLUE of an estimable function of $\boldsymbol{\beta}_1$ in $\mathcal{M}$. The unbiasedness condition requires that there should be a vector $\boldsymbol{k}$ such that

$\boldsymbol{l}'\boldsymbol{y} = \boldsymbol{k}'\boldsymbol{y}$ almost surely and $\boldsymbol{X}_2'\boldsymbol{k} = \boldsymbol{0}$ or $\boldsymbol{k}'\boldsymbol{y} = \boldsymbol{k}'(\boldsymbol{I} - \boldsymbol{P}_{X_2})\boldsymbol{y}$. Therefore, $\boldsymbol{l}'\boldsymbol{y}$ or $\boldsymbol{k}'\boldsymbol{y}$ is an unbiased estimator of the same estimable function in $\mathcal{M}$ and $\mathcal{M}^*$. Since it is uncorrelated with the LZF's under either model it must be the BLUE. Similarly, any BLUE in $\mathcal{M}^*$ is also the BLUE of its expectation (which must be a function of $\boldsymbol{\beta}_1$ alone) in $\mathcal{M}$. This proves part (c).

Part (d) can be proved using (7.4) and the fact that $(\boldsymbol{I}-\boldsymbol{P}_{(I-P_{X_2})X_1})(\boldsymbol{I}-\boldsymbol{P}_{X_2})\boldsymbol{V} = (\boldsymbol{I} - \boldsymbol{P}_X)\boldsymbol{V}$, which can be proved along the lines of the proof of part (a).

Part (e) follows from part (a), the expression (7.7), and the fact that $D((\boldsymbol{I} - \boldsymbol{P}_X)\boldsymbol{y}) = \sigma^2(\boldsymbol{I} - \boldsymbol{P}_X)\boldsymbol{V}(\boldsymbol{I} - \boldsymbol{P}_X)$ even under $\mathcal{M}^*$.

To prove part (f), observe that

$$\begin{aligned}
&\rho((\boldsymbol{I} - \boldsymbol{P}_{X_2})\boldsymbol{V}(\boldsymbol{I} - \boldsymbol{P}_{X_2}) : (\boldsymbol{I} - \boldsymbol{P}_{X_2})\boldsymbol{X}_1) - \rho((\boldsymbol{I} - \boldsymbol{P}_{X_2})\boldsymbol{X}_1)\\
&= \rho((\boldsymbol{I} - \boldsymbol{P}_{X_2})(\boldsymbol{V} : \boldsymbol{X}_1) - \rho((\boldsymbol{I} - \boldsymbol{P}_{X_2})\boldsymbol{X}_1)\\
&= [\rho(\boldsymbol{V} : \boldsymbol{X}_1 : \boldsymbol{X}_2) - \rho(\boldsymbol{X}_2)] - [\rho(\boldsymbol{X}_1 : \boldsymbol{X}_2) - \rho(\boldsymbol{X}_2)].
\end{aligned}$$

The last expression simplifies to $\rho(\boldsymbol{V} : \boldsymbol{X})-\rho(\boldsymbol{X})$, which is the error degrees of freedom for $\mathcal{M}$. □

The last two parts of the above proposition imply that even the usual unbiased estimator of σ^2 under the reduced model is identical to that under the original model. We can use the methodology developed in the earlier sections to analyse the reduced model which eliminates the nuisance parameters.

Remark 7.46. In the special case of the homoscedastic linear model ($\boldsymbol{V} = \boldsymbol{I}$), the BLUE of $(\boldsymbol{I} - \boldsymbol{P}_{X_2})\boldsymbol{X}_1\boldsymbol{\beta}_1$ can be obtained from (7.1) by substituting $\boldsymbol{I} - \boldsymbol{P}_{X_2}$ for $\boldsymbol{V}$, $(\boldsymbol{I} - \boldsymbol{P}_{X_2})\boldsymbol{X}_1$ for $\boldsymbol{X}$ and $(\boldsymbol{I} - \boldsymbol{P}_{X_2})\boldsymbol{y}$ for $\boldsymbol{y}$. The expression simplifies to

$$(\boldsymbol{I} - \boldsymbol{P}_{X_2})\boldsymbol{X}_1\widehat{\boldsymbol{\beta}}_1 = \boldsymbol{P}_{(I-P_{X_2})X_1}\boldsymbol{y}.$$

It follows that a 'substitution' estimator of $\boldsymbol{\beta}_1$ that produces BLUEs of estimable functions of $\boldsymbol{\beta}_1$ must satisfy the equation

$$\begin{aligned}
\boldsymbol{X}_1'(\boldsymbol{I}-\boldsymbol{P}_{X_2})\boldsymbol{X}_1\boldsymbol{\beta}_1 &= \boldsymbol{X}_1'\boldsymbol{P}_{(I-P_{X_2})X_1}\boldsymbol{y}\\
&= \boldsymbol{X}_1'(\boldsymbol{I}-\boldsymbol{P}_{X_2})\boldsymbol{X}_1[\boldsymbol{X}_1'(\boldsymbol{I}-\boldsymbol{P}_{X_2})\boldsymbol{X}_1]^-\boldsymbol{X}_1'(\boldsymbol{I}-\boldsymbol{P}_{X_2})\boldsymbol{y}\\
&= \boldsymbol{X}_1'(\boldsymbol{I}-\boldsymbol{P}_{X_2})\boldsymbol{y}.
\end{aligned}$$

The equation $\boldsymbol{X}_1'(\boldsymbol{I} - \boldsymbol{P}_{X_2})\boldsymbol{X}_1\boldsymbol{\beta}_1 = \boldsymbol{X}_1'(\boldsymbol{I} - \boldsymbol{P}_{X_2})\boldsymbol{y}$ is called the *reduced normal equation* for $\boldsymbol{\beta}_1$. It can also be verified that

$$D((\boldsymbol{I} - \boldsymbol{P}_{X_2})\boldsymbol{X}_1\widehat{\boldsymbol{\beta}}_1) = \sigma^2\boldsymbol{P}_{(I-P_{X_2})X_1},$$

which follows from (7.4) by appropriate substitution. Likewise, the usual unbiased estimator of σ^2, obtained from (7.6) and (7.7), are

$$\widehat{\sigma^2} = \frac{\text{SSE}}{\rho(\boldsymbol{V} : \boldsymbol{X}) - \rho(\boldsymbol{X})} = \frac{\|(\boldsymbol{I} - \boldsymbol{P}_{(I-P_{X_2})X_1})(\boldsymbol{I} - \boldsymbol{P}_{X_2})\boldsymbol{y}\|^2}{\rho(\boldsymbol{I} - \boldsymbol{P}_{X_2}) - \rho((\boldsymbol{I} - \boldsymbol{P}_{X_2})\boldsymbol{X}_1)}. \qquad \square$$

There have been attempts to obtain simpler reduced models that would also produce the appropriate results. Two such models are:

$$\mathcal{M}_1^* = ((\boldsymbol{I} - \boldsymbol{P}_{X_2})\boldsymbol{y}, (\boldsymbol{I} - \boldsymbol{P}_{X_2})\boldsymbol{X}_1\boldsymbol{\beta}_1, \sigma^2\boldsymbol{V})$$
$$\mathcal{M}_2^* = (\boldsymbol{y}, (\boldsymbol{I} - \boldsymbol{P}_{X_2})\boldsymbol{X}_1\boldsymbol{\beta}_1, \sigma^2\boldsymbol{V}).$$

Bhimasankaram and SahaRay (1996) point out that $\mathcal{M}_1^*$ cannot be a valid model in general, because the dispersion of $(\boldsymbol{I} - \boldsymbol{P}_{X_2})\boldsymbol{y}$ must be $(\boldsymbol{I} - \boldsymbol{P}_{X_2})\boldsymbol{V}(\boldsymbol{I} - \boldsymbol{P}_{X_2})$. In spite of this observation, there has been a flurry of research work on this model. The model $\mathcal{M}_2^*$ can only be meaningful if the response satisfies the consistency condition $\boldsymbol{y} \in \mathcal{C}(\boldsymbol{V} : (\boldsymbol{I} - \boldsymbol{P}_{X_2})\boldsymbol{X}_1)$, which is stronger than the consistency condition of the original model, $\boldsymbol{y} \in \mathcal{C}(\boldsymbol{V} : \boldsymbol{X})$. Bhimasankaram and SahaRay (1996) show that when $\mathcal{C}(\boldsymbol{V}\boldsymbol{X}_2) \subseteq \mathcal{C}(\boldsymbol{X}_2)$ and $\boldsymbol{V}$ is nonsingular, $\mathcal{M}_2^*$ indeed produces the right BLUE of $(\boldsymbol{I} - \boldsymbol{P}_{X_2})\boldsymbol{X}_1\boldsymbol{\beta}_1$ and the right dispersion matrix, but the wrong estimator of σ^2. The condition of nonsingularity of $\boldsymbol{V}$ is relaxed to some extent by Puntanen (1997).

7.11 Tests of hypotheses

Suppose $\boldsymbol{y} \sim N(\boldsymbol{X\beta}, \sigma^2\boldsymbol{V})$. If the hypothesis $\mathcal{H}_0 : \boldsymbol{A\beta} = \boldsymbol{\xi}$ is to be tested statistically against the hypothesis $\mathcal{H}_1 : \boldsymbol{A\beta} \neq \boldsymbol{\xi}$, we have to make sure that the following conditions hold.

(a) The model under the null hypothesis must be consistent, that is, $\boldsymbol{y} \in \mathcal{C}(\boldsymbol{X} : \boldsymbol{V})$ or $(\boldsymbol{I} - \boldsymbol{P}_V)\boldsymbol{y} \in \mathcal{C}((\boldsymbol{I} - \boldsymbol{P}_V)\boldsymbol{X})$.

(b) The hypothesis must be testable, i.e. $\mathcal{C}(\boldsymbol{A}') \subseteq \mathcal{C}(\boldsymbol{X}')$.

(c) The equation $\boldsymbol{A\beta} = \boldsymbol{\xi}$ must be algebraically consistent, i.e. $\boldsymbol{\xi} \in \mathcal{C}(\boldsymbol{A})$.

(d) The model under the alternative hypothesis must be consistent, i.e. $\boldsymbol{y} - \boldsymbol{XA}^-\boldsymbol{\xi} \in \mathcal{C}(\boldsymbol{X}(\boldsymbol{I} - \boldsymbol{A}^-\boldsymbol{A}) : \boldsymbol{V})$ or $(\boldsymbol{I} - \boldsymbol{P}_V)(\boldsymbol{y} - \boldsymbol{XA}^-\boldsymbol{\xi}) \in \mathcal{C}((\boldsymbol{I} - \boldsymbol{P}_V)\boldsymbol{X}(\boldsymbol{I} - \boldsymbol{A}^-\boldsymbol{A}))$.

We have seen in Examples 7.1 and 4.7 how conditions (a) or (b) may be violated. If condition (a) does not hold, then the model $(\boldsymbol{y}, \boldsymbol{X\beta}, \sigma^2\boldsymbol{V})$ is inconsistent with the data, and we do not even have a basis for testing statistically the hypothesis $\boldsymbol{A\beta} = \boldsymbol{\xi}$. If condition (b) is violated, then we have to work with the testable part of the hypothesis as per Proposition 4.13. Condition (c) essentially says that we cannot test statements such as $\begin{pmatrix} \boldsymbol{p'\beta} \\ \boldsymbol{p'\beta} \end{pmatrix} = \begin{pmatrix} 0 \\ 1 \end{pmatrix}$, which is self-contradicting. The next example shows how condition (d) may be violated, even if conditions (a)–(c) are satisfied. If either of (c) and (d) is violated, then the null hypothesis may be rejected without conducting a statistical test. Conditions (a) and (d) are automatically satisfied when $\boldsymbol{V}$ is nonsingular. A statistical test may be conducted if all the four conditions hold.

Example 7.47. Let the observed response for the model of Exercise 7.12 be $\boldsymbol{y} = (1 : 2 : 3 : 4)'$. It is easy to see that $\boldsymbol{u}_4'\boldsymbol{y} = 0$, so that $\boldsymbol{y} \in \mathcal{C}(\boldsymbol{V} : \boldsymbol{X})$, i.e. condition (a) holds. Consider the hypothesis $\beta_2 - \beta_3 = 0$. Since $y_2 - y_3$ is an LUE of $\beta_2 - \beta_3$, the hypothesis is testable. Further, a hypothesis with a single degree of freedom is always algebraically consistent. Thus, conditions (b) and (c) are satisfied. However, condition (d) is violated, as $\mathcal{C}(\boldsymbol{X}(\boldsymbol{I} - \boldsymbol{A}^-\boldsymbol{A})) = \mathcal{C}(\boldsymbol{u}_2)$ and this column space does not contain $\boldsymbol{y}$. In order to understand what goes wrong, note that the BLUE of $\beta_2 - \beta_3$ is $\widehat{y}_2 - \widehat{y}_3 = (y_1 + y_2 - y_3 - y_4)/2 = -2$. The expression of $D(\widehat{\boldsymbol{y}})$ obtained in Example 7.14 implies that $Var(\widehat{y}_2 - \widehat{y}_3) = 0$. Thus, it is known from the data *with certainty* that $\beta_2 - \beta_3 = -2$. Since the restricted model incorporates the null hypothesis $\beta_2 - \beta_3 = 0$, the observed data is inconsistent with it. □

Proposition 7.48. *Under the above set-up, the GLRT at level α is equivalent to rejecting $\mathcal{H}_0$ if*

$$\frac{R_H^2 - R_0^2}{R_0^2} \cdot \frac{n' - r}{m} > F_{m,n'-r,\alpha}$$

where $n' = \rho(\boldsymbol{X} : \boldsymbol{V})$, $r = \rho(\boldsymbol{X})$ and $m = \rho(D(\boldsymbol{A}\widehat{\boldsymbol{\beta}}))$.

Proof. See Exercise 7.21. □

A general version of the ANOVA table of Section 4.2.5 is given in Table 7.1.

Multiple comparisons of a number of single-degree-of-freedom hypothesis can be made using the ideas of Section 4.2.7. Consider the collection of testable hypotheses

$$\mathcal{H}_{0j} : \boldsymbol{a}_j'\boldsymbol{\beta} = \xi_j, \quad \text{against} \quad \mathcal{H}_{1j} : \boldsymbol{a}_j'\boldsymbol{\beta} \neq \xi_j,$$

Table 7.1 Analysis of variance Table for the hypothesis $\boldsymbol{A\beta} = \boldsymbol{\xi}$

Source	Sum of Squares	Degrees of Freedom	Mean Square
Deviation from $\mathcal{H}_0$	$R_H^2 - R_0^2 = (\boldsymbol{A}\widehat{\boldsymbol{\beta}} - \boldsymbol{\xi})'[\frac{1}{\sigma^2}D(\boldsymbol{A}\widehat{\boldsymbol{\beta}} - \boldsymbol{\xi})]^-(\boldsymbol{A}\widehat{\boldsymbol{\beta}} - \boldsymbol{\xi})$	$m = \rho(D(\boldsymbol{A}\widehat{\boldsymbol{\beta}} - \boldsymbol{\xi}))$	$\frac{R_H^2 - R_0^2}{m}$
Error	$R_0^2 = \min_{(\boldsymbol{y}-\boldsymbol{X\beta})\in\mathcal{C}(\boldsymbol{V})} (\boldsymbol{y}-\boldsymbol{X\beta})'\boldsymbol{V}^-(\boldsymbol{y}-\boldsymbol{X\beta})$	$n' - r = \rho(\boldsymbol{X}:\boldsymbol{V}) - \rho(\boldsymbol{X})$	$\frac{R_0^2}{n'-r}$
Total	$R_H^2 = \min_{\substack{(\boldsymbol{y}-\boldsymbol{X\beta})\in\mathcal{C}(\boldsymbol{V}) \\ \boldsymbol{A\beta} = \boldsymbol{\xi}}} (\boldsymbol{y}-\boldsymbol{X\beta})'\boldsymbol{V}^-(\boldsymbol{y}-\boldsymbol{X\beta})$	$n' - r + m$	

$j = 1, \ldots, q$. Let $\boldsymbol{A}' = (\boldsymbol{a}_1 : \boldsymbol{a}_2 : \cdots : \boldsymbol{a}_q)$ and $\boldsymbol{\xi} = (\xi_1 : \xi_2 : \cdots : \xi_q)'$. Using the Bonferroni inequality, we obtain a set of conservative tests that reject $\mathcal{H}_{0j}$ if

$$\frac{(\boldsymbol{a}_j'\widehat{\boldsymbol{\beta}} - \xi_j)^2}{\widehat{\sigma^2}\boldsymbol{a}_j'\boldsymbol{X}^- D(\widehat{\boldsymbol{y}})(\boldsymbol{X}^-)'\boldsymbol{a}_j} > F_{1,n'-r,\frac{\alpha}{2q}},$$

$j = 1, 2, \ldots, q$. The probability of erroneous rejection of at least one of the hypotheses, when all of them actually hold, is at most α. Using Scheffé's technique, we have another set of conservative tests that reject $\mathcal{H}_{0j}$ if

$$\frac{(\boldsymbol{a}_j'\widehat{\boldsymbol{\beta}} - \xi_j)^2}{\widehat{\sigma^2}\boldsymbol{a}_j'\boldsymbol{X}^- D(\widehat{\boldsymbol{y}})(\boldsymbol{X}^-)'\boldsymbol{a}_j} > mF_{m,n'-r,\alpha},$$

$j = 1, 2, \ldots, q$, where $m = \rho(D(\widehat{\boldsymbol{A\beta}})) = \rho(\boldsymbol{AX}^- D(\widehat{\boldsymbol{y}})(\boldsymbol{X}^-)'\boldsymbol{A}')$.

7.12 Confidence regions

If $\boldsymbol{y} \sim N(\boldsymbol{X\beta}, \sigma^2\boldsymbol{V})$ and $\boldsymbol{p}'\boldsymbol{\beta}$ is an estimable LPF, then it follows from the discussion of Sections 7.3 and 7.4 that

$$\frac{\boldsymbol{p}'\widehat{\boldsymbol{\beta}} - \boldsymbol{p}'\boldsymbol{\beta}}{\sqrt{\widehat{\sigma^2}\boldsymbol{p}'\boldsymbol{X}^-\boldsymbol{D}(\boldsymbol{X}^-)'\boldsymbol{p}}} \sim t_{n'-r},$$

where $\boldsymbol{D} = \sigma^{-2}D(\widehat{\boldsymbol{y}})$, $n' = \rho(\boldsymbol{X} : \boldsymbol{V})$ and $r = \rho(\boldsymbol{X})$. Thus, a left-sided $100(1-\alpha)\%$ confidence interval for $\boldsymbol{p}'\boldsymbol{\beta}$ is

$$\left(-\infty, \boldsymbol{p}'\widehat{\boldsymbol{\beta}} + t_{n'-r,\alpha}\sqrt{\widehat{\sigma^2}\boldsymbol{p}'\boldsymbol{X}^-\boldsymbol{D}(\boldsymbol{X}^-)'\boldsymbol{p}}\,\right].$$

As in Section 4.3, we can also find a right-sided or two-sided confidence interval. If the jth component of $\boldsymbol{\beta}$ is estimable, the corresponding one- and two-sided confidence intervals are obtained by replacing '$\boldsymbol{p}$' in these intervals by the jth column of the $k \times k$ identity matrix.

Under the above set-up, a $100(1-\alpha)\%$ ellipsoidal confidence region for the estimable vector parameter $\boldsymbol{A\beta}$ is

$$\left\{\boldsymbol{A\beta} : (\boldsymbol{A\beta} - \boldsymbol{A}\widehat{\boldsymbol{\beta}})'[\boldsymbol{AX}^{-}\boldsymbol{D}(\boldsymbol{X}^{-})'\boldsymbol{A}']^{-}(\boldsymbol{A\beta} - \boldsymbol{A}\widehat{\boldsymbol{\beta}}) \leq \frac{m\widehat{\sigma^2}F_{m,n'-r,\alpha}}{n'-r}\right\},$$

where $m = \rho(D(\boldsymbol{A}\widehat{\boldsymbol{\beta}}))$. If the entire vector parameter $\boldsymbol{\beta}$ is estimable, the corresponding confidence region is as given above with $\boldsymbol{A} = \boldsymbol{I}$ and $r = k$.

If $\boldsymbol{a}_1', \boldsymbol{a}_2', \ldots, \boldsymbol{a}_q'$ are the rows of the matrix $\boldsymbol{A}$, then simultaneous confidence intervals for the estimable LPFs $\boldsymbol{a}_1'\boldsymbol{\beta}, \boldsymbol{a}_2'\boldsymbol{\beta}, \ldots, \boldsymbol{a}_q'\boldsymbol{\beta}$ can be constructed as in Section 4.3.3. The Bonferroni confidence intervals with confidence coefficient $(1-\alpha)$ are

$$\begin{aligned} I_j^{(b)} = \Bigg[&\boldsymbol{a}_j'\widehat{\boldsymbol{\beta}} - t_{n'-r,\frac{\alpha}{2q}}\sqrt{\widehat{\sigma^2}\boldsymbol{a}_j'\boldsymbol{X}^{-}\boldsymbol{D}(\boldsymbol{X}^{-})'\boldsymbol{a}_j}, \\ &\boldsymbol{a}_j'\widehat{\boldsymbol{\beta}} + t_{n'-r,\frac{\alpha}{2q}}\sqrt{\widehat{\sigma^2}\boldsymbol{a}_j'\boldsymbol{X}^{-}\boldsymbol{D}(\boldsymbol{X}^{-})'\boldsymbol{a}_j}\Bigg], \quad j = 1, 2, \ldots, q. \end{aligned}$$

The corresponding Scheffé confidence intervals are

$$\begin{aligned} I_j^{(sc)} = \Bigg[&\boldsymbol{a}_j'\widehat{\boldsymbol{\beta}} - \sqrt{mF_{m,n'-r,\alpha}\boldsymbol{a}_j'\boldsymbol{X}^{-}\boldsymbol{D}(\boldsymbol{X}^{-})'\boldsymbol{a}_j\widehat{\sigma^2}}, \\ &\boldsymbol{a}_j'\widehat{\boldsymbol{\beta}} + \sqrt{mF_{m,n'-r,\alpha}\boldsymbol{a}_j'\boldsymbol{X}^{-}\boldsymbol{D}(\boldsymbol{X}^{-})'\boldsymbol{a}_j\widehat{\sigma^2}}\Bigg], \quad j = 1, 2, \ldots, q. \end{aligned}$$

In the context of linear regression, we may obtain a confidence band for the regression surface $(\boldsymbol{x}'\widehat{\boldsymbol{\beta}})$ by adapting Proposition 4.34 to the general linear model. The confidence band is

$$\begin{aligned} \Bigg[&\boldsymbol{x}'\widehat{\boldsymbol{\beta}} - \sqrt{m'F_{m',n'-r,\alpha}\boldsymbol{x}'\boldsymbol{X}^{-}\boldsymbol{D}(\boldsymbol{X}^{-})'\boldsymbol{x}\widehat{\sigma^2}}, \\ &\boldsymbol{x}'\widehat{\boldsymbol{\beta}} + \sqrt{m'F_{m',n'-r,\alpha}\boldsymbol{x}'\boldsymbol{X}^{-}\boldsymbol{D}(\boldsymbol{X}^{-})'\boldsymbol{x}\widehat{\sigma^2}}\Bigg], \end{aligned}$$

where $m' = \rho(D(\boldsymbol{X}\widehat{\boldsymbol{\beta}})) = \dim(\mathcal{C}(\boldsymbol{X}) \cap \mathcal{C}(\boldsymbol{V}))$. This band covers the regression surface with probability $1-\alpha$.

7.13 Prediction

7.13.1 *Best linear unbiased predictor*

Consider the linear model

$$\left(\begin{pmatrix} \boldsymbol{y} \\ y_0 \end{pmatrix}, \begin{pmatrix} \boldsymbol{X} \\ \boldsymbol{x}_0' \end{pmatrix}, \sigma^2 \begin{pmatrix} \boldsymbol{V} & \boldsymbol{v}_0 \\ \boldsymbol{v}_0' & v_0 \end{pmatrix}\right),$$

where $\boldsymbol{y}$ is observed but y_0 is not. If the dispersion matrix is known, the above model can serve as a vehicle for the prediction of y_0 in terms of $\boldsymbol{y}$. It follows from Proposition 2.23 that the BLP of y_0 given $\boldsymbol{y}$ is

$$\widehat{E}(y_0|\boldsymbol{y}) = \boldsymbol{x}_0'\boldsymbol{\beta} + \boldsymbol{v}_0'\boldsymbol{V}^-(\boldsymbol{y} - \boldsymbol{X}\boldsymbol{\beta}).$$

If $\boldsymbol{\beta}$ is not known, we have to look for the best linear unbiased predictor (BLUP). This predictor should (i) be of the form $\boldsymbol{a}'\boldsymbol{y} + b$, (ii) satisfy the condition $E(y_0 - \boldsymbol{a}'\boldsymbol{y} - b) = 0$ for all $\boldsymbol{\beta}$, and (iii) minimize $E[y_0 - \boldsymbol{a}'\boldsymbol{y} - b]^2$.

Proposition 7.49. *In the above set-up, let $\mathcal{M}$ denote the linear model $(\boldsymbol{y}, \boldsymbol{X}\boldsymbol{\beta}, \sigma^2\boldsymbol{V})$ and $\boldsymbol{V}^-$ be a particular g-inverse of $\boldsymbol{V}$. Then*

(a) *If $\boldsymbol{x}_0'\boldsymbol{\beta}$ is not estimable under the model $\mathcal{M}$, then a BLUP of y_0 does not exist.*
(b) *If $\boldsymbol{x}_0'\boldsymbol{\beta}$ is estimable under the model $\mathcal{M}$, then a BLUP of y_0 is given by*

$$\widehat{y}_0 = \widehat{\boldsymbol{x}_0'\boldsymbol{\beta}} + \boldsymbol{v}_0'\boldsymbol{V}^-\boldsymbol{e},$$

where $\widehat{\boldsymbol{x}_0'\boldsymbol{\beta}}$ and $\boldsymbol{e}$ are the BLUE of $\boldsymbol{x}_0'\boldsymbol{\beta}$ and the residual vector, respectively, from the model $\mathcal{M}$.
(c) *The BLUP described in part (b) is unique in the sense that any other BLUP is equal to it with probability 1.*
(d) *The mean square prediction error of the BLUP of part (b) is*

$$\sigma^2(v_0 - \boldsymbol{v}_0'\boldsymbol{V}^-\boldsymbol{v}_0) + (\boldsymbol{x}_0'\boldsymbol{X}^- - \boldsymbol{v}_0'\boldsymbol{V}^-)D(\boldsymbol{X}\widehat{\boldsymbol{\beta}})(\boldsymbol{X}'^-\boldsymbol{x}_0 - \boldsymbol{V}^-\boldsymbol{v}_0).$$

Proof. If $\boldsymbol{a}'\boldsymbol{y} + b$ is a linear unbiased predictor of y_0, then it is a linear unbiased estimator of $\boldsymbol{x}_0'\boldsymbol{\beta}$ under the model $\mathcal{M}$, i.e. $\boldsymbol{x}_0'\boldsymbol{\beta}$ is estimable. This proves part (a) by contradiction. In order to prove the remaining three parts, let $\boldsymbol{x}_0 \in \mathcal{C}(\boldsymbol{X}')$ and $\boldsymbol{a}'\boldsymbol{y} + b$ be a linear unbiased predictor of y_0. Consider the decomposition

$$y_0 - a'\boldsymbol{y} - b = (y_0 - \widehat{E}(y_0|\boldsymbol{y})) - (\widehat{y}_0 - \widehat{E}(y_0|\boldsymbol{y})) + (\widehat{y}_0 - a'\boldsymbol{y} - b).$$

The first term on the right-hand side is the prediction error of the BLP $\widehat{E}(y_0|\boldsymbol{y})$, which must be uncorrelated with $\boldsymbol{y}$ (see Proposition 2.23, part (b)).

Therefore, this term is uncorrelated with the other two terms. Further, the second term is the estimation error of the BLUE of $\boldsymbol{x}_0'\boldsymbol{\beta} - \boldsymbol{v}_0'\boldsymbol{V}^-\boldsymbol{X}\boldsymbol{\beta}$ in $\mathcal{M}$, while the third term is a linear zero function in this model. Therefore, these two terms are also uncorrelated. Consequently

$$E[y_0 - a'\boldsymbol{y} - b]^2 = E[y_0 - \widehat{E}(y_0|\boldsymbol{y})]^2 + E[\widehat{y}_0 - \widehat{E}(y_0|\boldsymbol{y})]^2 + E[\widehat{y}_0 - a'\boldsymbol{y} - b]^2.$$

The above is minimized if and only if the LZF $\widehat{y}_0 - a'\boldsymbol{y} - b$ is almost surely equal to zero. This proves parts (b) and (c). By setting $a'\boldsymbol{y} + b = \widehat{y}_0$ in the above equation, we have

$$\begin{aligned} E[y_0 - \widehat{y}_0]^2 &= E[y_0 - \widehat{E}(y_0|\boldsymbol{y})]^2 + E[\widehat{y}_0 - \widehat{E}(y_0|\boldsymbol{y})]^2 \\ &= \sigma^2(v_0 - \boldsymbol{v}_0'\boldsymbol{V}^-\boldsymbol{v}_0) + Var(\widehat{\boldsymbol{x}_0'\boldsymbol{\beta} - \boldsymbol{v}_0'\boldsymbol{V}^-\boldsymbol{X}\boldsymbol{\beta}}) \\ &= \sigma^2(v_0 - \boldsymbol{v}_0'\boldsymbol{V}^-\boldsymbol{v}_0) + Var((\boldsymbol{x}_0'\boldsymbol{X}^- - \boldsymbol{v}_0'\boldsymbol{V}^-)\boldsymbol{X}\widehat{\boldsymbol{\beta}}), \end{aligned}$$

which leads to the expression of part (d). □

When $\boldsymbol{V} = \boldsymbol{I}$, the expression of BLUP given in part (b) of Proposition 7.49 coincides with the BLUE $\widehat{\boldsymbol{x}_0'\boldsymbol{\beta}}$ of the expected value of the predicted observation. In the general case, $\widehat{\boldsymbol{x}_0'\boldsymbol{\beta}}$ is still a linear unbiased predictor, but the additional term $\boldsymbol{v}_0'\boldsymbol{V}^-\boldsymbol{e}$ serves to maximally reduce the prediction error. The expression for the mean squared prediction error of the BLUP given in part (d) is also a sum of two terms. The first term is the mean squared prediction error of the BLP. The second term represents the increase in the mean squared prediction error because $\boldsymbol{X}\boldsymbol{\beta}$ has to be estimated.

7.13.2 *Prediction and tolerance intervals*

Under the assumption of normality, the $100(1-\alpha)\%$ symmetric prediction interval for y_0 is

$$[\widehat{y}_0 - a,\ \widehat{y}_0 + a],$$

where

$$\begin{aligned} \widehat{y}_0 &= \boldsymbol{x}_0'\widehat{\boldsymbol{\beta}} + \boldsymbol{v}_0'\boldsymbol{V}^-\boldsymbol{e}, \\ a &= t_{\rho(X:V)-\rho(X),\alpha/2}(\widehat{\sigma^2 b})^{1/2}, \\ b &= v_0 - \boldsymbol{v}_0'\boldsymbol{V}^-\boldsymbol{v}_0 + (\boldsymbol{x}_0'\boldsymbol{X}^- - \boldsymbol{v}_0'\boldsymbol{V}^-)(D(\boldsymbol{X}\widehat{\boldsymbol{\beta}})/\sigma^2)^-(\boldsymbol{X}'^-\boldsymbol{x}_0 - \boldsymbol{V}^-\boldsymbol{v}_0). \end{aligned}$$

When $\boldsymbol{v}_0 = \boldsymbol{0}$, the quantity b simplifies to $v_0 + Var(\boldsymbol{x}_0'\widehat{\boldsymbol{\beta}})/\sigma^2$. The resulting expression of a is similar to that obtained in Section 4.4.2.

A tolerance interval for y_0 can also be obtained by using the idea of Section 4.4.4. Note that on the average $100(1-\gamma)\%$ of all replications of y_0 must satisfy the inequality

$$|y_0 - \boldsymbol{x}_0'\boldsymbol{\beta} - \boldsymbol{v}_0'\boldsymbol{V}^-(\boldsymbol{y} - \boldsymbol{X\beta})| < z_{\gamma/2}\sqrt{\sigma^2(v_0 - \boldsymbol{v}_0'\boldsymbol{V}^-\boldsymbol{v}_0)},$$

$z_{\gamma/2}$ being the $1-\gamma/2$ quantile of the standard normal distribution. Using the usual $100(1-\alpha/2)\%$ two-sided confidence interval of $(\boldsymbol{x}_0'\boldsymbol{X}^- - \boldsymbol{v}_0'\boldsymbol{V}^-)\boldsymbol{X\beta}$ and a $100(1-\alpha/2)\%$ upper confidence limit for σ^2 together with the Bonferroni inequality, we have the $100(1-\alpha)\%$ two-sided tolerance interval for inclusion of $100(1-\gamma)\%$ of all replications of y_0,

$$\left[\widehat{y}_0 - t_{\rho(X:V)-\rho(X),\alpha/4}\sqrt{\widehat{c\sigma^2}} - z_{\gamma/2}\sqrt{\widehat{d\sigma^2}}\,,\right.$$
$$\left.\widehat{y}_0 + t_{\rho(X:V)-\rho(X),\alpha/4}\sqrt{\widehat{c\sigma^2}} + z_{\gamma/2}\sqrt{\widehat{d\sigma^2}}\right],$$

where

$$\begin{aligned}
\widehat{y}_0 &= \boldsymbol{x}_0'\widehat{\boldsymbol{\beta}} + \boldsymbol{v}_0'\boldsymbol{V}^-\boldsymbol{e},\\
c &= (\boldsymbol{x}_0'\boldsymbol{X}^- - \boldsymbol{v}_0'\boldsymbol{V}^-)(D(\boldsymbol{X}\widehat{\boldsymbol{\beta}})/\sigma^2)^-(\boldsymbol{X}'^-\boldsymbol{x}_0 - \boldsymbol{V}^-\boldsymbol{v}_0),\\
d &= (\rho(X:V) - \rho(X))(v_0 - \boldsymbol{v}_0'\boldsymbol{V}^-\boldsymbol{v}_0)\Big/\chi^2_{\rho(X:V)-\rho(X),1-\alpha/2}\,.
\end{aligned}$$

Simultaneous prediction or tolerance intervals can also be obtained as in Sections 4.4.3 and 4.4.4 (see Exercises 7.22 and 7.23).

7.13.3 *Inference in finite population sampling**

Characteristics of a finite population are often estimated from a sample. Let $\boldsymbol{y}_s$ represent the vector of observed values of a particular variable in the sample (when the units are drawn without replacement), and let $\boldsymbol{y}_r$ represent the values in the rest of the population that are unobserved. Let the combined vector for the population, $(\boldsymbol{y}_s' : \boldsymbol{y}_r)'$ be denoted by $\boldsymbol{y}_t$. The objective is to estimate a function of $\boldsymbol{y}_t$ by means of a function of the observable $\boldsymbol{y}_s$. The present discussion is confined to estimating *linear* functions of $\boldsymbol{y}_t$ such as the population mean and the population total.

The population characteristic can be estimated better if there are some auxiliary variables carrying information about the main variable of interest, and these are known for the entire population. Let $\boldsymbol{X}_s$ be the matrix of auxiliary variables in the sample (each row representing a single unit), and $\boldsymbol{X}_r$ be the corresponding matrix for the rest of the population. We may seek to estimate the desired population characteristic by predicting $\boldsymbol{y}_r$ by means of the observables, $\boldsymbol{y}_s$, $\boldsymbol{X}_s$ and $\boldsymbol{X}_r$. The prediction is typically made on the basis of a linear model of the form

$$E\begin{pmatrix}\boldsymbol{y}_s\\ \boldsymbol{y}_r\end{pmatrix} = \begin{pmatrix}\boldsymbol{X}_s\\ \boldsymbol{X}_r\end{pmatrix}\boldsymbol{\beta}, \qquad D\begin{pmatrix}\boldsymbol{y}_s\\ \boldsymbol{y}_r\end{pmatrix} = \sigma^2\begin{pmatrix}\boldsymbol{V}_{ss} & \boldsymbol{V}_{sr}\\ \boldsymbol{V}_{rs} & \boldsymbol{V}_{rr}\end{pmatrix}, \tag{7.21}$$

where $\boldsymbol{\beta}$ is an unspecified vector parameter, and the dispersion matrix is known up to the scale factor σ^2.

Let $\gamma_t'\boldsymbol{y}_t$ be the function to be estimated, where γ_t is a known coefficient vector. It can be written as $\gamma_s'\boldsymbol{y}_s + \gamma_r'\boldsymbol{y}_r$, where $\gamma_t = (\gamma_s' : \gamma_r')'$. Since $\gamma_s'\boldsymbol{y}_s$ is exactly known, the task of 'estimating' $\gamma_t'\boldsymbol{y}_t$ is equivalent to that of predicting $\gamma_r'\boldsymbol{y}_r$. If the model (7.21) is assumed, then the theory of best linear unbiased prediction can be used for this purpose. The BLUP of $\gamma_r'\boldsymbol{y}_r$ is given by Proposition 7.49, with the following substitutions:

$$\boldsymbol{y} = \boldsymbol{y}_s,\ \boldsymbol{X} = \boldsymbol{X}_s,\ \boldsymbol{V} = \boldsymbol{V}_{ss},\ \boldsymbol{x}_0 = \boldsymbol{X}_r'\gamma_r,\ v_0 = \gamma_r'\boldsymbol{V}_{rr}\gamma_r,\ \boldsymbol{v}_0 = \boldsymbol{V}_{sr}\gamma_r.$$

According to Proposition 7.49, the BLUP exists and is unique if and only if $\boldsymbol{X}_r'\gamma_r \in \mathcal{C}(\boldsymbol{X}_s')$. If the BLUP exists, it is given by

$$\gamma_r'\widehat{\boldsymbol{y}}_r = \gamma_r'\boldsymbol{X}_r\boldsymbol{X}_s^-\widehat{\boldsymbol{X}_s\boldsymbol{\beta}} + \gamma_r'\boldsymbol{V}_{rs}\boldsymbol{V}_{ss}^-(\boldsymbol{y}_s - \widehat{\boldsymbol{X}_s\boldsymbol{\beta}}),$$

where

$$\widehat{\boldsymbol{X}_s\boldsymbol{\beta}} = \left[\boldsymbol{I} - \boldsymbol{V}_{ss}\left(\boldsymbol{I}-\boldsymbol{P}_{X_s}\right)\left\{\left(\boldsymbol{I}-\boldsymbol{P}_{X_s}\right)\boldsymbol{V}\left(\boldsymbol{I}-\boldsymbol{P}_{X_s}\right)\right\}^-\left(\boldsymbol{I}-\boldsymbol{P}_{X_s}\right)\right]\boldsymbol{y}_s.$$

Therefore, the *model-based estimator* of $\gamma_t'\boldsymbol{y}_t$ is

$$\widehat{\gamma_t'\boldsymbol{y}_t} = \gamma_s'\boldsymbol{y}_s + \gamma_r'[\boldsymbol{X}_r\boldsymbol{X}_s^-\widehat{\boldsymbol{X}_s\boldsymbol{\beta}} + \boldsymbol{V}_{rs}\boldsymbol{V}_{ss}^-(\boldsymbol{y}_s - \widehat{\boldsymbol{X}_s\boldsymbol{\beta}})]. \tag{7.22}$$

According to part (d) of Proposition 7.49, the mean square prediction error of $\widehat{\gamma_t'\boldsymbol{y}_t}$ is

$$\begin{aligned} MSEP &= \sigma^2\gamma_r'(\boldsymbol{V}_{rr} - \boldsymbol{V}_{rs}\boldsymbol{V}_{ss}^-\boldsymbol{V}_{sr})\gamma_r \\ &\quad + \gamma_r'(\boldsymbol{X}_r\boldsymbol{X}_s^- - \boldsymbol{V}_{rs}\boldsymbol{V}_{ss}^-)D(\widehat{\boldsymbol{X}_s\boldsymbol{\beta}})(\boldsymbol{X}_s'^-\boldsymbol{X}_r' - \boldsymbol{V}_{ss}^-\boldsymbol{V}_{sr})\gamma_r. \end{aligned}$$

If $\boldsymbol{V}_{rs} = \boldsymbol{0}$, then the estimator and its MSEP simplify to

$$\begin{aligned} \widehat{\gamma_t'\boldsymbol{y}_t} &= \gamma_s'\boldsymbol{y}_s + \gamma_r'\boldsymbol{X}_r\boldsymbol{X}_s^-\widehat{\boldsymbol{X}_s\boldsymbol{\beta}}, \\ MSEP &= \sigma^2\gamma_r'\boldsymbol{V}_{rr}\gamma_r + \gamma_r'\boldsymbol{X}_r\boldsymbol{X}_s^-D(\widehat{\boldsymbol{X}_s\boldsymbol{\beta}})\boldsymbol{X}_s'^-\boldsymbol{X}_r'\gamma_r. \end{aligned}$$

If $\boldsymbol{V}_{rs} = \boldsymbol{0}$ and $\boldsymbol{V}_{ss}$ is nonsingular, then the expressions further simplify to

$$\widehat{\gamma_t'\boldsymbol{y}_t} = \gamma_s'\boldsymbol{y}_s + \gamma_r'\boldsymbol{X}_r(\boldsymbol{X}_s'\boldsymbol{V}_{ss}^{-1}\boldsymbol{X}_s)^-\boldsymbol{X}_s'\boldsymbol{V}_{ss}^{-1}\boldsymbol{y}_s, \tag{7.23}$$

$$MSEP = \sigma^2\gamma_r'[\boldsymbol{V}_{rr} + \boldsymbol{X}_r(\boldsymbol{X}_s'\boldsymbol{V}_{ss}^{-1}\boldsymbol{X}_s)^-\boldsymbol{X}_r']\gamma_r. \tag{7.24}$$

When $\boldsymbol{V}_{rs} = \mathbf{0}$ and $\boldsymbol{V}_{ss} = \boldsymbol{I}$, the estimator and its MSEP are

$$\widehat{\gamma_t'\boldsymbol{y}_t} = \gamma_s'\boldsymbol{y}_s + \gamma_r'\boldsymbol{X}_r(\boldsymbol{X}_s'\boldsymbol{X}_s)^-\boldsymbol{X}_s'\boldsymbol{y}_s, \tag{7.25}$$

$$MSEP = \sigma^2\gamma_r'[\boldsymbol{V}_{rr} + \boldsymbol{X}_r(\boldsymbol{X}_s'\boldsymbol{X}_s)^-\boldsymbol{X}_r']\gamma_r. \tag{7.26}$$

In the following examples, n denotes the sample size and N is the population size, which is assumed known.

Example 7.50. (No auxiliary variable) If there is no auxiliary variable, a plausible model is $E(\boldsymbol{y}_t) = \mu\mathbf{1}$, $D(\boldsymbol{y}_t) = \sigma^2\boldsymbol{I}$. The BLUP of the population total $\mathbf{1}'\boldsymbol{y}_t$ simplifies from (7.25) to $N\mathbf{1}'\boldsymbol{y}_s/n$ or $N\bar{y}_s$. This is known as the *expansion estimator* of population total. The MSEP, given by (7.26), simplifies to $(N-n)N\sigma^2/n$.

The expansion estimator also arises naturally from simple random sampling without replacement (SRSWOR). According to the sampling design, $D(\boldsymbol{y}_s) = s^2(\boldsymbol{I} - N^{-1}\mathbf{1}\mathbf{1}')$, where s^2 is the true population variance, and consequently the variance of the expansion estimator is $N(N-n)s^2/n$ (see Exercise 7.27). As the parameters μ and σ^2 of the above prediction model are essentially the same as the population mean, $N^{-1}\mathbf{1}'\boldsymbol{y}_t$, and the population variance, s^2, respectively, we find that the variance expression obtained from the design-based approach is identical to the MSEP obtained from the model-based approach. □

Example 7.51. (One auxiliary variable) Let there be a single auxiliary variable, so that $\boldsymbol{X}_s = (\mathbf{1} : \boldsymbol{x}_s)$ and $\boldsymbol{X}_r = (\mathbf{1} : \boldsymbol{x}_r)$, and $D(\boldsymbol{y}_t) = \sigma^2\boldsymbol{I}$. The computations are simplified using a reparametrization, with $\boldsymbol{X}_s$ and $\boldsymbol{X}_r$ replaced by $\boldsymbol{X}_s^* = (\mathbf{1} : \boldsymbol{x}_s - \bar{x}_s\mathbf{1})$ and $\boldsymbol{X}_r^* = (\mathbf{1} : \boldsymbol{x}_r - \bar{x}_s\mathbf{1})$, respectively, where $\bar{x}_s$ is the sample mean of the auxiliary variable or $n^{-1}\mathbf{1}'\boldsymbol{x}_s$. The expression (7.25) for the BLUP of the population total $\mathbf{1}'\boldsymbol{y}_t$ simplifies to

$$N\left[\bar{y}_s + \frac{(\boldsymbol{x}_s - \bar{x}_s\mathbf{1})'(\boldsymbol{y}_s - \bar{y}_s\mathbf{1})}{\|\boldsymbol{x}_s - \bar{x}_s\mathbf{1}\|^2}\cdot(\bar{x} - \bar{x}_s)\right],$$

where $\bar{y}_s = n^{-1}\mathbf{1}'\boldsymbol{y}_s$ and $\bar{x} = N^{-1}\mathbf{1}'\boldsymbol{x}$. This estimator is known as the *regression estimator* of population total. The MSEP of this estimator, given by (7.26), simplifies to

$$\sigma^2\left[\frac{(N-n)N}{n} + \frac{N^2(\bar{x} - \bar{x}_s)^2}{\|\boldsymbol{x}_s - \bar{x}_s\mathbf{1}\|^2}\right]. \qquad \square$$

Example 7.52. (One auxiliary variable with heteroscedasticity) Let there be a single auxiliary variable but no intercept term, so that $\boldsymbol{X}_s$ and $\boldsymbol{X}_r$ can be written as $\boldsymbol{x}_s$ and $\boldsymbol{x}_r$, respectively, and $E(\boldsymbol{y}_s' : \boldsymbol{y}_r')' = (\boldsymbol{x}_s' : \boldsymbol{x}_r')'\beta$.

Further, let $D(\boldsymbol{y}_t)$ be equal to σ^2 times a diagonal matrix with the elements of $(\boldsymbol{x}_s' : \boldsymbol{x}_r')$ as its diagonal element. The BLUP of the population total $\boldsymbol{1}'\boldsymbol{y}_t$ is given by (7.23), which simplifies to $\boldsymbol{1}'\boldsymbol{y}_s(1 + \boldsymbol{1}'\boldsymbol{x}_r/\boldsymbol{1}'\boldsymbol{x}_s)$ or $N\bar{y}_s\frac{\bar{x}}{\bar{x}_s}$, $\bar{x}$ being the population mean of the auxiliary variable and $\bar{y}_s$ and $\bar{x}_s$ being the sample means of the main and auxiliary variables, respectively. This estimator of the population total is known as the *ratio estimator*, and it arises naturally in the context of probability proportional to size (PPS) sampling with the auxiliary variable used as 'size'. The MSEP of the ratio estimator is given by (7.24), which simplifies to $\sigma^2\frac{(N-n)N}{n}\frac{\bar{x}_r\bar{x}}{\bar{x}_s}$, $\bar{x}_r$ being the average value of the auxiliary variable among non-samples. □

It may appear from the theory of model-based inference and the preceding examples that the results hold irrespective of the sampling design. However, the assumed model may not be valid for all sampling designs. For example, sampling only from units which have a large value of the auxiliary variable may lead to wrong conclusions. Further, the worth of model-based prediction depends crucially on the validity of the model. The model has to be chosen with utmost care. If sampling with replacement takes place, then there may be replications within the sample. In such a case, one may have to use a model with singular dispersion matrix.

A combination of design-based and model-based approaches leads to the design-assisted approach, including the general regression (GREG) estimator. Valliant et al. (2000) give a detailed treatment of model-based and model-assisted inference in finite population sampling.

7.14 Complements/Exercises

Exercises with solutions given in Appendix C

7.1 Prove Proposition 3.34 for the general linear model.

7.2 If $\mathcal{C}(\boldsymbol{X}) \subseteq \mathcal{C}(\boldsymbol{V})$, show that the linear model $(\boldsymbol{y}, \boldsymbol{X\beta}, \sigma^2\boldsymbol{V})$ can be viewed as a linearly transformed version of another model of the form $(\boldsymbol{y}_*, \boldsymbol{X}_*\boldsymbol{\beta}, \sigma^2\boldsymbol{I})$.

7.3 Prove Proposition 7.17 By transforming $\boldsymbol{y}$ to $\boldsymbol{C}^{-1}\boldsymbol{y}$, where $\boldsymbol{CC}'$ is a rank-factorization of $\boldsymbol{V}$.

7.4 Let $\boldsymbol{p}'\boldsymbol{\beta}$ be an estimable LPF in the model $(\boldsymbol{y}, \boldsymbol{X\beta}, \sigma^2\boldsymbol{V})$, $\boldsymbol{p}'\widehat{\boldsymbol{\beta}}$ be its BLUE and $\widehat{\boldsymbol{p}'\boldsymbol{\beta}}_{LU}$ be another LUE. Define the *efficiency* of $\widehat{\boldsymbol{p}'\boldsymbol{\beta}}_{LU}$ as

$$\eta_p = \begin{cases} Var(\boldsymbol{p}'\widehat{\boldsymbol{\beta}})/Var(\widehat{\boldsymbol{p}'\boldsymbol{\beta}}_{LU}) & \text{if } Var(\widehat{\boldsymbol{p}'\boldsymbol{\beta}}_{LU}) > 0, \\ 1 & \text{if } Var(\widehat{\boldsymbol{p}'\boldsymbol{\beta}}_{LU}) = 0. \end{cases}$$

Show that $1-\eta_p$ is equal to the squared multiple correlation coefficient of $\widehat{\boldsymbol{p}'\boldsymbol{\beta}}_{LU}$ with any generating set of LZFs. Is the above notion of efficiency consistent with the definition given on page 627?

7.5 Consider the modified model $(\boldsymbol{y}_*, \boldsymbol{X\beta}, \sigma^2\boldsymbol{W})$ of Section 7.7.1 where $\boldsymbol{W} = \boldsymbol{V} + \boldsymbol{XUX}'$ and $\boldsymbol{U}$ is a symmetric, nonnegative definite matrix such that $\mathcal{C}(\boldsymbol{W}) = \mathcal{C}(\boldsymbol{X} : \boldsymbol{V})$. Show that

$$D(\widehat{\boldsymbol{y}}_*) = \sigma^2\boldsymbol{X}(\boldsymbol{X}'\boldsymbol{W}^-\boldsymbol{X})^-\boldsymbol{X}'.$$

If $D(\widehat{\boldsymbol{y}})$ is obtained as in Section 7.3 from the model $(\boldsymbol{y}, \boldsymbol{X\beta},\ \sigma^2\boldsymbol{V})$, then observe that

$$D(\widehat{\boldsymbol{y}}) \leq D(\widehat{\boldsymbol{y}}_*)$$

in the sense of the Löwner order. When does the above relation hold with equality?

7.6 Prove the statement of Remark 7.20.

7.7 Prove Proposition 7.22 using (7.3).

7.8 If $\boldsymbol{V}$ and $\boldsymbol{U}$ are symmetric and nonnegative definite matrices of appropriate order, then show that $\mathcal{C}(\boldsymbol{V}) \subseteq \mathcal{C}(\boldsymbol{V} + \boldsymbol{XUX}') \subseteq \mathcal{C}(\boldsymbol{V} : \boldsymbol{X})$.

7.9 This exercise aims at finding equivalent sufficient conditions for the results of Proposition 7.30. Let $\boldsymbol{W} = \boldsymbol{V} + \boldsymbol{XUX}'$ where $\boldsymbol{V}$ and $\boldsymbol{U}$ are symmetric and nonnegative definite matrices. Prove that the following three conditions are equivalent.

(a) $\mathcal{C}(\boldsymbol{W}) = \mathcal{C}(\boldsymbol{V} : \boldsymbol{X})$.
(b) $\mathcal{C}(\boldsymbol{X}) \subseteq \mathcal{C}(\boldsymbol{W})$.
(c) $\rho(\boldsymbol{W}) = \rho(\boldsymbol{V} : \boldsymbol{X})$.

7.10 Derive a principal components estimator of $\boldsymbol{X\beta}$ in the model $(\boldsymbol{y}, \boldsymbol{X\beta}, \sigma^2\boldsymbol{V})$ where $\boldsymbol{V}$ is nonsingular. When does it have smaller trace of mean squared error compared to the BLUE?

7.11 Let $\boldsymbol{FF}'$ be a rank-factorization of $\boldsymbol{V}$, $\boldsymbol{Q}$ be a nonsingular matrix such that $\boldsymbol{QX}$ has the lower trapezoidal form with $\rho(\boldsymbol{X})$ nonzero rows, and $\boldsymbol{P}$ be an orthogonal matrix such that $\boldsymbol{QFP}$ has the lower trapezoidal form. Partition $\boldsymbol{Q}$ and $\boldsymbol{P}$ as $(\boldsymbol{Q}_1' : \boldsymbol{Q}_2')'$ and $(\boldsymbol{P}_1 : \boldsymbol{P}_2)$, respectively, where $\boldsymbol{Q}_2$ has $\rho(\boldsymbol{X})$ rows and $\boldsymbol{P}_1$ has $\rho(\boldsymbol{V} : \boldsymbol{X}) - \rho(\boldsymbol{X})$ columns. Note that $\boldsymbol{Q}_1\boldsymbol{X} = \boldsymbol{0}$, $\boldsymbol{Q}_1\boldsymbol{FP}_2 = \boldsymbol{0}$, and $\boldsymbol{P}$ can be chosen to ensure that $\boldsymbol{Q}_1\boldsymbol{FP}_1$ and $\boldsymbol{Q}_2\boldsymbol{FP}_2$ have full column rank. Prove that a solution to the constrained minimization problem of Proposition 7.36 is given by $\widehat{\boldsymbol{\beta}}$ and $\boldsymbol{P}_1\widehat{\boldsymbol{u}}_1$, where $\widehat{\boldsymbol{\beta}}$ and $\widehat{\boldsymbol{u}}_1$ satisfy the equation

$$\begin{pmatrix} \boldsymbol{Q}_1\boldsymbol{FP}_1 & \boldsymbol{0} \\ \boldsymbol{Q}_2\boldsymbol{FP}_1 & \boldsymbol{Q}_2\boldsymbol{X} \end{pmatrix} \begin{pmatrix} \widehat{\boldsymbol{u}}_1 \\ \widehat{\boldsymbol{\beta}} \end{pmatrix} = \begin{pmatrix} \boldsymbol{Q}_1\boldsymbol{y} \\ \boldsymbol{Q}_2\boldsymbol{y} \end{pmatrix}.$$

Further, show that the elements of $\widehat{\boldsymbol{u}}_1$ form a basis set of LZFs with variance σ^2 and that the dispersion of $\boldsymbol{X}\widehat{\boldsymbol{\beta}}$ is $\sigma^2\boldsymbol{F}\boldsymbol{P}_2\boldsymbol{P}_2'\boldsymbol{F}'$.

7.12 Prove Proposition 7.30 without the condition that the matrix $\boldsymbol{U}$ is nonnegative definite.

7.13 Prove the statements made in Remark 7.39.

7.14 Let $\boldsymbol{y} = \boldsymbol{X\beta} + \sigma\boldsymbol{F}\boldsymbol{u}$, where $\boldsymbol{F}\boldsymbol{F}$ is a rank-factorization of $\boldsymbol{V}$, and the $\rho(\boldsymbol{V})$ elements of the random vector $\boldsymbol{u}$ are independent and identically distributed with mean 0, variance 1 and density $h(\cdot)$ satisfying $h(-u) = h(u)$ for all u. Assuming that the necessary partial derivatives and the integrals exist, derive the Cramer-Rao lower bound for the dispersion of an unbiased estimator of an estimable parameter $\boldsymbol{A\beta}$, and show that it is in general smaller than the bound in the case where h is the density of the standard normal distribution.

7.15 Let $\mathcal{M}_R$ and $\mathcal{M}$ be the model $(\boldsymbol{y}, \boldsymbol{X\beta}, \sigma^2\boldsymbol{V})$ with and without the restrictions $\boldsymbol{A\beta} = \boldsymbol{\xi}$, respectively, with $\boldsymbol{A\beta}$ not necessarily estimable in $\mathcal{M}$. Suppose $\boldsymbol{X}\widehat{\boldsymbol{\beta}}$ and $\boldsymbol{X}\widehat{\boldsymbol{\beta}}_R$ are the BLUEs of $\boldsymbol{X\beta}$ under $\mathcal{M}$ and $\mathcal{M}_R$, respectively.

(a) Show that $\boldsymbol{X}\widehat{\boldsymbol{\beta}}$ is the BLUE of $\boldsymbol{X\beta}$ in $\mathcal{M}_R$ with probability 1 if and only if $\mathcal{C}(\boldsymbol{V}) \cap \mathcal{C}(\boldsymbol{X}) \subseteq \mathcal{C}(\boldsymbol{X}(\boldsymbol{I} - \boldsymbol{P}_{A'}))$.

(b) Simplify the condition of part (a) when $\boldsymbol{V}$ is nonsingular.

[See Yang, Cui and Sun (1987) and the references therein for a discussion of this problem.]

7.16 Show that the MSE matrix of the BLUE of $\boldsymbol{X\beta}$ under the model $(\boldsymbol{y}, \boldsymbol{X\beta}, \sigma^2\boldsymbol{V})$ with the restriction $\boldsymbol{A\beta} = \boldsymbol{\xi}$ is smaller than the MSE matrix of its unrestricted BLUE whenever (7.19) holds. [Assume that $\boldsymbol{A\beta}$ is estimable but not equal to $\boldsymbol{\xi}$, and its unrestricted BLUE has a positive definite dispersion matrix.]

7.17 Determine when the MSE matrix of the BLUE of $\boldsymbol{X\beta}$ under the model $(\boldsymbol{y}, \boldsymbol{X\beta}, \sigma^2\boldsymbol{V})$ with the stochastic restriction $\boldsymbol{A\beta} = \boldsymbol{\xi} + \boldsymbol{\delta}$ (described in Section 7.9.3) is smaller than the MSE matrix of its unrestricted BLUE.

7.18 Find the estimator of $\boldsymbol{X\beta}$ that minimizes $(\boldsymbol{y} - \boldsymbol{X\beta})'\boldsymbol{V}^-(\boldsymbol{y} - \boldsymbol{X\beta})$ subject to the conditions $(\boldsymbol{y} - \boldsymbol{X\beta}) \in \mathcal{C}(\boldsymbol{V})$ and $\boldsymbol{p}'\boldsymbol{\beta} \le b$, where $\boldsymbol{p}'\boldsymbol{\beta}$ is estimable in $(\boldsymbol{y}, \boldsymbol{X\beta}, \sigma^2\boldsymbol{V})$.

7.19 Prove Proposition 3.53 for the general linear model with possibly singular dispersion matrix.

7.20 Compare the BLUEs of $(\boldsymbol{I} - \boldsymbol{P}_{X_2})\boldsymbol{X}_1\boldsymbol{\beta}_1$, their dispersions and the usual estimators of σ^2 under the models $\mathcal{M} = (\boldsymbol{y}, \boldsymbol{X}_1\boldsymbol{\beta}_1 + \boldsymbol{X}_2\boldsymbol{\beta}_2, \sigma^2\boldsymbol{I})$ and $\mathcal{M}^* = (\boldsymbol{y}, (\boldsymbol{I} - \boldsymbol{P}_{X_2})\boldsymbol{X}_1\boldsymbol{\beta}_1, \sigma^2\boldsymbol{I})$.

7.21 Prove Proposition 7.48, using the proof of Proposition 4.21 as a model.

7.22 Suppose the response vector of the normal-error linear model

$$\left(\begin{pmatrix} \boldsymbol{y} \\ \boldsymbol{y}_0 \end{pmatrix}, \begin{pmatrix} \boldsymbol{X} \\ \boldsymbol{X}_0 \end{pmatrix}\boldsymbol{\beta}, \sigma^2 \begin{pmatrix} \boldsymbol{V} & \boldsymbol{V}_0 \\ \boldsymbol{V}_0' & \boldsymbol{V}_{00} \end{pmatrix}\right)$$

is only partially observed, i.e. $\boldsymbol{y}_0$ is unobserved. The purpose of this exercise is to provide a region where $\boldsymbol{y}_0$ must lie with probability $1-\alpha$.

(a) Show that $\boldsymbol{y}_0$ is contained with probability $1-\alpha$ in the ellipsoidal 'prediction region'

$$\begin{aligned}&(\boldsymbol{y}_0-\widehat{\boldsymbol{y}}_0)'[(\boldsymbol{X}_0\boldsymbol{X}^- - \boldsymbol{V}_0'\boldsymbol{V}^-)\left\{\frac{1}{\sigma^2}D(\boldsymbol{X}\widehat{\boldsymbol{\beta}})\right\}(\boldsymbol{X}_0\boldsymbol{X}^- - \boldsymbol{V}_0'\boldsymbol{V}^-)' \\ &\quad + (\boldsymbol{V}_{00}-\boldsymbol{V}_0'\boldsymbol{V}^-\boldsymbol{V}_0)]^-(\boldsymbol{y}_0-\widehat{\boldsymbol{y}}_0) \\ &\quad \le m\widehat{\sigma^2}F_{m,n'-r,\alpha},\end{aligned}$$

where $\widehat{\boldsymbol{y}}_0 = \boldsymbol{X}_0\widehat{\boldsymbol{\beta}} + \boldsymbol{V}_0\boldsymbol{V}^-\boldsymbol{e}$, $\widehat{\boldsymbol{\beta}}$ and $\boldsymbol{e}$ are as in (7.2) and (7.3), respectively, $n' = \rho(X : V)$, $r = \rho(X)$ and $m = \rho[(\boldsymbol{X}_0\boldsymbol{X}^- - \boldsymbol{V}_0'\boldsymbol{V}^-)\{\sigma^{-2}D(\boldsymbol{X}\widehat{\boldsymbol{\beta}})\}(\boldsymbol{X}_0\boldsymbol{X}^- - \boldsymbol{V}_0'\boldsymbol{V}^-)' + (\boldsymbol{V}_{00} - \boldsymbol{V}_0'\boldsymbol{V}^-\boldsymbol{V}_0)]$.

(b) If $\boldsymbol{y}_0 = (y_{01} : \cdots : y_{0q})'$, $\boldsymbol{X}_0 = (\boldsymbol{x}_{01} : \cdots : \boldsymbol{x}_{0q})'$, $\boldsymbol{V}_0 = (\boldsymbol{v}_{01} : \cdots : \boldsymbol{v}_{0q})$ and v_{0i} is the ith diagonal element of $\boldsymbol{V}_{00}$, $i = 1, \ldots, q$, then show that the generalized version of Scheffé prediction intervals for $y_{01}, \ldots, y_{0q}$ given in Section 4.4.3 are

$$[\widehat{y}_{0i} - (m\widehat{\sigma^2}c_iF_{m,n'-r,\alpha})^{1/2}, \widehat{y}_{0i} + (m\widehat{\sigma^2}c_iF_{m,n'-r,\alpha})^{1/2}],$$

where

$$\begin{aligned}c_i = {}&(\boldsymbol{x}_{0i}'\boldsymbol{X}^- - \boldsymbol{v}_{0i}'\boldsymbol{V}^-)\{\sigma^{-2}D(\boldsymbol{X}\widehat{\boldsymbol{\beta}})\}^-((\boldsymbol{X}^-)'\boldsymbol{x}_{0i} - \boldsymbol{V}^-\boldsymbol{v}_{0i}) \\ &+ (v_{0i} - \boldsymbol{v}_{0i}'\boldsymbol{V}^-\boldsymbol{v}_{0i}), \qquad i = 1, \ldots, q.\end{aligned}$$

7.23 Derive simultaneous tolerance intervals for the components of $\boldsymbol{y}_0$, given the model of Exercise 7.22, as follows.

(a) Consider the prediction of a single sample of the entire vector $\boldsymbol{y}_0$ at a time. Show that on the average, at least $100(1-\gamma)\%$ of all replications of $\boldsymbol{y}_0$ must satisfy the simultaneous inequalities

$$|y_{0i} - \boldsymbol{x}_{0i}'\boldsymbol{\beta} - \boldsymbol{v}_{0i}'\boldsymbol{V}^-(\boldsymbol{y} - \boldsymbol{X}\boldsymbol{\beta})| < \sqrt{\chi^2_{s,\gamma}\sigma^2(v_{0i} - \boldsymbol{v}_{0i}'\boldsymbol{V}^-\boldsymbol{v}_{0i})},$$

$i = 1, \ldots, q$, where $s = \rho(\boldsymbol{V}_{00} - \boldsymbol{V}_0'\boldsymbol{V}^-\boldsymbol{V}_0)$.

(b) Using the result of part (a), $100(1-\alpha/2)\%$ Scheffé confidence intervals of $\boldsymbol{x}_{0i}'\boldsymbol{\beta} - \boldsymbol{v}_{0i}'\boldsymbol{V}^{-}\boldsymbol{X}\boldsymbol{\beta}$, $i = 1, \ldots, q$, and $100(1-\alpha/2)\%$ upper confidence limit for σ^2 together with the Bonferroni inequality, show that the intervals

$$\left[\widehat{y}_{0i} - \sqrt{m' F_{m',n'-r,\alpha/2} c_i \widehat{\sigma^2}} - \sqrt{\chi^2_{s,\gamma} d_i \widehat{\sigma^2}}\,,\right.$$
$$\left.\widehat{y}_{0i} + \sqrt{m' F_{m',n'-r,\alpha/2} c_i \widehat{\sigma^2}} + \sqrt{\chi^2_{s,\gamma} d_i \widehat{\sigma^2}}\right],$$

where

$$\begin{aligned}
\widehat{y}_{0i} &= \boldsymbol{x}_{0i}'\widehat{\boldsymbol{\beta}} + \boldsymbol{v}_{0i}'\boldsymbol{V}^{-}\boldsymbol{e},\\
c_i &= (\boldsymbol{x}_{0i}'\boldsymbol{X}^{-} - \boldsymbol{v}_{0i}'\boldsymbol{V}^{-})(D(\boldsymbol{X}\widehat{\boldsymbol{\beta}})/\sigma^2)(\boldsymbol{X}'^{-}\boldsymbol{x}_{0i} - \boldsymbol{V}^{-}\boldsymbol{v}_{0i}),\\
d_i &= (n'-r)(v_{0i} - \boldsymbol{v}_{0i}'\boldsymbol{V}^{-}\boldsymbol{v}_{0i})/\chi^2_{n'-r,1-\alpha/2},\\
m' &= \rho(D(\boldsymbol{X}\widehat{\boldsymbol{\beta}})) = \dim(\mathcal{C}(\boldsymbol{X}) \cap \mathcal{C}(\boldsymbol{V}))
\end{aligned}$$

contain at least $100(1-\gamma)\%$ of all replications of $\boldsymbol{y}_0$ with probability not less than $100(1-\alpha)\%$.

(c) If $\boldsymbol{V}_{00} - \boldsymbol{V}_0'\boldsymbol{V}^{-}\boldsymbol{V}_0$ is a diagonal matrix, then show that the intervals

$$[\widehat{y}_{0i} - \widehat{\sigma} b_i, \widehat{y}_{0i} + \widehat{\sigma} b_i]\,, \qquad i = 1, \ldots, q,$$

where

$$b_i = \sqrt{m' F_{m',n'-r,\alpha/2} c_i} + z_{\gamma/2}\sqrt{d_i},$$

contain with probability $1-\alpha$ at least $100(1-\gamma)\%$ of all replications of any combination of $y_{01}, \ldots, y_{0q}$.

7.24 Suppose sample units are drawn from a number of strata of a finite population, and the main variable is observed for all the sampled units. There is no auxiliary variable. The population mean of the variable in the various strata may be different. Identify a suitable linear model of the form (7.21), assuming $D(\boldsymbol{y}_t) = \sigma^2\boldsymbol{I}$, and obtain the BLUP of the population total. Determine the MSEP of the BLUP.

7.25 In Exercise 7.24 let the units in the ith stratum have variance σ_i^2, every pair of units within the ith stratum have correlation ρ_i, and the units from different strata be uncorrelated. Identify a suitable linear model of the form (7.21), and obtain the BLUP of the population total. Determine the MSEP of the BLUP.

Additional exercises

7.26 For each of the following situations describe an appropriate general linear model with no constraint on the parameters, and indicate whether the dispersion matrix is singular.

(a) Uncorrelated and homoscedastic observations following the model $y_{ij} = \boldsymbol{x}_i'\boldsymbol{\beta} + \varepsilon_{ij}$, $j = 1, \ldots, n_i$, $i = 1, \ldots, m$ are averaged. The only available data are $n_i^{-1}\sum_{j=1}^{n_i} y_{ij}$, $\boldsymbol{x}_i$ and n_i for $i = 1, \ldots, m$.

(b) For the stack loss data of Table 3.3, it is desired that a simple linear regression model is used to describe the relationship of the stack loss with air flow — after suitable linear adjustment for the other explanatory variables.

(c) From a complete set of data on response and explanatory variables on a number of randomly selected individuals, some information are discarded in order to protect privacy: the response is expressed in terms of deviations from the sample mean, and each explanatory variable is scaled so that the sum of squared values over all the individuals is equal to 1.

(d) An expensive but error-free instrument is used to measure the response variable once. Twenty additional measurements of the response by means of an inexpensive but erroneous instrument are also available. These measurements are unbiased and independent. There are two explanatory variables which are measured free of error.

7.27 Let the vector $\boldsymbol{y} = (y_{i_1} : y_{i_2} : \cdots : y_{i_n})'$ consist of units sampled from a *finite population* $y_1, y_2, \ldots, y_N$, where the units are selected according to simple random sampling without replacement (SRSWOR). The population mean $\bar{y} = N^{-1}\sum_{i=1}^{N} y_i$ and the population variance $s^2 = (N-1)^{-1}\sum_{i=1}^{N}(y_i - \bar{y})^2$ are unknown. Show that the vector of sampled units follows the linear model $(\boldsymbol{y}, \boldsymbol{X\beta}, \sigma^2\boldsymbol{V})$ with $\boldsymbol{X} = \boldsymbol{1}$, $\boldsymbol{\beta} = \bar{y}$, $\sigma^2 = s^2$ and $\boldsymbol{V} = \boldsymbol{I} - N^{-1}\boldsymbol{11}'$. Is $\boldsymbol{V}$ singular? Obtain the BLUE of $\bar{y}$, according to this model, and its variance.

7.28 Consider a linear parametric function $\boldsymbol{p}'\boldsymbol{\beta}$ in the possibly singular linear model $(\boldsymbol{y}, \boldsymbol{X\beta}, \sigma^2\boldsymbol{V})$. Show that there is an unbiased estimator of $\boldsymbol{p}'\boldsymbol{\beta}$ having the form $\boldsymbol{k}'\boldsymbol{y} + c$ if and only if $\boldsymbol{p} \in \mathcal{C}(\boldsymbol{X}')$. [Hint: Follow the proof of Proposition 7.4.]

7.29 Show that the estimator of (7.2) is uniquely defined if and only if $\boldsymbol{X}$ has full column rank, in which case it is the BLUE of $\boldsymbol{\beta}$.

7.30 If $\boldsymbol{l}'\boldsymbol{y}$ and $\boldsymbol{m}'\boldsymbol{y}$ are BLUEs of their respective expectations under the model $(\boldsymbol{y}, \boldsymbol{X\beta}, \sigma^2\boldsymbol{V})$, show that $\boldsymbol{l}'\boldsymbol{y} + \boldsymbol{m}'\boldsymbol{y}$ is also the BLUE of its expectation.

7.31 If $\boldsymbol{l}'\boldsymbol{y}$ is uncorrelated with all BLUEs in the model $(\boldsymbol{y}, \boldsymbol{X\beta}, \sigma^2\boldsymbol{V})$, is it necessarily an LZF?

7.32 Show that the estimator of σ^2 given by (7.9) is unbiased.

7.33 Show that a choice of $\boldsymbol{U}$ that ensures $\mathcal{C}(\boldsymbol{V} + \boldsymbol{XUX}') = \mathcal{C}(\boldsymbol{V} : \boldsymbol{X})$ is $\boldsymbol{U} = \boldsymbol{I}$. Show that $\boldsymbol{X}(\boldsymbol{X}'(\boldsymbol{V} + \boldsymbol{XX}')^-\boldsymbol{X})^-\boldsymbol{X}'(\boldsymbol{V} + \boldsymbol{XX}')^-\boldsymbol{y}$ is the BLUE of $\boldsymbol{X\beta}$ in the model $(\boldsymbol{y}, \boldsymbol{X\beta}, \sigma^2\boldsymbol{V})$.

7.34 Examine possible simplifications in the forms of the BLUE of $\boldsymbol{X\beta}$ in the model $(\boldsymbol{y}, \boldsymbol{X\beta}, \sigma^2\boldsymbol{V})$, the dispersion of the BLUE, the residual vector and the usual unbiased estimator of σ^2 when

(a) $\mathcal{C}(\boldsymbol{X}) \subseteq \mathcal{C}(\boldsymbol{V})$,
(b) $\mathcal{C}(\boldsymbol{V}) \subseteq \mathcal{C}(\boldsymbol{X})$,
(c) $\mathcal{C}(\boldsymbol{X})$ is orthogonal to $\mathcal{C}(\boldsymbol{V})$,
(d) $\mathcal{C}(\boldsymbol{X})$ and $\mathcal{C}(\boldsymbol{V})$ are virtually disjoint.

7.35 *Small area estimation.* The units in a finite population are cross-classified into c classes and d domains. The number of units in each cell (i.e. each combination of class and domain) is known. Let $\boldsymbol{y}_{sij}$ be the vector of sample values from the ijth cell, and $\boldsymbol{y}_{rij}$ be the corresponding vector of nonsamples. Assume the following model for $\boldsymbol{y}_{tij} = (\boldsymbol{y}'_{sij} : \boldsymbol{y}'_{rij})'$:

$$\begin{aligned} E(\boldsymbol{y}_{tij}) &= \mu_{ij}\boldsymbol{1}, & i &= 1, \ldots, c, \\ D(\boldsymbol{y}_{tij}) &= \sigma^2_{ij}[(1 - \rho_{ij})\boldsymbol{I} + \rho_{ij}\boldsymbol{11}'], & j &= 1, \ldots, d, \\ Cov(\boldsymbol{y}_{tij}, \boldsymbol{y}_{ti'j'}) &= \boldsymbol{0}, \quad \text{when } i \neq i' \text{ or } j \neq j'. \end{aligned}$$

(a) Obtain the BLUP of each domain total and the corresponding MSEP, and observe that the BLUP for a domain total has a large MSEP if the sample size from any particular cell in that domain is small, and the BLUP cannot be obtained if there is no sampled unit from a particular cell in that domain.
(b) Simplify the model by assuming $E(\boldsymbol{y}_{tij}) = \mu_i\boldsymbol{1}$, and obtain the resulting BLUP of the domain totals and the corresponding variances. Observe that the BLUP can be obtained as long as there is at least one sampled unit from each class.
(c) By comparing the MSEP expressions of parts (a) and (b), describe how the MSEP is reduced in the simplified model.

Chapter 8

Misspecified or Unknown Dispersion

The results of Chapters 3, 4 and 7 are based on the crucial assumption that the error dispersion matrix $\sigma^2 \boldsymbol{V}$ in the linear model $(\boldsymbol{y}, \boldsymbol{X\beta}, \sigma^2\boldsymbol{V})$ is known, up to the unspecified scale factor σ^2. The expression for the BLUE of an estimable parametric function, for instance, depends on this dispersion matrix and cannot be computed when the matrix $\boldsymbol{V}$ is unknown. As we shall see in this chapter however, there are many practical situations where the dispersion matrix is unknown.

In models with unknown dispersion, a simple strategy may be to use the least squares estimator (LSE), which is known to be unbiased. This amounts to using the BLUE with a linear model with *misspecified* dispersion matrix. In Section 8.1, we look at the consequences of using an incorrect dispersion matrix. The intention is to check if such misspecification may not matter in some situations, and measure how much it matters in other situations.

Sometimes one may have information about the dispersion matrix, say an estimated $\boldsymbol{V}$ from previous data. The possibility of inserting this estimate in the expression for the BLUE is examined in Section 8.2. If no information at all is available about the error dispersion matrix and it is *completely unspecified*, then it is impossible to derive any reasonable inference procedure. This is because the number of unknown parameters far exceeds the size of the data set. In fact, the number of unknown parameters in the dispersion matrix alone is $n(n+1)/2$, all of which have to be estimated using just n observations of the response and the k explanatory variables! Thus, we can proceed only if there is at least partial knowledge of the dispersion matrix, say in terms of a functional form for the elements of the matrix, making these depend on some reasonably small number of unknowns. In such a case, the inference problem at hand involves the estimation of the unspecified parameters that determine $\boldsymbol{V}$, *as well as* that of $\boldsymbol{\beta}$. A few general strategies of estimation are considered in Section 8.2.

In the subsequent sections we discuss estimation strategies that exploit the functional forms of $\boldsymbol{V}$ in various special cases. A very important special case of partially unknown dispersion matrix is the mixed effects linear model, also known as the variance components model. This model is considered in Section 8.3. The situations where correlation of observations is attributable to their temporal or spatial proximity are dealt with in Section 8.4. The case of uncorrelated errors with unequal variances is discussed in Section 8.5. Some related problems of signal processing are outlined in Section 8.6.

8.1 Misspecified dispersion matrix

Apart from the possibility of oversight, incorrect specification of the dispersion matrix can occur for various other reasons. If the dispersion matrix is unknown, one is tempted to work with the least squares method, which amounts to using the best linear unbiased estimator *after assuming a homogeneous and uncorrelated error structure.* After all, the LSE of $\boldsymbol{\beta}$ is proven to be unbiased (see Exercise 5.47). For high dimensional data (with a large number of explanatory variables), it is a common practice to use a simplified form of the dispersion structure to control statistical as well as computational errors. This is another example of misspecified dispersion matrix, whose consequences need to be understood. Whatever be the presumed form of the dispersion matrix $\boldsymbol{V}$, an iterative method is often used to estimate it, and an LSE is a common choice of initial iterate. The quality of the initial iterate may be crucial to the convergence of the iterative procedure. Some iterative procedures for fitting the generalized linear model (see Section 5.7) consist of estimating the dispersion matrix and computing a weighted least squares estimator WLSE at every stage of the iteration. The estimated dispersion matrix at any given stage is likely to be different from the 'true' dispersion matrix.

The extent of misspecification of $\boldsymbol{V}$ can sometimes be marginal, for instance, in the final stages of an iterative procedure. The effect of small perturbations in $\boldsymbol{V}$ on the WLSE is studied by several authors (see Strand 1974, Neuwirth 1984, Štulajter, 1990). In this section we consider possibly larger misspecifications, but confine the discussion to the case where the 'assumed' dispersion matrix is $\sigma^2\boldsymbol{I}$, so that the BLUE under the assumed model is the LSE.

The consequences of incorrect specification of the dispersion matrix may be appreciated through the following example.

Example 8.1. Suppose the true model is $(\boldsymbol{y}, \boldsymbol{X}\boldsymbol{\beta}, \sigma^2\boldsymbol{V})$, where

$$\boldsymbol{X} = \begin{pmatrix} 1 & 0 & 1 \\ 1 & 0 & -1 \\ 1 & 0 & 1 \\ 1 & 0 & -1 \\ 1 & 1 & 1 \\ 1 & 1 & -1 \\ 1 & 1 & 1 \\ 1 & 1 & -1 \end{pmatrix}, \quad \text{and} \quad \boldsymbol{V} = \begin{pmatrix} 1 & 0 & 0 & 0 & 0 & 0 & 0 & 0 \\ 0 & 1 & 0 & 0 & 0 & 0 & 0 & 0 \\ 0 & 0 & 1 & 0 & 0 & 0 & 0 & 0 \\ 0 & 0 & 0 & 1 & 0 & 0 & 0 & 0 \\ 0 & 0 & 0 & 0 & a & 0 & 0 & 0 \\ 0 & 0 & 0 & 0 & 0 & a & 0 & 0 \\ 0 & 0 & 0 & 0 & 0 & 0 & a & 0 \\ 0 & 0 & 0 & 0 & 0 & 0 & 0 & a \end{pmatrix},$$

and a is a positive number (not necessarily equal to 1). How does the dispersion of the LSE (which would be the BLUE if $\boldsymbol{V}$ had been equal to $\boldsymbol{I}$) compare with that of the BLUE?

The dispersion of the LSE is $\sigma^2(\boldsymbol{X}'\boldsymbol{X})^{-1}\boldsymbol{X}'\boldsymbol{V}\boldsymbol{X}(\boldsymbol{X}'\boldsymbol{X})^{-1}$, which in this example, turns out to be

$$D\left(\widehat{\boldsymbol{\beta}}_{LS}\right) = \sigma^2 \begin{pmatrix} 1/4 & -1/4 & 0 \\ -1/4 & (1+a)/4 & 0 \\ 0 & 0 & (1+a)/16 \end{pmatrix}.$$

On the other hand, the dispersion of the BLUE of $\boldsymbol{\beta}$ is $\sigma^2(\boldsymbol{X}'\boldsymbol{V}^{-1}\boldsymbol{X})^{-1}$, which simplifies to

$$D\left(\widehat{\boldsymbol{\beta}}_{BLU}\right) = \sigma^2 \begin{pmatrix} 1/4 & -1/4 & 0 \\ -1/4 & (1+a)/4 & 0 \\ 0 & 0 & a/4(1+a) \end{pmatrix}.$$

If we write $\boldsymbol{\beta}$ as $(\beta_0 : \beta_1 : \beta_2)'$, then it is clear that $Var(\widehat{\beta}_{i,LS}) = Var(\widehat{\beta}_{i,BLUE})$ for $i = 0, 1$, but $Var(\widehat{\beta}_{2,LS})/Var(\widehat{\beta}_{2,BLUE}) = (1+a)^2/4a$, a factor which grows without bound as a moves away from 1. Thus, while the LSE can sometimes be as good as the BLUE, it can also be much worse.

Note that when a is very small, the last four elements of the response vector carry very accurate information about $\beta_0 + \beta_1 + \beta_2$ and $\beta_0 + \beta_1 - \beta_2$. A combination of the last four observations may be used to estimate β_2 precisely, irrespective of the values of the first four observations. The LSE fails to exploit this advantage. Conversely, when a is very large, the LSE fails to attach less importance to the last four observations, thus inheriting the large amount of uncertainty associated with them. □

8.1.1 *Tolerable misspecification**

Proposition 8.2. *The BLUE of all estimable LPFs in the linear model* $(\boldsymbol{y}, \boldsymbol{X\beta}, \sigma^2\boldsymbol{V})$ *are the same as the corresponding LSEs with probability 1 if and only if the matrices* $\boldsymbol{X}$ *and* $\boldsymbol{V}$ *satisfy one of the following equivalent conditions.*
(a) $\mathcal{C}(\boldsymbol{VX}) \subseteq \mathcal{C}(\boldsymbol{X})$,
(b) $\boldsymbol{P}_{\!X}\boldsymbol{V}$ *is symmetric.*

Proof. We do not really have to consider *all* estimable LPFs; it is enough to consider $\boldsymbol{X\beta}$ only. The LSE of $\boldsymbol{X\beta}$ is $\boldsymbol{P}_{\!X}\boldsymbol{y}$, which is unbiased. A necessary and sufficient condition for this to be the BLUE with probability 1 is that it is uncorrelated with all LZFs. The latter condition is the same as $\boldsymbol{P}_{\!X}\boldsymbol{V}(\boldsymbol{I}-\boldsymbol{P}_{\!X}) = 0$, i.e. $\mathcal{C}(\boldsymbol{VP}_{\!X}) \subseteq \mathcal{C}(\boldsymbol{X})$. Since $\mathcal{C}(\boldsymbol{VP}_{\!X}) = \mathcal{C}(\boldsymbol{VX})$, the necessary and sufficient condition reduces to $\mathcal{C}(\boldsymbol{VX}) \subseteq \mathcal{C}(\boldsymbol{X})$. This proves part (a).

It is clear from the above arguments that the condition (a) is equivalent to $\boldsymbol{P}_{\!X}\boldsymbol{V}(\boldsymbol{I}-\boldsymbol{P}_{\!X}) = 0$. This can hold only if $\boldsymbol{P}_{\!X}\boldsymbol{V} = \boldsymbol{P}_{\!X}\boldsymbol{VP}_{\!X}$, i.e. $\boldsymbol{P}_{\!X}\boldsymbol{V}$ is symmetric. The reverse implication is obvious. □

Example 8.3. (Intra-class correlation structure) Suppose $\boldsymbol{1} \in \mathcal{C}(\boldsymbol{X})$ and $\boldsymbol{V}$ has the intra-class correlation structure, $\boldsymbol{V} = (1-\alpha)\boldsymbol{I} + \alpha\boldsymbol{11}'$. This structure amounts to assuming that all the observations have the same variance, and all pairs of observations have the same correlation. In order that $\boldsymbol{V}$ is nonnegative definite, α should not be less than $-1/(n-1)$. It is easy to see that $\mathcal{C}(\boldsymbol{VX}) \subset \mathcal{C}(\boldsymbol{X})$ in this case. Therefore, the LSE of any estimable LPF would be the corresponding BLUE here. □

Example 8.4. (One-way classified data with between-groups heterogeneity) Consider the model

$$y_{ij} = \mu + \tau_i + \varepsilon_{ij}, \quad j = 1,2,\ldots,n_i, \quad i = 1,2,\ldots,t,$$

with uncorrelated zero-mean errors such that $Var(\varepsilon_{ij}) = \sigma_i^2$. Let $\boldsymbol{y} = (y_{11} : \cdots : y_{1n_1} : \cdots\cdots : y_{t1} : \cdots : y_{tn_t})'$ and $\boldsymbol{\beta} = (\mu : \tau_1 : \cdots : \tau_t)'$. Once the corresponding $\boldsymbol{X}$ and $\boldsymbol{V}$ matrices are identified, it is easy to check that $\boldsymbol{VX} = \boldsymbol{XT}$, where

$$\boldsymbol{T} = \begin{pmatrix} 0 & 0 & 0 & \ldots & 0 \\ \sigma_1^2 & \sigma_1^2 & 0 & \ldots & 0 \\ \sigma_2^2 & 0 & \sigma_2^2 & \ldots & 0 \\ \vdots & \vdots & \vdots & \ddots & \vdots \\ \sigma_t^2 & 0 & 0 & \ldots & \sigma_t^2 \end{pmatrix}.$$

It follows that the LSE of every estimable LPF would be its BLUE, in spite of the heterogeneity between the groups. □

Example 8.5. (Two-way classified data with interaction and heterogeneity between groups) Consider the model

$$y_{ijk} = \mu + \tau_i + \beta_j + \gamma_{ij} + \varepsilon_{ijk}, \quad k = 1, \ldots, n_{ij},\ i = 1, \ldots, t,\ j = 1, \ldots, b,$$

with uncorrelated zero-mean errors such that $Var(\varepsilon_{ijk}) = \sigma_{ij}$. Instead of using the messy expression of $\boldsymbol{VX}$, write $\boldsymbol{V}$ as $\sum_{i,j} \boldsymbol{V}_{ij}$, where $\boldsymbol{V}_{ij}$ is obtained from $\boldsymbol{V}$ by replacing with 0 all the diagonal elements except those in the n_{ij} positions where σ_{ij} occurs. The multiplication of $\boldsymbol{V}_{ij}$ with $\boldsymbol{X}$ would involve only those rows of $\boldsymbol{X}$ which correspond to $y_{ij1}, y_{ij2}, \ldots, y_{ijn_{ij}}$. These rows of $\boldsymbol{X}$ are identical to one another. The product $\boldsymbol{V}_{ij}\boldsymbol{X}$, therefore, consists of repeated rows at the locations corresponding to $y_{ij1}, y_{ij2}, \ldots, y_{ijn_{ij}}$, and zero everywhere else. This is a matrix of rank one, and $\mathcal{C}(\boldsymbol{V}_{ij}\boldsymbol{X})$ is spanned by the single column of $\boldsymbol{X}$ that corresponds to the ijth interaction term. It follows that $\mathcal{C}(\boldsymbol{VX}) \subseteq \mathcal{C}(\boldsymbol{X})$. Therefore, the LSE of an estimable LPF is robust against heterogeneity between the groups featuring different combinations of τ_is and β_js.

Another way to appreciate this result is to view the two-way model with interactions as a reparametrization of the one-way model with $p \times q$ groups. The latter set-up has already been explored in the previous example. □

Example 8.6. (Seemingly Unrelated Regression (SUR) model) This model consists of a few apparently unrelated models with equal number of observations,

$$\boldsymbol{y}_i = \boldsymbol{X}_i\boldsymbol{\beta}_i + \boldsymbol{\varepsilon}_i,\ E(\boldsymbol{\varepsilon}_i) = 0,\ D(\boldsymbol{\varepsilon}_i) = \sigma_{i,i}\boldsymbol{I},\ i = 1, 2, \ldots, p,$$
$$Cov(\boldsymbol{\varepsilon}_i, \boldsymbol{\varepsilon}_j) = \sigma_{i,j}\boldsymbol{I},\ i, j = 1, 2, \ldots, p.$$

The only connection among the models $(\boldsymbol{y}_i, \boldsymbol{X}_i\boldsymbol{\beta}_i, \sigma_{i,i}\boldsymbol{I})$, $i = 1, \ldots, p$ is through the covariance condition. The special case where $\boldsymbol{X}_i$ is the same for all i can be interpreted as a multivariate linear model, with the ith equation describing the ith characteristic of the response. Once the models are combined to form a single model, $y_{ij1}, y_{ij2}, \ldots, y_{ijn_{ij}}$ it is fairly easy to see that $\boldsymbol{P}_X$ is block diagonal with $\boldsymbol{P}_{X_1}, \ldots, \boldsymbol{P}_{X_p}$ along its diagonals. Also, $\boldsymbol{V}$ can be partitioned into $p \times p$ blocks so that $\sigma_{i,j}\boldsymbol{I}$ in the ijth block. The condition $\boldsymbol{P}_X\boldsymbol{V} = \boldsymbol{V}\boldsymbol{P}_X$ is equivalent to $\sigma_{i,j}(\boldsymbol{P}_{X_i} - \boldsymbol{P}_{X_j}) = 0$ for all $i \neq j$. This condition holds if $\sigma_{ij} = 0$ for all $i \neq j$, that is, the 'seemingly' unrelated models are really uncorrelated. Another sufficient condition is $\boldsymbol{P}_{X_i} = \boldsymbol{P}_{X_j}$ for all $i \neq j$, which is essentially the case of the linear model with multivariate response. □

Proposition 8.2 only gives necessary and sufficient conditions to check whether the dispersion matrix $\boldsymbol{V}$ has a form that one can afford to ignore. These conditions happens to be satisfied by the matrix $\boldsymbol{V}$ for the special cases considered in the foregoing examples. However, for a more complete understanding of the class of $\boldsymbol{V}$ for which the LSE can serve as BLUE, we need a characterization of its structure, which is provided by the following result.

Proposition 8.7. *The BLUE of all estimable LPFs in the linear model $(\boldsymbol{y}, \boldsymbol{X\beta}, \sigma^2\boldsymbol{V})$ are the same as the corresponding LSEs with probability 1 if and only if $\boldsymbol{V}$ can be written in the form*

$$\boldsymbol{V} = \boldsymbol{P}_X\boldsymbol{A}\boldsymbol{P}_X + (\boldsymbol{I} - \boldsymbol{P}_X)\boldsymbol{B}(\boldsymbol{I} - \boldsymbol{P}_X) + c\boldsymbol{I},$$

where $\boldsymbol{A}$ and $\boldsymbol{B}$ are symmetric nonnegative definite matrices and c is a nonnegative constant.

Proof. It is easy to see that if $\boldsymbol{V}$ has the prescribed form, then $\boldsymbol{P}_X\boldsymbol{V}$ is symmetric, and hence Proposition 8.2 can be used. In order to prove the converse, let $\boldsymbol{P}_X\boldsymbol{V} = \boldsymbol{V}\boldsymbol{P}_X$, and write $\boldsymbol{V}$ as

$$\boldsymbol{V} = [\boldsymbol{P}_X + (\boldsymbol{I} - \boldsymbol{P}_X)]\boldsymbol{V}[\boldsymbol{P}_X + (\boldsymbol{I} - \boldsymbol{P}_X)].$$

If the expression on the right-hand side is expanded, four terms are obtained. The two cross terms turn out to be zero because of the condition $\boldsymbol{P}_X\boldsymbol{V} = \boldsymbol{V}\boldsymbol{P}_X$. Therefore, $\boldsymbol{V} = \boldsymbol{P}_X\boldsymbol{V}\boldsymbol{P}_X + (\boldsymbol{I} - \boldsymbol{P}_X)\boldsymbol{V}(\boldsymbol{I} - \boldsymbol{P}_X)$. The last expression is of the form prescribed in the proposition. □

Example 8.8. (A mixed effects model) Consider the model

$$\boldsymbol{y} = \sum_{i=1}^{p} \boldsymbol{X}_i(\boldsymbol{\beta}_i + \boldsymbol{\gamma}_i) + \boldsymbol{\varepsilon},$$

where $\boldsymbol{\beta}_1, \ldots \boldsymbol{\beta}_p$ are fixed parameters and $\boldsymbol{\varepsilon}$ and $\boldsymbol{\gamma}_1, \ldots, \boldsymbol{\gamma}_p$ are pair-wise uncorrelated, zero mean random vectors with $D(\boldsymbol{\varepsilon}) = \sigma^2\boldsymbol{I}$ and $D(\boldsymbol{\gamma}_i) = \boldsymbol{V}_i$, $i = 1, \ldots, p$. The model equation can be rewritten by putting together all the random terms, so that the effective dispersion matrix, $\boldsymbol{V} = D(\sum_{i=1}^{p} \boldsymbol{X}_i\boldsymbol{\gamma}_i + \boldsymbol{\varepsilon}) = \sigma^2\boldsymbol{I} + \sum_{i=1}^{p} \boldsymbol{X}_i\boldsymbol{V}_i\boldsymbol{X}_i'$. This is clearly in the form described in Proposition 8.7, where $c = \sigma^2$, $\boldsymbol{B} = \boldsymbol{0}$ and $\boldsymbol{A}$ is a block diagonal matrix with the matrices $(\boldsymbol{X}_i'\boldsymbol{X}_i)\boldsymbol{X}_i'\boldsymbol{V}_i\boldsymbol{X}_i(\boldsymbol{X}_i'\boldsymbol{X}_i)^-$, $i = 1, \ldots, p$ appearing as the diagonal blocks. The LSEs should be good enough for $\boldsymbol{\beta}$ in this model, even if σ^2 and $\boldsymbol{V}_1, \ldots, \boldsymbol{V}_p$ are unspecified. □

Apart from the three equivalent conditions given in Propositions 8.2 and 8.7, various other equivalent conditions have been derived by Rao (1967), Zyskind (1967) and several other authors. Puntanen and Styan (1989) and Lin (1993) survey the literature and catalog about 30 different equivalent conditions (see also Styan, 1973)! Kempthorne, in his discussion of Puntanen and Styan's (1989) article rightly points out that most of these 'equivalent' conditions are algebraic exercises that do not provide much additional insight to the problem. Nevertheless, the problem has continued to interest researchers; see Tian (2007), Tian and Puntanen (2009), Isotalo and Puntanen (2009), Liu (2009), Haslett and Puntanen (2010) and Haslett et al. (2014). Krämer (1980) and Mathew (1985) consider the possibility that the LSE may coincide with the BLUE if the observation vector $\boldsymbol{y}$ happens to lie in a particular subspace of $\mathbb{R}^n$. Mathew and Bhimasankaram (1983b), Mathew (1983) and Hauke et al. (2012) give some conditions under which an LPF would have a common BLUE under the models $(\boldsymbol{y}, \boldsymbol{X\beta}, \sigma^2\boldsymbol{V})$ and $(\boldsymbol{y}, \boldsymbol{X\beta}, \sigma^2\boldsymbol{U})$.

Even if the LSE coincides with the BLUE, does this mean that the dispersion structure can be completely ignored? This question may be answered by examining the usual estimator of the variance of the LSE of an estimable LPF. The following proposition provides conditions under which this estimator is unaffected, when $\boldsymbol{V}$ is 'assumed' to be $\boldsymbol{I}$.

Proposition 8.9. *Let $\mathcal{M}_V$ and $\mathcal{M}_I$ denote the models $(\boldsymbol{y}, \boldsymbol{X\beta}, \sigma^2\boldsymbol{V})$ and $(\boldsymbol{y}, \boldsymbol{X\beta}, \sigma^2\boldsymbol{I})$, respectively, such that $\rho(\boldsymbol{X} : \boldsymbol{V}) = n$.*

(a) The usual estimator of variance of the 'BLUE' of every estimable LPF, computed from the model $\mathcal{M}_I$, is appropriate for the model $\mathcal{M}_V$ if and only if $\boldsymbol{P_X V P_X} + (\boldsymbol{I} - \boldsymbol{P_X})\boldsymbol{V}(\boldsymbol{I} - \boldsymbol{P_X}) = c\boldsymbol{I}$ for some $c \geq 0$.
(b) The BLUE of every estimable LPF and its usual estimator of variance computed from the model $\mathcal{M}_I$ are both appropriate for the model $\mathcal{M}_V$ if and only if $\boldsymbol{V} = c\boldsymbol{I}$ for some $c \geq 0$.

Proof. We assume that $\mathcal{M}_V$ is the right model but work with the expressions obtained from the model $\mathcal{M}_I$. If $\boldsymbol{p}'\boldsymbol{\beta}$ is an estimable LPF, the variance of its LSE, as estimated from $\mathcal{M}_I$, is

$$\widehat{Var}(\boldsymbol{p}'\widehat{\boldsymbol{\beta}}_{LS})\Big|_{\mathcal{M}_I} = \frac{\boldsymbol{y}'(\boldsymbol{I} - \boldsymbol{P_X})\boldsymbol{y}}{n - \rho(\boldsymbol{X})} \cdot \boldsymbol{l}'\boldsymbol{P_X}\boldsymbol{l},$$

where $\boldsymbol{l}$ is such that $\boldsymbol{X}'\boldsymbol{l} = \boldsymbol{p}$. The variance of the LSE under the 'true' model is

$$\widehat{Var}(\boldsymbol{p}'\widehat{\boldsymbol{\beta}}_{LS})\Big|_{\mathcal{M}_V} = \frac{\boldsymbol{y}'(\boldsymbol{I}-\boldsymbol{P}_X)\{(\boldsymbol{I}-\boldsymbol{P}_X)\boldsymbol{V}(\boldsymbol{I}-\boldsymbol{P}_X)\}^-(\boldsymbol{I}-\boldsymbol{P}_X)\boldsymbol{y}}{\rho(\boldsymbol{X}:\boldsymbol{V})-\rho(\boldsymbol{X})}\cdot \boldsymbol{l}'\boldsymbol{P}_X\boldsymbol{V}\boldsymbol{P}_X\boldsymbol{l},$$

using the expression given in (7.7). The statement of the proposition stipulates that the two expressions given above must coincide for all $\boldsymbol{l}$ and all $\boldsymbol{y} \in \mathcal{C}(\boldsymbol{X}:\boldsymbol{V})$. Since $\rho(\boldsymbol{X}:\boldsymbol{V}) = n$, we must have

$$\frac{\boldsymbol{y}'(\boldsymbol{I}-\boldsymbol{P}_X)\boldsymbol{y}}{\boldsymbol{y}'(\boldsymbol{I}-\boldsymbol{P}_X)\{(\boldsymbol{I}-\boldsymbol{P}_X)\boldsymbol{V}(\boldsymbol{I}-\boldsymbol{P}_X)\}^-(\boldsymbol{I}-\boldsymbol{P}_X)\boldsymbol{y}} = \frac{\boldsymbol{l}'\boldsymbol{P}_X\boldsymbol{V}\boldsymbol{P}_X\boldsymbol{l}}{\boldsymbol{l}'\boldsymbol{P}_X\boldsymbol{l}}$$

for all $\boldsymbol{y}$ and $\boldsymbol{l}$. Substituting $\boldsymbol{y} = \boldsymbol{V}(\boldsymbol{I}-\boldsymbol{P}_X)\boldsymbol{m}$ in the above expression, we have

$$\frac{\boldsymbol{m}'(\boldsymbol{I}-\boldsymbol{P}_X)\boldsymbol{V}(\boldsymbol{I}-\boldsymbol{P}_X)\boldsymbol{V}(\boldsymbol{I}-\boldsymbol{P}_X)\boldsymbol{m}}{\boldsymbol{m}'(\boldsymbol{I}-\boldsymbol{P}_X)\boldsymbol{V}(\boldsymbol{I}-\boldsymbol{P}_X)\boldsymbol{m}} = \frac{\boldsymbol{l}'\boldsymbol{P}_X\boldsymbol{V}\boldsymbol{P}_X\boldsymbol{l}}{\boldsymbol{l}'\boldsymbol{P}_X\boldsymbol{l}} \quad \text{for all } \boldsymbol{m} \text{ and } \boldsymbol{l}. \tag{8.1}$$

Each ratio should therefore, be equal to a constant $c > 0$ that does not depend on $\boldsymbol{m}$ or $\boldsymbol{l}$. Setting the first ratio equal to c, we have

$$c\boldsymbol{m}'(\boldsymbol{I}-\boldsymbol{P}_X)\boldsymbol{V}(\boldsymbol{I}-\boldsymbol{P}_X)\boldsymbol{m} = \boldsymbol{m}'[(\boldsymbol{I}-\boldsymbol{P}_X)\boldsymbol{V}(\boldsymbol{I}-\boldsymbol{P}_X)]^2\boldsymbol{m} \quad \text{for all } \boldsymbol{m}.$$

Therefore, all eigenvalues of the matrix $c^{-1}(\boldsymbol{I}-\boldsymbol{P}_X)\boldsymbol{V}(\boldsymbol{I}-\boldsymbol{P}_X)$ are equal to their respective squares. Hence, this matrix must be an idempotent matrix which is also symmetric. It must be the orthogonal projection matrix (see Exercise A.14) for $\mathcal{C}((\boldsymbol{I}-\boldsymbol{P}_X)\boldsymbol{V})$. The latter is in general a subset of $\mathcal{C}(\boldsymbol{I}-\boldsymbol{P}_X)$. However, the condition $\rho(\boldsymbol{X}:\boldsymbol{V}) = n$ ensures that the dimensions of these two spaces are equal. Hence, the two column spaces are identical. By equating the orthogonal projection matrices of the two column spaces, we have

$$c^{-1}(\boldsymbol{I}-\boldsymbol{P}_X)\boldsymbol{V}(\boldsymbol{I}-\boldsymbol{P}_X) = \boldsymbol{I}-\boldsymbol{P}_X.$$

Since the right-hand side of (8.1) is also equal to c, we have

$$\boldsymbol{P}_X\boldsymbol{V}\boldsymbol{P}_X = c\boldsymbol{P}_X.$$

Putting the two conditions together, we have the necessary and sufficient condition $\boldsymbol{P}_X\boldsymbol{V}\boldsymbol{P}_X + (\boldsymbol{I}-\boldsymbol{P}_X)\boldsymbol{V}(\boldsymbol{I}-\boldsymbol{P}_X) = c\boldsymbol{I}$. This proves part (a).

In order to prove part (b), write $\boldsymbol{V}$ as

$$\begin{aligned}\boldsymbol{V} &= [\boldsymbol{P}_X + (\boldsymbol{I}-\boldsymbol{P}_X)]\boldsymbol{V}[\boldsymbol{P}_X + (\boldsymbol{I}-\boldsymbol{P}_X)]\\ &= \boldsymbol{P}_X\boldsymbol{V}\boldsymbol{P}_X + (\boldsymbol{I}-\boldsymbol{P}_X)\boldsymbol{V}(\boldsymbol{I}-\boldsymbol{P}_X) + \boldsymbol{P}_X\boldsymbol{V}(\boldsymbol{I}-\boldsymbol{P}_X) + (\boldsymbol{I}-\boldsymbol{P}_X)\boldsymbol{V}\boldsymbol{P}_X.\end{aligned}$$

In order that the BLUEs under the models $\boldsymbol{M}_I$ and $\boldsymbol{M}_V$ coincide, $\boldsymbol{P}_X\boldsymbol{V}$ must be symmetric, that is, the last two summands of the last expression should be zero. Part (a) implies that the estimated variances of the BLUEs for the two models agree if and only if the sum of the first two summands is $c\boldsymbol{I}$ for some $c > 0$. The two conditions hold simultaneously if and only if $\boldsymbol{V} = c\boldsymbol{I}$ for some $c > 0$. □

Example 8.10. (Intra-class correlation structure, continued) For the model of Example 8.3 assume that $\mathbf{1} \in \mathcal{C}(\boldsymbol{X})$. Then the dispersion of the BLUE of $\boldsymbol{X\beta}$ is

$$D(\boldsymbol{P}_X\boldsymbol{y}) = \sigma^2\boldsymbol{P}_X\boldsymbol{V}\boldsymbol{P}_X = \sigma^2\boldsymbol{P}_X[(1-\alpha)\boldsymbol{I} + \alpha\mathbf{1}\mathbf{1}']\boldsymbol{P}_X$$
$$= \sigma^2[(1-\alpha)\boldsymbol{P}_X + \alpha\mathbf{1}\mathbf{1}'].$$

The usual estimator of σ^2, computed from (7.6) and (7.7) is

$$\widehat{\sigma^2} = \frac{\boldsymbol{y}'(\boldsymbol{I} - \boldsymbol{P}_X)\boldsymbol{y}}{(1-\alpha)(n - \rho(\boldsymbol{X}))}.$$

Therefore, the correctly (and unbiasedly) estimated dispersion matrix of the BLUE of $\boldsymbol{X\beta}$ is

$$\widehat{\sigma^2}\boldsymbol{P}_X\boldsymbol{V}\boldsymbol{P}_X = \frac{\boldsymbol{y}'(\boldsymbol{I} - \boldsymbol{P}_X)\boldsymbol{y}}{n - \rho(\boldsymbol{X})}\left[\boldsymbol{P}_X + \frac{\alpha}{1-\alpha}\mathbf{1}\mathbf{1}'\right].$$

In contrast, the dispersion matrix computed by wrongly assuming $\alpha = 0$ (i.e. $\boldsymbol{V} = \boldsymbol{I}$) is

$$\frac{\boldsymbol{y}'(\boldsymbol{I} - \boldsymbol{P}_X)\boldsymbol{y}}{n - \rho(\boldsymbol{X})}\boldsymbol{P}_X,$$

which is clearly an underestimate. □

Part (b) of Proposition 8.9 raises a serious question about the usefulness of a large body of research done on correct estimation with misspecified dispersion matrix. It says that even if the estimators are alright, a misspecified dispersion matrix would seriously jeopardize some other aspect of inference.

Several researchers consider robustness of inference under dispersion misspecification. Kariya (1980) provides a general structure of $\boldsymbol{V}$ such that the estimator of σ^2 under two models would be identical. Jeyaratnam (1982) obtains conditions on $\boldsymbol{V}$ that ensure the validity of the likelihood ratio test which is appropriate for $\boldsymbol{V} = \boldsymbol{I}$. Bischoff (1993) discusses the robustness of D-optimal designs under dispersion misspecification, such that the point estimators of estimable LPFs remain the same. According to Proposition 8.9, the analysis of data arising out of such an experiment would be questionable for any further inference (for instance, for tests of hypotheses), unless the misspecification is rectified at that stage.

Mathew and Bhimasankaram (1983a, 1983b), like a number of researchers before them, consider the validity of the GLRT of a linear hypothesis. An interesting aspect of their work is that they look for invariance of inference for a *specific* vector LPF $\boldsymbol{A\beta}$, rather than that of the entire vector $\boldsymbol{X\beta}$. They also find conditions under which the test with a misspecified model would be a *conservative* one, even if the test statistic is wrong. For instance, they show that the likelihood ratio test of any linear hypothesis of the form $\boldsymbol{A\beta} = \boldsymbol{0}$ would be a conservative one if the true dispersion matrix has the intra-class correlation structure with $\alpha > 0$. This is perhaps one of the few studies where useful conclusions are drawn in this context of a linear model with misspecified dispersion matrix.

If we cannot get full mileage out of the LSE, we may try to do the next best thing: ask how good it is in relation to the BLUE, as we do in the next section.

8.1.2 *Efficiency of least squares estimators**

Suppose we are interested in an estimable LPF $\boldsymbol{p}'\boldsymbol{\beta}$ with $\boldsymbol{p}'\widehat{\boldsymbol{\beta}}_{BLU}$ and $\boldsymbol{p}'\widehat{\boldsymbol{\beta}}_{LS}$ representing its BLUE and LSE, respectively. When will $\boldsymbol{p}'\widehat{\boldsymbol{\beta}}_{LS}$ perform poorly? We use as an indicator of its efficiency the number

$$\eta_p = \begin{cases} Var(\boldsymbol{p}'\widehat{\boldsymbol{\beta}}_{BLU})/Var(\boldsymbol{p}'\widehat{\boldsymbol{\beta}}_{LS}) & \text{if } Var(\boldsymbol{p}'\widehat{\boldsymbol{\beta}}_{LS}) > 0, \\ 1 & \text{if } Var(\boldsymbol{p}'\widehat{\boldsymbol{\beta}}_{LS}) = 0. \end{cases}$$

Note that when $Var(\boldsymbol{p}'\widehat{\boldsymbol{\beta}}_{LS}) = 0$, $Var(\boldsymbol{p}'\widehat{\boldsymbol{\beta}}_{BLU})$ is also equal to zero, and so we define the efficiency to be equal to 1 in this case. In general η_p is a number between 0 and 1. If $\boldsymbol{V}$ is singular, then an LSE may have zero efficiency, as in the case of β_3 of Example 8.1 with $a = 0$. It follows from Exercise 7.4 that $1 - \eta_p$ is the squared multiple correlation coefficient of $\boldsymbol{p}'\widehat{\boldsymbol{\beta}}_{LS}$ with any generating set of LZFs.

Let us examine the worst case scenario for the LSE. It can be shown that

$$\eta_p \geq \frac{4\lambda_{max}(\boldsymbol{V})\lambda_{min}(\boldsymbol{V})}{(\lambda_{max}(\boldsymbol{V}) + \lambda_{min}(\boldsymbol{V}))^2}, \tag{8.2}$$

where $\lambda_{max}(\boldsymbol{V})$ and $\lambda_{min}(\boldsymbol{V})$ are the largest and smallest eigenvalues, respectively, of $\boldsymbol{V}$. See Hannan (1970) for a proof of this result when $\boldsymbol{X}$ and $\boldsymbol{V}$ have full column rank, and Wang and Chow (1994) for a proof in the general case where $\boldsymbol{X}$ may be rank deficient. When $\boldsymbol{V}$ is rank-deficient, the inequality holds trivially. It is clear that the lower bound on η is close to 1 when $\lambda_{min}(\boldsymbol{V})$ is close to $\lambda_{max}(\boldsymbol{V})$ (recall that $\lambda_{min}(\boldsymbol{V}) = \lambda_{max}(\boldsymbol{V})$ if and only if $\boldsymbol{V} = c\boldsymbol{I}$ for some $c > 0$). The bound would be close to zero if the extreme eigenvalues of $\boldsymbol{V}$ are far apart.

Example 8.11. Consider the model of Example 8.1. Since $\boldsymbol{V}$ is diagonal, the diagonal elements are its eigenvalues. The lower bound on the efficiency is $4a/(1+a)^2$. This bound is evidently attained in the case of the LSE of β_2. □

Even though the lower bound on the efficiency happens to be sharp in the above example, this is not always the case. For instance, if the third column of the $\boldsymbol{X}$-matrix of Example 8.1 is removed, then the matrices $\boldsymbol{X}$ and $\boldsymbol{V}$ satisfy the condition $\mathcal{C}(\boldsymbol{VX}) \subset \mathcal{C}(\boldsymbol{X})$. Therefore, by Proposition 8.2, $\eta_p = 1$ for all estimable $\boldsymbol{p}'\boldsymbol{\beta}$. The lower bound, however, remains $4a/(1+a)^2$ as $\boldsymbol{V}$ is not changed. The bound (8.2) is based on a worst-case scenario for a given $\boldsymbol{V}$. For a given *pair* $\boldsymbol{X}$ and $\boldsymbol{V}$, the efficiency of the LSE would depend on the interplay between these two matrices.

The next proposition provides a basis for understanding of the situations which are favourable or unfavourable to the LSE.

Proposition 8.12. *Let $\boldsymbol{p}'\boldsymbol{\beta}$ be an estimable LPF in the linear model $(\boldsymbol{y}, \boldsymbol{X\beta}, \sigma^2\boldsymbol{V})$. If the LSE of $\boldsymbol{p}'\boldsymbol{\beta}$ has nonzero variance, then its efficiency η_p is bounded from above and below by*

$$1 - \lambda_{max}(\boldsymbol{U}_2'\boldsymbol{U}_1\boldsymbol{U}_1'\boldsymbol{U}_2) \le \eta_p \le 1 - \lambda_{min}(\boldsymbol{U}_2'\boldsymbol{U}_1\boldsymbol{U}_1'\boldsymbol{U}_2),$$

where the columns of $\boldsymbol{U}_1$ and $\boldsymbol{U}_2$ form an orthonormal basis of $\mathcal{C}(\boldsymbol{C}'(\boldsymbol{I} - \boldsymbol{P}_X))$ and $\mathcal{C}(\boldsymbol{C}'\boldsymbol{P}_X)$, respectively, and $\boldsymbol{CC}'$ is a rank factorization of $\boldsymbol{V}$. The bounds are sharp.

Proof. Suppose $\boldsymbol{p}'\boldsymbol{\beta} = \boldsymbol{l}'\boldsymbol{X\beta}$, so that the LSE of $\boldsymbol{p}'\boldsymbol{\beta}$ is $\boldsymbol{l}'\boldsymbol{P}_X\boldsymbol{y}$ and the BLUE is $\boldsymbol{l}'\boldsymbol{X}\widehat{\boldsymbol{\beta}}_{BLU}$. It follows that

$$\eta_p = \frac{\boldsymbol{l}'D(\boldsymbol{X}\widehat{\boldsymbol{\beta}}_{BLU})\boldsymbol{l}}{\boldsymbol{l}'D(\boldsymbol{P}_X\boldsymbol{y})\boldsymbol{l}}.$$

Further, the difference between the above two estimators is an LZF. Therefore,

$$\begin{aligned}
D(\boldsymbol{P}_X\boldsymbol{y}) &= Cov(\boldsymbol{X}\widehat{\boldsymbol{\beta}}_{BLU} + (\boldsymbol{P}_X\boldsymbol{y} - \boldsymbol{X}\widehat{\boldsymbol{\beta}}_{BLU}), \boldsymbol{P}_X\boldsymbol{y}) \\
&= Cov(\boldsymbol{X}\widehat{\boldsymbol{\beta}}_{BLU}, \boldsymbol{P}_X\boldsymbol{y}) + Cov((\boldsymbol{P}_X\boldsymbol{y} - \boldsymbol{X}\widehat{\boldsymbol{\beta}}_{BLU}), \boldsymbol{P}_X\boldsymbol{y}) \\
&= D(\boldsymbol{X}\widehat{\boldsymbol{\beta}}_{BLU}) + Cov((\boldsymbol{P}_X - \boldsymbol{X}\widehat{\boldsymbol{\beta}}_{BLU}), \boldsymbol{P}_X\boldsymbol{y}).
\end{aligned}$$

It follows that

$$\eta_p = 1 - \frac{\boldsymbol{l}'Cov((\boldsymbol{P_X} - \boldsymbol{X}\widehat{\boldsymbol{\beta}}_{BLU}), \boldsymbol{P_X y})\boldsymbol{l}}{\boldsymbol{l}'D(\boldsymbol{P_X y})\boldsymbol{l}}.$$

By virtue of (7.1) the covariance term simplifies as below:

$$\begin{aligned}
&\sigma^{-2}Cov((\boldsymbol{P_X y} - \boldsymbol{X}\widehat{\boldsymbol{\beta}}_{BLU}), \boldsymbol{P_X y}) \\
&= \boldsymbol{P_X V P_X} - \boldsymbol{V P_X} + \boldsymbol{V}(\boldsymbol{I}-\boldsymbol{P_X})[(\boldsymbol{I}-\boldsymbol{P_X})\boldsymbol{V}(\boldsymbol{I}-\boldsymbol{P_X})]^-(\boldsymbol{I}-\boldsymbol{P_X})\boldsymbol{V P_X} \\
&= \boldsymbol{B'B} - \boldsymbol{CB} + \boldsymbol{CA}[\boldsymbol{A'A}]^-\boldsymbol{A'B} \\
&= \boldsymbol{B'B} - \boldsymbol{C}(\boldsymbol{I}-\boldsymbol{P_A})\boldsymbol{B} \;=\; \boldsymbol{B'B} - (\boldsymbol{B}' + \boldsymbol{A}')(\boldsymbol{I}-\boldsymbol{P_A})\boldsymbol{B} \\
&= \boldsymbol{B'B} - \boldsymbol{B}'(\boldsymbol{I}-\boldsymbol{P_A})\boldsymbol{B} \;=\; \boldsymbol{B'P_A B},
\end{aligned}$$

where $\boldsymbol{CC}'$ is a rank factorization of $\boldsymbol{V}$, $\boldsymbol{A} = \boldsymbol{C}'(\boldsymbol{I} - \boldsymbol{P_X})$ and $\boldsymbol{B} = \boldsymbol{C}'\boldsymbol{P_X}$. Hence,

$$\eta_p = 1 - \frac{\boldsymbol{l}'\boldsymbol{B}'\boldsymbol{P_A}\boldsymbol{B}\boldsymbol{l}}{\boldsymbol{l}'\boldsymbol{B}'\boldsymbol{B}\boldsymbol{l}}.$$

Let $\boldsymbol{U}_1$ and $\boldsymbol{U}_2$ be matrices with columns forming an orthonormal basis of $\mathcal{C}(\boldsymbol{A})$ and $\mathcal{C}(\boldsymbol{B})$, respectively. Then $\boldsymbol{P_A} = \boldsymbol{U}_1\boldsymbol{U}_1'$, and $\boldsymbol{Bl}$ can always be written as $\boldsymbol{U}_2\boldsymbol{q}$ for some vector $\boldsymbol{q}$. Therefore,

$$\eta_p = 1 - \frac{\boldsymbol{q}'\boldsymbol{U}_2'\boldsymbol{U}_1\boldsymbol{U}_1'\boldsymbol{U}_2\boldsymbol{q}}{\boldsymbol{q}'\boldsymbol{U}_2'\boldsymbol{U}_2\boldsymbol{q}} = 1 - \frac{\boldsymbol{q}'\boldsymbol{U}_2'\boldsymbol{U}_1\boldsymbol{U}_1'\boldsymbol{U}_2\boldsymbol{q}}{\boldsymbol{q}'\boldsymbol{q}}.$$

Since $\boldsymbol{q}$ is a completely arbitrary vector, the statement of the proposition follows (see Proposition A.26 and the subsequent discussion). □

It is clear from the above proposition that the efficiency of the LSE depends directly on the relationship between the semi-orthogonal matrices $\boldsymbol{U}_1$ and $\boldsymbol{U}_2$. Two special cases are particularly interesting.

When $\boldsymbol{U}_1'\boldsymbol{U}_2 = \boldsymbol{0}$, the lower bound is 1 from Proposition 8.12, so that the LSE of every estimable function has efficiency 1. The condition $\boldsymbol{U}_1'\boldsymbol{U}_2 = \boldsymbol{0}$ indicates orthogonality of the column spaces of $\boldsymbol{C}'\boldsymbol{P_X}$ and $\boldsymbol{C}'(\boldsymbol{I} - \boldsymbol{P_X})$, which is also equivalent to $\boldsymbol{P_X V}(\boldsymbol{I} - \boldsymbol{P_X}) = \boldsymbol{0}$. This leads us back to the condition $\boldsymbol{P_X V} = \boldsymbol{V P_X}$ which is necessary and sufficient for the equivalence of LSE and BLUE of every estimable LPF.

The other interesting special case occurs when the column spaces spanned by $\boldsymbol{U}_1$ and $\boldsymbol{U}_2$ have something in common, i.e. $\mathcal{C}(\boldsymbol{U}_1) \cap \mathcal{C}(\boldsymbol{U}_2) \neq \{\boldsymbol{0}\}$. If the vector $\boldsymbol{q}$ in the proof of Proposition 8.12 is such that $\boldsymbol{U}_2\boldsymbol{q} \in \mathcal{C}(\boldsymbol{U}_1)$, then the efficiency drops to zero. Thus, if

$$\boldsymbol{p}'\boldsymbol{\beta} \text{ is such that } \boldsymbol{p} = \boldsymbol{X}'\boldsymbol{l} \text{ and } \boldsymbol{V P_X l} \in \mathcal{C}(\boldsymbol{V}(\boldsymbol{I} - \boldsymbol{P_X})), \tag{8.3}$$

then the LSE of $\boldsymbol{p}'\boldsymbol{\beta}$ would have zero efficiency.

Remark 8.13. Let $\boldsymbol{U}_3$ be a matrix whose columns form an orthonormal basis of $\mathcal{C}(\boldsymbol{C}'(\boldsymbol{I}-\boldsymbol{P}_X))^{\perp}$. It follows that $\boldsymbol{U}_1\boldsymbol{U}_1' + \boldsymbol{U}_3\boldsymbol{U}_3' = \boldsymbol{I}$, under the notations of Proposition 8.12. Therefore, the bound of Proposition 8.12 can also be written as

$$\lambda_{min}(\boldsymbol{U}_2'\boldsymbol{U}_3\boldsymbol{U}_3'\boldsymbol{U}_2) \le \eta_p \le \lambda_{max}(\boldsymbol{U}_2'\boldsymbol{U}_3\boldsymbol{U}_3'\boldsymbol{U}_2).$$

When the number of observations in the model is much smaller than the number of parameters, $\boldsymbol{U}_3$ would have fewer columns than $\boldsymbol{U}_1$, and be easier to handle. □

Example 8.14. For the given forms of $\boldsymbol{X}$ and $\boldsymbol{V}$ in the model of Example 8.1, one can choose $\boldsymbol{C}$ as a diagonal matrix with diagonal elements given as square roots of those of $\boldsymbol{V}$. The column space of $\boldsymbol{X}$ is easily seen to be spanned by the orthogonal vectors

$$\boldsymbol{U}_1 = \begin{pmatrix} 0\\0\\0\\0\\1\\1\\1\\1 \end{pmatrix}, \qquad \boldsymbol{U}_2 = \begin{pmatrix} 1\\1\\1\\1\\0\\0\\0\\0 \end{pmatrix}, \qquad \boldsymbol{U}_3 = \begin{pmatrix} 1\\-1\\1\\-1\\1\\-1\\1\\-1 \end{pmatrix}.$$

Therefore, $\mathcal{C}(\boldsymbol{C}'\boldsymbol{P}_X)$ is spanned by the vectors $\boldsymbol{C}'\boldsymbol{U}_1$, $\boldsymbol{C}\boldsymbol{U}_2$ and $\boldsymbol{C}\boldsymbol{U}_3$, which can be easily orthogonalized. It follows that $\boldsymbol{U}_2$ can be chosen as

$$\boldsymbol{U}_2 - \begin{pmatrix} 0 & 1/2 & 1/2(1+a)^{1/2}\\ 0 & 1/2 & -1/2(1+a)^{1/2}\\ 0 & 1/2 & 1/2(1+a)^{1/2}\\ 0 & 1/2 & -1/2(1+a)^{1/2}\\ 1/2 & 0 & a^{1/2}/2(1+a)^{1/2}\\ 1/2 & 0 & -a^{1/2}/2(1+a)^{1/2}\\ 1/2 & 0 & a^{1/2}/2(1+a)^{1/2}\\ 1/2 & 0 & -a^{1/2}/2(1+a)^{1/2} \end{pmatrix}.$$

Using the representation $\boldsymbol{P}_X = \sum_{i=1}^{3} \boldsymbol{u}_i\boldsymbol{u}_i'/\|\boldsymbol{u}_i\|^2$ (see Proposition A.8), it can be verified that

$$C'(I - P_X)C$$
$$= \frac{1}{8}\begin{pmatrix} 5 & -1 & -3 & -1 & -a^{1/2} & a^{1/2} & -a^{1/2} & a^{1/2} \\ -1 & 5 & -1 & -3 & a^{1/2} & -a^{1/2} & a^{1/2} & -a^{1/2} \\ -3 & -1 & 5 & -1 & -a^{1/2} & a^{1/2} & -a^{1/2} & a^{1/2} \\ -1 & -3 & -1 & 5 & a^{1/2} & -a^{1/2} & a^{1/2} & -a^{1/2} \\ -a^{1/2} & a^{1/2} & -a^{1/2} & a^{1/2} & 5a & -a & -3a & -a \\ a^{1/2} & -a^{1/2} & a^{1/2} & -a^{1/2} & -a & 5a & -a & -3a \\ -a^{1/2} & a^{1/2} & -a^{1/2} & a^{1/2} & -3a & -a & 5a & -a \\ a^{1/2} & -a^{1/2} & a^{1/2} & -a^{1/2} & -a & -3a & -a & 5a \end{pmatrix}.$$

An orthonormal basis for $\mathcal{C}(C(I - P_X))^{\perp}$ is obtained from the three eigenvectors of the above matrix which correspond to zero eigenvalues. A possible choice of this basis is the set of columns of the matrix

$$U_3 = \begin{pmatrix} 1/8^{1/2} & 1/8^{1/2} & a^{1/2}/2(1+a)^{1/2} \\ 1/8^{1/2} & 1/8^{1/2} & -a^{1/2}/2(1+a)^{1/2} \\ 1/8^{1/2} & 1/8^{1/2} & a^{1/2}/2(1+a)^{1/2} \\ 1/8^{1/2} & 1/8^{1/2} & -a^{1/2}/2(1+a)^{1/2} \\ 1/8^{1/2} & -1/8^{1/2} & 1/2(1+a)^{1/2} \\ 1/8^{1/2} & -1/8^{1/2} & -1/2(1+a)^{1/2} \\ 1/8^{1/2} & -1/8^{1/2} & 1/2(1+a)^{1/2} \\ 1/8^{1/2} & -1/8^{1/2} & -1/2(1+a)^{1/2} \end{pmatrix}.$$

We are now ready to compute the bounds on η_p: Remark 8.13 tells us that these bounds are the extreme eigenvalues of $U_2'U_3U_3'U_2$, (i.e. the extreme singular values of the matrix $U_3'U_2$). It follows from the expressions of U_2 and U_3 that

$$U_3'U_2 = \begin{pmatrix} 1/2^{1/2} & 1/2^{1/2} & 0 \\ -1/2^{1/2} & -1/2^{1/2} & 0 \\ 0 & 0 & 2a^{1/2}/(1+a) \end{pmatrix},$$

which has singular values 1, 1 and $2a^{1/2}/(1+a)$. Consequently, we have for all p

$$\frac{4a}{(1+a)^2} \le \eta_p \le 1.$$

We have earlier found a p (equal to $(0:0:1)'$) for which the lower bound of efficiency is achieved, and two other values of p (equal to $(1:0:0)'$ and $(0:1:0)'$) for which the upper bound is achieved. Note that in the special case $V = I$ (i.e. $a = 1$), the lower bound is also equal to 1.

Let us briefly look into the special case $a = 0$. The choice $\boldsymbol{p} = (0:0:1)'$ corresponds to $\boldsymbol{p} = \boldsymbol{X}'\boldsymbol{l}$ with $\boldsymbol{l} = (0:0:0:0:0:0:\frac{1}{2}:-\frac{1}{2})'$. It is easy to see that $\boldsymbol{V}\boldsymbol{P}_X\boldsymbol{l} = \frac{1}{8}(1:-1:1:-1:0:0:0:0)'$. Also, the vector $\boldsymbol{u}_4 = (1:-1:1:-1:-1:1:-1:1)'$ is such that $\boldsymbol{V}\boldsymbol{u}_4$ is proportional to $\boldsymbol{V}\boldsymbol{P}_X\boldsymbol{l}$ while $\boldsymbol{u}_4 \in \mathcal{C}(\boldsymbol{I}-\boldsymbol{P}_X)$. Therefore, $\boldsymbol{V}\boldsymbol{P}_X\boldsymbol{l} \in \mathcal{C}(\boldsymbol{V}(\boldsymbol{I}-\boldsymbol{P}_X))$, and $\boldsymbol{p}'\boldsymbol{\beta}$ satisfies the condition of (8.3). As expected, the LSE of $\boldsymbol{p}'\boldsymbol{\beta}$ has zero efficiency in this case. □

When $\boldsymbol{V}$ and $\boldsymbol{X}$ are both full-rank, one can consider an indicator of the efficiency of the LSE of the vector parameter $\boldsymbol{\beta}$. One such measure is

$$\eta = \frac{\det(D(\widehat{\boldsymbol{\beta}}_{BLU}))}{\det(D(\widehat{\boldsymbol{\beta}}_{LS}))}.$$

Bloomfield and Watson (1975) and Knott (1975) show that

$$\eta \geq \prod_{i=1}^{k} \frac{4\lambda_i\lambda_{n-i+1}}{(\lambda_i + \lambda_{n-i+1})^2},$$

where $\lambda_1 \geq \cdots \geq \lambda_n$ are the eigenvalues of $\boldsymbol{V}$, and the number of observations (n) is assumed to be at least twice as large as the number of parameters (k). It is clear that the lower bound can be quite small when the eigenvalues are not of the same order. Like (8.2), the above lower bound also ignores the interplay between $\mathcal{C}(\boldsymbol{X})$ and $\mathcal{C}(\boldsymbol{V})$, and assumes a worst case scenario for $\boldsymbol{X}$. Watson (1967) shows that η can be expressed as

$$\eta = \prod_{i=1}^{k}(1-\rho_i^2),$$

where $\rho_1, \ldots, \rho_k$ are the canonical correlations between $\boldsymbol{X}\widehat{\boldsymbol{\beta}}_{LS}$ and the LZF vector $(\boldsymbol{I}-\boldsymbol{P}_X)\boldsymbol{y}$. This result provides an interesting interpretation of η. The vector $\boldsymbol{X}\widehat{\boldsymbol{\beta}}_{LS}$ is the sum of $\boldsymbol{X}\widehat{\boldsymbol{\beta}}_{BLU}$ and a vector of LZFs. The added LZFs account for the larger dispersion of $\boldsymbol{X}\widehat{\boldsymbol{\beta}}_{LS}$ than the corresponding BLUE. The canonical correlations measure the extent of contamination of the BLUEs by the LZFs.

Krämer and Donninger (1987) work with yet another ratio,

$$\frac{\mathrm{tr}(D(\boldsymbol{X}\widehat{\boldsymbol{\beta}}_{BLU}))}{\mathrm{tr}(D(\boldsymbol{X}\widehat{\boldsymbol{\beta}}_{LS}))},$$

as an indicator of efficiency of the LSE. Puntanen (1987) provides a review of various measures of efficiency of the LSE. Tilke (1993) obtains efficiency expressions for covariance structures arising in spatial data.

8.1.3 *Effect on the estimated variance of LSEs**

Let us now consider the effect of misspecified error dispersion matrix on the usual estimator of the *variance* of the LSE of an estimable LPF $\boldsymbol{p}'\boldsymbol{\beta}$. Let the true dispersion matrix be $\sigma^2\boldsymbol{V}$. If $\boldsymbol{V}$ is positive definite, Swindel (1968) shows that

$$\frac{\lambda_{k+1}+\cdots+\lambda_n}{(n-k)\lambda_1} \le \frac{E[\widehat{Var}(\boldsymbol{p}'\widehat{\boldsymbol{\beta}}_{LS})]}{Var(\boldsymbol{p}'\widehat{\boldsymbol{\beta}}_{LS})} \le \frac{\lambda_1+\cdots+\lambda_{n-k}}{(n-k)\lambda_n}, \qquad (8.4)$$

where $\lambda_1,\ldots,\lambda_n$ are the eigenvalues of $\boldsymbol{V}$ in the decreasing order, and k is the number of elements in $\boldsymbol{\beta}$. When all the eigenvalues are equal, both the bounds are equal to one. If the eigenvalues of $\boldsymbol{V}$ are scattered over several orders of magnitude, the above lower and upper bounds are much smaller and larger than 1, respectively, indicating considerable scope of under- or over-estimation of the variance.

However, for a given combination of $\boldsymbol{X}$ and $\boldsymbol{V}$ matrices, the bounds of (8.4) may not be sharp. This happens because the inequalities of (8.4) are based on the worst-case scenario for $\boldsymbol{X}$, as we have seen in the case of the bounds of efficiency given in (8.2). The following proposition would produce sharper and attainable bounds on the bias of the estimated variance of $\boldsymbol{p}'\boldsymbol{\beta}$.

Proposition 8.15. *In the above set-up, suppose $\boldsymbol{U}$ is a matrix whose columns form an orthonormal basis of $\mathcal{C}(\boldsymbol{X})$, and let $Var(\boldsymbol{p}'\widehat{\boldsymbol{\beta}}_{LS}) > 0$. Then*

$$\frac{1}{\lambda_{max}(\boldsymbol{U}'\boldsymbol{V}\boldsymbol{U})}\cdot\frac{\mathrm{tr}((\boldsymbol{I}-\boldsymbol{P}_X)\boldsymbol{V})}{n-\rho(\boldsymbol{X})} \le \frac{E[\widehat{Var}(\boldsymbol{p}'\widehat{\boldsymbol{\beta}}_{LS})]}{Var(\boldsymbol{p}'\widehat{\boldsymbol{\beta}}_{LS})} \le \frac{1}{\lambda_{min}(\boldsymbol{U}'\boldsymbol{V}\boldsymbol{U})}\cdot\frac{\mathrm{tr}((\boldsymbol{I}-\boldsymbol{P}_X)\boldsymbol{V})}{n-\rho(\boldsymbol{X})}.$$

Proof. The estimated variance of the LSE of $\boldsymbol{p}'\boldsymbol{\beta}$ is

$$\widehat{Var}(\boldsymbol{p}'\widehat{\boldsymbol{\beta}}_{LS}) = \frac{\boldsymbol{y}'(\boldsymbol{I}-\boldsymbol{P}_X)\boldsymbol{y}}{n-\rho(\boldsymbol{X})}\cdot\boldsymbol{l}'\boldsymbol{P}_X\boldsymbol{l},$$

where $\boldsymbol{l}$ is such that $\boldsymbol{p}=\boldsymbol{X}'\boldsymbol{l}$. The correct variance is $\sigma^2\boldsymbol{l}'\boldsymbol{P}_X\boldsymbol{V}\boldsymbol{P}_X\boldsymbol{l}$. If $\boldsymbol{U}$ is as described in the proposition, we can write $\boldsymbol{P}_X\boldsymbol{l}$ as $\boldsymbol{U}\boldsymbol{v}$ for some vector $\boldsymbol{v}$. Therefore,

$$\frac{E[\widehat{Var}(\boldsymbol{p}'\widehat{\boldsymbol{\beta}}_{LS})]}{Var(\boldsymbol{p}'\widehat{\boldsymbol{\beta}}_{LS})} = \frac{\mathrm{tr}((\boldsymbol{I}-\boldsymbol{P}_X)E(\boldsymbol{y}\boldsymbol{y}'))\cdot\boldsymbol{l}'\boldsymbol{P}_X\boldsymbol{l}}{n-\rho(\boldsymbol{X})\cdot\sigma^2\boldsymbol{l}'\boldsymbol{P}_X\boldsymbol{V}\boldsymbol{P}_X\boldsymbol{l}}$$
$$= \frac{\boldsymbol{l}'\boldsymbol{P}_X\boldsymbol{l}}{\boldsymbol{l}'\boldsymbol{P}_X\boldsymbol{V}\boldsymbol{P}_X\boldsymbol{l}}\cdot\frac{\mathrm{tr}((\boldsymbol{I}-\boldsymbol{P}_X)\boldsymbol{V})}{n-\rho(\boldsymbol{X})} = \frac{\boldsymbol{v}'\boldsymbol{U}'\boldsymbol{U}\boldsymbol{v}}{\boldsymbol{v}'\boldsymbol{U}'\boldsymbol{V}\boldsymbol{U}\boldsymbol{v}}\cdot\frac{\mathrm{tr}((\boldsymbol{I}-\boldsymbol{P}_X)\boldsymbol{V})}{n-\rho(\boldsymbol{X})}.$$

Since $U'U = I$ and v is completely arbitrary, the statement of the proposition follows (see Proposition A.26 and the subsequent discussion). □

The case $Var(p'\widehat{\beta}_{LS}) = 0$, omitted in Proposition 8.15, is dealt with in Exercise 8.4.

Example 8.16. (Intra-class correlation structure, continued) Consider the model of Example 8.3 and suppose $\mathbf{1} \in \mathcal{C}(X)$ and $V = (1-\alpha)I + \alpha\mathbf{1}\mathbf{1}'$. The eigenvalues of V are $1 + (n-1)\alpha$ and $1-\alpha$, with the latter having multiplicity $n-1$. It follows that the bounds obtained from (8.4) are $(1-\alpha)/(1+(n-1)\alpha)$ and $1 + n\alpha/(n-k)(1-\alpha)$, respectively.

Let us now look for better bounds using Proposition 8.15. Simple calculations show that $\text{tr}((I - P_X)V)/(n - \rho(X)) = 1 - \alpha$. Further, $U'VU = (1-\alpha)I + \alpha U'\mathbf{1}\mathbf{1}'U$. One eigenvalue of this matrix is $1+(n-1)\alpha$, while the other eigenvalues are $1-\alpha$. Therefore, we have

$$\frac{1-\alpha}{1+(n-1)\alpha} \le \frac{E[\widehat{Var}(p'\widehat{\beta}_{LS})]}{Var(p'\widehat{\beta}_{LS})} \le 1,$$

when $\alpha > 0$. In this case we have a tighter upper bound than (8.4), and find that the variance of the LSE may be underestimated. When α is negative, the expressions of the lower and upper bounds interchange, indicating the possibility of overestimation of the variance of the LSE. Underestimation is ruled out in this case, and this conclusion could not have been reached by merely using (8.4). Sharpness of this pair of bounds can be demonstrated (see Exercise 8.21). □

Example 8.17. Consider the model of Example 8.1. A possible choice of U is

$$U = \left(\frac{U_1}{\|U_1\|} \; \frac{U_2}{\|U_2\|} \; \frac{U_3}{\|U_3\|} \right),$$

where U_1, U_2 and U_3 are as described on page 407. It follows that $U'VU$ is a diagonal matrix having elements a, 1 and $(1+a)/2$. Further, $\text{tr}((I - P_X)V)$ is the same as $\text{tr}(C'(I - P_X)C)$, where $V = CC'$. Using the expression of $C'(I - P_X)C$ given on page 408, we have $\text{tr}((I - P_X)V) = 5(a+1)/2$.

When $a < 1$, the lower and upper bounds given by Proposition 8.15 are 1 and $(1+a)/2a$, respectively. Evidently the variance of the LSE tends to be overestimated. The lower bound is achieved by the estimated variances of $\widehat{\beta}_1$ and $\widehat{\beta}_2$, while the upper bound is sharp in the case of $\widehat{\beta}_0 + \widehat{\beta}_1$. The bounds obtained from (8.4) are $(4a + 1)/5$ and $(4 + a)/5a$, respectively. Neither of these bounds is sharp.

When $a>1$, the lower and upper bounds of Proposition 8.15 are $(1 + a)/2a$ and 1, respectively, which indicates a tendency of underestimation of the variance of the LSE in this case. The lower bound is sharp for the estimated variance of $\widehat{\beta}_0 + \widehat{\beta}_1$, while the upper bound is achieved in the cases of $\widehat{\beta}_1$ and $\widehat{\beta}_2$. The bounds given by (8.4) are not sharp. □

8.2 Unknown dispersion: the general case

When the error dispersion matrix is unknown, a simple strategy may be to plug in an estimate of it in the expression for the BLUE. This estimate may be based on historical data or other prior information. Alternatively, the estimate of the dispersion matrix may be based on the data at hand. We shall show that in either case the plug-in estimator is unbiased, under mild conditions. We also consider in this section likelihood-based estimation of the dispersion matrix.

8.2.1 *An estimator based on prior information**

Let $\widehat{\boldsymbol{V}}$ be an estimate of $\boldsymbol{V}$ in the linear model $(\boldsymbol{y}, \boldsymbol{X\beta}, \sigma^2\boldsymbol{V})$, such that $\widehat{\boldsymbol{V}}$ is independent of $\boldsymbol{y}$. Once $\widehat{\boldsymbol{V}}$ has been estimated, $\boldsymbol{X\beta}$ may be estimated by replacing $\boldsymbol{V}$ with $\widehat{\boldsymbol{V}}$ in the expression of its BLUE. We shall refer to this estimator as the plug-in estimator, $\widehat{\boldsymbol{X\beta}}_{pi}$.

Proposition 8.18. *Under the above set-up, let $\mathcal{C}(\widehat{\boldsymbol{V}}) = \mathcal{C}(\boldsymbol{V})$ with probability 1. Then the plug-in estimator is unbiased for $\boldsymbol{X\beta}$.*

Proof. The result follows from the form of the BLUE given in Proposition 7.7, after replacing $\boldsymbol{V}$ with $\widehat{\boldsymbol{V}}$ and taking conditional expectation of the resulting expression given $\widehat{\boldsymbol{V}}$. □

Remark 8.19. Even though the plug-in estimator of Proposition 8.18 is unbiased, it may not be close to the BLUE. On the contrary, it may even have a larger dispersion than the LSE. To see this, note that the dispersion of $\widehat{\boldsymbol{X\beta}}_{pi}$ is

$$D(\widehat{\boldsymbol{X\beta}}_{pi}) = E[D(\widehat{\boldsymbol{X\beta}}_{pi}|\widehat{\boldsymbol{V}})] + D[E(\widehat{\boldsymbol{X\beta}}_{pi}|\widehat{\boldsymbol{V}})] = E[D(\widehat{\boldsymbol{X\beta}}_{pi}|\widehat{\boldsymbol{V}})].$$

The assumption $\mathcal{C}(\widehat{\boldsymbol{V}}) = \mathcal{C}(\boldsymbol{V})$ implies that $\widehat{\boldsymbol{X\beta}}_{pi} \in \mathcal{C}(\boldsymbol{X})$ almost surely (see Exercise 8.5). Therefore,

$$D(\widehat{\boldsymbol{X\beta}}_{pi}|\widehat{\boldsymbol{V}}) = D(\boldsymbol{P}_{\!X}\widehat{\boldsymbol{X\beta}}_{pi}|\widehat{\boldsymbol{V}}) = D(\boldsymbol{P}_{\!X}\boldsymbol{y} - \boldsymbol{P}_{\!X}\boldsymbol{e}_{pi}|\widehat{\boldsymbol{V}}),$$

where $\boldsymbol{e}_{pi}$ is the residual vector corresponding to $\widehat{\boldsymbol{X\beta}}_{pi}$. It follows that

$$\sigma^{-2}D(\widehat{\boldsymbol{X\beta}}_{pi}) = \boldsymbol{P}_X\boldsymbol{V}\boldsymbol{P}_X - E[Cov(\boldsymbol{P}_X\boldsymbol{y}, \boldsymbol{P}_X\boldsymbol{e}_{pi}|\widehat{\boldsymbol{V}})] \\ - E[Cov(\boldsymbol{P}_X\boldsymbol{e}_{pi}, \boldsymbol{P}_X\boldsymbol{y}|\widehat{\boldsymbol{V}})] + E[D(\boldsymbol{P}_X\boldsymbol{e}_{pi}|\widehat{\boldsymbol{V}})].$$

Now consider the situation which is most favourable to the LSE. The LSE coincides with the BLUE when $\boldsymbol{P}_X\boldsymbol{V} = \boldsymbol{P}_X\boldsymbol{V}\boldsymbol{P}_X$ (see Proposition 8.2). Whenever this condition holds, the covariance terms in the above expression are equal to zero. In such a case, the dispersion of the LSE of $\boldsymbol{X\beta}$, $\sigma^2\boldsymbol{P}_X\boldsymbol{V}\boldsymbol{P}_X$, is smaller than the dispersion of the plug-in estimator. Even if this condition holds approximately, the plug-in estimator based on prior information on $\boldsymbol{V}$ is not likely to be an improvement upon the LSE. □

Rao (1967) obtains exact confidence regions for the plug-in estimator under the assumption of normality of the errors, Wishart distribution of $\widehat{\boldsymbol{V}}$ and nonsingularity of $\boldsymbol{V}$.

The prior information on $\boldsymbol{V}$ may also be available in the form of a distribution. See Exercise 8.6 for properties of an estimator which utilizes such information.

8.2.2 *Maximum likelihood estimator*

Let us now suppose $\boldsymbol{V}$ is a function of an unknown vector parameter $\boldsymbol{\theta}$. When the scale factor (σ^2) is unspecified, we include it in $\boldsymbol{\theta}$ for notational simplicity. Thus, the model is $(\boldsymbol{y}, \boldsymbol{X\beta}, \boldsymbol{V}(\boldsymbol{\theta}))$. We assume that the error distribution is normal.

If the rank of $\boldsymbol{V}(\boldsymbol{\theta})$ is less than the sample size (n), the joint distribution of $\boldsymbol{y}$ is singular normal, having the density given in Section 2.1.4. The joint likelihood of $\boldsymbol{\beta}$ and $\boldsymbol{\theta}$ is

$$L(\boldsymbol{\beta}, \boldsymbol{\theta}) = (2\pi)^{-\frac{\rho(\boldsymbol{V}(\boldsymbol{\theta}))}{2}}|\boldsymbol{C}'(\boldsymbol{\theta})\boldsymbol{C}(\boldsymbol{\theta})|^{-\frac{1}{2}}\exp\left[-\frac{1}{2}(\boldsymbol{y}-\boldsymbol{X\beta})'\boldsymbol{V}^-(\boldsymbol{\theta})(\boldsymbol{y}-\boldsymbol{X\beta})\right],$$

where $\boldsymbol{C}(\boldsymbol{\theta})\boldsymbol{C}'(\boldsymbol{\theta})$ is a rank factorization of $\boldsymbol{V}(\boldsymbol{\theta})$. Note that the determinant $|\boldsymbol{C}'(\boldsymbol{\theta})\boldsymbol{C}(\boldsymbol{\theta})|$ reduces to $|\boldsymbol{V}(\boldsymbol{\theta})|$ when $\boldsymbol{V}(\boldsymbol{\theta})$ is nonsingular. When $\boldsymbol{V}(\boldsymbol{\theta})$ is singular, the ranges of $\boldsymbol{\theta}$ and $\boldsymbol{\beta}$ have to be restricted so that $\boldsymbol{y} - \boldsymbol{X\beta}$ is always in $\mathcal{C}(\boldsymbol{V}(\boldsymbol{\theta}))$. Further, if $\rho(\boldsymbol{V}(\boldsymbol{\theta}))$ depends on the value of $\boldsymbol{\theta}$, then the likelihood function is not bounded. Therefore, we also have to restrict the range of $\boldsymbol{\theta}$ so that the rank of $\boldsymbol{V}(\boldsymbol{\theta})$ is constant.

Since $\boldsymbol{\beta}$ may not always be estimable, we work with $\boldsymbol{X\beta}$. It follows, along the lines of the argument given in Section 7.5, that

$$\widehat{\boldsymbol{X\beta}}_{ML} = \arg\min_{\boldsymbol{X\beta}}[(\boldsymbol{y}-\boldsymbol{X\beta})\boldsymbol{V}^-(\widehat{\boldsymbol{\theta}}_{ML})(\boldsymbol{y}-\boldsymbol{X\beta})],$$

$$\widehat{\boldsymbol{\theta}}_{ML} = \arg\min_{\boldsymbol{\theta}}[\log|\boldsymbol{C}'(\boldsymbol{\theta})\boldsymbol{C}(\boldsymbol{\theta})| + (\boldsymbol{y}-\widehat{\boldsymbol{X\beta}}_{ML})'\boldsymbol{V}^-(\boldsymbol{\theta})(\boldsymbol{y}-\widehat{\boldsymbol{X\beta}}_{ML})].$$

For every value of $\boldsymbol{\theta}$ in its allowable range (such that $\boldsymbol{y} \in \mathcal{C}(\boldsymbol{X} : \boldsymbol{V}(\boldsymbol{\theta}))$ and $\rho(\boldsymbol{V}(\boldsymbol{\theta}))$ is constant), one may take $\boldsymbol{V}(\boldsymbol{\theta})$ as the true dispersion matrix and compute the BLUE of $\boldsymbol{X\beta}$ and the corresponding error sum of squares. If the latter is denoted by $R_0^2(\boldsymbol{\theta})$, then the MLE of $\boldsymbol{\theta}$ is the minimizer of

$$\log|\boldsymbol{C}'(\boldsymbol{\theta})\boldsymbol{C}(\boldsymbol{\theta})| + R_0^2(\boldsymbol{\theta})$$

(see Proposition 7.22 and the subsequent discussion).

Example 8.20. (Serially correlated errors) Suppose the errors in the linear model $(\boldsymbol{y}, \boldsymbol{X\beta}, \boldsymbol{V}(\boldsymbol{\theta}))$ follow the autoregressive model

$$\varepsilon_i = \phi\varepsilon_{i-1} + \delta_i, \qquad i = 2, 3, \ldots, n,$$

$\delta_2, \ldots, \delta_n$ being uncorrelated, each with variance σ^2. This model is the same as (5.12). In such a case, the parameter $\boldsymbol{\theta}$ consists of σ^2 and ϕ. The dispersion matrix of $\boldsymbol{\varepsilon}$ is

$$\boldsymbol{V}(\sigma^2,\phi) = \sigma^2(1-\phi^2)^{-1}\begin{pmatrix} 1 & \phi & \phi^2 & \cdots & \phi^{n-1} \\ \phi & 1 & \phi & \cdots & \phi^{n-2} \\ \phi^2 & \phi & 1 & \cdots & \phi^{n-3} \\ \vdots & \vdots & \vdots & \ddots & \vdots \\ \phi^{n-1} & \phi^{n-2} & \phi^{n-3} & \cdots & 1 \end{pmatrix},$$

which is full rank, as long as $|\phi| < 1$. A possible factorization of $\boldsymbol{V}(\boldsymbol{\theta})$ is $\boldsymbol{C}(\boldsymbol{\theta})\boldsymbol{C}'(\boldsymbol{\theta})$, where

$$\boldsymbol{C}(\boldsymbol{\theta}) = \sigma\begin{pmatrix} (1-\phi^2)^{-1/2} & 0 & 0 & \cdots & 0 \\ \phi(1-\phi^2)^{-1/2} & 1 & 0 & \ldots & 0 \\ \phi^2(1-\phi^2)^{-1/2} & \phi & 1 & \ldots & 0 \\ \vdots & \vdots & \vdots & \ddots & \vdots \\ \phi^{n-1}(1-\phi^2)^{-1/2} & \phi^{n-2} & \phi^{n-3} & \cdots & 1 \end{pmatrix}.$$

It follows that $|\boldsymbol{C}'(\boldsymbol{\theta})\boldsymbol{C}(\boldsymbol{\theta})| = \sigma^{2n}(1-\phi^2)^{n/2-1}$. Since $\boldsymbol{C}'(\boldsymbol{\theta})$ is nonsingular, one way to obtain R_0^2 for a given $\boldsymbol{\theta}$ is through the least squares analysis of the model $(\boldsymbol{C}^{-1}(\boldsymbol{\theta})\boldsymbol{y}, \boldsymbol{C}^{-1}(\boldsymbol{\theta})\boldsymbol{X}\boldsymbol{\beta}, \sigma^2\boldsymbol{I})$. Note that

$$\boldsymbol{C}^{-1}(\boldsymbol{\theta}) = \sigma^{-1}\begin{pmatrix} (1-\phi^2)^{1/2} & 0 & 0 & \cdots & 0 & 0 \\ -\phi & 1 & 0 & \cdots & 0 & 0 \\ 0 & -\phi & 1 & \cdots & 0 & 0 \\ \vdots & \vdots & \vdots & \ddots & \vdots & \vdots \\ 0 & 0 & 0 & \cdots & 1 & 0 \\ 0 & 0 & 0 & \cdots & -\phi & 1 \end{pmatrix}.$$

The MLEs of σ^2 and ϕ are obtained by minimizing $n\log\sigma^2 + (n/2-1)\log(1-\phi^2) + R_0^2(\sigma^2,\phi)$, where

$$R_0^2(\sigma^2,\phi) = \boldsymbol{y}'\boldsymbol{C}^{-1'}(\boldsymbol{\theta})\left(\boldsymbol{I} - \boldsymbol{P}_{C^{-1}(\theta)X}\right)\boldsymbol{C}^{-1}(\boldsymbol{\theta})\boldsymbol{y} = R_0^2(1,\phi)/\sigma^2.$$

It follows that the MLE of σ^2 is $R_0^2(1,\phi)/n$ and the MLE of ϕ is the minimizer of

$$(n/2-1)\log(1-\phi^2) + n\log R_0^2(1,\phi).$$

The MLE of $\boldsymbol{X}\boldsymbol{\beta}$ is its BLUE from the model $(\boldsymbol{y}, \boldsymbol{X}\boldsymbol{\beta}, \sigma^2\boldsymbol{V})$ with $\boldsymbol{V}$ replaced by $\boldsymbol{V}(\widehat{\boldsymbol{\theta}}_{ML})$. □

In general closed form expressions of the MLEs of $\boldsymbol{\theta}$ and $\boldsymbol{\beta}$ are not available. One may have to adopt a recursive strategy of alternately optimizing over $\boldsymbol{\theta}$ and $\boldsymbol{\beta}$ (see Section 8.4.1). We now describe a variation of the *maximum likelihood* (ML) method that has some useful properties.

8.2.3 *Translation invariance and REML*

Consider the model $(\boldsymbol{y}, \boldsymbol{X}\boldsymbol{\beta}, \sigma^2\boldsymbol{V}(\boldsymbol{\theta}))$. For any vector $\boldsymbol{l}$ of appropriate dimension, the perturbed response $\boldsymbol{y}+\boldsymbol{X}\boldsymbol{l}$ follows the model $(\boldsymbol{y}+\boldsymbol{X}\boldsymbol{l}, \boldsymbol{X}(\boldsymbol{\beta}+\boldsymbol{l}), \sigma^2\boldsymbol{V})$. Since the parameter $\boldsymbol{\beta}$ is unspecified, the addition of $\boldsymbol{l}$ to $\boldsymbol{\beta}$ should not change the model. If we are interested in estimating $\boldsymbol{\theta}$, then the models $(\boldsymbol{y}, \boldsymbol{X}\boldsymbol{\beta}, \sigma^2\boldsymbol{V}(\boldsymbol{\theta}))$ and $(\boldsymbol{y}+\boldsymbol{X}\boldsymbol{l}, \boldsymbol{X}\boldsymbol{\beta}, \sigma^2\boldsymbol{V}(\boldsymbol{\theta}))$ should be equivalent for this purpose. We shall refer to an estimator of $\boldsymbol{\theta}$ as *translation invariant* if it remains the same when $\boldsymbol{y}$ is replaced by $\boldsymbol{y}+\boldsymbol{X}\boldsymbol{l}$ for any $\boldsymbol{l}$. This property is also referred to as *translation invariance* in the literature. If the error distribution is such that the MLE of $\boldsymbol{\theta}$ exists, then it must be translation invariant.

Proposition 8.21. *In the above set-up, an estimator of $\boldsymbol{\theta}$ is translation invariant if and only if it depends on $\boldsymbol{y}$ through the linear zero functions alone.*

Proof. If $\widehat{\theta}(y)$ is a translation invariant estimator of θ, then

$$\widehat{\theta}(y) = \widehat{\theta}((I - P_X)y + X((X'X)^- X'y)) = \widehat{\theta}((I - P_X)y),$$

which depends on y only through $(I - P_X)y$, and the latter is a vector of LZFs. Conversely, if $\widehat{\theta}(y)$ depends on y only through LZFs, it must be a function of any generating set of LZFs. In particular, it is a function of $(I - P_X)y$. Let us express $\widehat{\theta}(y)$ as $\eta((I - P_X)y)$. Then for every vector l of appropriate dimension we have

$$\widehat{\theta}(y + Xl) = \eta((I - P_X)(y + Xl) = \eta((I - P_X)(y) = \widehat{\theta}(y).$$

Thus, $\widehat{\theta}(y)$ is translation invariant. □

The LZFs carry information about the model error (see Remark 3.16). Therefore, translation invariance is a reasonable property that we can expect an estimator of θ to possess.

As pointed out at the beginning of Section 7.3, whatever be the true dispersion, every LZF must be a function of $(I - P_X)y$, the least squares residual vector. It follows that an estimator of θ is translation-invariant if and only if it depends on y through $(I - P_X)y$.

The emphasis on the least squares residual vector can be carried further by considering the likelihood of θ constructed from it. Note that $(I - P_X)y$ is the response in the reduced linear model $((I - P_X)y, 0, \sigma^2(I - P_X)V(\theta)(I - P_X))$. The MLE of θ obtained by maximizing the likelihood function constructed from this model is called the *residual maximum likelihood* (REML) estimator. Because of the restriction of translation invariance, it is also called the *restricted maximum likelihood estimator.* In the normal case, assuming that $G(\theta)G(\theta)'$ is a rank factorization of $(I - P_X)V(\theta)(I - P_X)$, the REML estimator of θ minimizes

$$\log |G'(\theta)G(\theta)| + y'(I - P_X)[G(\theta)G(\theta)']^-(I - P_X)y$$

over all allowable θ such that $(I - P_X)y \in \mathcal{C}(G(\theta))$ and the rank of $G'(\theta)G(\theta)$ is constant.

It follows from Remark 3.48 that $y'(I - P_X)[G(\theta)G(\theta)']^-(I - P_X)y$ is the same as the error sum of squares, $R_0^2(\theta)$ computed from the model $(y, X\beta, \sigma^2 V(\theta))$. Therefore, the ML and REML methods for estimating θ differ only in the first term of the objective function that is minimized. Both the estimators are translation invariant. However, unlike the MLE, the REML estimator often accounts for the degrees of freedom utilized for estimation of the regression parameters. For instance, the 'natural' unbiased estimator of variance derived in Section 7.4 happens to be the REML estimator in the normal case (see Exercise 8.22).

Remark 8.22. Note that $|\boldsymbol{G}'(\boldsymbol{\theta})\boldsymbol{G}(\boldsymbol{\theta})|$ is the product of the nonzero eigenvalues of $\boldsymbol{G}(\boldsymbol{\theta})\boldsymbol{G}'(\boldsymbol{\theta})$. If $\boldsymbol{I} - \boldsymbol{P}_X$ is written as $\boldsymbol{U}\boldsymbol{U}'$ where $\boldsymbol{U}$ is a semi-orthogonal matrix, then the nonzero eigenvalues of $(\boldsymbol{I} - \boldsymbol{P}_X)\boldsymbol{V}(\boldsymbol{\theta})(\boldsymbol{I} - \boldsymbol{P}_X)$ and $\boldsymbol{U}'\boldsymbol{V}(\boldsymbol{\theta})\boldsymbol{U}\boldsymbol{U}'\boldsymbol{U}$ are identical. The latter matrix simplifies to $\boldsymbol{U}'\boldsymbol{V}(\boldsymbol{\theta})\boldsymbol{U}$. This matrix has full rank whenever $\boldsymbol{V}(\boldsymbol{\theta})$ has full rank. In such a case, the REML estimator of $\boldsymbol{\theta}$ is the minimizer of $\log|\boldsymbol{U}'\boldsymbol{V}(\boldsymbol{\theta})\boldsymbol{U}| + \boldsymbol{R}_0^2(\boldsymbol{\theta})$. □

Example 8.23. (Autocorrelated errors, continued) Consider the linear model of Example 8.20. Let $\boldsymbol{U}\boldsymbol{U}'$ be a rank factorization of the matrix $\boldsymbol{I}-\boldsymbol{P}_X$. Note that $\boldsymbol{U}$ is a semi-orthogonal matrix. Since $\boldsymbol{V}(\boldsymbol{\theta})$ is nonsingular for the specified range of ϕ, Remark 8.22 implies that the REML estimators of σ^2 and ϕ are found by minimizing

$$\begin{aligned}\log|\boldsymbol{U}'\boldsymbol{V}(\sigma^2,\phi)\boldsymbol{U}| &+ R_0^2(\sigma^2,\phi)\\ &= (n-k)\log\sigma^2 + \log|\boldsymbol{U}'\boldsymbol{V}(1,\phi)\boldsymbol{U}| + R_0^2(1,\phi)/\sigma^2.\end{aligned}$$

It follows that the REML estimator of σ^2 is $R_0^2(1,\phi)/(n-k)$, which is larger than the corresponding MLE. The REML of ϕ is the minimizer of

$$\log|\boldsymbol{U}'\boldsymbol{V}(1,\phi)\boldsymbol{U}| + (n-k)\log R_0^2(1,\phi).$$

In contrast, the MLE is the minimizer of $\log|\boldsymbol{V}(1,\phi)| + n\log R_0^2(1,\phi)$. □

Note that the ML and REML estimates may lie at the boundary of the parameter space and that these may not be unique. One usually has to find these estimates through iterative procedures.

Once the REML estimator of $\boldsymbol{\theta}$ is obtained, one may substitute it in $\boldsymbol{V}(\boldsymbol{\theta})$, and then substitute the latter in the expression of Proposition 7.7 to get an estimator of any estimable LPF of $\boldsymbol{\beta}$. The estimator obtained in this manner belongs to a larger class of substitution estimators, discussed next.

8.2.4 *A two-stage estimator*

Let $\boldsymbol{V}(\widehat{\boldsymbol{\theta}})$ be an estimator of $\boldsymbol{V}(\boldsymbol{\theta})$, based on the response vector $\boldsymbol{y}$ under the model $(\boldsymbol{y}, \boldsymbol{X\beta}, \boldsymbol{V}(\boldsymbol{\theta}))$. Let $\widehat{\boldsymbol{X\beta}}_{ts}$ be the estimator of $\boldsymbol{X\beta}$ obtained by plugging in $\boldsymbol{V}(\widehat{\boldsymbol{\theta}})$ for $\boldsymbol{V}(\boldsymbol{\theta})$ in the expression of its BLUE. If $\boldsymbol{V}(\widehat{\boldsymbol{\theta}})$ is a translation invariant estimator, then it is a function of $(\boldsymbol{I} - \boldsymbol{P}_X)\boldsymbol{y}$, the vector of least squares residuals. Thus, the estimation procedure for $\boldsymbol{X\beta}$ can notionally be said to have two stages: an initial stage of least squares estimation (and subsequent estimation of the nuisance parameter, $\boldsymbol{\theta}$) followed by a second stage of best linear unbiased estimation using $\boldsymbol{V}(\widehat{\boldsymbol{\theta}})$ as the dispersion matrix. We refer to this estimator as the two-stage estimator.

Proposition 8.24. *In the above set-up, let the model error* $\boldsymbol{\varepsilon} = \boldsymbol{y} - \boldsymbol{X\beta}$ *have a symmetric distribution about* $\mathbf{0}$, *and* $\boldsymbol{V}(\widehat{\boldsymbol{\theta}}) = \boldsymbol{H}(\boldsymbol{y})$ *be a translation invariant estimator of* $\boldsymbol{V}(\boldsymbol{\theta})$ *such that* $\mathcal{C}(\boldsymbol{V}(\widehat{\boldsymbol{\theta}})) = \mathcal{C}(\boldsymbol{V})$ *for all* $\boldsymbol{y} \in \mathcal{C}(\boldsymbol{X} : \boldsymbol{V})$ *and* $\boldsymbol{H}(-\boldsymbol{y}) = \boldsymbol{H}(\boldsymbol{y})$. *Then the distribution of* $\widehat{\boldsymbol{X\beta}}_{ts} - \boldsymbol{X\beta}$ *is symmetric about* $\mathbf{0}$.

Proof. The expression of the BLUE of $\boldsymbol{X\beta}$ given in Proposition 7.7 implies that

$$\widehat{\boldsymbol{X\beta}}_{ts} - \boldsymbol{X\beta} = [\boldsymbol{I} - \boldsymbol{H}(\boldsymbol{\varepsilon})(\boldsymbol{I} - \boldsymbol{P}_X)\{(\boldsymbol{I} - \boldsymbol{P}_X)\boldsymbol{H}(\boldsymbol{\varepsilon})(\boldsymbol{I} - \boldsymbol{P}_X)\}^-(\boldsymbol{I} - \boldsymbol{P}_X)]\boldsymbol{\varepsilon}.$$

The result follows from the fact that the expression on the right-hand side is multiplied by -1 whenever $\boldsymbol{\varepsilon}$ is replaced by $-\boldsymbol{\varepsilon}$. □

Thus, if $E(\widehat{\boldsymbol{X\beta}}_{ts})$ exists, then $\widehat{\boldsymbol{X\beta}}_{ts}$ is unbiased for $\boldsymbol{X\beta}$. This result is proved in the case of nonsingular $\boldsymbol{V}$ in Wang and Chow (1994).

Remark 8.25. The twin conditions of translation invariance and symmetry with respect to the data are satisfied by most of the common estimators of $\boldsymbol{V}$ that are applicable to the special cases considered in the next few sections. Proposition 8.24 implies that in all these cases the two-stage estimator would be unbiased as long as its mean exists and the error distribution is symmetric about $\mathbf{0}$. In particular, the two-stage estimator of $\boldsymbol{X\beta}$ based on the ML or REML estimator of $\boldsymbol{\theta}$ is unbiased under these conditions. □

Remark 8.26. Suppose $\boldsymbol{\eta}((\boldsymbol{I} - \boldsymbol{P}_X)\boldsymbol{y})$ is a translation invariant estimator of $\boldsymbol{\theta}$. Consider the following iterative estimation scheme, where the subscript i denotes the estimator at the ith stage of iteration.

$$\begin{aligned}
\widehat{\boldsymbol{\theta}}_i &= \boldsymbol{\eta}(\boldsymbol{y} - \boldsymbol{X}\widehat{\boldsymbol{\beta}}_{i-1}) \\
\boldsymbol{X}\widehat{\boldsymbol{\beta}}_i &= [\boldsymbol{I} - \boldsymbol{V}(\widehat{\boldsymbol{\theta}}_i)(\boldsymbol{I} - \boldsymbol{P}_X)\{(\boldsymbol{I} - \boldsymbol{P}_X)\boldsymbol{V}(\widehat{\boldsymbol{\theta}}_i)(\boldsymbol{I} - \boldsymbol{P}_X)\}^-(\boldsymbol{I} - \boldsymbol{P}_X)]\boldsymbol{y}.
\end{aligned}$$

The above recursions hold for $i \geq 1$, and $\boldsymbol{X}\widehat{\boldsymbol{\beta}}_0 = \boldsymbol{P}_X\boldsymbol{y}$. If $\widehat{\boldsymbol{\theta}}_i$ is translation invariant, then $\boldsymbol{y} - \boldsymbol{X}\widehat{\boldsymbol{\beta}}_i$ is a function of $(\boldsymbol{I} - \boldsymbol{P}_X)\boldsymbol{y}$, and hence $\widehat{\boldsymbol{\theta}}_{i+1}$ is also translation invariant. Thus, if the error distribution is symmetric about $\mathbf{0}$, and $E(\boldsymbol{X}\widehat{\boldsymbol{\beta}}_i)$ exists, then $\boldsymbol{X}\widehat{\boldsymbol{\beta}}_i$ is unbiased for every i. □

As in the case of the plug-in estimator described in Section 8.2.1, other properties of the two-stage estimator of $\boldsymbol{X\beta}$ cannot be derived without further assumptions. Eaton (1985) and Christensen (1991) show that if $\boldsymbol{V}(\widehat{\boldsymbol{\theta}};\boldsymbol{y})$ is an unbiased estimator of $\boldsymbol{V}(\boldsymbol{\theta})$, then under certain conditions on the error distribution, the dispersion of the two-stage estimator of $\boldsymbol{X\beta}$ is larger than that of the corresponding BLUE (a hypothetical estimator that is a function of the unknown $\boldsymbol{\theta}$). Further, if the dispersion of the two-stage estimator is computed in the usual way by treating the estimated $\boldsymbol{V}(\boldsymbol{\theta})$ as 'true', then under the above conditions this estimated dispersion is expected to be smaller than the dispersion of the BLUE. In other words, the two-stage estimator may have an excessively large dispersion which is likely to be underestimated.

There is some good news on the asymptotic front however (see e.g. Ullah et al., 1983) involving special structures of $\boldsymbol{V}(\boldsymbol{\theta})$ and consistent estimators of $\boldsymbol{\theta}$. These results indicate that the asymptotic dispersion of the two-stage estimator of $\boldsymbol{X\beta}$, as the sample size goes to infinity, may be the same as that of the BLUE based on known $\boldsymbol{\theta}$.

8.3 Mixed effects and variance components

The general form of the mixed effects model (also known as the mixed model) is

$$\boldsymbol{y} = \boldsymbol{X\beta} + \sum_{i=1}^{k} \boldsymbol{U}_i\boldsymbol{\gamma}_i, \tag{8.5}$$

where $\boldsymbol{U}_1, \ldots, \boldsymbol{U}_k$ are known matrices, $\boldsymbol{\beta}$ is a fixed but unspecified parameter, and $\boldsymbol{\gamma}_1, \ldots, \boldsymbol{\gamma}_k$ are random vector parameters such that $E(\boldsymbol{\gamma}_i) = 0$ and $D(\boldsymbol{\gamma}_i) = \sigma_i^2\boldsymbol{I}$ for $i = 1, \ldots, k$ and $Cov(\boldsymbol{\gamma}_i, \boldsymbol{\gamma}_j) = \boldsymbol{0}$ for $i \neq j$. The case of $k = 1$ coincides with the model $(\boldsymbol{y}, \boldsymbol{X\beta}, \sigma_1^2\boldsymbol{U}_1\boldsymbol{U}_1')$ which has been dealt with in the previous chapter. In the present context this special case is referred to as the 'fixed effects' model. Another special case where $\boldsymbol{X}$ consists of a single intercept column is referred to as the 'random effects' model. We shall refer to the fixed and random parameters of the mixed model as fixed and random *effects*, respectively.

The random effects part of the mixed model represents a special type of influence exerted by the $\boldsymbol{U}_i$'s on the response $\boldsymbol{y}$. According to the model, the effects of these are linear, but change from case to case. For instance, the effect of a batch in a production process is thought to be better represented as a random effect than as a fixed effect. Since the coefficients of the $\boldsymbol{U}_i$'s are random, it does not make sense to 'estimate' them. It may be somewhat unrealistic to presume that the mean of a random effect is always zero. However, the mean is nonrandom, and therefore it can be clubbed together with the fixed effects whenever the need arises.

It is easy to see that the model (8.5) is a special case of the model

$$(\boldsymbol{y}, \boldsymbol{X\beta}, \boldsymbol{V}(\boldsymbol{\theta})), \quad \boldsymbol{V}(\boldsymbol{\theta}) = \sum_{i=1}^{k} \sigma_i^2 \boldsymbol{V}_i, \qquad \boldsymbol{\theta} = (\sigma_1^2, \cdots \sigma_k^2)', \tag{8.6}$$

and $\boldsymbol{V}_1, \ldots, \boldsymbol{V}_k$ are known nonnegative definite matrices. This model is known as the *variance components model.* The mixed effects model (8.5) corresponds to the choice $\boldsymbol{V}_i = \boldsymbol{U}_i\boldsymbol{U}_i'$, $i = 1, 2, \ldots, k$. Conversely, any model of the above form can always be represented by (8.5) with suitable choices of the 'random effects'. We shall treat these models as equivalent to one another. Sometimes the models (8.5) and (8.6) are written in a slightly different way: by showing an additional term that represents homogeneous and uncorrelated errors. We prefer to absorb this term in the $\boldsymbol{U}_i$'s and $\boldsymbol{V}_i$'s.

We have seen in Section 8.1 that the knowledge of the parameter $\boldsymbol{\theta}$ is usually necessary for inference on $\boldsymbol{\beta}$. However, inference on $\boldsymbol{\theta}$ in the variance components model is also an important problem by its own right. This is needed, for instance, to examine the importance of various random effects or to assess the quality of estimation or prediction.

8.3.1 *Identifiability and estimability*

Recall that in the special case of the fixed effects model, a quadratic function of $\boldsymbol{y}$ turned out to be a natural estimator of σ^2 that is unbiased and translation invariant. In the general case also we may look for quadratic and unbiased estimators of $\sigma_1^2, \ldots, \sigma_k^2$. At the outset it is important to observe that one cannot always expect to to be able to identify or estimate $\sigma_1^2, \ldots, \sigma_k^2$ separately. For instance, if $k = 2$ and $\boldsymbol{V}_1 = \boldsymbol{V}_2$, then there is essentially a single variance component and σ_1^2 and σ_2^2 cannot possibly be estimated separately. Thus, the issue of identifiability (see Definition 3.26) has to be addressed first. Further, we have to examine which linear functions of $\boldsymbol{\theta}$ can be unbiasedly estimated by a quadratic estimator that may also be translation invariant. Some characterizations in this context are given below.

Proposition 8.27. *Consider the estimation of $\boldsymbol{p}'\boldsymbol{\theta}$ under the variance components model (8.6), and let the matrices $\boldsymbol{F} = ((f_{i,j}))$, $\boldsymbol{G} = ((g_{i,j}))$ and*

$\boldsymbol{H} = ((h_{i,j}))$ *be defined as*

$$f_{i,j} = \mathrm{tr}(\boldsymbol{V}_i\boldsymbol{V}_j); \qquad g_{i,j} = f_{i,j} - \mathrm{tr}(\boldsymbol{P}_X\boldsymbol{V}_i\boldsymbol{P}_X\boldsymbol{V}_j);$$
$$h_{i,j} = \mathrm{tr}((\boldsymbol{I}-\boldsymbol{P}_X)\boldsymbol{V}_i(\boldsymbol{I}-\boldsymbol{P}_X)\boldsymbol{V}_j).$$

(a) $\boldsymbol{p}'\boldsymbol{\theta}$ *is identifiable if and only if* $\boldsymbol{p} \in \mathcal{C}(\boldsymbol{F})$.
(b) There is a quadratic and unbiased estimator of $\boldsymbol{p}'\boldsymbol{\theta}$ *if and only if* $\boldsymbol{p} \in \mathcal{C}(\boldsymbol{G})$.
(c) There is a translation invariant, quadratic and unbiased estimator of $\boldsymbol{p}'\boldsymbol{\theta}$ *if and only if* $\boldsymbol{p} \in \mathcal{C}(\boldsymbol{H})$.

Proof. According to the definition of identifiability given on page 81, $\boldsymbol{p}'\boldsymbol{\theta}$ is identifiable if and only if $\boldsymbol{p}'\boldsymbol{\theta}_1 \neq \boldsymbol{p}'\boldsymbol{\theta}_2$ implies that $\boldsymbol{V}(\boldsymbol{\theta}_1) - \boldsymbol{V}(\boldsymbol{\theta}_2) \neq 0$, where $\boldsymbol{\theta}_1$ and $\boldsymbol{\theta}_2$ are any two plausible values of $\boldsymbol{\theta}$. Another way of writing this condition is

$$\|\boldsymbol{V}(\boldsymbol{\theta}_1) - \boldsymbol{V}(\boldsymbol{\theta}_2)\|_F^2 = 0 \quad \Rightarrow \quad \boldsymbol{p}'(\boldsymbol{\theta}_1 - \boldsymbol{\theta}_2) = 0.$$

The above condition is equivalent to

$$(\boldsymbol{\theta}_1 - \boldsymbol{\theta}_2)'\boldsymbol{F}(\boldsymbol{\theta}_1 - \boldsymbol{\theta}_2) = 0 \quad \Rightarrow \quad \boldsymbol{p}'(\boldsymbol{\theta}_1 - \boldsymbol{\theta}_2) = 0,$$

which simplifies to $\boldsymbol{F\theta} = \boldsymbol{0} \Rightarrow \boldsymbol{p}'\boldsymbol{\theta} = 0$. The statement of part (a) follows immediately.

In order to prove part (b), let $\boldsymbol{y}'\boldsymbol{Q}\boldsymbol{y}$ be an unbiased estimator of $\boldsymbol{p}'\boldsymbol{\theta}$, and assume without loss of generality that $\boldsymbol{Q}$ is symmetric. Then we must have $E(\boldsymbol{y}'\boldsymbol{Q}\boldsymbol{y}) = \boldsymbol{\beta}'\boldsymbol{X}'\boldsymbol{Q}\boldsymbol{X}\boldsymbol{\beta} + \sum_{i=1}^k \sigma_i^2\mathrm{tr}(\boldsymbol{Q}\boldsymbol{V}_i) = \boldsymbol{p}'\boldsymbol{\theta}$ for all appropriate $\boldsymbol{\beta}$ and $\boldsymbol{\theta}$. This gives us a pair of necessary conditions: (i) $\boldsymbol{\beta}'\boldsymbol{X}'\boldsymbol{Q}\boldsymbol{X}'\boldsymbol{\beta} = 0$ for all $\boldsymbol{\beta}$ such that $\left(\boldsymbol{I} - \boldsymbol{P}_{V(\theta)}\right)\boldsymbol{X}\boldsymbol{\beta} = \left(\boldsymbol{I} - \boldsymbol{P}_{V(\theta)}\right)\boldsymbol{y}$ and (ii) $\sum_{i=1}^k \sigma_i^2\mathrm{tr}(\boldsymbol{Q}\boldsymbol{V}_i) = \boldsymbol{p}'\boldsymbol{\theta}$ for all nonnegative $\sigma_1^2, \ldots \sigma_k^2$. The first condition essentially means that without loss of generality we can assume $\boldsymbol{X}'\boldsymbol{Q}\boldsymbol{X} = \boldsymbol{0}$ (see Exercise 8.10), which implies that $\boldsymbol{Q}$ must be of the form $\boldsymbol{T} - \boldsymbol{P}_X\boldsymbol{T}\boldsymbol{P}_X$ where $\boldsymbol{T}$ is another symmetric matrix (see Exercise A.31). The second condition is $\mathrm{tr}(\boldsymbol{Q}\boldsymbol{V}_i) = p_i$ for $i = 1, \ldots, k$, p_i being the ith component of $\boldsymbol{p}$. A consequence of the two conditions is

$$\boldsymbol{p} = \begin{pmatrix} \mathrm{tr}((\boldsymbol{T} - \boldsymbol{P}_X\boldsymbol{T}\boldsymbol{P}_X)\boldsymbol{V}_1) \\ \vdots \\ \mathrm{tr}((\boldsymbol{T} - \boldsymbol{P}_X\boldsymbol{T}\boldsymbol{P}_X)\boldsymbol{V}_k) \end{pmatrix} = \begin{pmatrix} (\mathrm{vec}(\boldsymbol{V}_1) - \mathrm{vec}(\boldsymbol{P}_X\boldsymbol{V}_1\boldsymbol{P}_X))' \\ \vdots \\ (\mathrm{vec}(\boldsymbol{V}_k) - \mathrm{vec}(\boldsymbol{P}_X\boldsymbol{V}_k\boldsymbol{P}_X)) \end{pmatrix} \mathrm{vec}(\boldsymbol{T}).$$

If we denote the matrix in the last expression by $\boldsymbol{A}$, the above condition implies that $\boldsymbol{p} \in \mathcal{C}(\boldsymbol{A}) = \mathcal{C}(\boldsymbol{A}\boldsymbol{A}') = \mathcal{C}(\boldsymbol{G})$. Conversely, if $\boldsymbol{p} \in \mathcal{C}(\boldsymbol{G})$, then we can write $\boldsymbol{p}$ as $\boldsymbol{A}\boldsymbol{t}$ for some vector $\boldsymbol{t}$. Let $\boldsymbol{T}$ be a square matrix such that

$\text{vec}(\boldsymbol{T}) = \boldsymbol{t}$, and $\boldsymbol{T}_s$ be its symmetrized version, given by $(\boldsymbol{T} + \boldsymbol{T}')/2$. Let us define $\boldsymbol{Q} = \boldsymbol{T}_s - \boldsymbol{P}_X \boldsymbol{T}_s \boldsymbol{P}_X$. It can be verified that $\boldsymbol{y}'\boldsymbol{Q}\boldsymbol{y}$ is an unbiased estimator of $\boldsymbol{p}'\boldsymbol{\theta}$.

In order to prove part (c), note that a translation invariant estimator must depend on $\boldsymbol{y}$ through $(\boldsymbol{I} - \boldsymbol{P}_X)\boldsymbol{y}$ (see Proposition 8.21). The result follows by applying part (b) to the model $((\boldsymbol{I} - \boldsymbol{P}_X)\boldsymbol{y}, \boldsymbol{0}, (\boldsymbol{I} - \boldsymbol{P}_X)\boldsymbol{V}(\boldsymbol{\theta})(\boldsymbol{I} - \boldsymbol{P}_X))$ with variance components $\sigma_i^2(\boldsymbol{I} - \boldsymbol{P}_X)\boldsymbol{V}_i(\boldsymbol{I} - \boldsymbol{P}_X)$, $i = 1, \ldots, k$. □

Remark 8.28. It can be shown that quadratic and translation invariant 'estimability' of $\boldsymbol{p}'\boldsymbol{\theta}$ implies its quadratic 'estimability' (in the sense of the above proposition), which in turn implies its identifiability (Exercise 8.9). The reverse implications are disproved via the counterexamples given in Exercises 8.23 and 8.24 (see also Rao and Kleffe, 1988). This is in contrast with the linear parametric functions of the 'fixed effects', for which the notions of identifiability and (linear) estimability coincide (see Proposition 3.27). □

We shall henceforth assume the quadratic and translation invariant estimability of the parameters of interest, without explicitly mentioning this assumption.

8.3.2 *ML and REML methods*

Consider the ML method described in Section 8.2.2 in the special case of the variance components model of (8.6), where $\boldsymbol{\theta} = (\sigma_1^2 : \cdot : \sigma_k^2)'$. We assume that the random effects have independent normal distributions, and provide the MLEs of $\boldsymbol{\theta}$ and $\boldsymbol{X\beta}$ in the next proposition.

Proposition 8.29. *In the above set-up the MLEs of $\boldsymbol{\theta} = (\sigma_1^2 : \cdots : \sigma_k^2)'$ and $\boldsymbol{X\beta}$, satisfy the equations*

$$\text{tr}(\boldsymbol{V}^-(\widehat{\boldsymbol{\theta}}_{ML})\boldsymbol{V}_i) = (\boldsymbol{y} - \boldsymbol{X}\widehat{\boldsymbol{\beta}}_{ML})'\boldsymbol{V}^-(\widehat{\boldsymbol{\theta}}_{ML})\boldsymbol{V}_i\boldsymbol{V}^-(\widehat{\boldsymbol{\theta}}_{ML})(\boldsymbol{y} - \boldsymbol{X}\widehat{\boldsymbol{\beta}}_{ML}), \quad i = 1, \ldots, k,$$

$$\boldsymbol{X}\widehat{\boldsymbol{\beta}}_{ML} = [\boldsymbol{I} - \boldsymbol{V}(\widehat{\boldsymbol{\theta}}_{ML})(\boldsymbol{I} - \boldsymbol{P}_X)\{(\boldsymbol{I} - \boldsymbol{P}_X)\boldsymbol{V}(\widehat{\boldsymbol{\theta}}_{ML})(\boldsymbol{I} - \boldsymbol{P}_X)\}^-(\boldsymbol{I} - \boldsymbol{P}_X)]\boldsymbol{y},$$

provided the MLEs of $\sigma_1, \ldots, \sigma_k^2$ are greater than 0. The above equations do not depend on the choice of the g-inverse of $\boldsymbol{V}(\boldsymbol{\theta})$.

Proof. It can be shown that as long as $\sigma_i^2 > 0$, $i = 1, \ldots, k$, $\mathcal{C}(\boldsymbol{V}(\boldsymbol{\theta})) = \mathcal{C}(\boldsymbol{V}_1 : \boldsymbol{V}_2 : \cdots : \boldsymbol{V}_k)$ (see Exercise 8.11). Therefore, $\mathcal{C}(\boldsymbol{V}(\boldsymbol{\theta}))$ and $\rho(\boldsymbol{V}(\boldsymbol{\theta}))$ do not depend on $\boldsymbol{\theta}$. We first prove the proposition in the special case where $\boldsymbol{V}(\boldsymbol{\theta})$ has full rank, and then generalize it to the possibly singular case.

When $\boldsymbol{V}(\boldsymbol{\theta})$ is nonsingular, it follows from the discussion of Section 8.2.2 that $\boldsymbol{X}\widehat{\boldsymbol{\beta}}_{ML}$ is as described above, and $\widehat{\boldsymbol{\theta}}_{ML}$ minimizes

$$\log|\boldsymbol{V}(\boldsymbol{\theta})| + (\boldsymbol{y} - \boldsymbol{X}\widehat{\boldsymbol{\beta}}_{ML})'\boldsymbol{V}^{-1}(\boldsymbol{\theta})(\boldsymbol{y} - \boldsymbol{X}\widehat{\boldsymbol{\beta}}_{ML}).$$

We now obtain the derivative of the two terms with respect to σ_i^2. We write $\boldsymbol{V}(\boldsymbol{\theta})$ as

$$\boldsymbol{V}(\boldsymbol{\theta}) = \sum_{j=1}^{k} \sigma_j^2 \boldsymbol{V}_j = \left(\sum_{\substack{j=1 \\ j \neq i}}^{n} \sigma_j^2 \boldsymbol{V}_j + \sigma_0^2 \boldsymbol{V}_i \right) + \phi \boldsymbol{V}_i = \boldsymbol{A} + \phi \boldsymbol{V}_i,$$

where σ_0^2 is a fixed positive number smaller than σ_i^2 and $\phi = \sigma_i^2 - \sigma_0^2$. If $\boldsymbol{C}\boldsymbol{C}'$ is a rank-factorization of $\boldsymbol{A}$ and $\boldsymbol{V}_i$ is expressed as $\boldsymbol{C}\boldsymbol{L}\boldsymbol{L}'\boldsymbol{C}'$, then

$$|\boldsymbol{V}(\boldsymbol{\theta})| = |\boldsymbol{A} + \phi \boldsymbol{V}_i| = |\boldsymbol{C}(\boldsymbol{I} + \phi \boldsymbol{L}\boldsymbol{L}')\boldsymbol{C}'| = |\boldsymbol{C}'\boldsymbol{C}| \cdot |\boldsymbol{I} + \phi \boldsymbol{L}\boldsymbol{L}'|.$$

If $\lambda_1, \ldots, \lambda_n$ are the eigenvalues $\boldsymbol{L}\boldsymbol{L}'$ (including possible multiplicities and zero eigenvalues), then $|\boldsymbol{V}(\boldsymbol{\theta})| = |\boldsymbol{C}'\boldsymbol{C}| \prod_{j=1}^{n}(1 + \phi\lambda_j)$. Hence,

$$\begin{aligned}
\frac{\partial \log|\boldsymbol{V}(\boldsymbol{\theta})|}{\partial \sigma_i^2} = \frac{\partial \log|\boldsymbol{V}(\boldsymbol{\theta})|}{\partial \phi} &= \sum_{j=1}^{n} \frac{\partial}{\partial \phi} \log(1 + \phi\lambda_j) \\
&= \sum_{j=1}^{n} \frac{\lambda_j}{1 + \phi\lambda_j} = \mathrm{tr}[(\boldsymbol{I} + \phi \boldsymbol{L}\boldsymbol{L}')^{-1}\boldsymbol{L}\boldsymbol{L}'] \\
&= \mathrm{tr}[(\boldsymbol{C}\boldsymbol{C}' + \phi \boldsymbol{C}\boldsymbol{L}\boldsymbol{L}'\boldsymbol{C}')^{-1}\boldsymbol{C}\boldsymbol{L}\boldsymbol{L}'\boldsymbol{C}'] \\
&= \mathrm{tr}[(\boldsymbol{A} + \phi \boldsymbol{V}_i)^{-1}\boldsymbol{V}_i] = \mathrm{tr}[\boldsymbol{V}^{-1}(\boldsymbol{\theta})\boldsymbol{V}_i].
\end{aligned}$$

Further, by differentiating both sides of the matrix identity $\boldsymbol{I} = \boldsymbol{V}(\boldsymbol{\theta})\boldsymbol{V}^{-1}(\boldsymbol{\theta})$ with respect to σ_i^2, we have

$$\boldsymbol{0} = \frac{\partial}{\partial \sigma_i^2}[\boldsymbol{V}(\boldsymbol{\theta})\boldsymbol{V}^{-1}(\boldsymbol{\theta})] = \boldsymbol{V}_i\boldsymbol{V}^{-1}(\boldsymbol{\theta}) + \boldsymbol{V}(\boldsymbol{\theta})\frac{\partial}{\partial \sigma_i^2}\boldsymbol{V}^{-1}(\boldsymbol{\theta}).$$

Hence, $\frac{\partial}{\partial \sigma_i^2}\boldsymbol{V}^{-1}(\boldsymbol{\theta}) = -\boldsymbol{V}^{-1}(\boldsymbol{\theta})\boldsymbol{V}_i\boldsymbol{V}^{-1}(\boldsymbol{\theta})$. Using these derivatives in the defining expression of $\widehat{\boldsymbol{\theta}}_{ML}$, we have the estimating equations

$$\mathrm{tr}(\boldsymbol{V}^{-1}(\widehat{\boldsymbol{\theta}}_{ML})\boldsymbol{V}_i) = (\boldsymbol{y} - \boldsymbol{X}\widehat{\boldsymbol{\beta}}_{ML})'\boldsymbol{V}^{-1}(\widehat{\boldsymbol{\theta}}_{ML})\boldsymbol{V}_i\boldsymbol{V}^{-1}(\widehat{\boldsymbol{\theta}}_{ML})(\boldsymbol{y} - \boldsymbol{X}\widehat{\boldsymbol{\beta}}_{ML})$$

for $i = 1, \ldots, k$.

Now we allow $\boldsymbol{V}(\boldsymbol{\theta})$ to be singular. Let $\boldsymbol{U}\boldsymbol{D}(\boldsymbol{\theta})\boldsymbol{U}'$ be a spectral decomposition of $\boldsymbol{V}(\boldsymbol{\theta})$, where $\boldsymbol{D}(\boldsymbol{\theta})$ is a positive definite diagonal matrix. Note that $\boldsymbol{U}$ cannot depend on $\boldsymbol{\theta}$ because $\boldsymbol{U}\boldsymbol{U}'$ is the orthogonal projection matrix for $\mathcal{C}(\boldsymbol{V}(\boldsymbol{\theta}))$, which does not depend on $\boldsymbol{\theta}$. Further, $[\boldsymbol{U}\boldsymbol{D}^{1/2}(\boldsymbol{\theta})][\boldsymbol{U}\boldsymbol{D}^{1/2}(\boldsymbol{\theta})]'$ is a rank-factorization of $\boldsymbol{V}(\boldsymbol{\theta})$, and a choice of $\boldsymbol{V}^-(\boldsymbol{\theta})$ is $\boldsymbol{U}\boldsymbol{D}(\boldsymbol{\theta})^{-1}\boldsymbol{U}'$. Therefore, it follows from the discussion of Section 8.2.2 that the MLE of $\boldsymbol{\theta}$ is obtained by minimizing

$$\log|\boldsymbol{D}(\boldsymbol{\theta})| + (\boldsymbol{U}'\boldsymbol{y} - \boldsymbol{U}'\widehat{\boldsymbol{X}\boldsymbol{\beta}}_{ML})'\boldsymbol{D}^{-1}(\boldsymbol{\theta})(\boldsymbol{U}'\boldsymbol{y} - \boldsymbol{U}'\widehat{\boldsymbol{X}\boldsymbol{\beta}}_{ML})$$

with respect to $\boldsymbol{\theta}$. This is essentially the case of a variance components model $(\boldsymbol{U}'\boldsymbol{y}, \boldsymbol{U}'\boldsymbol{X}\boldsymbol{\beta}, \boldsymbol{D}(\boldsymbol{\theta}))$ with the nonsingular dispersion matrix $\boldsymbol{D}(\boldsymbol{\theta}) = \sum_{i=1}^k \sigma_i^2 \boldsymbol{U}'\boldsymbol{V}_i\boldsymbol{U}$. Therefore, whenever the MLE's of $\sigma_1^2, \ldots, \sigma_k^2$ are positive, these satisfy the simultaneous equations

$$\begin{aligned}\mathrm{tr}(\boldsymbol{D}^{-1}(\boldsymbol{\theta})\boldsymbol{U}'\boldsymbol{V}_i\boldsymbol{U}) = (\boldsymbol{U}'\boldsymbol{y} - \boldsymbol{U}'\widehat{\boldsymbol{X}\boldsymbol{\beta}}_{ML})'&\boldsymbol{D}^{-1}(\boldsymbol{\theta})\boldsymbol{U}'\boldsymbol{V}_i\boldsymbol{U}\boldsymbol{D}^{-1}(\boldsymbol{\theta})\\ &(\boldsymbol{U}'\boldsymbol{y} - \boldsymbol{U}'\widehat{\boldsymbol{X}\boldsymbol{\beta}}_{ML}), \qquad i = 1, \ldots, k.\end{aligned}$$

The equations given in the statement of the proposition follow from the facts that $\mathrm{tr}(\boldsymbol{D}^{-1}(\boldsymbol{\theta})\boldsymbol{U}'\boldsymbol{V}_i\boldsymbol{U}) = \mathrm{tr}(\boldsymbol{U}\boldsymbol{D}^{-1}(\boldsymbol{\theta})\boldsymbol{U}'\boldsymbol{V}_i)$ and that the matrix $\boldsymbol{U}\boldsymbol{D}^{-1}(\boldsymbol{\theta})\boldsymbol{U}'$ is a choice of $V^-(\boldsymbol{\theta})$.

In order to show that the equations do not depend on the choice of the g-inverse of $\boldsymbol{V}(\boldsymbol{\theta})$, note that $\mathrm{tr}(\boldsymbol{V}^-(\boldsymbol{\theta})\boldsymbol{V}_i) = \mathrm{tr}(\boldsymbol{F}_i'\boldsymbol{V}^-(\boldsymbol{\theta})\boldsymbol{F}_i)$, where $\boldsymbol{F}_i\boldsymbol{F}_i'$ is a rank factorization of $\boldsymbol{V}_i$. Since $\mathcal{C}(\boldsymbol{F}_i) = \mathcal{C}(\boldsymbol{V}_i) \subseteq \mathcal{C}(\boldsymbol{V}(\boldsymbol{\theta}))$, the matrix $\boldsymbol{F}_i'\boldsymbol{V}^-(\boldsymbol{\theta})\boldsymbol{F}_i$ does not depend on the choice of the g-inverse of $\boldsymbol{V}(\boldsymbol{\theta})$. Also, since $\widehat{\boldsymbol{X}\boldsymbol{\beta}}_{ML}$ is the BLUE of $\boldsymbol{X}\boldsymbol{\beta}$ in the model $(\boldsymbol{y}, \boldsymbol{X}\boldsymbol{\beta}, \boldsymbol{V}(\boldsymbol{\theta}))$ with $\boldsymbol{\theta}$ replaced by its MLE, the residual vector $\boldsymbol{y} - \widehat{\boldsymbol{X}\boldsymbol{\beta}}_{ML}$ belongs to $\mathcal{C}(\boldsymbol{V}(\boldsymbol{\theta}))$ (see (7.5)). This fact implies that the right-hand side of each equation given in the statement of the proposition does not depend on the choice of the g-inverse of $\boldsymbol{V}(\boldsymbol{\theta})$. □

Remark 8.30. An alternative form of the estimating equations of $\widehat{\boldsymbol{\theta}}_{ML}$ given in Proposition 8.29 is

$$\sum_{j=1}^k \sigma_j^2 \mathrm{tr}(\boldsymbol{V}^-(\boldsymbol{\theta})\boldsymbol{V}_i\boldsymbol{V}^-(\boldsymbol{\theta})\boldsymbol{V}_j) = \boldsymbol{a}(\boldsymbol{\theta})'\boldsymbol{V}_i\boldsymbol{a}(\boldsymbol{\theta}), \quad i = 1, \ldots, k,$$

where

$$\boldsymbol{a}(\boldsymbol{\theta}) = (\boldsymbol{I} - \boldsymbol{P}_X)\{(\boldsymbol{I} - \boldsymbol{P}_X)\boldsymbol{V}(\boldsymbol{\theta})(\boldsymbol{I} - \boldsymbol{P}_X)\}^-(\boldsymbol{I} - \boldsymbol{P}_X)\boldsymbol{y}.$$

This is a consequence of (7.1) and the fact that $\boldsymbol{V}_i = \boldsymbol{V}_i\boldsymbol{V}^-(\boldsymbol{\theta})\boldsymbol{V}(\boldsymbol{\theta}) = \sum_{j=1}^k \sigma_j^2 \boldsymbol{V}_i\boldsymbol{V}^-(\boldsymbol{\theta})\boldsymbol{V}_j$. This representation lends itself to recursive computation of the MLE of $\boldsymbol{\theta}$. The current iterates can be used to compute $\boldsymbol{V}(\boldsymbol{\theta})$, while the next iterates are obtained by solving the system of linear equations in $\sigma_1^2, \ldots, \sigma_k^2$. □

Remark 8.31. If $\boldsymbol{V}(\boldsymbol{\theta})$ is nonsingular, the equations of Proposition 8.29 can be further simplified as (see Exercise 8.12)

$$\sum_{j=1}^{k} \sigma_j^2 \mathrm{tr}(\boldsymbol{V}^{-1}(\boldsymbol{\theta})\boldsymbol{V}_j\boldsymbol{V}^{-1}(\boldsymbol{\theta})\boldsymbol{V}_i) = \boldsymbol{e}(\boldsymbol{\theta})'\boldsymbol{V}^{-1}(\boldsymbol{\theta})\boldsymbol{V}_i\boldsymbol{V}^{-1}(\boldsymbol{\theta})\boldsymbol{e}(\boldsymbol{\theta}),$$

for $i = 1, \ldots, k$, where

$$\boldsymbol{e}(\boldsymbol{\theta}) = [\boldsymbol{I} - \boldsymbol{X}'(\boldsymbol{X}'\boldsymbol{V}^{-1}(\boldsymbol{\theta})\boldsymbol{X})^{-}\boldsymbol{X}'\boldsymbol{V}^{-1}(\boldsymbol{\theta})]\boldsymbol{y}. \qquad \square$$

The computation of the REML estimator can proceed in a similar manner. It follows from the discussion of Section 8.2.3 that the REML estimator of $\boldsymbol{\theta}$ can be viewed as its MLE in a reduced model where $\boldsymbol{y}$, $\boldsymbol{X\beta}$ and $\boldsymbol{V}(\boldsymbol{\theta})$ are replaced by $(\boldsymbol{I}-\boldsymbol{P}_X)\boldsymbol{y}$, $\boldsymbol{0}$ and $(\boldsymbol{I}-\boldsymbol{P}_X)\boldsymbol{V}(\boldsymbol{\theta})(\boldsymbol{I}-\boldsymbol{P}_X)$, respectively. The corresponding decomposition of the dispersion matrix is

$$(\boldsymbol{I}-\boldsymbol{P}_X)\boldsymbol{V}(\boldsymbol{\theta})(\boldsymbol{I}-\boldsymbol{P}_X) = \sum_{i=1}^{k} \sigma_i^2 (\boldsymbol{I}-\boldsymbol{P}_X)\boldsymbol{V}_i(\boldsymbol{I}-\boldsymbol{P}_X).$$

Thus, the next proposition follows easily from Remark 8.30.

Proposition 8.32. *In the above set-up if the random effects are independent and normally distributed, then the REML estimators of* $\sigma_1^2, \ldots, \sigma_k^2$ *satisfy the equations*

$$\sum_{j=1}^{k} \sigma_j^2 \mathrm{tr}(\boldsymbol{W}^{-}(\boldsymbol{\theta})\boldsymbol{W}_i\boldsymbol{W}^{-}(\boldsymbol{\theta})\boldsymbol{W}_j) = \boldsymbol{b}(\boldsymbol{\theta})'\boldsymbol{W}_i\boldsymbol{b}(\boldsymbol{\theta}), \quad i = 1, \ldots, k,$$

where

$$\begin{aligned} \boldsymbol{W}(\boldsymbol{\theta}) &= (\boldsymbol{I}-\boldsymbol{P}_X)\boldsymbol{V}(\boldsymbol{\theta})(\boldsymbol{I}-\boldsymbol{P}_X); \\ \boldsymbol{W}_i &= (\boldsymbol{I}-\boldsymbol{P}_X)\boldsymbol{V}_i(\boldsymbol{I}-\boldsymbol{P}_X), \quad i = 1, \ldots, k; \\ \boldsymbol{b}(\boldsymbol{\theta}) &= \boldsymbol{W}^{-}(\boldsymbol{\theta})(\boldsymbol{I}-\boldsymbol{P}_X)\boldsymbol{y} \end{aligned}$$

provided the estimates are positive. The above equations do not depend on the choice of the g-inverse of $\boldsymbol{W}(\boldsymbol{\theta})$. $\square$

The iterative procedure outlined for the MLE in Remark 8.30 can be used to solve the equations for the REML estimator.

Example 8.33. (Balanced one-way classified random effects model) Consider the model

$$y_{ij} = \mu + \tau_i + \varepsilon_{ij}, \quad i = 1, \ldots, t, \ j = 1, \ldots, m,$$

where the τ_i's are the i.i.d. random effects having the $N(0, \sigma_1^2)$ distribution, and the ε_{ij}'s are the i.i.d. model errors (independent of the τ_i's) having the $N(0, \sigma_2^2)$ distribution.

In this case $\boldsymbol{X} = \mathbf{1}$, $\boldsymbol{\theta} = (\sigma_1^2 : \sigma_2^2)'$, and $\boldsymbol{V}(\boldsymbol{\theta})$ is a block-diagonal matrix with each $m \times m$ diagonal block given by $\sigma_1^2 \mathbf{1}\mathbf{1}' + \sigma_2^2 \boldsymbol{I}$. Specifically,

$$\boldsymbol{V}_1 = \begin{pmatrix} \mathbf{1}\mathbf{1}' & \cdots & \mathbf{0} \\ \vdots & \ddots & \vdots \\ \mathbf{0} & \cdots & \mathbf{1}\mathbf{1}' \end{pmatrix}; \qquad \boldsymbol{V}_2 = \boldsymbol{I}.$$

$\boldsymbol{V}^{-1}(\boldsymbol{\theta})$ is also a block diagonal matrix with each diagonal block given by $\sigma_2^{-2}(\boldsymbol{I} - \frac{\sigma_1^2}{\sigma_2^2 + m\sigma_1^2}\mathbf{1}\mathbf{1}')$. It is easy to see that $\mathcal{C}(\boldsymbol{V}(\boldsymbol{\theta})\boldsymbol{X}) \subseteq \mathcal{C}(\boldsymbol{X})$, so the MLE of μ is its LSE, i.e. the sample mean of the observations. Therefore, the least squares residuals may be used in the equations of Proposition 8.29. The equation for $i = 2$ amounts to

$$\text{tr}(\boldsymbol{V}^{-1}(\boldsymbol{\theta})) = \|\boldsymbol{V}^{-1}(\boldsymbol{\theta})(\boldsymbol{y} - \bar{y}\mathbf{1})\|^2.$$

The two sides of the equation simplify as follows.

$$\sum_{i=1}^{t} \text{tr}\left[\sigma_2^{-2}\left(\boldsymbol{I} - \frac{\sigma_1^2}{\sigma_2^2 + m\sigma_1^2}\mathbf{1}\mathbf{1}'\right)\right] = \sum_{i=1}^{t} \left\|\sigma_2^{-2}\left(\boldsymbol{y}_i - \bar{y}\mathbf{1} - \frac{\sigma_1^2 m(\bar{y}_i - \bar{y})}{\sigma_2^2 + m\sigma_1^2}\mathbf{1}\right)\right\|^2,$$

$$\text{i.e.} \quad \frac{tm}{\sigma_2^2}\left(1 - \frac{\sigma_1^2}{\sigma_2^2 + m\sigma_1^2}\right) = \sum_{i=1}^{t} \left\| \frac{\boldsymbol{y}_i - \bar{y}_i\mathbf{1}}{\sigma_2^2} - \frac{\bar{y} - \bar{y}_i}{\sigma_2^2 + m\sigma_1^2}\mathbf{1} \right\|^2,$$

$$\text{i.e.} \quad \frac{tm(\sigma_2^2 + (m-1)\sigma_1^2)}{\sigma_2^2(\sigma_2^2 + m\sigma_1^2)} = \frac{\sum_{i,j}(y_{ij} - \bar{y}_i)^2}{\sigma_2^4} + \frac{m\sum_i(\bar{y}_i - \bar{y})^2}{(\sigma_2^2 + m\sigma_1^2)^2},$$

where $\bar{y}$ is the sample mean of all the observations, $\bar{y}_i$ is the ith cell mean and $\boldsymbol{y}_i$ is the sub-vector of $\boldsymbol{y}$ corresponding to the ith cell.

The equation for $i = 1$, as per Proposition 8.29, is

$$\text{tr}(\boldsymbol{V}^{-1}(\boldsymbol{\theta})\boldsymbol{V}_1) = (\boldsymbol{y} - \bar{y}\mathbf{1})'\boldsymbol{V}^{-1}(\boldsymbol{\theta})\boldsymbol{V}_1\boldsymbol{V}^{-1}(\boldsymbol{\theta})(\boldsymbol{y} - \bar{y}\mathbf{1}).$$

After some algebraic manipulations, this equation simplifies to

$$\frac{tm}{\sigma_2^2 + m\sigma_1^2} = \frac{m^2\sum_i(\bar{y}_i - \bar{y})^2}{(\sigma_2^2 + m\sigma_1^2)^2}.$$

The two equations lead to the following solution:

$$\begin{aligned} \widehat{\sigma_1^2} &= \frac{1}{t}\sum_i(\bar{y}_i - \bar{y})^2 - \frac{\widehat{\sigma_2^2}}{m}, \\ \widehat{\sigma_2^2} &= \frac{1}{t(m-1)}\sum_{i,j}(y_{ij} - \bar{y}_i)^2. \end{aligned} \tag{8.7}$$

In order to compute the REML estimators we can use the following simplified form of the equations given in Proposition 8.32:

$$\mathrm{tr}(\boldsymbol{W}^-(\boldsymbol{\theta})\boldsymbol{W}_i) = \boldsymbol{b}(\boldsymbol{\theta})'\boldsymbol{W}_i\boldsymbol{b}(\boldsymbol{\theta}), \quad i = 1, 2.$$

Note that the right-hand sides of the estimating equations of Remark 8.30 and Proposition 8.32 are identical. In the present case, this has already been simplified for the computation of the MLE, for $i = 1, 2$. The matrices on the left-hand side simplify as follows:

$$\boldsymbol{W}_1 = \boldsymbol{V}_1 - \frac{1}{t}\mathbf{1}\mathbf{1}', \quad \boldsymbol{W}_2 = \boldsymbol{I} - \frac{1}{tm}\mathbf{1}\mathbf{1}', \quad \boldsymbol{W}(\boldsymbol{\theta}) = \boldsymbol{V} - \left(\frac{\sigma_1^2}{t} + \frac{\sigma_2^2}{tm}\right)\mathbf{1}\mathbf{1}'.$$

Since $\mathbf{1}'\boldsymbol{V}^{-1}\mathbf{1} = (\sigma_1^2/t + \sigma_2^2/tm)^{-1}$, it follows that a choice of $\boldsymbol{W}^-(\boldsymbol{\theta})$ is $\boldsymbol{V}^{-1}(\boldsymbol{\theta})$. Further algebraic manipulations lead to the following form of the two equations.

$$\frac{(tm-1)\sigma_2^2 + tm(m-1)\sigma_1^2}{\sigma_2^2(\sigma_2^2 + m\sigma_1^2)} = \frac{\sum_{i,j}(y_{ij} - \bar{y}_i)^2}{\sigma_2^4} + \frac{m\sum_i(\bar{y}_i - \bar{y})^2}{(\sigma_2^2 + m\sigma_1^2)^2},$$

$$\frac{(t-1)m}{\sigma_2^2 + m\sigma_1^2} = \frac{m^2\sum_i(\bar{y}_i - \bar{y})^2}{(\sigma_2^2 + m\sigma_1^2)^2}.$$

The resulting estimators are

$$\begin{aligned} \widehat{\sigma_1^2} &= \frac{1}{t-1}\sum_i(\bar{y}_i - \bar{y})^2 - \frac{\widehat{\sigma_2^2}}{m}, \\ \widehat{\sigma_2^2} &= \frac{1}{t(m-1)}\sum_{i,j}(y_{ij} - \bar{y}_i)^2. \end{aligned} \tag{8.8}$$

It is interesting to note that the ML and REML estimators of σ_2^2 coincide, while the REML estimator of σ_1^2 is larger than the corresponding MLE. We shall show later (see page 430) that the REML estimators of the two parameters are unbiased. These also happen to have the minimum variance among all unbiased estimators (see page 436).

The solution for σ_1^2 obtained from the ML or REML estimating equations may turn out to be negative. If this happens to be the case, the MLE of σ_1^2 should be 0. Thus, one has to ignore the presence of the first component of the variance. The MLE of σ_2^2 under this revised model is $\frac{1}{tm}\sum_{ij}(y_{ij} - \bar{y})^2$, and the REML estimator is $\frac{1}{tm-1}\sum_{ij}(y_{ij} - \bar{y})^2$. □

Apart from the iterative method mentioned in this section, one can try and find the ML or REML estimators using other iterative methods such as Newton-Raphson, steepest ascent, scoring and the EM algorithm. See Rao (1997) for some details on these algorithms in the context of variance components estimation.

We now turn our attention to some methods which deal specifically with the variance components model.

8.3.3 *ANOVA methods*

Two major problems of the ML and REML methods are the need of an iterative algorithm to solve them and the possibility of negative variance estimates. Faster computers have alleviated the first problem to some extent. Yet, the quality of the solutions of iterative algorithms often depend on the quality of the initial values. In this section we consider some simple estimators which are not only useful as initial values, but also quite meaningful in a number of special cases.

The ANOVA methods try to exploit the fact that the linear zero functions do not depend on the fixed effects parameters, and thereby carry information about the random effects or variance components. Suppose we have a set of quadratic forms of the LZFs, $q_i = \boldsymbol{y}'(\boldsymbol{I} - \boldsymbol{P}_X)\boldsymbol{Q}_i(\boldsymbol{I} - \boldsymbol{P}_X)\boldsymbol{y}$, $i = 1, \ldots, k$, where the $\boldsymbol{Q}_i$'s are known nonrandom matrices. Note that for $i = 1, \ldots, k$

$$\begin{aligned} E(q_i) &= E(\operatorname{tr}(\widetilde{\boldsymbol{Q}}_i\boldsymbol{y}\boldsymbol{y}')) = \operatorname{tr}(\widetilde{\boldsymbol{Q}}_i E(\boldsymbol{y}\boldsymbol{y}')) \\ &= \operatorname{tr}(\widetilde{\boldsymbol{Q}}_i \boldsymbol{V}(\boldsymbol{\theta}) + \widetilde{\boldsymbol{Q}}_i \boldsymbol{X}\boldsymbol{\beta}\boldsymbol{\beta}'\boldsymbol{X}') = \sum_{j=1}^{k} \sigma_j^2 \operatorname{tr}(\widetilde{\boldsymbol{Q}}_i \boldsymbol{V}_j), \end{aligned}$$

where $\widetilde{\boldsymbol{Q}}_i = (\boldsymbol{I}-\boldsymbol{P}_X)\boldsymbol{Q}_i(\boldsymbol{I}-\boldsymbol{P}_X)$. Thus, the mean of each q_i is a linear function of $\sigma_1^2, \ldots, \sigma_k^2$. Consider the system of equations

$$\begin{pmatrix} \operatorname{tr}(\widetilde{\boldsymbol{Q}}_1\boldsymbol{V}_1) & \cdots & \operatorname{tr}(\widetilde{\boldsymbol{Q}}_1\boldsymbol{V}_k) \\ \vdots & \ddots & \vdots \\ \operatorname{tr}(\widetilde{\boldsymbol{Q}}_k\boldsymbol{V}_1) & \cdots & \operatorname{tr}(\widetilde{\boldsymbol{Q}}_k\boldsymbol{V}_k) \end{pmatrix} \begin{pmatrix} \sigma_1^2 \\ \vdots \\ \sigma_k^2 \end{pmatrix} = \begin{pmatrix} \boldsymbol{y}'\widetilde{\boldsymbol{Q}}_1\boldsymbol{y} \\ \vdots \\ \boldsymbol{y}'\widetilde{\boldsymbol{Q}}_k\boldsymbol{y} \end{pmatrix}. \tag{8.9}$$

Thus, if the weight matrices are chosen suitably, then the above matrix would be invertible, and a unique set of solutions to the above equations would exist. It is easy to see that the resulting estimators of $\sigma_1^2, \ldots, \sigma_k^2$ are unbiased. Since these estimators are functions of LZFs, they are also translation invariant.

A general problem with the above class of estimators is that it is not clear how one should select the matrices $\widetilde{\boldsymbol{Q}}_1, \ldots, \widetilde{\boldsymbol{Q}}_k$. Depending on the choice of these matrices, one might obtain several versions of ANOVA estimators of the variance components. Some specific applications provide intuitively meaningful choices of the matrices. In the case of balanced data, the ANOVA estimators are often found to have the minimum variance among all unbiased estimators that are quadratic functions of the response.

Henderson proposed a series of methods in the early 1950's, which remained quite popular for the next few decades. These are basically ANOVA methods with various choices of the quadratic functions.

Example 8.34. (Henderson's Method III) Consider the mixed linear model

$$\boldsymbol{y} = \boldsymbol{X}\boldsymbol{\beta} + \sum_{i=1}^{k} \boldsymbol{U}_i\boldsymbol{\gamma}_i,$$

where $\boldsymbol{U}_k = \boldsymbol{I}$. The model can alternatively be written as (8.6) with $\boldsymbol{V}_k = \boldsymbol{I}$. Let

$$\begin{aligned}
\boldsymbol{P}_0 &= \boldsymbol{P}_{(X:U_1:\cdots:U_{k-1})}; \\
\boldsymbol{Q}_i &= \boldsymbol{P}_0 - \boldsymbol{P}_{(X:U_1:\cdots:U_{i-1}:U_{i+1}:\cdots:U_{k-1})}, \qquad i = 1, \ldots, k-1; \\
\boldsymbol{Q}_k &= \boldsymbol{I} - \boldsymbol{P}_0.
\end{aligned}$$

Since $\mathcal{C}(\boldsymbol{X} : \boldsymbol{U}_1 : \cdots : \boldsymbol{U}_{k-1})^\perp \subseteq \mathcal{C}(\boldsymbol{X})^\perp$, we have $\widetilde{\boldsymbol{Q}}_k = \boldsymbol{Q}_k$. Likewise, $\widetilde{\boldsymbol{Q}}_i = \boldsymbol{Q}_i$ for $i = 1, \ldots, k-1$. The quadratic form $\boldsymbol{y}'\boldsymbol{Q}_k\boldsymbol{y}$ can be interpreted as the error sum of squares in the model where $\boldsymbol{\gamma}_k$ is the vector of uncorrelated errors and the remaining random effects are assumed to be fixed effects. The quadratic form $\boldsymbol{y}'\boldsymbol{Q}_i\boldsymbol{y}$ can be seen as the sum of squares due to deviation from the hypothesis of no significant effect of $\boldsymbol{U}_i$ (with $\boldsymbol{\gamma}_i$ treated as a fixed effect). Henderson's Method III consists of setting these sums of squares to their respective expected values under the mixed effects model, and solving for the parameters $\sigma_1^2, \ldots, \sigma_k^2$.

In this special case of the ANOVA method, the coefficient matrix of equation (8.9) reduces to

$$\begin{pmatrix}
\operatorname{tr}(\boldsymbol{Q}_1\boldsymbol{V}_1) & 0 & \cdots & 0 & \operatorname{tr}(\boldsymbol{Q}_1) \\
0 & \operatorname{tr}(\boldsymbol{Q}_2\boldsymbol{V}_2) & \cdots & 0 & \operatorname{tr}(\boldsymbol{Q}_2) \\
\vdots & \vdots & \ddots & \vdots & \vdots \\
0 & 0 & \cdots & \operatorname{tr}(\boldsymbol{Q}_{k-1}\boldsymbol{V}_{k-1}) & \operatorname{tr}(\boldsymbol{Q}_{k-1}) \\
0 & 0 & \cdots & 0 & \operatorname{tr}(\boldsymbol{Q}_k)
\end{pmatrix}.$$

Consequently the explicit solutions to the simultaneous equations are

$$\begin{aligned}
\widehat{\sigma}_i^2 &= \frac{\boldsymbol{y}'\boldsymbol{Q}_i\boldsymbol{y} - \widehat{\sigma}_k^2\operatorname{tr}(\boldsymbol{Q}_i)}{\operatorname{tr}(\boldsymbol{Q}_i\boldsymbol{V}_i)}, \qquad i = 1, \ldots, k-1; \\
\widehat{\sigma}_k^2 &= \frac{\boldsymbol{y}'\boldsymbol{Q}_k\boldsymbol{y}}{\operatorname{tr}\boldsymbol{Q}_k} = \frac{\boldsymbol{y}'(\boldsymbol{I} - \boldsymbol{P}_0)\boldsymbol{y}}{\operatorname{tr}(\boldsymbol{I} - \boldsymbol{P}_0)}.
\end{aligned}$$

The best aspect of this method is its computational simplicity. The interpretability of the quadratic forms has also given the method an oblique justification. While the estimators are unbiased, they are not known to have any optimal property in general. □

Example 8.35. (Balanced one-way classified random effects model, continued) In the case of the model of Example 8.33, Henderson's Method III estimators simplify further. In fact, the estimators of $\widehat{\sigma}_1^2$ and $\widehat{\sigma}_2^2$ coincide with the corresponding REML estimator given in (8.8). Since the ANOVA estimators are generally unbiased, the REML estimators are unbiased in this case. □

The ANOVA-type methods have the advantage that these work without any distributional assumption. In the case of some balanced designs, some natural quadratic forms can be found (see Hocking, 2013). One may also consider using more than k quadratic forms, and try a least squares fit on the extended system of equations of the form (8.9). See Searle et al. (2006) for details.

8.3.4 *Minimum norm quadratic unbiased estimator*

Suppose the 'random effects' $\gamma_1, \ldots, \gamma_k$ in the mixed effects model (8.5) are somehow observed. If this is the case, a 'natural' estimator of σ_i^2 is $\|\gamma_i\|^2/d_i$, where d_i is the dimension of the vector γ_i, $i = 1, \ldots, k$. A natural estimator of a linear function of the parameters, $\sum_{i=1}^k p_i\sigma_i^2$, is $\sum_{i=1}^k \|\gamma_i\|^2 p_i/d_i$.

Now suppose the same parameter, $\sum_{i=1}^k p_i\sigma_i^2$, is estimated by a quadratic function of the response. As in the case of the ANOVA methods, we shall insist on translation invariance of the estimator. This restricts our choice to quadratic forms in the LZF vector, $(\boldsymbol{I} - \boldsymbol{P}_X)\boldsymbol{y}$. We write the quadratic form as $\boldsymbol{y}'(\boldsymbol{I} - \boldsymbol{P}_X)\boldsymbol{Q}(\boldsymbol{I} - \boldsymbol{P}_X)\boldsymbol{y}$ or simply $\boldsymbol{y}'\widetilde{\boldsymbol{Q}}\boldsymbol{y}$, where $\widetilde{\boldsymbol{Q}}$ is of the form $(\boldsymbol{I} - \boldsymbol{P}_X)\boldsymbol{Q}(\boldsymbol{I} - \boldsymbol{P}_X)$. We assume without loss of generality that $\boldsymbol{Q}$ and $\widetilde{\boldsymbol{Q}}$ are symmetric matrices.

The development of the estimator has so far taken place along the lines of the ANOVA method. We now make a crucial choice that would help us select a suitable matrix $\widetilde{\boldsymbol{Q}}$. We rewrite the estimator as

$$\boldsymbol{y}'\widetilde{\boldsymbol{Q}}\boldsymbol{y} = \left(\sum_{i=1}^k \boldsymbol{U}_i\gamma_i\right)' \widetilde{\boldsymbol{Q}} \left(\sum_{i=1}^k \boldsymbol{U}_i\gamma_i\right) = \sum_{i=1}^k \sum_{j=1}^k \gamma_i'\boldsymbol{U}_i'\widetilde{\boldsymbol{Q}}\boldsymbol{U}_j\gamma_j,$$

and try to bring it as close as possible to the 'natural' estimator, described earlier. The difference between the estimators is

$$\sum_{i=1}^{k}\sum_{j=1}^{k}\gamma_i'\boldsymbol{U}_i'\widetilde{\boldsymbol{Q}}\boldsymbol{U}_j\gamma_j - \sum_{i=1}^{k}\gamma_i'(p_i/d_i)\boldsymbol{I}\gamma_i.$$

Suppose our initial guess of the parameters $\sigma_1^2, \ldots, \sigma_k^2$ be $w_1, \ldots, w_k$. Then we can write $\gamma_i = w_i^{1/2}\varepsilon_i$, $i = 1, \ldots, k$, where all the components of the vectors $\varepsilon_1, \ldots, \varepsilon_k$ have approximately the same variance, provided the prior guess is not too bad. Using the re-scaled random effects, we can write the difference of the two estimators as $\varepsilon'\boldsymbol{A}\varepsilon$, where

$$\boldsymbol{A} = \begin{pmatrix} w_1^{1/2}\boldsymbol{U}_1' \\ w_2^{1/2}\boldsymbol{U}_2' \\ \vdots \\ w_k^{1/2}\boldsymbol{U}_k' \end{pmatrix} \widetilde{\boldsymbol{Q}} \begin{pmatrix} w_1^{1/2}\boldsymbol{U}_1' \\ w_2^{1/2}\boldsymbol{U}_2' \\ \vdots \\ w_k^{1/2}\boldsymbol{U}_k' \end{pmatrix}' - \begin{pmatrix} \frac{w_1p_1}{d_1}\boldsymbol{I} & \boldsymbol{0} & \cdots & \boldsymbol{0} \\ \boldsymbol{0} & \frac{w_2p_2}{d_2}\boldsymbol{I} & \cdots & \boldsymbol{0} \\ \vdots & \vdots & \ddots & \vdots \\ \boldsymbol{0} & \cdots & \boldsymbol{0} & \frac{w_kp_k}{d_k}\boldsymbol{I} \end{pmatrix},$$

and $\varepsilon' = (\varepsilon_1' : \varepsilon_2' : \cdots : \varepsilon_k')$. In order to ensure that the quadratic form $\varepsilon'\boldsymbol{A}\varepsilon$ is small, we would require that the matrix $\boldsymbol{A}$ be small. This objective can be reached by minimizing a norm of this matrix. A popular norm in this context is the Frobenius norm, denoted by $\|\cdot\|_F$ (see page 588). Thus, we have the task of minimizing

$$\|\boldsymbol{A}\|_F^2 = \sum_{i=1}^{k} w_i^2 \left\| \boldsymbol{U}_i'\widetilde{\boldsymbol{Q}}\boldsymbol{U}_i - \frac{p_i}{d_i}\boldsymbol{I} \right\|_F^2 + \sum_{\substack{i=1 \\ i\neq j}}^{k}\sum_{j=1}^{k} w_iw_j\|\boldsymbol{U}_i'\widetilde{\boldsymbol{Q}}\boldsymbol{U}_j\|_F^2.$$

The minimization of the above with respect to the matrix $\widetilde{\boldsymbol{Q}}$ leads us to the estimator $\boldsymbol{y}'\widetilde{\boldsymbol{Q}}\boldsymbol{y}$, which is referred to as the minimum norm quadratic estimator (MINQE). Iterative techniques are usually needed in order to determine this estimator. A detailed description of such techniques may be found in Rao and Kleffe (1988).

Note that

$$E[\boldsymbol{y}'\widetilde{\boldsymbol{Q}}\boldsymbol{y}] = \text{tr}[\widetilde{\boldsymbol{Q}}E(\boldsymbol{y}\boldsymbol{y}')] = \sum_{i=1}^{k}\sigma_i^2\text{tr}[\boldsymbol{U}_i'\widetilde{\boldsymbol{Q}}\boldsymbol{U}_i].$$

Therefore, in order that $\boldsymbol{y}'\widetilde{\boldsymbol{Q}}\boldsymbol{y}$ is an *unbiased* estimator of $\sum_{i=1}^{k} p_i\sigma_i^2$, we must have

$$\text{tr}[\boldsymbol{U}_i'\widetilde{\boldsymbol{Q}}\boldsymbol{U}_i] = p_i, \qquad i = 1, \ldots, k. \tag{8.10}$$

Subject to this additional condition, together with the fact $\|\boldsymbol{A}\|_F^2 = \text{tr}(\boldsymbol{A}\boldsymbol{A}')$, we have the simplification

$$\|\boldsymbol{A}\|_F^2 + \sum_{i=1}^{k}\frac{w_i^2p_i^2}{d_i} = \sum_{i=1}^{k}\sum_{j=1}^{k} w_iw_j\|\boldsymbol{U}_i'\widetilde{\boldsymbol{Q}}\boldsymbol{U}_j\|_F^2. \tag{8.11}$$

Therefore, the *minimum norm quadratic unbiased estimator* (MINQUE) is $\boldsymbol{y}'\widetilde{\boldsymbol{Q}}\boldsymbol{y}$ such that $\widetilde{\boldsymbol{Q}}$ minimizes the right-hand side of (8.11) under the constraint (8.10).

In a remarkable work, Mitra (1971) shows that the problem of finding the MINQUE can be reformulated as that of obtaining the BLUE of an estimable LPF, assuming that $w_i = 1$ for $i = 1, \ldots, k$ and $D(\boldsymbol{y})$ is positive definite. We now provide a set of estimating equations for the MINQUE, derived by using an extension of Mitra's argument that does not require these assumptions. The estimating equations are like normal equations, and give rise to closed form solutions. In the following proposition $\boldsymbol{\theta}$ and $\boldsymbol{V}(\boldsymbol{\theta})$ are as in (8.6), $\boldsymbol{p} = (p_1 : \cdots : p_k)'$, and $\boldsymbol{w} = (w_1 : \cdots : w_k)'$ represents the 'guessed value' of $\boldsymbol{\theta}$.

Proposition 8.36. *In the above set-up let* $\mathbf{p}'\boldsymbol{\theta}$ *be estimable through a translation invariant, quadratic and unbiased estimator under the model (8.5), and* $\mathcal{C}(\boldsymbol{V}(\boldsymbol{w})) = \mathcal{C}(\boldsymbol{V}(\boldsymbol{\theta}))$. *Then the unique MINQUE of* $\mathbf{p}'\boldsymbol{\theta}$, *which minimizes (8.11) subject to the constraint (8.10), is* $\mathbf{p}'\widehat{\boldsymbol{\theta}}$, *where* $\widehat{\boldsymbol{\theta}}$ *is any solution to the set of equations*

$$\sum_{j=1}^{k} \sigma_j^2 \mathrm{tr}(\boldsymbol{W}^-(\boldsymbol{w})\boldsymbol{W}_i\boldsymbol{W}^-(\boldsymbol{w})\boldsymbol{W}_j) = \boldsymbol{b}(\boldsymbol{w})'\boldsymbol{W}_i\boldsymbol{b}(\boldsymbol{w}), \quad i = 1, \ldots, k,$$

where $\boldsymbol{W}(\cdot)$, $\boldsymbol{b}(\cdot)$ *and* $\boldsymbol{W}_1, \ldots, \boldsymbol{W}_k$ *are as defined in Proposition 8.32.*

Proof. Let $\boldsymbol{G}\boldsymbol{G}'$ be a rank-factorization of $\boldsymbol{W}(\boldsymbol{w})$, and $\boldsymbol{F}$ be a matrix such that $\boldsymbol{P}_W$, the orthogonal projection matrix for $\mathcal{C}(\boldsymbol{W}(\boldsymbol{w}))$, can be written as $\boldsymbol{G}\boldsymbol{F}$. Since $(\boldsymbol{I}-\boldsymbol{P}_X)\boldsymbol{y} \in \mathcal{C}(\boldsymbol{W}(\boldsymbol{w}))$ with probability 1 (see Proposition 2.13), we can rewrite the quadratic form $\boldsymbol{y}'\widetilde{\boldsymbol{Q}}\boldsymbol{y}$ as

$$\boldsymbol{y}'\widetilde{\boldsymbol{Q}}\boldsymbol{y} = \boldsymbol{y}'(\boldsymbol{I} - \boldsymbol{P}_X)\boldsymbol{P}_W\boldsymbol{Q}\boldsymbol{P}_W(\boldsymbol{I} - \boldsymbol{P}_X)\boldsymbol{y} = \boldsymbol{z}'\boldsymbol{C}\boldsymbol{z},$$

where $\boldsymbol{C} = \boldsymbol{G}'\boldsymbol{Q}\boldsymbol{G}$ and $\boldsymbol{z} = \boldsymbol{F}(\boldsymbol{I} - \boldsymbol{P}_X)\boldsymbol{y}$. Further, let $\boldsymbol{c} = \mathrm{vec}(\boldsymbol{C})$ and $\boldsymbol{t} = \mathrm{vec}(\boldsymbol{z}\boldsymbol{z}')$. Then

$$\boldsymbol{y}'\widetilde{\boldsymbol{Q}}\boldsymbol{y} = \boldsymbol{z}'\boldsymbol{C}\boldsymbol{z} = \mathrm{tr}(\boldsymbol{C}\boldsymbol{z}\boldsymbol{z}') = \boldsymbol{c}'\boldsymbol{t}, \tag{8.12}$$

where we have used the fact that $\boldsymbol{C}$ is a symmetric matrix.

Note that $E(\boldsymbol{z}) = \boldsymbol{0}$ and

$$E(\boldsymbol{z}\boldsymbol{z}') = D(\boldsymbol{z}) = \boldsymbol{F}(\boldsymbol{I} - \boldsymbol{P}_X)\boldsymbol{V}(\boldsymbol{\theta})(\boldsymbol{I} - \boldsymbol{P}_X)\boldsymbol{F} = \sum_{i=1}^{k} \sigma_i^2 \boldsymbol{F}\boldsymbol{W}_i\boldsymbol{F}'.$$

Therefore,

$$E(\boldsymbol{t}) = \sum_{i=1}^{k} \sigma_i^2 \boldsymbol{\xi}_i = \boldsymbol{X}_t\boldsymbol{\theta}, \tag{8.13}$$

where $\boldsymbol{\xi}_i = \mathrm{vec}(\boldsymbol{F}\boldsymbol{W}_i\boldsymbol{F}')$, $i = 1, \ldots, k$, and $\boldsymbol{X}_t = (\boldsymbol{\xi}_1 : \cdots : \boldsymbol{\xi}_k)$.

We now turn to the quantity that a MINQUE is supposed to minimize. The right-hand side of (8.11) simplifies as follows

$$\sum_{i=1}^{k}\sum_{j=1}^{k} w_iw_j\|\boldsymbol{U}_i'\widetilde{\boldsymbol{Q}}\boldsymbol{U}_j\|_F^2 = \sum_{i=1}^{k}\sum_{j=1}^{k} w_iw_j\mathrm{tr}(\boldsymbol{U}_i'\widetilde{\boldsymbol{Q}}\boldsymbol{U}_j\boldsymbol{U}_j'\widetilde{\boldsymbol{Q}}\boldsymbol{U}_i)$$
$$= \sum_{i=1}^{k}\sum_{j=1}^{k} w_iw_j\mathrm{tr}(\boldsymbol{Q}\boldsymbol{W}_j'\boldsymbol{Q}\boldsymbol{W}_i) = \mathrm{tr}(\boldsymbol{Q}\boldsymbol{W}(\boldsymbol{w})'\boldsymbol{Q}\boldsymbol{W}(\boldsymbol{w}))$$
$$= \mathrm{tr}(\boldsymbol{Q}\boldsymbol{G}\boldsymbol{G}'\boldsymbol{Q}\boldsymbol{G}\boldsymbol{G}') = \mathrm{tr}(\boldsymbol{G}'\boldsymbol{Q}\boldsymbol{G}\boldsymbol{G}'\boldsymbol{Q}\boldsymbol{G}) = \mathrm{tr}(\boldsymbol{C}\boldsymbol{C}) = \boldsymbol{c}'\boldsymbol{c}. \tag{8.14}$$

From (8.12), (8.13) and (8.14) we conclude that $\boldsymbol{c}'\boldsymbol{t}$ is a MINQUE of $\boldsymbol{p}'\boldsymbol{\theta}$ (where $E(\boldsymbol{t}) = \boldsymbol{X}_t\boldsymbol{\theta}$) if it is an unbiased estimator of the latter and $\boldsymbol{c}'\boldsymbol{c}$ has the smallest possible value. Therefore, the problem of finding the MINQUE is computationally equivalent to finding the BLUE of $\boldsymbol{p}'\boldsymbol{\theta}$ from the linear model $(\boldsymbol{t}, \boldsymbol{X}_t\boldsymbol{\theta}, \boldsymbol{I})$. It is well-known that such an estimator exists if and only if $\boldsymbol{p} \in \mathcal{C}(\boldsymbol{X}_t')$. Since $E(\boldsymbol{t})$ in this model is the same as that obtained from (8.5), and translation invariance is ensured by the construction of the model, we conclude that the assumptions of the proposition imply $\boldsymbol{p} \in \mathcal{C}(\boldsymbol{X}_t')$. It follows from Propositions 3.33 and 3.38 (Gauss-Markov Theorem) that the MINQUE is unique and is given by $\boldsymbol{p}'\widehat{\boldsymbol{\theta}}$ where $\widehat{\boldsymbol{\theta}}$ is any solution to the normal equation $\boldsymbol{X}_t'\boldsymbol{X}_t\boldsymbol{\theta} = \boldsymbol{X}_t'\boldsymbol{t}$. In order to complete the proof, we only have to show that the normal equation simplifies to the set of equations described in the statement of the proposition. Indeed, the equation simplifies to

$$\sum_{j=1}^{k} \boldsymbol{\xi}_i'\boldsymbol{\xi}_j\sigma_j^2 = \boldsymbol{\xi}_i'\boldsymbol{t}, \quad i = 1, \ldots, k.$$

Further, we have

$$\boldsymbol{\xi}_i'\boldsymbol{\xi}_j = \mathrm{vec}(\boldsymbol{F}\boldsymbol{W}_i\boldsymbol{F}')'\mathrm{vec}(\boldsymbol{F}\boldsymbol{W}_j\boldsymbol{F}') = \mathrm{tr}(\boldsymbol{F}\boldsymbol{W}_i\boldsymbol{F}'\boldsymbol{F}\boldsymbol{W}_j\boldsymbol{F}')$$
$$= \mathrm{tr}(\boldsymbol{F}'\boldsymbol{F}\boldsymbol{W}_i\boldsymbol{F}'\boldsymbol{F}\boldsymbol{W}_j) = \mathrm{tr}(\boldsymbol{W}^-(\boldsymbol{w})\boldsymbol{P}_{\boldsymbol{W}}\boldsymbol{W}_i\boldsymbol{P}_{\boldsymbol{W}}\boldsymbol{W}^-(\boldsymbol{w})\boldsymbol{P}_{\boldsymbol{W}}\boldsymbol{W}_j\boldsymbol{P}_{\boldsymbol{W}})$$
$$= \mathrm{tr}(\boldsymbol{W}^-(\boldsymbol{w})\boldsymbol{W}_i\boldsymbol{W}^-(\boldsymbol{w})\boldsymbol{W}_j),$$

where we have made use of the fact

$$\boldsymbol{F}'\boldsymbol{F} = \boldsymbol{F}'\boldsymbol{P}_{\boldsymbol{G}'}\boldsymbol{F} = \boldsymbol{F}'\boldsymbol{G}'(\boldsymbol{G}\boldsymbol{G}')^-\boldsymbol{G}\boldsymbol{F} = \boldsymbol{P}_{\boldsymbol{W}}\boldsymbol{W}^-(\boldsymbol{w})\boldsymbol{P}_{\boldsymbol{W}}$$

(as $\boldsymbol{G}$ has full column rank). Likewise,

$$\boldsymbol{\xi}_i'\boldsymbol{t} = \mathrm{tr}[\boldsymbol{F}\boldsymbol{W}_i\boldsymbol{F}'\boldsymbol{F}(\boldsymbol{I} - \boldsymbol{P}_{\boldsymbol{X}})\boldsymbol{y}\boldsymbol{y}'(\boldsymbol{I} - \boldsymbol{P}_{\boldsymbol{X}})\boldsymbol{F}']$$
$$= \boldsymbol{y}'(\boldsymbol{I} - \boldsymbol{P}_{\boldsymbol{X}})\boldsymbol{F}'\boldsymbol{F}\boldsymbol{W}_i\boldsymbol{F}'\boldsymbol{F}(\boldsymbol{I} - \boldsymbol{P}_{\boldsymbol{X}})\boldsymbol{y}$$
$$= \boldsymbol{y}'(\boldsymbol{I} - \boldsymbol{P}_{\boldsymbol{X}})\boldsymbol{W}^-(\boldsymbol{w})\boldsymbol{W}_i\boldsymbol{W}^-(\boldsymbol{w})(\boldsymbol{I} - \boldsymbol{P}_{\boldsymbol{X}})\boldsymbol{y} = \boldsymbol{b}(\boldsymbol{w})'\boldsymbol{W}_i\boldsymbol{b}(\boldsymbol{w}).$$

This completes the proof. □

Remark 8.37. The model $(\boldsymbol{t}, \boldsymbol{X}_t\boldsymbol{\theta}, \boldsymbol{I})$ used in the proof of Proposition 8.36 implies that $D(\boldsymbol{t}) = \boldsymbol{I}$, which is different from its dispersion computed from (8.5). However, this discrepancy does not come in the way of the main argument of the proof. Also, the solution to the normal equations may be such that the matrix $\boldsymbol{C}$ (obtained from $\boldsymbol{c}$) is not symmetric. It can then be replaced by $(\boldsymbol{C}+\boldsymbol{C}')/2$ without altering the MINQUE, which is unique. The corresponding choice of $\boldsymbol{Q}$ is nonunique. □

Example 8.38. (Balanced one-way classified random effects model, continued) Consider the model of Example 8.33. Let the initial estimators of σ_1^2 and σ_2^2 be w_1 and w_2, respectively. Using the forms of $\boldsymbol{W}_1$, $\boldsymbol{W}_2$ and $\boldsymbol{W}^-(\boldsymbol{\theta})$ given in Example 8.33, we have after some simplification

$$\begin{aligned}
\mathrm{tr}(\boldsymbol{W}^-(\boldsymbol{w})\boldsymbol{W}_1\boldsymbol{W}^-(\boldsymbol{w})\boldsymbol{W}_1) &= \frac{m^2(t-1)}{(w_2+mw_1)^2}\\
\mathrm{tr}(\boldsymbol{W}^-(\boldsymbol{w})\boldsymbol{W}_1\boldsymbol{W}^-(\boldsymbol{w})\boldsymbol{W}_2) &= \frac{m(t-1)}{(w_2+mw_1)^2}\\
\mathrm{tr}(\boldsymbol{W}^-(\boldsymbol{w})\boldsymbol{W}_2\boldsymbol{W}^-(\boldsymbol{w})\boldsymbol{W}_2) &= \frac{(t-1)}{(w_2+mw_1)^2}+\frac{(m-1)t}{w_2^2}.
\end{aligned}$$

Further, using the calculations of Example 8.33, we readily have

$$\begin{aligned}
\boldsymbol{b}(\boldsymbol{w})'\boldsymbol{W}_1\boldsymbol{b}(\boldsymbol{w}) &= \frac{m^2\sum_i(\bar{y}_i-\bar{y})^2}{(w_2+mw_1)^2},\\
\boldsymbol{b}(\boldsymbol{w})'\boldsymbol{W}_2\boldsymbol{b}(\boldsymbol{w}) &= \frac{m\sum_i(\bar{y}_i-\bar{y})^2}{(w_2+mw_1)^2}+\frac{\sum_{i,j}(y_{ij}-\bar{y}_i)^2}{w_2^2}.
\end{aligned}$$

Thus, the estimating equations of Proposition 8.36 simplify to

$$\frac{m(t-1)}{(w_2+mw_1)^2}(m\sigma_1^2+\sigma_2^2) = \frac{m^2\sum_i(\bar{y}_i-\bar{y})^2}{(mw_1+w_2)^2},$$

$$\frac{(t-1)}{(w_2+mw_1)^2}(m\sigma_1^2+\sigma_2^2)+\frac{(m-1)t}{w_2^2}\sigma_2^2 = \frac{m\sum_i(\bar{y}_i-\bar{y})^2}{(mw_1+w_2)^2}+\frac{\sum_{i,j}(y_{ij}-\bar{y}_i)^2}{w_2^2}.$$

The MINQUE of σ_1^2 and σ_2^2 obtained by solving these equations coincide with their respective (normal) REML estimators, irrespective of the values of w_1 and w_2. □

Proposition 8.36 has several interesting consequences. First, by comparing the estimating equations of the MINQUE and the REML estimator (see Proposition 8.32), we find that if the weights $w_1, \ldots, w_k$ are accurate guesses of the parameters, then these two estimators coincide. More importantly, if the MINQUE of $\sigma_1^2, \ldots, \sigma_k^2$ exist and these are used as weights in a second stage of MINQUE, and this procedure is repeated, then this iterative procedure (referred to as I-MINQUE) coincides with the iterative procedure for finding REML, described in Section 8.3.2. Thus, even when the errors are non-normal, the REML estimator can be interpreted as the I-MINQUE estimator. On the other hand, the MINQUE estimator can be thought of as a single step from the initially guessed values towards the (normal) REML estimator.

The MINQE and MINQUE estimators generally depend on the initial guesses. If no prior information on the parameters are available, these may be chosen as equal numbers.

8.3.5 *Best quadratic unbiased estimator*

Consider a translation invariant and quadratic function of the response, $\boldsymbol{y}'\widetilde{\boldsymbol{Q}}\boldsymbol{y}$, which is an unbiased estimator of a linear function of the parameters, $\sum_{i=1}^{k} p_i\sigma_i^2$. An estimator of this kind is called the minimum variance quadratic unbiased estimator (MIVQUE), or the best quadratic unbiased estimator (BQUE), if it has smaller variance than all other translation invariant, quadratic and unbiased estimators. Since the variance of a quadratic function of the response involves the third and fourth moments, a distributional assumption is needed to find the MIVQUE. We assume that the distribution is multivariate normal. Note that this assumption was made in the cases of the REML and ML estimators, but not in the case of the MINQUE and ANOVA estimators.

Under the assumption of normality, it can be shown that

$$Var(\boldsymbol{y}'\widetilde{\boldsymbol{Q}}\boldsymbol{y}) = 2\text{tr}[(\widetilde{\boldsymbol{Q}}\boldsymbol{V}(\boldsymbol{\theta}))^2]. \tag{8.15}$$

In order to find the MIVQUE, one has to minimize this quantity with respect to $\widetilde{\boldsymbol{Q}}$ subject to the condition (8.10) for unbiasedness. Also, $\widetilde{\boldsymbol{Q}}$ has to be of the form $(\boldsymbol{I} - \boldsymbol{P}_X)\boldsymbol{Q}(\boldsymbol{I} - \boldsymbol{P}_X)$ in order to ensure translation invariance. It can be shown that if the MIVQUE exists, then it must satisfy the condition of Proposition 8.36 with $\boldsymbol{w}$ replaced by the 'true value' of $\boldsymbol{\theta}$ (Exercise 8.14). In general the solution to these linear estimating equations is a function of the unknown parameters.

We may find an approximation of the MIVQUE using an approximation of $\boldsymbol{V}(\boldsymbol{\theta})$. If the approximation is of the form $\boldsymbol{V}(\boldsymbol{w})$, then the resulting estimator is identical with the MINQUE (Exercise 8.14). Thus, MINQUE can be interpreted as an approximation of MIVQUE in the normal case.

Any attempt to improve upon this estimator by recursively updating the estimated dispersion matrix would only lead us to the normal REML estimator. If $\boldsymbol{V}(\boldsymbol{\theta})$ in (8.15) is a function of $\boldsymbol{y}$ — as is expected in a recursive procedure — then the resulting matrix $\widetilde{\boldsymbol{Q}}$ also depends on $\boldsymbol{y}$ in general. Thus, the REML estimator obtained in the end of the recursive procedure is not necessarily a quadratic function of $\boldsymbol{y}$, let alone being the MIVQUE.

However, in some special cases the normal MIVQUE can be determined. Since the MINQUE minimizes (8.15) for $\boldsymbol{\theta} = \boldsymbol{w}$, we can conclude that whenever the MINQUE does not depend on $\boldsymbol{w}$ it minimizes (8.15) uniformly over all $\boldsymbol{\theta}$. In such a case, the MINQUE must be the same as the normal MIVQUE.

Example 8.39. (Balanced one-way classified random effects model, continued) Consider the model of Example 8.33. It was shown in Example 8.38 that the MINQUE of σ_1^2 and σ_2^2 do not depend on w_1 and w_2 and are equal to the corresponding REML estimators. Thus, the MIVQUE of σ_1^2 and σ_2^2 are identical to the REML estimators given in (8.8). This coincidence shows that the REML estimators in this case are not only unbiased but these also have the minimum variance among all quadratic and unbiased estimators. □

A review of the various methods of estimation in the mixed linear model may be found in Gumedze and Dunne (2011). For detailed discussion and R implementation, see Galecki and Burzykowski (2013).

8.3.6 *Further inference in the mixed model**

If the parameter $\boldsymbol{\theta}$ is known, the best linear unbiased predictor of the random effects of the model (8.5) can be obtained from Proposition 7.49. Specifically, the BLUPs are given by

$$\widehat{\boldsymbol{\gamma}}_i = \sigma_i^2 \boldsymbol{U}_i' \left(\sum_{j=1}^{k} \sigma_j^2 \boldsymbol{U}_j \boldsymbol{U}_j' \right)^{-} \boldsymbol{e}, \qquad (8.16)$$

where $\boldsymbol{e}$ is the residual vector given in page 352, with $\boldsymbol{V} = \sum_{j=1}^{k} \sigma_j^2 \boldsymbol{U}_j \boldsymbol{U}_j'$ (Exercise 8.26). The predicted value of $\boldsymbol{p}'\boldsymbol{\beta} + \boldsymbol{q}'\boldsymbol{\gamma}$ is $\widehat{\boldsymbol{p}'\boldsymbol{\beta}} + \boldsymbol{q}'\widehat{\boldsymbol{\gamma}}$ where $\widehat{\boldsymbol{p}'\boldsymbol{\beta}}$ is the BLUE of $\boldsymbol{p}'\boldsymbol{\beta}$ under the mixed effects model and $\widehat{\boldsymbol{\gamma}}$ is as described above. Rao and Kleffe (1988) give a computational method for simultaneously obtaining the BLUE of estimable LPFs of the fixed effects and the BLUPs of the random effects. This approach accommodates the possible rank deficiency of the matrices in the model, and is similar to the inverse partitioned matrix method for the fixed effects case (see Section 7.7.2).

The main difficulty in the problem of prediction is that the parameter $\boldsymbol{\theta}$ is in general not known. One can plug in estimators of these in the above expression. The resulting predictors would no longer be the 'best' predictor in any sense. As in the case of two-stage estimators of the fixed effects, such two-stage predictors of the random effects can be shown to have some reasonable properties (see for instance Toyooka, 1982).

The problem of testing hypotheses on variance components in the mixed linear model is not an easy one. See Khuri et al. (1998) for some illustrations of the difficulty of the general problem and tractable solutions in some special cases.

8.4 Other special cases with correlated error

8.4.1 *Serially correlated observations*

As discussed in Section 5.3.3, serial correlation can arise in observations recorded serially in time, which is common in Econometric data.

One way of dealing with serial correlation of the response variable in the linear model is to include some lagged (past) values of the response in the list of explanatory variables (see, for instance, Verbeek, 2017, p. 143). Such a model is referred to as a *dynamic model* or an *ARIMAX model* in the econometric literature (see Davidson and MacKinnon, 1993; Box et al., 2015). These models are beyond the scope of the present discussion.

Another popular model for serially correlated response is

$$\begin{aligned} y_i &= \boldsymbol{x}_i'\boldsymbol{\beta} + \varepsilon_i, \\ \varepsilon_i &= \sum_{j=1}^{p} \phi_j \varepsilon_{i-j} + \delta_i + \sum_{j=1}^{q} \theta_j \delta_{i-j}, \end{aligned}$$

where $\phi_1, \ldots, \phi_p, \theta_1, \ldots, \theta_q$ are constants and the δ_i's are uncorrelated errors each with variance σ^2. This linear model, which is a generalization of equation (5.12) of Section 5.3.3, can be written as $(\boldsymbol{y}, \boldsymbol{X\beta}, \boldsymbol{V}(\boldsymbol{\theta}))$, where $\boldsymbol{\theta} = (\sigma^2 : \phi_1 : \cdots : \phi_p : \theta_1 : \cdots : \theta_q)'$. The above description of ε_i coincides with the autoregressive moving average model of order p, q or ARMA(p, q) of (1.14). It is assumed that the dispersion matrix $\boldsymbol{V}(\boldsymbol{\theta})$ is positive definite. It follows from the discussion of Section 8.2.2 that the MLE of the ARMA parameters ($\phi_1, \ldots, \phi_p$ and $\theta_1, \ldots, \theta_q$), under the assumption of normal distribution, are obtained by minimizing

$$\left[\log|\boldsymbol{V}(\boldsymbol{\theta})| + n\log\{(\boldsymbol{y} - \widehat{\boldsymbol{X\beta}}_{ML})'\boldsymbol{V}^{-1}(\boldsymbol{\theta})(\boldsymbol{y} - \widehat{\boldsymbol{X\beta}}_{ML})\}\right]\Big|_{\sigma^2=1}, \tag{8.17}$$

while the MLE of σ^2 is

$$\widehat{\sigma}^2 = n^{-1}R_0^2(\widehat{\phi}_1 : \cdots : \widehat{\phi}_p : \widehat{\theta}_1 : \cdots : \widehat{\theta}_q),$$

where all the estimators in the right-hand side of the last expression are MLEs. The special case of these estimators for $p = 1$ and $\theta = 0$ was derived in Example 8.20.

Minimizing (8.17) is not an easy task. A complication arises because of some constraints on the parameter space which ensure that $\varepsilon_1, \ldots, \varepsilon_n$ are second order stationary time series. Harvey and Phillips (1979) have suggested a computational procedure for finding the MLEs of all the parameters based on a state-space representation of the ARMA model and the Kalman filter (see Section 9.1.6 and Exercise 9.5). Zinde-Walsh and Galbraith (1991) show that the MLE can be approximated by a class of two-stage estimators up to a reasonable degree of accuracy. The common two-stage estimators are similar in spirit to that obtained in Section 8.2.4, and are generally translation invariant.

The case of $q = 0$ corresponds to an AR(p) model of ε_i. There are several possibilities of approximating the MLE in this special case. For instance, we can drop the first p observations and work with the model

$$y_i - \sum_{j=1}^{p} \phi_j y_{i-j} = \boldsymbol{\beta}'\left(\boldsymbol{x}_i - \sum_{i=1}^{p} \phi_j \boldsymbol{x}_{i-j}\right) + \delta_i, \quad i = p+1, \ldots, n, \tag{8.18}$$

which has uncorrelated errors with variance σ^2. This model can also be written as

$$y_i - \boldsymbol{\beta}'\boldsymbol{x}_i = \sum_{j=1}^{p} \phi_j(y_{i-j} - \boldsymbol{\beta}'\boldsymbol{x}_{i-j}) + \delta_i, \quad i = p+1, \ldots, n. \tag{8.19}$$

The representation (8.18) may be used to estimate the parameters $\boldsymbol{\beta}$ for given values of the AR parameters, while (8.19) may be used to estimate the AR parameters for given $\boldsymbol{\beta}$, using any one of the standard methods (see Brockwell and Davis, 2016). One can use an initial stage of least squares (using (8.18) with all AR parameters set to 0), estimate the AR parameters from (8.19), and revise the estimate of $\boldsymbol{\beta}$ using (8.18) once again. This two-stage procedure is a generalization of the method given in page 226. One can also repeat the procedure for further improvement of the estimator, but the convergence of these iterations is not assured in general.

The case of $p = 1$ is the most common one. A wide range of solutions is available in this case. One can perform a grid search on the single AR parameter, ϕ, to minimize the objective function given in Example 8.20. This would produce the exact MLE. One can also follow the back-and-forth scheme for the AR(p) model given above, which simplifies somewhat for $p = 1$. In case ϕ is found to be very close to 1, an extremely simple strategy that works quite well is to assume $\phi = 1$. The implication of this assumption is that one can use the least squares method on differences of successive observations. It can be shown that the MLE has good efficiency compared to the BLUE for known ϕ. An illustration of this fact is given in Exercise 8.27.

Baille (1979) finds a decomposition of the asymptotic mean squared prediction error when estimated AR parameters are used in the linear model for the purpose of prediction. This result indicates that the variance of the error arising from the use of estimated AR parameters (instead of their 'true' values) decrease inversely with the sample size.

8.4.2 *Models for spatial data*

When an observation consists of attributes of a particular location, correlation among neighbouring entities is expected. A model that takes into account such correlation is

$$\boldsymbol{y} = \boldsymbol{X\beta} + \boldsymbol{\varepsilon}, \quad \boldsymbol{\varepsilon} = \alpha \boldsymbol{W\varepsilon} + \boldsymbol{\delta}, \quad E(\boldsymbol{\delta}) = \boldsymbol{0}, \quad D(\boldsymbol{\delta}) = \sigma^2 \boldsymbol{I},$$

where α is an unspecified constant and $\boldsymbol{W}$ is a known matrix whose elements represent the degree of association among pairs of locations. Usually $\boldsymbol{W}$ is chosen to have zero diagonal elements. The above model can be written as $(\boldsymbol{y}, \boldsymbol{X\beta}, \sigma^2\boldsymbol{V}(\alpha))$ where $\boldsymbol{V}(\alpha) = [(\boldsymbol{I} - \alpha\boldsymbol{W})(\boldsymbol{I} - \alpha\boldsymbol{W}')]^{-1}$. The parameter takes values in a right-neighbourhood of zero such that $\boldsymbol{V}(\alpha)$ is positive definite. Krämer and Donninger (1987) show that the LSE, which is the BLUE in the case $\alpha = 0$, may be grossly inefficient. Ord (1975) proposes an iterative technique for obtaining the MLEs of $\boldsymbol{\beta}$ and α under the assumption of the normal distribution. Several other ad hoc models for the spatial correlation of errors in the linear model have appeared in the literature.

Another approach of dealing with spatial correlation has been quite popular, particularly in the area of geostatistics. According to this approach, the response at various locations are viewed as samples of a stochastic process defined over a suitable space. The location of an observational point in this space is described by the vector $\boldsymbol{u}$. Thus, the ith component of the response vector $\boldsymbol{y}$ is a sample of the process $y(\boldsymbol{u})$ at the location $\boldsymbol{u} = \boldsymbol{U}_i$.

The ith row of $\boldsymbol{X}$ can also be viewed as the value of a function $\boldsymbol{x}(\boldsymbol{u})$ at the location $\boldsymbol{u} = \boldsymbol{U}_i$. Even though $\boldsymbol{x}(\boldsymbol{u})$ may itself be a stochastic process, it may be treated as a nonrandom quantity by conditioning $y(\boldsymbol{u})$ on it. It is assumed that

$$E(y(\boldsymbol{u})|\boldsymbol{x}(\cdot)) = \boldsymbol{\beta}'\boldsymbol{x}(\boldsymbol{u}); \qquad Cov((y(\boldsymbol{u}), y(\boldsymbol{v}))|\boldsymbol{x}(\cdot)) = g(\boldsymbol{u}, \boldsymbol{v}),$$

where g is an unknown function. This leads us back to the linear model with $\boldsymbol{V} = ((g(\boldsymbol{U}_i, \boldsymbol{u}_j)))$.

Some kind of assumption of stationarity of the stochastic process is needed so that inference on $\boldsymbol{\beta}$ and g is possible. Typically one assumes wide sense stationarity of $y(\boldsymbol{u}) - E(y(\boldsymbol{u})|\boldsymbol{x}(\cdot))$, which means that $g(\boldsymbol{u}, \boldsymbol{v})$ can be written as a function of $\boldsymbol{u} - \boldsymbol{v}$. With a minor abuse of notation we shall write it as $g(\boldsymbol{u} - \boldsymbol{v})$. Note that $g(\boldsymbol{u} - \boldsymbol{v}) = g(\boldsymbol{v} - \boldsymbol{u})$.

Under the above assumptions, $Var(y(\boldsymbol{u}) - y(\boldsymbol{u} + \boldsymbol{h})) = 2g(0) - 2g(\boldsymbol{h})$. This function is known as the *variogram* in geostatistical literature, while the half of this function is called the *semivariogram*. The latter function has traditionally been used for inference.

The semivariogram can be estimated nonparametrically. For instance, if the observations are taken on a spatial lattice, then a natural estimator of the semivariogram is

$$\frac{1}{2n(\boldsymbol{h})} \sum_{i=1}^{n(h)} [(y(\boldsymbol{U}_i) - \boldsymbol{\beta}'\boldsymbol{x}(\boldsymbol{U}_i)) - (y(\boldsymbol{U}_i + \boldsymbol{h}) - \boldsymbol{\beta}'\boldsymbol{x}(\boldsymbol{U}_i + \boldsymbol{h}))]^2,$$

where $n(\boldsymbol{h})$ is the number of pairs of observations which are $\boldsymbol{h}$ distance apart. Since $\boldsymbol{\beta}$ is not known, an estimator of it may be used in the above expression. This estimator of the semivariogram may have to be smoothed or locally averaged. Once the semivariogram is estimated, the matrix $\boldsymbol{V}$ can be estimated from it, and the parameter $\boldsymbol{\beta}$ recalculated. Iterations of this scheme is possible, although the convergence of such iterations is not always guaranteed. See Cressie (2015) for a description of nonparametric methods for estimating the semivariogram.

The semivariogram can also be estimated parametrically. Several parametric models of this function can be found in Olea (1999). The parameters of these models may be estimated by the ML or REML methods, or by a least squares approach which seeks to minimize the distance between the parametric function with a nonparametric estimator. A popular parametric model, written in terms of the covariance function g, is

$$g(\boldsymbol{h}) = \sum_{l=1}^{k} \sigma_l^2 g_l(\boldsymbol{h}),$$

where $g_1(\cdot), \ldots, g_k(\cdot)$ are known functions and $\sigma_1, \ldots, \sigma_k$ are unspecified parameters. This clearly leads us to the variance components model (8.6), with $\boldsymbol{V}_l = ((g_l(\boldsymbol{U}_i - \boldsymbol{u}_j)))$, $l = 1, \ldots, k$. Therefore, all the methods of variance components estimation are applicable here. Another class of parametric models that have been used for data on a spatial lattice is that of ARMA models. The methods for linear models with ARMA errors can be used here.

The problem of prediction in the case of spatial data is known as *kriging*. The general theory of BLUP given in Section 7.13 is applicable. If the linear model for the covariance function is used, then the BLUP is given by (8.16). Further details on kriging and parametric estimation of semivariogram may be found in Christensen (1991). Zimmerman and Cressie (1992) examine the performance of the predictor obtained by replacing the unknown parameters involved in the BLUP by their respective estimators. Their results suggest that the estimated mean squared prediction error of these predictors may be more reliable when the spatial correlation is stronger.

8.5 Special cases with uncorrelated error

Even if the model errors are uncorrelated, the least squares method may be inadequate because of unequal variances of the errors. We came across this phenomenon, referred to as *heteroscedasticity*, in Section 5.3.2. Heteroscedastic data may arise in various contexts, some of which are considered here.

8.5.1 *Combining experiments: meta-analysis*

Often one is faced with the task of combining information from various sources. The quality of data available from these sources may not be uniform. Sometimes the data are only available in a summarized form. The challenge of *meta-analysis* is to make improved inference (in comparison to what can be done with data taken from any single source) by judicious use of whatever information is available.

In the context of linear models, data from the various sources may carry information on a common set of fixed effects, but may have different levels of the model error. A simple model for this situation is

$$\boldsymbol{y}_j = \boldsymbol{X}_j\boldsymbol{\beta} + \boldsymbol{\varepsilon}_j, \quad E(\boldsymbol{\varepsilon}_j) = \boldsymbol{0}, \ D(\boldsymbol{\varepsilon}_j) = \sigma_j^2\boldsymbol{I}, \ Cov(\boldsymbol{\varepsilon}_i, \boldsymbol{\varepsilon}_j) = \boldsymbol{0},$$

for $i, j = 1, \ldots, m$, $i \neq j$. The m individual models $(\boldsymbol{y}_j, \boldsymbol{X}_j\boldsymbol{\beta}, \sigma_j^2\boldsymbol{I})$, $j = 1, \ldots, m$, can be represented by a single combined model $(\boldsymbol{y}, \boldsymbol{X\beta}, \boldsymbol{V}(\boldsymbol{\theta}))$, where

$$\boldsymbol{y} = \begin{pmatrix} \boldsymbol{y}_1 \\ \boldsymbol{y}_2 \\ \vdots \\ \boldsymbol{y}_m \end{pmatrix}, \quad \boldsymbol{X} = \begin{pmatrix} \boldsymbol{X}_1 \\ \boldsymbol{X}_2 \\ \vdots \\ \boldsymbol{X}_m \end{pmatrix}, \quad \boldsymbol{V}(\boldsymbol{\theta}) = \begin{pmatrix} \sigma_1^2\boldsymbol{I} & \boldsymbol{0} & \cdots & \boldsymbol{0} \\ \boldsymbol{0} & \sigma_2^2\boldsymbol{I} & \cdots & \boldsymbol{0} \\ \vdots & \vdots & \ddots & \vdots \\ \boldsymbol{0} & \boldsymbol{0} & \cdots & \sigma_m^2\boldsymbol{I} \end{pmatrix},$$

and $\boldsymbol{\theta} = (\sigma_1^2 : \cdots : \sigma_m^2)'$. Further, we can decompose $\boldsymbol{V}(\boldsymbol{\theta})$ as

$$\boldsymbol{V}(\boldsymbol{\theta}) = \sum_{j=1}^{m} \sigma_j^2 \boldsymbol{V}_j,$$

where $\boldsymbol{V}_j$ is a block diagonal matrix with $\boldsymbol{I}$ at the jth diagonal block and zero everywhere else. Therefore, this model is a special case of the variance components model, and the methods discussed in the previous section are directly applicable here.

The normal MLEs given in Section 8.2.2 satisfy the following simplified equations:

$$\widehat{\boldsymbol{X}_j\boldsymbol{\beta}} = \boldsymbol{X}_j \left(\sum_{i=1}^{m} \widehat{\sigma}_i^{-2}\boldsymbol{X}_i'\boldsymbol{X}_i\right)^{-} \left(\sum_{i=1}^{m} \widehat{\sigma}_i^{-2}\boldsymbol{X}_i'\boldsymbol{y}_i\right), \quad j = 1, \ldots, m, \tag{8.20}$$

$$\widehat{\sigma}_j^2 = n_j^{-1} \parallel \boldsymbol{y}_j - \widehat{\boldsymbol{X}_j\boldsymbol{\beta}} \parallel^2, \quad j = 1, \ldots, m, \tag{8.21}$$

where n_j is the number of elements of $\boldsymbol{y}_j$. The above equations lead to a natural way of obtaining the MLE: by iterating back and forth between the estimates of $\boldsymbol{X}_j\boldsymbol{\beta}$'s and σ_j^2's. The least squares estimators of the $\boldsymbol{X}_j\boldsymbol{\beta}$'s may be used as the initial iterate. The resulting estimators of the σ_j^2's are obviously nonnegative.

Even if the normal distribution is not appropriate for the response, equations (8.20)–(8.21) form the basis of several reasonable estimators. Fuller and Rao (1978) consider a two-stage estimator which is similar to the second iterate of the above iterative procedure. If the number of groups (m) is fixed and $\min_{j \leq m} n_j \to \infty$, the two-stage estimator of $\boldsymbol{X\beta}$ is as efficient as its BLUE computed from the model with 'known' σ_j^2's. Fuller and Rao derived the large sample properties of the estimator as $m \to \infty$, and the n_j's form a fixed sequence. Chen and Shao (1993) derive the large-sample properties of the estimators obtained at later stages of the iterations. They show that the estimator obtained after a finite, though unknown, number of iterations is asymptotically more efficient than the corresponding estimators at earlier stages, and suggest a stopping rule for the iterations. Hooper

(1993) suggests an iterative procedure with a modification of (8.21) which is based on a Bayesian model for the variances.

In the above discussion, we have assumed that the raw data from the various studies are available at the time of the meta-analysis. Generally one has only a summary of the information from each study. For instance, one may have the LSE $\widehat{\boldsymbol{\beta}}_{(j)} = (\boldsymbol{X}_j'\boldsymbol{X}_j)^{-1}\boldsymbol{X}_j'\boldsymbol{y}_j$, its estimated dispersion, $\widehat{D}(\widehat{\boldsymbol{\beta}}_{(j)}) = \widehat{\sigma}_j^2(\boldsymbol{X}_j'\boldsymbol{X}_j)^{-1}$, and the estimated error variance, $\widehat{\sigma}_j^2 = \boldsymbol{y}_j'(\boldsymbol{I} - \boldsymbol{P}_{X_j})\boldsymbol{y}_j/(n_j - k)$ for $j = 1, \ldots, m$, assuming that $\boldsymbol{\beta}$ is fully estimable from each study. In such a case we can bypass (8.21) and use the available estimates of $\sigma_1^2, \ldots, \sigma_m^2$ for the computation of (8.20). The resulting estimator of $\boldsymbol{\beta}$ is

$$\widehat{\boldsymbol{\beta}} = \left[\sum_{j=1}^{m}\left(\widehat{D}(\widehat{\boldsymbol{\beta}}_{(j)})\right)^{-1}\right]^{-1}\left[\sum_{j=1}^{m}\left(\widehat{D}(\widehat{\boldsymbol{\beta}}_{(j)})\right)^{-1}\widehat{\boldsymbol{\beta}}_{(j)}\right], \tag{8.22}$$

with estimated dispersion

$$\widehat{D}(\widehat{\boldsymbol{\beta}}) = \left[\sum_{j=1}^{m}\left(\widehat{D}(\widehat{\boldsymbol{\beta}}_{(j)})\right)^{-1}\right]^{-1}. \tag{8.23}$$

Note that the equations (8.22) and (8.23) describe the BLUE and its dispersion if the true (unknown) values of $\sigma_1^2 \ldots, \sigma_m^2$ are used in the expressions of $\widehat{D}(\widehat{\boldsymbol{\beta}}_{(j)})$, $j = 1, \ldots, m$ (Exercise 8.15). It can be shown that the estimator (8.22) with true and estimated values of $\sigma_1^2 \ldots, \sigma_m^2$ become distributionally equivalent to one another as $\min_{j \le m} n_j \to \infty$.

There are several other interesting problems relating to combinations of experiments and meta-analysis, such as the problem of estimation of fixed effects in the presence of nuisance parameters (see Hedayat and Majumdar, 1985, and Liu, 1996), and combination of tests from several studies (see Zhou and Mathew, 1993 and Mathew et al., 1993). These topics will not be dealt with here.

8.5.2 *Systematic heteroscedasticity*

We have seen in Section 5.3.2, the variances of the responses sometimes follow a definite pattern. In the case of time series data, the variance may be a function of time. In other contexts the variance may be found to be a function of the mean response, or a function of one or more of the explanatory variables. Mathematically we can model these three situations as $Var(y_i|\boldsymbol{x}_i) = g(i)$, $Var(y_i|\boldsymbol{x}_i) = g(\boldsymbol{x}_i'\boldsymbol{\beta})$ and $Var(y_i|\boldsymbol{x}_i) = g(\boldsymbol{x}_i)$, respectively, where $\boldsymbol{x}_i$ is the ith row of the matrix $\boldsymbol{X}$ and g is usually an unspecified function. As observed in Section 5.3.2, various plots based on standardized or studentized residuals can be used to guess the forms of these functions.

Carroll and Ruppert (1988) discuss formal methods of estimating the function g. Once $Var(y_i|\boldsymbol{x}_i)$ is estimated, these can be treated as known and an appropriate weighted least squares analysis can be carried out in order to estimate $\boldsymbol{\beta}$, which is the parameter of primary interest. Carroll (1982) shows that the cost of not knowing the variance in the second and third examples goes to zero as the sample size increases. Similar conclusions follow from van der Genugten's (1991) work in the case of the first example. These results are based on the first-order properties of the two-stage estimators of $\boldsymbol{\beta}$, and are quite reassuring when one has a lot of data.

A model of heteroscedasticity that includes all the examples given above as special cases is

$$Var(y_i|\boldsymbol{x}_i) = \sigma^2 g(\boldsymbol{z}_i, \boldsymbol{\beta}, \boldsymbol{\theta}),$$

where $\boldsymbol{z}_i$ is a a known vector (which may include some components of $\boldsymbol{x}_i$) and $\boldsymbol{\theta}$ is an unspecified vector parameter. Under the restrictive assumption that the function g is structurally known, one can use the ML method for estimation. Alternatively one can use a two-stage estimator where $\boldsymbol{\theta}$ is estimated on the basis of the least squares residuals, and plug these into the expression of BLUE of $\boldsymbol{\beta}$ for known dispersion matrix. Davidian and Carroll (1987) review some methods of estimating $\boldsymbol{\theta}$ and also consider the second-order properties of the two-stage estimator. Their findings indicate that although *any* consistent estimator of $\boldsymbol{\theta}$ used in the second stage of the two-stage method is good enough for large sample sizes, the quality of the estimator of $\boldsymbol{\theta}$ does matter for moderate sample sizes. Further iterations of the two-stage procedure (via back-and-forth estimation of $\boldsymbol{\theta}$ and $\boldsymbol{\beta}$) should improve the efficiency of the estimator of $\boldsymbol{\beta}$, particularly when the variance of y_i depends on its mean.

8.6 Some problems of signal processing

A classical model of signal processing is

$$y_t = \sum_{j=1}^{p} x_{tj} + \varepsilon_t, \qquad t = 1, \ldots, N. \tag{8.24}$$

In the above, the response is usually recorded serially in time. The terms in the summation are referred to as *signal* and the error term as the *noise*. The signal may have the following form:

$$x_{tj} = a_j s_{tj}, \qquad t = 1, \ldots, N, \; j = 1, \ldots, p. \tag{8.25}$$

Here, the s_{tj}'s are known. For instance, $s_{11}, \ldots, s_{N1}$ may represent consecutive time samples of a signal emitted by an active sonar or radar, while the y_t's represent the signal received after the emitted signal is reflected from an object of interest. The terms for $j = 2, \ldots, m$ may represent various lagged versions of a single emitted signal, where the lags represent the delays caused by the signal traversing various paths. This is known as the *multipath* effect. The unknown a_j's represent the decrease in amplitude of the signals (known as *attenuation*) as it travels from the source to the receiver via the various paths.

In the case of a passive sonar or radar receiver, which 'listens' but does not emit any signal, the signals originate from various sources of interest. In a multiple target situation the signal $s_{1j}, \ldots, s_{Nj}$ can be the engine noise of the jth target, which should be available from a database of signature tunes of commonly used engines.

The estimated amplitudes $a_1, \ldots, a_p$ carry information about the existence and/or distance of the objects of interest from the receiver. The 'noise' in the transmission medium is often correlated in time. Typically a time series model (such as AR(p)) is used for the correlation structure. Thus, the methods of Section 8.4.1 are applicable.

An important special case of (8.24) is

$$y_t = \sum_{j=1}^{p} a_j \cos(\omega_j t + \theta_j) + \varepsilon_t, \qquad i = 1, \ldots, N.$$

A version of this model with $p = 1$ had been considered in Exercise 1.9. If the sinusoidal frequencies $\omega_1, \ldots, \omega_p$ are known, then the jth signal can be rewritten as $(a_j \cos\theta_j)\cos(\omega_j t) - (a_j \sin\theta_j)\sin(\omega_j t)$. Thus, the standard techniques would work for the transformed parameters $a_j \cos\theta_j$ and $a_j \sin\theta_j$, $j = 1, \ldots, p$ (in lieu of the original parameters, a_j, θ_j, $j = 1, \ldots, p$. If the frequencies are unknown, the problem becomes much more complicated. Often it is necessary to estimate these frequencies in real-time. A discussion of such estimation procedures may be found in Kay (1999).

Sometimes the signal part of (8.24) is also random. A *narrow-band* random signal is of the form

$$x_{tj} = a_{tj} \cos(\omega_j t), \qquad t = 1, \ldots, N, \; j = 1, \ldots, p,$$

where a_{tj}, $t = 1, \ldots, N$, for each j constitute a sample from a distribution, which are uncorrelated with the noise. This model can be seen as a special case of the variance components model (8.6) when the frequencies $\omega_1, \ldots, \omega_p$ are known. A more general version of this problem with complex signals and unknown frequencies is well-known in the signal processing literature. The importance of this problem stems partly from its equivalence with the problem of estimating the direction of arrival of several random signals using measurements from an array of sensors (see Chapters 5, and 16–17 in Bose and Rao, 1993, and Chapters 3 and 7–9 in Haykin, 1991).

The following mixed effects model has applications in some signal processing problems.

$$y_t = \boldsymbol{x}_t'\boldsymbol{\beta} + \boldsymbol{z}_t'\boldsymbol{\gamma} + \varepsilon_t, \qquad t = 1, \ldots, N.$$

Koch (1999) gives an example of physical geodesy where the response represents the gravity at a certain location on the surface of the earth, the fixed effects represent the reference potential and the random effects represent the disturbing potential of the earth's gravity. The important problems in this context are smoothing (getting rid of the noise from the recorded observations) and prediction. The theory of BLUP and the methods of Section 8.3 can be used here.

8.7 Complements/Exercises

Exercises with solutions given in Appendix C

8.1 If $\mathbf{1} \in \mathcal{C}(\boldsymbol{X}_{n\times k})$ and $\boldsymbol{V}$ is a diagonal matrix with n distinct diagonal elements ($n > k$), show that the LSEs of all the estimable functions in the model $(\boldsymbol{y}, \boldsymbol{X\beta}, \sigma^2\boldsymbol{V})$ cannot be BLUE.

8.2 Suppose the dispersion matrix in the model $(\boldsymbol{y}, \boldsymbol{X\beta}, \sigma^2\boldsymbol{V})$ has the form

$$\boldsymbol{V} = \alpha\boldsymbol{P}_{\!X} + \boldsymbol{CC}',$$

where $\mathcal{C}(\boldsymbol{C}) \subset \mathcal{C}(\boldsymbol{X})^{\perp}$, $\boldsymbol{C}'\boldsymbol{C} = \boldsymbol{I}$, and $\alpha = \rho(\boldsymbol{C})/(n - \rho(\boldsymbol{X}))$.

(a) Show that if one erroneously uses the model $(\boldsymbol{y}, \boldsymbol{X\beta}, \sigma^2\boldsymbol{I})$ to compute the BLUE of $\boldsymbol{X\beta}$ *and* the usual estimator of its dispersion matrix, no mistake is committed.

(b) Does this fact contradict Proposition 8.9?

(c) Does the 'wrong model' lead to the correct error sum of squares?

(d) Does the 'wrong model' lead to the appropriate estimate of the dispersion matrix of the residual vector?

8.3 Consider the mixed effects model

$$\boldsymbol{y}_i = \boldsymbol{X}(\boldsymbol{\beta} + \boldsymbol{\eta}_i) + \boldsymbol{\varepsilon}_i, \qquad i = 1, 2, \ldots, p,$$

where $\boldsymbol{\beta}$ is a fixed parameter and $\boldsymbol{\varepsilon}_1, \ldots, \boldsymbol{\varepsilon}_p$ and $\boldsymbol{\eta}_1, \ldots, \boldsymbol{\eta}_p$ are pairwise uncorrelated, zero mean random vectors with $D(\boldsymbol{\varepsilon}_i) = \sigma^2 \boldsymbol{I}$ and $D(\boldsymbol{\eta}_i) = \boldsymbol{V}_0$, $i = 1, \ldots, p$. Show that the BLUE of all estimable functions of $\boldsymbol{\beta}$ coincide with the corresponding LSEs. [This model is used by Chow and Shao (1991) for the analysis of shelf-life of drugs.]

8.4 Show that the LSE of an estimable LPF can have zero variance if and only if the column spaces $\mathcal{C}(\boldsymbol{X})$ and $\mathcal{C}(\boldsymbol{V})^{\perp}$ are *not* virtually disjoint. Is the variance of a zero-variance LSE overestimated if $\boldsymbol{V}$ is incorrectly assumed to be equal to $\boldsymbol{I}$?

8.5 Show that the estimator $\boldsymbol{X}\widehat{\boldsymbol{\beta}}_{pi}$ described in Section 8.2.1 resides almost surely in $\mathcal{C}(\boldsymbol{X})$, provided $\mathcal{C}(\widehat{\boldsymbol{V}}) = \mathcal{C}(\boldsymbol{V})$ with probability 1.

8.6 For the linear model $(\boldsymbol{y}, \boldsymbol{X\beta}, \sigma^2\boldsymbol{V})$ consider the 'averaged' estimator

$$\boldsymbol{X}\widehat{\boldsymbol{\beta}}_{pia} = E_V[\boldsymbol{I} - \boldsymbol{V}(\boldsymbol{I}-\boldsymbol{P}_X)\{(\boldsymbol{I}-\boldsymbol{P}_X)\boldsymbol{V}(\boldsymbol{I}-\boldsymbol{P}_X)\}^-(\boldsymbol{I}-\boldsymbol{P}_X)]\boldsymbol{y},$$

where the expectation is with respect to a *presumed* distribution of $\boldsymbol{V}$ such that $\mathcal{C}(\boldsymbol{V})$ is the same for all points in the support of that distribution.

(a) Show that $\boldsymbol{X}\widehat{\boldsymbol{\beta}}_{pia}$ is unbiased for $\boldsymbol{X\beta}$.

(b) Derive an expression for the dispersion of this estimator, for fixed $\boldsymbol{V}$.

8.7 Suppose the elements of the vector $\boldsymbol{By}$ constitute a generating set of linear zero functions for the model $(\boldsymbol{y}, \boldsymbol{X\beta}, \boldsymbol{V}(\boldsymbol{\theta}))$, and that $D(\boldsymbol{By})$ according to this model is nonsingular. If the REML estimator of $\boldsymbol{\theta}$ exists, does it coincide with its MLE from the reduced model $(\boldsymbol{By}, \boldsymbol{0}, \boldsymbol{BV}(\boldsymbol{\theta})\boldsymbol{B}')$? You may assume that $\boldsymbol{y}$ has a multivariate (possibly singular) normal distribution. Does the MLE depend on the choice of $\boldsymbol{B}$?

8.8 If $\boldsymbol{\theta}$ is a scalar (written as θ) and $\boldsymbol{V}(\theta)$ has full rank, show that the normal MLE of θ in the linear model $(\boldsymbol{y}, \boldsymbol{X\beta}, \boldsymbol{V}(\theta))$ satisfies the estimating equation

$$\operatorname{tr}\left(\boldsymbol{V}^{-1}(\theta)\frac{\partial}{\partial\theta}\boldsymbol{V}(\theta)\right) = \boldsymbol{e}(\theta)'\boldsymbol{V}^{-1}(\theta)\frac{\partial \boldsymbol{V}(\theta)}{\partial\theta}\boldsymbol{V}^{-1}\boldsymbol{e}(\theta),$$

where $\boldsymbol{e}(\theta) = \boldsymbol{y} - \boldsymbol{X}(\boldsymbol{X}'\boldsymbol{V}^{-1}(\theta)\boldsymbol{X})^-\boldsymbol{X}'\boldsymbol{V}^{-1}(\theta)\boldsymbol{y}$. Give an estimating equation for the normal REML estimator.

8.9 Show that the condition of part (b) of Proposition 8.27 is weaker than that of part (c) but stronger than the condition of part (a).

8.10 If $\boldsymbol{y}'\boldsymbol{Q}\boldsymbol{y}$ is an unbiased estimator of $\boldsymbol{p}'\boldsymbol{\theta}$ in the variance components model (8.6), show that there exists a symmetric matrix $\boldsymbol{Q}_*$ such that $\boldsymbol{y}'\boldsymbol{Q}_*\boldsymbol{y} = \boldsymbol{y}'\boldsymbol{Q}\boldsymbol{y}$ with probability 1 and $\boldsymbol{X}'\boldsymbol{Q}_*\boldsymbol{X} = \boldsymbol{0}$.

8.11 Suppose $\boldsymbol{V}(\boldsymbol{\theta})$ is as in (8.6) and $\sigma_i^2 > 0$, $i = 1, \ldots, k$. Show that $\mathcal{C}(\boldsymbol{V}(\boldsymbol{\theta})) = \mathcal{C}(\boldsymbol{V}_1 : \boldsymbol{V}_2 : \cdots : \boldsymbol{V}_k)$.

8.12 Prove the alternative equations for the MLE of $\boldsymbol{\theta}$ given in Remark 8.31. State and prove the corresponding result for the REML estimator.

8.13 Consider the variance components model of the type (8.6) with $\boldsymbol{V}_k = \boldsymbol{I}$. Then the MINQUE corresponding to the choice $\boldsymbol{w} = (0 : \cdots : 0 : 1)'$, i.e. $\boldsymbol{V}(\boldsymbol{w}) = \boldsymbol{I}$ in the equation of Proposition 8.36, is sometimes referred to as MINQUE(0). Derive the expressions for the MINQUE(0) of the two variance parameters in the case of the model of Example 8.33. What happens when the model is not balanced, that is, there are m_i observations for the ith level of the random effect, $i = 1, \ldots, t$?

8.14 Suppose the parameter $\boldsymbol{p}'\boldsymbol{\theta}$ is estimable through a translation invariant, quadratic and unbiased estimator under the variance components model (8.5) with normally distributed random effects. Show that in order that $\boldsymbol{y}'\widetilde{\boldsymbol{Q}}\boldsymbol{y}$ is the MIVQUE of $\boldsymbol{p}'\boldsymbol{\theta}$, it must be of the form $\boldsymbol{p}\widehat{\boldsymbol{\theta}} = \sum_{j=1}^k p_j \widehat{\sigma^2}_j$, where $\widehat{\sigma^2}_1, \ldots, \widehat{\sigma^2}_k$ satisfy the equations

$$\sum_{j=1}^k \widehat{\sigma^2}_j \mathrm{tr}(\boldsymbol{W}^-(\boldsymbol{\theta})\boldsymbol{W}_i\boldsymbol{W}^-(\boldsymbol{\theta})\boldsymbol{W}_j) = \boldsymbol{b}(\boldsymbol{\theta})'\boldsymbol{W}_i\boldsymbol{b}(\boldsymbol{\theta}), \quad i = 1, \ldots, k,$$

where $\boldsymbol{W}(\cdot)$, $\boldsymbol{b}(\cdot)$ and $\boldsymbol{W}_1, \ldots, \boldsymbol{W}_k$ are as defined in Proposition 8.32, and $\boldsymbol{\theta}$ is the true value of the parameter. Also, show that an approximation of the MIVQUE, obtained by replacing $\boldsymbol{\theta}$ by a known vector in the objective function of (8.15), is a MINQUE.

8.15 Show that the equations (8.22) and (8.23) describe the BLUE and its dispersion if the true values of $\sigma_1^2 \ldots, \sigma_m^2$ are used in the expressions of $\widehat{D}(\widehat{\boldsymbol{\beta}}_{(j)})$, $j = 1, \ldots, m$.

8.16 In the above problem assume $\sigma_1^2 = \cdots = \sigma_m^2$. Find expressions for (a) the BLUE OF $\boldsymbol{\beta}$, (b) its dispersion and (c) the usual estimator of the common error variance, from the pooled data. The expressions should be in terms of the summary statistics of the individual studies.

8.17 Consider the problem of comparing the effects of two treatments, where summarized data from n_0 controlled comparative studies have to be combined with those from several uncontrolled studies on each of the treatments (a total of n_1 summaries on treatment 1 and n_2 summaries on treatment 2). Li and Begg (1994) formulate this problem of meta-analysis in terms of the mixed effects model (8.5) with

$$X = \begin{pmatrix} \mathbf{1}_{n_0} & \mathbf{0}_{n_0} \\ \mathbf{1}_{n_0} & \mathbf{1}_{n_0} \\ \mathbf{1}_{n_1} & \mathbf{0}_{n_1} \\ \mathbf{1}_{n_2} & \mathbf{1}_{n_2} \end{pmatrix}, \qquad \boldsymbol{\beta} = \begin{pmatrix} \beta_1 \\ \beta_2 \end{pmatrix}, \qquad k = 2,$$

$$U_1 = \begin{pmatrix} I_{n_0\times n_0} & \mathbf{0}_{n_1\times n_1} & \mathbf{0}_{n_2\times n_2} \\ I_{n_0\times n_0} & \mathbf{0}_{n_1\times n_1} & \mathbf{0}_{n_2\times n_2} \\ \mathbf{0}_{n_0\times n_0} & I_{n_1\times n_1} & \mathbf{0}_{n_2\times n_2} \\ \mathbf{0}_{n_0\times n_0} & \mathbf{0}_{n_1\times n_1} & I_{n_2\times n_2} \end{pmatrix}, \quad U_2 = \begin{pmatrix} \psi_1 & 0 & \cdots & 0 \\ 0 & \psi_2 & \cdots & 0 \\ \vdots & \vdots & \ddots & \vdots \\ 0 & 0 & \cdots & \psi_{2n_0+n_1+n_2} \end{pmatrix},$$

where γ_1 represents a baseline effect in the three sets of studies, and γ_2 pertain to the random effects of the various treatment-study combinations. Though U_2 is assumed to be known, in practice it is estimated from the respective studies. Consequently it is assumed that $\sigma_2^2 = 1$. The fixed parameter β_2 represents the differential impact of the second treatment. Let us denote the four groups of observations as G_{0a}, G_{0b}, G_1 and G_2, respectively. Consider the following class of quadratic functions of $\boldsymbol{y}$ based on summary statistic:

$$q(w_0, w_1, w_2) = w_0 s_0^2 + w_1 s_1^2 + w_2 s_2^2,$$

where s_0^2 is the average of the sample variances in G_{0a} and G_{0b}, and s_1^2 and s_2^2 are the sample variances in G_1 and G_2, respectively. Assuming that the average of ψ_is in every group is known, find conditions on the weights w_0, w_1 and w_2 so that $q(w_0, w_1, w_2)$ is translation invariant and unbiased for σ_1^2. Can w_2 be equal to w_1?

Additional exercises

8.18 Consider the nested classification model with homogeneity within subsamples, given by $y_{ijk} = \mu + \alpha_i + \beta_{ij} + \varepsilon_{ijk}$, $k = 1, 2, \ldots, n_{ij}$, $j = 1, 2, \ldots, q_i$, $i = 1, 2, \ldots, p$, having uncorrelated zero-mean errors with $Var(\varepsilon_{ij}) = \sigma_{ij}$. Show that the LSEs of the estimable LPFs coincide with the corresponding BLUEs.

8.19 Consider Example 8.5 with no interaction between cells. Show that the LSEs of the estimable LPFs would coincide with the corresponding BLUEs only if the σ_{ij}'s are the same for all i and j.

8.20 Consider the linear model $\boldsymbol{y} = \boldsymbol{X\beta} + \boldsymbol{\varepsilon}$ with zero-mean errors having a spatial correlation structure modelled by the equation $\boldsymbol{\varepsilon} = \alpha \boldsymbol{W\varepsilon} + \boldsymbol{\delta}$, where $\boldsymbol{W}$ is a known 'weight' matrix with nonnegative elements, α is an unknown positive 'correlation parameter' such that $\alpha^2 \text{tr}(\boldsymbol{W}'\boldsymbol{W}) \leq 1$ and $\boldsymbol{\delta}$ is a vector of uncorrelated errors of equal variance [see Section 8.4.2]. Show that the LSE of any estimable function would coincide with its BLUE under the above model whenever $\mathcal{C}(\boldsymbol{WX}) \subseteq \mathcal{C}(\boldsymbol{X})$ and $\mathcal{C}(\boldsymbol{W}'\boldsymbol{X}) \subseteq \mathcal{C}(\boldsymbol{X})$.

8.21 Find estimable LPFs for which the upper and lower bounds obtained in Example 8.16 are achieved.

8.22 Consider the linear model $(\boldsymbol{y}, \boldsymbol{X\beta}, \sigma^2\boldsymbol{V})$ with normal errors where $\boldsymbol{V}$ is possibly singular but completely known. Derive the REML estimator of σ^2, and show that unlike the MLE, this estimator is unbiased.

8.23 Consider the linear model $(\boldsymbol{y}, \boldsymbol{X\beta}, \boldsymbol{V}(\boldsymbol{\theta}))$ with

$$\boldsymbol{X} = \begin{pmatrix} 1 & 0 \\ 1 & 0 \\ 0 & 1 \\ 0 & 1 \end{pmatrix}, \quad \boldsymbol{V}(\boldsymbol{\theta}) = \begin{pmatrix} \sigma_1^2 & 0 & 0 & 0 \\ 0 & \sigma_2^2 & 0 & 0 \\ 0 & 0 & \sigma_1^2 & 0 \\ 0 & 0 & 0 & \sigma_2^2 \end{pmatrix}, \quad \boldsymbol{\theta} = \begin{pmatrix} \sigma_1^2 \\ \sigma_2^2 \end{pmatrix}.$$

Show that there is no translation invariant, quadratic and unbiased estimator of σ_1^2 or σ_2^2, even though there is a quadratic and unbiased estimator of each of them. Find a quadratic and unbiased estimator of σ_1^2.

8.24 If $\boldsymbol{V}_1 = \boldsymbol{XX}'$ and $\boldsymbol{V}_2 = \boldsymbol{I}$ in the model (8.6) and $\boldsymbol{X}$ is such that $\text{tr}(\boldsymbol{XX}'\boldsymbol{XX}')\text{tr}(\boldsymbol{I}_{n\times n}) \neq [\text{tr}(\boldsymbol{XX}')]^2$, show that there is no quadratic and unbiased estimator of σ_1^2 even though it is identifiable.

8.25 Find the MINQUE and normal MIVQUE estimators of σ^2 in the fixed effects linear model $(\boldsymbol{y}, \boldsymbol{X\beta}, \sigma^2\boldsymbol{V})$ where $\boldsymbol{V}$ is a known nonnegative definite matrix.

8.26 Show that the BLUP of the random effects in the mixed effects model (8.5) are indeed as described in (8.16).

8.27 Consider the linear model $(\boldsymbol{y}, \boldsymbol{X\beta}, \boldsymbol{V}(\sigma^2, \phi))$, where the error sequence follows the model of Example 8.20. Calculate the minimum efficiency of an LSE from (8.2), for $\phi = 0.95$ and sample size 10. Compare this with the minimum efficiency of an LSE in the transformed model with sample size 9, where the observations (response as well as explanatory variables) consist of differences of the successive observations in the original model. Also compute the bounds on the expected value of the estimated variance of an LSE (given in (8.4)) for the two models, assuming $\boldsymbol{X}$ has rank 2. What can you conclude from these comparisons?

Chapter 9

Updates in the General Linear Model

Consider the linear model $(\boldsymbol{y}, \boldsymbol{X\beta}, \sigma^2\boldsymbol{V})$ where the parameters $\boldsymbol{\beta}$ and σ^2 are unknown. The statistical quantities of interest include the best linear unbiased estimators (BLUEs) of the estimable parametric functions, variance-covariance matrices of such estimators, the error sum of squares and the likelihood ratio tests for testable linear hypotheses. In this chapter we are concerned with the changes in these quantities when some observations are included or excluded, as well as when some explanatory variables are included or excluded.

The update problem for additional observations is important not only for computational purpose but also for theoretical reasons. A proper understanding of the update mechanism can provide insight into strategies for sequential design and inference. Updating in the case of exclusion of observations has implications in deletion diagnostics, studied in Section 5.4. The inclusion and exclusion of explanatory variables are relevant for comparison of various subset models.

The focus in this chapter will be on statistical interpretation and understanding of the mechanism of update. The LZFs and the principle of decorrelation will serve as the main tools in the derivation of the updates. This approach is based on the works of Bhimasankaram and Jammalamadaka (1994b) and Jammalamadaka and Sengupta (1999). Expressions in some special cases are obtained by Plackett (1950), Mitra and Bhimasankaram (1971), McGilchrist and Sandland (1979), Haslett (1985) and Bhimasankaram et al. (1995).

The update formulae given in the following sections and in the articles mentioned above are not focussed specifically for the purpose of computation. There is a great deal of literature on numerically stable methods of recursive estimation in the linear model, see for instance Chambers (1975),

Gragg et al. (1979), Kourouklis and Paige (1981), Farebrother (1988) and Björk (1996).

We use a special notational convention in this chapter. When it is necessary to display the sample size explicitly, we indicate it by a subscript. On the other hand, when the number of parameters has to be displayed, we use subscripts within parentheses.

9.1 Inclusion of observations

Let us denote the linear model with n observations by

$$\mathcal{M}_n = (\boldsymbol{y}_n, \boldsymbol{X}_n\boldsymbol{\beta}, \sigma^2\boldsymbol{V}_n).$$

In this section we track the transition from $\mathcal{M}_m = (\boldsymbol{y}_m, \boldsymbol{X}_m\boldsymbol{\beta}, \sigma^2\boldsymbol{V}_m)$ to $\mathcal{M}_n$ for $n > m$. We refer to $\mathcal{M}_m$ as the 'initial' model and $\mathcal{M}_n$ as the 'augmented' model. Note that each LZF in the initial model $\mathcal{M}_m$ is also an LZF in the augmented model $\mathcal{M}_n$. According to Proposition 7.19, the number of nontrivial and uncorrelated LZFs exclusive to the augmented model, which are uncorrelated with the LZFs common to both the models, is $[\rho(\boldsymbol{X}_n : \boldsymbol{V}_n) - \rho(\boldsymbol{X}_n)] - [\rho(\boldsymbol{X}_m : \boldsymbol{V}_m) - \rho(\boldsymbol{X}_m)]$. The clue to the update relationships lies in the identification of these LZFs.

9.1.1 *A simple case*

Let us first consider the case $n = m + 1$ and $\boldsymbol{V}_n = \boldsymbol{I}_{n\times n}$. We partition $\boldsymbol{y}_{m+1}$ and $\boldsymbol{X}_{m+1}$ as

$$\boldsymbol{y}_{m+1} = \begin{pmatrix} \boldsymbol{y}_m \\ y_{m+1} \end{pmatrix}; \qquad \boldsymbol{X}_{m+1} = \begin{pmatrix} \boldsymbol{X}_m \\ \boldsymbol{x}'_{m+1} \end{pmatrix}. \tag{9.1}$$

We consider two cases:
(a) $\boldsymbol{x}_{m+1} \notin \mathcal{C}(\boldsymbol{X}'_m)$, i.e. $\rho(\boldsymbol{X}_{m+1}) = \rho(\boldsymbol{X}_m) + 1$, and
(b) $\boldsymbol{x}_{m+1} \in \mathcal{C}(\boldsymbol{X}'_m)$, i.e. $\rho(\boldsymbol{X}_{m+1}) = \rho(\boldsymbol{X}_m)$.

Recall from page 94 that $\rho(\boldsymbol{X})$ is the effective number of parameters/explanatory variables in a linear model with model matrix $\boldsymbol{X}$. Thus in case (a) when $\rho(\boldsymbol{X}_{m+1}) - \rho(\boldsymbol{X}_m) = 1$, there is effectively one additional explanatory variable in the augmented model. This variable does not affect the fit of $\boldsymbol{y}_m$, but ensures *exact* fit of the last observation. As the last observation is the BLUE of its own expectation, there is no new LZF exclusive to the augmented model. Consequently there need be no revision in the BLUE of any function that is estimable under the initial model. The dispersion of such a BLUE, as well as R_0^2 would also remain unchanged (see Proposition 9.9 and the discussion preceding it for formal proofs of these statements in a more general case).

In case (b) $\boldsymbol{x}'_{m+1}\boldsymbol{\beta}$ is estimable under $\mathcal{M}_m$. Let $\boldsymbol{x}'_{m+1}\widehat{\boldsymbol{\beta}}_m$ be the BLUE of this function under $\mathcal{M}_m$. Then it is uncorrelated with every LZF of $\mathcal{M}_m$. Consequently the linear statistic

$$w_{m+1} = y_{m+1} - \boldsymbol{x}'_{m+1}\widehat{\boldsymbol{\beta}}_m \tag{9.2}$$

is an LZF of $\mathcal{M}_{m+1}$ which is uncorrelated with every LZF of $\mathcal{M}_m$. Since $\rho(\boldsymbol{I}-\boldsymbol{P}_{X_{m+1}}) = \rho(\boldsymbol{I}-\boldsymbol{P}_{X_m})+1$, a standardized basis set of LZFs of $\mathcal{M}_{m+1}$ can be obtained by augmenting a standardized basis set of LZFs of $\mathcal{M}_m$ with a standardized version of w_{m+1}. Since the BLUEs under $\mathcal{M}_m$ are already uncorrelated with the LZFs of $\mathcal{M}_m$, decorrelation with w_{m+1} would produce the updated BLUE under $\mathcal{M}_{m+1}$. These observations lead to the following update equations.

Proposition 9.1. *Under the above set-up, let $\boldsymbol{x}_{m+1} \in \mathcal{C}(\boldsymbol{X}'_m)$. Suppose further that $\boldsymbol{A\beta}$ is estimable, and w_{m+1} is as in (9.2). Further, let $h = \boldsymbol{x}'_{m+1}(\boldsymbol{X}'_m\boldsymbol{X}_m)^-\boldsymbol{x}_{m+1}$ and $\boldsymbol{c} = \boldsymbol{X}_m(\boldsymbol{X}'_m\boldsymbol{X}_m)^-\boldsymbol{x}_{m+1}$. Then*

(a) $\boldsymbol{X}_m\widehat{\boldsymbol{\beta}}_{m+1} = \boldsymbol{X}_m\widehat{\boldsymbol{\beta}}_m + \dfrac{w_{m+1}}{1+h}\boldsymbol{c}.$

(b) $D(\boldsymbol{X}_m\widehat{\boldsymbol{\beta}}_{m+1}) = D(\boldsymbol{X}_m\widehat{\boldsymbol{\beta}}_m) - \dfrac{\sigma^2}{1+h}\boldsymbol{cc}'.$

(c) $R^2_{0_n} = R^2_{0_m} + \dfrac{w^2_{m+1}}{1+h}.$

(d) The change in R^2_H corresponding to the hypothesis $\boldsymbol{A\beta} = \boldsymbol{\xi}$ is $R^2_{H_n} = R^2_{H_m} + \dfrac{(w_{m+1} - \boldsymbol{a}'\boldsymbol{D}_A^-(\boldsymbol{A}\widehat{\boldsymbol{\beta}}_m - \boldsymbol{\xi}))^2}{1+h-\boldsymbol{a}'\boldsymbol{D}_A^-\boldsymbol{a}}$, where $\boldsymbol{D}_A = \boldsymbol{A}(\boldsymbol{X}'_m\boldsymbol{X}_m)^-\boldsymbol{A}'$ and $\boldsymbol{a} = \boldsymbol{A}(\boldsymbol{X}'_m\boldsymbol{X}_m)^-\boldsymbol{x}_{m+1}$.

(e) The degrees of freedom of R_0^2 and R_H^2 increase by 1 as a result of the inclusion of the additional observation.

Proof. Note that $\boldsymbol{X}_m\widehat{\boldsymbol{\beta}}_m$ is an unbiased estimator of $\boldsymbol{X}_m\boldsymbol{\beta}$ that is already uncorrelated with the LZFs of $\mathcal{M}_m$. By making it uncorrelated with the new LZF w_{m+1} through Proposition 2.28, we have

$$\boldsymbol{X}_m\widehat{\boldsymbol{\beta}}_{m+1} = \boldsymbol{X}_m\widehat{\boldsymbol{\beta}}_m - Cov(\boldsymbol{X}_m\widehat{\boldsymbol{\beta}}_m, w_{m+1})w_{m+1}/Var(w_{m+1}).$$

Part (a) is proved by simplifying the above expression.

Since $\boldsymbol{X}_m\widehat{\boldsymbol{\beta}}_{m+1}$ must be uncorrelated with the increment term in part (a), we have

$$D(\boldsymbol{X}_m\widehat{\boldsymbol{\beta}}_m) = D(\boldsymbol{X}_m\widehat{\boldsymbol{\beta}}_{m+1}) + D\left(\frac{w_{m+1}}{1+h}\boldsymbol{c}\right).$$

Simplification of this expression leads to the relation given in part (b).

Part (c) follows from the characterization of R_0^2 through a standardized basis set of linear zero functions, and by simplifying the increment, $\frac{\sigma^2 w_{m+1}^2}{Var(w_{m+1}^2)}$.

As far as the restricted model is concerned, the role of w_{m+1} is played by the quantity

$$w_{m+1} - \boldsymbol{a}'\boldsymbol{D}_A^-(\boldsymbol{A}\widehat{\boldsymbol{\beta}}_m - \boldsymbol{\xi}),$$

which is obtained from w_{m+1} by decorrelating it from the LZF $(\boldsymbol{A}\widehat{\boldsymbol{\beta}}_m - \boldsymbol{\xi})$. The variance of this quantity is easily seen to be $Var(w_{m+1}) - \sigma^2\boldsymbol{a}'\boldsymbol{D}_A^-\boldsymbol{a}$. The result of part (d) is similar to that of part (c) with these adjustments.

Part (e) follows from the fact that the additional observation results in only one additional LZF having variance σ^2 which is uncorrelated with the existing LZFs — both for the restricted and unrestricted models. □

Update equations like those given in Proposition 9.1 are obtained by Plackett (1950) and Mitra and Bhimasankaram (1971).

The quantity w_{m+1} holds the key to the update equations given in Proposition 9.1. It can be interpreted as the prediction error of the BLUP of y_{m+1} computed from the first m observations (see Proposition 7.49). Brown et al. (1975) call this quantity the *recursive residual* of the newly included observation.

We now go back to the general case where $\boldsymbol{V}_n$ is not necessarily $\boldsymbol{I}_n$ and several observations may be included simultaneously $(n - m > 1)$.

9.1.2 *General case: linear zero functions gained*

Let $\boldsymbol{y}_n$, $\boldsymbol{X}_n$ and $\boldsymbol{V}_n$ be partitioned as shown below:

$$\boldsymbol{y}_n = \begin{pmatrix} \boldsymbol{y}_m \\ \boldsymbol{y}_l \end{pmatrix}; \qquad \boldsymbol{X}_n = \begin{pmatrix} \boldsymbol{X}_m \\ \boldsymbol{X}_l \end{pmatrix}; \qquad \boldsymbol{V}_n = \begin{pmatrix} \boldsymbol{V}_m & \boldsymbol{V}_{ml} \\ \boldsymbol{V}_{lm} & \boldsymbol{V}_l \end{pmatrix}, \tag{9.3}$$

where $l = n - m$. Let $l_* = \rho(\boldsymbol{X}_n : \boldsymbol{V}_n) - \rho(\boldsymbol{X}_m : \boldsymbol{V}_m)$. Note that

$$0 \le \rho(\boldsymbol{X}_n) - \rho(\boldsymbol{X}_m) \le l_* \le l.$$

The following cases can arise:

(a) $0 < \rho(\boldsymbol{X}_n) - \rho(\boldsymbol{X}_m) = l_*$;
(b) $0 = \rho(\boldsymbol{X}_n) - \rho(\boldsymbol{X}_m) < l_*$, that is, $\mathcal{C}(\boldsymbol{X}_l') \subseteq \mathcal{C}(\boldsymbol{X}_m')$;
(c) $0 = \rho(\boldsymbol{X}_n) - \rho(\boldsymbol{X}_m) = l_*$;
(d) $0 < \rho(\boldsymbol{X}_n) - \rho(\boldsymbol{X}_m) < l_*$.

Remark 9.2. Case (a) implies that there are some additional estimable LPFs in the augmented model, but no new LZF. Case (b) corresponds to some additional LZFs in the augmented model, but no new estimable LPF. Case (c) corresponds to no new LZF or estimable LPF. Case (d) indicates that there are some additional LZFs as well as additional estimable LPFs in the augmented model (see Exercise 9.1). □

We have already come across cases (a) and (b) in Section 9.1.1. Case (c) can only arise when $\boldsymbol{V}_n$ is singular. Case (d) can arise only if $l > 1$.

There is no new LZF to be identified in cases (a) and (c). In case (d), we can permute the rows of $\boldsymbol{X}_l$ in such a way that each of the top few rows, when appended successively to the rows of $\boldsymbol{X}_m$, increase the rank of the matrix by 1, and the remaining rows belong to the row space of the concatenated matrix. This permuted version of $\boldsymbol{X}_l$ can be partitioned as $(\boldsymbol{X}_{l_1}' : \boldsymbol{X}_{l_2}')'$, where $\boldsymbol{X}_{l_1}$ has $\rho(\boldsymbol{X}_n) - \rho(\boldsymbol{X}_m)$ rows and

$$\rho\begin{pmatrix}\boldsymbol{X}_m\\ \boldsymbol{X}_{l_1}\end{pmatrix} = \rho(\boldsymbol{X}_n).$$

The elements of $\boldsymbol{y}_l$, $\boldsymbol{V}_{ml}$, $\boldsymbol{V}_{lm}$ and $\boldsymbol{V}_l$ can also be permuted accordingly. With this permutation, the inclusion of the l observations can be viewed as a two-step process: the inclusion of the first set of observations entails additional estimable LPFs but no new LZF, as in case (a), while the inclusion of the remaining observations result in additional LZFs but no new estimable LPF, as in case (b). Thus, it is enough to identify the set of new LZFs in the augmented model in case (b), which we do through the next proposition.

Proposition 9.3. *In the above set-up, let $l_* > 0$ and $\mathcal{C}(\boldsymbol{X}_l') \subset \mathcal{C}(\boldsymbol{X}_m')$. Then a vector of LZFs of the model $\mathcal{M}_n$ that is uncorrelated with all the LZFs of $\mathcal{M}_m$ is given by*

$$\boldsymbol{w}_l = \boldsymbol{y}_l - \boldsymbol{X}_l\widehat{\boldsymbol{\beta}}_m - \boldsymbol{V}_{ml}'\boldsymbol{V}_m^-(\boldsymbol{y}_m - \boldsymbol{X}_m\widehat{\boldsymbol{\beta}}_m). \tag{9.4}$$

Further, all LZFs of the augmented model are linear combinations of $\boldsymbol{w}_l$ and the LZFs of the initial model.

Proof. It is easy to see that $\boldsymbol{y}_l - \boldsymbol{X}_l\widehat{\boldsymbol{\beta}}_m$ is indeed an LZF in the augmented model. The expression for $\boldsymbol{w}_l$ is obtained by decorrelating this LZF from $(\boldsymbol{I}_m - \boldsymbol{P}_{X_m})\boldsymbol{y}_m$ through Proposition 2.28, and simplifying it.

We shall prove the second part of the proposition by showing that there is no LZF of the augmented model which is uncorrelated with $\boldsymbol{w}_l$ and the

LZFs of the initial model. Suppose, for contradiction, that $\boldsymbol{u}'(\boldsymbol{I}-\boldsymbol{P}_{X_n})\boldsymbol{y}_n$ is such an LZF. Consequently it is uncorrelated with $(\boldsymbol{I}-\boldsymbol{P}_{X_m})\boldsymbol{y}_m$ and $(\boldsymbol{y}_l-\boldsymbol{X}_l\widehat{\boldsymbol{\beta}}_m)$. Therefore

$$(\boldsymbol{I}-\boldsymbol{P}_{X_m})(\boldsymbol{V}_m:\boldsymbol{V}_{ml})(\boldsymbol{I}-\boldsymbol{P}_{X_n})\boldsymbol{u}=0$$
$$(\boldsymbol{V}_{lm}:\boldsymbol{V}_l)(\boldsymbol{I}-\boldsymbol{P}_{X_n})\boldsymbol{u}-\boldsymbol{X}_l\boldsymbol{X}_m^-(\boldsymbol{V}_m:\boldsymbol{V}_{ml})(\boldsymbol{I}-\boldsymbol{P}_{X_n})\boldsymbol{u}=0.$$

The first condition is equivalent to $(\boldsymbol{V}_m:\boldsymbol{V}_{ml})(\boldsymbol{I}-\boldsymbol{P}_{X_n})\boldsymbol{u}\in\mathcal{C}(\boldsymbol{X}_m)$. It follows from this and the second condition that

$$\begin{pmatrix}\boldsymbol{X}_m\\ \boldsymbol{X}_l\end{pmatrix}\boldsymbol{X}_m^-(\boldsymbol{V}_m:\boldsymbol{V}_{ml})(\boldsymbol{I}-\boldsymbol{P}_{X_n})\boldsymbol{u}=\begin{pmatrix}\boldsymbol{V}_m & \boldsymbol{V}_{ml}\\ \boldsymbol{V}_{lm} & \boldsymbol{V}_l\end{pmatrix}(\boldsymbol{I}-\boldsymbol{P}_{X_n})\boldsymbol{u},$$

i.e. $\boldsymbol{V}(\boldsymbol{I}-\boldsymbol{P}_{X_n})\boldsymbol{u}\in\mathcal{C}(\boldsymbol{X}_n)$. This implies that $\boldsymbol{u}'(\boldsymbol{I}-\boldsymbol{P}_{X_n})\boldsymbol{y}_n$ is a trivial LZF with zero variance. □

The crucial LZF $\boldsymbol{w}_l$ is a generalization of w_{m+1} defined in (9.2) for the special case $l=1$.

Remark 9.4. A standardized basis set of LZFs in the augmented model has l_* extra elements, in comparison with a corresponding set for the initial model. Since all the LZFs of the augmented model that are uncorrelated with those of the initial model have to be linear functions of $\boldsymbol{w}_l$, the rank of $D(\boldsymbol{w}_l)$ must be l_*. □

Remark 9.5. It follows from Proposition 7.49 that the LZF $\boldsymbol{w}_l$ can be written as the prediction error $\boldsymbol{y}_l-\widehat{\boldsymbol{y}}_l$, where $\widehat{\boldsymbol{y}}_l$ is the BLUP of $\boldsymbol{y}_l$ on the basis of the model $\mathcal{M}_m$. □

Remark 9.6. There is no unique choice of the LZF with the properties stated in Proposition 9.3. Any linear function of $\boldsymbol{w}_l$ having the same rank of the dispersion matrix would suffice. However, the expression in (9.4) is invariant under the choice of the g-inverse of $\boldsymbol{V}_m$ (this follows from Proposition 7.15). □

Remark 9.7. Let $\boldsymbol{d}_l(\boldsymbol{\beta})=\boldsymbol{y}_l-\boldsymbol{X}_l\boldsymbol{\beta}-\boldsymbol{V}_{lm}\boldsymbol{V}_m^-(\boldsymbol{y}_m-\boldsymbol{X}_m\boldsymbol{\beta})$, the error part of $\boldsymbol{y}_l$ decorrelated from the error part of $\boldsymbol{y}_m$. The LZF $\boldsymbol{w}_l$ can be seen as $\boldsymbol{d}_l(\widehat{\boldsymbol{\beta}}_m)$, the prediction of $\boldsymbol{d}_l(\boldsymbol{\beta})$ based on the first m observations. The implications of this interpretation will be clear in Section 9.2. □

McGilchrist and Sandland (1979) extend the *recursive residual* of Brown et al. (1975) to the case of any positive definite $\boldsymbol{V}$. The expression of (9.4) for $l=1$ can be seen as a further generalization to the case of singular $\boldsymbol{V}$.

Recursive residuals have been quite popular (particularly when there is a natural order among the observations) because of the fact that these are uncorrelated. These are used as diagnostic tools (see Kianifard and Swallow, 1996). It was seen in Proposition 9.1 that the recursive residual plays the central role in obtaining updates of various quantities of interest. The same holds in the general case, as we shall see in Proposition 9.8.

Haslett (1985) extends the recursive residuals to the case of multiple observations ($l \geq 1$), assuming that $\boldsymbol{V}$ is positive definite. Jammalamadaka and Sengupta (1999) further extend it to the case of possibly singular $\boldsymbol{V}$ in the following way. Suppose $\boldsymbol{F}\boldsymbol{F}'$ is a rank-factorization of $\sigma^{-2}D(\boldsymbol{w}_l)$, and $\boldsymbol{F}^{-L}$ is a left-inverse of $\boldsymbol{F}$. Then the LZF, $\boldsymbol{F}^{-L}\boldsymbol{w}_l$ can be defined as a *recursive group residual* for the observation vector $\boldsymbol{y}_l$. The recursive group residual is not uniquely defined whenever $D(\boldsymbol{w}_l)$ is a singular matrix. However, the sum of squares of the recursive group residuals is uniquely defined and is equal to $\sigma^2\boldsymbol{w}_l'[D(\boldsymbol{w}_l)]^-\boldsymbol{w}_l$. The vector $\boldsymbol{w}_l$ is also uniquely defined given the order of inclusion of the observations. Moreover, the components of $\boldsymbol{w}_l$ have one-to-one correspondence with those of $\boldsymbol{y}_l$. We can call $\boldsymbol{w}_l$ the *unscaled recursive group residual* for $\boldsymbol{y}_l$.

9.1.3 *General case: update equations*

It follows from Remark 9.2 and the subsequent discussion that the main case of interest for data augmentation is case (b). We already have from Proposition 9.3 a vector LZF which accounts for the additional LZFs of the augmented model. We now use it to update various statistics.

Proposition 9.8. *Under the set-up of Section 9.1.2, let* $\mathcal{C}(\boldsymbol{X}_l') \subset \mathcal{C}(\boldsymbol{X}_m')$ *and let* $l_* = \rho(\boldsymbol{X}_n : \boldsymbol{V}_n) - \rho(\boldsymbol{X}_m : \boldsymbol{V}_m) > 0$. *Suppose further that* $\boldsymbol{A\beta}$ *is estimable with* $D(\boldsymbol{A}\widehat{\boldsymbol{\beta}}_m)$ *not identically zero, and* $\boldsymbol{w}_l$ *is the recursive residual given in (9.4). Then*

(a) $\boldsymbol{X}_m\widehat{\boldsymbol{\beta}}_n = \boldsymbol{X}_m\widehat{\boldsymbol{\beta}}_m - Cov(\boldsymbol{X}_m\widehat{\boldsymbol{\beta}}_m, \boldsymbol{w}_l)[D(\boldsymbol{w}_l)]^-\boldsymbol{w}_l$.

(b) $D(\boldsymbol{X}_m\widehat{\boldsymbol{\beta}}_n) = D(\boldsymbol{X}_m\widehat{\boldsymbol{\beta}}_m) - Cov(\boldsymbol{X}_m\widehat{\boldsymbol{\beta}}_m, \boldsymbol{w}_l)[D(\boldsymbol{w}_l)]^-Cov(\boldsymbol{w}_l, \boldsymbol{X}_m\widehat{\boldsymbol{\beta}}_m)$.

(c) $R^2_{0_n} = R^2_{0_m} + \sigma^2\boldsymbol{w}_l'[D(\boldsymbol{w}_l)]^-\boldsymbol{w}_l$.

(d) *The change in* R^2_H *corresponding to the hypothesis* $\boldsymbol{A\beta} = \boldsymbol{\xi}$ *is* $R^2_{H_n} = R^2_{H_m} + \sigma^2\boldsymbol{w}_{l*}'[D(\boldsymbol{w}_{l*})]^-\boldsymbol{w}_{l*}$, *where*

$$\boldsymbol{w}_{l*} = \boldsymbol{w}_l - Cov(\boldsymbol{w}_l, \boldsymbol{A}\widehat{\boldsymbol{\beta}}_m)[D(\boldsymbol{A}\widehat{\boldsymbol{\beta}}_m)]^-(\boldsymbol{A}\widehat{\boldsymbol{\beta}}_m - \boldsymbol{\xi}).$$

(e) *Inclusion of the* l *additional observations increases the degrees of freedom of* R^2_0 *and* R^2_H *by* l_* *and* $\rho(D(\boldsymbol{w}_{l*}))$, *respectively.*

Proof. The proofs of parts (a), (b) and (c) are similar to the proofs of the corresponding parts of Proposition 9.1. Substitution of these three update formulae into (7.17) leads us to (d) after some algebraic manipulation. Part (e) is a consequence of the fact that the additional error degrees of freedom coincide with the number of nontrivial LZFs of the augmented model that are uncorrelated with the old ones as well as among themselves. □

The variances and covariances involved in the update formulae can be computed from the expressions given in Sections 7.3 and 7.7. The explicit algebraic expressions in the general case are somewhat ungainly, as found out by Pordzik (1992a) and Bhimasankaram et al. (1995) who use the inverse partitioned matrix approach of Section 7.7.2 as a vehicle for deriving the updates. Simpler expressions can be found in some special cases.

When a single observation is included ($l = 1$), $D(\boldsymbol{w}_l)$ reduces to a scalar. Here, the assumptions of Proposition 9.8 imply that $\rho(D(\boldsymbol{w}_l))$ is equal to 1. The rank of $D(\boldsymbol{w}_{l*})$ must also be equal to 1 (it is zero if and only if $\boldsymbol{w}_l$ is a linear function of the BLUEs of $\mathcal{M}_m$, which is impossible).

If $\boldsymbol{V}_m$ is nonsingular, the unscaled recursive group residual defined in (9.4) can be written as

$$\begin{aligned} \boldsymbol{w}_l &= \boldsymbol{s}_l - \widehat{\boldsymbol{s}}_l, \\ \text{where } \boldsymbol{s}_l &= \boldsymbol{y}_l - \boldsymbol{V}_{ml}'\boldsymbol{V}_m^{-1}\boldsymbol{y}_m, \\ \widehat{\boldsymbol{s}}_l &= \boldsymbol{Z}_l\widehat{\boldsymbol{\beta}}_m, \\ \text{and } \boldsymbol{Z}_l &= (\boldsymbol{X}_l - \boldsymbol{V}_{ml}'\boldsymbol{V}_m^{-1}\boldsymbol{X}_m). \end{aligned}$$

(A similar decomposition is possible even if $\boldsymbol{V}_m$ is singular, but the quantities $\boldsymbol{s}_l$ and $\widehat{\boldsymbol{s}}_l$ are not uniquely defined in such a case.) The quantity $\boldsymbol{s}_l$ is a part of $\boldsymbol{y}_l$ which is uncorrelated with $\boldsymbol{y}_m$. In contrast, $\widehat{\boldsymbol{s}}_l$ can be interpreted as the BLUP of $\boldsymbol{s}_l$ under the model $(\boldsymbol{y}_m, \boldsymbol{X}\boldsymbol{\beta}, \sigma^2\boldsymbol{V}_m)$. Clearly, $Cov(\boldsymbol{s}_l, \widehat{\boldsymbol{s}}_l) = \boldsymbol{0}$. It follows that

$$\begin{aligned} D(\boldsymbol{w}_l) &= D(\boldsymbol{s}_l) + D(\widehat{\boldsymbol{s}}_l), \\ Cov(\boldsymbol{X}_m\widehat{\boldsymbol{\beta}}_m, \boldsymbol{w}_l) &= -Cov(\boldsymbol{X}_m\widehat{\boldsymbol{\beta}}_m, \widehat{\boldsymbol{s}}_l). \end{aligned}$$

If, in addition, $\boldsymbol{X}_m$ has full column rank, then we can work directly with $\widehat{\boldsymbol{\beta}}_m$ (instead of $\boldsymbol{X}_m\widehat{\boldsymbol{\beta}}_m$). Thus, we have the following simplifications:

$$\begin{aligned} D(\boldsymbol{s}_l) &= \sigma^2(\boldsymbol{V}_l - \boldsymbol{V}_{ml}'\boldsymbol{V}_m^{-}\boldsymbol{V}_{ml}), \\ D(\widehat{\boldsymbol{s}}_l) &= \sigma^2\boldsymbol{Z}_l(\boldsymbol{X}_m'\boldsymbol{V}_m^{-1}\boldsymbol{X}_m)^{-1}\boldsymbol{Z}_l', \\ Cov(\widehat{\boldsymbol{\beta}}_m, \widehat{\boldsymbol{s}}_l) &= \sigma^2(\boldsymbol{X}_m'\boldsymbol{V}_m^{-1}\boldsymbol{X}_m)^{-1}\boldsymbol{Z}_l' \quad = \; -Cov(\widehat{\boldsymbol{\beta}}_m, \boldsymbol{w}_l), \end{aligned}$$

$$\widehat{\beta}_n = \widehat{\beta}_m + Cov(\widehat{\beta}_m, \widehat{s}_l)[D(s_l) + D(\widehat{s}_l)]^-(s_l - \widehat{s}_l),$$
$$D(\widehat{\beta}_n) = D(\widehat{\beta}_m) - Cov(\widehat{\beta}_m, \widehat{s}_l)[D(s_l) + D(\widehat{s}_l)]^- Cov(\widehat{\beta}_m, \widehat{s}_l)',$$
$$R^2_{0_n} = R^2_{0_m} + \sigma^2(s_l - \widehat{s}_l)'[D(s_l) + D(\widehat{s}_l)]^-(s_l - \widehat{s}_l).$$

The above formulae for $\widehat{\beta}_n$, $D(\widehat{\beta}_n)$ and $R^2_{0_n}$ are essentially the same as those given by McGilchrist and Sandland (1979) (for $l = 1$) and Haslett (1985) (for $l \geq 1$).

Further simplifications occur when $\boldsymbol{V} = \boldsymbol{I}$, in which case

$$s_l = \boldsymbol{y}_l,$$
$$\widehat{s}_l = \boldsymbol{X}_l\widehat{\beta}_m,$$
$$D(s_l) = \sigma^2\boldsymbol{I},$$
$$D(\widehat{s}_l) = \sigma^2\boldsymbol{X}_l(\boldsymbol{X}_m'\boldsymbol{X}_m)^{-1}\boldsymbol{X}_l',$$
$$Cov(\widehat{\beta}_m, \widehat{s}_l) = \sigma^2(\boldsymbol{X}_m'\boldsymbol{X}_m)^{-1}\boldsymbol{X}_l'.$$

The resulting simplified forms of the update formulae are similar to those obtained in Proposition 9.1.

The general expression of $R^2_{H_n}$ given in Proposition 9.8(e) can be somewhat simplified. Note that the unscaled recursive group residual under the restriction $\boldsymbol{A}\beta = \boldsymbol{\xi}$ is $\boldsymbol{w}_{l*} = \boldsymbol{w}_l - \widehat{\boldsymbol{w}}_l$, where $\widehat{\boldsymbol{w}}_l = Cov(\boldsymbol{w}_l, \boldsymbol{A}\widehat{\beta}_m)[D(\boldsymbol{A}\widehat{\beta}_m)]^-(\boldsymbol{A}\widehat{\beta}_m - \boldsymbol{\xi})$, the linear regression of $\boldsymbol{w}_l$ on $\boldsymbol{A}\widehat{\beta}_m - \boldsymbol{\xi}$. It follows that $\boldsymbol{w}_{l*}$ and $\widehat{\boldsymbol{w}}_l$ are uncorrelated, and hence,

$$D(\boldsymbol{w}_{l*}) = D(\boldsymbol{w}_l) - D(\widehat{\boldsymbol{w}}_l).$$

In the special case of $l = l_* = 1$, the update formula for error sum of squares under the restriction is

$$R^2_{H_n} = R^2_{H_m} + \sigma^2(\boldsymbol{w}_l - \widehat{\boldsymbol{w}}_l)^2/[D(\boldsymbol{w}_l) - D(\widehat{\boldsymbol{w}}_l)].$$

Bhimasankaram and Jammalamadaka (1994b) gave another formula for $R^2_{H_n}$ essentially in terms of $\boldsymbol{w}_l$, $\widehat{\boldsymbol{w}}_l$, $D(\boldsymbol{w}_l)$ and $D(\widehat{\boldsymbol{w}}_l)$, using other notations. It contained a minor error and the corrected expression given above is much simpler.

If $l_* \geq 1$ and $\boldsymbol{X}_m$ and $\boldsymbol{V}_m$ have full column rank, the expressions of $\widehat{\boldsymbol{w}}_l$ and $D(\widehat{\boldsymbol{w}}_l)$ simplify as follows.

$$\widehat{\boldsymbol{w}}_l = -\boldsymbol{Z}_l D(\widehat{\beta}_m)\boldsymbol{A}'[\boldsymbol{A}D(\widehat{\beta}_m)\boldsymbol{A}']^-(\boldsymbol{A}\widehat{\beta}_m - \boldsymbol{\xi}),$$
$$D(\widehat{\boldsymbol{w}}_l) = \boldsymbol{Z}_l D(\widehat{\beta}_m)\boldsymbol{A}'[\boldsymbol{A}D(\widehat{\beta}_m)\boldsymbol{A}']^-\boldsymbol{A}D(\widehat{\beta}_m)\boldsymbol{Z}_l'.$$

We now turn to cases (a), (c) and (d) of page 454.

In case (c), the additional observations of the augmented model are essentially linear functions of the initial model (see Exercise 9.2). Therefore, the linear zero functions and the BLUEs remain the same in the appended model. There is no change whatsoever in any statistic of interest.

It has been explained in the discussion following Remark 9.2 that data augmentation in case (d) essentially consists of two steps of augmentation classifiable as cases (a) and (b), respectively.

In case (a), there is no additional LZF in the augmented model. Hence, the BLUEs of the LPFs which are estimable in $\mathcal{M}_m$, their dispersions, the error sum of squares and the corresponding degrees of freedom are the same under the two models. The error sum of squares under the restriction $\boldsymbol{A\beta} = \boldsymbol{\xi}$ and the corresponding degrees of freedom also remains the same after data augmentation. However, the additional observations contribute to the estimation of the LPFs that are estimable only under the augmented model, as shown in the next proposition.

Proposition 9.9. *Under the set-up used in this section, let* $\rho(\boldsymbol{X}_n') - \rho(\boldsymbol{X}_m') = l_*$. *Then*

(a) $\boldsymbol{X}_l\widehat{\boldsymbol{\beta}}_n = \boldsymbol{y}_l - \boldsymbol{V}_{lm}\boldsymbol{V}_m^-(\boldsymbol{y}_m - \boldsymbol{X}_m\widehat{\boldsymbol{\beta}}_m)$.
(b) $D(\boldsymbol{X}_l\widehat{\boldsymbol{\beta}}_n) = \sigma^2\boldsymbol{V}_l - \boldsymbol{V}_{lm}\boldsymbol{V}_m^- D(\boldsymbol{y}_m - \boldsymbol{X}_m\widehat{\boldsymbol{\beta}}_m)\boldsymbol{V}_m^-\boldsymbol{V}_{ml}$.

Proof. The LZFs of the augmented and original models coincide (see Remark 9.2). Therefore, the BLUE of $\boldsymbol{X}_l\boldsymbol{\beta}$ is obtained by adjusting $\boldsymbol{y}_l$ for its covariance with the LZFs of the original model. We choose $\boldsymbol{y}_m - \boldsymbol{X}_m\widehat{\boldsymbol{\beta}}_m$ as a representative vector of LZFs.

If we write this vector, according to (7.3), as

$$\begin{aligned}
&\boldsymbol{y}_m - \boldsymbol{X}_m\widehat{\boldsymbol{\beta}}_m \\
&= \boldsymbol{V}_m(\boldsymbol{I} - \boldsymbol{P}_{X_m})\{(\boldsymbol{I} - \boldsymbol{P}_{X_m})\boldsymbol{V}_m^-(\boldsymbol{I} - \boldsymbol{P}_{X_m})\}^-(\boldsymbol{I} - \boldsymbol{P}_{X_m})\boldsymbol{y}_m) \\
&= \boldsymbol{V}_m\boldsymbol{R}_m\boldsymbol{y}_m,
\end{aligned}$$

then the required BLUE is

$$\begin{aligned}
\boldsymbol{X}_l\widehat{\boldsymbol{\beta}}_n &= \boldsymbol{y}_l - Cov(\boldsymbol{y}_l, \boldsymbol{y}_m - \boldsymbol{X}_m\widehat{\boldsymbol{\beta}}_m)[D(\boldsymbol{y}_m - \boldsymbol{X}_m\widehat{\boldsymbol{\beta}}_m)]^-(\boldsymbol{y}_m - \boldsymbol{X}_m\widehat{\boldsymbol{\beta}}_m) \\
&= \boldsymbol{y}_l - Cov(\boldsymbol{y}_l, \boldsymbol{V}_m\boldsymbol{R}_m\boldsymbol{y}_m)[D(\boldsymbol{V}_m\boldsymbol{R}_m\boldsymbol{y}_m)]^-(\boldsymbol{V}_m\boldsymbol{R}_m\boldsymbol{y}_m) \\
&= \boldsymbol{y}_l - \boldsymbol{V}_{lm}\boldsymbol{V}_m^- D(\boldsymbol{V}_m\boldsymbol{R}_m\boldsymbol{y}_m)[D(\boldsymbol{V}_m\boldsymbol{R}_m\boldsymbol{y}_m)]^-(\boldsymbol{V}_m\boldsymbol{R}_m\boldsymbol{y}_m) \\
&= \boldsymbol{y}_l - \boldsymbol{V}_{lm}\boldsymbol{V}_m^-(\boldsymbol{y}_m - \boldsymbol{X}_m\widehat{\boldsymbol{\beta}}_m).
\end{aligned}$$

The expression in part (b) follows immediately. □

When $\boldsymbol{V}_{lm} = \boldsymbol{0}$, it is clear that the fitted value of $\boldsymbol{y}_l$ is equal to its observed value, and the corresponding dispersion is equal to the dispersion of $\boldsymbol{y}_l$. This is not at all surprising, considering that the l parameters can take any value to make the fit of $\boldsymbol{y}_l$ as good as possible. Let us consider an example to understand why $\boldsymbol{y}_l$ is not necessarily exactly fitted when $\boldsymbol{V}_{lm} \neq \boldsymbol{0}$.

Example 9.10. Let $m = 2$, $l = 1$, $\boldsymbol{\beta} = (\beta_1 : \beta_2)'$ and

$$\boldsymbol{y}_n = \begin{pmatrix} y_1 \\ y_2 \\ y_3 \end{pmatrix}, \quad \boldsymbol{X}_n = \begin{pmatrix} 1 & 0 \\ 0 & 0 \\ 0 & 1 \end{pmatrix}, \quad \boldsymbol{V}_n = \begin{pmatrix} 1 & 0 & 1 \\ 0 & 1 & 1 \\ 1 & 1 & 3 \end{pmatrix}.$$

It is easy to see that only β_1 is estimable from the first two observations. Moreover, the second observation does not carry any information about β_1. It follows that $\widehat{\beta}_1 = y_1$, and the residuals for the first two observations are 0 and y_2, respectively. Further, the dispersion of the fitted values of the first two observations is

$$\sigma^2 \begin{pmatrix} 1 & 0 \\ 0 & 0 \end{pmatrix}.$$

According to Proposition 9.9, the fitted value of y_3 is $y_3 - y_2$.

The reason why the fitted value of y_3 is not y_3 itself can be understood by examining the covariance of y_3 with the other two observations. Out of these, y_1 carries information about β_1. Therefore, y_2 is the only available observation which carries exclusive information about the model error. As a consequence, the BLUP of the error component of y_3, based on the first two observations, is y_2. Since the third observation does not introduce any new LZF, it cannot change the estimator of β_1, and consequently, the prediction of the model error. The estimator of β_2 adjusts itself to ensure that the residual of the third observation is the same as its predicted value from the first two observations! □

The argument given in Example 9.10 can be extended to the general case also. The fitted value of $\boldsymbol{y}_l$ from the augmented model must be such that the corresponding residual is identical to the BLUP of $\boldsymbol{\varepsilon}_l$ from the original model, which is given by $\boldsymbol{V}_{lm}\boldsymbol{V}_m^-(\boldsymbol{y}_m - \boldsymbol{X}_m\widehat{\boldsymbol{\beta}}_m)$. This reduces to zero when the augmented observations are uncorrelated with the original observations ($\boldsymbol{V}_{lm} = \boldsymbol{0}$). Even if this residual is nonzero, it does not alter the error sum of squares, because it is a function of the LZFs of the initial model. The degrees of freedom also do not change.

An expression of the BLUE of a general LPF which is estimable under the augmented model is given in Exercise 9.14.

9.1.4 *Application to model diagnostics*

The *deleted* residual mentioned in Remark 5.10 is an important tool in regression diagnostics. Simply stated, the deleted residual for the ith observation is the prediction error arising from the linear prediction of this observation in terms of all the other observations. If the data set is permuted so that the ith observation is the last one, then the recursive residual (9.2) for this observation is the ith deleted residual.

We have seen in Section 5.3 how the standardized residuals (5.7) and the studentized residuals (5.8) are used to diagnose different forms of model inadequacy such as nonlinearity, heteroscedasticity, correlation among observations and non-normality. The index plot of either of these forms of residuals, which is generally used to detect serial correlation, can also detect structural change in the model (e.g. sudden change in location or variance of the response from a particular time). Haslett and Haslett (2007) review the different types of residuals that can be used for the general linear model. Since the recursive residuals are uncorrelated, their scaled versions provide an attractive alternative to the standardized and the studentized residuals, particularly when there is a natural order among the observations. Galpin and Hawkins (1984) and Hawkins (1991) give a good exposition of these diagnostic methods. A popular variation of the index plot of scaled residuals is the *CUSUM plot*, where the cumulative sums of the scaled recursive residuals are plotted against the index. Movement away from zero is interpreted as indication of a structural change in the model. This plot is proposed by Brown et al. (1975), who also gives formal cut-offs for fluctuations of the plot when there is no structural change. Several modifications and generalizations are suggested by subsequent researchers. McGilchrist et al. (1983) use the plot of the recursive estimates of the regression coefficients vs. the index number in order to detect structural change in the model.

A number of formal tests for the violations of various assumptions can also be constructed on the basis of the recursive residuals. See Kianifard and Swallow (1996) for a review of these methods.

9.1.5 *Design augmentation*

Suppose a set of m observations has already been collected, and one is interested in a particular estimable function $\boldsymbol{p}'\boldsymbol{\beta}$. Consider the problem of choosing an additional design point (i.e. an additional row of the design matrix $\boldsymbol{X}_m$) optimally, so that the variance of the BLUE of $\boldsymbol{p}'\boldsymbol{\beta}$ is minimized.

In the absence of any constraint, the variance can be made indefinitely close to zero (e.g. by choosing the additional row of $\boldsymbol{X}_m$ as a very large multiple of $\boldsymbol{p}$. A reasonable constraint may be to set an upper bound on the variance of the estimated mean of the additional observation, calculated on the basis of the first m observations. Of course, one can choose alternative constraints. The purpose of this section is only to show how the update formulae derived earlier can be utilized in solving some design problems.

The simple case of homoscedastic model errors admits an intuitively meaningful solution to this problem: the new row of the design matrix should be proportional to $\boldsymbol{p}$. We now derive a solution in the general case of heteroscedastic and possibly singular error dispersion matrix, by making use of the results of Section 9.1.3.

Note that in the present context $l = 1$. In order to simplify the notations, we denote $\boldsymbol{X}_m$, $\boldsymbol{X}_l$, $\boldsymbol{y}_m$, $\boldsymbol{y}_l$, $\boldsymbol{V}_m$, $\boldsymbol{V}_{ml}$, V_l, $\boldsymbol{w}_l$ and $\boldsymbol{d}_l(\cdot)$ by $\boldsymbol{X}$, $\boldsymbol{x}'$, $\boldsymbol{y}$, y, $\boldsymbol{V}$, $\boldsymbol{v}$, v, w and $d(\cdot)$, respectively. The task is to minimize the variance of $\boldsymbol{p}'\widehat{\boldsymbol{\beta}}_{m+1}$ with respect to $\boldsymbol{x}$, subject to the constraint $Var(\boldsymbol{x}'\widehat{\boldsymbol{\beta}}_m) \leq \alpha\sigma^2$ where α is a known positive number.

It is clear that the new design point $\boldsymbol{x}$ carries no information about $\boldsymbol{p}'\boldsymbol{\beta}$ if it is not in $\mathcal{C}(\boldsymbol{X}')$. Therefore $\boldsymbol{x}$ has to be of the form $\boldsymbol{X}'\boldsymbol{u}$. In such a case, choosing $\boldsymbol{x}$ is equivalent to choosing $\boldsymbol{u}$. It was argued in Section 9.1.2 that whenever $\boldsymbol{x} \in \mathcal{C}(\boldsymbol{X}')$, there must be an additional LZF with nonzero variance, unless the new observation error is perfectly correlated with the first m errors of the model. The latter case is not interesting, since the $Var(\boldsymbol{x}'\widehat{\boldsymbol{\beta}}_{m+1})$ happens to be the same as $Var(\boldsymbol{x}'\widehat{\boldsymbol{\beta}}_m)$. In the following discussion we assume that $\boldsymbol{x} = \boldsymbol{X}'\boldsymbol{u}$ and $Var(w) > 0$.

In view of Part (b) of Proposition 9.8, minimizing $Var(\boldsymbol{p}'\widehat{\boldsymbol{\beta}}_{m+1})$ is equivalent to maximizing $[Cov(\boldsymbol{p}'\widehat{\boldsymbol{\beta}}_m, w)]^2/Var(w)$. Writing w as $d(\boldsymbol{\beta}) + [d(\widehat{\boldsymbol{\beta}}_m) - d(\boldsymbol{\beta})]$, a sum of uncorrelated parts (see Remark 9.7), it follows that

$$\begin{aligned} Cov(\boldsymbol{p}'\widehat{\boldsymbol{\beta}}_m, w) &= Cov(\boldsymbol{p}'\widehat{\boldsymbol{\beta}}_m, d(\widehat{\boldsymbol{\beta}}_m) - d(\boldsymbol{\beta})), \\ Var(w) &= Var(d(\boldsymbol{\beta})) + Var(d(\widehat{\boldsymbol{\beta}}_m) - d(\boldsymbol{\beta})). \end{aligned}$$

Let $\theta = Var(d(\boldsymbol{\beta}))/\sigma^2$ and the vectors $\boldsymbol{a}$ and $\boldsymbol{b}$ satisfy $\boldsymbol{p} = \boldsymbol{X}'\boldsymbol{a}$ and $\boldsymbol{v} = \boldsymbol{V}\boldsymbol{b}$, respectively. Then $d(\widehat{\boldsymbol{\beta}}_m) - d(\boldsymbol{\beta}) = (\boldsymbol{b} - \boldsymbol{u})'\boldsymbol{X}(\widehat{\boldsymbol{\beta}}_m - \boldsymbol{\beta})$. Denoting $\sigma^{-2}D(\boldsymbol{X}\widehat{\boldsymbol{\beta}}_m)$ by $\boldsymbol{S}\boldsymbol{S}'$, we have

$$\begin{aligned} Cov(\boldsymbol{p}'\widehat{\boldsymbol{\beta}}_m, w) &= -\sigma^2\boldsymbol{a}'\boldsymbol{S}\boldsymbol{S}'(\boldsymbol{u} - \boldsymbol{b}), \\ Var(w) &= \sigma^2[\theta + (\boldsymbol{u} - \boldsymbol{b})'\boldsymbol{S}\boldsymbol{S}'(\boldsymbol{u} - \boldsymbol{b})], \\ Var(\boldsymbol{x}'\widehat{\boldsymbol{\beta}}_m) &= \sigma^2\boldsymbol{u}'\boldsymbol{S}\boldsymbol{S}'\boldsymbol{u}. \end{aligned}$$

Thus the optimization problem reduces to

$$\max_{\boldsymbol{u}} \frac{[\boldsymbol{a}'\boldsymbol{S}\boldsymbol{S}'(\boldsymbol{u}-\boldsymbol{b})]^2}{\theta+(\boldsymbol{u}-\boldsymbol{b})'\boldsymbol{S}\boldsymbol{S}'(\boldsymbol{u}-\boldsymbol{b})}, \qquad \text{such that} \quad \boldsymbol{u}'\boldsymbol{S}\boldsymbol{S}'\boldsymbol{u} \le \alpha. \tag{9.5}$$

A further simplification occurs if we let $\boldsymbol{u}_1 = \boldsymbol{P}_{\boldsymbol{S}'\boldsymbol{a}}\boldsymbol{S}'\boldsymbol{u}$, $\boldsymbol{b}_1 = \boldsymbol{P}_{\boldsymbol{S}'\boldsymbol{a}}\boldsymbol{S}'\boldsymbol{b}$, $\boldsymbol{u}_2 = \boldsymbol{S}'\boldsymbol{u} - \boldsymbol{u}_1$ and $\boldsymbol{b}_2 = \boldsymbol{S}'\boldsymbol{b} - \boldsymbol{b}_1$. The solution to (9.5) can be obtained from the solution to the following problem.

$$\max_{\boldsymbol{u}_1,\boldsymbol{u}_2} \frac{(\boldsymbol{u}_1-\boldsymbol{b}_1)'(\boldsymbol{u}_1-\boldsymbol{b}_1)}{\theta+(\boldsymbol{u}_2-\boldsymbol{b}_2)'(\boldsymbol{u}_2-\boldsymbol{b}_2)},$$

$$\text{such that} \quad \boldsymbol{u}_1 \in \mathcal{C}(\boldsymbol{S}'\boldsymbol{a}), \quad \boldsymbol{u}_2 \in \mathcal{C}((\boldsymbol{I}-\boldsymbol{P}_{\boldsymbol{S}'\boldsymbol{a}})\boldsymbol{S}'), \quad \boldsymbol{u}_1'\boldsymbol{u}_1 + \boldsymbol{u}_2'\boldsymbol{u}_2 \le \alpha. \tag{9.6}$$

Note that the objective function of (9.6) is equivalent to, but not identical with that of (9.5).

Sengupta (1995) arrives at a similar formulation of the problem using the inverse partitioned matrix method.

Proposition 9.11. *The solution to the optimization problem (9.6) is as follows.*

(a) If $\boldsymbol{b}_1 = \boldsymbol{b}_2 = 0$, *the maximum is attained if and only if* $\boldsymbol{u}_2 = 0$ *and* $\boldsymbol{u}_1 = \pm(\alpha/\boldsymbol{a}'\boldsymbol{S}\boldsymbol{S}'\boldsymbol{a})^{1/2}\boldsymbol{S}'\boldsymbol{a}$.

(b) If $\boldsymbol{b}_1 \ne 0$ *and* $\boldsymbol{b}_2 = 0$, *the maximum is attained if and only if* $\boldsymbol{u}_1 = -(\alpha/\boldsymbol{b}_1'\boldsymbol{S}\boldsymbol{S}'\boldsymbol{b}_1)^{1/2}\boldsymbol{b}_1$ *and* $\boldsymbol{u}_2 = 0$.

(c) If $\boldsymbol{b}_1 = 0$ *and* $\boldsymbol{b}_2 \ne 0$, *the maximum is attained if and only if* $\boldsymbol{u}_2 = c_1\boldsymbol{b}_2$, *where*

$$c_1 = \frac{\boldsymbol{b}_2'\boldsymbol{b}_2+\alpha+\theta}{2\boldsymbol{b}_2'\boldsymbol{b}_2}\left[1-\left(1-\frac{4\alpha\boldsymbol{b}_2'\boldsymbol{b}_2}{(\boldsymbol{b}_2'\boldsymbol{b}_2+\alpha+\theta)^2}\right)^{1/2}\right],$$

and $\boldsymbol{u}_1 = \pm[(\alpha - c_1^2\boldsymbol{b}_2'\boldsymbol{b}_2)/\boldsymbol{a}'\boldsymbol{S}\boldsymbol{S}'\boldsymbol{a}]^{1/2}\boldsymbol{S}'\boldsymbol{a}$.

(d) If $\boldsymbol{b}_1$ *and* $\boldsymbol{b}_2$ *are both nonzero, then the maximum is attained if and only if* $\boldsymbol{u}_2 = c_2\boldsymbol{b}_2$ *where* c_2 *maximizes* $[(\alpha - c_2^2\boldsymbol{b}_2'\boldsymbol{b}_2)^{1/2} + (\boldsymbol{b}_1'\boldsymbol{b}_1)^{1/2}]^2/[\theta+\boldsymbol{b}_2'\boldsymbol{b}_2(c_2-1)^2]$ *over the range* $0 \le c_2 \le (\alpha/\boldsymbol{b}_2'\boldsymbol{b}_2)^{1/2}$, *and* $\boldsymbol{u}_1 = \pm[(\alpha - c_2^2\boldsymbol{b}_2'\boldsymbol{b}_2)/\boldsymbol{b}_1'\boldsymbol{b}_1]^{1/2}\boldsymbol{b}_2$.

Proof. The proofs of parts (a) and (b) are straightforward. The other two parts are proved by holding $\boldsymbol{u}_2$ fixed, maximizing the numerator of (9.6) subject to the constraint $\boldsymbol{u}_1'\boldsymbol{u}_1 \le \alpha - \boldsymbol{u}_2'\boldsymbol{u}_2$, and maximizing the resulting expression with respect to $\boldsymbol{u}_2$. For details, we refer the reader to Sengupta (1995). □

Remark 9.12. The solution of part (b) coincides with one of the two solutions of part (a). □

Remark 9.13. Suppose r_1 is the correlation coefficient between y and $\boldsymbol{p}'\widehat{\boldsymbol{\beta}}_m$, and r_2 is the multiple correlation coefficient of y with $\boldsymbol{X}\widehat{\boldsymbol{\beta}}_m$. Then $\boldsymbol{b}_1'\boldsymbol{b}_1 = vr_1^2$ and $\boldsymbol{b}_2'\boldsymbol{b}_2 = v(r_2^2 - r_1^2)$. Thus the four different cases of Proposition 9.11 have direct statistical interpretation. □

Remark 9.14. Proposition 9.11 leads us to a choice of $\boldsymbol{S}'\boldsymbol{u}$ in each of the four special cases. The choice in each case is of the form $\boldsymbol{S}'\boldsymbol{t}$ for some $\boldsymbol{t}$. It is clear that $\boldsymbol{S}'\boldsymbol{u} = \boldsymbol{S}'\boldsymbol{t}$ if and only if $\boldsymbol{u}$ is of the form $\boldsymbol{u} = \boldsymbol{t} + \boldsymbol{t}_1$ where $\boldsymbol{S}'\boldsymbol{t}_1 = 0$. On the other hand, the condition $\boldsymbol{S}'\boldsymbol{t}_1 = 0$ holds if and only if $\boldsymbol{t}_1$ is orthogonal to $\mathcal{C}(D(\boldsymbol{X}\widehat{\boldsymbol{\beta}}_m))$, which is the same as $\mathcal{C}(\boldsymbol{X}) \cap \mathcal{C}(\boldsymbol{V})$. Thus, $\boldsymbol{t}_1$ must be of the form $(\boldsymbol{I} - \boldsymbol{P}_X)\boldsymbol{t}_2 + (\boldsymbol{I} - \boldsymbol{P}_V)\boldsymbol{t}_0$. Therefore, the condition $\boldsymbol{S}'\boldsymbol{u} = \boldsymbol{S}'\boldsymbol{t}$ is equivalent to $\boldsymbol{X}\boldsymbol{u} = \boldsymbol{X}\boldsymbol{t} + \boldsymbol{X}(\boldsymbol{I}-\boldsymbol{P}_V)\boldsymbol{t}_0$ for some vector $\boldsymbol{t}_0$. □

The above observations allow one to translate the choice of $\boldsymbol{S}'\boldsymbol{u}$ obtained from Proposition 9.11 into a choice of $\boldsymbol{x}$, as follows.

Proposition 9.15. *The choice of $\boldsymbol{x}$ that minimizes $Var(\boldsymbol{p}'\widehat{\boldsymbol{\beta}}_{m+1})$ subject to $\sigma^{-2}Var(\boldsymbol{x}'\widehat{\boldsymbol{\beta}}_m) \le \alpha$ is given as follows.*

$$\boldsymbol{x} = \begin{cases} \pm(\alpha/v_p)^{1/2}\boldsymbol{p} + \boldsymbol{x}_0 & \text{if } r_2 = 0, \\ -(\alpha/vr_1^2)^{1/2}\boldsymbol{X}'\boldsymbol{V}^-\boldsymbol{v} + \boldsymbol{x}_0 & \text{if } r_2^2 = r_1^2 > 0, \\ [(\alpha - c_1^2vr_2^2)/v_p]^{1/2} + c_1\boldsymbol{X}'\boldsymbol{V}^-\boldsymbol{v} + \boldsymbol{x}_0 & \text{if } r_2 > 0 = r_1, \\ -\left[c_2 + \left\{\dfrac{\alpha - c_2^2v(r_2^2 - r_1^2)}{vr_1^2}\right\}^{1/2}\right](v/v_p)^{1/2}r_1\boldsymbol{p} & \\ \qquad + c_2\boldsymbol{X}'\boldsymbol{V}^-\boldsymbol{v} + \boldsymbol{x}_0 & \text{if } r_2^2 > r_1^2 > 0, \end{cases}$$

where $v_p = Var(\boldsymbol{p}'\widehat{\boldsymbol{\beta}}_m)/\sigma^2$, $\boldsymbol{x}_0$ is an arbitrary vector in $\mathcal{C}(\boldsymbol{X}(\boldsymbol{I} - \boldsymbol{P}_V))$, r_1 and r_2 are as in Remark 9.13, and

$$c_1 = \left(\frac{1}{2} + \frac{\alpha + \theta}{2vr_2^2}\right)\left[1 - \left(1 - \frac{4\alpha vr_2^2}{(\alpha + \theta + vr_2^2)^2}\right)^{1/2}\right],$$

$$c_2 = \arg \max_{c \in [0, \{\alpha/v(r_2^2 - r_1^2)\}^{1/2}]} \frac{\left[\{\alpha - c^2v(r_2^2 - r_1^2)\}^{1/2} + \{vr_1^2\}^{1/2}\right]^2}{\theta + v(r_2^2 - r_1^2)(c-1)^2}.$$

Proof. The results follow from Proposition 9.11 and Remark 9.14 after some algebra. □

Remark 9.16. The ambiguity in the choice of $\boldsymbol{V}^-$ can be removed by replacing $\boldsymbol{X}'\boldsymbol{V}^-\boldsymbol{v}$ by $\boldsymbol{X}'\boldsymbol{P}_V\boldsymbol{V}^-\boldsymbol{v}$. The difference between the two terms is absorbed by the arbitrary vector $\boldsymbol{x}_0$. □

Remark 9.17. The intuitive solution of choosing $\boldsymbol{x}$ in the direction of $\boldsymbol{p}$ is optimal not only in the homoscedastic case, but whenever $r_2 = -r_1 > 0$. If $r_2 = r_1 > 0$, the opposite direction is optimal. Both of these cases correspond to the situation when the multiple correlation of y with $\boldsymbol{X}\widehat{\boldsymbol{\beta}}_m$ is the same (in magnitude) as its correlation with $\boldsymbol{p}'\widehat{\boldsymbol{\beta}}_m$ alone. Both the solutions are optimal when $r_2 = 0$. The assumption of uncorrelated error variances is a special case when $r_2 = 0$. □

Sengupta (1995) also considers the design problem when there are several LPFs of interest. Bhaumik and Mathew (2001) consider a similar problem when several additional observations have to be designed.

9.1.6 *Recursive prediction and Kalman filter*

When observations are collected over a period of time, the linear model is sometimes used as a vehicle for predicting future values of the response. This prediction is recursively updated as newer observations become available. Using Theorem 7.49 and the notations used in this chapter, the BLUP of $\boldsymbol{y}_l$ on the basis of data $\boldsymbol{y}_m$ and $\boldsymbol{X}_n$ is seen to be

$$\widehat{\boldsymbol{y}}_l = \boldsymbol{X}_l\widehat{\boldsymbol{\beta}}_m - \boldsymbol{V}'_{ml}\boldsymbol{V}^-_m(\boldsymbol{y}_m - \boldsymbol{X}_m\widehat{\boldsymbol{\beta}}_m),$$

assuming that $\boldsymbol{X}_l\boldsymbol{\beta}$ is estimable under the model $\mathcal{M}_m$. The dispersion of the corresponding prediction error is

$$D(\boldsymbol{y}_l - \widehat{\boldsymbol{y}}_l) = (\boldsymbol{V}'_{ml}\boldsymbol{V}^-_m - \boldsymbol{X}_l\boldsymbol{X}^-_m)D(\boldsymbol{X}_m\widehat{\boldsymbol{\beta}}_m)(\boldsymbol{V}'_{ml}\boldsymbol{V}^-_m - \boldsymbol{X}_l\boldsymbol{X}^-_m)'.$$

Part (a) of Theorem 9.8 shows how the actual prediction error $\boldsymbol{w}_l = \boldsymbol{y}_l - \widehat{\boldsymbol{y}}_l$ can be utilized, once $\boldsymbol{y}_l$ becomes available, to obtain the estimator of $\boldsymbol{X}_n\boldsymbol{\beta}$ and its dispersion. These updated quantities can be used to predict future values of the response in terms of the corresponding values of the explanatory variables.

The assumption of a linear model with fixed coefficients is unsuitable for predicting the response, if the underlying mechanism changes with time. A very versatile model for a time-varying system is the *state-space model*, given by the recursive relation

$$\boldsymbol{x}_t = \boldsymbol{B}_t\boldsymbol{x}_{t-1} + \boldsymbol{u}_t, \quad (9.7)$$

$$\boldsymbol{z}_t = \boldsymbol{H}_t\boldsymbol{x}_t + \boldsymbol{v}_t, \quad (9.8)$$

for $t = 1, 2, \ldots$. In the above model, which had been briefly mentioned in Section 1.6, the *state vector* $\boldsymbol{x}_t$ is unobservable, but the *measurement vector*

$\boldsymbol{z}_t$ is observable. The error vectors $\boldsymbol{u}_t$ and $\boldsymbol{v}_t$ have zero mean, and

$$\begin{aligned} Cov(\boldsymbol{u}_s, \boldsymbol{u}_t) &= \boldsymbol{Q}_u(s,t), \quad s,t = 1,2,\ldots, \\ Cov(\boldsymbol{v}_s, \boldsymbol{v}_t) &= \boldsymbol{Q}_v(s,t), \quad s,t = 1,2,\ldots, \\ Cov(\boldsymbol{u}_s, \boldsymbol{v}_t) &= \boldsymbol{Q}_{uv}(s,t), \quad s,t = 1,2,\ldots. \end{aligned}$$

The matrices $\boldsymbol{Q}_u(s,t)$, $\boldsymbol{Q}_v(s,t)$ and $\boldsymbol{Q}_{u,v}(s,t)$, $s,t = 1,2,\ldots$ are assumed to be known. The *state transition matrix* $\boldsymbol{B}_t$ and the *measurement matrix* $\boldsymbol{H}_t$, $t = 1,2,\ldots$, are also assumed to be known. The objective is to predict the state vector $\boldsymbol{x}_t$ by a linear function of the observations $\boldsymbol{z}_1, \boldsymbol{z}_2, \ldots, \boldsymbol{z}_t$ and the initial state $\boldsymbol{x}_0$. In some applications the measurement vector $\boldsymbol{z}_t$ also has to be predicted by a linear function of $\boldsymbol{x}_0, \boldsymbol{z}_1, \ldots, \boldsymbol{z}_{t-1}$. The linear predictors should have the smallest possible mean squared prediction error. The vector $\boldsymbol{x}_0$ may itself be an estimator, where the corresponding estimation error is absorbed in $\boldsymbol{u}_1$. The analysis given here is conditional on a fixed value of $\boldsymbol{x}_0$.

A recursive solution to the above problem is given by the *Kalman filter* (Kalman, 1960, Kalman and Bucy, 1961). The state-space model and the Kalman filter have a wide range of applications. It will be shown here that the Kalman filter equations can be derived from the update formulae of Section 9.1.3 in an intuitive manner.

The first step in the derivation is to show that the minimum mean squared error linear predictor is given by a BLUE in a fixed effects linear model — as pointed out by Duncan and Horn (1972). A simpler version of their argument is used here, but a stronger result (with possibly singular dispersion matrices) is proved.

Proposition 9.18. *Let $\boldsymbol{h}$ be a known nonrandom vector and $\boldsymbol{x}$ and $\boldsymbol{z}$ be random vectors following the model*

$$\begin{pmatrix} \boldsymbol{h} \\ \boldsymbol{z} \end{pmatrix} = \begin{pmatrix} \boldsymbol{F} \\ \boldsymbol{G} \end{pmatrix} \boldsymbol{x} + \begin{pmatrix} \boldsymbol{u} \\ \boldsymbol{v} \end{pmatrix}, \quad E\begin{pmatrix} \boldsymbol{u} \\ \boldsymbol{v} \end{pmatrix} = \boldsymbol{0}, \quad D\begin{pmatrix} \boldsymbol{u} \\ \boldsymbol{v} \end{pmatrix} = \boldsymbol{V} \tag{9.9}$$

where $\boldsymbol{F}$, $\boldsymbol{G}$ and $\boldsymbol{V}$ are known matrices which may not have full row or column rank, and $\mathcal{C}(\boldsymbol{G}') \subseteq \mathcal{C}(\boldsymbol{F}')$. Then for an arbitrary matrix $\boldsymbol{C}$ of appropriate dimension satisfying $\mathcal{C}(\boldsymbol{C}') \subseteq \mathcal{C}(\boldsymbol{F}')$

(a) a minimum mean squared error linear predictor of $\boldsymbol{Cx}$ having the form $\boldsymbol{A}_1\boldsymbol{h} + \boldsymbol{A}_2\boldsymbol{z} + \boldsymbol{a}_3$ must be unbiased in the sense that the expected value of its prediction error is zero for all values of $E(\boldsymbol{x})$;

(b) the BLUE of $C\beta$ from the fixed effects model $(y, X\beta, V)$, where

$$y = \begin{pmatrix} h \\ z \end{pmatrix}, \quad \text{and} \quad X = \begin{pmatrix} F \\ G \end{pmatrix},$$

is a linear predictor of Cx based on z and h, having the minimum mean squared error;

(c) the mean squared prediction error of the predictor of part (b) is the same as the dispersion matrix of the BLUE of $C\beta$ from the above fixed effects linear model.

Proof. Let $A_1h + A_2z + a_3$ be a linear predictor of Cx. The matrix of mean squared prediction error for this predictor is

$$\begin{aligned} &E[(A_1h + A_2z + a_3 - Cx)(A_1h + A_2z + a_3 - Cx)'] \\ &= E(A_1h + A_2z + a_3 - Cx)E(A_1h + A_2z + a_3 - Cx)' \\ &\quad + D(A_1h + A_2z + a_3 - Cx) \\ &= [(A_1F + A_2G - C)E(x) + a_3][(A_1F + A_2G - C)E(x) + a_3]' \\ &\quad + D(A_1h + A_2z - Cx). \end{aligned}$$

Since h is nonrandom, the dispersion depends only on A_2. For a given choice of A_2, the bias term can be made equal to zero by choosing $A_1 = (C - A_2G)F^-$ and $a_3 = 0$. Therefore, a linear predictor with minimum mean square prediction error cannot have nonzero bias. This proves part (a).

In order to prove part (b), let $A_1h + A_2z + a_3$ be a linear predictor of Cx and $B = ((C - A_2G)F^- : A_2)$. Let us also write $\varepsilon = (u' : v')'$. It follows that

$$\begin{aligned} &E[(A_1h + A_2z + a_3 - Cx)(A_1h + A_2z + a_3 - Cx)'] \\ &\geq E[(By - Cx)(By - Cx)'] \\ &= D(By - Cx) = D\left(B\varepsilon - ((C - A_2G)F^- : A_2)\begin{pmatrix} F \\ G \end{pmatrix} x - Cx\right) \\ &= D(B\varepsilon) = BVB'. \end{aligned}$$

Let $C = LX$ and $B_* = LR$ where

$$R = I - V(I - P_X)\{(I - P_X)V(I - P_X)\}^-(I - P_X). \tag{9.10}$$

According to Proposition 7.7, B_*y is the BLUE of $C\beta$ from the model $(y, X\beta, V)$. Moreover, $B_*X = LX = C$. Consequently,

$$\begin{aligned} BVB' &= (B - B_* + B_*)V(B - B_* + B_*)' \\ &= B_*VB_*' + (B - B_*)V(B - B_*)' \\ &\quad + B_*V(B - B_*)' + (B - B_*)VB_*'. \end{aligned}$$

The dispersion of the BLUE $\boldsymbol{Ry}$ given in (7.4) can be written as $\boldsymbol{VR}'$. Proposition 7.15 implies that $\mathcal{C}(\boldsymbol{VR}') \subseteq \mathcal{C}(\boldsymbol{X})$. It follows that $\boldsymbol{VB_*}'$ can be written as $\boldsymbol{XK}$ for some matrix $\boldsymbol{K}$. Hence,

$$(\boldsymbol{B}-\boldsymbol{B_*})\boldsymbol{VB_*}' = (\boldsymbol{BX}-\boldsymbol{B_*X})\boldsymbol{K} = (\boldsymbol{C}-\boldsymbol{C})\boldsymbol{K} = \boldsymbol{0}.$$

Consequently

$$\begin{aligned} E[(\boldsymbol{A}_1\boldsymbol{h}+\boldsymbol{A}_2\boldsymbol{z}+\boldsymbol{a}_3-\boldsymbol{Cx})(\boldsymbol{A}_1\boldsymbol{h}+\boldsymbol{A}_2\boldsymbol{z}+\boldsymbol{a}_3-\boldsymbol{Cx})'] &\geq \boldsymbol{BVB}' \\ = \boldsymbol{B_*VB_*}' + (\boldsymbol{B}-\boldsymbol{B_*})\boldsymbol{V}(\boldsymbol{B}-\boldsymbol{B_*})' \\ \geq \boldsymbol{B_*VB_*}' \;=\; E[(\boldsymbol{B_*y}-\boldsymbol{Cx})(\boldsymbol{B_*y}-\boldsymbol{Cx})'] \end{aligned}$$

This proves part (b). Part (c) follows from the simplification

$$E[(\boldsymbol{B_*y}-\boldsymbol{Cx})(\boldsymbol{B_*y}-\boldsymbol{Cx})'] \;=\; \boldsymbol{B_*VB_*}' = \boldsymbol{LVR'L}',$$

the last expression being the dispersion matrix of the BLUE of $\boldsymbol{C\beta}$ from the model $(\boldsymbol{y}, \boldsymbol{X\beta}, \boldsymbol{V})$. □

Proposition 9.18 generalizes a result of Duncan and Horn (1972), where $\boldsymbol{V}$ was assumed to be block-diagonal and nonsingular, and $\boldsymbol{F}$ and $\boldsymbol{L}$ were chosen as $\boldsymbol{I}$. The best linear predictor described in this proposition happens to be a BLUP.

Note that the equations (9.7)–(9.8) up to time t can be written as

$$\boldsymbol{y}_t = \boldsymbol{X}_t\boldsymbol{\gamma}_t + \boldsymbol{\varepsilon}_t, \tag{9.11}$$

where $\boldsymbol{\gamma}_t = (\boldsymbol{x}_1' : \boldsymbol{x}_2' : \cdots : \boldsymbol{x}_t')'$ and

$$\boldsymbol{y}_t = \begin{pmatrix} \boldsymbol{B}_1\boldsymbol{x}_0 \\ \boldsymbol{0} \\ \vdots \\ \boldsymbol{0} \\ \\ \boldsymbol{z}_1 \\ \boldsymbol{z}_2 \\ \vdots \\ \boldsymbol{z}_t \end{pmatrix}, \quad \boldsymbol{X}_t = \begin{pmatrix} \boldsymbol{I} & \boldsymbol{0} & \cdots & \boldsymbol{0} \\ -\boldsymbol{B}_2 & \boldsymbol{I} & \cdots & \boldsymbol{0} \\ \vdots & \ddots & \ddots & \vdots \\ \boldsymbol{0} & \cdots & -\boldsymbol{B}_t & \boldsymbol{I} \\ \\ \boldsymbol{H}_1 & \boldsymbol{0} & \cdots & \boldsymbol{0} \\ \boldsymbol{0} & \boldsymbol{H}_2 & \cdots & \boldsymbol{0} \\ \vdots & \vdots & \ddots & \vdots \\ \boldsymbol{0} & \boldsymbol{0} & \cdots & \boldsymbol{H}_t \end{pmatrix}, \quad \boldsymbol{\varepsilon}_t = \begin{pmatrix} -\boldsymbol{u}_1 \\ -\boldsymbol{u}_2 \\ \vdots \\ -\boldsymbol{u}_t \\ \\ \boldsymbol{v}_1 \\ \boldsymbol{v}_2 \\ \vdots \\ \boldsymbol{v}_t \end{pmatrix}.$$

This is a special case of (9.9) with $\boldsymbol{F}$ nonsingular. We shall denote $D(\boldsymbol{\varepsilon}_t)$ by $\boldsymbol{V}_t$, and use the notation $\mathcal{M}_t$ to describe the model $(\boldsymbol{y}_t, \boldsymbol{X}_t\boldsymbol{\gamma}_t, \boldsymbol{V}_t)$.

The state update and measurement equations up to time t can also be written as

$$\boldsymbol{y}_t = (\boldsymbol{X}_t : \boldsymbol{0})\boldsymbol{\gamma}_{t+1} + \boldsymbol{\varepsilon}_t. \tag{9.12}$$

We shall denote by $\mathcal{M}_t^\dagger$ the model $(\boldsymbol{y}_t, (\boldsymbol{X}_t : \boldsymbol{0})\boldsymbol{\gamma}_{t+1}, \boldsymbol{V}_t)$, which also fits into the framework of (9.9). However, the condition $\mathcal{C}(\boldsymbol{C}') \subseteq \mathcal{C}(\boldsymbol{F}')$ of Proposition 9.18 means that the result can be used only to predict linear functions of $\boldsymbol{\gamma}_t$, and not for all functions of $\boldsymbol{\gamma}_{t+1}$.

The state update equations (9.7) up to time t and the measurement equations (9.8) up to time $t-1$ can be combined into the single equation

$$\boldsymbol{y}_{t|t-1} = \boldsymbol{X}_{t|t-1}\boldsymbol{\gamma}_t + \boldsymbol{\varepsilon}_{t|t-1}, \tag{9.13}$$

where $\boldsymbol{\gamma}_t$ is as in (9.11) and

$$\boldsymbol{y}_{t|t-1} = \begin{pmatrix} \boldsymbol{B}_1\boldsymbol{x}_0 \\ \boldsymbol{0} \\ \vdots \\ \boldsymbol{0} \\ \\ \boldsymbol{z}_1 \\ \vdots \\ \boldsymbol{z}_{t-1} \end{pmatrix}, \quad \boldsymbol{X}_{t|t-1} = \begin{pmatrix} \boldsymbol{I} & \boldsymbol{0} & \cdots & \boldsymbol{0} \\ -\boldsymbol{B}_2 & \boldsymbol{I} & \cdots & \boldsymbol{0} \\ \vdots & \ddots & \ddots & \vdots \\ \boldsymbol{0} & \cdots & -\boldsymbol{B}_t & \boldsymbol{I} \\ \\ \boldsymbol{H}_1 & \cdots & \boldsymbol{0} & \boldsymbol{0} \\ \vdots & \ddots & \vdots & \vdots \\ \boldsymbol{0} & \cdots & \boldsymbol{H}_{t-1} & \boldsymbol{0} \end{pmatrix}, \quad \boldsymbol{\varepsilon}_{t|t-1} = \begin{pmatrix} -\boldsymbol{u}_1 \\ -\boldsymbol{u}_2 \\ \vdots \\ -\boldsymbol{u}_t \\ \\ \boldsymbol{v}_1 \\ \vdots \\ \boldsymbol{v}_{t-1} \end{pmatrix}.$$

We shall denote $D(\boldsymbol{\varepsilon}_{t|t-1})$ by $\boldsymbol{V}_{t|t-1}$ and use the notation $\mathcal{M}_{t|t-1}$ for the model $(\boldsymbol{y}_{t|t-1}, \boldsymbol{X}_{t|t-1}\boldsymbol{\gamma}_t, \boldsymbol{V}_{t|t-1})$. This is also a special case of (9.9) with $\boldsymbol{F}$ nonsingular.

Recursive prediction of the state vector consists of the following cycle of steps.

(I) Given the prediction of $\boldsymbol{x}_{t-1}$ based on $\boldsymbol{x}_0, \boldsymbol{z}_1, \ldots, \boldsymbol{z}_{t-1}$ and the dispersion of the prediction error, predict $\boldsymbol{x}_t$ and the dispersion matrix.

(II) Given the above quantities, update these by taking into account the additional measurement $\boldsymbol{z}_t$.

The above discussion and Proposition 9.18 imply that the best linear predictor of the state vector and at every stage is given by a BLUE in a suitable 'equivalent' linear model.

This is where the update equations of Section 9.1.3 have a role to play. Using the 'BLUE' of $\boldsymbol{x}_{t-1}$ and its dispersion under the linear model (9.11) (with t replaced by $t-1$), we can find the 'BLUE' of $\boldsymbol{x}_t$ and its dispersion under the model (9.11) by tracking the following three transitions: (Ia) from $\mathcal{M}_{t-1}$ to $\mathcal{M}_{t-1}^\dagger$, (Ib) from $\mathcal{M}_{t-1}^\dagger$ to $\mathcal{M}_{t|t-1}$ and (II) from $\mathcal{M}_{t|t-1}$ to $\mathcal{M}_t$.

At this point we assume that the covariance matrices given on page 467 have the special form: $\boldsymbol{Q}_{uv}(s,t) = \boldsymbol{0}$ for all s, t, $R_u(s,t) = \boldsymbol{0}$ for $s \neq t$ and $R_v(s,t) = \boldsymbol{0}$ for $s \neq t$. This is done only to simplify the algebra. The derivation can easily be extended to the general case.

Step Ia: transition from $\mathcal{M}_{t-1}$ to $\mathcal{M}_{t-1}^{\dagger}$.
Let us denote the BLUE of $\boldsymbol{x}_{t-1}$ computed from the model $\mathcal{M}_{t-1}$ by $\widehat{\boldsymbol{x}}_{t-1}$ and its dispersion matrix by $\boldsymbol{P}_{t-1}$. Using Proposition 9.18 for (9.11), with t replaced by $t-1$ and $\boldsymbol{C} = (\boldsymbol{0} : \cdots : \boldsymbol{0} : \boldsymbol{I})$, $\widehat{\boldsymbol{x}}_{t-1}$ and $\boldsymbol{P}_{t-1}$ may be identified as the minimum mean squared linear predictor of $\boldsymbol{x}_{t-1}$ based on $\boldsymbol{x}_0, \boldsymbol{z}_1, \ldots, \boldsymbol{z}_{t-1}$, and the dispersion matrix of the corresponding prediction error.

The transition from $\mathcal{M}_{t-1}$ to $\mathcal{M}_{t-1}^{\dagger}$ should involve *no change* in the BLUE or the dispersion matrix, since the model $\mathcal{M}_{t-1}^{\dagger}$ is only a reparametrization of $\mathcal{M}_{t-1}$. Applying Proposition 9.18 to (9.12), with t replaced by $t-1$, we observe that the best linear predictor and the dispersion matrix of the prediction error remain the same.

Step Ib: transition from $\mathcal{M}_{t-1}^{\dagger}$ to $\mathcal{M}_{t|t-1}$.
Let $\widehat{\boldsymbol{x}}_{t|t-1}$ and $\boldsymbol{P}_{t|t-1}$ denote the BLUE of $\boldsymbol{x}_t$ and its dispersion matrix, computed from the model $\mathcal{M}_{t|t-1}$. Applying Proposition 9.18 to (9.13), $\widehat{\boldsymbol{x}}_{t|t-1}$ and $\boldsymbol{P}_{t|t-1}$ may be identified as the best linear predictor of $\boldsymbol{x}_t$ based on $\boldsymbol{x}_0, \boldsymbol{z}_1, \ldots, \boldsymbol{z}_{t-1}$, and the dispersion matrix of the corresponding prediction error.

The model $\mathcal{M}_{t|t-1}$ is obtained from the model $\mathcal{M}_{t-1}^{\dagger}$ by including some additional observations. Note that $\rho(\boldsymbol{X}_{t|t-1}) - \rho(\boldsymbol{X}_{t-1} : \boldsymbol{0})$ is equal to the size of the vector $\boldsymbol{x}_t$. Therefore, there is no *new* LZF. The BLUE of γ_{t-1} and its dispersion remains unchanged. We can use Proposition 9.9 in order to obtain $\widehat{\boldsymbol{x}}_{t|t-1}$ and $P_{t|t-1}$ in terms of the previously computed quantities. Specifically, we have

$$\begin{aligned} -\boldsymbol{B}_t\widehat{\boldsymbol{x}}_{t-1} + \widehat{\boldsymbol{x}}_{t|t-1} &= \boldsymbol{y}_*, \\ D(-\boldsymbol{B}_t\widehat{\boldsymbol{x}}_{t-1} + \widehat{\boldsymbol{x}}_{t|t-1}) &= \boldsymbol{Q}_u(t,t), \end{aligned}$$

where $\boldsymbol{y}_*$ is the observed value of the additional part of the $\boldsymbol{y}$-vector. This happens to be $\boldsymbol{0}$, but that should not matter while we simplify the second equation. What matters is that $\boldsymbol{y}_*$ is uncorrelated with $\boldsymbol{y}_{t-1}$. Thus, we have

$$Cov(\widehat{\boldsymbol{x}}_{t|t-1}, \widehat{\boldsymbol{x}}_{t-1}) = Cov(\boldsymbol{y}_* + \boldsymbol{B}_t\widehat{\boldsymbol{x}}_{t-1}, \widehat{\boldsymbol{x}}_{t-1}) = \boldsymbol{B}_t D(\widehat{\boldsymbol{x}}_{t-1}).$$

Consequently,

$$\begin{aligned} \boldsymbol{Q}_u(t,t) = D(\boldsymbol{B}_t\widehat{\boldsymbol{x}}_{t-1}) + \boldsymbol{P}_{t|t-1} - Cov(\boldsymbol{B}_t\widehat{\boldsymbol{x}}_{t-1}, \widehat{\boldsymbol{x}}_{t|t-1}) \\ - Cov(\widehat{\boldsymbol{x}}_{t|t-1}, \boldsymbol{B}_t\widehat{\boldsymbol{x}}_{t-1}) \quad = \quad \boldsymbol{P}_{t|t-1} - \boldsymbol{B}_t\boldsymbol{P}_{t-1}\boldsymbol{B}_t'. \end{aligned}$$

Now we substitute $\boldsymbol{y}_* = \boldsymbol{0}$ in the earlier equation and have the updates

$$\widehat{\boldsymbol{x}}_{t|t-1} = \boldsymbol{B}_t\widehat{\boldsymbol{x}}_{t-1}, \tag{9.14}$$

$$\boldsymbol{P}_{t|t-1} = \boldsymbol{B}_t\boldsymbol{P}_{t-1}\boldsymbol{B}_t' + \boldsymbol{Q}_u(t,t). \tag{9.15}$$

Step II: transition from $\mathcal{M}_{t|t-1}$ to $\mathcal{M}_t$.
The model $\mathcal{M}_t$ is obtained from the model $\mathcal{M}_{t|t-1}$ by including some additional observations. Since $\boldsymbol{X}_{t|t-1}$ has full column rank, there is no newly estimable LPF. In the present case, the recursive residual of Proposition 9.3 is identified as $\boldsymbol{w}_t = \boldsymbol{z}_t - \widehat{\boldsymbol{z}}_t$, where

$$\widehat{\boldsymbol{z}}_t = \boldsymbol{H}_t\widehat{\boldsymbol{x}}_{t|t-1}. \tag{9.16}$$

The requisite variance and covariances are

$$D(\boldsymbol{w}_t) = D(\boldsymbol{z}_t) + \boldsymbol{H}_t D(\widehat{\boldsymbol{x}}_{t|t-1})\boldsymbol{H}_t' = \boldsymbol{Q}_v(t,t) + \boldsymbol{H}_t\boldsymbol{P}_{t|t-1}\boldsymbol{H}_t',$$

$$Cov(\widehat{\boldsymbol{x}}_{t|t-1}, \boldsymbol{w}_t) = -\boldsymbol{P}_{t|t-1}\boldsymbol{H}_t'. \tag{9.17}$$

Substitution of $\boldsymbol{w}_t$, $D(\boldsymbol{w}_t)$ and $Cov(\widehat{\boldsymbol{x}}_{t|t-1}, \boldsymbol{w}_t)$ in parts (a) and (b) of Proposition 9.8 produces

$$\widehat{\boldsymbol{x}}_t = \widehat{\boldsymbol{x}}_{t|t-1} + \boldsymbol{P}_{t|t-1}\boldsymbol{H}_t V'(\boldsymbol{Q}_v(t,t) + \boldsymbol{H}_t\boldsymbol{P}_{t|t-1}\boldsymbol{H}_t')^-(\boldsymbol{z}_t - \boldsymbol{H}_t\widehat{\boldsymbol{x}}_{t|t-1}), \tag{9.18}$$

$$\boldsymbol{P}_t = \boldsymbol{P}_{t|t-1} - \boldsymbol{P}_{t|t-1}\boldsymbol{H}_t'(\boldsymbol{Q}_v(t,t) + \boldsymbol{H}_t\boldsymbol{P}_{t|t-1}\boldsymbol{H}_t')^-\boldsymbol{H}_t\boldsymbol{P}_{t|t-1}. \tag{9.19}$$

The recursive relations (9.14)–(9.15) and (9.18)–(9.19) constitute the Kalman filter. These relations hold for $t \geq 2$. The initial iterates are $\widehat{\boldsymbol{x}}_{1|0} = \boldsymbol{B}_1\boldsymbol{x}_0$ and $P_{1|0} = \boldsymbol{Q}_u(1,1)$. The minimum mean squared error linear predictor of the measurement vector $\boldsymbol{z}_t$ (in terms of $\boldsymbol{x}_0, \boldsymbol{z}_1, \ldots, \boldsymbol{z}_{t-1}$) and the dispersion matrix of the corresponding prediction error are given by (9.16) and (9.17), respectively.

It may be observed that Proposition 9.18 holds with no condition on the nature of the matrix $\boldsymbol{V}_t$. Allowance for the singularity of $\boldsymbol{V}_t$ is important in many practical applications (see, for instance, Harvey and Phillips, 1979). Proposition 9.8 also allows the matrix $\boldsymbol{V}_{ml}$ to be nonzero. Therefore, the above derivation can be readily generalized to incorporate correlation of the error vectors $\boldsymbol{u}_t$ and $\boldsymbol{v}_t$ in the state-space model (9.7)–(9.8). Temporal correlation can also be handled. Thus, the derivation of the Kalman filter through the update equations of the linear model has several theoretical advantages.

Haslett (1996) uses the linear model update equations to derive the Kalman filter. However, he assumes $\boldsymbol{V}_t$ to be nonsingular and uses a more complicated set-up for linear model updates, where data and parameters are augmented simultaneously. Nieto and Guerrero (1995) derive the Kalman filter in the singular dispersion case from a different set-up, and use the Moore-Penrose inverse where any g-inverse would suffice. Sengupta (2004) provides a more general derivation in this case.

9.2 Exclusion of observations

Recall the models $\mathcal{M}_m$ and $\mathcal{M}_n$ defined in Section 9.1. In this section we track the transition from the model $\mathcal{M}_n$ to $\mathcal{M}_m$. We refer to $\mathcal{M}_n$ as the 'initial' model and $\mathcal{M}_m$ as the 'deleted' model. The deleted model has $l = n - m$ fewer observations than the initial model.

9.2.1 *A simple case*

Once again we first consider the case $\boldsymbol{V}_n = \boldsymbol{I}$ and $l = 1$, and compare the models $\mathcal{M}_n$ and $\mathcal{M}_{n-1}$. We partition $\boldsymbol{y}_n$ and $\boldsymbol{X}_n$ as

$$\boldsymbol{y}_n = \begin{pmatrix} \boldsymbol{y}_{n-1} \\ y_n \end{pmatrix}; \qquad \boldsymbol{X}_n = \begin{pmatrix} \boldsymbol{X}_{n-1} \\ \boldsymbol{x}_n' \end{pmatrix}. \tag{9.20}$$

In Section 9.1.1 the recursive residual played a pivotal role in determining the updates in the augmented model. The recursive residual corresponding to y_n is expressed in terms of the predicted value of y_n from the deleted model, which does not suit the present context. We need a pivot that is expressed in terms of the quantities computed for the initial model. For this purpose we use the ordinary residual, $e_n = y_n - \boldsymbol{x}_n'\widehat{\boldsymbol{\beta}}_n$. Note that $\widehat{\boldsymbol{\beta}}_n$ is uncorrelated with every LZF, and in particular with every LZF of the deleted model. Further, y_n is also uncorrelated with the LZFs of the deleted model, as it is uncorrelated with $\boldsymbol{y}_{n-1}$. Thus, e_n is uncorrelated with every LZF of the deleted model.

Since the last recursive residual and the corresponding ordinary residual are linear functions that are uncorrelated with the same sets of BLUEs and LZFs, and according to the rank condition there cannot be two linearly independent linear functions having this property, these two residuals must be multiples of one another with probability one. Part (a) of Exercise 5.14 had been a restatement of this fact.

Decorrelation of $\boldsymbol{X}_{n-1}\widehat{\boldsymbol{\beta}}_{n-1}$ from e_n yields

$$\boldsymbol{X}_{n-1}\widehat{\boldsymbol{\beta}}_n = \boldsymbol{X}_{n-1}\widehat{\boldsymbol{\beta}}_{n-1} - Cov(X_{n-1}\widehat{\boldsymbol{\beta}}_{n-1}, e_n)e_n/Var(e_n), \qquad (9.21)$$

assuming that $Var(e_n) > 0$. (If $Var(e_n) = 0$, then no decorrelation is necessary, and $\boldsymbol{X}_{n-1}\widehat{\boldsymbol{\beta}}_{n-1} = \boldsymbol{X}_{n-1}\widehat{\boldsymbol{\beta}}_n$.) Rearrangement of the terms of (9.21) gives $\boldsymbol{X}_{n-1}\widehat{\boldsymbol{\beta}}_{n-1}$ in terms of $\boldsymbol{X}_{n-1}\widehat{\boldsymbol{\beta}}_n$. In order to obtain a simple expression of $Cov(X_{n-1}\widehat{\boldsymbol{\beta}}_{n-1})$, we calculate the covariance of both sides of (9.21) with y_n. This yields

$$\begin{aligned} Cov(\boldsymbol{X}_{n-1}\widehat{\boldsymbol{\beta}}_n, y_n) &= 0 - Cov(X_{n-1}\widehat{\boldsymbol{\beta}}_{n-1}, e_n)Cov(e_n, y_n)/Var(e_n) \\ &= -Cov(X_{n-1}\widehat{\boldsymbol{\beta}}_{n-1}, e_n). \end{aligned}$$

The last equation follows from the fact that

$$Cov(e_n, y_n) = Cov(e_n, \boldsymbol{x}_n'\widehat{\boldsymbol{\beta}}_n) + Var(e_n) = Var(e_n).$$

Thus,

$$Cov(X_{n-1}\widehat{\boldsymbol{\beta}}_{n-1}, e_n) = -Cov(\boldsymbol{X}_{n-1}\widehat{\boldsymbol{\beta}}_n, y_n) = -\sigma^2\boldsymbol{X}_{n-1}(\boldsymbol{X}_n'\boldsymbol{X}_n)^-\boldsymbol{x}_n.$$

This simplification, together with (9.21), produces

$$\boldsymbol{X}_{n-1}\widehat{\boldsymbol{\beta}}_{n-1} = \boldsymbol{X}_{n-1}\widehat{\boldsymbol{\beta}}_n - \boldsymbol{X}_{n-1}(\boldsymbol{X}_n'\boldsymbol{X}_n)^-\boldsymbol{x}_n e_n/(1-h_n), \qquad (9.22)$$

where h_n is $\boldsymbol{x}_n'(\boldsymbol{X}_n'\boldsymbol{X}_n)^-\boldsymbol{x}_n$, the leverage of the nth observation. The update equations resulting from (9.22) are given in the next proposition.

Proposition 9.19. *Consider the initial model $\mathcal{M}_n$ and the deleted model $\mathcal{M}_{n-1}$, and let $\mathbf{c} = \boldsymbol{X}_{n-1}(\boldsymbol{X}_n'\boldsymbol{X}_n)^-\boldsymbol{x}_n$ and $h_n = \boldsymbol{x}_n'(\boldsymbol{X}_n'\boldsymbol{X}_n)^-\boldsymbol{x}_n < 1$. Further, let $\boldsymbol{A\beta}$ be estimable in the models $\mathcal{M}_n$ and $\mathcal{M}_{n-1}$. Then the updated statistics for the deleted model are as follows:*

(a) $\boldsymbol{X}_{n-1}\widehat{\boldsymbol{\beta}}_{n-1} = \boldsymbol{X}_{n-1}\widehat{\boldsymbol{\beta}}_n - \mathbf{c}e_n/(1-h_n)$.
(b) $D(\boldsymbol{X}_{n-1}\widehat{\boldsymbol{\beta}}_{n-1}) = D(\boldsymbol{X}_{n-1}\widehat{\boldsymbol{\beta}}_n) + \sigma^2\mathbf{c}\mathbf{c}'/(1-h_n)$.
(c) $R^2_{0_{n-1}} = R^2_{0_n} - e_n^2/(1-h_n)$.
(d) The change in the error sum of squares R_H^2 under the restriction $\boldsymbol{A\beta} = \boldsymbol{\xi}$ is

$$R^2_{H_{n-1}} = R^2_{H_n} - \frac{[e_n + \boldsymbol{a}'\boldsymbol{D}_A^-(\boldsymbol{A}\widehat{\boldsymbol{\beta}}_n - \boldsymbol{\xi})]^2}{1 - h_n + \boldsymbol{a}'\boldsymbol{D}_A^-\boldsymbol{a}},$$

where $\boldsymbol{a} = \boldsymbol{A}'(\boldsymbol{X}_n'\boldsymbol{X}_n)^-\boldsymbol{x}_n$ and $\boldsymbol{D}_A = \boldsymbol{A}'(\boldsymbol{X}_n'\boldsymbol{X}_n)^-\boldsymbol{A}$.
(e) The degrees of freedom of R_0^2 and R_H^2 decrease by 1 when the nth observation is excluded.

Proof. Parts (a)–(c) follow immediately from the discussion leading to (9.22) and Proposition 9.8. In order to prove part (d), let

$$e_{n*} = e_n + \boldsymbol{a}'\boldsymbol{D}_A^-(\boldsymbol{A}\widehat{\boldsymbol{\beta}}_n - \boldsymbol{\xi}).$$

It is easy to see that e_{n*} is uncorrelated with all the LZFs of the deleted model. Further, we have from part (a)

$$\begin{aligned} Cov(e_n^*, \boldsymbol{A}\widehat{\boldsymbol{\beta}}_{n-1}) &= Cov(e_n + \boldsymbol{a}'\boldsymbol{D}_A^-(\boldsymbol{A}\widehat{\boldsymbol{\beta}}_n - \boldsymbol{\xi}), \boldsymbol{A}\widehat{\boldsymbol{\beta}}_n - \boldsymbol{a}e_n/(1-h_n)) \\ &= \sigma^2(\boldsymbol{0} - \boldsymbol{a}' + \boldsymbol{a}' - \boldsymbol{0}) \\ &= \boldsymbol{0}. \end{aligned}$$

In view of Proposition 7.41, e_n^* is uncorrelated with *every* LZF of the deleted and restricted model. Thus, it can play a pivotal role in tracking the effect of data exclusion in the restricted model. The stated result follows from the fact that $Var(e_n^*) = \sigma^2(1-h_n+\boldsymbol{a}'\boldsymbol{D}_A^-\boldsymbol{a})$. Part (e) follows from part (e) of Proposition 9.1. □

Remark 9.20. The condition $h_n = 1$ is equivalent to $\boldsymbol{x}_n \notin \mathcal{C}(\boldsymbol{X}'_{n-1})$ or $\rho(\boldsymbol{X}_n) = \rho(\boldsymbol{X}_{n-1}) + 1$. If $h_n = 1$, then it follows from the discussion of Section 9.1.1 that the exclusion of y_n does not change any of the quantities of interest, except that $\boldsymbol{x}_n'\boldsymbol{\beta}$ becomes non-estimable. □

9.2.2 *General case: linear zero functions lost*

Let us consider once again the four cases described in Section 9.1.2. No LZF is lost in cases (a) and (c). Case (d) can be thought of as a two-step exclusion where the steps correspond to cases (b) and (a), respectively. Therefore, we deal mainly with case (b) and identify the LZFs lost.

As we have seen in the simple case of data exclusion, the unscaled recursive group residual ($\boldsymbol{w}_l$) of Section 9.1.2 is an LZF of $\mathcal{M}_n$ which is uncorrelated with the LZFs of $\mathcal{M}_m$, and these two sets of LZFs together form a generating set of LZFs of $\mathcal{M}_n$. This is why $\boldsymbol{w}_l$ was used as a pivot for obtaining the updates in Section 9.1.3. However, $\boldsymbol{w}_l$ is expressed in terms of the residuals of $\mathcal{M}_m$, which is generally not available before the data exclusion takes place. Of course, we can express $\boldsymbol{w}_l$ directly in terms of $\boldsymbol{y}_n$ as

$$\begin{aligned} \boldsymbol{w}_l = \boldsymbol{y}_l - \boldsymbol{X}_l\boldsymbol{X}_m^-\boldsymbol{y}_m + (\boldsymbol{X}_l\boldsymbol{X}_m^- - \boldsymbol{V}_{lm}\boldsymbol{V}_m^-)\boldsymbol{V}_m(\boldsymbol{I} - \boldsymbol{P}_{\boldsymbol{X}_m}) \\ \times [(\boldsymbol{I} - \boldsymbol{P}_{\boldsymbol{X}_m})\boldsymbol{V}_m(\boldsymbol{I} - \boldsymbol{P}_{\boldsymbol{X}_m})]^-(\boldsymbol{I} - \boldsymbol{P}_{\boldsymbol{X}_m})\boldsymbol{y}_m. \end{aligned}$$

This expression does not depend on the choice of the various g-inverses. However, its computation essentially entails fresh computation of $\boldsymbol{X}\widehat{\boldsymbol{\beta}}_m$.

We need a modification of $\boldsymbol{w}_l$ which can be used in the present context. We now give such an LZF via the next proposition in the special case where $\boldsymbol{V}_n$ is nonsingular. Note that in such a case, $l_* = \rho(\boldsymbol{X}_n : \boldsymbol{V}_n) - \rho(\boldsymbol{X}_m : \boldsymbol{V}_m)$ simplifies to l.

Proposition 9.21. *In the set-up of Section 9.1.2, let $l > 0$. Then a vector of LZFs of the model $\mathcal{M}_n$ that is uncorrelated with all the LZFs of $\mathcal{M}_m$ is given by*

$$\boldsymbol{r}_l = \boldsymbol{d}_l(\widehat{\boldsymbol{\beta}}_n) = \boldsymbol{y}_l - \boldsymbol{X}_l\widehat{\boldsymbol{\beta}}_n - \boldsymbol{V}_{lm}\boldsymbol{V}_m^-(\boldsymbol{y}_m - \boldsymbol{X}_m\widehat{\boldsymbol{\beta}}_n), \tag{9.23}$$

where $\boldsymbol{d}_l(\cdot)$ is as defined in Remark 9.7. If $\rho(\boldsymbol{V}_n) = n$, then there is no nontrivial LZF of $\mathcal{M}_n$ which is uncorrelated with $\boldsymbol{r}_l$ and the LZFs of $\mathcal{M}_m$.

Proof. If $\boldsymbol{e}_n$ is the residual vector for $\mathcal{M}_n$, then $\boldsymbol{r}_l = [-\boldsymbol{V}_{lm}\boldsymbol{V}_m^- : \boldsymbol{I}]\boldsymbol{e}_n$. Therefore, by writing the LZF $(\boldsymbol{I} - \boldsymbol{P}_{X_m})\boldsymbol{y}_m$ as $\boldsymbol{L}(\boldsymbol{I} - \boldsymbol{P}_{X_n})\boldsymbol{y}_n$ for some matrix $\boldsymbol{L}$, we have from (7.5)

$$\begin{aligned}
Cov(\boldsymbol{r}_l, (\boldsymbol{I} - \boldsymbol{P}_{X_m})\boldsymbol{y}_m) &= [-\boldsymbol{V}_{lm}\boldsymbol{V}_m^- : \boldsymbol{I}]Cov(\boldsymbol{e}_n, (\boldsymbol{I} - \boldsymbol{P}_{X_n})\boldsymbol{y}_n)\boldsymbol{L}' \\
&= [-\boldsymbol{V}_{lm}\boldsymbol{V}_m^- : \boldsymbol{I}]Cov(\boldsymbol{y}_n, (\boldsymbol{I} - \boldsymbol{P}_{X_n})\boldsymbol{y}_n)\boldsymbol{L}' \\
&= Cov\left((-\boldsymbol{V}_{lm}\boldsymbol{V}_m^- : \boldsymbol{I})\boldsymbol{y}_n, (\boldsymbol{I} - \boldsymbol{P}_{X_m})\boldsymbol{y}_m\right) \\
&= \boldsymbol{0}.
\end{aligned}$$

In order to prove the remaining part, we show that

$$\rho(\boldsymbol{r}_l) = l_* - [\rho(\boldsymbol{X}_n) - \rho(\boldsymbol{X}_m)]$$

whenever $\boldsymbol{V}_n$ has full rank. Note that in this case $l_* = l$. Let $\boldsymbol{C}\boldsymbol{C}'$ be a rank-factorization of $\boldsymbol{V}_n$ such that $\boldsymbol{C}' = (\boldsymbol{C}_1' : \boldsymbol{C}_2')$ and $\boldsymbol{V}_m = \boldsymbol{C}_1\boldsymbol{C}_1'$. Then

$$\begin{aligned}
D(\boldsymbol{r}_l) &= \sigma^2(-\boldsymbol{V}_{lm}\boldsymbol{V}_m^{-1} : \boldsymbol{I})[\boldsymbol{V}_n - \boldsymbol{X}_n(\boldsymbol{X}_n'\boldsymbol{V}_n^{-1}\boldsymbol{X}_n)^-\boldsymbol{X}_n']\begin{pmatrix}-\boldsymbol{V}_m^-\boldsymbol{V}_{ml}\\ \boldsymbol{I}\end{pmatrix} \\
&= \sigma^2(-\boldsymbol{C}_2\boldsymbol{C}_1'(\boldsymbol{C}_1\boldsymbol{C}_1')^- : \boldsymbol{I})\boldsymbol{C}\left(\boldsymbol{I} - \boldsymbol{P}_{C^{-1}X_n}\right)\boldsymbol{C}'\begin{pmatrix}-(\boldsymbol{C}_1\boldsymbol{C}_1')^-\boldsymbol{C}_1\boldsymbol{C}_2'\\ \boldsymbol{I}\end{pmatrix} \\
&= \sigma^2\left(\boldsymbol{C}_2\left(\boldsymbol{I} - \boldsymbol{P}_{C_1'}\right)\right)\left(\boldsymbol{I} - \boldsymbol{P}_{C^{-1}X_n}\right)\left(\left(\boldsymbol{I} - \boldsymbol{P}_{C_1'}\right)\boldsymbol{C}_2'\right).
\end{aligned}$$

If $\boldsymbol{L}\boldsymbol{L}'$ is a rank-factorization of $\boldsymbol{I} - \boldsymbol{P}_{C_1'}$, then we have

$$\begin{aligned}
\rho(D(\boldsymbol{r}_l)) &= \rho\left(\left(\boldsymbol{I} - \boldsymbol{P}_{C^{-1}X_n}\right)\left(\left(\boldsymbol{I} - \boldsymbol{P}_{C_1'}\right)\boldsymbol{C}_2'\right)\right) \\
&= \rho\left(\left(\boldsymbol{I} - \boldsymbol{P}_{C^{-1}X_n}\right)\left(\left(\boldsymbol{I} - \boldsymbol{P}_{C_1'}\right)\boldsymbol{P}_{C_2'}\right)\right)
\end{aligned}$$

$$
\begin{aligned}
&= \rho\left(\left(I - P_{C^{-1}X_n}\right)\left(P_{C_1':C_2'} - P_{C_1'}\right)\right)\\
&= \rho\left(\left(I - P_{C^{-1}X_n}\right)\left(I - P_{C_1'}\right)\right)\\
&= \rho\left(\left(I - P_{C^{-1}X_n}\right)L\right)\\
&= \rho((C^{-1}X_n : L)) - \rho(C^{-1}X_n)\\
&= \rho((X_n : CL)) - \rho(X_n)\\
&= \rho\begin{pmatrix} X_m & 0 \\ X_l & C_2L \end{pmatrix} - \rho(X_n)\\
&= \rho(X_m) + \rho(C_2L) - \rho(X_n)\\
&= \rho(C_2LL') - [\rho(X_n) - \rho(X_m)]\\
&= \rho\left(\left(I - P_{C_1'}\right)C_2'\right) - [\rho(X_n) - \rho(X_m)]\\
&= \rho(C_1' : C_2') - \rho(C_1') - [\rho(X_n) - \rho(X_m)]\\
&= n - m - [\rho(X_n) - \rho(X_m)]\\
&= l - [\rho(X_n) - \rho(X_m)].
\end{aligned}
$$

This completes the proof. □

It can be shown that whenever $\mathcal{C}(X_l') \subseteq \mathcal{C}(X_m')$ and V_n is nonsingular, r_l and w_l are linearly transformed versions of one another (see Exercise 9.7). The advantage of r_l over w_l is that the former is expressed in terms of the estimator $X_n\widehat{\beta}_n$.

When V_n is singular, w_l may not be a function of r_l. In particular, r_l may even have zero dispersion whereas the dispersion matrix of w_l must have rank l_*. Evidently r_l can serve as a pivot for updates in the general linear model if and only if $\rho(D(r_l)) = l_* - [\rho(X_n) - \rho(X_m)]$. The latter condition is satisfied when V_n is nonsingular. Jammalamadaka and Sengupta (1999) overlook the necessity of the rank condition on $D(r_l)$ (see Remark 9.24).

Note that the condition $\mathcal{C}(X_l') \subseteq \mathcal{C}(X_m')$ was *not* needed in the proof of Proposition 9.21. Thus, case (d) of Section 9.1.2 (that is, the case where some LZFs and estimable LPFs are lost due to data exclusion) is well within the scope of this proposition.

9.2.3 *General case: update equations*

Let us assume that $0 < l_* - [\rho(X_n) - \rho(X_m)] = \rho(D(r_l))$, that is, some LZFs (represented adequately by r_l) are lost because of data exclusion. In the light of Remark 9.6, we have

$$\boldsymbol{X}_m\widehat{\boldsymbol{\beta}}_m = \boldsymbol{X}_m\widehat{\boldsymbol{\beta}}_n + Cov(\boldsymbol{X}_m\widehat{\boldsymbol{\beta}}_m, \boldsymbol{r}_l)[D(\boldsymbol{r}_l)]^-\boldsymbol{r}_l. \tag{9.24}$$

The covariance on the right-hand side remains to be expressed in terms of the known quantities in the current model. From (9.24) it follows that

$$\begin{aligned} &Cov(\boldsymbol{X}_m\widehat{\boldsymbol{\beta}}_m, \boldsymbol{d}_l(\boldsymbol{\beta})) \\ &= Cov(\boldsymbol{X}_m\widehat{\boldsymbol{\beta}}_n, \boldsymbol{d}_l(\boldsymbol{\beta})) + Cov(\boldsymbol{X}_m\widehat{\boldsymbol{\beta}}_m, \boldsymbol{r}_l)[D(\boldsymbol{r}_l)]^- Cov(\boldsymbol{r}_l, \boldsymbol{d}_l(\boldsymbol{\beta})). \end{aligned}$$

Since $\boldsymbol{d}_l(\boldsymbol{\beta})$ is uncorrelated with $\boldsymbol{y}_m$ while $\boldsymbol{X}_m\widehat{\boldsymbol{\beta}}_m$ is a linear function of it, the left-hand side is zero. Also $Cov(\boldsymbol{r}_l, \boldsymbol{d}_l(\boldsymbol{\beta})) = D(\boldsymbol{r}_l)$, since $Cov(\boldsymbol{r}_l, \boldsymbol{d}_l(\boldsymbol{\beta})) - D(\boldsymbol{r}_l)$ is the covariance of $\boldsymbol{r}_l$ with a BLUE in $\mathcal{M}_n$ which must be zero. Therefore the second term in the right-hand side reduces to $Cov(\boldsymbol{X}_m\widehat{\boldsymbol{\beta}}_m, \boldsymbol{r}_l)$, which can be replaced by $-Cov(\boldsymbol{X}_m\widehat{\boldsymbol{\beta}}_n, \boldsymbol{d}_l(\boldsymbol{\beta}))$ in (9.24). This leads to the update relationships given below.

Proposition 9.22. *Let* $0 < l_* - [\rho(\boldsymbol{X}_n) - \rho(\boldsymbol{X}_m)] = \rho(D(\boldsymbol{r}_l))$ *and* $\boldsymbol{A\beta}$ *be estimable in either model with* $D(\boldsymbol{A}\widehat{\boldsymbol{\beta}}_n)$ *not identically zero. Then the updated statistics for the deleted model are as follows:*

(a) $\boldsymbol{X}_m\widehat{\boldsymbol{\beta}}_m = \boldsymbol{X}_m\widehat{\boldsymbol{\beta}}_n - Cov(\boldsymbol{X}_m\widehat{\boldsymbol{\beta}}_n, \boldsymbol{d}_l(\boldsymbol{\beta}))[D(\boldsymbol{r}_l)]^-\boldsymbol{r}_l.$
(b) $D(\boldsymbol{X}_m\widehat{\boldsymbol{\beta}}_m) = D(\boldsymbol{X}_m\widehat{\boldsymbol{\beta}}_n) + Cov(\boldsymbol{X}_m\widehat{\boldsymbol{\beta}}_n, \boldsymbol{d}_l(\boldsymbol{\beta}))[D(\boldsymbol{r}_l)]^- Cov(\boldsymbol{d}_l(\boldsymbol{\beta}), \boldsymbol{X}_m\widehat{\boldsymbol{\beta}}_n).$
(c) $R^2_{0_m} = R^2_{0_n} - \sigma^2\boldsymbol{r}_l'[D(\boldsymbol{r}_l)]^-\boldsymbol{r}_l.$
(d) The reduction in the error sum of squares under the restriction $\boldsymbol{A\beta} = \boldsymbol{\xi}$ *is given by* $R^2_{H_m} = R^2_{H_n} - \sigma^2\boldsymbol{r}_{l*}'[D(\boldsymbol{r}_{l*})]^-\boldsymbol{r}_{l*}$*, where*

$$\boldsymbol{r}_{l*} = \boldsymbol{r}_l + Cov(\boldsymbol{d}_l(\boldsymbol{\beta}), \boldsymbol{A}\widehat{\boldsymbol{\beta}}_n)[\boldsymbol{D}(\boldsymbol{A}\widehat{\boldsymbol{\beta}}_n)]^-(\boldsymbol{A}\widehat{\boldsymbol{\beta}}_n - \boldsymbol{\xi}).$$

(e) The degrees of freedom of R_0^2 *and* R_H^2 *reduce by* l_* *and* $\rho(D(\boldsymbol{r}_{l*}))$*, respectively, as a result of data exclusion.*

Proof. Parts (a)–(c) and (e) follow immediately from the above discussion and Proposition 9.8. Part (d) is proved by substituting the update formulae of parts (a) and (b) into equation (7.17) and simplifying. □

Remark 9.23. Bhimasankaram and Jammalamadaka (1994a) give algebraic expressions for the updates given in Proposition 9.22 in the special case when $l = 1$ and $\boldsymbol{V}_n$ is nonsingular. Bhimasankaram and Jammalamadaka (1994b) give statistical interpretations of these results along the lines of Proposition 9.22. Another set of interpretations in the multivariate normal case is given by Chib et al. (1987). Bhimasankaram et al. (1995) give update equations for data exclusion in all possible cases, using the inverse partition matrix approach. □

Remark 9.24. The difficulty of finding an update equation in the case $\rho(D(\boldsymbol{r}_l)) < l_* - [\rho(\boldsymbol{X}_n) - \rho(\boldsymbol{X}_m)]$ can be appreciated by considering the model with

$$\boldsymbol{y}_n = \begin{pmatrix} \boldsymbol{y}_m \\ y_{m+1} \\ y_{m+2} \end{pmatrix}, \quad \boldsymbol{X}_n = \begin{pmatrix} \boldsymbol{X}_m \\ 1\ 0 \\ 1\ 1 \end{pmatrix}, \quad \boldsymbol{\beta} = \begin{pmatrix} \beta_0 \\ \beta_1 \end{pmatrix}, \quad \boldsymbol{V}_n = \begin{pmatrix} \boldsymbol{V}_m & \mathbf{0} & \mathbf{0} \\ \mathbf{0} & 0 & 0 \\ \mathbf{0} & 0 & 0 \end{pmatrix}.$$

If $\rho(\boldsymbol{X}_m) = 2$ and $\boldsymbol{V}_m = \boldsymbol{I}_{m\times m}$, then $l_* - [\rho(\boldsymbol{X}_n) - \rho(\boldsymbol{X}_m)] = 2$, while $\rho(D(\boldsymbol{r}_l)) = \mathbf{0}$. It is clear that $\widehat{\boldsymbol{\beta}}_n = (y_{m+1} : y_{m+2} - y_{m+1})'$ and $D(\widehat{\boldsymbol{\beta}}_n) = \mathbf{0}$, but $\widehat{\boldsymbol{\beta}}_m$ has to be calculated afresh. There is no way of 'utilizing' the computations of the model with n observations. □

9.2.4 *Deletion diagnostics*

The theory developed above is now used to obtain general versions of a few diagnostic measures based on case deletion, introduced in Section 5.4, and to gain some insight. There are two aspects of this generalization: we permit *any* known error dispersion matrix and simultaneous deletion of *multiple* cases. It is assumed here that every estimable LPF of the full model remains estimable after exclusion of the observations.

Suppose l out of the n original observations, having index set I_l, are dropped. Let the modified versions of $\boldsymbol{X}_n$, $\widehat{\boldsymbol{\beta}}_n$ and $\boldsymbol{V}_n$ be denoted by $\boldsymbol{X}_m$, $\widehat{\boldsymbol{\beta}}_m$ and $\boldsymbol{V}_m$, respectively. For notational parity with the foregoing sections one can think of I_l as $\{m+1,\ldots,n\}$, i.e. as if the *last* few observations are deleted. This is not important however, as any set of l observations can be made to occur in the end by a suitable permutation. Let us assume

$$\rho(D(\boldsymbol{r}_l)) = [\rho((\boldsymbol{X}_n : \boldsymbol{V}_n)) - \rho((\boldsymbol{X}_m : \boldsymbol{V}_m))] - [\rho(\boldsymbol{X}_n) - \rho(\boldsymbol{X}_m)].$$

The consequent change in the BLUE of an estimable LPF $\boldsymbol{p}'\boldsymbol{\beta}$, obtained from part (a) of Proposition 9.22, is the difference

$$DFBETA_{I_l,p} = \boldsymbol{p}'\widehat{\boldsymbol{\beta}}_n - \boldsymbol{p}'\widehat{\boldsymbol{\beta}}_m = Cov(\boldsymbol{p}'\widehat{\boldsymbol{\beta}}_n, \boldsymbol{d}_l(\boldsymbol{\beta}))[D(\boldsymbol{r}_l)]^-\boldsymbol{r}_l. \tag{9.25}$$

The variance of $\boldsymbol{p}'\widehat{\boldsymbol{\beta}}_n$ is estimated by replacing σ^2 in the expression of $Var(\boldsymbol{p}'\widehat{\boldsymbol{\beta}}_n)$ by

$$\sigma^2_{(-I_l)} = \frac{R^2_{0_n} - \sigma^2\boldsymbol{r}_l'[D(\boldsymbol{r}_l)]^-\boldsymbol{r}_l}{\rho(\boldsymbol{X}_m : \boldsymbol{V}_m) - \rho(\boldsymbol{X}_m)}. \tag{9.26}$$

Let us denote this estimator by $\widehat{Var}(\boldsymbol{p}'\widehat{\boldsymbol{\beta}}_n)$. The quantity

$$DFBETAS_{I_l,p} = \frac{DFBETA_{I_l,p}}{[\widehat{Var}(\boldsymbol{p}'\widehat{\boldsymbol{\beta}}_n)]^{1/2}} \tag{9.27}$$

can be used as a scaled measure of impact of the observations with index set I_l on the BLUE of $\boldsymbol{p}'\boldsymbol{\beta}$. The actual algebraic formula for $DFBETAS_{I_l,p}$ would depend on the values of the model matrices and the chosen computational method (see, for instance, Bhimasankaram et al., 1995). When $I_l = \{i\}$ and $\boldsymbol{V}_n = \boldsymbol{I}$, this measure simplifies (see Remark 9.23) to

$$DFBETAS_{i,p} = \frac{\boldsymbol{p}'(\boldsymbol{X}_n'\boldsymbol{X}_n)^-\boldsymbol{x}_i e_i}{\widehat{\sigma}_{(-i)}(1-h_i)[\boldsymbol{p}'(\boldsymbol{X}_n'\boldsymbol{X}_n)^-\boldsymbol{p}]^{1/2}},$$

where

$$\widehat{\sigma}^2_{(-i)} = \frac{R^2_{0_n} - e_i^2/(1-h_i)}{n - \rho(\boldsymbol{X}_n) - 1}.$$

We had discussed in Section 5.4 the special case of this measure where $\boldsymbol{p}$ is the jth column of the identity matrix.

A special case of (9.27) for $I_l = \{i\}$ and $\boldsymbol{p} = \boldsymbol{x}_i$ is

$$DFFITS_i = \frac{\sigma^2}{\sigma^2_{(-i)}} \cdot \frac{\boldsymbol{x}_i'\widehat{\boldsymbol{\beta}}_n - \boldsymbol{x}_n'\widehat{\boldsymbol{\beta}}_m}{(Var(\boldsymbol{x}_i'\widehat{\boldsymbol{\beta}}_n))^{1/2}}.$$

It is clear that $DFFITS_i$ is the change in the fitted value of the ith observation when the latter is dropped. If $\boldsymbol{V}_n = \boldsymbol{I}$, the above expression simplifies to (5.17).

Let us now turn to the change in the overall fit when the observations I_l are dropped. A measure of this change is the following generalization of Cook's distance

$$\begin{aligned} COOKD_{I_l} &= \frac{\sigma^2(\boldsymbol{X}_n\widehat{\boldsymbol{\beta}}_n - \boldsymbol{X}_n\widehat{\boldsymbol{\beta}}_m)'[D(\boldsymbol{X}_n\widehat{\boldsymbol{\beta}}_n)]^-(\boldsymbol{X}_n\widehat{\boldsymbol{\beta}}_n - \boldsymbol{X}_n\widehat{\boldsymbol{\beta}}_m)}{\widehat{\sigma}^2_n\rho(\boldsymbol{X}_n)} \\ &= \frac{\sigma^2\boldsymbol{r}_l'[D(\boldsymbol{r}_l)]^-\boldsymbol{C}_n'[D(\boldsymbol{X}_n\widehat{\boldsymbol{\beta}}_n)]^-\boldsymbol{C}_n[D(\boldsymbol{r}_l)]^-\boldsymbol{r}_l}{\widehat{\sigma}^2_n\rho(\boldsymbol{X}_n)}, \end{aligned}$$

$$\text{where} \quad \boldsymbol{C}_n = Cov(\boldsymbol{X}_n\widehat{\boldsymbol{\beta}}_n, \boldsymbol{d}_l(\boldsymbol{\beta})).$$

If $I_l = \{i\}$ and $\boldsymbol{V}_n = \boldsymbol{I}$, the Cook's distance simplifies (see Remark 9.23) to

$$COOKD_i = \frac{e_i^2 h_i[n - \rho(\boldsymbol{X}_n)]}{(1-h_i)^2\rho(\boldsymbol{X}_n)R^2_{0_n}} = \frac{r_i^2}{\rho(\boldsymbol{X}_n)} \cdot \left(\frac{h_i}{1-h_i}\right),$$

which is similar to (5.19).

A key assumption for the computation of these diagnostics is that the matrix $\boldsymbol{V}_n$ is known. If it is estimated, as discussed in Chapter 8, exclusion of observations alters the estimator of $\boldsymbol{V}_n$ also. If the estimator of $\boldsymbol{V}_n$ based on the complete data is used in the above formulae, the resulting diagnostics would only be approximations.

A nice interpretation of the above diagnostic measures can be given in terms of a well-known result. Note that the vector $\boldsymbol{w}_l$ introduced in Section 9.1.2 is the prediction error for the BLUP of $\boldsymbol{y}_l$ in terms of $\boldsymbol{y}_m$ (see Remark 9.5). The BLUP itself is $\boldsymbol{y}_l - \boldsymbol{w}_l$. Let $\boldsymbol{y}_{n(-I_l)} = (\boldsymbol{y}_m' : (\boldsymbol{y}_l - \boldsymbol{w}_l)')'$, and $\mathcal{M}_{n(-I_l)}$ be the model $(\boldsymbol{y}_{n(-I_l)}, \boldsymbol{X}_n\boldsymbol{\beta}_n, \sigma^2\boldsymbol{V}_n)$. This is a data-augmented version of the model $\mathcal{M}_m$. It is easy to see that the recursive residual described in Proposition 9.3 reduces to zero in this case. Consequently the BLUEs of $\mathcal{M}_{n(-I_l)}$, their dispersions and the error sum of squares coincide with those of the model $\mathcal{M}_m$. This fact is a confirmation of the intuitively reasonable idea that if one predicts a few observations on the basis of a linear model, and pretends as if the predicted values are actual data, then the estimators of the parameters of the model are not altered by taking into account these additional 'data'. If the BLUE of $\boldsymbol{X}_n\boldsymbol{\beta}$ in the model $\mathcal{M}_n$ is written as $\boldsymbol{B}_n\boldsymbol{y}_n$, then the above discussion implies that $\boldsymbol{B}_n\boldsymbol{y}_{n(-I_l)} = \boldsymbol{X}_n\widehat{\boldsymbol{\beta}}_m$. Consequently

$$\boldsymbol{X}_n\widehat{\boldsymbol{\beta}}_m = \boldsymbol{X}_n\widehat{\boldsymbol{\beta}}_n - \boldsymbol{B}_n \begin{pmatrix} \mathbf{0} \\ \boldsymbol{w}_l \end{pmatrix}. \tag{9.28}$$

This update formula is strikingly simple. The reason for its simplicity is that, unlike the propositions of Sections 9.1.3 and 9.2.3, this device makes no attempt to use the summary statistics of $\mathcal{M}_m$ or $\mathcal{M}_n$ exclusively. Specifically, the matrix $\boldsymbol{B}_n$ is an attribute of $\mathcal{M}_n$, while $\boldsymbol{w}_l$ is computed on the basis of $\mathcal{M}_m$. Therefore, (9.28) is not suitable for practical computation. Nevertheless, it provides an important interpretation of the update. Haslett (1999) proves this result in the case of nonsingular $\boldsymbol{V}_n$.

It follows from (9.28) that

$$DFBETAS_{I_l,p} = \frac{\boldsymbol{p}'\boldsymbol{X}_n^-\boldsymbol{B}_n \begin{pmatrix} \mathbf{0} \\ \boldsymbol{w}_l \end{pmatrix}}{[(\widehat{\sigma}^2_{(-I_l)}/\sigma^2)Var(\boldsymbol{p}'\widehat{\boldsymbol{\beta}}_n)]^{1/2}},$$

where $\widehat{\sigma}^2_{(-I_l)}$ is given by (9.26) or as

$$\sigma^2_{(-I_l)} = \frac{R^2_{0_n} - \sigma^2\boldsymbol{w}_l'[D(\boldsymbol{w}_l)]^-\boldsymbol{w}_l}{\rho(\boldsymbol{X}_m : \boldsymbol{V}_m) - \rho(\boldsymbol{X}_m)}.$$

Cook's distance also has the simple representation

$$COOKD_{I_l} = \frac{\sigma^2(\mathbf{0} : \boldsymbol{w}_l')\boldsymbol{B}_n'[D(\boldsymbol{X}_n\widehat{\boldsymbol{\beta}}_n)]^-\boldsymbol{B}_n \begin{pmatrix} \mathbf{0} \\ \boldsymbol{w}_l \end{pmatrix}}{\widehat{\sigma}^2_n\rho(\boldsymbol{X}_n)}.$$

9.2.5 *Missing plot substitution*

Missing observations sometimes create problems in designed experiments. The BLUEs and various sums of squares of interest in a designed experiment often have closed form and simple expressions owing to the special structure of the design matrix. Even a single missing observation may render the standard computational formulae useless, typically by turning a balanced set-up into an unbalanced one.

One of the methods of dealing with this problem is missing plot substitution, which was introduced in Section 6.3.4. The idea is to proceed with the algebra, pretending as if all the data are available, and then to minimize the 'error sum of squares' with respect to the missing observation(s).

To see why this should work, let us assume for the time being that the requisite parameters remain estimable even with the missing observation(s). Consider the update equation of R_0^2 in Proposition 9.8. It is clear that $R_{0_n}^2 \geq R_{0_m}^2$, and that the equality is achieved if and only if the recursive residual, $\boldsymbol{w}_l$, is $\boldsymbol{0}$. Thus, the error sum of squares is minimized when $\boldsymbol{y}_l$ happens to be equal to its BLUP computed on the basis of the rest of the data. It was explained on page 481 why the substitution of $\boldsymbol{y}_l$ by its BLUP amounts to estimating the parameters from the depleted model. It is clear that the BLUEs, their dispersions and R_0^2 for $\mathcal{M}_m$ would be properly computed from the full model with the substituted 'data'. The appropriate number of degrees of freedom associated with R_0^2 would however be $\rho(\boldsymbol{V}_m : \boldsymbol{X}_m) - \rho(\boldsymbol{X}_m)$ (rather than $\rho(\boldsymbol{V}_n : \boldsymbol{X}_n) - \rho(\boldsymbol{X}_n)$).

These substituted values of the missing observations should not be used for computing R_H^2. It can be shown that this substitution makes R_H^2 larger than what it should be (see Kshirsagar, 1983). The appropriate R_H^2 is obtained from the full model with another substitution: by replacing the missing observations by their BLUP in terms of the available data, *subject to the appropriate linear restriction* (see Exercise 9.19). Since this substitution minimizes the R_H^2 of the full model with respect to the missing observations, any other substitution (such as the unrestricted BLUP) may result in an inflated R_H^2. The number of degrees of freedom associated with the appropriate R_H^2 is $\rho(\boldsymbol{V}_m : \boldsymbol{X}_m) - \rho(\boldsymbol{X}_m) + \rho(D(\boldsymbol{A}\widehat{\boldsymbol{\beta}}_m))$.

The missing plot substitution technique can be extended to the case where the missing observations render some LPFs non-estimable. Shah and Deo (1991) proved that the principle of substitution works when $\boldsymbol{V} = \boldsymbol{I}$. The following proposition gives a stronger result.

Proposition 9.25. *Let the models $\mathcal{M}_n$ and $\mathcal{M}_m$ be defined as in Section 9.1, with $\rho(\boldsymbol{X}_n)$ not necessarily equal to $\rho(\boldsymbol{X}_m)$.*

(a) The BLUEs of all estimable functions of $\mathcal{M}_m$ and their respective dispersions are the same as those obtained from $\mathcal{M}_n$, provided $\boldsymbol{y}_l$ assumes a value that minimizes $R^2_{0_n}$.
(b) The minimized value of $R^2_{0_n}$, described in part (a), is equal to $R^2_{0_m}$.
(c) The error sum of squares under the restriction $\boldsymbol{A\beta} = \boldsymbol{\xi}$, $R^2_{H_m}$, is equal to the minimized value of $R^2_{H_n}$ with respect to $\boldsymbol{y}_l$ under this restriction.

Proof. Let $\boldsymbol{w}_l$ be a vector of LZFs, which form a generating set of the LZFs of $\mathcal{M}_n$ that are uncorrelated to the LZFs of $\mathcal{M}_m$. Since $\rho(\boldsymbol{X}_m)$ is not necessarily equal to $\rho(\boldsymbol{X}_n)$, it is not possible to construct $\boldsymbol{w}_l$ by (9.4). In any case, $R^2_{0_n} = R^2_{0_m} + \boldsymbol{w}_l[D(\boldsymbol{w}_l)]^-\boldsymbol{w}_l$. We shall show that it is possible to choose $\boldsymbol{y}_l$ such that $\boldsymbol{w}_l$ is equal to zero with probability 1, which ensures $R^2_{0_n} = R^2_{0_m}$.

The BLUE of an estimable LPF of $\mathcal{M}_m$ is uncorrelated with every LZF of $\mathcal{M}_m$. The BLUE of this LPF under $\mathcal{M}_n$ is obtained by decorrelating the earlier BLUE from $\boldsymbol{w}_l$. The two BLUEs are related via an equation similar to the update formula of part (a) of Proposition 9.8, where $\boldsymbol{w}_l$ is as defined above. The two estimators would be identical if $\boldsymbol{w}_l = \boldsymbol{0}$.

Let $\boldsymbol{t}'\boldsymbol{y}_n$ be an LZF of $\mathcal{M}_n$ which is uncorrelated with all the LZFs of $\mathcal{M}_m$. In order to complete the proof of parts (a) and (b), we shall now show that any such LZF is identically zero with probability 1 if $\boldsymbol{y}_l$ assumes the value

$$\widehat{\boldsymbol{y}}_l = \boldsymbol{X}_l\boldsymbol{P}_{\boldsymbol{X}'_m}\widehat{\boldsymbol{\beta}}_m + \boldsymbol{V}'_{ml}\boldsymbol{V}^-_m(\boldsymbol{y}_m - \boldsymbol{X}_m\widehat{\boldsymbol{\beta}}_m). \tag{9.29}$$

According to part (a) of Proposition 7.3, there is a vector $\boldsymbol{k}$ such that $\boldsymbol{t}'\boldsymbol{y} = \boldsymbol{k}'\boldsymbol{y}$ almost surely and $\boldsymbol{X}'_n\boldsymbol{k} = \boldsymbol{0}$. Let us partition $\boldsymbol{k}$ as $(\boldsymbol{k}'_m : \boldsymbol{k}'_l)'$, conformably with $\boldsymbol{X}_n$. Then $\boldsymbol{t}'\boldsymbol{y} = \boldsymbol{k}'_m\boldsymbol{y}_m + \boldsymbol{k}'_l\boldsymbol{y}_l$ and $\boldsymbol{X}'_m\boldsymbol{k}_m + \boldsymbol{X}'_l\boldsymbol{k}_l = \boldsymbol{0}$. Since this LZF is uncorrelated with $(\boldsymbol{I} - \boldsymbol{P}_{\boldsymbol{X}_m})\boldsymbol{y}_m$ (i.e. with all the LZFs of $\mathcal{M}_m$), we have

$$\boldsymbol{0} = Cov\left(\boldsymbol{k}'_m\boldsymbol{y}_m + \boldsymbol{k}'_l\boldsymbol{y}_l, \left(\boldsymbol{I} - \boldsymbol{P}_{\boldsymbol{X}_m}\right)\boldsymbol{y}_m\right) = (\boldsymbol{k}'_m\boldsymbol{V}_m + \boldsymbol{k}'_l\boldsymbol{V}'_{ml})\left(\boldsymbol{I} - \boldsymbol{P}_{\boldsymbol{X}_m}\right).$$

Consequently

$$\begin{aligned}\boldsymbol{k}'_m\boldsymbol{y}_m + \boldsymbol{k}'_l\widehat{\boldsymbol{y}}_l &= \boldsymbol{k}'_m\boldsymbol{y}_m + \boldsymbol{k}'_l\boldsymbol{X}_l\boldsymbol{P}_{\boldsymbol{X}'_m}\widehat{\boldsymbol{\beta}}_m + \boldsymbol{k}'_l\boldsymbol{V}'_{ml}\boldsymbol{V}^-_m(\boldsymbol{y}_m - \boldsymbol{X}_m\widehat{\boldsymbol{\beta}}_m)\\ &= \boldsymbol{k}'_m(\boldsymbol{y}_m - \boldsymbol{X}_m\boldsymbol{P}_{\boldsymbol{X}'_m}\widehat{\boldsymbol{\beta}}_m) + \boldsymbol{k}'_l\boldsymbol{V}'_{ml}\boldsymbol{V}^-_m(\boldsymbol{y}_m - \boldsymbol{X}_m\widehat{\boldsymbol{\beta}}_m)\\ &= (\boldsymbol{k}'_m + \boldsymbol{k}'_l\boldsymbol{V}'_{ml}\boldsymbol{V}^-_m)(\boldsymbol{y}_m - \boldsymbol{X}_m\boldsymbol{\beta}_m).\end{aligned}$$

According to part (a) of Proposition 2.13) and part (b) of Proposition 7.15,

$$(\boldsymbol{y}_m - \boldsymbol{X}_m\widehat{\boldsymbol{\beta}}_m) \in \mathcal{C}(D(\boldsymbol{y}_m - \boldsymbol{X}_m\widehat{\boldsymbol{\beta}}_m)) = \mathcal{C}\left(\boldsymbol{V}_m\left(\boldsymbol{I} - \boldsymbol{P}_{X_m}\right)\right)$$

with probability 1. Thus, we can write $\boldsymbol{y}_m - \boldsymbol{X}_m\widehat{\boldsymbol{\beta}}_m$ almost surely as $\boldsymbol{V}_m(\boldsymbol{I} - \boldsymbol{P}_{X_m})\boldsymbol{u}$ for some vector $\boldsymbol{u}$. Substituting this in the expression of $\boldsymbol{k}_m'\boldsymbol{y}_m + \boldsymbol{k}_l'\widehat{\boldsymbol{y}}_l$, we have

$$\begin{aligned}
\boldsymbol{k}_m'\boldsymbol{y}_m + \boldsymbol{k}_l'\widehat{\boldsymbol{y}}_l &= (\boldsymbol{k}_m' + \boldsymbol{k}_l'\boldsymbol{V}_{ml}'\boldsymbol{V}_m^-)\boldsymbol{V}_m(\boldsymbol{I} - \boldsymbol{P}_{X_m})\boldsymbol{u} \\
&= (\boldsymbol{k}_m'\boldsymbol{V}_m + \boldsymbol{k}_l'\boldsymbol{V}_{ml}')(\boldsymbol{I} - \boldsymbol{P}_{X_m})\boldsymbol{u} \\
&= \boldsymbol{0}
\end{aligned}$$

with probability 1. This completes the proof of parts (a) and (b).

Part (c) is obtained by repeating the above argument for the linear model

$$\left(\begin{pmatrix}\boldsymbol{y}_n \\ \boldsymbol{\xi}\end{pmatrix}, \begin{pmatrix}\boldsymbol{X}_n \\ \boldsymbol{A}\end{pmatrix}\boldsymbol{\beta}, \ \sigma^2\begin{pmatrix}\boldsymbol{V} & \boldsymbol{0} \\ \boldsymbol{0} & \boldsymbol{0}\end{pmatrix}\right),$$

which is equivalent to the restricted model (see Section 7.9). □

9.3 Exclusion of explanatory variables

There are several reasons why we may wish to study the effect of dropping some explanatory variables from a model. The issue of reducing the number of explanatory variables often arises from the consideration of costs vis-a-vis their utility. Alternatively, the motivation may come from the consideration of collinearity and possible lack of precision of the estimators. If the purpose of a regression analysis is prediction or study of the differential impact of a single variable or a small set of variables, then the pruning of unnecessary explanatory variables may be useful.

In the present section and the next, we examine the connection between the models

$$\mathcal{M}_{(k)} = (\boldsymbol{y}, \boldsymbol{X}_{(k)}\boldsymbol{\beta}_{(k)}, \sigma^2\boldsymbol{V})$$

and

$$\mathcal{M}_{(h)} = (\boldsymbol{y}, \boldsymbol{X}_{(h)}\boldsymbol{\beta}_{(h)}, \sigma^2\boldsymbol{V}) \quad (k > h),$$

where the subscript within parentheses represents the number of *explanatory variables* in the model, and

$$\boldsymbol{X}_{(k)} = (\boldsymbol{X}_{(h)} : \boldsymbol{X}_{(j)}), \qquad \boldsymbol{\beta}_{(k)} = \begin{pmatrix}\boldsymbol{\beta}_{(h)} \\ \boldsymbol{\beta}_{(j)}\end{pmatrix}.$$

We shall refer to $\mathcal{M}_{(k)}$ as the *larger model*, and to $\mathcal{M}_{(h)}$ as the *smaller model*.

The model $\mathcal{M}_{(h)}$ can be viewed as a restricted version of the model $\mathcal{M}_{(k)}$, where the restriction is $\boldsymbol{\beta}_{(j)} = \mathbf{0}$. When we dealt with a general linear restriction, we had to *construct* an equivalent unrestricted model. No such exercise is needed here, because we already *have* a simple unrestricted model, $\mathcal{M}_{(h)}$. We shall be able to use the results derived earlier in the general case, and shall gain further insight by exploiting the simplicity of this special case.

For the consistency of the smaller model with the data, $(\boldsymbol{I}-\boldsymbol{P}_V)\boldsymbol{y}$ must belong to $\mathcal{C}((\boldsymbol{I}-\boldsymbol{P}_V)\boldsymbol{X}_{(h)})$. (This is a simplified version of the consistency condition for a general linear restriction, given in (7.15).) We assume that this condition holds. It follows that the data is consistent with the larger model as well.

Here we consider the transition from the larger to the smaller model ($\mathcal{M}_{(k)}$ to $\mathcal{M}_{(h)}$). Analysis of the reverse transition will be the subject of Section 9.4.

9.3.1 *A simple case*

Let $\boldsymbol{V} = \boldsymbol{I}$ and $h = k - 1$. We partition $\boldsymbol{X}_{(k)}$ as $(\boldsymbol{X}_{(k-1)} : \boldsymbol{x}_{(k)})$ and $\boldsymbol{\beta}_{(k)}$ as $(\boldsymbol{\beta}'_{(k-1)} : \beta_{(k)})'$. A standardized basis of LZFs in $\mathcal{M}_{(k)}$ contains $n-\rho(\boldsymbol{X}_{(k)})$ elements. Since $\mathcal{C}(\boldsymbol{X}_{(k-1)}) \subset \mathcal{C}(\boldsymbol{X}_{(k)})$, this number may increase by 1 or remain the same when an explanatory variable is dropped. The case when there is no change corresponds to $\rho(\boldsymbol{X}_{(k-1)}) = \rho(\boldsymbol{X}_{(k)})$, i.e. $\boldsymbol{x}_{(k)} \in \mathcal{C}(\boldsymbol{X}_{(k-1)})$, which amounts to a reparametrization. We now assume that $\boldsymbol{x}_{(k)} \notin \mathcal{C}(\boldsymbol{X}_{(k-1)})$, i.e. $\rho(\boldsymbol{X}_{(k-1)}) = \rho(\boldsymbol{X}_{(k)}) - 1$. This means a standardized basis set of LZFs of the smaller model can be obtained by extending a basis set of LZFs of the larger model by a single LZF that is uncorrelated with the LZFs of the larger model. Proposition 7.41 indicates that a choice of this additional LZF is an appropriately scaled version of

$$\nu = \widehat{\beta}_{(k)}, \tag{9.30}$$

which is already decorrelated from the LZFs of the larger model. Indeed, ν is a BLUE in $\mathcal{M}_{(k)}$ and an LZF in $\mathcal{M}_{(k-1)}$. Clearly $Var(\nu) > 0$. Therefore, ν can be used as a pivot for obtaining the update equations. The detailed equations are given in the next proposition. In order to distinguish between the least squares estimators under the two models, we use a 'tilde' for the estimators under the smaller model and the usual 'hat' for those under the larger model.

Proposition 9.26. *Under the above set-up, let* $\rho(\boldsymbol{X}_{(k-1)}) = \rho(\boldsymbol{X}_{(k)}) - 1$ *and* $\boldsymbol{A\beta}_{(k-1)}$ *be estimable under the larger model. Further, let*

$$\boldsymbol{a} = \boldsymbol{B}(\boldsymbol{X}'_{(k)}\boldsymbol{X}_{(k)})^{-}\begin{pmatrix}\boldsymbol{0}\\1\end{pmatrix},$$

$$c = (\boldsymbol{0}:1)(\boldsymbol{X}'_{(k)}\boldsymbol{X}_{(k)})^{-}\begin{pmatrix}\boldsymbol{0}\\1\end{pmatrix},$$

$$\boldsymbol{K} = \boldsymbol{B}(\boldsymbol{X}'_{(k)}\boldsymbol{X}_{(k)})^{-}\boldsymbol{B}', \quad \textit{where } \boldsymbol{B} = (\boldsymbol{A}:\boldsymbol{0}).$$

Then

(a) $\boldsymbol{A}\widetilde{\boldsymbol{\beta}}_{(k-1)} = \boldsymbol{A}\widehat{\boldsymbol{\beta}}_{(k-1)} - \boldsymbol{a}\nu/c$.
(b) $D(\boldsymbol{A}\widetilde{\boldsymbol{\beta}}_{(k-1)}) = D(\boldsymbol{A}\widehat{\boldsymbol{\beta}}_{(k-1)}) - \sigma^2\boldsymbol{aa}'/c$.
(c) $R^2_{0_{(k-1)}} = R^2_{0_{(k)}} + \nu^2/c$.
(d) *The change in* R^2_H *corresponding to the restriction* $\boldsymbol{A\beta}_{(k-1)} = \boldsymbol{\xi}$ *is* $R^2_{H_{(k-1)}} = R^2_{H_{(k)}} + \sigma^2\nu_*^2/Var(\nu_*)$, *where* $\nu_* = \nu - \boldsymbol{a}'\boldsymbol{K}^{-}(\boldsymbol{A}\widehat{\boldsymbol{\beta}}_{(k-1)} - \boldsymbol{\xi})$ *and* $\sigma^{-2}Var(\nu_*) = c - \boldsymbol{a}'\boldsymbol{K}^{-}\boldsymbol{a}$.
(e) *The degrees of freedom of* R_0^2 *and* R^2_H *increase by 1 with the exclusion of the explanatory variables.* □

Proof. It can be shown along the lines of the proof of Proposition 9.1 that

$$\boldsymbol{A}\widetilde{\boldsymbol{\beta}}_{(k-1)} = \boldsymbol{A}\widehat{\boldsymbol{\beta}}_{(k-1)} - Cov(\boldsymbol{A}\widehat{\boldsymbol{\beta}}_{(k-1)}, \nu)\nu/Var(\nu),$$

$$D(\boldsymbol{A}\widetilde{\boldsymbol{\beta}}_{(k-1)}) = D(\boldsymbol{A}\widehat{\boldsymbol{\beta}}_{(k-1)}) - Cov(\boldsymbol{A}\widehat{\boldsymbol{\beta}}_{(k-1)}, \nu)Cov(\nu, \boldsymbol{A}\widehat{\boldsymbol{\beta}}_{(k-1)})/Var(\nu),$$

$$R^2_{0_{(k-1)}} = R^2_{0_{(k)}} + \sigma^2\nu^2/Var(\nu),$$

where ν is as in (9.30). The statements (a)–(c) are obtained by simplifying these expressions. A pivot for changes under the restriction $\boldsymbol{A\beta}_{(k-1)} = \boldsymbol{\xi}$ is obtained by decorrelating ν from $\boldsymbol{A}\widehat{\boldsymbol{\beta}}_{(k-1)}$. Thus we have the LZF

$$\nu_* = \nu - Cov(\nu, \boldsymbol{A}\widehat{\boldsymbol{\beta}}_{(k-1)})[D(\boldsymbol{A}\widehat{\boldsymbol{\beta}}_{(k-1)})]^{-}(\boldsymbol{A}\widehat{\boldsymbol{\beta}}_{(k-1)} - \boldsymbol{\xi}).$$

Consequently we have the result of part (d). The proof of part (e) is left as an exercise. □

9.3.2 *General case: linear zero functions gained*

According to Proposition 7.40, every LZF in the larger model is an LZF in the smaller model. A standardized basis of LZFs for the model with k parameters contains $\rho(\boldsymbol{X}_{(k)} : \boldsymbol{V}) - \rho(\boldsymbol{X}_{(k)})$ LZFs (see Proposition 7.19). If this set is extended to a standardized basis for the smaller model, then the number of uncorrelated LZFs exclusive to the smaller model is $j_* = \rho(\boldsymbol{X}_{(h)} : \boldsymbol{V}) - \rho(\boldsymbol{X}_{(k)} : \boldsymbol{V}) - \rho(\boldsymbol{X}_{(h)}) + \rho(\boldsymbol{X}_{(k)})$. It is clear that $0 \le j_* \le \rho(\boldsymbol{X}_{(j)})$.

We first show that the above expression for j_* can be simplified to $\rho(\boldsymbol{X}_{(k)}) - \rho(\boldsymbol{X}_{(h)})$, if we dispose of a pathological special case. Suppose $\boldsymbol{x}$ is an explanatory variable exclusive to the larger model which is not in $\mathcal{C}(\boldsymbol{X}_{(h)} : \boldsymbol{V})$. Then $\boldsymbol{l} = (\boldsymbol{I} - \boldsymbol{P}_{X_{(h)}:V})\boldsymbol{x}$ must be a nontrivial vector. Consistency of the smaller model dictates that $\boldsymbol{l}'\boldsymbol{y} = 0$ with probability 1, while that of the larger model requires $\boldsymbol{l}'\boldsymbol{y} = (\boldsymbol{l}'\boldsymbol{x})\beta = \|\boldsymbol{l}\|^2\beta$, β being the coefficient of $\boldsymbol{x}$ in the larger model. These two conditions hold simultaneously only if β is identically zero, that is, $\boldsymbol{x}$ is *useless* as an explanatory variable. *We now assume that there is no useless explanatory variable in the larger model, i.e.* $\rho(\boldsymbol{X}_{(k)} : \boldsymbol{V}) = \rho(\boldsymbol{X}_{(h)} : \boldsymbol{V})$. Consequently $j_* = \rho(\boldsymbol{X}_{(k)}) - \rho(\boldsymbol{X}_{(h)})$.

Another trivial case occurs when $j_* = 0$. Under this condition, the explanatory variables exclusive to the larger model are *redundant* in the presence of the other explanatory variables, so that the two models are reparametrizations of one another. The various statistics of interest under the two models are essentially the same. *The case of real interest is* $0 < j_* \le \rho(\boldsymbol{X}_{(j)})$.

Recall that j_* is the maximum number of uncorrelated LZFs in the smaller model that are uncorrelated with all the LZFs in the larger model. A vector of LZFs having this property must be a BLUE in the larger model. In contrast to the simple case considered in Section 9.3.1, we cannot use Proposition 7.41 to get hold of these BLUE-turned-LZFs, because $\boldsymbol{\beta}_{(j)}$ may not be estimable. The following result provides an adequate set of such linear functions.

Proposition 9.27. *The linear function* $\boldsymbol{\nu} = (\boldsymbol{I} - \boldsymbol{P}_{X_{(h)}})\boldsymbol{X}_{(j)}\widehat{\boldsymbol{\beta}}_{(j)}$, *is a vector of BLUEs in the model* $\mathcal{M}_{(k)}$ *and a vector of LZFs in the model* $\mathcal{M}_{(h)}$. *Further,* $\rho(D(\boldsymbol{\nu})) = j_*$.

Proof. The parametric function $(\boldsymbol{I} - \boldsymbol{P}_{X_{(h)}})\boldsymbol{X}_{(k)}\boldsymbol{\beta}_{(k)}$ is estimable in the larger model. The BLUE of this function is $\boldsymbol{\nu}$. It is easy to see that $E(\boldsymbol{\nu}) = \boldsymbol{0}$ under the smaller model. Since the column space of $D(\boldsymbol{X}_{(k)}\widehat{\boldsymbol{\beta}}_{(k)})$ is $\mathcal{C}(\boldsymbol{X}_{(k)}) \cap \mathcal{C}(\boldsymbol{V})$ (see part (a) of Proposition 7.15), that of $D(\boldsymbol{\nu})$ must be $\mathcal{C}\left(\left(\boldsymbol{I} - \boldsymbol{P}_{X_{(h)}}\right)\boldsymbol{X}_{(k)}\right) \cap \mathcal{C}((\boldsymbol{I} - \boldsymbol{P}_{X_{(h)}})\boldsymbol{V})$. Note that

$$\mathcal{C}\left(\left(\boldsymbol{I} - \boldsymbol{P}_{X_{(h)}}\right)\boldsymbol{X}_{(k)}\right) \subseteq \mathcal{C}\left(\left(\boldsymbol{I} - \boldsymbol{P}_{X_{(h)}}\right)(\boldsymbol{X}_{(k)} : \boldsymbol{V})\right)$$
$$= \mathcal{C}\left(\left(\boldsymbol{I} - \boldsymbol{P}_{X_{(h)}}\right)(\boldsymbol{X}_{(h)} : \boldsymbol{V})\right) = \mathcal{C}\left(\left(\boldsymbol{I} - \boldsymbol{P}_{X_{(h)}}\right)\boldsymbol{V}\right).$$

Hence, $\mathcal{C}(D(\boldsymbol{\nu})) = \mathcal{C}((\boldsymbol{I} - \boldsymbol{P}_{X_{(h)}})\boldsymbol{X}_{(k)})$. Consequently $\rho(D(\boldsymbol{\nu})) = \rho((\boldsymbol{I} - \boldsymbol{P}_{X_{(h)}})\boldsymbol{X}_{(k)}) = j_*$. □

It is easy to see that the quantity $\boldsymbol{\nu}$ introduced in the above proposition is just a special case of $\boldsymbol{A}\widehat{\boldsymbol{\beta}} - \boldsymbol{\xi}$ with $\boldsymbol{A} = (\boldsymbol{I} - \boldsymbol{P}_{X_{(h)}})\boldsymbol{X}_{(k)}$ and $\boldsymbol{\xi} = \boldsymbol{0}$. Thus, we have finally found an equivalent linear restriction that would serve the purpose. It is essentially the 'testable part' of the generally untestable restriction $\boldsymbol{\beta}_{(j)} = \boldsymbol{0}$ (see Exercise 9.9).

9.3.3 *General case: update equations*

Before trying to find update formulae for BLUEs, let us examine if all LPFs can be meaningfully updated. If we think of the smaller model as a restricted model, then Proposition 3.52 says that *all* LPFs which are estimable under the larger model are estimable under the smaller model. (While estimating such an LPF from the smaller model, we can formally use the restriction $\boldsymbol{\beta}_{(j)} = \boldsymbol{0}$.) However, our present interest lies in the linear functions of $\boldsymbol{\beta}_{(h)}$. Note that the only functions of $\boldsymbol{\beta}_{(h)}$ that are estimable under the larger model are linear combinations of $(\boldsymbol{I} - \boldsymbol{P}_{X_{(j)}})\boldsymbol{X}_{(h)}\boldsymbol{\beta}_{(h)}$. The estimable functions in the smaller model are linear combinations of $\boldsymbol{X}_{(h)}\boldsymbol{\beta}_{(h)}$. Therefore, the estimable functions of $\boldsymbol{\beta}_{(h)}$ in the larger model are estimable under the smaller model, but the converse is not true in general. The rank of $(\boldsymbol{I} - \boldsymbol{P}_{X_{(j)}})\boldsymbol{X}_{(h)}$ is j_*, the maximum number of uncorrelated LZFs which are exclusive to the smaller model. Hence, a necessary and sufficient condition for all the estimable functions in the *smaller* model to be estimable under the larger model is that $j_* = \rho(\boldsymbol{X}_{(j)})$. (In such a case $\boldsymbol{X}_{(h)}\boldsymbol{\beta}_{(h)}$ and $\boldsymbol{X}_{(j)}\boldsymbol{\beta}_{(j)}$ are both estimable under the larger model.)

Even if $0 < j_* < \rho(\boldsymbol{X}_{(j)})$, there may be *some* functions of $\boldsymbol{\beta}_{(h)}$ that are estimable under both the models. We now proceed to obtain the update of the BLUE of such a function when the last j explanatory variables are dropped from the larger model. Once again, we use a 'tilde' for the estimators under the smaller model and a 'hat' for those under the larger model.

The results given below follow along the lines of Proposition 9.8.

Proposition 9.28. *Let $\boldsymbol{A}\boldsymbol{\beta}_{(h)}$ be estimable under the larger model. Then*

(a) $\boldsymbol{A}\widetilde{\boldsymbol{\beta}}_{(h)} = \boldsymbol{A}\widehat{\boldsymbol{\beta}}_{(h)} - Cov(\boldsymbol{A}\widehat{\boldsymbol{\beta}}_{(h)}, \boldsymbol{\nu})[D(\boldsymbol{\nu})]^{-}\boldsymbol{\nu}$, *where* $\boldsymbol{\nu} = (\boldsymbol{I} - \boldsymbol{P}_{X_{(h)}})\boldsymbol{X}_{(j)}\widehat{\boldsymbol{\beta}}_{(j)}$.

(b) $D(\boldsymbol{A}\widetilde{\boldsymbol{\beta}}_{(h)}) = D(\boldsymbol{A}\widehat{\boldsymbol{\beta}}_{(h)}) - Cov(\boldsymbol{A}\widehat{\boldsymbol{\beta}}_{(h)}, \boldsymbol{\nu})[D(\boldsymbol{\nu})]^{-}Cov(\boldsymbol{\nu}, \boldsymbol{A}\widehat{\boldsymbol{\beta}}_{(h)})$.

(c) $R^2_{0_{(h)}} = R^2_{0_{(k)}} + \boldsymbol{\nu}'[\sigma^{-2}D(\boldsymbol{\nu})]^-\boldsymbol{\nu}$.

(d) The change in R^2_H *corresponding to the hypothesis* $\boldsymbol{A\beta}_{(h)} = \boldsymbol{\xi}$ *is* $R^2_{H_{(h)}} = R^2_{H_{(k)}} + \boldsymbol{\nu}'_*[\sigma^{-2}D(\boldsymbol{\nu}_*)]^-\boldsymbol{\nu}_*$, *where*

$$\boldsymbol{\nu}_* = \boldsymbol{\nu} - Cov(\boldsymbol{\nu}, \boldsymbol{A}\widehat{\boldsymbol{\beta}}_{(h)})[D(\boldsymbol{A}\widehat{\boldsymbol{\beta}}_{(h)})]^-(\boldsymbol{A}\widehat{\boldsymbol{\beta}}_{(h)} - \boldsymbol{\xi}).$$

(e) As a result of exclusion of the explanatory variables, the degrees of freedom of R^2_0 *and* R^2_H *increase by* j_* *and* $\rho(D(\boldsymbol{\nu}_*))$, *respectively.* □

Remark 9.29. vector $\boldsymbol{\nu}_*$ is the BLUE of $(\boldsymbol{I} - \boldsymbol{P}_{X_{(h)}})\boldsymbol{X}_{(j)}\boldsymbol{\beta}_{(j)}$ in the larger model under the restriction $\boldsymbol{A\beta}_{(h)} = \boldsymbol{\xi}$. □

Remark 9.30. Depending on the special case at hand, one may use a different form of $\boldsymbol{\nu}$ that would have the requisite properties. For instance, if $j_* = \rho(\boldsymbol{X}_{(j)})$, it can be chosen as $\boldsymbol{X}_{(j)}\widehat{\boldsymbol{\beta}}_{(j)}$. If $j_* = j$, $\boldsymbol{\nu}$ can be chosen as $\widehat{\boldsymbol{\beta}}_{(j)}$. □

Remark 9.31. If $\boldsymbol{\beta}_{(k)}$ is entirely estimable under the original model, we have

$$\widetilde{\boldsymbol{\beta}}_{(h)} = \widehat{\boldsymbol{\beta}}_{(h)} - Cov(\widehat{\boldsymbol{\beta}}_{(h)}, \widehat{\boldsymbol{\beta}}_{(j)})[D(\widehat{\boldsymbol{\beta}}_{(j)})]^-\widehat{\boldsymbol{\beta}}_{(j)},$$
$$D(\widetilde{\boldsymbol{\beta}}_{(h)}) = D(\widehat{\boldsymbol{\beta}}_{(h)}) - Cov(\widehat{\boldsymbol{\beta}}_{(h)}, \widehat{\boldsymbol{\beta}}_{(j)})[D(\widehat{\boldsymbol{\beta}}_{(j)})]^-Cov(\widehat{\boldsymbol{\beta}}_{(h)}, \widehat{\boldsymbol{\beta}}_{(j)})'.$$

These updates only involve $\widehat{\boldsymbol{\beta}}_{(k)}$ and its dispersion. □

Bhimasankaram and Jammalamadaka (1994b) give the update formulae for the exclusion of a single explanatory variable when $\boldsymbol{V}$ is nonsingular. These can be obtained as a special case of Proposition 9.28 after routine algebra.

9.3.4 *Consequences of omitted variables*

The BLUE-turned-LZF, $\boldsymbol{\nu}$, is the key quantity that controls the updates of the BLUEs and their dispersion. If the larger model is correct, part (a) of Proposition 9.28 implies that the bias of the estimator $\boldsymbol{A}\widetilde{\boldsymbol{\beta}}_{(h)}$ depends on the *mean* of $\boldsymbol{\nu}$ under the larger model. The bias is not substantial for a BLUE in the smaller model when the mean of $\boldsymbol{\nu}$ is small. Note that $E(\boldsymbol{\nu}) = (\boldsymbol{I} - \boldsymbol{P}_{X_{(h)}})\boldsymbol{X}_{(j)}\boldsymbol{\beta}_{(j)}$, and it can be small when $(\boldsymbol{I} - \boldsymbol{P}_{X_{(h)}})\boldsymbol{X}_{(j)}$ is a matrix with very small elements. This happens if the dropped columns of the model matrix are almost linear combinations of the columns that are retained, which is possible when there is collinearity. On the other hand, the reduction of the dispersion depends only on the *covariance* of

$A\widehat{\beta}_{(h)}$ with ν, which need not be small even if $E(\nu)$ is small. Thus, in the presence of collinearity involving the dropped columns, there is a possibility of reducing dispersion substantially without picking up too much bias. The trade-off between bias and variance in the case $V = I$ was considered in Section 5.1.1.

9.3.5 *Sequential linear restrictions*

We have already mentioned that deleting explanatory variables is equivalent to introducing linear restrictions. If there is a need to revise the statistical quantities of interest in view of a linear restriction of the form $A\beta = \xi$, the appropriate equations can easily be formed along the lines of Proposition 9.28. The main idea is to capture the 'testable part' of the restriction, and use the BLUE of the corresponding LPF under the unrestricted model as the key LZF in the restricted model. These recursions would enable one to incorporate several linear restrictions serially. Kala and Klaczynski (1988) and Pordzik (1992b) obtain the explicit algebraic formulae when V is nonsingular and only one restriction is incorporated at a time.

9.4 Inclusion of explanatory variables

We now consider the transition from the model $\mathcal{M}_{(h)} = (y, X_{(h)}\beta_{(h)}, \sigma^2 V)$ to the model $\mathcal{M}_{(k)} = (y, X_{(k)}\beta_{(k)}, \sigma^2 V)$ $(k > h)$, where $X_{(k)} = (X_{(h)} : X_{(j)})$, and $\beta_{(k)} = (\beta'_{(h)} : \beta_{(j)})'$. As in Section 9.3, we refer to $\mathcal{M}_{(k)}$ as the *larger model*, and to $\mathcal{M}_{(h)}$ as the *smaller model*.

9.4.1 *A simple case*

Let $V = I$ and $k = h+1$. We partition $X_{(h+1)}$ as $(X_{(h)} : x_{(h+1)})$ and $\beta_{(h+1)}$ as $(\beta'_{(k)} : \beta_{(h+1)})'$. The LZFs in the larger model are a subset of those in the smaller model. We show that the quantity

$$t = x'_{(h+1)}\left(I - P_{X_{(h)}}\right) y \qquad (9.31)$$

can be used as a pivot for the updates. It is easily seen that t is an LZF in $\mathcal{M}_{(h)}$. Since $(I - P_{X_{(h)}})x_{(h+1)} \in \mathcal{C}(X_{(h+1)})$, t is uncorrelated with $(I - P_{X_{(h+1)}})y$. Therefore, t is a BLUE in $\mathcal{M}_{(h+1)}$. We use t as a pivot for the updates. If $x_{(h+1)} \in \mathcal{C}(X_{(h)})$, then we only have a reparametrization, and the quantities of interest do not change. Assuming that $x_{(h+1)} \notin$

$\mathcal{C}(\boldsymbol{X}_{(h)})$, and using 'tilde' for the estimators under the smaller model and a 'hat' for those under the larger model, we have the updates given by the following proposition.

Proposition 9.32. *Under the above set-up, let* $\rho(\boldsymbol{X}_{(h+1)}) = \rho(\boldsymbol{X}_{(h)}) + 1$ *and* $\boldsymbol{A\beta}_{(h)}$ *be estimable under the larger model. Further, suppose* $\boldsymbol{a} = \boldsymbol{A}\boldsymbol{X}^-_{(h+1)}(\boldsymbol{I} - \boldsymbol{P}_{X_{(h)}})\boldsymbol{x}_{(h+1)}$ *where* $\boldsymbol{X}^-_{(h+1)}$ *is any g-inverse of* $\boldsymbol{X}_{(h+1)}$, $c = \boldsymbol{x}'_{(h+1)}(\boldsymbol{I} - \boldsymbol{P}_{X_{(h)}})\boldsymbol{x}_{(h+1)}$ *and* t *be as in (9.31). Then*

(a) $\widehat{\boldsymbol{A\beta}}_{(h)} = \widetilde{\boldsymbol{A\beta}}_{(h)} + \boldsymbol{a}t/c$.

(b) $D(\widehat{\boldsymbol{A\beta}}_{(h)}) = D(\widetilde{\boldsymbol{A\beta}}_{(h)}) + \sigma^2\boldsymbol{a}\boldsymbol{a}'/c$.

(c) $R^2_{0_{(h+1)}} = R^2_{0_{(h)}} - t^2/c$.

(d) $R^2_{H_{(h+1)}} = R^2_{H_{(h)}} - t^2_*/[c - \boldsymbol{a}'\{\sigma^{-2}D(\widetilde{\boldsymbol{A\beta}}_{(h)}) + c^{-1}\boldsymbol{a}\boldsymbol{a}'\}^-\boldsymbol{a}]$, *where*

$$t_* = t - \boldsymbol{a}'[\sigma^{-2}D(\widetilde{\boldsymbol{A\beta}}_{(h)}) + c^{-1}\boldsymbol{a}\boldsymbol{a}']^-(\widetilde{\boldsymbol{A\beta}}_{(h)} + \boldsymbol{a}t/c - \boldsymbol{\xi}).$$

(e) The degrees of freedom of R^2_0 *and* R^2_H *decrease by 1 with the exclusion of the explanatory variables.*

Proof. Since t given by (9.31) is an LZF of the smaller model and a BLUE in the larger model,

$$\widetilde{\boldsymbol{A\beta}}_{(h)} = \widehat{\boldsymbol{A\beta}}_{(h)} - Cov(\widehat{\boldsymbol{A\beta}}_{(h)}, t)t/Var(t).$$

Write $\widehat{\boldsymbol{A\beta}}_{(h)}$ as

$$\widehat{\boldsymbol{A\beta}}_{(h)} = \boldsymbol{A}\boldsymbol{X}^-_{(k)}[\boldsymbol{X}_{(k)}\widehat{\boldsymbol{\beta}}_{(k)}] = \boldsymbol{A}\boldsymbol{X}^-_{(k)}\boldsymbol{y} - \boldsymbol{A}\boldsymbol{X}^-_{(k)}[\boldsymbol{y} - \boldsymbol{X}_{(k)}\widehat{\boldsymbol{\beta}}_{(k)}],$$

where $k = h+1$. The second term is an LZF in the larger model and hence is uncorrelated with t. Therefore $Cov(\widehat{\boldsymbol{A\beta}}_{(h)}, t) = Cov(\boldsymbol{A}\boldsymbol{X}_{(k)}{}^-\boldsymbol{y},\, t)$, and we have

$$\widehat{\boldsymbol{A\beta}}_{(h)} = \widetilde{\boldsymbol{A\beta}}_{(h)} + Cov(\boldsymbol{A}\boldsymbol{X}^-_{(k)}\boldsymbol{y}, t)t/Var(t),$$

which after simplification leads to the expression given in part (a). The results of parts (b) and (c) follow from the basic expressions

$$D(\widehat{\boldsymbol{A\beta}}_{(h)}) = D(\widetilde{\boldsymbol{A\beta}}_{(h)}) + Cov(\boldsymbol{A}\boldsymbol{X}^-_{(k)}\boldsymbol{y}, t)Cov(\boldsymbol{A}\boldsymbol{X}^-_{(k)}\boldsymbol{y}, t)'/Var(t),$$
$$R^2_{0_{(k)}} = R^2_{0_{(h)}} - \sigma^2t^2/Var(t).$$

Decorrelation of t with $\widehat{\boldsymbol{A\beta}}_{(h)} - \boldsymbol{\xi}$ yields

$$t_* = t - Cov(t, \widehat{\boldsymbol{A\beta}}_{(h)})[D(\widehat{\boldsymbol{A\beta}}_{(h)})]^-(\widehat{\boldsymbol{A\beta}}_{(h)} - \boldsymbol{\xi}),$$

which simplifies to the form given in part (d), by virtue of the results of parts (a) and (b). The expression for $R^2_{H_{(h+1)}}$ follows immediately. Part (e) is a restatement of part (e) of Proposition 9.26. □

9.4.2 General case: linear zero functions lost

We now remove the assumptions $V = I$ and $k = h+1$. We need a pivot which can be computed in terms of the statistics of the smaller model. Such a vector is presented below.

Proposition 9.33. *A vector of LZFs in the smaller model that is also a BLUE in the larger model is*

$$t = X'_{(j)}\left(I - P_{X_{(h)}}\right)\left\{\left(I - P_{X_{(h)}}\right)V\left(I - P_{X_{(h)}}\right)\right\}^{-}\left(I - P_{X_{(h)}}\right)y. \tag{9.32}$$

Further, $\rho(D(t)) = j_*$.

Proof. It is clear that t is an LZF in the smaller model. Let $l'y$ be an LZF in the augmented model. In view of Proposition 7.3(b), we can conclude without loss of generality that $X'_{(j)}l = 0$ and $X'_{(h)}l = 0$. Writing l as $(I - P_{X_{(h)}})s$, we have, by virtue of Remark 7.9),

$$\begin{aligned} Cov(t, l'y) &= \sigma^2 X'_{(j)}\left(I - P_{X_{(h)}}\right)\left\{\left(I - P_{X_{(h)}}\right)V\left(I - P_{X_{(h)}}\right)\right\}^{-} \\ &\qquad \cdot\left(I - P_{X_{(h)}}\right)V\left(I - P_{X_{(h)}}\right)s \\ &= \sigma^2 X'_{(j)}\left(I - P_{X_{(h)}}\right)s = \sigma^2 X'_{(j)}l = 0. \end{aligned}$$

In the above we have used the fact that $\mathcal{C}(I - P_{X_{(h)}})X_{(j)})$ is a subset of $\mathcal{C}((I - P_{X_{(h)}})V)$ (identical to $\mathcal{C}((I - P_{X_{(h)}})V(I - P_{X_{(h)}})))$, which follows from the assumption $X_{(j)} \in \mathcal{C}(X_{(h)} : V)$. Being uncorrelated with all LZFs in the larger model, t must be a BLUE there. The rank condition follows from the fact that $\mathcal{C}(D(y - X_{(h)}\widetilde{\beta}_{(h)})) = \mathcal{C}(V(I - P_{X_{(h)}}))$ (see Proposition 7.15), which implies $\mathcal{C}(D(t)) = \mathcal{C}(X'_{(j)}(I - P_{X_{(h)}}))$. □

Remark 9.34. Recall that $\mathcal{C}(X_{(j)})$ is assumed to be a subset of $\mathcal{C}(X_{(h)} : V)$. If $X_{(j)} = X_{(h)}B + VC$, then t is the same as $C'y_{res}$, where y_{res} is the residual of y from the smaller model. (Specifically, $y_{res} = Ry$ where $R = V(I - P_{X_{(h)}})\{(I - P_{X_{(h)}})V(I - P_{X_{(h)}})\}^{-}(I - P_{X_{(h)}})$, as seen from Remark 7.9.) The vector t can also be interpreted as $X'_{(j)_{res}}V^{-}y_{res}$ where $X_{(j)_{res}} = RX_{(j)}$, the 'residual' of $X_{(j)}$ when regressed (one column at a time) on $X_{(h)}$. Similarly, $D(t)$ is the same as $\sigma^2 X'_{(j)_{res}}V^{-}X_{(j)_{res}}$. □

Remark 9.35. The expectations of ν and t, defined in Propositions 9.27 and 9.33, respectively, are linear functions of $\beta_{(j)}$. These linear parametric functions are estimable in the model $(y_{res}, X_{(j)_{res}}\beta_{(j)}, \sigma^2 W)$, where

$\boldsymbol{W} = \boldsymbol{RV}$. Moreover, $\boldsymbol{\nu}$ and $\boldsymbol{t}$ are BLUEs of the corresponding parametric functions in this 'residual' model, which is obtained from the original (larger) model by pre-multiplying both the systematic and error parts by $\boldsymbol{R}$ (see Exercise 9.11). See Exercise 9.10 for a direct relation between $\boldsymbol{\nu}$ and $\boldsymbol{t}$. □

Remark 9.36. When $\boldsymbol{V}$ is positive definite and a *single* explanatory variable is included, the BLUE of the coefficient of the new variable in the augmented model is proportional to the 'lost' LZF. In this special case the BLUE can be interpreted as the estimated (simple) regression coefficient in the 'residual' model. □

9.4.3 *General case: update equations*

We now provide the update relations for the larger model where the BLUE is denoted with a 'hat', in terms of the statistics of the smaller model, where the BLUE is denoted with a 'tilde'.

Proposition 9.37. *If $\boldsymbol{A\beta}_{(h)}$ is estimable under the larger model, then*

(a) $\boldsymbol{A}\widehat{\boldsymbol{\beta}}_{(h)} = \boldsymbol{A}\widetilde{\boldsymbol{\beta}}_{(h)} + Cov(\boldsymbol{A}\boldsymbol{X}_{(k)}^{-}\boldsymbol{y}, \boldsymbol{t})[D(\boldsymbol{t})]^{-}\boldsymbol{t}$, *where* $\boldsymbol{t}$ *is as in (9.32).*
(b) $D(\boldsymbol{A}\widehat{\boldsymbol{\beta}}_{(h)}) = D(\boldsymbol{A}\widetilde{\boldsymbol{\beta}}_{(h)}) + Cov(\boldsymbol{A}\boldsymbol{X}_{(k)}^{-}\boldsymbol{y}, \boldsymbol{t})[D(\boldsymbol{t})]^{-}Cov(\boldsymbol{t}, \boldsymbol{A}\boldsymbol{X}_{(k)}^{-}\boldsymbol{y})$.
(c) $R^2_{0_{(k)}} = R^2_{0_{(h)}} - \sigma^2\boldsymbol{t}'[D(\boldsymbol{t})]^{-}\boldsymbol{t}$.
(d) $R^2_{H_{(k)}} = R^2_{H_{(h)}} - \sigma^2\boldsymbol{t}_*'[D(\boldsymbol{t}_*)]^{-}\boldsymbol{t}_*$, *where*

$$\boldsymbol{t}_* = \boldsymbol{t} - Cov(\boldsymbol{t}, \boldsymbol{A}\widehat{\boldsymbol{\beta}}_{(h)})[D(\boldsymbol{A}\widehat{\boldsymbol{\beta}}_{(h)})]^{-}(\boldsymbol{A}\widehat{\boldsymbol{\beta}}_{(h)} - \boldsymbol{\xi}).$$

(e) The increase in the degrees of freedom of R_0^2 and R_H^2 with the exclusion of the explanatory variables are given by j_* and $\rho(D(\boldsymbol{t}_*))$, respectively.

Proof. Since $\boldsymbol{t}$ contains j_* uncorrelated LZFs of the current model that turn into BLUEs in the larger model,

$$\boldsymbol{A}\widetilde{\boldsymbol{\beta}}_{(h)} = \boldsymbol{A}\widehat{\boldsymbol{\beta}}_{(h)} - Cov(\boldsymbol{A}\widehat{\boldsymbol{\beta}}_{(h)}, \boldsymbol{t})[D(\boldsymbol{t})]^{-}\boldsymbol{t}.$$

Following the argument given in the proof of Proposition 9.32, we have $Cov(\boldsymbol{A}\widehat{\boldsymbol{\beta}}_{(h)}, \boldsymbol{t}) = Cov(\boldsymbol{A}\boldsymbol{X}_{(k)}{}^{-}\boldsymbol{y}, \boldsymbol{t})$. Parts (a), (b) and (c) follow immediately. Part (d) is proved by substituting the results of these three parts into (7.17). Part (e) is easy to prove. □

Remark 9.38. The vector $\boldsymbol{A}\boldsymbol{X}_{(k)}^{-}\boldsymbol{y}$ depends on the choice of the generalized inverse of $\boldsymbol{X}_{(k)}$, but its covariance with $\boldsymbol{t}$ does not. □

Remark 9.39. The vector $\boldsymbol{t}_*$ used in parts (d) and (e) may be expressed in terms of the statistics of the original model using parts (a) and (b). The expression simplifies to

$$\boldsymbol{t}_* = D(\boldsymbol{t})\Big[D(\boldsymbol{t}) + Cov(\boldsymbol{t}, \boldsymbol{A}\boldsymbol{X}_{(k)}{}^-\boldsymbol{y})[D(\boldsymbol{A}\widetilde{\boldsymbol{\beta}}_{(h)})]^- Cov(\boldsymbol{t}, \boldsymbol{A}\boldsymbol{X}_{(k)}{}^-\boldsymbol{y})'\Big]^- \cdot\Big[\boldsymbol{t} + Cov(\boldsymbol{t}, \boldsymbol{A}\boldsymbol{X}_{(k)}{}^-\boldsymbol{y})[D(\boldsymbol{A}\widetilde{\boldsymbol{\beta}}_{(h)})]^-(\boldsymbol{A}\widetilde{\boldsymbol{\beta}}_{(h)} - \boldsymbol{\xi})\Big]. \qquad \square$$

9.4.4 *Application to regression model building*

We have already come across the added variable plot or partial regression plot in Sections 3.11 and 5.3.1 (see pages 104 and 207) for examining the relevance of an additional explanatory variable in the homoscedastic linear model. Let us relate it with the foregoing developments.

Suppose $\boldsymbol{X}_{(h)}$ represents the columns of explanatory variables already present in the model, and $\boldsymbol{x}_{(j)}$ is the column of the additional explanatory variable. Let $\beta_{(j)}$ be the coefficient of $\boldsymbol{x}_{(j)}$ in the larger model. Remarks 9.35 and 9.36 imply that the whenever $\boldsymbol{V}$ is nonsingular, the BLUE of $\beta_{(j)}$ from the larger model is the same as its BLUE from the single-parameter linear model $(\boldsymbol{y}_{res}, \boldsymbol{x}_{(j)_{res}}\beta_{(j)}, \sigma^2\boldsymbol{V})$, where $\boldsymbol{y}_{res}$ is the vector of residuals from the model $(\boldsymbol{y}, \boldsymbol{X}_{(h)}\boldsymbol{\beta}_{(h)}, \sigma^2\boldsymbol{V})$, and $\boldsymbol{x}_{(j)_{res}}\beta_{(j)}$ is the 'residual' from the model $(\boldsymbol{x}_{(j)}, \boldsymbol{X}_{(h)}\boldsymbol{\beta}_{(h)}, \sigma^2\boldsymbol{V})$. Indeed, these residuals are versions of $\boldsymbol{y}$ and $\boldsymbol{x}_{(j)}$, respectively, after they have been decorrelated from $\boldsymbol{X}_{(h)}$.

The BLUE of $\beta_{(j)}$ from the model $(\boldsymbol{y}_{res}, \boldsymbol{x}_{(j)_{res}}\beta_{(j)}, \sigma^2\boldsymbol{V})$ is the crucial LZF that controls the update terms of Section 9.4.3. If this BLUE is very small in comparison to its variance, its effect on the updates would be minimal. This fact is utilized in the homoscedastic case (i.e. when $\boldsymbol{V}$ is proportional to $\boldsymbol{I}$) by the added variable plot for the jth variable, which is the scatter plot of $\boldsymbol{y}_{res}$ against $\boldsymbol{x}_{(j)_{res}}$. The strength of their linear relationship is brought out by the p-value of the t-test for $\beta_{(j)} = 0$.

The matrix $\boldsymbol{V}$ may not be proportional to $\boldsymbol{I}$ if, e.g., the response has the intra-class correlation structure (Example 8.3) or serial correlation (Example 5.19). In such a case, one can modify the added variable plot by replacing $\boldsymbol{y}_{res}$ and $\boldsymbol{x}_{(j)_{res}}$ with $\boldsymbol{C}'\boldsymbol{y}_{res}$ and $\boldsymbol{C}'\boldsymbol{x}_{(j)_{res}}$, respectively, where $\boldsymbol{C}\boldsymbol{C}'$ is a rank-factorization of $\boldsymbol{V}^{-1}$.

9.5 Data exclusion and variable inclusion

There is a very interesting connection between the exclusion of observations from the homoscedastic linear model and inclusion of some special variables to it. The result has been known to some researchers for a long time (see e.g. Bartlett, 1937a; Schall and Dunne, 1988).

Consider the model $(\boldsymbol{y}, \boldsymbol{X\beta}, \sigma^2\boldsymbol{I})$. If we wish to drop the last l observations, then the corresponding updates are given in Proposition 9.22. This proposition uses a key LZF, $\boldsymbol{r}_l$, which is uncorrelated with all the LZFs of the depleted model. This LZF is lost when the observations are dropped. The expression for $\boldsymbol{r}_l$ (see (9.23)) reduces in the homoscedastic case to $\boldsymbol{e}_l$, the residuals of the last l observations.

If, instead of dropping l observations, we seek to include l explanatory variables (in the form of an $n \times l$ matrix $\boldsymbol{Z}$ concatenated to the columns of $\boldsymbol{X}$), then the appropriate 'lost' LZF is given by $\boldsymbol{t}_l$ (see (9.32)). This LZF reduces to $\boldsymbol{Ze}$ in the present case, $\boldsymbol{e}$ being the residual vector in the original model.

The key LZFs in the two cases would be identical if $\boldsymbol{Z}$ is chosen to be the last l columns of an $n \times n$ identity matrix. Since the LZFs are identical, all the updates would naturally be identical. Thus, the dropping of the observations is equivalent to the inclusion of the explanatory variables.

The following is an intuitive explanation of this remarkable connection. When $\boldsymbol{X}$ is replaced by $(\boldsymbol{X} : \boldsymbol{Z})$, we introduce l additional parameters. The above choice of $\boldsymbol{Z}$ ensures that each additional parameter contributes to the mean of exactly one observation. Thus, each of the last l observations can be exactly fitted with the help of the parameter which is exclusive to it. Therefore, the last few observations determine the BLUEs of the additional parameters. The remaining parameters are estimated by the remaining observations.

An application of this result in the analysis of unbalanced data in designed experiments (using the analysis of covariance model) was given in Section 6.3.4.

9.6 Complements/Exercises

Exercises with solutions given in Appendix C

9.1 Justify the interpretations given in Remark 9.2.

9.2 Show that the condition of case (c) of page 454 implies that the initial and augmented models are transformed versions of one another.

9.3 Given the set-up and notations of Proposition 9.8, show that $\boldsymbol{w}_{l*} = \boldsymbol{y}_l - \widetilde{\boldsymbol{y}}_l$, where $\widetilde{\boldsymbol{y}}_l$ is the BLUP of $\boldsymbol{y}_l$ from the model $\mathcal{M}_m$ subject to the restriction $\boldsymbol{A\beta} = \boldsymbol{\xi}$.

9.4 Consider the update problem of Section 9.1, and assume that the model errors are uncorrelated. Examine if the updates of a BLUE and its dispersion can be obtained as a special case of the Kalman filter equations (9.14)–(9.19). If this is possible, compare the equations with those of Section 9.1.3.

9.5 Suppose the sequence of response values $y_1, y_2, \ldots$ follow the model

$$y_t = \boldsymbol{\alpha}_t'\boldsymbol{\beta} + \varepsilon_t,$$
$$\varepsilon_t = \sum_{j=1}^{r} \phi_j \varepsilon_{t-j} + \delta_t + \sum_{j=1}^{r} \theta_j \delta_{t-j},$$

where $\phi_1, \ldots, \phi_r$ and $\theta_1, \ldots, \theta_r$ are known constants some of which may be zero, $\boldsymbol{\alpha}_1, \boldsymbol{\alpha}_2, \ldots$ are vectors of observed explanatory variables, $\boldsymbol{\beta}$ is an unknown vector parameter and $\delta_1, \delta_2, \ldots$ are uncorrelated errors with unknown variance σ^2. Note that this model fits into the usual $(\boldsymbol{y}, \boldsymbol{X\beta}, \sigma^2\boldsymbol{V})$ form, but the expression for $\boldsymbol{V}$ is quite complicated (see page 437). Show that this model can also be written in the state-space form (9.7)–(9.8) with $\boldsymbol{x}_t = (\boldsymbol{\beta}' : \varepsilon_t : v_{1,t} : \cdots : v_{r-1,t})'$ and $\boldsymbol{z}_t = y_t$, where

$$v_{k,t} = \sum_{j=1}^{r-k} \phi_{j+k}\varepsilon_{t-j} + \sum_{j=0}^{r-k} \theta_{j+k}\delta_{t-j}.$$

Identify the other components of the state-space model in this case. If the Kalman filter is used for estimating $\boldsymbol{\beta}$, what would be the update formulae? [Harvey and Phillips (1979) use the above formulation as a basis for estimation when the parameters $\phi_1, \ldots, \phi_r$ and $\theta_1, \ldots, \theta_r$ are unknown.]

9.6 Suppose the sequence of vectors $\boldsymbol{u}_t$ and $\boldsymbol{v}_t$, $t = 1, 2, \ldots$ and $\boldsymbol{x}_0$ in the state-space model (9.7)–(9.8) are independent and have normal distributions. Show that the predictors of the state vectors described by the Kalman filter (9.14)–(9.19) have the smallest mean squared error among all (possibly nonlinear) predictors based on the same information.

9.7 Show that whenever $\mathcal{C}(\boldsymbol{X}_l') \subseteq \mathcal{C}(\boldsymbol{X}_m')$, the LZF $\boldsymbol{r}_l$ defined in Proposition 9.21 is a linear function of $\boldsymbol{w}_l$. Is $\boldsymbol{w}_l$ necessarily a linear function of $\boldsymbol{r}_l$?

9.8 Prove part (e) of Proposition 9.26.

9.9 Show that the hypothesis $(\boldsymbol{I} - \boldsymbol{P}_{X_{(h)}})\boldsymbol{X}_{(k)}\boldsymbol{\beta}_{(k)} = \boldsymbol{0}$ in the model $\mathcal{M}_{(k)}$ of Section 9.3.2 is equivalent to the 'testable part' of the hypothesis $\boldsymbol{\beta}_{(j)} = \boldsymbol{0}$, as per Proposition 4.13.

9.10 Show that the random vectors $\boldsymbol{\nu}$ and $\boldsymbol{t}$ defined in Propositions 9.27 and 9.33, respectively, are related to one another as

$$\boldsymbol{\nu} = \left(\boldsymbol{I} - \boldsymbol{P}_{X_{(h)}}\right)\boldsymbol{X}_{(j)}[\sigma^{-2}D(\boldsymbol{t})]^{-}\boldsymbol{t},$$

$$\boldsymbol{t} = \boldsymbol{X}'_{(j)}\left(\boldsymbol{I} - \boldsymbol{P}_{X_{(h)}}\right)\left\{\left(\boldsymbol{I} - \boldsymbol{P}_{X_{(h)}}\right)\boldsymbol{V}\left(\boldsymbol{I} - \boldsymbol{P}_{X_{(h)}}\right)\right\}^{-}\boldsymbol{\nu}.$$

9.11 Prove the statements of Remark 9.35.

9.12 Given the two-way classified data model of (6.12), obtain a diagnostic to check which block is most influential to the computation of (a) error sum of squares, (b) between treatments sum of squares and (c) the GLRT for equivalence of treatments.

9.13 Describe how the various tests of hypotheses would change when a single observation is missing from the model of (6.29).

Additional exercises

9.14 Given the models $\mathcal{M}_m$ and $\mathcal{M}_n$ defined in Section 9.1 and the partition of (9.3), let $\rho(\boldsymbol{X}_n) - \rho(\boldsymbol{X}_m) = l_* = \rho(\boldsymbol{X}_n : \boldsymbol{V}_n) - \rho(\boldsymbol{X}_n) - \rho(\boldsymbol{X}_m : \boldsymbol{V}_m)$. Show that the BLUE of any LPF $\boldsymbol{A\beta}$ which is estimable in the model $\mathcal{M}_n$ is given by

$$\widehat{\boldsymbol{A\beta}}_n = \boldsymbol{L}_m\boldsymbol{X}_m\widehat{\boldsymbol{\beta}}_m + \boldsymbol{L}_l\boldsymbol{y}_l - \boldsymbol{L}_l\boldsymbol{V}_{lm}\boldsymbol{V}_m^{-}(\boldsymbol{y}_m - \boldsymbol{X}_m\widehat{\boldsymbol{\beta}}_m),$$

where $\boldsymbol{L}_m$ and $\boldsymbol{L}_l$ are such that $\boldsymbol{A} = (\boldsymbol{L}_m : \boldsymbol{L}_l)(\boldsymbol{X}'_m : \boldsymbol{X}'_l)'$. Derive a formula of the dispersion of this estimator.

9.15 Prove that whenever $h_i < 1$, the quantity $\widehat{\sigma^2}_{(-i)}$ used in (5.8) is equal to $[(n-r)\widehat{\sigma^2} - e_i^2/(1-h_i)]/(n-r-1)$, where r is the rank of $\boldsymbol{X}$.

9.16 Let r_i and t_i be the standardized and studentized residuals, defined by (5.7) and (5.8), respectively, for the ith observation in the linear model $(\boldsymbol{y}, \boldsymbol{X\beta}, \sigma^2\boldsymbol{I})$.

(a) Show that $r_i^2 \leq n - \rho(\boldsymbol{X})$. When does this result hold with equality?

(b) If $h_i < 1$, show that

$$t_i = r_i\left(\frac{n-\rho(\boldsymbol{X})-1}{n-\rho(\boldsymbol{X})-r_i^2}\right)^{1/2}.$$

Can r_i be written explicitly in terms of t_i?

(c) What happens when $h_i = 1$?

9.17 Let $\boldsymbol{u}_i$ be the ith column of the $n \times n$ identity matrix. Show that the uniformly most powerful test for the hypothesis $\mathcal{H}_0 : \gamma = 0$ in the model $(\boldsymbol{y}, \boldsymbol{X\beta} + \gamma\boldsymbol{u}_i, \sigma^2\boldsymbol{I})$, with n observations, leads to the test statistic t_i given by (5.8).

9.18 Obtain an expression for $COVRATIO_i$ in terms of the leverage (h_i) and the standardized residual (r_i). Also prove (5.21).

9.19 Consider the set-up of Section 9.1.3, and let $\boldsymbol{M}_n$ correspond to a designed experiment, while the observation $\boldsymbol{y}_l$ is missing. Assume that $\mathcal{C}(\boldsymbol{X}_m') = \mathcal{C}(\boldsymbol{X}_n')$, and let $\rho(\boldsymbol{X}_n : \boldsymbol{V}_n) - \rho(\boldsymbol{X}_m : \boldsymbol{V}_m) > 0$. Show that the restricted sum of squares $R^2_{H_m}$ for the linear hypothesis $\boldsymbol{A\beta} = \boldsymbol{\xi}$ is given by $R^2_{H_n}$ for the model $\mathcal{M}_n$ where $\boldsymbol{y}_l$ has been replaced by $\widetilde{\boldsymbol{y}}_l$, its BLUP from $\mathcal{M}_m$ under the restriction $\boldsymbol{A\beta} = \boldsymbol{\xi}$.

9.20 Find an expression for the change in the value of the coefficient of determination (see page 129) when a single observation is excluded from the model $(\boldsymbol{y}_n, \boldsymbol{X}_n\boldsymbol{\beta}_n, \sigma^2\boldsymbol{I}_n)$, and give a statistical interpretation of this quantity.

Chapter 10

Multivariate Linear Model

Suppose we wish to determine the efficacy of a new drug by observing n patients over a period of time. Consider the situation where the response of the ith patient ($i = 1, \ldots, n$) is measured via the value of the set of q variables $(y_{i1}, \ldots, y_{iq})$ which are quantitative measures of relief, observed at the different time points $1, \ldots, q$ after the treatment begins. As in typical regression, each response may depend on several explanatory variables such as the drug used (new or conventional), the age and gender of the patient etc. A linear model for such multivariate response can take the form

$$y_{ij} = \beta_{0j} + \sum_{l=1}^{p} \beta_{lj} x_{il} + \varepsilon_{ij}, \; i = 1, \ldots, n, \quad j = 1, \ldots, q.$$

Note that the coefficients of the explanatory variables in the above model depend on the time-point j, as the influence of these variables may depend on the time of measurement. The above model is of the form (1.3). However, the observations on a given patient at different time points may be correlated. The error variance for the various time points may also be different. Since these variances and covariances may not be known, the error model (1.5) with a known $\boldsymbol{V}$ will not be adequate.

Our goal in this chapter is to study the above linear model, commonly referred to as the "multivariate linear model", under suitable assumptions. After describing the general features of the model in Section 10.1, we discuss best linear unbiased estimation of the model coefficients and unbiased estimation of the error variances and covariances in Sections 10.2 and 10.3, respectively. In Section 10.4, we deal with maximum likelihood estimation of these parameters in the case of normally distributed errors. The effect of linear restrictions is discussed in Section 10.5. Sections 10.6 considers tests of linear hypotheses. Prediction and confidence regions are briefly discussed in Section 10.7. Section 10.8 provides some applications.

10.1 Description of the multivariate linear model

The general form of the multivariate linear model can be written as

$$\boldsymbol{Y} = \boldsymbol{X}\mathcal{B} + \mathcal{E}. \tag{10.1}$$

In the above equation $\boldsymbol{Y}_{n\times q}$ is the matrix of observations of the response variables, with each row representing a case (or observation set) and each column representing a characteristic or component of the response. The matrix $\boldsymbol{X}_{n\times k}$ is the observed matrix of the corresponding explanatory variables (as in the univariate response linear model considered earlier). The matrix $\mathcal{B}_{k\times q}$ contains the unspecified parameters, while the matrix $\mathcal{E}_{n\times q}$ contains the model errors. It is assumed that

$$E(\mathcal{E}) = \boldsymbol{0}, \qquad D(\text{vec}(\mathcal{E})) = \boldsymbol{\Sigma}_{q\times q} \otimes \boldsymbol{V}_{n\times n}.$$

We allow the matrices $\boldsymbol{\Sigma}$ and $\boldsymbol{V}$ involved in the Kronecker product to be singular. Typically the matrix $\boldsymbol{V}$ is assumed to be known and the matrix $\boldsymbol{\Sigma}$, unknown with specified rank. Clearly when $q = 1$, (10.1) reduces to the univariate linear model (1.4).

In the example mentioned at the beginning of the chapter, note that every row of $\boldsymbol{Y}$ and $\boldsymbol{X}$ correspond to a patient, every column of $\boldsymbol{Y}$ and $\mathcal{B}$ correspond to a particular time point and every column of $\boldsymbol{X}$ (and the corresponding row of $\mathcal{B}$) correspond to an explanatory variable or the intercept term. Assuming that the responses for the various patients are uncorrelated, we can define $\boldsymbol{V} = \boldsymbol{I}$. The variance-covariance matrix of the response for a particular patient (given the explanatory variables) is $\boldsymbol{\Sigma}$.

Using the result of Exercise A.29, we can rewrite the model (10.1) as

$$\text{vec}(\boldsymbol{Y}) = (\boldsymbol{I} \otimes \boldsymbol{X})\text{vec}(\mathcal{B}) + \text{vec}(\mathcal{E}), \quad E(\text{vec}(\mathcal{E})) = \boldsymbol{0}, \quad D(\text{vec}(\mathcal{E})) = \boldsymbol{\Sigma} \otimes \boldsymbol{V}. \tag{10.2}$$

When $\boldsymbol{\Sigma}$ is unknown, the linear model $(\text{vec}(\boldsymbol{Y}), (\boldsymbol{I} \otimes \boldsymbol{X})\text{vec}(\mathcal{B}), \boldsymbol{\Sigma} \otimes \boldsymbol{V})$ has a partially specified dispersion matrix, and hence it falls under the purview of Section 8.2. However, the special structure of the dispersion matrix in this case lends itself to a somewhat simpler analysis.

Note that we allow both $\boldsymbol{\Sigma}$ and $\boldsymbol{V}$ to be singular. The importance of the singular model in the case of univariate response was described in detail in Section 7.1. Those reasons are equally valid in the multivariate response case (see for instance Section 10.5). It follows from Proposition 2.13 that

$$\text{vec}(\mathcal{E}) \in \mathcal{C}(\boldsymbol{\Sigma} \otimes \boldsymbol{V}),$$

that is, *there is a matrix* $\boldsymbol{L}$ *such that* $\mathcal{E} = \boldsymbol{V}\boldsymbol{L}\boldsymbol{\Sigma}$ *with probability* 1. Hence,

$$\mathcal{C}((\boldsymbol{I} - \boldsymbol{P}_{X})\boldsymbol{Y}) \subset \mathcal{C}((\boldsymbol{I} - \boldsymbol{P}_{X})\boldsymbol{V}), \quad \text{and } \mathcal{C}(\boldsymbol{Y}'(\boldsymbol{I} - \boldsymbol{P}_{X})) \subset \mathcal{C}(\boldsymbol{\Sigma}),$$

with probability 1. These two conditions must be satisfied by the data. The first condition is equivalent to $\mathcal{C}((\boldsymbol{I}-\boldsymbol{P}_V)\boldsymbol{Y}) \subset \mathcal{C}((\boldsymbol{I}-\boldsymbol{P}_V)\boldsymbol{X})$ with probability 1. Even though $\boldsymbol{\Sigma}$ is unknown, the second condition is verifiable as long as $\mathcal{C}(\boldsymbol{\Sigma})$ is known (for example, from some restrictions giving rise to the singularity of $\boldsymbol{\Sigma}$).

10.2 Best linear unbiased estimation

As mentioned in the earlier Section 10.1, the model (10.1) can also be written in the form (10.2). Even though the dispersion matrix of (10.2) involves several unspecified parameters, much of the theory of Chapter 7 is directly applicable to this model. On the other hand, the inference problems for the multivariate linear model are posed with respect to model (10.1). Therefore, we shall have to move back and forth between these two representations (10.1) and (10.2).

Note that a vector-valued linear function of vec$(\mathcal{B})$ has the general representation $\sum_{j=1}^q \boldsymbol{A}_j\mathcal{B}\boldsymbol{u}_j$, where $(\boldsymbol{u}_1 : \cdots : \boldsymbol{u}_q) = \boldsymbol{I}_{q\times q}$, and $\boldsymbol{A}_1, \ldots, \boldsymbol{A}_q$ are arbitrary matrices of appropriate dimension. Likewise, a vector-valued linear function of vec$(\boldsymbol{Y})$ is of the form $\sum_{j=1}^q \boldsymbol{K}_j\boldsymbol{Y}\boldsymbol{u}_j$, where $\boldsymbol{K}_1, \ldots, \boldsymbol{K}_q$ are arbitrary matrices of appropriate dimension.

Consider the problem of estimating the linear parametric function $\sum_{j=1}^q \boldsymbol{A}_j\mathcal{B}\boldsymbol{u}_j$ by a linear function of the response, $\sum_{j=1}^q \boldsymbol{K}_j\boldsymbol{Y}\boldsymbol{u}_j$. The characterizations of linear unbiased estimator, linear zero function and estimable linear parametric function are given in the next proposition.

Proposition 10.1. *Consider the linear model (10.1) where $\boldsymbol{V}$ may be singular.*

(a) The linear function $\sum_{j=1}^q \boldsymbol{K}_j\boldsymbol{Y}\boldsymbol{u}_j$ is a LUE of $\sum_{j=1}^q \boldsymbol{A}_j\mathcal{B}\boldsymbol{u}_j$ if and only if there are matrices $\boldsymbol{L}_1, \ldots, \boldsymbol{L}_q$ such that $\boldsymbol{L}_j\boldsymbol{X} = \boldsymbol{A}_j$ for $j = 1, \ldots, q$ and $\sum_{j=1}^q \boldsymbol{L}_j\boldsymbol{Y}\boldsymbol{u}_j = \sum_{j=1}^q \boldsymbol{K}_j\boldsymbol{Y}\boldsymbol{u}_j$ with probability 1.

(b) The linear function $\sum_{j=1}^q \boldsymbol{K}_j\boldsymbol{Y}\boldsymbol{u}_j$ is a LZF if and only if there are matrices $\boldsymbol{L}_1, \ldots, \boldsymbol{L}_q$ such that $\boldsymbol{L}_j\boldsymbol{X} = \boldsymbol{0}$ for $j = 1, \ldots, q$ and $\sum_{j=1}^q \boldsymbol{L}_j\boldsymbol{Y}\boldsymbol{u}_j = \sum_{j=1}^q \boldsymbol{K}_j\boldsymbol{Y}\boldsymbol{u}_j$ with probability 1.

(c) The LPF $\sum_{j=1}^q \boldsymbol{A}_j\mathcal{B}\boldsymbol{u}_j$ is estimable if and only if $\mathcal{C}(\boldsymbol{A}_j') \subset \mathcal{C}(\boldsymbol{X}')$ for $j = 1, \ldots, q$.

(d) The LPF $\sum_{j=1}^q \boldsymbol{A}_j\mathcal{B}\boldsymbol{u}_j$ is identifiable if and only if it is estimable.

Proof. Let $\boldsymbol{k}'$ be the first row of $(\boldsymbol{K}_1 : \cdots : \boldsymbol{K}_q)$. Using part (a) of Proposition 7.3 for the model (vec$(\boldsymbol{Y})$, $(\boldsymbol{I}\otimes\boldsymbol{X})vec(\mathcal{B})$, $\boldsymbol{\Sigma}\otimes\boldsymbol{V}$), we have the existence of a vector $\boldsymbol{l}$ such that $\boldsymbol{l}'\text{vec}(\boldsymbol{Y}) = \boldsymbol{k}'\text{vec}(\boldsymbol{Y})$ almost surely and that $\boldsymbol{l}'(\boldsymbol{I} \otimes \boldsymbol{X})$ is equal to first element of the vector $(\boldsymbol{A}_1 : \cdots : \boldsymbol{A}_q)\text{vec}(\mathcal{B})$. Define the first row of $(\boldsymbol{L}_1 : \cdots : \boldsymbol{L}_q)$ as $\boldsymbol{l}'$. The other rows of this matrix can be defined similarly. Thus, we have $\sum_{j=1}^q \boldsymbol{L}_j \boldsymbol{Y} \boldsymbol{u}_j = \sum_{j=1}^q \boldsymbol{K}_j \boldsymbol{Y} \boldsymbol{u}_j$ with probability 1 and

$$(\boldsymbol{A}_1 : \cdots : \boldsymbol{A}_q)\text{vec}(\mathcal{B}) = (\boldsymbol{L}_1 : \cdots : \boldsymbol{L}_q)(\boldsymbol{I} \otimes \boldsymbol{X}) = (\boldsymbol{L}_1\boldsymbol{X} : \cdots : \boldsymbol{L}_q\boldsymbol{X}). \tag{10.3}$$

Part (a) follows immediately. Part (b) is obtained by setting $\boldsymbol{A}_i = \boldsymbol{0}$ for $i = 1, \ldots, q$ in part (a). In order to prove part (c), we use Proposition 7.4. The condition obtained from this proposition is $\mathcal{C}((\boldsymbol{A}_1 : \cdots : \boldsymbol{A}_q)') \subset \mathcal{C}((\boldsymbol{I} \otimes \boldsymbol{X})')$. This holds if and only if there is a matrix $(\boldsymbol{L}_1 : \cdots : \boldsymbol{L}_q)$ such that (10.3) holds, i.e. $\mathcal{C}(\boldsymbol{A}_j') \subset \mathcal{C}(\boldsymbol{X}')$ for $j = 1, \ldots, q$. Part (d) follows directly from Proposition 7.6. □

The next proposition presents the BLUE of an estimable linear parametric function.

Proposition 10.2. *If $\sum_{j=1}^q \boldsymbol{A}_j \mathcal{B} \boldsymbol{u}_j$ is an estimable vector LPF of the model (10.1), then its BLUE is $\sum_{j=1}^q \boldsymbol{A}_j \boldsymbol{X}^- \widehat{\boldsymbol{X}\mathcal{B}} \boldsymbol{u}_j$, where*

$$\widehat{\boldsymbol{X}\mathcal{B}} = [\boldsymbol{I} - \boldsymbol{V}(\boldsymbol{I} - \boldsymbol{P}_X)\{(\boldsymbol{I} - \boldsymbol{P}_X)\boldsymbol{V}(\boldsymbol{I} - \boldsymbol{P}_X)\}^-(\boldsymbol{I} - \boldsymbol{P}_X)]\boldsymbol{Y}.$$

Further, the BLUE is unique.

Proof. According to Proposition 7.7, which holds even when the dispersion matrix is unknown, the BLUE of $\text{vec}(\widehat{\boldsymbol{X}\mathcal{B}})$ or $(\boldsymbol{I} \otimes \boldsymbol{X})\text{vec}(\mathcal{B})$ in the model (10.1) is given by the right-hand side of (7.1), with $\boldsymbol{X}$, $\boldsymbol{V}$ and $\boldsymbol{y}$ replaced by $\boldsymbol{I} \otimes \boldsymbol{X}$, $\boldsymbol{\Sigma} \otimes \boldsymbol{V}$ and $\text{vec}(\boldsymbol{Y})$, respectively. Using algebraic simplifications such as $(\boldsymbol{AC}) \otimes (\boldsymbol{BD}) = (\boldsymbol{A} \otimes \boldsymbol{B})(\boldsymbol{C} \otimes \boldsymbol{D})$ and $\boldsymbol{P}_{A\otimes B} = \boldsymbol{P}_A \otimes \boldsymbol{P}_B$ (see page 588 and Exercise A.27), we can simplify it to

$$\text{vec}(\widehat{\boldsymbol{X}\mathcal{B}}) = (\boldsymbol{I} \otimes \boldsymbol{X})\text{vec}(\widehat{\mathcal{B}}) = [\boldsymbol{I} - (\boldsymbol{\Sigma\Sigma}^-) \otimes \boldsymbol{M}]\text{vec}(\boldsymbol{Y}),$$

where $\boldsymbol{M} = \boldsymbol{V}(\boldsymbol{I} - \boldsymbol{P}_X)\{(\boldsymbol{I} - \boldsymbol{P}_X)\boldsymbol{V}(\boldsymbol{I} - \boldsymbol{P}_X)\}^-(\boldsymbol{I} - \boldsymbol{P}_X)$. Since $\boldsymbol{MX} = \boldsymbol{0}$ and $\text{vec}(\boldsymbol{Y})$ can almost surely be written as $[(\boldsymbol{\Sigma} \otimes \boldsymbol{V})\boldsymbol{a} + (\boldsymbol{I} \otimes \boldsymbol{X})\boldsymbol{b}]$ (see the discussion at the end of Section 10.1), we have the simplification

$$\begin{aligned}
\text{vec}(\widehat{\boldsymbol{X}\mathcal{B}}) &= [\boldsymbol{I} - (\boldsymbol{\Sigma\Sigma}^-) \otimes \boldsymbol{M}][(\boldsymbol{\Sigma} \otimes \boldsymbol{V})\boldsymbol{a} + (\boldsymbol{I} \otimes \boldsymbol{X})\boldsymbol{b}] \\
&= [\boldsymbol{\Sigma} \otimes \boldsymbol{V} - \boldsymbol{\Sigma} \otimes (\boldsymbol{MV})]\boldsymbol{a} + (\boldsymbol{I} \otimes \boldsymbol{X})\boldsymbol{b} \\
&= [\boldsymbol{I} \otimes \boldsymbol{I} - \boldsymbol{I} \otimes \boldsymbol{M}](\boldsymbol{\Sigma} \otimes \boldsymbol{V})\boldsymbol{a} + (\boldsymbol{I} \otimes \boldsymbol{X})\boldsymbol{b} \\
&= [\boldsymbol{I} \otimes (\boldsymbol{I} - \boldsymbol{M})][(\boldsymbol{\Sigma} \otimes \boldsymbol{V})\boldsymbol{a} + (\boldsymbol{I} \otimes \boldsymbol{X})\boldsymbol{b}] \\
&= [\boldsymbol{I} \otimes (\boldsymbol{I} - \boldsymbol{M})]\text{vec}(\boldsymbol{Y}) = [\boldsymbol{I} \otimes (\boldsymbol{I} - \boldsymbol{M})]\text{vec}(\boldsymbol{Y}) \\
&= \text{vec}((\boldsymbol{I} - \boldsymbol{M})\boldsymbol{Y}),
\end{aligned}$$

as stated in the proposition. It has mean $X\mathcal{B}$ and is uncorrelated with every LZF. Therefore, $\sum_{j=1}^{q} A_j X^- \widehat{X\mathcal{B}} u_j$ has mean $\sum_{j=1}^{q} A_j \mathcal{B} u_j$ and is uncorrelated with every LZF. This proves the first part of the proposition. Since $\mathcal{C}(\widehat{X\mathcal{B}}) \subset \mathcal{C}(X)$ with probability 1 (see Remark 10.7) and $\mathcal{C}(A_j') \subset \mathcal{C}(X')$ (see Proposition 10.1), the BLUE $\sum_{j=1}^{q} A_j X^- \widehat{X\mathcal{B}} u_j$ does not depend on the choice of the g-inverse of X. Uniqueness or nonexistence of a different BLUE follows from Proposition 7.7. □

We denote $A_j X^- \widehat{X\mathcal{B}}$ by $A_j \widehat{\mathcal{B}}$, so that the BLUE of $\sum_{j=1}^{q} A_j \mathcal{B} u_j$ is $\sum_{j=1}^{q} A_j \widehat{\mathcal{B}} u_j$.

Remark 10.3. When $V = I$, the BLUE $\widehat{XB}$ simplifies to $P_X Y$. When V is nonsingular, it simplifies to $X(X'V^{-1}X)^- X'V^{-1}Y$, according to Proposition 7.17. □

Remark 10.4. When $A' \subset \mathcal{C}(X')$, all the elements of the matrix $A\mathcal{B}$ are estimable. It can be observed that $\mathrm{vec}(A\mathcal{B})$ is a special case of $\sum_{j=1}^{q} A_j \mathcal{B} u_j$ where $A_j = u_j \otimes A$. Direct substitution of the BLUE of $X\mathcal{B}$ shows that the BLUE of $A\mathcal{B}$ is $AX^- \widehat{XB}$. We denote this BLUE by $A\widehat{\mathcal{B}}$. □

Example 10.5. (Egyptian skulls) Table 10.1 shows four measurements of skulls (maximal breadth or MB, basibregmatic height or BH, basialveolar length or BL and nasal height or NH, all in millimeters) from five different time periods ranging from 4000 BC to 150 AD. It is claimed that a gradual change in skull size over time is evidence of interbreeding of the Egyptians with immigrant populations over the years. We would examine if there is any difference in the skull sizes between the time periods. The response is a vector consisting of the four measurements. The period 4000 BC is chosen as reference, and the indicators of all the other periods are the explanatory variables. The following lines of code produce the estimated parameters.

```
data(skulls)
mlm <- lm(cbind(MB, BH, BL, NH) ~ factor(Year), data = skulls)
coef(mlm)
```

The resulting output is given below.

```
                          MB          BH        BL          NH
(Intercept)       131.366667 133.600000 99.166667 50.53333333
factor(Year)-3300   1.000000  -0.900000 -0.100000 -0.30000000
factor(Year)-1850   3.100000   0.200000 -3.133333  0.03333333
```

Table 10.1 Measurements of Egyptian skulls from different time periods (data object `skulls` in R package `lmreg`, source: Thomson and Randall-Maciver, 1905)

Year 4000 BC				Year 3300 BC				year 1850 BC				Year 200 BC				Year 150 AD			
MB	BH	BL	NH	MB	BH	BL	NH	MB	BH	BL	NH	MB	BH	BL	NH	MB	BH	BL	NH
131	138	89	49	124	138	101	48	137	141	96	52	137	134	107	54	137	123	91	50
125	131	92	48	133	134	97	48	129	133	93	47	141	128	95	53	136	131	95	49
131	132	99	50	138	134	98	45	132	138	87	48	141	130	87	49	128	126	91	57
119	132	96	44	148	129	104	51	130	134	106	50	135	131	99	51	130	134	92	52
136	143	100	54	126	124	95	45	134	134	96	45	133	120	91	46	138	127	86	47
138	137	89	56	135	136	98	52	140	133	98	50	131	135	90	50	126	138	101	52
139	130	108	48	132	145	100	54	138	138	95	47	140	137	94	60	136	138	97	58
125	136	93	48	133	130	102	48	136	145	99	55	139	130	90	48	126	126	92	45
131	134	102	51	131	134	96	50	136	131	92	46	140	134	90	51	132	132	99	55
134	134	99	51	133	125	94	46	126	136	95	56	138	140	100	52	139	135	92	54
129	138	95	50	133	136	103	53	137	129	100	53	132	133	90	53	143	120	95	51
134	121	95	53	131	139	98	51	137	139	97	50	134	134	97	54	141	136	101	54
126	129	109	51	131	136	99	56	136	126	101	50	135	135	99	50	135	135	95	56
132	136	100	50	138	134	98	49	137	133	90	49	133	136	95	52	137	134	93	53
141	140	100	51	130	136	104	53	129	142	104	47	136	130	99	55	142	135	96	52
131	134	97	54	131	128	98	45	135	138	102	55	134	137	93	52	139	134	95	47
135	137	103	50	138	129	107	53	129	135	92	50	131	141	99	55	138	125	99	51
132	133	93	53	123	131	101	51	134	125	90	60	129	135	95	47	137	135	96	54
139	136	96	50	130	129	105	47	138	134	96	51	136	128	93	54	133	125	92	50
132	131	101	49	134	130	93	54	136	135	94	53	131	125	88	48	145	129	89	47
126	133	102	51	137	136	106	49	132	130	91	52	139	130	94	53	138	136	92	46
135	135	103	47	126	131	100	48	133	131	100	50	144	124	86	50	131	129	97	44
134	124	93	53	135	136	97	52	138	137	94	51	141	131	97	53	143	126	88	54
128	134	103	50	129	126	91	50	130	127	99	45	130	131	98	53	134	124	91	55
130	130	104	49	134	139	101	49	136	133	91	49	133	128	92	51	132	127	97	52
138	135	100	55	131	134	90	53	134	123	95	52	138	126	97	54	137	125	85	57
128	132	93	53	132	130	104	50	136	137	101	54	131	142	95	53	129	128	81	52
127	129	106	48	130	132	93	52	133	131	96	49	136	138	94	55	140	135	103	48
131	136	114	54	135	132	98	54	138	133	100	55	132	136	92	52	147	129	87	48
124	138	101	46	130	128	101	51	138	133	91	46	135	130	100	51	136	133	97	51

```
factor(Year)-200     4.133333  -1.300000 -4.633333  1.43333333
factor(Year)150      4.800000  -3.266667 -5.666667  0.83333333
```

The first row (intercept) contains the estimated mean values of the four measurements for the oldest group of skulls (4000 BC). The increasing values of the other coefficients in the first column (MB) shows that the maximal breadth has increased steadily over the years. The next two columns show a steady decline in basibregmatic height and basialveolar length in successively more recent periods, while the nasal height has had some ups and downs. □

We call $\widehat{X\mathcal{B}}$ the *matrix of fitted values* and denote it by $\widehat{Y}$. We refer to the matrix $E = Y - \widehat{X\mathcal{B}}$ as the *matrix of residuals.* The dispersion matrices of $\text{vec}(\widehat{Y})$ and $\text{vec}(E)$ are as in (7.4) and (7.5), respectively, with X, V and y replaced by $I \otimes X$, $\Sigma \otimes V$ and $\text{vec}(Y)$, respectively. These simplify to

$$D(\text{vec}(\widehat{Y})) = \Sigma \otimes T, \tag{10.4}$$
$$D(\text{vec}(E)) = \Sigma \otimes (V - T), \tag{10.5}$$
$$\text{where } T = V - V(I - P_X)\{(I - P_X)V(I - P_X)\}^-(I - P_X)V. \tag{10.6}$$

Note that $A_j\mathcal{B}u_j = (u_j' \otimes (A_jX^-))\text{vec}(X\mathcal{B})$. It follows from (10.4) that the dispersion of the BLUE $\sum_{j=1}^q A_j\widehat{\mathcal{B}}u_j$ is

$$D\left(\sum_{j=1}^q A_j\widehat{\mathcal{B}}u_j\right) = \sum_{i=1}^q\sum_{j=1}^q \sigma_{i,j}D_{ij}, \tag{10.7}$$

where $((\sigma_{i,j})) = \Sigma$, $D_{ij} = A_iX^-T(X^-)'A_j'$ for $i, j = 1, \ldots, q$ and T is as in (10.6).

Consider the special case $A_j = u_j \otimes A$, $j = 1, \ldots, q$. If $A\mathcal{B}$ is a matrix of estimable LPFs, then $\text{vec}(A\mathcal{B}) = (I_{q\times q} \otimes (AX^-))\text{vec}(X\mathcal{B})$. It follows directly from (10.4) that

$$D(\text{vec}(A\widehat{\mathcal{B}})) = \Sigma \otimes [AX^-T(X^-)'A']. \tag{10.8}$$

When V is nonsingular, (10.4) simplifies to

$$D(\text{vec}(\widehat{Y})) = \Sigma \otimes [X(X'V^{-1}X)^-X].$$

When $V = I$, $D(\text{vec}(\widehat{Y}))$ further simplifies to $\Sigma \otimes P_X$. The expressions for the dispersions of $\text{vec}(E)$ and $\sum_{j=1}^q A_j\widehat{\mathcal{B}}u_j$ also simplify accordingly.

Remark 10.6. Suppose we are only interested in the estimable linear parametric function $A_j\mathcal{B}u_j$ for a *fixed* j. We may ignore all but the jth variable of the response vector and use the univariate response linear model formulation of Chapter 7. The resulting BLUE and its dispersion would be same as those obtained from Proposition 10.2 and (10.7). Therefore, there is no need to invoke the multivariate linear model for this purpose. However, analysis from the univariate linear model will not be adequate if we are interested in inference involving more than one component of the response vector, as the cross-terms of (10.7) corresponding to $\sigma_{i,j}$ for $i \neq j$ are in general not equal to zero. □

Remark 10.7. Comparison of the BLUE of $\boldsymbol{X}\mathcal{B}$ given in Proposition 10.2 and (7.4) reveals that every column of $\widehat{\boldsymbol{Y}}$ belongs to $\mathcal{C}(\boldsymbol{X})$ with probability 1 (see Remark 7.16). Therefore, $\mathcal{C}(\widehat{\boldsymbol{Y}}) \subset \mathcal{C}(\boldsymbol{X})$ with probability 1. Likewise, vec$(\boldsymbol{E})$ almost surely belongs to $\mathcal{C}(\boldsymbol{\Sigma} \otimes (\boldsymbol{V}(\boldsymbol{I} - \boldsymbol{P}_X)))$, and therefore the residual matrix must have the representation

$$\boldsymbol{E} = \boldsymbol{V}\left(\boldsymbol{I} - \boldsymbol{P}_X\right)\boldsymbol{L}\boldsymbol{\Sigma} \quad \text{almost surely,}$$

for some matrix $\boldsymbol{L}$ (see Exercise 10.1). □

10.3 Unbiased estimation of error dispersion

In order to estimate $\boldsymbol{\Sigma}$, we have to rely on the LZFs which are functions of the model errors. We would like to consider an adequate number of vector LZFs having dispersion matrix equal to $\boldsymbol{\Sigma}$.

Definition 10.8. A vector of LZFs of the multivariate linear model (10.1) is called a *normalized linear zero function* (NLZF) if its dispersion matrix is proportional to $\boldsymbol{\Sigma}$.

Definition 10.9. A set of NLZFs is called a *generating set of NLZFs* if every NLZF is almost surely a linear combination of the NLZFs contained in it.

As an example, the rows of the residual matrix $\boldsymbol{E}$ constitute a generating set of NLZFs. Another example is the set of rows of $(\boldsymbol{I} - \boldsymbol{P}_X)\boldsymbol{Y}$ (see Exercise 10.3).

Definition 10.10. A generating set of NLZFs is called a *standardized basis set of NLZFs* if every pair of NLZFs contained in it is uncorrelated, and each NLZF has dispersion equal to $\boldsymbol{\Sigma}$.

The NLZFs are akin to the rows of $\mathcal{E}$. A standardized basis set contains the maximum possible number of uncorrelated sets of NLZFs, which can be utilized to estimate $\boldsymbol{\Sigma}$. The next proposition proves an invariance which is crucial to the derivation of a meaningful estimator.

Proposition 10.11. *If $\boldsymbol{Z}$ is any matrix whose rows constitute a standardized basis set of NLZFs, then*

(a) $\boldsymbol{Z}$ has $\rho(\boldsymbol{V} : \boldsymbol{X}) - \rho(\boldsymbol{X})$ rows;
(b) the value of $\boldsymbol{Z}'\boldsymbol{Z}$ does not depend on the choice of the standardized basis set.

Proof. Let $\boldsymbol{Z}$ be a matrix whose rows constitute a standardized basis set of NLZFs, and let ρ_1 be the number of its rows. Since the set of rows of $\boldsymbol{Z}_{\rho_1\times q}$ as well as that of $\boldsymbol{E}_{n\times q}$ are generating sets of NLZFs, there are matrices $\boldsymbol{B}_{\rho_1\times n}$ and $\boldsymbol{C}_{n\times\rho_1}$ such that $\boldsymbol{E}=\boldsymbol{CZ}$ and $\boldsymbol{Z}=\boldsymbol{BE}$. It follows from Exercise A.27 that

$$\rho(D(\mathrm{vec}(\boldsymbol{Z})))=\rho(\boldsymbol{\Sigma}\otimes\boldsymbol{I}_{\rho_1\times\rho_1})=\rho_1\rho(\boldsymbol{\Sigma}).$$

Also,

$$\begin{aligned}\rho(D(\mathrm{vec}(\boldsymbol{Z})))&=\rho(D[(\boldsymbol{I}\otimes\boldsymbol{B})\mathrm{vec}(\boldsymbol{E})])\le\rho(D(\mathrm{vec}(\boldsymbol{E})))\\&=\rho(D[(\boldsymbol{I}\otimes\boldsymbol{C})\mathrm{vec}(\boldsymbol{Z})])\\&=\rho([(\boldsymbol{I}\otimes\boldsymbol{C})(\boldsymbol{\Sigma}\otimes\boldsymbol{I})(\boldsymbol{I}\otimes\boldsymbol{C}')])\\&=\rho(\boldsymbol{\Sigma}\otimes(\boldsymbol{CC}'))=\rho(\boldsymbol{\Sigma})\rho(\boldsymbol{CC}')\le\rho_1\rho(\boldsymbol{\Sigma}).\end{aligned}$$

The last step is a consequence of the fact that $\rho(\boldsymbol{C})\le\rho_1$, since ρ_1 is the number of columns of $\boldsymbol{C}$. In summary, we have the following chain of equalities:

$$\rho_1\rho(\boldsymbol{\Sigma})=\rho(D(\mathrm{vec}(\boldsymbol{Z})))\le\rho(D(\mathrm{vec}(\boldsymbol{E})))\le\rho_1\rho(\boldsymbol{\Sigma}).$$

All the terms should therefore be the same. Hence, from (10.5) and Proposition 7.15,

$$\rho_1\rho(\boldsymbol{\Sigma})=\rho(D(\mathrm{vec}(\boldsymbol{E})))=\rho(\boldsymbol{\Sigma})\rho(\boldsymbol{V}(\boldsymbol{I}-\boldsymbol{P}_{\boldsymbol{X}})).$$

Assuming $\rho(\boldsymbol{\Sigma})>0$, we have $\rho_1=\rho(\boldsymbol{V}(\boldsymbol{I}-\boldsymbol{P}_{\boldsymbol{X}}))=\rho(\boldsymbol{V}:\boldsymbol{X})-\rho(\boldsymbol{X})$ (see Proposition A.14(b)). This proves part (a).

In order to prove part (b), note that

$$\begin{aligned}\boldsymbol{\Sigma}\otimes\boldsymbol{I}_{\rho_1\times\rho_1}&=D(\mathrm{vec}(\boldsymbol{Z}))=D[(\boldsymbol{I}\otimes\boldsymbol{B})\mathrm{vec}(\boldsymbol{E})]\\&=D[(\boldsymbol{I}\otimes\boldsymbol{B})(\boldsymbol{I}\otimes\boldsymbol{C})\mathrm{vec}(\boldsymbol{Z})]=D[(\boldsymbol{I}\otimes(\boldsymbol{BC}))\mathrm{vec}(\boldsymbol{Z})]\\&=(\boldsymbol{I}\otimes(\boldsymbol{BC}))(\boldsymbol{\Sigma}\otimes\boldsymbol{I}_{\rho_1\times\rho_1})(\boldsymbol{I}\otimes(\boldsymbol{C}'\boldsymbol{B}'))\\&=\boldsymbol{\Sigma}\otimes(\boldsymbol{BCC}'\boldsymbol{B}').\end{aligned}$$

Therefore, $\boldsymbol{BCC}'\boldsymbol{B}'=\boldsymbol{I}_{\rho_1\times\rho_1}$. Hence, the $\rho_1\times\rho_1$ matrix $\boldsymbol{BC}$ is orthogonal, and $\boldsymbol{C}'\boldsymbol{B}'\boldsymbol{BC}=\boldsymbol{I}$. Consequently, $\boldsymbol{B}'\boldsymbol{B}$ is a g-inverse of $\boldsymbol{CC}'$, and

$$\boldsymbol{Z}'\boldsymbol{Z}=\boldsymbol{E}'\boldsymbol{B}'\boldsymbol{BE}=\boldsymbol{E}'(\boldsymbol{CC}')^-\boldsymbol{E}.$$

Since $D(\mathrm{vec}(\boldsymbol{E}))=\boldsymbol{\Sigma}\otimes(\boldsymbol{CC}')$, comparison with (10.5) reveals that $\boldsymbol{CC}'=\boldsymbol{V}-\boldsymbol{T}$, where $\boldsymbol{T}$ does not depend on the choice of $\boldsymbol{Z}$. Also, $\mathrm{vec}(\boldsymbol{E})\in\mathcal{C}(\boldsymbol{\Sigma}\otimes(\boldsymbol{CC}'))$ almost surely, so that the columns of $\boldsymbol{E}$ are in $\mathcal{C}(\boldsymbol{CC}')$. Thus, the quantity $\boldsymbol{E}'(\boldsymbol{CC}')^-\boldsymbol{E}$ is uniquely defined for all choices of the g-inverse. □

The matrix $\boldsymbol{R}_0 = \boldsymbol{Z}'\boldsymbol{Z}$ is invariant under the choice of the standardized basis of NLZFs. It is a generalization of the error sum of squares (R_0^2) to the multivariate linear model.

Definition 10.12. If $\boldsymbol{Z}$ is a matrix such that its rows constitute a standardized basis set of NLZFs, then the matrix $\boldsymbol{R}_0 = \boldsymbol{Z}'\boldsymbol{Z}$ is called the *error sum of squares and products* matrix.

Part (b) of Proposition 10.11 ensures that there is no ambiguity in the definition of $\boldsymbol{R}_0$. Part (a) of this proposition implies that

$$E(\boldsymbol{R}_0) = E(\boldsymbol{Z}'\boldsymbol{Z}) = (\rho(\boldsymbol{V} : \boldsymbol{X}) - \rho(\boldsymbol{X}))\,\boldsymbol{\Sigma}.$$

Therefore, an unbiased estimator of $\boldsymbol{\Sigma}$ is

$$\widehat{\boldsymbol{\Sigma}} = (\rho(\boldsymbol{V} : \boldsymbol{X}) - \rho(\boldsymbol{X}))^{-1}\,\boldsymbol{R}_0. \tag{10.9}$$

We conclude this section by presenting a few alternate expressions for $\boldsymbol{R}_0$, the error sum of squares and products matrix, beginning with (Exercises 10.3 and 10.4)

$$\begin{aligned}\boldsymbol{R}_0 &= \boldsymbol{E}'[\boldsymbol{V}(\boldsymbol{I}-\boldsymbol{P}_{\boldsymbol{X}})\{(\boldsymbol{I}-\boldsymbol{P}_{\boldsymbol{X}})\boldsymbol{V}(\boldsymbol{I}-\boldsymbol{P}_{\boldsymbol{X}})\}^-(\boldsymbol{I}-\boldsymbol{P}_{\boldsymbol{X}})\boldsymbol{V}]^-\boldsymbol{E} &(10.10)\\ &= \boldsymbol{Y}'(\boldsymbol{I}-\boldsymbol{P}_{\boldsymbol{X}})\{(\boldsymbol{I}-\boldsymbol{P}_{\boldsymbol{X}})\boldsymbol{V}(\boldsymbol{I}-\boldsymbol{P}_{\boldsymbol{X}})\}^-(\boldsymbol{I}-\boldsymbol{P}_{\boldsymbol{X}})\boldsymbol{Y}. &(10.11)\end{aligned}$$

These alternative forms will be useful later in this chapter.

Let us write the expression of (10.10) as $\boldsymbol{E}'\boldsymbol{K}^-\boldsymbol{E}$, where $\boldsymbol{K} = \boldsymbol{V}\boldsymbol{M}$ and

$$\boldsymbol{M} = (\boldsymbol{I}-\boldsymbol{P}_{\boldsymbol{X}})\{(\boldsymbol{I}-\boldsymbol{P}_{\boldsymbol{X}})\boldsymbol{V}(\boldsymbol{I}-\boldsymbol{P}_{\boldsymbol{X}})\}^-(\boldsymbol{I}-\boldsymbol{P}_{\boldsymbol{X}})\boldsymbol{V}.$$

Note that if $\boldsymbol{U}$ is any symmetric matrix, then

$$\boldsymbol{K} = (\boldsymbol{V}+\boldsymbol{X}\boldsymbol{U}\boldsymbol{X}')\boldsymbol{M} = \boldsymbol{M}'(\boldsymbol{V}+\boldsymbol{X}\boldsymbol{U}\boldsymbol{X}')\boldsymbol{M}.$$

Since $\boldsymbol{\Sigma}\otimes\boldsymbol{K}$ is the dispersion matrix of $\boldsymbol{E}$ (see (10.5)), there must be a matrix $\boldsymbol{L}$ of appropriate order such that $\mathrm{vec}(\boldsymbol{E}) = (\boldsymbol{\Sigma}\otimes\boldsymbol{K})\mathrm{vec}(\boldsymbol{L})$, i.e. $\boldsymbol{E} = \boldsymbol{K}\boldsymbol{L}\boldsymbol{\Sigma}$ (see Exercise A.29). It follows that

$$\begin{aligned}\boldsymbol{E}'(\boldsymbol{V}+\boldsymbol{X}\boldsymbol{U}\boldsymbol{X}')^-\boldsymbol{E} &= \boldsymbol{\Sigma}\boldsymbol{L}'\boldsymbol{K}(\boldsymbol{V}+\boldsymbol{X}\boldsymbol{U}\boldsymbol{X}')^-\boldsymbol{K}\boldsymbol{L}\boldsymbol{\Sigma}\\ &= \boldsymbol{\Sigma}\boldsymbol{L}'\boldsymbol{M}'(\boldsymbol{V}+\boldsymbol{X}\boldsymbol{U}\boldsymbol{X}')\boldsymbol{M}\boldsymbol{L}\boldsymbol{\Sigma} = \boldsymbol{\Sigma}\boldsymbol{L}'\boldsymbol{K}\boldsymbol{L}\boldsymbol{\Sigma}\\ &= \boldsymbol{\Sigma}\boldsymbol{L}'\boldsymbol{K}\boldsymbol{K}^-\boldsymbol{K}\boldsymbol{L}\boldsymbol{\Sigma} = \boldsymbol{E}'\boldsymbol{K}^-\boldsymbol{E} = \boldsymbol{R}_0.\end{aligned}$$

Consequently, $\boldsymbol{R}_0$ can be written as $\boldsymbol{E}'(\boldsymbol{V}+\boldsymbol{X}\boldsymbol{U}\boldsymbol{X}')^-\boldsymbol{E}$ where $\boldsymbol{U}$ is *any* symmetric matrix, and any g-inverse can be used in this expression. In particular,

$$\boldsymbol{R}_0 = \boldsymbol{E}'\boldsymbol{V}^-\boldsymbol{E} \tag{10.12}$$

$$\text{and } \widehat{\boldsymbol{\Sigma}} = (\rho(\boldsymbol{V} : \boldsymbol{X}) - \rho(\boldsymbol{X}))^{-1}\,\boldsymbol{E}'\boldsymbol{V}^-\boldsymbol{E}. \tag{10.13}$$

Remark 10.13. Let $\rho_1 = \rho(\boldsymbol{V} : \boldsymbol{X}) - \rho(\boldsymbol{X})$ and $\boldsymbol{Z}_{\rho_1 \times q}$ be as in Proposition 10.11. According to Proposition 2.13, every column of $\boldsymbol{Z}'$ is in $\mathcal{C}(\boldsymbol{\Sigma})$ with probability 1. Therefore, $\mathcal{C}(\boldsymbol{Z}') \subset \mathcal{C}(\boldsymbol{\Sigma})$ almost surely. Let $\boldsymbol{B}\boldsymbol{B}'$ be a rank-factorization of $\boldsymbol{\Sigma}$. Then it can be verified that the $\rho(\boldsymbol{\Sigma}) \times \rho_1$ matrix $\boldsymbol{B}^{-L}\boldsymbol{Z}'$ has uncorrelated elements, each having mean zero and variance 1. If the joint distribution of these elements have a density over the entire $\rho_1\rho(\boldsymbol{\Sigma})$-dimensional Euclidean space, then it can be shown that the rank of $\boldsymbol{B}^{-L}\boldsymbol{Z}'$ is almost surely equal to the minimum of ρ_1 and $\rho(\boldsymbol{\Sigma})$ (see Okamoto, 1973). Therefore, whenever $\rho_1 \geq \rho(\boldsymbol{\Sigma})$, we have

$$\rho(\boldsymbol{Z}'\boldsymbol{Z}) \geq \rho(\boldsymbol{B}^{-L}\boldsymbol{Z}'\boldsymbol{Z}\boldsymbol{B}^{-L'}) = \rho(\boldsymbol{\Sigma}) \quad \text{almost surely.}$$

Comparing this with the earlier observation on column spaces, we have $\mathcal{C}(\boldsymbol{R}_0) = \mathcal{C}(\boldsymbol{Z}'\boldsymbol{Z}) = \mathcal{C}(\boldsymbol{\Sigma})$ and $\rho(\boldsymbol{R}_0) = \rho(\boldsymbol{\Sigma})$ with probability 1, whenever $\rho_1 \geq \rho(\boldsymbol{\Sigma})$. □

Example 10.14. (Egyptian skulls, continued) For the data of Table 10.1, the error sum of squares matrix $\boldsymbol{R}_0$ simplifies to $\boldsymbol{Y}'(\boldsymbol{I} - \boldsymbol{P}_X)\boldsymbol{Y}$ and the unbiased estimator $\widehat{\boldsymbol{\Sigma}}$ is equal to $\boldsymbol{R}_0/(150-5)$. The latter matrix is computed as follows.

```
data(skulls)
Y <- as.matrix(skulls[,1:4])
mlm <- lm(Y ~ factor(Year), data = skulls)
X <- model.matrix(mlm)
PX <- projector(X)
R0 <- t(Y)%*%(Y-PX%*%Y)
r1 <- dim(X)[1] - dim(X)[2]
Sighat <- R0 / r1; Sighat
```

The value of `Sighat` is given below.

```
            MB          BH          BL        NH
MB 21.11080460  0.03678161  0.07908046  2.008966
BH  0.03678161 23.48459770  5.20000000  2.845057
BL  0.07908046  5.20000000 24.17908046  1.133333
NH  2.00896552  2.84505747  1.13333333 10.152644
```

If one is only interested in the estimated standard deviations, i.e. the square roots of the diagonal elements of the above matrix, these can be obtained by the additional command `sigma(mlm)`.

In view of (10.8), the variance-covariance matrix of vec($\mathcal{B}$) is $\boldsymbol{\Sigma} \otimes (\boldsymbol{X}'\boldsymbol{X})^{-1}$. The estimated dispersion matrix can be computed by using either of the commands `kronecker(Sighat,solve(t(X)%*%X))` and `vcov(mlm)`.

The output is omitted for brevity. The estimated standard deviations of the regression coefficients and the corresponding t- and p-values are obtained through the command `summary(mlm)`, which produces the analysis of individual response variables, taken one at a time. This output is also omitted for brevity. □

10.4 Maximum likelihood estimation

10.4.1 *Estimator of mean*

Let $\text{vec}(\boldsymbol{Y}_{n\times q}) \sim N(\text{vec}(\boldsymbol{X}_{n\times k}\mathcal{B}_{k\times q}), \boldsymbol{\Sigma}_{q\times q}\otimes\boldsymbol{V}_{n\times n})$. The task of finding the MLE of $\boldsymbol{X}\mathcal{B}$ and $\boldsymbol{\Sigma}$ is similar to that considered in Section 7.5, in the case $q = 1$. It follows from Proposition 7.24 that the MLE of $\boldsymbol{X}\mathcal{B}$ coincides with its BLUE, for fixed $\boldsymbol{\Sigma}\otimes\boldsymbol{V}$. Proposition 10.2 shows that the BLUE does not depend on $\boldsymbol{\Sigma}$. Therefore, the unique MLE of $\boldsymbol{X}\mathcal{B}$ is given by

$$\widehat{\boldsymbol{X}\mathcal{B}}_{ML} = [\boldsymbol{I} - \boldsymbol{V}(\boldsymbol{I} - \boldsymbol{P}_{\!X})\{(\boldsymbol{I} - \boldsymbol{P}_{\!X})\boldsymbol{V}(\boldsymbol{I} - \boldsymbol{P}_{\!X})\}^{-}(\boldsymbol{I} - \boldsymbol{P}_{\!X})]\boldsymbol{Y}. \quad (10.14)$$

The dispersion matrix of the MLE is given by (10.4).

The above value of $\boldsymbol{X}\mathcal{B}$ maximizes the likelihood, and in the process minimizes the exponent,

$$\text{vec}(\boldsymbol{Y} - \boldsymbol{X}\mathcal{B})'(\boldsymbol{\Sigma}\otimes\boldsymbol{V})^{-}\text{vec}(\boldsymbol{Y} - \boldsymbol{X}\mathcal{B}),$$

which can also be written as $\text{tr}[(\boldsymbol{Y} - \boldsymbol{X}\mathcal{B})'\boldsymbol{V}^{-}(\boldsymbol{Y} - \boldsymbol{X}\mathcal{B})\boldsymbol{\Sigma}^{-})$. The smallest or residual value of above the quadratic function of $\mathcal{B}$ happens to be $\text{tr}(\boldsymbol{E}'\boldsymbol{V}^{-}\boldsymbol{E}\boldsymbol{\Sigma}^{-})$. The corresponding value of the sum of squares and products matrix, $(\boldsymbol{Y} - \boldsymbol{X}\mathcal{B})'\boldsymbol{V}^{-}(\boldsymbol{Y} - \boldsymbol{X}\mathcal{B})$, is $\boldsymbol{E}'\boldsymbol{V}^{-}\boldsymbol{E}$. Thus, the error sum of squares and products matrix can also be called the 'residual sum of squares and products matrix'.

10.4.2 *Estimator of error dispersion*

We derive the MLE of $\boldsymbol{\Sigma}$ without assuming that it is positive definite, and without invoking any calculus that can be rather messy. The MLE is obtained by maximizing the likelihood function with respect to $\boldsymbol{\Sigma}$, after substituting $\boldsymbol{X}\mathcal{B}$ with its MLE, $\widehat{\boldsymbol{X}\mathcal{B}}$. Simplifying the expression of the density given in Section 7.5, we have the partially maximized log-likelihood (also called log-likelihood *profile*)

$$-\frac{\rho(\boldsymbol{V}\otimes\boldsymbol{\Sigma})}{2}\log(2\pi) - \frac{1}{2}\log|(\boldsymbol{B}'\otimes\boldsymbol{C}')(\boldsymbol{C}\otimes\boldsymbol{B})| - \frac{1}{2}\text{vec}(\boldsymbol{E})'(\boldsymbol{\Sigma}\otimes\boldsymbol{V})^{-}\text{vec}(\boldsymbol{E}),$$

where BB' and CC' are rank-factorizations of Σ and V, respectively (see Exercise A.27). The log-likelihood profile further simplifies to

$$-\frac{\rho(V)\rho(\Sigma)}{2}\log(2\pi) - \frac{1}{2}\log|(B'B)\otimes(C'C)| - \frac{1}{2}\text{tr}(E'V^{-}E\Sigma^{-}).$$

According to the result of Exercise A.28,

$$|(B'B)\otimes(C'C)| = |B'B|^{\rho(V)}\cdot|C'C|^{\rho(\Sigma)}.$$

Consequently, the log-likelihood profile is maximized when we minimize

$$\rho(V)\log|B'B| + \text{tr}(R_0\Sigma^{-})$$

with respect to B. Let B_*B_*' be a rank-factorization of $R_0/\rho(V)$. It follows from Remark 10.13 that B_* and B have the same column space, with probability 1. Let Q be an invertible matrix such that $B_* = BQ$. In order to maximize the log-likelihood profile, we have to minimize the following with respect to Q:

$$\begin{aligned}\log|B'B| + \text{tr}(B_*B_*'(BB')^{-}) &= \log|Q^{-1'}B_*'B_*Q^{-1}| + \text{tr}(B_*'(BB')^{-}B_*)\\ &= \log|B_*'B_*Q^{-1}Q^{-1'}| + \text{tr}(Q'P_{B'}Q)\\ &= \log|B_*'B_*| - \log|Q'Q| + \text{tr}(Q'Q).\end{aligned}$$

The last equality follows from the fact that $P_{B'} = I$ whenever B has full column rank. If $\lambda_1,\ldots,\lambda_{\rho(\Sigma)}$ are the eigenvalues of $Q'Q$, then

$$\text{tr}(Q'Q) - \log|Q'Q| = \sum_{j=1}^{\rho(\Sigma)}\lambda_i - \log\lambda_i.$$

The quantity $x - \log x$ is always greater than or equal to 1 for all positive x, and is equal to 1 only when $x = 1$. Therefore, the log-likelihood profile is minimized when all the eigenvalues of $Q'Q$ are 1. This happens if and only if $Q'Q = I = QQ'$, that is, when

$$\Sigma = BB' = B_*Q^{-1}(Q^{-1})'B_*' = B_*B_*' = R_0/\rho(V).$$

Therefore,

$$\widehat{\Sigma}_{ML} = \frac{1}{\rho(V)}R_0 = \frac{1}{\rho(V)}E'V^{-}E. \tag{10.15}$$

Comparing with the unbiased estimator of (10.13) we find that the MLE of Σ is negatively biased.

10.4.3 *REML estimator of error dispersion*

By taking a cue from Section 8.2.3, let us now derive the residual maximum likelihood estimator of $\boldsymbol{\Sigma}$, assuming again that $\text{vec}(\boldsymbol{Y}_{n\times q}) \sim N(\boldsymbol{X}_{n\times k}\mathcal{B}_{k\times q}, \boldsymbol{\Sigma}_{q\times q} \otimes \boldsymbol{V}_{n\times n})$. The REML estimator maximizes the likelihood function computed from the joint density of $(\boldsymbol{I} - \boldsymbol{I} \otimes \boldsymbol{P}_X)vec(\boldsymbol{Y})$. It is easy to see that

$$(\boldsymbol{I} - \boldsymbol{I} \otimes \boldsymbol{P}_X)vec(\boldsymbol{Y}) \sim N(\boldsymbol{0}, \boldsymbol{\Sigma} \otimes [(\boldsymbol{I} - \boldsymbol{P}_X)\boldsymbol{V}(\boldsymbol{I} - \boldsymbol{P}_X)]).$$

The task is similar to maximizing the likelihood profile in the case of the MLE, with $\boldsymbol{E}$ replaced by $(\boldsymbol{I} - \boldsymbol{P}_X)\boldsymbol{Y}$ and $\boldsymbol{V}$ replaced by $(\boldsymbol{I} - \boldsymbol{P}_X)\boldsymbol{V}(\boldsymbol{I} - \boldsymbol{P}_X)$. Therefore, the REML estimator can be obtained by making these substitutions in (10.15). Therefore,

$$\begin{aligned}
\widehat{\boldsymbol{\Sigma}}_{REML} &= \frac{1}{\rho((\boldsymbol{I} - \boldsymbol{P}_X)\boldsymbol{V}(\boldsymbol{I} - \boldsymbol{P}_X))} \\
&\qquad \cdot \boldsymbol{Y}'(\boldsymbol{I} - \boldsymbol{P}_X)\{(\boldsymbol{I} - \boldsymbol{P}_X)\boldsymbol{V}(\boldsymbol{I} - \boldsymbol{P}_X)\}^-(\boldsymbol{I} - \boldsymbol{P}_X)\boldsymbol{Y} \\
&= \frac{1}{\rho(\boldsymbol{V}(\boldsymbol{I} - \boldsymbol{P}_X))}\boldsymbol{R}_0 \quad = \quad \frac{1}{\rho(\boldsymbol{V} : \boldsymbol{X}) - \rho(\boldsymbol{X})}\boldsymbol{R}_0. \qquad (10.16)
\end{aligned}$$

The simplification occurs due to (10.11). Thus, the REML estimator of $\boldsymbol{\Sigma}$ coincides with the unbiased estimator (10.13) derived earlier.

10.5 Effect of linear restrictions

10.5.1 *Effect on estimable LPFs, LZFs and BLUEs*

Consider the linear restriction $\boldsymbol{A}\mathcal{B} = \boldsymbol{\Psi}$ on the parameters of the linear model (10.1). The restriction can be interpreted as a set of observations with zero error, and appended to the other observations. Thus, we have the model equation

$$\begin{pmatrix} \boldsymbol{Y} \\ \boldsymbol{\Psi} \end{pmatrix} = \begin{pmatrix} \boldsymbol{X} \\ \boldsymbol{A} \end{pmatrix} \mathcal{B} + \begin{pmatrix} \mathcal{E} \\ \boldsymbol{0} \end{pmatrix}. \qquad (10.17)$$

We shall refer to the above model as $\mathcal{M}_R$, and use the notation $\mathcal{M}$ for the linear model of (10.1). Thus,

$$\begin{aligned}
\mathcal{M} &= (\text{vec}(\boldsymbol{Y}), (\boldsymbol{I} \otimes \boldsymbol{X})\text{vec}(\mathcal{B}), \boldsymbol{\Sigma} \otimes \boldsymbol{V}), \\
\mathcal{M}_R &= \left(\text{vec}\begin{pmatrix} \boldsymbol{Y} \\ \boldsymbol{\Psi} \end{pmatrix}, \left(\boldsymbol{I} \otimes \begin{pmatrix} \boldsymbol{X} \\ \boldsymbol{A} \end{pmatrix}\right) \text{vec}(\mathcal{B}), \boldsymbol{\Sigma} \otimes \begin{pmatrix} \boldsymbol{V} & \boldsymbol{0} \\ \boldsymbol{0} & \boldsymbol{0} \end{pmatrix}\right).
\end{aligned}$$

The restriction must satisfy the condition $\mathcal{C}(\boldsymbol{\Psi}) \subset \mathcal{C}(\boldsymbol{A})$ for algebraic consistency. Also, in order that the restrictions are consistent with the observed data, the response matrix $\boldsymbol{Y}$ must satisfy the condition

$$\mathcal{C}\begin{pmatrix}\boldsymbol{Y}\\ \boldsymbol{\Psi}\end{pmatrix} \subseteq \mathcal{C}\left(\boldsymbol{\Sigma}\otimes\begin{pmatrix}\boldsymbol{V} & \boldsymbol{0}\\ \boldsymbol{0} & \boldsymbol{0}\end{pmatrix} : \boldsymbol{I}\otimes\begin{pmatrix}\boldsymbol{X}\\ \boldsymbol{A}\end{pmatrix}\right) \quad \text{almost surely.} \qquad (10.18)$$

We adapt Proposition 7.40 to the present situation and state it below.

Proposition 10.15. *Let $\boldsymbol{A}\mathcal{B} = \boldsymbol{\Psi}$ be a consistent restriction on the model $\mathcal{M}$.*

(a) All estimable LPFs of the unrestricted model $\mathcal{M}$ are estimable under the restricted model $\mathcal{M}_R$.
(b) All LZFs of the unrestricted model are LZFs under the restricted model.
(c) The restriction cannot increase the dispersion of the BLUE of $\text{vec}(\boldsymbol{X}\mathcal{B})$*, in the sense of the Löwner order.*
(d) The restriction cannot reduce the error sum of squares and products matrix, in the sense of the Löwner order.

The proof proceeds along the lines of that of Proposition 7.40, with no major change in the multivariate case. □

10.5.2 Change in error sum of squares and products

Let us now assume that $\boldsymbol{A}\mathcal{B}$ is estimable, i.e. $\mathcal{C}(\boldsymbol{A}') \subset \mathcal{C}(\boldsymbol{X}')$. The BLUEs of the unrestricted model which turn into LZFs under restrictions are identified in Proposition 7.41. Presently we are interested in those *groups of* BLUEs in $\mathcal{M}$ which may turn into NLZFs because of the restriction — thus affecting the error sum of squares and products matrix. The following result is an extension of Proposition 7.41 in this direction.

Proposition 10.16. *Let $\mathcal{C}(\boldsymbol{\Psi}) \subset \mathcal{C}(\boldsymbol{A})$ and $\mathcal{C}(\boldsymbol{A}') \subset \mathcal{C}(\boldsymbol{X}')$. Let $\boldsymbol{A}\widehat{\mathcal{B}}$ be the BLUE of $\boldsymbol{A}\mathcal{B}$ under the model $\mathcal{M}$.*

(a) $\boldsymbol{A}\widehat{\mathcal{B}} - \boldsymbol{\Psi}$ is a matrix whose rows are NLZFs under the model $\mathcal{M}_R$.
(b) The elements of $\boldsymbol{A}\widehat{\mathcal{B}} - \boldsymbol{\Psi}$ are uncorrelated with all NLZFs of $\mathcal{M}$.
(c) There is no nontrivial NLZF of $\mathcal{M}_R$ which is uncorrelated with $\boldsymbol{A}\widehat{\mathcal{B}} - \boldsymbol{\Psi}$ and the NLZFs of $\mathcal{M}$.

Proof. According to the model $\mathcal{M}_R$, the expected value of $\boldsymbol{A}\widehat{\mathcal{B}}$ is $\boldsymbol{0}$. The dispersion of $\text{vec}(\boldsymbol{A}\widehat{\mathcal{B}})$ is given by (10.8). Therefore, the dispersion of the any row of $\boldsymbol{A}\widehat{\mathcal{B}}$ is proportional to $\boldsymbol{\Sigma}$. This proves part (a). Part (b) follows from the fact that $A\widehat{\mathcal{B}}$ is a BLUE of $\mathcal{M}$, which must be uncorrelated with all LZFs in $\mathcal{M}$, and in particular with the NLZFs. Part (c) is a consequence of part (c) of Proposition 7.41. □

Proposition 10.16 shows that a generating set of NLZFs of $\mathcal{M}_R$ can be obtained by augmenting a generating set of NLZFs of $\mathcal{M}$ (say, the rows of $\boldsymbol{E}$) with the rows of $A\widehat{\mathcal{B}} - \boldsymbol{\Psi}$, and that the two sets of NLZFs are uncorrelated. If we denote the error sum of squares and products matrix of $\mathcal{M}_R$ by $\boldsymbol{R}_H$, then we have from (10.5), (10.8) and Exercise 10.4

$$\begin{aligned}\boldsymbol{R}_H &= (\boldsymbol{E}' : (\boldsymbol{A}\widehat{\mathcal{B}} - \boldsymbol{\Psi})')\begin{pmatrix}\boldsymbol{V}-\boldsymbol{T} & \boldsymbol{0}\\ \boldsymbol{0} & \boldsymbol{A}\boldsymbol{X}^-\boldsymbol{T}(\boldsymbol{X}^-)'\boldsymbol{A}'\end{pmatrix}^-\begin{pmatrix}\boldsymbol{E}\\ \boldsymbol{A}\widehat{\mathcal{B}} - \boldsymbol{\Psi}\end{pmatrix}\\ &= \boldsymbol{E}'(\boldsymbol{V}-\boldsymbol{T})^-\boldsymbol{E} + (\boldsymbol{A}\widehat{\mathcal{B}} - \boldsymbol{\Psi})'[\boldsymbol{A}\boldsymbol{X}^-\boldsymbol{T}(\boldsymbol{X}^-)'\boldsymbol{A}']^-(\boldsymbol{A}\widehat{\mathcal{B}} - \boldsymbol{\Psi})\\ &= \boldsymbol{R}_0 + (\boldsymbol{A}\widehat{\mathcal{B}} - \boldsymbol{\Psi})'[\boldsymbol{A}\boldsymbol{X}^-\boldsymbol{T}(\boldsymbol{X}^-)'\boldsymbol{A}']^-(\boldsymbol{A}\widehat{\mathcal{B}} - \boldsymbol{\Psi}),\end{aligned} \tag{10.19}$$

where $\boldsymbol{T}$ is as in (10.6). This decomposition of the error sum of squares and products matrix under the restriction $\boldsymbol{A}\mathcal{B} = \boldsymbol{\Psi}$ is similar to (7.17) obtained in the case of univariate response.

10.5.3 *Change in 'BLUE' and MSE matrix*

Suppose the restriction $\boldsymbol{A}\mathcal{B} = \boldsymbol{\Psi}$ is not necessarily true, but it is imposed anyway to reduce dispersion of the estimators, possibly at the expense of bias. Let the matrices $\boldsymbol{\Sigma}$ and $[\boldsymbol{A}\boldsymbol{X}^-\boldsymbol{T}(\boldsymbol{X}^-)'\boldsymbol{A}']$ used in (10.8) be positive definite. It follows from Proposition 10.16 that the BLUE of $\boldsymbol{X}\mathcal{B}$ under the restriction is obtained from the unrestricted BLUE by decorrelating the latter from $\boldsymbol{A}\widehat{\mathcal{B}}-\boldsymbol{\Psi}$ (see Proposition 2.13). Thus,

$$\begin{aligned}&\text{vec}(\widehat{\boldsymbol{X}\mathcal{B}_R})\\ &\quad = \text{vec}(\widehat{\boldsymbol{X}\mathcal{B}}) - Cov(\text{vec}(\widehat{\boldsymbol{X}\mathcal{B}}), \text{vec}(\boldsymbol{A}\widehat{\mathcal{B}}))[D(\text{vec}(\boldsymbol{A}\widehat{\mathcal{B}}))]^-\text{vec}(\boldsymbol{A}\widehat{\mathcal{B}}-\boldsymbol{\Psi}).\end{aligned}$$

In view of (10.4) and (10.8), this expression simplifies to

$$\text{vec}(\widehat{\boldsymbol{X}\mathcal{B}_R}) = \text{vec}(\widehat{\boldsymbol{X}\mathcal{B}}) - \text{vec}\left(\boldsymbol{T}(\boldsymbol{X}^-)'\boldsymbol{A}'[\boldsymbol{A}\boldsymbol{X}^-\boldsymbol{T}(\boldsymbol{X}^-)'\boldsymbol{A}']^{-1}(\boldsymbol{A}\widehat{\mathcal{B}}-\boldsymbol{\Psi})\right).$$

This is similar to the expression given in Section 7.9.2 in the case of univariate response. Following that derivation, we obtain that

$$MSE(\text{vec}(\widehat{\boldsymbol{X}\mathcal{B}_R})) \leq MSE(\text{vec}(\widehat{\boldsymbol{X}\mathcal{B}}))$$

in the sense of Löwner order if

$$[\text{vec}(\boldsymbol{A}\mathcal{B} - \boldsymbol{\Psi})]'[\boldsymbol{\Sigma} \otimes (\boldsymbol{A}\boldsymbol{X}^-\boldsymbol{T}(\boldsymbol{X}^-)'\boldsymbol{A}')]^{-1}[\text{vec}(\boldsymbol{A}\mathcal{B} - \boldsymbol{\Psi})] \leq 1.$$

This condition can also be written as

$$\text{tr}[(\boldsymbol{A}\mathcal{B} - \boldsymbol{\Psi})'(\boldsymbol{A}\boldsymbol{X}^-\boldsymbol{T}(\boldsymbol{X}^-)'\boldsymbol{A}')^{-1}(\boldsymbol{A}\mathcal{B} - \boldsymbol{\Psi})\boldsymbol{\Sigma}^{-1}] \leq 1$$

which is satisfied if $\boldsymbol{\Psi}$ is close to the true value of $\boldsymbol{A}\mathcal{B}$ or $\boldsymbol{\Sigma}$ is large.

10.6 Tests of linear hypotheses

We now assume that

$$\text{vec}(\boldsymbol{Y}_{n\times q}) \sim N(\text{vec}(\boldsymbol{X}_{n\times k}\mathcal{B}_{k\times q}), \boldsymbol{\Sigma}_{q\times q} \otimes \boldsymbol{V}_{n\times n}).$$

Suppose we wish to test the null hypothesis

$$\mathcal{H}_0 \;:\; \boldsymbol{A}\mathcal{B} = \boldsymbol{\Psi} \tag{10.20}$$

against the alternative hypothesis

$$\mathcal{H}_1 \;:\; \boldsymbol{A}\mathcal{B} \neq \boldsymbol{\Psi}. \tag{10.21}$$

Let us suppose the data conforms to the consistency condition (10.18). The issue of testability of this hypothesis is similar to that in the univariate response case (see Section 4.2.2). We assume that the hypothesis $\mathcal{H}_0$ is completely testable, i.e. $\mathcal{C}(\boldsymbol{A}') \subseteq \mathcal{C}(\boldsymbol{X}')$. We also assume that there is no algebraic inconsistency in the hypothesis, i.e. $\mathcal{C}(\boldsymbol{\Psi}) \subseteq \mathcal{C}(\boldsymbol{A})$.

The decomposition (10.19) suggests that the data supports the null hypothesis if the matrix $\boldsymbol{R}_0$ is not too small compared to $\boldsymbol{R}_H$. There is no unique way to measure the 'smallness' of one matrix compared to another. We shall consider a few tests which essentially compare this pair of matrices in different ways.

10.6.1 *Generalized likelihood ratio test*

Recall from Section 10.4.2 that the log-likelihood function, after maximization with respect to $\boldsymbol{X}\mathcal{B}$ and $\boldsymbol{\Sigma}$, depends linearly on

$$\rho(\boldsymbol{V}) \log |\boldsymbol{B}_*'\boldsymbol{B}_*|,$$

where $\boldsymbol{B}_*\boldsymbol{B}_*'$ is a rank-factorization of $\boldsymbol{R}_0$. This result was derived *without assuming that $\boldsymbol{\Sigma}$ or $\boldsymbol{V}$ is positive definite.* The linear model (10.1) under the hypothesis $\mathcal{H}_0$ is equivalent to the unrestricted model (10.17). The error sum of squares and products matrix for this model is $\boldsymbol{R}_H$. Therefore, the log-likelihood function, after maximization with respect to $\boldsymbol{X}\mathcal{B}$ and $\boldsymbol{\Sigma}$ subject to the restriction $\boldsymbol{A}\mathcal{B} = \boldsymbol{\Psi}$, is a linear function of

$$\rho(\boldsymbol{V}) \log |\boldsymbol{B}_\dagger'\boldsymbol{B}_\dagger|,$$

where $\boldsymbol{B}_\dagger\boldsymbol{B}_\dagger'$ is a rank-factorization of $\boldsymbol{R}_H$. (Note that the rank of the error dispersion matrix of (10.17) is $\rho(\boldsymbol{V})$.) It follows from (B.4) that the GLRT is a monotonically increasing function of

$$\Lambda = \frac{|\boldsymbol{B}_*'\boldsymbol{B}_*|}{|\boldsymbol{B}_\dagger'\boldsymbol{B}_\dagger|}, \tag{10.22}$$

small values of which should lead to the rejection of $\mathcal{H}_0$. This statistic, proposed by Wilks (1932), is known as *Wilks' Λ statistic.* It follows from Remark 10.13 that

$$\mathcal{C}(\boldsymbol{B}_*) = \mathcal{C}(\boldsymbol{B}_\dagger) = \mathcal{C}(\boldsymbol{B}) = \mathcal{C}(\boldsymbol{\Sigma}).$$

As a result, the matrices $\boldsymbol{B}_*$, $\boldsymbol{B}_\dagger$ and $\boldsymbol{B}$, each being of order $q \times \rho_0$, have the same rank. In the special case where $\boldsymbol{\Sigma}$ is positive definite, the Wilks' Λ statistic simplifies to

$$\Lambda = \frac{|\boldsymbol{R}_0|}{|\boldsymbol{R}_H|}. \tag{10.23}$$

Returning to the general case, we now show that the distribution of Λ under $\mathcal{H}_0$ depends only on the following numbers:

$$\begin{aligned} \rho_0 &= \rho(\boldsymbol{\Sigma}), \\ \rho_1 &= \rho(\boldsymbol{V} : \boldsymbol{X}) - \rho(\boldsymbol{X}), \\ \rho_2 &= \rho(\boldsymbol{A}\boldsymbol{X}^-\boldsymbol{T}(\boldsymbol{X}^-)'\boldsymbol{A}'), \end{aligned}$$

where $\boldsymbol{T}$ is as in (10.6). We assume that $\rho_1 > \rho_0$. Since $\mathcal{C}(\boldsymbol{B}_*) = \mathcal{C}(\boldsymbol{B})$, $\boldsymbol{B}_*$ can be written as $\boldsymbol{B}\boldsymbol{B}^{-L}\boldsymbol{B}_*$. Hence,

$$\begin{aligned} |\boldsymbol{B}_*'\boldsymbol{B}_*| &= |\boldsymbol{B}_*'(\boldsymbol{B}^{-L})'\boldsymbol{B}'\boldsymbol{B}\boldsymbol{B}^{-L}\boldsymbol{B}_*| \\ &= |\boldsymbol{B}^{-L}\boldsymbol{B}_*\boldsymbol{B}_*'(\boldsymbol{B}^{-L})'| \cdot |\boldsymbol{B}'\boldsymbol{B}| \\ &= |\boldsymbol{B}^{-L}\boldsymbol{R}_0(\boldsymbol{B}^{-L})'| \cdot |\boldsymbol{B}'\boldsymbol{B}|. \end{aligned}$$

If $\boldsymbol{Z}_1$ is a matrix whose rows constitute a standardized basis set of NLZFs of (10.1), then $\boldsymbol{R}_0 = \boldsymbol{Z}_1'\boldsymbol{Z}_1$, the rows of the $\rho_0 \times q$ matrix $\boldsymbol{Z}_1$ being independent and distributed as $N(\boldsymbol{0}, \boldsymbol{\Sigma})$. Therefore,

$$|\boldsymbol{B}_*'\boldsymbol{B}_*| = |\boldsymbol{B}^{-L}\boldsymbol{Z}_1'\boldsymbol{Z}_1(\boldsymbol{B}^{-L})'| \cdot |\boldsymbol{B}'\boldsymbol{B}|.$$

Note that the elements of the $\rho_1 \times \rho_0$ matrix $\boldsymbol{Z}_1(\boldsymbol{B}^{-L})'$ are independent and have the standard normal distribution. Likewise, if $\boldsymbol{Z}_2$ is a matrix whose rows, together with those of $\boldsymbol{Z}_1$, constitute a standardized basis set of NLZFs of (10.17), then

$$|\boldsymbol{B}_\dagger'\boldsymbol{B}_\dagger| = |\boldsymbol{B}^{-L}\boldsymbol{Z}_1'\boldsymbol{Z}_1(\boldsymbol{B}^{-L})' + \boldsymbol{B}^{-L}\boldsymbol{Z}_2'\boldsymbol{Z}_2(\boldsymbol{B}^{-L})'| \cdot |\boldsymbol{B}'\boldsymbol{B}|.$$

In the above, the $\rho_2 \times \rho_0$ matrix $\boldsymbol{Z}_2(\boldsymbol{B}^{-L})'$ is independent of $\boldsymbol{Z}_1(\boldsymbol{B}^{-L})'$, and has independent elements with the standard normal distribution. It follows that

$$\Lambda = \frac{|\boldsymbol{Z}_0'\boldsymbol{Z}_0|}{|\boldsymbol{Z}_0'\boldsymbol{Z}_0 + \boldsymbol{Z}_h'\boldsymbol{Z}_h|},$$

where the elements of the $\rho_1 \times \rho_0$ matrix $\boldsymbol{Z}_0 = \boldsymbol{Z}_1(\boldsymbol{B}^{-L})'$ and the $\rho_2 \times \rho_0$ matrix $\boldsymbol{Z}_h = \boldsymbol{Z}_2(\boldsymbol{B}^{-L})'$ are independent and have the standard normal distribution. Therefore, the distribution of Λ depends only on ρ_i, $i = 0, 1, 2$.

The joint distribution of the elements of $\boldsymbol{Z}_0'\boldsymbol{Z}_0$ is called the *standard Wishart distribution* with parameters (ρ_0, ρ_1). We shall denote it by W_{ρ_0,ρ_1}. The density of this distribution is proportional to

$$|\boldsymbol{Z}_0'\boldsymbol{Z}_0|^{(\rho_1-\rho_0-1)/2}\exp[-\mathrm{tr}(\boldsymbol{Z}_0'\boldsymbol{Z}_0)/2].$$

Obviously the joint density of the elements of $\boldsymbol{Z}_1'\boldsymbol{Z}_1$ is W_{ρ_0,ρ_2}. See Bhimasankaram and Sengupta (1991) for a more general form of this distribution resulting from singular normal distributions.

The distribution of Λ is called the *Wilks' Λ distribution* with parameters (ρ_0, ρ_1, ρ_2). The distribution is the same as that of the product of ρ_0 independent beta-distributed random variables with parameters

$$\left(\frac{\rho_1 - \rho_0 + 1}{2}, \frac{\rho_2}{2}\right), \ldots, \left(\frac{\rho_1}{2}, \frac{\rho_2}{2}\right).$$

See Rao (1973) for some approximations to this distribution. The exact distribution in an important special case is derived in Section 10.6.3.

10.6.2 *Roy's union-intersection test*

Roy (1953) had introduced an interesting approach to the problem of testing multiple hypotheses. The use of this approach in the present context leads to a useful test.

The null hypothesis (10.20) consists of a matrix equality involving $\mathcal{B}$. It holds if and only if the vector equations $\boldsymbol{A}\mathcal{B}\boldsymbol{l} = \boldsymbol{\Psi}\boldsymbol{l}$ hold for all $\boldsymbol{l}$. Thus, we can think of $\mathcal{H}_0$ as the intersection of all the hypotheses of the form

$$\mathcal{H}_{0l} \;:\; \boldsymbol{A}\mathcal{B}\boldsymbol{l} = \boldsymbol{\Psi}\boldsymbol{l}$$

for all $\boldsymbol{l}$, that is,

$$\mathcal{H}_0 = \cap_l \mathcal{H}_{0l}.$$

The alternative hypothesis corresponding to $\mathcal{H}_{0l}$ for a fixed $\boldsymbol{l}$ is

$$\mathcal{H}_{1l} \;:\; \boldsymbol{A}\mathcal{B}\boldsymbol{l} \neq \boldsymbol{\Psi}\boldsymbol{l}.$$

The overall alternative hypothesis can be written as the union

$$\mathcal{H}_1 = \cup_l \mathcal{H}_{1l}.$$

If we fix $\boldsymbol{l}$ for the time being, then we can frame the problem of testing $\mathcal{H}_{0l}$ against $\mathcal{H}_{1l}$ in the context of the univariate response linear model

$$(\boldsymbol{Y}\boldsymbol{l}, \boldsymbol{X}\mathcal{B}\boldsymbol{l}, (\boldsymbol{l}'\Sigma\boldsymbol{l})\boldsymbol{V}).$$

The GLRT for this problem was derived in Section 7.11. The test rejects $\mathcal{H}_{0l}$ if the ratio $(R^2_{Hl} - R^2_{0l})/R^2_{0l}$ is too large, where R^2_{0l} is the error sum of squares for the above model and R^2_{Hl} is the error sum of squares under the hypothesis $\mathcal{H}_{0l}$. It is easy to see that $R^2_{0l} = \boldsymbol{l}'\boldsymbol{R}_0\boldsymbol{l}$ and $R^2_{Hl} = \boldsymbol{l}'\boldsymbol{R}_H\boldsymbol{l}$. Therefore, $\mathcal{H}_{0l}$ should be rejected if the ratio $\boldsymbol{l}'(\boldsymbol{R}_H - \boldsymbol{R}_0)\boldsymbol{l}/(\boldsymbol{l}'\boldsymbol{R}_0\boldsymbol{l})$ is sufficiently large.

Let us now return to the original hypothesis, $\mathcal{H}_0$. Since it is the intersection of all the hypotheses of the form $\mathcal{H}_{0l}$, it should be rejected if the data carries evidence against *any* one of the sub-hypotheses. In other words, $\mathcal{H}_0$ should be rejected if

$$T_R = \sup_{l} \frac{\boldsymbol{l}'(\boldsymbol{R}_H - \boldsymbol{R}_0)\boldsymbol{l}}{\boldsymbol{l}'\boldsymbol{R}_0\boldsymbol{l}}$$

is too large. The statistic T_R is called the *union-intersection statistic* for $\mathcal{H}_0$.

Suppose $\boldsymbol{B}_*\boldsymbol{B}_*'$ is a rank factorization of $\boldsymbol{R}_0$. Since $\mathcal{C}(\boldsymbol{B}_*)$, $\mathcal{C}(\boldsymbol{R}_H)$ and $\mathcal{C}(\boldsymbol{\Sigma})$ are identical with probability 1 (see Remark 10.13), we can write $\boldsymbol{R}_H$ as $\boldsymbol{B}_*\boldsymbol{B}_*^{-L}\boldsymbol{R}_H$. Therefore,

$$\begin{aligned} T_R &= \sup_{l} \frac{\boldsymbol{l}'\boldsymbol{B}_*\boldsymbol{B}_*^{-L}\boldsymbol{R}_H(\boldsymbol{B}_*^{-L})'\boldsymbol{B}_*'\boldsymbol{l}}{\boldsymbol{l}'\boldsymbol{B}_*\boldsymbol{B}_*\boldsymbol{l}} - 1 \\ &= \sup_{k} \frac{\boldsymbol{k}'\boldsymbol{B}_*^{-L}\boldsymbol{R}_H(\boldsymbol{B}_*^{-L})'\boldsymbol{k}}{\boldsymbol{k}'\boldsymbol{k}} - 1. \end{aligned}$$

It follows from Proposition A.26 that $T_R + 1$ is the largest eigenvalue of the matrix $\boldsymbol{B}_*^{-L}\boldsymbol{R}_H(\boldsymbol{B}_*^{-L})'$. If $\boldsymbol{B}_\dagger\boldsymbol{B}_\dagger'$ is a rank-factorization of $\boldsymbol{R}_H$, then T_R+1 is also the largest eigenvalue of $\boldsymbol{B}_\dagger'(\boldsymbol{B}_*^{-L})'\boldsymbol{B}_*^{-L}\boldsymbol{B}_\dagger$, that is, the largest eigenvalue of the matrix $\boldsymbol{B}_\dagger'\boldsymbol{R}_0^-\boldsymbol{B}_\dagger$. Proposition 10.17 of the next section guarantees that when $\mathcal{H}_0$ holds, the distribution of T_R does not depend on $\boldsymbol{\Sigma}$. Like Wilks' Λ statistic, the union-intersection statistic also has a distribution that depends only on the parameters ρ_0, ρ_1 and ρ_2, described in the previous section.

When $\boldsymbol{\Sigma}$ is positive definite, $\boldsymbol{R}_0$ is also positive definite with probability 1. In this special case the union-intersection statistic reduces to the largest eigenvalue of $(\boldsymbol{R}_H - \boldsymbol{R}_0)\boldsymbol{R}_0^{-1}$. The distribution of T_R in another special case is derived in Section 10.6.3.

10.6.3 *Other tests*

Let $\boldsymbol{B}_*\boldsymbol{B}_*'$ and $\boldsymbol{B}_\dagger\boldsymbol{B}_\dagger'$ be rank factorizations of $\boldsymbol{R}_0$ and $\boldsymbol{R}_H$, respectively. By making use of the congruence of the column spaces of $\boldsymbol{R}_0$ and $\boldsymbol{R}_H$, the

Wilks' Λ test can alternatively be expressed as

$$\begin{aligned}
\Lambda &= \frac{|\boldsymbol{B}_*'\boldsymbol{B}_*|}{|\boldsymbol{B}_\dagger'\boldsymbol{B}_\dagger|} \\
&= \frac{|\boldsymbol{B}_*'\boldsymbol{B}_*|}{|\boldsymbol{B}_\dagger'(\boldsymbol{B}_*^{-L})'\boldsymbol{B}_*'\boldsymbol{B}_*\boldsymbol{B}_*^{-L}\boldsymbol{B}_\dagger|} \\
&= \frac{|\boldsymbol{B}_*'\boldsymbol{B}_*|}{|\boldsymbol{B}_*'\boldsymbol{B}_*\boldsymbol{B}_\dagger'(\boldsymbol{B}_*^{-L})'\boldsymbol{B}_*^{-L}\boldsymbol{B}_\dagger|} \\
&= \frac{|\boldsymbol{B}_*'\boldsymbol{B}_*|}{|\boldsymbol{B}_*'\boldsymbol{B}_*|\cdot|\boldsymbol{B}_\dagger'(\boldsymbol{B}_*^{-L})'\boldsymbol{B}_*^{-L}\boldsymbol{B}_\dagger|} \\
&= \frac{1}{|\boldsymbol{B}_\dagger'\boldsymbol{R}_0^-\boldsymbol{B}_\dagger|}.
\end{aligned}$$

Thus, Λ and T_R are both functions of the matrix $\boldsymbol{B}_\dagger'\boldsymbol{R}_0^-\boldsymbol{B}_\dagger$. We shall now show that under $\mathcal{H}_0$, this matrix is invariant of $\boldsymbol{\Sigma}$.

Proposition 10.17. *Under the above set-up, the matrix $\boldsymbol{B}_\dagger'\boldsymbol{R}_0^-\boldsymbol{B}_\dagger$ does not depend on $\boldsymbol{\Sigma}$.*

Proof. Let $\boldsymbol{B}\boldsymbol{B}'$ be a rank-factorization of $\boldsymbol{\Sigma}$. Since the column spaces of the matrices $\boldsymbol{B}$, $\boldsymbol{B}_*$ and $\boldsymbol{B}_\dagger$ are identical with probability 1 (see Remark 10.13), we can write

$$\begin{aligned}
\boldsymbol{B}_\dagger'\boldsymbol{R}_0^-\boldsymbol{B}_\dagger &= [\boldsymbol{B}_\dagger'(\boldsymbol{B}^{-L})'\boldsymbol{B}']\boldsymbol{R}_0^-[\boldsymbol{B}\boldsymbol{B}^{-L}\boldsymbol{B}_\dagger] \\
&= [\boldsymbol{B}_\dagger'(\boldsymbol{B}^{-L})'][\boldsymbol{B}^{-L}\boldsymbol{R}_0(\boldsymbol{B}^{-L})']^{-1}[\boldsymbol{B}^{-L}\boldsymbol{B}_\dagger].
\end{aligned}$$

It was shown in Section 10.6.1 that $\boldsymbol{B}^{-L}\boldsymbol{R}_0(\boldsymbol{B}^{-L})'$ does not depend on $\boldsymbol{\Sigma}$. Likewise, $\boldsymbol{B}^{-L}\boldsymbol{R}_H(\boldsymbol{B}^{-L})'$ is free of $\boldsymbol{\Sigma}$, and $[\boldsymbol{B}^{-L}\boldsymbol{B}_\dagger][\boldsymbol{B}^{-L}\boldsymbol{B}_\dagger]'$ can be any rank-factorization of $\boldsymbol{B}^{-L}\boldsymbol{R}_H(\boldsymbol{B}^{-L})'$. The result follows. □

The (almost surely) nonsingular matrix $\boldsymbol{B}_\dagger'\boldsymbol{R}_0^-\boldsymbol{B}_\dagger$ holds the key to this testing problem. The distribution of this matrix under $\mathcal{H}_0$ depends only on the parameters ρ_0, ρ_1 and ρ_2, defined in Section 10.6.1. We have already seen that the Wilks' Λ and union-intersection statistics are scalar functions of this matrix. Other scalar functions can also be used. Lawley (1938) and Hotelling (1951) suggest a test which amounts to rejecting $\mathcal{H}_0$ when the trace (T_{LH}) of the matrix $[\boldsymbol{B}_\dagger'\boldsymbol{R}_0^-\boldsymbol{B}_\dagger - \boldsymbol{I}]$ is too large. A multiple of this trace, $(\rho(\boldsymbol{V} : \boldsymbol{X}) - \rho(\boldsymbol{X}))[\boldsymbol{B}_\dagger'\boldsymbol{R}_0^-\boldsymbol{B}_\dagger - \boldsymbol{I}]$ is generally denoted by T^2. Generalization of another test suggested by Pillai (1955) leads to the rejection of $\mathcal{H}_0$ when the trace (T_P) of the matrix $\boldsymbol{I} - (\boldsymbol{B}_\dagger'\boldsymbol{R}_0^-\boldsymbol{B}_\dagger)^{-1}$ is too large. All the four statistics can be expressed in terms of simple functions of the eigenvalues of $B_\dagger' R_0^- B_\dagger$. When Σ is positive definite, these eigenvalues coincide with those of $R_H R_0^{-1}$. See Arnold (1981, Chapter 19) for asymptotic distributions of these test statistics.

Example 10.18. (Egyptian skulls, continued) For the data of Table 10.1, let us consider the hypothesis of homogeneity of the group means. The sum of squares under this null hypothesis is $R_H = Y'(I - P_1)Y$. The test statistics Λ, T_R, T_{LH} and T_P are functions of the eigenvalues of the matrix $B_\dagger' R_0^- B_\dagger$, which coincide with those of $R_0^- B_\dagger B_\dagger'$ or $R_0^- R_H$. Continuing with the codes given in Examples 10.5, the additional lines of code given below produces the matrices $R_H - R_0$ and R_0 and carries out the four tests.

```
library(car)
linearHypothesis(mlm, hypothesis.matrix = c("factor(Year)-3300=0",
"factor(Year)-1850=0", "factor(Year)-200=0", "factor(Year)150=0"))
```

The output is as follows.

```
Sum of squares and products for the hypothesis:
          MB          BH         BL          NH
MB  502.8267 -228.14667 -626.6267  135.43333
BH -228.1467  229.90667  292.2800  -66.06667
BL -626.6267  292.28000  803.2933 -180.73333
NH  135.4333  -66.06667 -180.7333   61.20000

Sum of squares and products for error:
            MB          BH          BL         NH
MB 3061.066667    5.333333    11.46667  291.3000
BH    5.333333 3405.266667   754.00000  412.5333
BL   11.466667  754.000000 3505.96667  164.3333
NH  291.300000  412.533333   164.33333 1472.1333

Multivariate Tests:
                 Df test stat  approx F num Df   den Df       Pr(>F)
Pillai            4 0.3533056  3.512037     16 580.0000 4.6753e-06
Wilks             4 0.6635858  3.900928     16 434.4548 7.0102e-07
Hotelling-Lawley  4 0.4818191  4.230974     16 562.0000 8.2782e-08
Roy               4 0.4250954 15.409707      4 145.0000 1.5883e-10
```

All the tests indicate heterogeneity of skull dimensions across the five time periods.

It may be verified that the matrix $\boldsymbol{R}_0$ reported above is the same as R0 computed (though not reported) in Example 10.14. For independent computation of the matrix $\boldsymbol{R}_H$ and the integer parameters ρ_0, ρ_1 and ρ_2 of the Wilks' Λ statistic (see (10.23) and the discussion after it), one can use the code given below.

```
one <- rep(1,dim(Y)[1])
P1 <- projector(one)
RH <- t(Y)%*%(diag(one)-P1)%*%Y
r0 <- dim(Y)[2]
r1 <- dim(X)[1] - dim(X)[2]
r2 <- dim(X)[2] - 1
```

The three parameters are found to be 4, 145 and 4. Computation of the four statistics can be verified, in accordance with the foregoing discussion, through the following code.

```
sum(diag(solve(RH)%*%(RH-R0)))          # Pillai test
det(R0)/det(RH)                         # Wilks test
sum(diag((RH-R0)%*%solve(R0)))          # Lawley-Hotelling
eigen(RH%*%solve(R0))$values[1] - 1     # Roy test
```

The four test statistics turn out to be 0.3533, 0.6636, 0.4818 and 0.4251 respectively, as computed previously. □

We now consider the special case where $\rho_2 = 1$, i.e. $\boldsymbol{R}_H - \boldsymbol{R}_0$ is a matrix of rank 1. Some examples of this case are given in Section 10.8. We show that the four statistics described so far are equivalent in this case.

Proposition 10.19. *In the above set-up, let $\boldsymbol{R}_H - \boldsymbol{R}_0$ be a matrix of rank 1. Then the GLRT, Roy's union-intersection test, the Lawley-Hotelling test and Pillai's test are equivalent to rejecting the null hypothesis for large values of $\boldsymbol{r}_H'\boldsymbol{R}_0^-\boldsymbol{r}_H$, where $\boldsymbol{R}_H - \boldsymbol{R}_0 = \boldsymbol{r}_H\boldsymbol{r}_H'$.*

Proof. Let $\boldsymbol{B}_*\boldsymbol{B}_*'$ be a rank factorization of $\boldsymbol{R}_0$. Since $\mathcal{C}(\boldsymbol{R}_H) = \mathcal{C}(\boldsymbol{R}_0)$ with probability 1 (see Remark 10.13), we have $\boldsymbol{r}_H \in \mathcal{C}(\boldsymbol{R}_0)$ almost surely. Thus, $\boldsymbol{r}_H'\boldsymbol{R}_0^-\boldsymbol{r}_H$ is well-defined for any choice of the g-inverse.

It has already been observed that the four test statistics are functions of the eigenvalues of $\boldsymbol{B}_\dagger'\boldsymbol{R}_0^-\boldsymbol{B}_\dagger$, where $\boldsymbol{B}_\dagger\boldsymbol{B}_\dagger'$ is a rank-factorization of $\boldsymbol{R}_H$. The set of eigenvalues of $\boldsymbol{B}_\dagger'\boldsymbol{R}_0^-\boldsymbol{B}_\dagger$ are the same as the set of *nonzero* eigenvalues of $\boldsymbol{R}_0^-\boldsymbol{B}_\dagger\boldsymbol{B}_\dagger'$, that is, the set of nonzero eigenvalues of $\boldsymbol{R}_0^-(\boldsymbol{R}_0 + \boldsymbol{r}_H\boldsymbol{r}_H')$. By expressing $\boldsymbol{r}_H$ as $\boldsymbol{B}_*\boldsymbol{r}$ for some vector $\boldsymbol{r}$, we have

$$\boldsymbol{R}_0^-(\boldsymbol{R}_0 + \boldsymbol{r}_H\boldsymbol{r}_H') = (\boldsymbol{B}_*\boldsymbol{B}_*')^-\boldsymbol{B}_*[\boldsymbol{I}_{\rho(\Sigma)\times\rho(\Sigma)} + \boldsymbol{r}\boldsymbol{r}']\boldsymbol{B}_*'.$$

The nonzero eigenvalues of the latter matrix are the same as the eigenvalues of the nonsingular matrix $\boldsymbol{P}_{\boldsymbol{B}_*'}(\boldsymbol{I}+\boldsymbol{r}\boldsymbol{r}')$, which simplifies to $\boldsymbol{I}+\boldsymbol{r}\boldsymbol{r}'$. This matrix has $\rho(\boldsymbol{\Sigma})$ eigenvalues, one of which is $1+\boldsymbol{r}'\boldsymbol{r}$ while the others are equal to 1. Since $\boldsymbol{r}'\boldsymbol{r} = \boldsymbol{r}_H'(\boldsymbol{B}_*^-)'\boldsymbol{B}_*^-\boldsymbol{r}_H = \boldsymbol{r}_H'\boldsymbol{R}_0^-\boldsymbol{r}_H$, we conclude that $\rho(\boldsymbol{\Sigma})-1$ eigenvalues of the matrix $\boldsymbol{B}_\dagger'\boldsymbol{R}_0^-\boldsymbol{B}_\dagger$ are equal to 1 and the remaining one is equal to $1+\boldsymbol{r}_H'\boldsymbol{R}_0^-\boldsymbol{r}_H$. It follows that

$$\begin{aligned}
\Lambda &= \frac{1}{1+\boldsymbol{r}_H'\boldsymbol{R}_0^-\boldsymbol{r}_H},\\
T_R &= \boldsymbol{r}_H'\boldsymbol{R}_0^-\boldsymbol{r}_H,\\
T_{LH} &= \boldsymbol{r}_H'\boldsymbol{R}_0^-\boldsymbol{r}_H = \frac{T^2}{\rho(\boldsymbol{V}:\boldsymbol{X})-\rho(\boldsymbol{X})},\\
T_P &= \frac{\boldsymbol{r}_H'\boldsymbol{R}_0^-\boldsymbol{r}_H}{1+\boldsymbol{r}_H'\boldsymbol{R}_0^-\boldsymbol{r}_H}.
\end{aligned}$$

Therefore, all the tests are equivalent to rejecting the null hypothesis when $\boldsymbol{r}_H'\boldsymbol{R}_0^-\boldsymbol{r}_H$ is too large. □

The statistic T^2 described in the context of Proposition 10.19 is known as *Hotelling's* T^2 statistic. It is a generalization of the two-sample t-test for univariate data. We now prove a result which leads to the null distribution of the statistic $\boldsymbol{r}_H'\boldsymbol{R}_0^-\boldsymbol{r}_H$.

Proposition 10.20. *Let $\boldsymbol{u}_0,\boldsymbol{u}_1,\ldots,\boldsymbol{u}_n$ be independent random vectors of order $q\times 1$, having the distribution $N(\boldsymbol{0},\boldsymbol{\Sigma})$. Let $\boldsymbol{Z}=(\boldsymbol{u}_1:\cdots:\boldsymbol{u}_n)'$ and $q_*=\rho(\boldsymbol{\Sigma})\le n$. Then $\boldsymbol{u}_0'(\boldsymbol{Z}'\boldsymbol{Z})^-\boldsymbol{u}_0(n-q_*+1)/q_*$ has the $F_{q_*,\,n-q_*+1}$ distribution.*

Proof. Let $\boldsymbol{F}_{q\times q_*}$ be such that $\boldsymbol{F}\boldsymbol{F}'$ is a rank-factorization of $\boldsymbol{\Sigma}$ and $\boldsymbol{v}_j = \boldsymbol{F}^{-L}\boldsymbol{u}_j$, $j=0,1,\ldots,n$, for a fixed left-inverse of $\boldsymbol{F}$. Note that the independent random vectors $\boldsymbol{v}_0,\boldsymbol{v}_1,\ldots,\boldsymbol{v}_n$, have the distribution $N(\boldsymbol{0},\boldsymbol{I}_{q_*\times q_*})$. It follows from Proposition 2.13 and Remark 10.13 that $\boldsymbol{u}_0\in\mathcal{C}(\boldsymbol{\Sigma})=\mathcal{C}(\boldsymbol{F})=\mathcal{C}(\boldsymbol{Z}')$ with probability 1. Therefore,

$$\boldsymbol{u}_0'(\boldsymbol{Z}'\boldsymbol{Z})^-\boldsymbol{u}_0 = \boldsymbol{u}_0'(\boldsymbol{F}^{-L})'\boldsymbol{F}'(\boldsymbol{Z}'\boldsymbol{Z})^-\boldsymbol{F}\boldsymbol{F}^{-L}\boldsymbol{u}_0 = \boldsymbol{v}_0'\left(\sum_{j=1}^n \boldsymbol{v}_j\boldsymbol{v}_j'\right)^{-1}\boldsymbol{v}_0.$$

This reduction shows that it is enough to prove the statement of the proposition for $\boldsymbol{\Sigma}=\boldsymbol{I}$.

We now assume that $\boldsymbol{\Sigma}=\boldsymbol{I}$, replace $(\boldsymbol{Z}'\boldsymbol{Z})^-$ by $(\boldsymbol{Z}'\boldsymbol{Z})^{-1}$, and do not make a distinction between q and q_*. Let $\boldsymbol{d}=\|\boldsymbol{u}_0\|^{-1}\boldsymbol{u}_0$ and $\boldsymbol{C}$ be a

$q_* \times (q_* - 1)$ matrix such that $\boldsymbol{B}' = (\boldsymbol{C} : \boldsymbol{d})$ is an orthogonal matrix. Given $\boldsymbol{u}_0$, the vectors $\boldsymbol{w}_j = \boldsymbol{B}\boldsymbol{u}_j$, $j = 1, \ldots, n$ are independent and have the distribution $N(\boldsymbol{0}, \boldsymbol{I}_{q_* \times q_*})$. Let $\boldsymbol{Z}_* = (\boldsymbol{w}_1 : \cdots : \boldsymbol{w}_n)' = \boldsymbol{Z}\boldsymbol{B}'$. Then the ratio

$$\frac{\boldsymbol{u}_0'(\boldsymbol{Z}'\boldsymbol{Z})^{-1}\boldsymbol{u}_0}{\boldsymbol{u}_0'\boldsymbol{u}_0} = \boldsymbol{d}'(\boldsymbol{Z}'\boldsymbol{Z})^{-1}\boldsymbol{d},$$

is seen to be the last diagonal element of $\boldsymbol{B}(\boldsymbol{Z}'\boldsymbol{Z})^{-1}\boldsymbol{B}'$, that is, the last diagonal element of $(\boldsymbol{Z}_*'\boldsymbol{Z}_*)^{-1}$. Using the block matrix inversion formula (see page 593) for the matrix

$$\boldsymbol{Z}_*'\boldsymbol{Z}_* = \begin{pmatrix} (\boldsymbol{Z}\boldsymbol{C})'\boldsymbol{Z}\boldsymbol{C} & (\boldsymbol{Z}\boldsymbol{C})'\boldsymbol{Z}\boldsymbol{d} \\ (\boldsymbol{Z}\boldsymbol{d})'\boldsymbol{Z}\boldsymbol{C} & (\boldsymbol{Z}\boldsymbol{d})'\boldsymbol{Z}\boldsymbol{d} \end{pmatrix} = \begin{pmatrix} \boldsymbol{X}_*'\boldsymbol{X}_* & \boldsymbol{X}_*'\boldsymbol{y}_* \\ \boldsymbol{y}_*'\boldsymbol{X}_* & \boldsymbol{y}_*'\boldsymbol{y}_* \end{pmatrix},$$

where $\boldsymbol{X}_* = \boldsymbol{Z}\boldsymbol{C}$ and $\boldsymbol{y}_* = \boldsymbol{Z}\boldsymbol{d}$, we have the following expression for the last diagonal element of its inverse.

$$\boldsymbol{d}'(\boldsymbol{Z}'\boldsymbol{Z})^{-1}\boldsymbol{d} = [\boldsymbol{y}_*'\boldsymbol{y}_* - \boldsymbol{y}_*'\boldsymbol{X}_*(\boldsymbol{X}_*'\boldsymbol{X}_*)^{-1}\boldsymbol{X}_*'\boldsymbol{y}_*]^{-1} = \frac{1}{\boldsymbol{y}_*'(\boldsymbol{I} - \boldsymbol{P}_{X_*})\boldsymbol{y}_*}.$$

Consequently

$$\frac{\boldsymbol{u}_0'\boldsymbol{u}_0}{\boldsymbol{u}_0'(\boldsymbol{Z}'\boldsymbol{Z})^{-}\boldsymbol{u}_0} = \frac{\boldsymbol{u}_0'\boldsymbol{u}_0}{\boldsymbol{u}_0'(\boldsymbol{Z}'\boldsymbol{Z})^{-1}\boldsymbol{u}_0} = \boldsymbol{y}_*'(\boldsymbol{I} - \boldsymbol{P}_{X_*})\boldsymbol{y}_*.$$

For given $\boldsymbol{u}_0$, the above quantity is the error sum of squares for the linear model $(\boldsymbol{y}_*, \boldsymbol{X}_*\boldsymbol{\beta}, \sigma^2\boldsymbol{I})$. Since the elements of $\boldsymbol{y}_*$ and $\boldsymbol{X}_*$ are independent and have the standard normal distribution (given $\boldsymbol{u}_0$), it follows that the error sum of squares has the $\chi^2_{n-\rho(X_*)}$ distribution. Note that $\rho(\boldsymbol{X}_*) = \rho(\boldsymbol{C}) = q_* - 1$, and that the above conditional distribution does not depend on the $\boldsymbol{u}_0$. Therefore, the conditional distribution is the same as the unconditional distribution and the chi-square statistic is independent of $\boldsymbol{u}_0'\boldsymbol{u}_0$. Therefore, the ratio

$$\boldsymbol{u}_0'(\boldsymbol{Z}'\boldsymbol{Z})^{-}\boldsymbol{u}_0 \times \frac{n - \rho(\boldsymbol{X}_*)}{q_*} = \frac{\boldsymbol{u}_0'\boldsymbol{u}_0/q_*}{\left(\dfrac{\boldsymbol{u}_0'\boldsymbol{u}_0}{\boldsymbol{u}_0'(\boldsymbol{Z}'\boldsymbol{Z})^{-}\boldsymbol{u}_0}\right) \Big/ (n - q_* + 1)}$$

has the stated F distribution. □

It follows from Propositions 10.19 and 10.20 that under the null hypothesis, the statistic $\boldsymbol{r}_H'\boldsymbol{R}_0^{-}\boldsymbol{r}_H(\rho_1 - \rho_0 + 1)/\rho_0$ has the $F_{\rho_0,\ \rho_1-\rho_0+1}$ distribution, where ρ_0 and ρ_1 are as defined in Section 10.6.1. Distribution under the alternative hypothesis is generally difficult to obtain; see Fang et al. (2000) and the references therein for approximations.

Example 10.21. (Egyptian skulls, continued) For the data given in Table 10.1, let us treat Year as a continuous variable. The hypothesis of homogeneity of the group means would then reduce to the coefficient of this regressor being 0. In this situation, $\boldsymbol{R}_H - \boldsymbol{R}_0 = \boldsymbol{Y}'\boldsymbol{P}_x\boldsymbol{Y}$, where $\boldsymbol{x}$ is the mean corrected version of the Year vector. In other words, $\boldsymbol{R}_H - \boldsymbol{R}_0 = \boldsymbol{r}_H\boldsymbol{r}_H'$, where $\boldsymbol{r}_H = \boldsymbol{Y}'\boldsymbol{x}/\|\boldsymbol{x}\|$. Accordingly, one can carry out the single test that is equivalent to all the four tests, through the code given below.

```
data(skulls)
Y <- as.matrix(skulls[,1:4]); x <- skulls$Year
X <- cbind(1,x)
PX <- projector(X)
R0 <- t(Y)%*%(Y-PX%*%Y)
r1 <- dim(X)[1] - dim(X)[2]
r0 <- dim(Y)[2]
x <- x - mean(x)
rH <- t(Y)%*%x/sqrt(sum(x^2))
teststat <- t(rH)%*%solve(R0,rH) * (r1 - r0 + 1) / r0
teststat; pf(teststat,r0,r1-r0+1,lower.tail = FALSE)
```

The test statistic turns out to be 15.219, and its p-value is 2.0604×10^{-10}. The same computation can be done directly by the following lines of code.

```
data(skulls)
mlm <- lm(cbind(MB, BH, BL, NH) ~ Year, data = skulls)
library(car)
linearHypothesis(mlm, hypothesis.matrix = c("factor(Year)-3300=0",
"factor(Year)-1850=0", "factor(Year)-200=0", "factor(Year)150=0"))
```

The output (omitted here) shows that even though the four test statistics are not the same, the corresponding F-ratio is 15.219 in all the cases, with 4 and 145 degrees of freedom, and the p-value is as reported above. □

10.6.4 *A more general hypothesis*

The tests of Sections 10.6.1–10.6.3 can be used for any hypothesis of the form $\boldsymbol{A}\mathcal{B}\boldsymbol{C} = \boldsymbol{\Psi}$, against the alternative hypothesis $\boldsymbol{A}\mathcal{B}\boldsymbol{C} \neq \boldsymbol{\Psi}$, where $\boldsymbol{C}$ is a known matrix having full column rank. To see this, transform the response matrix $\boldsymbol{Y}$ linearly into $\boldsymbol{YC}$, and consider the model $(\text{vec}(\boldsymbol{YC}), (\boldsymbol{I} \otimes \boldsymbol{X})\text{vec}(\mathcal{B}_*), \boldsymbol{\Sigma}_* \otimes \boldsymbol{V})$, where $\mathcal{B}_* = \mathcal{B}\boldsymbol{C}$ and $\boldsymbol{\Sigma}_* = \boldsymbol{C}'\boldsymbol{\Sigma}\boldsymbol{C}$.

The null and alternative hypotheses reduce to $\boldsymbol{A}\mathcal{B}_* = \boldsymbol{\Psi}$ and $\boldsymbol{A}\mathcal{B}_* \neq \boldsymbol{\Psi}$, respectively.

Example 10.22. (Profile analysis) Suppose heights of some children with a growth disorder are measured at the exact ages of $k_0+1,\ldots,k_0+k_1$ years. Complete data on n_1 girls and n_2 boys are available. Let μ_{jk} be the population mean of the height of the jth group at age k_0+k, $k=1,\ldots,k_1$; $j=1$ indicates girls and $j=2$ indicates boys. The task is to compare the plots of μ_{jk} vs. k (average height vs. age) for the two groups. We assume that the height (y_{ijk}) of the ith subject of the jth group at age k_0+k years follows the linear model

$$y_{ijk} = \mu_{jk} + \varepsilon_{ijk}, \quad i=1,\ldots,n_j,\ j=1,2,\ k=1,\ldots,k_1.$$

The model can be written as $\boldsymbol{Y} = \boldsymbol{X}\mathcal{B} + \mathcal{E}$, where

$$\boldsymbol{Y} = \begin{pmatrix} y_{111} & \cdots & y_{11k_1} \\ \vdots & \ddots & \vdots \\ y_{n_1 11} & \cdots & y_{n_1 1k_1} \\ y_{121} & \cdots & y_{12k_1} \\ \vdots & \ddots & \vdots \\ y_{n_2 21} & \cdots & y_{n_2 2k_1} \end{pmatrix}, \quad \boldsymbol{X} = \begin{pmatrix} 1 & 0 \\ \vdots & \vdots \\ 1 & 0 \\ 0 & 1 \\ \vdots & \vdots \\ 0 & 1 \end{pmatrix}, \quad \mathcal{B} = \begin{pmatrix} \mu_{11} & \cdots & \mu_{1k_1} \\ \mu_{21} & \cdots & \mu_{2k_1} \end{pmatrix}.$$

Consider the following three hypothesis: (a) $\mathcal{H}_p$, that the two plots are parallel (same 'velocity' of mean height for boys and girls), (b) $\mathcal{H}_e$, that the two plots are identical (same mean height for both the groups at any given age) and (c) $\mathcal{H}_c$, that the lines are horizontal (no gain in mean height with age). Let

$$\boldsymbol{A} = (1 : -1), \qquad \boldsymbol{C}_{k_1\times(k_1-1)} = \begin{pmatrix} 1 & 1 & \cdots & 1 \\ -1 & 0 & \cdots & 0 \\ 0 & -1 & \cdots & 0 \\ \vdots & \vdots & \ddots & \vdots \\ 0 & 0 & \cdots & -1 \end{pmatrix}.$$

Then the three null hypotheses can be written as $\boldsymbol{A}\mathcal{B}\boldsymbol{C} = \boldsymbol{0}$, $\boldsymbol{A}\mathcal{B} = \boldsymbol{0}$ and $\mathcal{B}\boldsymbol{C} = \boldsymbol{0}$, respectively. Assuming that $\text{vec}(\boldsymbol{Y}) \sim N((\boldsymbol{I}\otimes\boldsymbol{X})\text{vec}(\mathcal{B}), \boldsymbol{\Sigma}\otimes\boldsymbol{I})$, we can use the methods of Sections 10.6.1–10.6.3 to test $\mathcal{H}_e$ against the general alternative hypothesis of no pattern in the average height profiles of boys and girls. The tests of the other two hypotheses against the same alternative hypothesis can be made on the basis of $\text{vec}(\boldsymbol{Y}_*) \sim N((\boldsymbol{I}\otimes\boldsymbol{X})\text{vec}(\mathcal{B}_*), \boldsymbol{\Sigma}_*\otimes\boldsymbol{I})$, where $\boldsymbol{Y}_* = \boldsymbol{Y}\boldsymbol{C}$, $\mathcal{B}_* = \mathcal{B}\boldsymbol{C}$ and $\boldsymbol{\Sigma}_* = \boldsymbol{C}'\boldsymbol{\Sigma}\boldsymbol{C}$. □

10.6.5 *Multiple comparisons*

The Bonferroni inequality can be used in the multivariate case to conduct simultaneous tests of hypotheses (see Section 4.2.7). Another procedure for multiple comparisons follows from Roy's union-intersection test (see Section 10.6.2). For instance, consider the three hypotheses

$$\mathcal{H}_{kl} : \boldsymbol{k}'\boldsymbol{A}\mathcal{B}\boldsymbol{l} = \boldsymbol{k}'\boldsymbol{\Psi}\boldsymbol{l}, \quad \mathcal{H}_l : \boldsymbol{A}\mathcal{B}\boldsymbol{l} = \boldsymbol{\Psi}\boldsymbol{l}, \quad \mathcal{H}_0 : \boldsymbol{A}\mathcal{B} = \boldsymbol{\Psi}.$$

Let $\boldsymbol{R}_H$ and $\boldsymbol{R}_0$ be as in Section 10.6.2, $R_{0l}^2 = \boldsymbol{l}'\boldsymbol{R}_0\boldsymbol{l}$, and $R_{H_{kl}}^2$ and $R_{H_l}^2$ be the error sum of squares for the model $(\boldsymbol{Y}\boldsymbol{l}, \boldsymbol{X}(\mathcal{B}\boldsymbol{l}), (\boldsymbol{l}'\boldsymbol{\Sigma}\boldsymbol{l})\boldsymbol{I})$ under $\mathcal{H}_{kl}$ and $\mathcal{H}_l$, respectively. It follows from the decomposition (7.17) and Exercise A.32 that $R_{H_l}^2 - R_{0l}^2$ is the largest possible value of $R_{H_{kl}}^2 - R_{0l}^2$ for all $\boldsymbol{k}$. If t_R is the level α cutoff for Roy's T_R statistic for $\mathcal{H}_0$, then under $\mathcal{H}_0$ we have

$$\begin{aligned} P\left(\frac{R_{H_{kl}}^2 - R_{0l}^2}{R_{0l}^2} > t_R\right) &\le P\left(\sup_{\boldsymbol{k}} \frac{R_{H_{kl}}^2 - R_{0l}^2}{R_{0l}^2} > t_R\right) = P\left(\frac{R_{H_l}^2 - R_{0l}^2}{R_{0l}^2} > t_R\right) \\ &\le P\left(\sup_{\boldsymbol{l}} \frac{\boldsymbol{l}'(\boldsymbol{R}_H - \boldsymbol{R}_0)\boldsymbol{l}}{\boldsymbol{l}'\boldsymbol{R}_0\boldsymbol{l}} > t_R\right) = P(T_R > t_R) = \alpha. \end{aligned}$$

Thus, the test $(R_{H_{kl}}^2 - R_{0l}^2)/R_{0l}^2 > t_R$ for $\mathcal{H}_{kl}$ has the probability of type I error at most α, even if this test is carried out along with an arbitrary number of tests of the same kind (with other choices for $\boldsymbol{k}$ and $\boldsymbol{l}$).

10.6.6 *Test for additional information*

All the q components of the response may not be important in understanding how the response depends on the explanatory variables. Suppose we partition the response $\boldsymbol{Y}$ as $(\boldsymbol{Y}_1 : \boldsymbol{Y}_2)$, where $\boldsymbol{Y}_j$ has q_j components, $j = 1, 2$, and $q_1 + q_2 = q$. It is clear from (10.1) that

$$E(\boldsymbol{Y}_j|\boldsymbol{X}) = \boldsymbol{X}\mathcal{B}_j \quad \text{for } j = 1, 2,$$

where $(\mathcal{B}_1 : \mathcal{B}_2)$ is a partition of $\mathcal{B}$ such that $\mathcal{B}_1$ has q_1 columns. Assuming the multivariate normality of $\boldsymbol{Y}$ and partitioning $\boldsymbol{\Sigma}$ conformably with $\boldsymbol{Y}$ as $\begin{pmatrix}\boldsymbol{\Sigma}_{11} & \boldsymbol{\Sigma}_{12} \\ \boldsymbol{\Sigma}_{21} & \boldsymbol{\Sigma}_{22}\end{pmatrix}$, we have

$$E(\boldsymbol{Y}_2|\boldsymbol{Y}_1, \boldsymbol{X}) = \boldsymbol{X}\mathcal{B}_2 + (\boldsymbol{Y}_1 - \boldsymbol{X}\mathcal{B}_1)\boldsymbol{\Sigma}_{11}^{-}\boldsymbol{\Sigma}_{12}, \tag{10.24}$$

$$D(\mathrm{vec}(\boldsymbol{Y}_2)|\boldsymbol{Y}_1, \boldsymbol{X}) = (\boldsymbol{\Sigma}_{22} - \boldsymbol{\Sigma}_{21}\boldsymbol{\Sigma}_{11}^{-}\boldsymbol{\Sigma}_{12}) \otimes \boldsymbol{V}. \tag{10.25}$$

It is possible that $E(\boldsymbol{Y}_2|\boldsymbol{Y}_1, \boldsymbol{X})$ does not depend on $\boldsymbol{X}$ at all. If this happens, then the knowledge of $\boldsymbol{Y}_1$ is sufficient for obtaining the mean of

$\boldsymbol{Y}_2$, and the knowledge of $\boldsymbol{X}$ is superfluous for this purpose. In other words, the components included in $\boldsymbol{Y}_1$ determine how all the components of the response depend on the explanatory variables, and the components included in $\boldsymbol{Y}_2$ do not carry any additional information in this regard. In practice, this may hold only in an approximate sense, that is, some components of the response may carry *most of the* relevant information regarding the dependence on the explanatory variables. Elimination of components with little information would produce a more parsimonious model.

Since the aim is to retain only the essential components, let us assume that there is no linear dependence among the retained components, i.e. $\boldsymbol{\Sigma}_{11}$ is positive definite. Then we can rewrite (10.24) as

$$E(\boldsymbol{Y}_2|\boldsymbol{Y}_1, \boldsymbol{X}) = \boldsymbol{Y}_1\mathcal{B}_a + \boldsymbol{X}\mathcal{B}_b = (\boldsymbol{Y}_1 : \boldsymbol{X})\begin{pmatrix}\mathcal{B}_a\\ \mathcal{B}_b\end{pmatrix},$$

where $\mathcal{B}_a = \boldsymbol{\Sigma}_{11}^{-1}\boldsymbol{\Sigma}_{12}$ and $\mathcal{B}_b = \mathcal{B}_2 - \mathcal{B}_1\boldsymbol{\Sigma}_{11}^{-1}\boldsymbol{\Sigma}_{12}$. The hypothesis '$\boldsymbol{X}\mathcal{B}_b = \boldsymbol{0}$' can be interpreted as 'no additional information carried by the last q_2 elements' of the response vector. The model for $\boldsymbol{Y}_2$ given $\boldsymbol{Y}_1$ is

$$\left(\mathrm{vec}(\boldsymbol{Y}_2), (\boldsymbol{I}\otimes(\boldsymbol{Y}_1 : \boldsymbol{X}))\mathrm{vec}\begin{pmatrix}\mathcal{B}_a\\ \mathcal{B}_b\end{pmatrix}, (\boldsymbol{\Sigma}_{22} - \boldsymbol{\Sigma}_{21}\boldsymbol{\Sigma}_{11}^{-}\boldsymbol{\Sigma}_{12})\otimes\boldsymbol{V}\right).$$

The essential difference of this model with (10.1) is that some of the response variables of (10.1) are regarded here as explanatory variables. It is with respect to this model that the hypothesis $(\boldsymbol{0} : \boldsymbol{X})\begin{pmatrix}\mathcal{B}_a\\ \mathcal{B}_b\end{pmatrix} = \boldsymbol{0}$ (or $\boldsymbol{X}\mathcal{B}_b = \boldsymbol{0}$) has to be tested. This problem is well within the general hypothesis testing framework of Sections 10.6.1–10.6.3.

10.7 Linear prediction and confidence regions

Suppose $\boldsymbol{Y}$ follows the multivariate linear model (10.1) and that we have to predict a new observation $\boldsymbol{y}_0$. The combined set of observations follow the model

$$\begin{pmatrix}\boldsymbol{Y}\\ \boldsymbol{y}_0'\end{pmatrix} = \begin{pmatrix}\boldsymbol{X}\\ \boldsymbol{x}_0'\end{pmatrix}\mathcal{B} + \begin{pmatrix}\mathcal{E}\\ \boldsymbol{\varepsilon}'\end{pmatrix}, \quad E\begin{pmatrix}\mathcal{E}\\ \boldsymbol{\varepsilon}'\end{pmatrix} = \boldsymbol{0}, \quad D\begin{pmatrix}\mathcal{E}\\ \boldsymbol{\varepsilon}'\end{pmatrix} = \boldsymbol{\Sigma}_{q\times q}\otimes\begin{pmatrix}\boldsymbol{V} & \boldsymbol{v}_0\\ \boldsymbol{v}_0' & v_0\end{pmatrix}.$$

The result of Exercise 2.9 implies that the BLP of $\boldsymbol{y}_0$ given $\boldsymbol{Y}$ is

$$\widehat{E}(\boldsymbol{y}_0|\boldsymbol{Y}) = [\boldsymbol{x}_0'\mathcal{B} + \boldsymbol{v}_0'\boldsymbol{V}^-(\boldsymbol{Y} - \boldsymbol{X}\mathcal{B})]',$$

and that the mean squared prediction error of the BLP is $\boldsymbol{\Sigma}\otimes(v_0 - \boldsymbol{v}_0'\boldsymbol{V}^-\boldsymbol{v}_0)$. Since $\mathcal{B}$ is unknown, the BLP cannot be computed. Therefore, we look for a linear predictor of the form $\boldsymbol{Ya}+\boldsymbol{b}$ where $\boldsymbol{a}$ and $\boldsymbol{b}$ do not depend on $\mathcal{B}$. This linear predictor is unbiased if $E(\boldsymbol{Ya}+\boldsymbol{b}) = E(\boldsymbol{y}_0)$ and is the best linear unbiased predictor (BLUP) if it minimizes the mean squared error matrix $E[(\boldsymbol{y}_0 - \boldsymbol{Ya} - \boldsymbol{b})(\boldsymbol{y}_0 - \boldsymbol{Ya} - \boldsymbol{b})']$ in the sense of the Löwner order. The BLUP is given by the following extension of Proposition 7.49.

Proposition 10.23. *The following statements hold in the above set-up.*

(a) If $\boldsymbol{x}_0'\mathcal{B}$ is not estimable under the model (10.1), then a BLUP of $\boldsymbol{y}_0$ does not exist.

(b) If $\boldsymbol{x}_0'\mathcal{B}$ is estimable under the model (10.1), then a BLUP of $\boldsymbol{y}_0$ is

$$\widehat{\boldsymbol{y}}_0 = [\widehat{\boldsymbol{x}_0'\mathcal{B}} + \boldsymbol{v}_0'\boldsymbol{V}^-\boldsymbol{E}]',$$

where $\widehat{\boldsymbol{x}_0'\mathcal{B}}$ and $\boldsymbol{E}$ are the BLUE of $\boldsymbol{x}_0'\mathcal{B}$ and the residual matrix from the model (10.1), respectively.

(c) The BLUP described in part (b) is unique in the sense that any other BLUP is equal to it with probability 1.

(d) The mean square prediction error matrix of the BLUP of part (b) is

$$[(v_0 - \boldsymbol{v}_0'\boldsymbol{V}^-\boldsymbol{v}_0) + (\boldsymbol{x}_0'\boldsymbol{X}^- - \boldsymbol{v}_0'\boldsymbol{V}^-)\boldsymbol{T}((\boldsymbol{X}^-)'\boldsymbol{x}_0 - \boldsymbol{V}^-\boldsymbol{v}_0)]\boldsymbol{\Sigma},$$

where $\boldsymbol{T}$ is as in (10.6).

Proof. $\boldsymbol{Ya}+\boldsymbol{b}$ is a linear unbiased predictor of $\boldsymbol{y}_0$ if and only if it is a linear unbiased estimator of $\boldsymbol{x}_0'\mathcal{B}$ under the model (10.1). Part (a) follows from the fact that an LUE of $\boldsymbol{x}_0'\mathcal{B}$ exists only if $\boldsymbol{x}_0'\mathcal{B}$ is estimable. In order to prove the remaining three parts, let $\boldsymbol{x}_0 \in \mathcal{C}(\boldsymbol{X}')$ and $\boldsymbol{Ya}+\boldsymbol{b}$ be a linear unbiased predictor of $\boldsymbol{y}_0$. Consider the decomposition

$$\boldsymbol{y}_0 - \boldsymbol{Ya} - \boldsymbol{b} = (\boldsymbol{y}_0 - \widehat{E}(\boldsymbol{y}_0|\boldsymbol{Y})) - (\widehat{\boldsymbol{y}}_0 - \widehat{E}(\boldsymbol{y}_0|\boldsymbol{Y})) + (\widehat{\boldsymbol{y}}_0 - \boldsymbol{Ya} - \boldsymbol{b}).$$

The first term on the right-hand side is the prediction error of the BLP $\widehat{E}(\boldsymbol{y}_0|\boldsymbol{Y})$, which must be uncorrelated with $\boldsymbol{Y}$ according to the result of Exercise 2.9. Therefore, this term is uncorrelated with the other two terms. The second term is the estimation error of the BLUE of $\boldsymbol{x}_0'\mathcal{B} - \boldsymbol{v}_0'\boldsymbol{V}^-\boldsymbol{X}\mathcal{B}$ in (10.1), while the third term is a linear zero function in this model. Therefore, these two terms are also uncorrelated. Consequently

$$E[(\boldsymbol{y}_0 - \boldsymbol{Ya} - \boldsymbol{b})(\boldsymbol{y}_0 - \boldsymbol{Ya} - \boldsymbol{b})'] = E[(\boldsymbol{y}_0 - \widehat{E}(\boldsymbol{y}_0|\boldsymbol{Y}))(\boldsymbol{y}_0 - \widehat{E}(\boldsymbol{y}_0|\boldsymbol{Y}))']$$
$$+ E[(\widehat{\boldsymbol{y}}_0 - \widehat{E}(\boldsymbol{y}_0|\boldsymbol{Y}))(\widehat{\boldsymbol{y}}_0 - \widehat{E}(\boldsymbol{y}_0|\boldsymbol{Y}))'] + E[(\widehat{\boldsymbol{y}}_0 - \boldsymbol{Ya} - \boldsymbol{b})(\widehat{\boldsymbol{y}}_0 - \boldsymbol{Ya} - \boldsymbol{b})'].$$

The above expression is minimized if and only if the LZF $\widehat{\boldsymbol{y}}_0 - \boldsymbol{Ya} - \boldsymbol{b}$ is almost surely equal to zero. This proves parts (b) and (c). By setting

$\boldsymbol{Ya}+\boldsymbol{b}=\widehat{\boldsymbol{y}}_0$ in the above equation, we have

$$\begin{aligned}
&E[(\boldsymbol{y}_0-\widehat{\boldsymbol{y}}_0)(\boldsymbol{y}_0-\widehat{\boldsymbol{y}}_0)']\\
&=E[(\boldsymbol{y}_0-\widehat{E}(\boldsymbol{y}_0|\boldsymbol{Y}))(\boldsymbol{y}_0-\widehat{E}(\boldsymbol{y}_0|\boldsymbol{Y}))']+E[(\widehat{\boldsymbol{y}}_0-\widehat{E}(\boldsymbol{y}_0|\boldsymbol{Y}))(\widehat{\boldsymbol{y}}_0-\widehat{E}(\boldsymbol{y}_0|\boldsymbol{Y}))']\\
&=\boldsymbol{\Sigma}\otimes(v_0-\boldsymbol{v}_0'\boldsymbol{V}^-\boldsymbol{v}_0)+D((\widehat{\boldsymbol{x}_0'\mathcal{B}}-\boldsymbol{v}_0'\boldsymbol{V}^-\widehat{\boldsymbol{X}\mathcal{B}})')\\
&=\boldsymbol{\Sigma}\otimes(v_0-\boldsymbol{v}_0'\boldsymbol{V}^-\boldsymbol{v}_0)+D(\text{vec}((\boldsymbol{x}_0'\boldsymbol{X}^- -\boldsymbol{v}_0'\boldsymbol{V}^-)\widehat{\boldsymbol{X}\mathcal{B}}))\\
&=\boldsymbol{\Sigma}\otimes(v_0-\boldsymbol{v}_0'\boldsymbol{V}^-\boldsymbol{v}_0)+D((\boldsymbol{I}\otimes(\boldsymbol{x}_0'\boldsymbol{X}^- -\boldsymbol{v}_0'\boldsymbol{V}^-))\text{vec}(\widehat{\boldsymbol{X}\mathcal{B}}))\\
&=\boldsymbol{\Sigma}\otimes(v_0-\boldsymbol{v}_0'\boldsymbol{V}^-\boldsymbol{v}_0)+\boldsymbol{\Sigma}\otimes[(\boldsymbol{x}_0'\boldsymbol{X}^- -\boldsymbol{v}_0'\boldsymbol{V}^-)\boldsymbol{T}((\boldsymbol{X}^-)'\boldsymbol{x}_0-\boldsymbol{V}^-\boldsymbol{v}_0),
\end{aligned}$$

which justifies the expression of part (d). □

When the joint distribution of $\boldsymbol{Y}$ and $\boldsymbol{y}_0$ is multivariate normal, $\boldsymbol{y}_0-\widehat{\boldsymbol{y}}_0$ is also multivariate normal, and is independent of the estimator $\widehat{\boldsymbol{\Sigma}}$ given in (10.9). It follows from Proposition 10.20 that the statistic

$$\frac{(\boldsymbol{y}_0-\widehat{\boldsymbol{y}}_0)'\widehat{\boldsymbol{\Sigma}}^-(\boldsymbol{y}_0-\widehat{\boldsymbol{y}}_0)}{(v_0-\boldsymbol{v}_0'\boldsymbol{V}^-\boldsymbol{v}_0)+(\boldsymbol{x}_0'\boldsymbol{X}^- -\boldsymbol{v}_0'\boldsymbol{V}^-)\boldsymbol{T}((\boldsymbol{X}^-)'\boldsymbol{x}_0-\boldsymbol{V}^-\boldsymbol{v}_0)} \times\frac{\rho(\boldsymbol{V}:\boldsymbol{X})-\rho(\boldsymbol{X})+1-\rho(\boldsymbol{\Sigma})}{\rho(\boldsymbol{\Sigma})\cdot(\rho(\boldsymbol{V}:\boldsymbol{X})-\rho(\boldsymbol{X}))}$$

has the $F_{\rho(\Sigma),\ \rho(V:X)-\rho(X)+1-\rho(\Sigma)}$ distribution. A $100(1-\alpha)\%$ prediction region for $\boldsymbol{y}_0$ is

$$\begin{aligned}
&(\boldsymbol{y}_0-\widehat{\boldsymbol{y}}_0)'\widehat{\boldsymbol{\Sigma}}^-(\boldsymbol{y}_0-\widehat{\boldsymbol{y}}_0)\\
&\le F_{\rho(\Sigma),\ \rho(V:X)-\rho(X)+1-\rho(\Sigma),\ \alpha}\times\frac{\rho(\boldsymbol{\Sigma})\cdot(\rho(\boldsymbol{V}:\boldsymbol{X})-\rho(\boldsymbol{X}))}{\rho(\boldsymbol{V}:\boldsymbol{X})-\rho(\boldsymbol{X})+1-\rho(\boldsymbol{\Sigma})}\\
&\quad\times[(v_0-\boldsymbol{v}_0'\boldsymbol{V}^-\boldsymbol{v}_0)+(\boldsymbol{x}_0'\boldsymbol{X}^- -\boldsymbol{v}_0'\boldsymbol{V}^-)\boldsymbol{T}((\boldsymbol{X}^-)'\boldsymbol{x}_0-\boldsymbol{V}^-\boldsymbol{v}_0)], \qquad (10.26)
\end{aligned}$$

where $F_{\rho(\Sigma),\ \rho(V:X)-\rho(X)+1-\rho(\Sigma),\ \alpha}$ is the $(1-\alpha)$ quantile of the F distribution with $\rho(\boldsymbol{\Sigma})$ and $\rho(\boldsymbol{V}:\boldsymbol{X})-\rho(\boldsymbol{X})+1-\rho(\boldsymbol{\Sigma})$ degrees of freedom. When $\boldsymbol{V}=\boldsymbol{I}$, $\boldsymbol{v}_0=\boldsymbol{0}$ and $v_0=1$, the point prediction of $\boldsymbol{y}_0$ simplifies to $\widehat{\boldsymbol{x}_0'\mathcal{B}}$, its mean square prediction error matrix is $[1+\boldsymbol{x}_0'(\boldsymbol{X}'\boldsymbol{X})^-\boldsymbol{x}_0]\boldsymbol{\Sigma}$ and the $100(1-\alpha)\%$ prediction region for $\boldsymbol{y}_0$ reduces to

$$\begin{aligned}
&(\boldsymbol{y}_0-\widehat{\boldsymbol{y}}_0)'\widehat{\boldsymbol{\Sigma}}^-(\boldsymbol{y}_0-\widehat{\boldsymbol{y}}_0)\\
&\le F_{\rho(\Sigma),\ n-\rho(X)+1-\rho(\Sigma),\ \alpha}\times\frac{\rho(\boldsymbol{\Sigma})\cdot(n-\rho(\boldsymbol{X}))}{n-\rho(\boldsymbol{X})+1-\rho(\boldsymbol{\Sigma})}\times[1+\boldsymbol{x}_0'(\boldsymbol{X}'\boldsymbol{X})^-\boldsymbol{x}_0].
\end{aligned}$$

An elliptical confidence region for $\mathcal{B}'\boldsymbol{x}_0$ is

$$\begin{aligned}
&(\mathcal{B}'\boldsymbol{x}_0-\widehat{\boldsymbol{y}}_0)'\widehat{\boldsymbol{\Sigma}}^-(\mathcal{B}'\boldsymbol{x}_0-\widehat{\boldsymbol{y}}_0)\\
&\le F_{\rho(\Sigma),\ \rho(V:X)-\rho(X)+1-\rho(\Sigma),\ \alpha}\times\frac{\rho(\boldsymbol{\Sigma})\cdot(\rho(\boldsymbol{V}:\boldsymbol{X})-\rho(\boldsymbol{X}))}{\rho(\boldsymbol{V}:\boldsymbol{X})-\rho(\boldsymbol{X})+1-\rho(\boldsymbol{\Sigma})}\\
&\quad\times[(\boldsymbol{x}_0'\boldsymbol{X}^- -\boldsymbol{v}_0'\boldsymbol{V}^-)\boldsymbol{T}((\boldsymbol{X}^-)'\boldsymbol{x}_0-\boldsymbol{V}^-\boldsymbol{v}_0)], \qquad (10.27)
\end{aligned}$$

which can be derived along the lines of (10.26). If $\boldsymbol{V} = \boldsymbol{I}$, this region simplifies to

$$(\mathcal{B}'\boldsymbol{x}_0 - \widehat{\boldsymbol{y}}_0)'\widehat{\boldsymbol{\Sigma}}^-(\mathcal{B}'\boldsymbol{x}_0 - \widehat{\boldsymbol{y}}_0)$$
$$\leq F_{\rho(\Sigma),\, n-\rho(X)+1-\rho(\Sigma),\, \alpha} \times \frac{\rho(\boldsymbol{\Sigma})\cdot(n-\rho(\boldsymbol{X}))}{n-\rho(\boldsymbol{X})+1-\rho(\boldsymbol{\Sigma})} \times \boldsymbol{x}_0'(\boldsymbol{X}'\boldsymbol{X})^-\boldsymbol{x}_0.$$

Simultaneous confidence intervals for linear parametric functions can be constructed, using the ideas described in Section 10.6.5. Tolerance intervals in the spirit of Section 7.13.2 can also be obtained. See Tian and Wang (2017) for simultaneous prediction in the multivariate general linear model.

10.8 Applications

10.8.1 *One-sample problem*

Suppose there are n independent samples from the q-variate normal distribution $N(\boldsymbol{\mu}, \boldsymbol{\Sigma})$, with $\boldsymbol{\mu}$ and $\boldsymbol{\Sigma}$ unspecified. The data can be organized as a matrix so that it follows the model (10.1) with $\boldsymbol{X} = \mathbf{1}_{n\times 1}$, $\mathcal{B} = \boldsymbol{\mu}'$ and $\boldsymbol{V} = \boldsymbol{I}$. Following Bhimasankaram and Sengupta (1991), we allow $\boldsymbol{\Sigma}$ to be singular. The one-sample problem is to test the hypothesis $\boldsymbol{\mu} = \boldsymbol{\mu}_0$ for a specified vector $\boldsymbol{\mu}_0$. The hypothesis is of the form $\boldsymbol{A}\mathcal{B} = \boldsymbol{\Psi}$ with $\boldsymbol{A} = 1$ and $\boldsymbol{\Psi} = \boldsymbol{\mu}_0'$. It is easy to see that the error sum of squares and products matrix $\boldsymbol{R}_0$ simplifies to $\boldsymbol{Y}'(\boldsymbol{I} - n^{-1}\mathbf{1}\mathbf{1}')\boldsymbol{Y}$. On the other hand, the decomposition (10.19) simplifies to

$$\boldsymbol{R}_H - \boldsymbol{R}_0 = n(\widehat{\boldsymbol{\mu}} - \boldsymbol{\mu}_0)(\widehat{\boldsymbol{\mu}} - \boldsymbol{\mu}_0)',$$

where $\widehat{\boldsymbol{\mu}}$ is the BLUE of $\boldsymbol{\mu}$, given by $n^{-1}\boldsymbol{Y}'\mathbf{1}$. As $R_H^2 - R_0^2$ is a matrix of rank 1, the four statistics mentioned in Sections 10.6.1–10.6.3 are equivalent to one another (see Proposition 10.19). It is easy to see that Roy's union-intersection statistic simplifies to $T_R = n(\widehat{\boldsymbol{\mu}} - \boldsymbol{\mu}_0)'\boldsymbol{R}_0^-(\widehat{\boldsymbol{\mu}} - \boldsymbol{\mu}_0)$. The Lawley-Hotelling statistic turns out to be $T^2 = (n-1)T_R$. According to Proposition 10.20, the null distribution of the statistic $(n-q_*)T^2/[q_*(n-1)]$ is $F_{q_*, n-q_*}$, where $q_* = \rho(\boldsymbol{\Sigma})$.

10.8.2 *Two-sample problem*

Suppose we have n_1 and n_2 samples from the q-variate normal distributions $N(\boldsymbol{\mu}_1, \boldsymbol{\Sigma})$ and $N(\boldsymbol{\mu}_2, \boldsymbol{\Sigma})$, respectively. If $\boldsymbol{Y}$ is the $(n_1 + n_2) \times q$ matrix such that its top n_1 rows correspond to the n_1 samples from the first population and the remaining n_2 rows correspond to the n_2 samples from the second population, then $\boldsymbol{Y}$ follows the model (10.1) with

$$\boldsymbol{X} = \begin{pmatrix} \mathbf{1}_{n_1\times} & \mathbf{0}_{n_2\times 1} \\ \mathbf{0}_{n_1\times} & \mathbf{1}_{n_2\times 1} \end{pmatrix}, \quad \mathcal{B} = \begin{pmatrix} \boldsymbol{\mu}_1' \\ \boldsymbol{\mu}_2' \end{pmatrix}, \quad \boldsymbol{V} = \boldsymbol{I}.$$

The two-sample problem consists of testing the hypothesis $\boldsymbol{\mu}_1 = \boldsymbol{\mu}_2$. This hypothesis can be written as $\boldsymbol{A}\mathcal{B} = \boldsymbol{\Psi}$ where $\boldsymbol{A} = (1 : -1)$ and $\boldsymbol{\Psi} = \mathbf{0}_{1\times q}$. In this case the matrix $\boldsymbol{R}_0$ simplifies to

$$\boldsymbol{R}_0 = \boldsymbol{Y}_1'(\boldsymbol{I}_{n_1\times n_1} - n_1^{-1}\mathbf{1}_{n_1\times 1}\mathbf{1}_{n_1\times 1}')\boldsymbol{Y}_1 + \boldsymbol{Y}_2'(\boldsymbol{I}_{n_2\times n_2} - n_2^{-1}\mathbf{1}_{n_1\times 2}\mathbf{1}_{n_1\times 2}')\boldsymbol{Y}_2,$$

where $(\boldsymbol{Y}_1' : \boldsymbol{Y}_2') = \boldsymbol{Y}'$ and $\boldsymbol{Y}_1$ has order $n_1 \times q$. The matrix $\boldsymbol{R}_H - \boldsymbol{R}_0$ simplifies to

$$\boldsymbol{R}_H - \boldsymbol{R}_0 = (n_1^{-1} + n_2^{-1})^{-1}(\widehat{\boldsymbol{\mu}}_1 - \widehat{\boldsymbol{\mu}}_2)(\widehat{\boldsymbol{\mu}}_1 - \widehat{\boldsymbol{\mu}}_2)',$$

where $(\widehat{\boldsymbol{\mu}}_1 : \widehat{\boldsymbol{\mu}}_2)$ is the BLUE of $\mathcal{B}'$, given by $\widehat{\boldsymbol{\mu}}_j = n_j^{-1}\boldsymbol{Y}_j'\mathbf{1}_{n_j\times 1}$, $j = 1, 2$. Once again, the four statistics mentioned in Sections 10.6.1 and 10.6.3 are equivalent. Roy's union-intersection test statistic reduces to

$$T_R = (n_1^{-1} + n_2^{-1})^{-1}(\widehat{\boldsymbol{\mu}}_1 - \widehat{\boldsymbol{\mu}}_2)'\boldsymbol{R}_0^-(\widehat{\boldsymbol{\mu}}_1 - \widehat{\boldsymbol{\mu}}_2).$$

The Lawley-Hotelling statistic for the two-sample problem simplifies to $T^2 = (n_1 + n_2 - 2)T_R$. The statistics T_R and T^2 are also proportional to Mahalanobis' squared distance,

$$D^2 = (\widehat{\boldsymbol{\mu}}_1 - \widehat{\boldsymbol{\mu}}_2)\widehat{\boldsymbol{\Sigma}}^-(\widehat{\boldsymbol{\mu}}_1 - \widehat{\boldsymbol{\mu}}_2)' = (n_1 + n_2 - 2)(\widehat{\boldsymbol{\mu}}_1 - \widehat{\boldsymbol{\mu}}_2)R_0^-(\widehat{\boldsymbol{\mu}}_1 - \widehat{\boldsymbol{\mu}}_2)'.$$

Under the null hypothesis, Proposition 10.20 implies that the statistic $(n_1 + n_2 - q_* - 1)T^2/[q_*(n_1 + n_2 - 2)]$ has the $F_{q_*, n_1+n_2-q_*-1}$ distribution, where $q_* = \rho(\boldsymbol{\Sigma})$.

See Exercise 10.11 for an extension to the case $\boldsymbol{V} \neq \boldsymbol{I}$.

10.8.3 *Multivariate ANOVA*

Consider the model (10.1) with $\boldsymbol{V} = \boldsymbol{I}$ and suppose the elements of the matrix $\boldsymbol{X}$ are obtained from a designed experiment such as those described in Chapter 6. In that chapter we had attributed different parts of the total sum of squares to various sources. In a similar manner we can analyse the sum of squares and products matrix and attribute its parts to various sources. Such an analysis is called *multivariate analysis of variance* (MANOVA) or *analysis of dispersion*. The GLRT for various hypotheses in the univariate case had turned out to be a comparison of the ratio of estimated variances (under the respective hypotheses) with a suitable cut-off.

In the present case, the comparison shifts from variances to dispersions. As observed before, there are several ways making this comparison. The GLRT is based on the ratio of the determinants of the relevant dispersion matrices. Detailed calculations are available in textbooks of multivariate analysis such as Arnold (1981, Section 19.6).

A MANOVA table is similar in spirit to Table 6.11 for ANCOVA. The similarity is not superficial. When the ANCOVA table is expressed in terms of matrices (as in the case of Table 6.11), it is essentially a MANOVA table where the covariates are treated as additional elements of the response vector. Under the assumption of multivariate normality of the response, one can obtain the ANCOVA model by conditioning a single component of the response of a MANOVA model on the remaining components. Conditioning of *more than one* component of the response on the remaining components leads to the *multivariate ANCOVA* model.

10.8.4 *Growth models*

In Example 10.22 no specific relation among the μ_{jk}s was assumed. *Growth models* involve explicit assumption on the nature of dependence of the mean height (or any other dimension) with time. For instance, μ_{jk} can be a polynomial function of the kth time point, where the coefficients of the polynomial would depend on the group j. This amounts to assuming a linear structure of the matrix $\mathcal{B}$, such as

$$\mathcal{B} = \mathcal{B}_0 + \mathcal{A}\boldsymbol{H},$$

where $\mathcal{B}_0$ and $\boldsymbol{H}$ are specified matrices, and the matrix $\mathcal{A}$ has fewer columns than $\mathcal{B}$. The matrix $\boldsymbol{H}$ can always be chosen to have full row rank. Thus, a linear growth model is

$$\boldsymbol{Y} = \boldsymbol{X}\mathcal{B}_0 + \boldsymbol{X}\mathcal{A}\boldsymbol{H} + \mathcal{E}, \quad E(\mathcal{E}) = \boldsymbol{0}, \quad D(\mathrm{vec}(\mathcal{E})) = \boldsymbol{\Sigma} \otimes \boldsymbol{V}. \tag{10.28}$$

Let $\boldsymbol{G}$ be a *fixed* symmetric and positive definite matrix having the same order as $\boldsymbol{\Sigma}$, and $\boldsymbol{Z}\boldsymbol{Z}'$ be a rank factorization of $(\boldsymbol{I} - \boldsymbol{P}_{H})$. We can rewrite the model (10.28) as

$$\begin{aligned}(\boldsymbol{Y} - \boldsymbol{X}\mathcal{B}_0)&[\boldsymbol{G}\boldsymbol{H}'(\boldsymbol{H}\boldsymbol{G}\boldsymbol{H}')^{-1} : \boldsymbol{Z}]\\ &= [\boldsymbol{X}\mathcal{A} : \boldsymbol{0}] + \mathcal{E}[\boldsymbol{G}\boldsymbol{H}'(\boldsymbol{H}\boldsymbol{G}\boldsymbol{H}')^{-1} : \boldsymbol{Z}].\end{aligned}$$

Under the assumption of multivariate normality, we can condition $\boldsymbol{Y}_1 = (\boldsymbol{Y} - \boldsymbol{X}\mathcal{B}_0)\boldsymbol{G}\boldsymbol{H}'(\boldsymbol{H}\boldsymbol{G}\boldsymbol{H}')^{-1}$ on $\boldsymbol{Y}_2 = (\boldsymbol{Y} - \boldsymbol{X}\mathcal{B}_0)\boldsymbol{Z}$, as in Section 10.6.6, to obtain the model

$$\boldsymbol{Y}_1 = \boldsymbol{X}\mathcal{A} + \boldsymbol{Y}_2\mathcal{B}_a + \mathcal{E}_*, \quad E(\mathcal{E}_*) = \boldsymbol{0}, \quad D(\mathrm{vec}(\mathcal{E}_*)) = \boldsymbol{\Sigma}_* \otimes \boldsymbol{V} \tag{10.29}$$

where $\mathcal{B}_a$ is a matrix of unspecified parameters and

$$\Sigma_* = (\boldsymbol{HGH}')^{-1}\boldsymbol{HG}[\Sigma - \Sigma\boldsymbol{Z}(\boldsymbol{Z}'\Sigma\boldsymbol{Z})^{-1}\boldsymbol{Z}'\Sigma]\boldsymbol{GH}'(\boldsymbol{HGH}')^{-1}.$$

This model is a special case of (10.1). The analysis of this model can proceed along the usual lines. The choice of the matrix $\boldsymbol{G}$ is arbitrary. If $\boldsymbol{G} = \boldsymbol{\Sigma}^{-1}$, then the term $\mathcal{B}_a$ disappears and $\boldsymbol{\Sigma}_*$ simplifies to $(\boldsymbol{H}\boldsymbol{\Sigma}^{-1}\boldsymbol{H}')^{-1}$. If $\boldsymbol{G}$ is chosen as a reasonable approximation of $\boldsymbol{\Sigma}^{-1}$, then we can use the simplified model $\boldsymbol{Y}_1 = \boldsymbol{X}\mathcal{A}+\mathcal{E}_*$. See Rao (1973c, Section 8c.7) and Christensen (1991, Section 1.6) for more details on the analysis of growth models in the case $\boldsymbol{V} = \boldsymbol{I}$.

In general, the matrix $\mathcal{B}$ can have rank deficiency of unknown kind. This phenomenon is quite common in high-dimensional data. Inference under a reduced rank regression model (Izenman, 2013) can be adopted in such a case. Another interesting approach involving sparse projections has been proposed by Sun et al. (2015).

10.9 Complements/Exercises

Exercises with solutions given in Appendix C

10.1 Show that the residual matrix $\boldsymbol{E}$ defined on page 505 has the representation described in Remark 10.7.

10.2 Derive the multivariate linear model from a suitable multivariate normal distribution of all the variables.

10.3 Show that the rows of the matrices $(\boldsymbol{I}-\boldsymbol{P}_X)\boldsymbol{Y}$ and $\boldsymbol{E}$ (the residual matrix) constitute two generating sets of normalized linear zero functions in the model (10.1).

10.4 If the rows of a matrix $\boldsymbol{Z}$ constitute a generating set of normalized linear zero functions in the model (10.1), then show that $D(\text{vec}(\boldsymbol{Z}))$ is of the form $\boldsymbol{\Sigma} \otimes \boldsymbol{A}$, where $\boldsymbol{A}$ is a nonnegative definite matrix. Further, show that the error sum of squares and products matrix can be expressed as $\boldsymbol{R}_0 = \boldsymbol{Z}'\boldsymbol{A}^-\boldsymbol{Z}$.

10.5 *Profile analysis.* Explicitly identify the GLRT for the three hypotheses mentioned in Example 10.22.

10.6 Given the set-up of Example 10.22, how will you test the null hypothesis $\mathcal{H}_c$ against the alternative hypothesis $\mathcal{H}_p$?

Table 10.2 Fisher's Iris data (data object **iris** in R package **datasets**, source: Fisher, 1936; continued to page 535)

Iris setosa				*Iris versicolor*				*Iris virginica*			
l_s	w_s	l_p	w_p	l_s	w_s	l_p	w_p	l_s	w_s	l_p	w_p
5.1	3.5	1.4	0.2	7.0	3.2	4.7	1.4	6.3	3.3	6.0	2.5
4.9	3.0	1.4	0.2	6.4	3.2	4.5	1.5	5.8	2.7	5.1	1.9
4.7	3.2	1.3	0.2	6.9	3.1	4.9	1.5	7.1	3.0	5.9	2.1
4.6	3.1	1.5	0.2	5.5	2.3	4.0	1.3	6.3	2.9	5.6	1.8
5.0	3.6	1.4	0.2	6.5	2.8	4.6	1.5	6.5	3.0	5.8	2.2
5.4	3.9	1.7	0.4	5.7	2.8	4.5	1.3	7.6	3.0	6.6	2.1
4.6	3.4	1.4	0.3	6.3	3.3	4.7	1.6	4.9	2.5	4.5	1.7
5.0	3.4	1.5	0.2	4.9	2.4	3.3	1.0	7.3	2.9	6.3	1.8
4.4	2.9	1.4	0.2	6.6	2.9	4.6	1.3	6.7	2.5	5.8	1.8
4.9	3.1	1.5	0.1	5.2	2.7	3.9	1.4	7.2	3.6	6.1	2.5
5.4	3.7	1.5	0.2	5.0	2.0	3.5	1.0	6.5	3.2	5.1	2.0
4.8	3.4	1.6	0.2	5.9	3.0	4.2	1.5	6.4	2.7	5.3	1.9
4.8	3.0	1.4	0.1	6.0	2.2	4.0	1.0	6.8	3.0	5.5	2.1
4.3	3.0	1.1	0.1	6.1	2.9	4.7	1.4	5.7	2.5	5.0	2.0
5.8	4.0	1.2	0.2	5.6	2.9	3.6	1.3	5.8	2.8	5.1	2.4
5.7	4.4	1.5	0.4	6.7	3.1	4.4	1.4	6.4	3.2	5.3	2.3
5.4	3.9	1.3	0.4	5.6	3.0	4.5	1.5	6.5	3.0	5.5	1.8
5.1	3.5	1.4	0.3	5.8	2.7	4.1	1.0	7.7	3.8	6.7	2.2
5.7	3.8	1.7	0.3	6.2	2.2	4.5	1.5	7.7	2.6	6.9	2.3
5.1	3.8	1.5	0.3	5.6	2.5	3.9	1.1	6.0	2.2	5.0	1.5
5.4	3.4	1.7	0.2	5.9	3.2	4.8	1.8	6.9	3.2	5.7	2.3
5.1	3.7	1.5	0.4	6.1	2.8	4.0	1.3	5.6	2.8	4.9	2.0
4.6	3.6	1.0	0.2	6.3	2.5	4.9	1.5	7.7	2.8	6.7	2.0
5.1	3.3	1.7	0.5	6.1	2.8	4.7	1.2	6.3	2.7	4.9	1.8
4.8	3.4	1.9	0.2	6.4	2.9	4.3	1.3	6.7	3.3	5.7	2.1

Additional exercises

10.7 (*Fisher's Iris data*). The data set given in Table 10.2 represents 150 measurements of sepal length (l_s), sepal width (w_s), petal length (l_p) and petal width (w_p) of flowers of three species of the plant Iris (*Iris setosa, Iris versicolor*, and *Iris virginica*). This classic data set is taken from Fisher (1936). Let $\boldsymbol{Y}$ be the 150×4 matrix of the observations given in the table (each species accounting for a 50×4 block of $\boldsymbol{Y}$). Let $\boldsymbol{X}$ be a 150×4 binary matrix, where the first column contains 1 in all the rows, the second column contains 1 in the rows corresponding to the first species and 0 elsewhere, and the last two columns contain 1 in the rows corresponding to the second and third species, respectively, and 0 elsewhere. Assume that the data follows the linear model (10.1) with $\boldsymbol{V} = \boldsymbol{I}$.

Table 10.2 Fisher's Iris data (continued from page 534)

Iris setosa				*Iris versicolor*				*Iris virginica*			
l_s	w_s	l_p	w_p	l_s	w_s	l_p	w_p	l_s	w_s	l_p	w_p
5.0	3.0	1.6	0.2	6.6	3.0	4.4	1.4	7.2	3.2	6.0	1.8
5.0	3.4	1.6	0.4	6.8	2.8	4.8	1.4	6.2	2.8	4.8	1.8
5.2	3.5	1.5	0.2	6.7	3.0	5.0	1.7	6.1	3.0	4.9	1.8
5.2	3.4	1.4	0.2	6.0	2.9	4.5	1.5	6.4	2.8	5.6	2.1
4.7	3.2	1.6	0.2	5.7	2.6	3.5	1.0	7.2	3.0	5.8	1.6
4.8	3.1	1.6	0.2	5.5	2.4	3.8	1.1	7.4	2.8	6.1	1.9
5.4	3.4	1.5	0.4	5.5	2.4	3.7	1.0	7.9	3.8	6.4	2.0
5.2	4.1	1.5	0.1	5.8	2.7	3.9	1.2	6.4	2.8	5.6	2.2
5.5	4.2	1.4	0.2	6.0	2.7	5.1	1.6	6.3	2.8	5.1	1.5
4.9	3.1	1.5	0.2	5.4	3.0	4.5	1.5	6.1	2.6	5.6	1.4
5.0	3.2	1.2	0.2	6.0	3.4	4.5	1.6	7.7	3.0	6.1	2.3
5.5	3.5	1.3	0.2	6.7	3.1	4.7	1.5	6.3	3.4	5.6	2.4
4.9	3.6	1.4	0.1	6.3	2.3	4.4	1.3	6.4	3.1	5.5	1.8
4.4	3.0	1.3	0.2	5.6	3.0	4.1	1.3	6.0	3.0	4.8	1.8
5.1	3.4	1.5	0.2	5.5	2.5	4.0	1.3	6.9	3.1	5.4	2.1
5.0	3.5	1.3	0.3	5.5	2.6	4.4	1.2	6.7	3.1	5.6	2.4
4.5	2.3	1.3	0.3	6.1	3.0	4.6	1.4	6.9	3.1	5.1	2.3
4.4	3.2	1.3	0.2	5.8	2.6	4.0	1.2	5.8	2.7	5.1	1.9
5.0	3.5	1.6	0.6	5.0	2.3	3.3	1.0	6.8	3.2	5.9	2.3
5.1	3.8	1.9	0.4	5.6	2.7	4.2	1.3	6.7	3.3	5.7	2.5
4.8	3.0	1.4	0.3	5.7	3.0	4.2	1.2	6.7	3.0	5.2	2.3
5.1	3.8	1.6	0.2	5.7	2.9	4.2	1.3	6.3	2.5	5.0	1.9
4.6	3.2	1.4	0.2	6.2	2.9	4.3	1.3	6.5	3.0	5.2	2.0
5.3	3.7	1.5	0.2	5.1	2.5	3.0	1.1	6.2	3.4	5.4	2.3
5.0	3.3	1.4	0.2	5.7	2.8	4.1	1.3	5.9	3.0	5.1	1.8

(a) Interpret the elements of the 4×4 parameter matrix $\mathcal{B}$ and determine which of the parameters are estimable.

(b) Find the BLUE of the difference between the mean responses of *Iris versicolor* and *Iris setosa*, and provide an estimate of the dispersion matrix of the estimation error.

10.8 Use the data given in Table 10.2 to determine whether there is significant difference between the mean responses of *Iris setosa* and *Iris versicolor*, by formulating the problem as the test of a linear hypothesis and carrying out an appropriate test. You can use the linear model (10.1) with multivariate normal distribution of the errors.

10.9 Use the data given in Table 10.2 and the model of Exercise 10.8 to determine whether there is significant variation of the four characteristics across the three species, by carrying out the appropriate GLRT.

10.10 The data set of Table 10.3, taken from Lunn and McNeil (1991, p. 127)

Table 10.3 Men's olympic sprint times in seconds (data object `olympic` in R package `lmreg`, source: Lunn and McNeil, 1991)

Year	100 m	200 m	400 m	800 m	1500 m
1900	10.80	22.20	49.40	121.40	246.00
1904	11.00	21.60	49.20	116.00	245.40
1908	10.80	22.40	50.00	112.80	243.40
1912	10.80	21.70	48.20	111.90	236.80
1920	10.80	22.00	49.60	113.40	241.80
1924	10.60	21.60	47.60	112.40	233.60
1928	10.80	21.80	47.80	111.80	233.20
1932	10.30	21.20	46.20	109.80	231.20
1936	10.30	20.70	46.50	112.90	227.80
1948	10.30	21.10	46.20	109.20	225.20
1952	10.40	20.70	45.90	109.20	225.20
1956	10.50	20.60	46.70	107.70	221.20
1960	10.20	20.50	44.90	106.30	215.60
1964	10.00	20.30	45.10	105.10	218.10
1968	9.95	19.83	43.80	104.30	214.90
1972	10.14	20.00	44.66	105.90	216.30
1976	10.06	20.23	44.26	103.50	219.20
1980	10.25	20.19	44.60	105.40	218.40
1984	9.99	19.80	44.27	103.00	212.50
1988	9.92	19.75	43.87	103.45	215.96

shows the times in seconds recorded by winners of men's olympic sprint finals from 1900 to 1988 (except for 1916, 1940 and 1944 when world wars prevented the olympic games from being held). Assume the model $\boldsymbol{Y} = \boldsymbol{X}\mathcal{B}+\boldsymbol{E}$ where $\boldsymbol{Y}$ consists of the log-values of the last five columns of Table 10.3, $\boldsymbol{X}$ consists of the intercept term and values of the 'year' variable measured with origin at 1950, and $\text{vec}(\boldsymbol{E}) \sim N(\boldsymbol{0}, \boldsymbol{\Sigma}_{5\times 5} \otimes \boldsymbol{I}_{20\times 20})$. Test for the following hypotheses: (a) the log-sprint times did not change significantly with time; (b) the log-sprint times of every distance category changed with time at the same rate.

10.11 Consider the two-sample problem of Section 10.8.2, and suppose the samples are correlated. Describe how the test procedure has to be adjusted, assuming that $\boldsymbol{V}$ is a known and possibly singular block-diagonal matrix, with $n_1 \times n_1$ and $n_2 \times n_2$ diagonal blocks.

10.12 Use the data given in Table 10.2 and the model of Exercise 10.8 to determine whether l_s and w_s are superfluous characteristics (for dependence of the response on the explanatory variables described in Exercise 10.7) in the presence of l_p and w_p, by carrying out the appropriate GLRT.

Chapter 11

Linear Inference — Other Perspectives

The classical theory of statistical inference (briefly reviewed in Section B.1 of Appendix B), has a strong parallel to inference about the parameter $\boldsymbol{\beta}$ in the linear model $(\boldsymbol{y}, \boldsymbol{X\beta}, \sigma^2\boldsymbol{V})$, if we restrict our attention to linear statistics of the form $\boldsymbol{Ly}$. Early work on such connections can be found in Barnard (1963) and Baksalary and Kala (1981). Drygas (1983) gives the theory a more elaborate structure, while subsequent work (see e.g. Kala et al., 2017) provides modifications and many extensions in various directions. In Section 11.1 we present a systematic exposition of the theory and show how it is connected to the definitions as well as the propositions contained in Chapters 3 and 7. This development culminates in a decomposition of the response vector in the general linear model into uncorrelated parts that are either BLUE or LZF and are either degenerate or having a common variance. Section 11.2 carries the theory of linear inference further by discussing linear versions of admissible, Bayes and minimax estimators. In order to complete the story, some other classes of linear estimators are discussed in Section 11.3.

Section 11.4 deals with the geometry of linear models, which has fascinated many mathematicians and statisticians. The ideas of orthogonality and projections can be used to derive an approximation of $\boldsymbol{X\beta}$ in the linear model in a completely mathematical way, and the prize catch that results is indeed the BLUE. Although our development of the theory in Chapters 3, 4 and 7 is based on statistical ideas, once that is done, the geometric perspective and its intuitive appeal can only help enrich and add to the understanding of linear models.

Section 11.5 discusses large sample properties of a BLUE in the general linear model, justifying the use of this estimator even when no distributional assumption is made.

11.1 Foundations of linear inference

11.1.1 *General theory*

We begin by adapting the characterization of ancillary statistic, given on page 618, to the case of linear functions of $\boldsymbol{y}$.

Definition 11.1. A statistic $\boldsymbol{Zy}$ in the model $(\boldsymbol{y}, \boldsymbol{X\beta}, \sigma^2\boldsymbol{V})$ is called *linearly ancillary* for $\boldsymbol{\beta}$ if any *linear* function of it has zero expectation for all $\boldsymbol{\beta}$. □

Definition 11.2. A linearly ancillary statistic $\boldsymbol{Zy}$ for $\boldsymbol{\beta}$ in the model $(\boldsymbol{y}, \boldsymbol{X\beta}, \sigma^2\boldsymbol{V})$ is called *linearly maximal ancillary* if any other linearly ancillary statistic is almost surely equal to a linear function of $\boldsymbol{Zy}$ for all $\boldsymbol{\beta}$. □

In other words, linearly ancillary statistics in a linear model are precisely the LZFs. A linearly maximal ancillary statistic is a vector whose elements constitute a generating set of LZFs.

Recall that the usual definition of sufficiency involves a conditional distribution. It is not suitable for adaptation to the linear case where we would like not to assume any distribution. Therefore, we make use of the alternative definition given in Section B.1, and replace the conditional expectation by the best linear predictor (BLP) defined on page 49, thus leading to:

Definition 11.3. A statistic $\boldsymbol{Ty}$ in the model $(\boldsymbol{y}, \boldsymbol{X\beta}, \sigma^2\boldsymbol{V})$ is called *linearly sufficient* for $\boldsymbol{\beta}$ if for every linear function $\boldsymbol{l}'\boldsymbol{y}$ of $\boldsymbol{y}$, the linear regression $\widehat{E}(\boldsymbol{l}'\boldsymbol{y}|\boldsymbol{Ty})$ (also called the BLP) is almost surely equal to a linear function of $\boldsymbol{Ty}$ which does not depend on $\boldsymbol{\beta}$. □

Definition 11.4. A linearly sufficient statistic $\boldsymbol{Ty}$ for $\boldsymbol{\beta}$ in the model $(\boldsymbol{y}, \boldsymbol{X\beta}, \sigma^2\boldsymbol{V})$ is called *linearly minimal sufficient* if $\boldsymbol{Ty}$ is almost surely equal to a linear function of any other linearly sufficient statistic for all $\boldsymbol{\beta}$. □

Definition 11.5. A statistic $\boldsymbol{Ty}$ in the model $(\boldsymbol{y}, \boldsymbol{X\beta}, \sigma^2\boldsymbol{V})$ is called *linearly complete* for $\boldsymbol{\beta}$ if no nontrivial[1] linear function of $\boldsymbol{Ty}$ is linearly ancillary. □

If a statistic is linearly sufficient and linearly complete at the same time, we shall refer to it as a *linearly complete and sufficient* statistic. It will be

[1]A nontrivial linear function is one which is not equal to zero almost surely.

proved later (see Proposition 11.11) that such a statistic coincides with a linearly minimal sufficient statistic.

Example 11.6. The statistic $(\boldsymbol{I}-\boldsymbol{P}_X)\boldsymbol{y}$ is a linearly maximal ancillary, and any function of the form $\boldsymbol{l}'(\boldsymbol{I}-\boldsymbol{P}_X)\boldsymbol{y}$ (i.e. any LZF) is a linear ancillary. A scalar $\boldsymbol{l}'\boldsymbol{y}$ which is not an LZF is linearly complete. The vector $\boldsymbol{A}\boldsymbol{y}$, where $\boldsymbol{A}$ is a square and nonsingular matrix, is linearly sufficient for $\boldsymbol{\beta}$. The vector of fitted values is a linearly complete and sufficient statistic (see Proposition 11.10). □

We now prove a result similar to Basu's theorem (see page 619).

Proposition 11.7. *A linearly complete and sufficient statistic is uncorrelated with every linearly ancillary statistic.*

Proof. Let $\boldsymbol{T}\boldsymbol{y}$ be a linearly complete and sufficient statistic for $\boldsymbol{\beta}$, and $\boldsymbol{z}'\boldsymbol{y}$ be a linearly ancillary statistic (i.e. an LZF). The BLP of $\boldsymbol{z}'\boldsymbol{y}$ given $\boldsymbol{T}\boldsymbol{y}$ is

$$\widehat{E}(\boldsymbol{z}'\boldsymbol{y}|\boldsymbol{T}\boldsymbol{y}) = \boldsymbol{z}'\boldsymbol{V}\boldsymbol{T}'(\boldsymbol{T}\boldsymbol{V}\boldsymbol{T}')^-(\boldsymbol{T}\boldsymbol{y}-\boldsymbol{T}\boldsymbol{X}\boldsymbol{\beta}).$$

Since $\boldsymbol{T}\boldsymbol{y}$ is linearly sufficient, the quantity on the right-hand side does not depend on $\boldsymbol{\beta}$, and is therefore equal to $\boldsymbol{z}'\boldsymbol{V}\boldsymbol{T}'(\boldsymbol{T}\boldsymbol{V}\boldsymbol{T}')^-\boldsymbol{T}\boldsymbol{y}$ for any choice of the g-inverse. The linear completeness of $\boldsymbol{T}\boldsymbol{y}$ implies that this quantity should be equal to 0 almost surely. Therefore, $\boldsymbol{z}'\boldsymbol{V}\boldsymbol{T}'$, the covariance of $\widehat{E}(\boldsymbol{z}'\boldsymbol{y}|\boldsymbol{T}\boldsymbol{y})$ with $\boldsymbol{T}\boldsymbol{y}$ must be zero. □

A linear version of the Rao-Blackwell theorem (Proposition B.9) follows.

Proposition 11.8. *Let $\boldsymbol{T}\boldsymbol{y}$ be linearly sufficient for $\boldsymbol{\beta}$ and $\boldsymbol{s}'\boldsymbol{y}$ be an estimator of a single LPF, $\boldsymbol{p}'\boldsymbol{\beta}$, in the linear model $(\boldsymbol{y}, \boldsymbol{X}\boldsymbol{\beta}, \sigma^2\boldsymbol{V})$. The mean square error of the "improved" estimator, $\widehat{E}[\boldsymbol{s}'\boldsymbol{y}|\boldsymbol{T}\boldsymbol{y}]$, is less than or equal to that of $\boldsymbol{s}'\boldsymbol{y}$.*

Proof. Let us denote $\widehat{E}[\boldsymbol{s}'\boldsymbol{y}|\boldsymbol{T}\boldsymbol{y}]$ by $\boldsymbol{h}'\boldsymbol{T}\boldsymbol{y}$. Proposition 2.23 implies that the linearly ancillary statistic $\boldsymbol{s}'\boldsymbol{y}-\boldsymbol{h}'\boldsymbol{T}\boldsymbol{y}$ is uncorrelated with $\boldsymbol{h}'\boldsymbol{T}\boldsymbol{y}$. Therefore,

$$\begin{aligned} E(\boldsymbol{s}'\boldsymbol{y}-\boldsymbol{p}'\boldsymbol{\beta})^2 &= E(\boldsymbol{h}'\boldsymbol{T}\boldsymbol{y}-\boldsymbol{p}'\boldsymbol{\beta})^2 + Var(\boldsymbol{s}'\boldsymbol{y}-\boldsymbol{h}'\boldsymbol{T}\boldsymbol{y}) \\ &\quad + 2E(\boldsymbol{h}'\boldsymbol{T}\boldsymbol{y}-\boldsymbol{p}'\boldsymbol{\beta})E(\boldsymbol{s}'\boldsymbol{y}-\boldsymbol{h}'\boldsymbol{T}\boldsymbol{y}) \\ &= E(\boldsymbol{h}'\boldsymbol{T}\boldsymbol{y}-\boldsymbol{p}'\boldsymbol{\beta})^2 + Var(\boldsymbol{s}'\boldsymbol{y}-\boldsymbol{h}'\boldsymbol{T}\boldsymbol{y}) \geq E(\boldsymbol{h}'\boldsymbol{T}\boldsymbol{y}-\boldsymbol{p}'\boldsymbol{\beta})^2. \end{aligned}$$

Thus, $\boldsymbol{h}'\boldsymbol{T}\boldsymbol{y}$ has smaller MSE than $\boldsymbol{s}'\boldsymbol{y}$. □

The above proposition implies that the variance of an LUE of $\boldsymbol{p}'\boldsymbol{\beta}$ can be reduced by regressing it on any linearly sufficient statistic. The LUE with minimum variance is of course the BLUE, which is the linear analogue of the UMVUE. Characterization of the BLUEs through the property of their being uncorrelated with LZFs (linear ancillaries) has already been given in Proposition 3.29, which is the linear version of Proposition B.10. This result directly leads us to the construction of the BLUE of any estimable LPF via Proposition 7.7. The proof of the uniqueness of the BLUE — if it exists — also follows. Such a constructive procedure for obtaining the UMVUE in the general case is not available, because a complete collection of all estimators of zero are not easy to get. Instead, one has to obtain the UMVUE from an unbiased estimator and a complete sufficient statistic, via the Lehmann-Scheffé theorem (Proposition B.11). A linear analog of this proposition is given below.

Proposition 11.9. *Let $\boldsymbol{p}'\boldsymbol{\beta}$ have an unbiased estimator $\boldsymbol{s}'\boldsymbol{y}$, and $\boldsymbol{T}\boldsymbol{y}$ be a linearly complete and sufficient statistic for $\boldsymbol{\beta}$ in the linear model $(\boldsymbol{y}, \boldsymbol{X}\boldsymbol{\beta}, \sigma^2\boldsymbol{V})$. Then the BLUE of $\boldsymbol{p}'\boldsymbol{\beta}$ exists and is almost surely equal to $\widehat{E}(\boldsymbol{s}'\boldsymbol{y}|\boldsymbol{T}\boldsymbol{y})$.*

Proof. Let $\boldsymbol{u}_1'\boldsymbol{T}\boldsymbol{y} = \widehat{E}(\boldsymbol{s}'\boldsymbol{y}|\boldsymbol{T}\boldsymbol{y})$. It is easy to see that $\boldsymbol{u}_1'\boldsymbol{T}\boldsymbol{y}$ is unbiased for $\boldsymbol{p}'\boldsymbol{\beta}$ (see Proposition 2.23(c)). To prove that it is the BLUE, let $\boldsymbol{u}'\boldsymbol{y}$ be another LUE of $\boldsymbol{p}'\boldsymbol{\beta}$ having strictly smaller variance than $\boldsymbol{u}_1'\boldsymbol{T}\boldsymbol{y}$. Let $\boldsymbol{u}_2'\boldsymbol{T}\boldsymbol{y} = \widehat{E}(\boldsymbol{u}'\boldsymbol{y}|\boldsymbol{T}\boldsymbol{y})$. Therefore, $\boldsymbol{u}_2'\boldsymbol{T}\boldsymbol{y}$ is also an LUE of $\boldsymbol{p}'\boldsymbol{\beta}$ having strictly smaller variance than $\boldsymbol{u}_1'\boldsymbol{T}\boldsymbol{y}$. Note that $\boldsymbol{u}_1'\boldsymbol{T}\boldsymbol{y} - \boldsymbol{u}_2'\boldsymbol{T}\boldsymbol{y}$ is a linearly ancillary statistic or LZF. Because of the linear completeness of $\boldsymbol{T}\boldsymbol{y}$, we must have $\boldsymbol{u}_1'\boldsymbol{T}\boldsymbol{y} - \boldsymbol{u}_2'\boldsymbol{T}\boldsymbol{y} = 0$ with probability 1 for all $\boldsymbol{\beta}$. Therefore, $\boldsymbol{u}_2'\boldsymbol{T}\boldsymbol{y}$ cannot have smaller variance than $\boldsymbol{u}_1'\boldsymbol{T}\boldsymbol{y}$. □

The construction outlined in the above proposition depends on the existence of a linearly complete and sufficient statistic. It is now shown that the vector of fitted values $\widehat{\boldsymbol{y}}$ described by (7.1) is such a statistic.

Proposition 11.10. *A linearly complete and sufficient statistic in the linear model $(\boldsymbol{y}, \boldsymbol{X}\boldsymbol{\beta}, \sigma^2\boldsymbol{V})$ is the vector of fitted values, $\widehat{\boldsymbol{y}}$.*

Proof. In view of (7.1), we have

$$\widehat{E}(\boldsymbol{l}'\boldsymbol{y}|\widehat{\boldsymbol{y}}) = \boldsymbol{l}'\boldsymbol{X}\boldsymbol{\beta} - \boldsymbol{l}'D(\widehat{\boldsymbol{y}})[D(\widehat{\boldsymbol{y}})]^-(\widehat{\boldsymbol{y}} - \boldsymbol{X}\boldsymbol{\beta}) = \boldsymbol{l}'\boldsymbol{X}\boldsymbol{\beta} - \boldsymbol{l}'(\widehat{\boldsymbol{y}} - \boldsymbol{X}\boldsymbol{\beta}) = \boldsymbol{l}'\widehat{\boldsymbol{y}},$$

which does not depend on $\boldsymbol{\beta}$. Therefore, $\widehat{\boldsymbol{y}}$ is a linearly sufficient statistic. Further, Proposition 3.29 and Remark 3.15 imply that $\widehat{\boldsymbol{y}}$ is uncorrelated with every linearly ancillary statistic (i.e. every LZF). In particular, if $\boldsymbol{a}'\widehat{\boldsymbol{y}}$

is an LZF, it is uncorrelated with itself, i.e. it must be zero almost surely. Hence, $\widehat{\boldsymbol{y}}$ is linearly complete and sufficient. □

Propositions 11.8–11.10 lead us to a linear version of Bahadur's (1957) result linking complete sufficiency with minimal sufficiency. Unlike in the general case, these two turn out to be equivalent in the linear case.

Proposition 11.11. *A linear statistic in the model $(\boldsymbol{y}, \boldsymbol{X\beta}, \sigma^2\boldsymbol{V})$ is linearly complete and sufficient if and only if it is linearly minimal sufficient.*

Proof. Let $\boldsymbol{Ty}$ be linearly complete and sufficient. Proposition 11.9 implies that every element of $\boldsymbol{Ty}$ is the BLUE of its expectation. Let $\boldsymbol{t}'\boldsymbol{y}$ be an element of $\boldsymbol{Ty}$ and $\boldsymbol{Sy}$ any other linearly sufficient statistic. According to Proposition 11.8, $\widehat{E}(\boldsymbol{t}'\boldsymbol{y}|\boldsymbol{Sy})$ has at least as small a variance as $\boldsymbol{t}'\boldsymbol{y}$. Since $\boldsymbol{t}'\boldsymbol{y}$ is the BLUE of its expectation, its variance must be the same as that of $\widehat{E}(\boldsymbol{t}'\boldsymbol{y}|\boldsymbol{Sy})$. Uniqueness of the BLUE implies that $\boldsymbol{t}'\boldsymbol{y}$ must be almost surely equal to $\widehat{E}(\boldsymbol{t}'\boldsymbol{y}|\boldsymbol{Sy})$, which is a linear function of $\boldsymbol{Sy}$. Therefore, $\boldsymbol{Ty}$ is almost surely equal to a linear function of every linearly sufficient statistic.

To prove the converse, let $\boldsymbol{Ty}$ be linearly minimal sufficient. According to Proposition 11.10, $\boldsymbol{Ty}$ must be almost surely equal to $\boldsymbol{A}\widehat{\boldsymbol{y}}$ for some matrix $\boldsymbol{A}$. If $\boldsymbol{l}'\boldsymbol{A}\widehat{\boldsymbol{y}}$ is linearly ancillary, Proposition 3.29 ensures that it must be uncorrelated with itself, and hence equal to zero almost surely. □

We are now ready for a characterization of linearly sufficient statistics in terms of BLUEs.

Proposition 11.12. *A statistic is linearly sufficient for $\boldsymbol{\beta}$ in the linear model $(\boldsymbol{y}, \boldsymbol{X\beta}, \sigma^2\boldsymbol{V})$ if and only if every BLUE is almost surely equal to a linear function of it.*

Proof. Every BLUE is almost surely equal to a linear function of the vector of fitted values. The latter in turn is almost surely equal to a linear function of every linearly sufficient statistic, according to Propositions 11.10 and 11.11. To prove the converse, let every BLUE be a linear function of the statistic $\boldsymbol{Ty}$. We shall show that for any $\boldsymbol{l}'\boldsymbol{y}$, $\widehat{E}(\boldsymbol{l}'\boldsymbol{y}|\boldsymbol{Ty})$ does not depend on $\boldsymbol{\beta}$. Since $\boldsymbol{y} = \widehat{\boldsymbol{y}} + \boldsymbol{e}$, it is enough to show that $\widehat{E}(\boldsymbol{l}'\widehat{\boldsymbol{y}}|\boldsymbol{Ty})$ and $\widehat{E}(\boldsymbol{l}'\boldsymbol{e}|\boldsymbol{Ty})$ do not depend on $\boldsymbol{\beta}$. The statement about $\widehat{E}(\boldsymbol{l}'\widehat{\boldsymbol{y}}|\boldsymbol{Ty})$ follows from the fact that $\widehat{\boldsymbol{y}}$ (and hence $\boldsymbol{l}'\widehat{\boldsymbol{y}}$) is a function of $\boldsymbol{Ty}$. To prove the other part, note that $\boldsymbol{l}'\boldsymbol{e} - \widehat{E}(\boldsymbol{l}'\boldsymbol{e}|\boldsymbol{Ty})$ is uncorrelated with $\boldsymbol{Ty}$. Hence it is uncorrelated with $\widehat{\boldsymbol{y}}$ and with $\boldsymbol{T}\widehat{\boldsymbol{y}}$. Setting the covariance with the latter equal to zero, we have after simplification

$$Cov(\boldsymbol{l}'\boldsymbol{e}, \boldsymbol{Ty})[D(\boldsymbol{Ty})]^- D(\boldsymbol{T}\widehat{\boldsymbol{y}}) = \boldsymbol{0}.$$

As $(\boldsymbol{T}\widehat{\boldsymbol{y}} - \boldsymbol{TX\beta}) \in \mathcal{C}(D(\boldsymbol{T}\widehat{\boldsymbol{y}}))$, we conclude that $Cov(\boldsymbol{l}'\boldsymbol{e}, \boldsymbol{Ty})[D(\boldsymbol{Ty})]^-$ $(\boldsymbol{T}\widehat{\boldsymbol{y}} - \boldsymbol{TX\beta}) = 0$, and consequently $Cov(\boldsymbol{l}'\boldsymbol{e}, \boldsymbol{Ty})[D(\boldsymbol{Ty})]^-(\boldsymbol{Ty} - \boldsymbol{TX\beta})$ is free of $\boldsymbol{\beta}$. □

Drygas (1983) *defines* a linearly sufficient statistic via the above characterization. See Müller et al. (1984) for characterizations through three other properties.

Proposition 11.12 shows that a linearly sufficient statistic for $\boldsymbol{\beta}$ is a vector whose elements contain a *generating set of BLUEs*, defined in Section 3.8. Proposition 11.7 implies that the elements of a linearly minimal sufficient statistic for $\boldsymbol{\beta}$ constitute a *basis set of BLUEs*. Apart from BLUEs, several linear estimators described in Sections 11.2 and 5.6 are functions of a linearly minimal sufficient statistic for $\boldsymbol{\beta}$. We shall illustrate in Section 11.1.3 the simultaneous construction of a linearly minimal sufficient statistic and a linearly maximal ancillary.

When the distribution of $\boldsymbol{y}$ is multivariate normal, the concepts of linear sufficiency and completeness reduce to usual sufficiency and completeness, respectively.

Proposition 11.13. *Let* $\boldsymbol{y} \sim N(\boldsymbol{X\beta}, \sigma^2\boldsymbol{V})$.

(a) The statistic $\boldsymbol{Ty}$ *is linearly sufficient for* $\boldsymbol{\beta}$ *if and only if it is sufficient for* $\boldsymbol{\beta}$.
(b) The statistic $\boldsymbol{Ty}$ *is linearly ancillary for* $\boldsymbol{\beta}$ *if and only if it is ancillary for* $\boldsymbol{\beta}$.
(c) The statistic $\boldsymbol{Ty}$ *is linearly minimal sufficient (that is, linearly complete and sufficient) for* $\boldsymbol{\beta}$ *if and only if it is complete and sufficient for* $\boldsymbol{\beta}$.

Proof. In the normal case $\widehat{E}[\boldsymbol{y}|\boldsymbol{Ty} = \boldsymbol{t}] = E[\boldsymbol{y}|\boldsymbol{Ty} = \boldsymbol{t}]$. Therefore $\boldsymbol{Ty}$ is linearly sufficient for $\boldsymbol{\beta}$ if and only if $E[\boldsymbol{y}|\boldsymbol{Ty} = \boldsymbol{t}]$ does not depend on $\boldsymbol{\beta}$, which in turn is equivalent to the conditional (normal) distribution of $\boldsymbol{y}$ given $\boldsymbol{Ty} = \boldsymbol{t}$ being not dependent on $\boldsymbol{\beta}$. This proves part (a).

If $\boldsymbol{Ty}$ is linearly ancillary for $\boldsymbol{\beta}$, then its (normal) distribution has zero mean, and hence it does not depend on $\boldsymbol{\beta}$. Therefore it is ancillary for $\boldsymbol{\beta}$. Conversely, if $\boldsymbol{Ty}$ is ancillary for $\boldsymbol{\beta}$, then $E(\boldsymbol{Ty}) = \boldsymbol{TX\beta}$ does not depend on $\boldsymbol{\beta}$, which means that $\boldsymbol{Ty}$ must be an LZF. This proves part (b).

In order to prove part (c), let $\boldsymbol{Ty}$ be complete and sufficient for $\boldsymbol{\beta}$. According to Basu's theorem, it must be uncorrelated with every LZF. Therefore, if the statistic $\boldsymbol{l}'\boldsymbol{Ty}$ is linearly ancillary, then it must be uncorrelated with itself. It follows that $\boldsymbol{l}'\boldsymbol{Ty}$ is almost surely equal to zero. This proves the linear completeness of $\boldsymbol{Ty}$. The linear sufficiency follows from part (a). See Exercise 11.1 for a proof of the converse. □

Drygas (1983) and Mueller (1987) give some algebraic characterizations of a matrix $\boldsymbol{T}$ so that $\boldsymbol{T}'\boldsymbol{y}$ is linearly sufficient, linearly complete or linearly complete and sufficient. These results hold for nonsingular $\boldsymbol{V}$ but there are some problems in the singular case. Such characterizations for the singular case, are given in Section 11.1.4.

The above theory leaves out the question of estimating σ^2. Since quadratic functions of $\boldsymbol{y}$ are generally needed to estimate it, one has to consider at least one quadratic function of $\boldsymbol{y}$ together with a linear sufficient statistic in order to make the pair sufficient for both $\boldsymbol{\beta}$ and σ^2 in some sense. See Drygas (1983) and Mueller (1987) for a definition and characterizations of quadratic sufficiency. Oktaba et al. (1988) look at the possible equivalence of the models $(\boldsymbol{y}, \boldsymbol{X\beta}, \sigma^2\boldsymbol{V})$ and the corresponding model for $\boldsymbol{Ty}$, $(\boldsymbol{Ty}, \boldsymbol{TX\beta}, \sigma^2\boldsymbol{TVT}')$, in terms of estimable functions, BLUEs, variance estimators and tests of hypotheses. They defined $\boldsymbol{Ty}$ as an *invariant linearly sufficient statistic*, and gave algebraic characterizations of such statistics. Shang and Zhang (1993) study linear sufficiency and linear completeness in the limited context of estimating a linear (vector) function of $\boldsymbol{\beta}$ only, and also for restricted linear models. Kornacki (1998) considers possible ordering of linear models in terms of classes of linearly and quadratically sufficient statistics. The issue of linear sufficiency has been considered in the context of linear prediction also; see Isotalo et al. (2018) for a collection of results on this topic. Kala et al. (2017) discuss relative linear sufficiency in respect of a transformed linear model.

11.1.2 *Basis set of BLUEs*

It was observed on page 542), the elements of a linearly minimal sufficient statistic for $\boldsymbol{\beta}$ constitute a basis set of BLUEs. Conversely, it can be verified that every basis set of BLUEs comprise a linearly minimal sufficient statistic.

In a singular linear model, it is possible that a BLUE would have zero variance (see Example 7.14). Therefore, some elements of a basis set of

BLUEs can also have zero variance. If this happens, one might ask if there is redundancy even in a basis set of BLUEs. Let us consider an example.

Example 11.14. Suppose we have five independent measurements on the weights of three objects. The last two observations are made with super-precise instruments. The weights β_1, β_2 and β_3 can be estimated from the model $\mathcal{M} = (\boldsymbol{y}, \boldsymbol{X\beta}, \sigma^2\boldsymbol{V})$, where

$$\boldsymbol{y} = \begin{pmatrix} y_1 \\ y_2 \\ y_3 \\ y_4 \\ y_5 \end{pmatrix}, \qquad \boldsymbol{X} = \begin{pmatrix} 1 & 0 & 0 \\ 0 & 1 & 0 \\ 0 & 0 & 1 \\ 1 & 0 & 0 \\ 0 & 1 & 0 \end{pmatrix}, \qquad \boldsymbol{V} = \begin{pmatrix} \boldsymbol{I}_{3\times 3} & \boldsymbol{0}_{3\times 2} \\ \boldsymbol{0}_{2\times 3} & \delta\boldsymbol{I}_{2\times 2} \end{pmatrix},$$

where δ is a known, small constant, which represents the relative precision of measurement for the last two cases. The model becomes singular in the limit as δ goes to zero. All the parameters in this model are estimable. The BLUEs are $\widehat{\beta}_1 = (\delta y_1 + y_4)/(1+\delta)$, $\widehat{\beta}_2 = (\delta y_2 + y_5)/(1+\delta)$, and $\widehat{\beta}_3 = y_3$. A basis set of BLUEs is given by the elements of the vector $\boldsymbol{Ty} = (\widehat{\beta}_1 : \widehat{\beta}_2 : \widehat{\beta}_3)'$, which reduces to $(y_4 : y_5 : y_3)'$ when $\delta = 0$, i.e. when $\boldsymbol{V}$ is singular.

It may be argued that in the singular case, there is a linear combination of the first two elements of $\boldsymbol{Ty}$ which is zero. Specifically, $\beta_2\widehat{\beta}_1 - \beta_1\widehat{\beta}_2 = 0$. However, we need not be bothered about this 'redundancy' in $\boldsymbol{Ty}$, as β_1 and β_2 are not known *a priori*. □

A model like the one in Example 11.14 may also arise from a linear restriction on the parameters (see the equivalent unrestricted model $\mathcal{M}_R$ described on page 369). For instance, the model of Example 11.14 could have come from the model $(\boldsymbol{y}, \boldsymbol{I}_{3\times 3}\boldsymbol{\beta}, \sigma^2\boldsymbol{I})$ under the restriction $\beta_1 = \beta_2 = 1$. In such a case, there is a *known* relation between two elements of $\boldsymbol{Ty}$, namely, $\widehat{\beta}_1 = \widehat{\beta}_2$. This relation corresponds to the relation $\beta_2\widehat{\beta}_1 - \beta_1\widehat{\beta}_2 = 0$ in Example 11.14, while in the present case we know *a priori* that $\beta_1 = \beta_2$. Thus the redundancy in the basis set of BLUEs results from the known restriction on the parameter space. The redundancy would disappear if the restrictions are incorporated via the equivalent unrestricted model $\mathcal{M}_r$ of page 369.

When there is no known restriction on the parameters space, a standardized basis set of BLUEs (defined on page 90) in a singular linear model in general contains a combination of elements with variance 0 and σ^2, none of which is redundant. The next proposition gives the number of elements of each kind.

Proposition 11.15. *Consider the linear model $(\boldsymbol{y}, \boldsymbol{X\beta}, \sigma^2\boldsymbol{V})$ with no known restriction on the parameters. If $\boldsymbol{z}$ is any vector of BLUEs whose elements constitute a standardized basis set, then*

(a) the total number of elements of $\boldsymbol{z}$ is $\rho(\boldsymbol{X})$;
(b) the number of elements of $\boldsymbol{z}$ which have variance equal to σ^2 is equal to the dimension of $\mathcal{C}(\boldsymbol{X}) \cap \mathcal{C}(\boldsymbol{V})$, while the remaining elements have zero variance.

Proof. Let $\boldsymbol{ZB}$ be a rank-factorization of $\boldsymbol{X}$, so that $\boldsymbol{Z}$ has $\rho(\boldsymbol{X})$ columns. If $\boldsymbol{\theta} = \boldsymbol{B\beta}$, then $(\boldsymbol{y}, \boldsymbol{Z\theta}, \sigma^2\boldsymbol{V})$ is a reparametrization of the original model $(\boldsymbol{y}, \boldsymbol{X\beta}, \sigma^2\boldsymbol{V})$, such that the vector parameter in the reparametrized model has the smallest possible size $(\rho(\boldsymbol{X}))$. Since $\boldsymbol{\theta}$ is fully estimable, any standardized basis set of BLUEs must have at least $\rho(\boldsymbol{X})$ elements. Let m be the number of elements of $\boldsymbol{z}$, which must be greater than or equal to $\rho(\boldsymbol{X})$. Let $m > \rho(\boldsymbol{X})$ and $\boldsymbol{z} = \boldsymbol{L}'\boldsymbol{y}$. Since the $m \times \rho(\boldsymbol{X})$ matrix $\boldsymbol{L}'\boldsymbol{Z}$ has more rows than columns, there is a nontrivial vector $\boldsymbol{l}$ such that $\boldsymbol{l}'\boldsymbol{L}'\boldsymbol{Z\theta} = 0$. It follows that $\boldsymbol{l}'\boldsymbol{z}$ is a linear combination of BLUEs which is an LZF! Since it has to be uncorrelated with all LZFs, $\boldsymbol{l}'\boldsymbol{z}$ must have zero variance. Therefore, $\boldsymbol{l}'\boldsymbol{z} = 0$ with probability 1. This contradicts the definition of a standardized basis set. Hence, m must be equal to $\rho(\boldsymbol{X})$.

In order to prove part (b), it is enough to show that the rank of the dispersion matrix of $\boldsymbol{z}$ is equal to the dimension of $\mathcal{C}(\boldsymbol{X}) \cap \mathcal{C}(\boldsymbol{V})$. Since $\boldsymbol{z}$ and $\widehat{\boldsymbol{y}}$ are both generating sets, there are $n \times m$ matrices $\boldsymbol{C}$ and $\boldsymbol{B}$ such that $\widehat{\boldsymbol{y}} = \boldsymbol{Cz}$ and $\boldsymbol{z} = \boldsymbol{B}'\widehat{\boldsymbol{y}}$. Therefore,

$$\rho(D(\boldsymbol{z})) = \rho(\boldsymbol{B}'D(\widehat{\boldsymbol{y}})\boldsymbol{B}) \leq \rho(D(\widehat{\boldsymbol{y}})) = \rho(\boldsymbol{C}D(\boldsymbol{z})\boldsymbol{C}) \leq \rho(D(\boldsymbol{z})).$$

Since all the inequalities given above must hold as equalities, we have $\rho(D(\boldsymbol{z})) = \rho(D(\widehat{\boldsymbol{y}}))$. The result follows from Proposition 7.15(a). □

As in the case of linearly minimal sufficient statistics, we can also think of a smallest set of linearly maximal ancillaries. This would coincide with a basis of LZFs, defined in Section 3.8. Part (a) of Proposition 7.19 implies that such a set should contain precisely $\rho(\boldsymbol{V} : \boldsymbol{X}) - \rho(\boldsymbol{X})$ LZFs.

11.1.3 *A decomposition of the response*

We now look for simultaneous construction of standardized bases for BLUEs and LZFs via a single transformation of the response. The next proposition provides these bases, and paves the way for a canonical decomposition of the sum of squares, as we have seen in Section 3.8.

Proposition 11.16. *Given the linear model $(\boldsymbol{y}, \boldsymbol{X\beta}, \sigma^2\boldsymbol{V})$ with possibly rank-deficient $\boldsymbol{X}$ and $\boldsymbol{V}$ but no known constraint on the parameter space, there is a nonsingular matrix $\boldsymbol{L}$ such that the vector $\boldsymbol{Ly}$ can be written as $(\boldsymbol{y}_1' : \boldsymbol{y}_2' : \boldsymbol{y}_3' : \boldsymbol{y}_4')'$, where*

(a) *$\boldsymbol{z} = (\boldsymbol{y}_1' : \boldsymbol{y}_2')'$ is a vector whose elements constitute a standardized basis set of BLUEs;*
(b) *$D(\boldsymbol{y}_1) = \sigma^2\boldsymbol{I}$ and $D(\boldsymbol{y}_2) = \boldsymbol{0}$;*
(c) *$\boldsymbol{y}_3$ is a vector whose elements constitute a standardized basis set of LZFs;*
(d) *$\boldsymbol{y}_4 = \boldsymbol{0}$ with probability 1;*
(e) *$\|\boldsymbol{y}_3\|^2$ is equal to the error sum of squares;*
(f) *$\|\boldsymbol{y}_2\|^2 = \|(\boldsymbol{I} - \boldsymbol{P}_V)\boldsymbol{y}\|^2$ with probability 1;*
(g) *The number of elements of $\boldsymbol{y}_1$, $\boldsymbol{y}_2$, $\boldsymbol{y}_3$ and $\boldsymbol{y}_4$ are $dim(\mathcal{C}(\boldsymbol{X}) \cap \mathcal{C}(\boldsymbol{V}))$, $\rho(\boldsymbol{V} : \boldsymbol{X}) - \rho(\boldsymbol{V})$, $\rho(\boldsymbol{V} : \boldsymbol{X}) - \rho(\boldsymbol{X})$ and $n - \rho(\boldsymbol{V} : \boldsymbol{X})$, respectively.*

Proof. Let $\boldsymbol{U\Lambda U}'$ be a spectral decomposition of $\boldsymbol{V}$ such that $\boldsymbol{\Lambda}$ is nonsingular. Let $\boldsymbol{U}_1$, $\boldsymbol{U}_2$, $\boldsymbol{U}_3$ and $\boldsymbol{U}_4$ be semi-orthogonal matrices and $\boldsymbol{\Lambda}_1$ be a nonsingular diagonal matrix such that

$$\boldsymbol{U}_1\boldsymbol{U}_1' = \boldsymbol{P}_{(I-P_V)X},$$
$$\boldsymbol{U}_2\boldsymbol{U}_2' = \boldsymbol{I} - \boldsymbol{P}_{V:X},$$
$$\boldsymbol{U}_3\boldsymbol{\Lambda}_1\boldsymbol{U}_3' \text{ is a spectral decomposition of } (\boldsymbol{I} - \boldsymbol{P}_X)\boldsymbol{V}(\boldsymbol{I} - \boldsymbol{P}_X),$$
$$\boldsymbol{U}_4\boldsymbol{U}_4' = \boldsymbol{P}_V - \boldsymbol{P}_{V(I-P_X)}.$$

Let $\boldsymbol{KK}'$ be a rank-factorization of the nonsingular matrix $\boldsymbol{U}_4'\boldsymbol{V}\boldsymbol{U}_4$. We define $\boldsymbol{L}$ as

$$\boldsymbol{L} = \begin{pmatrix} \boldsymbol{K}^{-1}\boldsymbol{U}_4' \\ \boldsymbol{U}_1' \\ \boldsymbol{\Lambda}_1^{-1/2}\boldsymbol{U}_3'(\boldsymbol{I} - \boldsymbol{P}_X) \\ \boldsymbol{U}_2' \end{pmatrix} = \begin{pmatrix} \boldsymbol{L}_1 \\ \boldsymbol{L}_2 \\ \boldsymbol{L}_3 \\ \boldsymbol{L}_4 \end{pmatrix}.$$

Let $\boldsymbol{y}_i = \boldsymbol{L}_i\boldsymbol{y}$, $i = 1, 2, 3, 4$. The number of elements of these vectors are the ranks (numbers of columns) of the semi-orthogonal matrices $\boldsymbol{U}_4$, $\boldsymbol{U}_1$, $\boldsymbol{U}_3$ and $\boldsymbol{U}_2$, respectively, which are easily seen to be as given in part (g). It also follows that $\boldsymbol{L}$ is a square matrix.

In order to show that $\boldsymbol{L}$ is nonsingular, let $\boldsymbol{l}$ be a vector satisfying $\boldsymbol{Ll} = \boldsymbol{0}$. A part of this condition, namely $\boldsymbol{L}_4\boldsymbol{l} = \boldsymbol{0}$ implies that $\boldsymbol{l} \in \mathcal{C}(\boldsymbol{V} : \boldsymbol{X})$, i.e.

$\boldsymbol{l}$ must be of the form $\boldsymbol{V}\boldsymbol{a} + (\boldsymbol{I} - \boldsymbol{P}_V)\boldsymbol{X}\boldsymbol{b}$. Another part, namely $\boldsymbol{L}_2\boldsymbol{l} = \boldsymbol{0}$ implies that $(\boldsymbol{I} - \boldsymbol{P}_V)\boldsymbol{X}\boldsymbol{b} = \boldsymbol{0}$, so that $\boldsymbol{l} = \boldsymbol{V}\boldsymbol{a}$. Then the part $L_3\boldsymbol{l} = \boldsymbol{0}$ implies that $(\boldsymbol{I} - \boldsymbol{P}_X)\boldsymbol{V}\boldsymbol{a} = \boldsymbol{0}$, while the part $L_1\boldsymbol{l} = \boldsymbol{0}$ implies that $\boldsymbol{V}\boldsymbol{a}$ must be of the form $\boldsymbol{V}(\boldsymbol{I} - \boldsymbol{P}_X)\boldsymbol{c}$ for some vector $\boldsymbol{c}$. The combined implication of the last two conclusions is that $\boldsymbol{V}\boldsymbol{a} = \boldsymbol{0}$. Thus, $\boldsymbol{l} = \boldsymbol{0}$, i.e. $\boldsymbol{L}$ must have full column rank.

Simple calculations show that $D(\boldsymbol{y}_1) = \sigma^2\boldsymbol{I}$, $D(\boldsymbol{y}_2) = \boldsymbol{0}$, $D(\boldsymbol{y}_3) = \sigma^2\boldsymbol{I}$, $D(\boldsymbol{y}_4) = \boldsymbol{0}$ and $Cov(\boldsymbol{y}_1, \boldsymbol{y}_3) = \boldsymbol{0}$. Further, $E(\boldsymbol{y}_3) = \boldsymbol{0}$ and $\boldsymbol{E}(\boldsymbol{y}_4) = \boldsymbol{0}$. We have proved parts (b) and (d). Since the number of uncorrelated LZFs contained in $\boldsymbol{y}_3$ is exactly $\rho(\boldsymbol{V} : \boldsymbol{X}) - \rho(\boldsymbol{X})$, part (c) is proved. The vectors $\boldsymbol{y}_1$ and $\boldsymbol{y}_2$ must be BLUEs of their respective expectations, as these are uncorrelated with the basis set of LZFs contained in $\boldsymbol{y}_3$. In order to prove part (a), partition $\boldsymbol{L}^{-1}$ conformably with $\boldsymbol{L}$ as $(\boldsymbol{M}_1 : \boldsymbol{M}_2 : \boldsymbol{M}_3 : \boldsymbol{M}_4)$. Since $\boldsymbol{L}_3\boldsymbol{X} = \boldsymbol{0}$ and $\boldsymbol{L}_4\boldsymbol{X} = \boldsymbol{0}$, it follows that $\boldsymbol{M}_1\boldsymbol{L}_1\boldsymbol{y} + \boldsymbol{M}_2\boldsymbol{L}_2\boldsymbol{y}$ is an unbiased estimator of $\boldsymbol{X}\boldsymbol{\beta}$, which must be the BLUE. Thus, $\widehat{\boldsymbol{y}}$ is a linear function of $\boldsymbol{z}$, and the elements of $\boldsymbol{z}$ constitute a standardized basis set of BLUEs.

Part (e) is proved by observing that

$$\boldsymbol{y}_3'\boldsymbol{y}_3 = \boldsymbol{y}'(\boldsymbol{I} - \boldsymbol{P}_X)\{(\boldsymbol{I} - \boldsymbol{P}_X)\boldsymbol{V}(\boldsymbol{I} - \boldsymbol{P}_X)\}^-(\boldsymbol{I} - \boldsymbol{P}_X)\boldsymbol{y} = R_0^2,$$

from (7.7). Part (f) follows from the fact that

$$\boldsymbol{y}'(\boldsymbol{I} - \boldsymbol{P}_V)\boldsymbol{y} = \boldsymbol{y}'(\boldsymbol{U}_1\boldsymbol{U}_1' + \boldsymbol{U}_2\boldsymbol{U}_2')\boldsymbol{y} = \boldsymbol{y}_2'\boldsymbol{y}_2 + \boldsymbol{y}_4'\boldsymbol{y}_4 = \boldsymbol{y}_2'\boldsymbol{y}_2$$

almost surely. □

The transformation of $\boldsymbol{y}$ given in the above theorem produces a vector with uncorrelated components. Some of these components are BLUEs of their respective expectations, while the others are LZFs. Some components are degenerate with zero variance, while the others have variance σ^2. The number of components belonging to each category is summarized in Table 11.1.

Table 11.1 Number of components of transformed $\boldsymbol{y}$ in various categories

	BLUE	LZF	total
with variance $= \sigma^2$	$\dim(\mathcal{C}(\boldsymbol{X}) \cap \mathcal{C}(\boldsymbol{V}))$	$\rho(\boldsymbol{V} : \boldsymbol{X}) - \rho(\boldsymbol{X})$	$\rho(\boldsymbol{V})$
with variance $= 0$	$\rho(\boldsymbol{V} : \boldsymbol{X}) - \rho(\boldsymbol{V})$	$n - \rho(\boldsymbol{V} : \boldsymbol{X})$	$n - \rho(\boldsymbol{V})$
total	$\rho(\boldsymbol{X})$	$n - \rho(\boldsymbol{X})$	n

Example 11.17. Consider the model $(\boldsymbol{y}, \boldsymbol{X\beta}, \sigma^2\boldsymbol{V})$ with four observations and two parameters,

$$\boldsymbol{X} = \begin{pmatrix} 1 & 0 \\ 1 & 0 \\ 0 & 1 \\ 0 & 1 \end{pmatrix}, \qquad \boldsymbol{V} = \begin{pmatrix} 1 & 0 & 0 & 0 \\ 0 & 1 & 0 & 0 \\ 0 & 0 & 0 & 0 \\ 0 & 0 & 0 & 0 \end{pmatrix}.$$

Here, $n = 4$, $\rho(\boldsymbol{V}) = \rho(\boldsymbol{X}) = 2$, $\rho(\boldsymbol{X} : \boldsymbol{V}) = 3$, $\dim(\mathcal{C}(\boldsymbol{X}) \cap \mathcal{C}(\boldsymbol{V})) = 1$. Therefore, there is exactly one component of each category described in Table 6.1. We can choose

$$\boldsymbol{U} = \begin{pmatrix} 1 & 0 \\ 0 & 1 \\ 0 & 0 \\ 0 & 0 \end{pmatrix}, \ \boldsymbol{U}_1 = \begin{pmatrix} 0 \\ 0 \\ \frac{1}{\sqrt{2}} \\ \frac{1}{\sqrt{2}} \end{pmatrix}, \ \boldsymbol{U}_2 = \begin{pmatrix} 0 \\ 0 \\ \frac{1}{\sqrt{2}} \\ -\frac{1}{\sqrt{2}} \end{pmatrix}, \ \boldsymbol{U}_3 = \begin{pmatrix} \frac{1}{\sqrt{2}} \\ -\frac{1}{\sqrt{2}} \\ 0 \\ 0 \end{pmatrix}, \ \boldsymbol{U}_4 = \begin{pmatrix} \frac{1}{\sqrt{2}} \\ \frac{1}{\sqrt{2}} \\ 0 \\ 0 \end{pmatrix}.$$

Then, the matrix $\boldsymbol{L}$ defined in Proposition 11.16 is

$$\boldsymbol{L} = \frac{1}{\sqrt{2}} \begin{pmatrix} 1 & 1 & 0 & 0 \\ 0 & 0 & 1 & 1 \\ 1 & -1 & 0 & 0 \\ 0 & 0 & 1 & -1 \end{pmatrix}.$$

Thus, $(y_1+y_2)/\sqrt{2}$ is a BLUE with variance σ^2, $(y_3+y_4)/\sqrt{2}$ is a BLUE with zero variance, $(y_1 - y_2)/\sqrt{2}$ is an LZF with variance σ^2, and $(y_3 - y_4)/\sqrt{2}$ is an LZF with zero variance. □

Remark 11.18. The vector $\boldsymbol{z}$ described in part (a) of Proposition 11.16 is a linearly minimal sufficient statistic. The vector $\boldsymbol{y}_3$ described in part (c) is a linearly maximal ancillary. □

Remark 11.19. When the parameter space of the model is constrained, Proposition 11.16 continues to hold with the following change in part (a): the vector $\boldsymbol{z}$ is a generating set of the BLUEs. In this case $\boldsymbol{y}_1$ and a sub-vector of $\boldsymbol{y}_2$ constitutes a standardized basis set. There is a possible over-counting of the number of BLUEs with zero variance in Table 11.1. There is also a corresponding under-counting of LZFs with zero variance. If $\boldsymbol{A\beta} = \boldsymbol{\xi}$ is the known restriction, then the correct numbers can be obtained by replacing $\boldsymbol{X}$ with $\boldsymbol{X}(\boldsymbol{I} - \boldsymbol{AA}^-)$ in that table. □

Nordström (1985) gives an additive decomposition of $\boldsymbol{y}$ into four subspaces of $\mathbb{R}^n$. This decomposition is similar to the transformation given in

Proposition 11.16 (see Exercise 11.5). The advantage of the transformation in Proposition 11.16 is that it provides the standardized basis sets of BLUEs and LZFs.

When $\mathcal{C}(\boldsymbol{X}) \subseteq \mathcal{C}(\boldsymbol{V})$ (a condition which holds if $\boldsymbol{V}$ is nonsingular), it can be shown that

$$\|\boldsymbol{y}_1\|^2 = \widehat{\boldsymbol{y}}'\boldsymbol{V}^-\widehat{\boldsymbol{y}}, \tag{11.1}$$

$$\|\boldsymbol{y}_2\|^2 = 0, \tag{11.2}$$

with probability 1. These facts supplement the results

$$\|\boldsymbol{y}_3\|^2 = \boldsymbol{e}'\boldsymbol{V}^-\boldsymbol{e}, \tag{11.3}$$

$$\|\boldsymbol{y}_4\|^2 = 0, \tag{11.4}$$

obtained from parts (d) and (e) of Proposition 11.16.

Instead of proving (11.1), we now prove a more general result.

Proposition 11.20. *Let $\boldsymbol{z}$ be any standardized basis of BLUEs in the linear model $(\boldsymbol{y}, \boldsymbol{X\beta}, \sigma^2\boldsymbol{V})$ with $\mathcal{C}(\boldsymbol{X}) \subseteq \mathcal{C}(\boldsymbol{V})$. Then $\boldsymbol{z}'\boldsymbol{z} = \widehat{\boldsymbol{y}}'\boldsymbol{V}^-\widehat{\boldsymbol{y}} = \boldsymbol{y}'\boldsymbol{V}^-\boldsymbol{y} - R_0^2$.*

Proof. Let $\boldsymbol{FF}'$ be a rank-factorization of $\boldsymbol{V}$, $\boldsymbol{C}$ a left-inverse of $\boldsymbol{F}$ and $\boldsymbol{C}\widehat{\boldsymbol{y}} = \boldsymbol{Bz}$. Using the fact that $\widehat{\boldsymbol{y}} = \boldsymbol{X}(\boldsymbol{X}'\boldsymbol{V}^-\boldsymbol{X})^-\boldsymbol{X}'\boldsymbol{V}^-\boldsymbol{y}$ (see Exercise 7.34) and equating the dispersions of the two sides, we have $\boldsymbol{P}_{\boldsymbol{CX}} = \boldsymbol{BB}'$. Therefore $\rho(\boldsymbol{B}) = \rho(\boldsymbol{CX}) = \rho(\boldsymbol{X})$, i.e. $\boldsymbol{B}$ has full column rank. It follows that $\boldsymbol{P}_{\boldsymbol{B}'} = \boldsymbol{I}$. Hence,

$$\begin{aligned}\boldsymbol{z}'\boldsymbol{z} = \boldsymbol{z}'\boldsymbol{P}_{\boldsymbol{B}'}\boldsymbol{z} &= \boldsymbol{z}'\boldsymbol{B}'(\boldsymbol{BB}')^-\boldsymbol{Bz} = \widehat{\boldsymbol{y}}'\boldsymbol{C}'(\boldsymbol{P}_{\boldsymbol{CX}})^-\boldsymbol{C}\widehat{\boldsymbol{y}}\\ &= \widehat{\boldsymbol{y}}'\boldsymbol{C}'\boldsymbol{P}_{\boldsymbol{CX}}\boldsymbol{C}\widehat{\boldsymbol{y}} = \widehat{\boldsymbol{y}}'\boldsymbol{C}'\boldsymbol{C}\widehat{\boldsymbol{y}} = \widehat{\boldsymbol{y}}'\boldsymbol{V}^-\widehat{\boldsymbol{y}}.\end{aligned}$$

Also,

$$\widehat{\boldsymbol{y}}'\boldsymbol{V}^-\widehat{\boldsymbol{y}} = \widehat{\boldsymbol{y}}'\boldsymbol{V}^-\boldsymbol{X}(\boldsymbol{X}'\boldsymbol{V}^-\boldsymbol{X})^-\boldsymbol{X}'\boldsymbol{V}^-\boldsymbol{y} = \widehat{\boldsymbol{y}}'\boldsymbol{V}^-\boldsymbol{y},$$

which means that $\widehat{\boldsymbol{y}}'\boldsymbol{V}^-\boldsymbol{e} = 0$. Therefore,

$$\boldsymbol{y}'\boldsymbol{V}^-\boldsymbol{y} = \widehat{\boldsymbol{y}}'\boldsymbol{V}^-\widehat{\boldsymbol{y}} + \boldsymbol{e}'\boldsymbol{V}^-\boldsymbol{e} = \boldsymbol{z}'\boldsymbol{z} + R_0^2.$$ □

The above proposition is a generalization of part (b) of Proposition 3.46, where it was assumed that $\boldsymbol{V} = \boldsymbol{I}$. The result can be further modified to the case where $\boldsymbol{z}$ is *any* basis set of BLUEs, which is not necessarily standardized (Exercise 11.19). However, the decomposition of Proposition 11.20 does not hold when $\mathcal{C}(\boldsymbol{X})$ is not contained in $\mathcal{C}(\boldsymbol{V})$. To see this, note that in the latter case there may be an element of $\boldsymbol{z}$ with zero variance. Multiplying this element with two would lead to another standardized basis set, and the value of $\boldsymbol{z}'\boldsymbol{z}$ would increase. Thus, the value of $\boldsymbol{z}'\boldsymbol{z}$ is not invariant of the choice of the standardized basis set of BLUEs. This is in contrast to the unique sum of squared elements of any standardized basis sets of LZFs.

11.1.4 *Estimation and error spaces*

The idea of Error and Estimation spaces was introduced in Section 3.2 (see Remark 3.35). We now define these formally.

Definition 11.21. The *Error Space* of the model $(\boldsymbol{y}, \boldsymbol{X\beta}, \sigma^2\boldsymbol{V})$ is defined as

$$\mathcal{E}_r = \{\boldsymbol{l} : \boldsymbol{l}'\boldsymbol{y} \text{ is an LZF of the linear model}\}. \qquad \square$$

Definition 11.22. The *Estimation Space* of the model $(\boldsymbol{y}, \boldsymbol{X\beta}, \sigma^2\boldsymbol{V})$ is defined as

$$\mathcal{E}_s = \{\boldsymbol{l} : \boldsymbol{l}'\boldsymbol{y} \text{ is a BLUE of the linear model}\}. \qquad \square$$

Remark 11.23. If there is no known restriction on the parameter space, and $\boldsymbol{L}_1$, $\boldsymbol{L}_2$, $\boldsymbol{L}_3$ and $\boldsymbol{L}_4$ are as in Proposition 11.16, then $\mathcal{E}_r = \mathcal{C}(\boldsymbol{L}_3' : \boldsymbol{L}_4')$, $\mathcal{E}_s = \mathcal{C}(\boldsymbol{L}_1' : \boldsymbol{L}_2' : \boldsymbol{L}_4')$. $\square$

It is easy to see that the error and estimation spaces conform to the definition of vector spaces given in Section A.3. The connection between these two spaces and the definitions given in Section 11.1.1 are given in the following proposition.

Proposition 11.24. *Let* $\boldsymbol{Ty}$ *be a linear statistic in the model* $\mathcal{M} = (\boldsymbol{y}, \boldsymbol{X\beta}, \sigma^2\boldsymbol{V})$.

(a) *The statistic* $\boldsymbol{Ty}$ *is linearly ancillary if and only if* $\mathcal{C}(\boldsymbol{T}') \subseteq \mathcal{E}_r$, *and linearly maximal ancillary if and only if* $\mathcal{C}(\boldsymbol{T}') = \mathcal{E}_r$.
(b) *The statistic* $\boldsymbol{Ty}$ *is linearly complete if and only if* $(\mathcal{C}(\boldsymbol{T}') \cap \mathcal{E}_r) \subseteq (\mathcal{E}_s \cap \mathcal{E}_r)$.
(c) *The statistic* $\boldsymbol{Ty}$ *is linearly sufficient if and only if* $\mathcal{E}_s \subseteq \mathcal{C}(\boldsymbol{T}')$.
(d) *The statistic* $\boldsymbol{Ty}$ *is linearly minimal sufficient if and only if* $\mathcal{C}(\boldsymbol{T}') = \mathcal{E}_s$.

Proof. See Exercise 11.4. $\square$

The above proposition shows that the various types of linear statistics considered in Section 11.1 can be characterized once the error and estimation spaces are characterized. We now provide characterizations of the latter.

Proposition 11.25. *Let* $\mathcal{M}$ *be the linear model* $(\boldsymbol{y}, \boldsymbol{X\beta}, \sigma^2\boldsymbol{V})$ *with no known restriction on the parameters. Then*

(a) $\mathcal{E}_r = \mathcal{C}(\boldsymbol{X})^\perp$;
(b) $\mathcal{E}_s = \mathcal{C}(\boldsymbol{V}(\boldsymbol{I} - \boldsymbol{P}_X))^\perp$;
(c) $\mathcal{E}_r \cap \mathcal{E}_s = \mathcal{C}(\boldsymbol{V} : \boldsymbol{X})^\perp$;
(d) $\mathcal{E}_r + \mathcal{E}_s = \mathbb{R}^n$.

Proof. Since there is no known restriction on the parameters, parts (a), (c) and (d) follow from Remark 11.23.

In order to prove part (b), note that $\boldsymbol{l}'\boldsymbol{y}$ is a BLUE in $\mathcal{M}$ if and only if it is uncorrelated with $(\boldsymbol{I} - \boldsymbol{P}_X)\boldsymbol{y}$. This condition is equivalent to $\boldsymbol{l}'\boldsymbol{V}(\boldsymbol{I} - \boldsymbol{P}_X) = \boldsymbol{0}$, or $\boldsymbol{l} \in \mathcal{C}(\boldsymbol{V}(\boldsymbol{I} - \boldsymbol{P}_X))^\perp$. □

Remark 11.26. The condition $\boldsymbol{l} \in \mathcal{C}(\boldsymbol{V}(\boldsymbol{I} - \boldsymbol{P}_X))^\perp$ holds if and only if $\boldsymbol{V}\boldsymbol{l} \in \mathcal{C}(\boldsymbol{X})$. Therefore, when $\boldsymbol{V}$ is nonsingular, the estimation space is $\mathcal{C}(\boldsymbol{V}^{-1}\boldsymbol{X})$. When $\boldsymbol{V} = \boldsymbol{I}$, $\mathcal{E}_s$ further simplifies to $\mathcal{C}(\boldsymbol{X})$. □

Part (c) of Proposition 11.25 shows that if $\boldsymbol{l}$ is a vector belonging to the estimation and error spaces simultaneously, then $\boldsymbol{l}'\boldsymbol{y}$ is zero almost surely, as $\boldsymbol{y} \in \mathcal{C}(\boldsymbol{V} : \boldsymbol{X})$ with probability one. Thus, the intersection of the two spaces plays no role in the values of the linear functions (BLUEs, LZFs and their linear combinations). If $\mathcal{C}(\boldsymbol{X} : \boldsymbol{V}) = \mathbb{R}^n$, the error and estimations spaces are virtually disjoint.

If $\boldsymbol{u}$ and $\boldsymbol{v}$ are in the estimation and error spaces, respectively, then $\boldsymbol{u}'\boldsymbol{V}\boldsymbol{v} = 0$. Part (d) of Proposition 11.25 indicates that the two spaces together span the entire $\mathbb{R}^n$. Thus, the two spaces have a complementary relationship. When $\boldsymbol{V}$ is nonsingular, they are in fact orthogonal complements of each other under the inner product defined through the positive definite matrix $\boldsymbol{V}$.

We are now ready for a characterization of a matrix $\boldsymbol{T}$ so that the statistic $\boldsymbol{T}\boldsymbol{y}$ is linearly ancillary, linearly complete, linearly sufficient or linearly minimal sufficient.

Proposition 11.27. *Let $\boldsymbol{T}\boldsymbol{y}$ be a linear statistic in the linear model $(\boldsymbol{y}, \boldsymbol{X}\boldsymbol{\beta}, \sigma^2\boldsymbol{V})$, denoted by $\mathcal{M}$, with no known restriction on the parameters. Then*

(a) The statistic $\boldsymbol{T}\boldsymbol{y}$ is linearly ancillary if and only if $\boldsymbol{T}\boldsymbol{X} = \boldsymbol{0}$, and linearly maximal ancillary if and only if $\mathcal{C}(\boldsymbol{T}') = \mathcal{C}(\boldsymbol{X})^\perp$;
(b) The statistic $\boldsymbol{T}\boldsymbol{y}$ is linearly complete if and only if $\mathcal{C}(\boldsymbol{T}\boldsymbol{V}) \subseteq \mathcal{C}(\boldsymbol{T}\boldsymbol{X})$;
(c) The statistic $\boldsymbol{T}\boldsymbol{y}$ is linearly sufficient if and only if $\mathcal{C}(\boldsymbol{V}(\boldsymbol{I} - \boldsymbol{P}_X))^\perp \subseteq \mathcal{C}(\boldsymbol{T}')$;

(d) *The statistic* $\boldsymbol{Ty}$ *is linearly minimal sufficient if and only if* $\mathcal{C}(\boldsymbol{V}(\boldsymbol{I}-\boldsymbol{P}_X))^{\perp} = \mathcal{C}(\boldsymbol{T}')$.

Proof. Part (a) follows from the definition. In order to prove part (b), let $\boldsymbol{Ty}$ be linearly complete and $\boldsymbol{l}$ be an arbitrary vector so that $\boldsymbol{l}'\boldsymbol{TX} = \boldsymbol{0}$. According to Proposition 11.25, $\boldsymbol{T}'\boldsymbol{l} \in \mathcal{E}_r$. Part (b) of Proposition 11.24 implies that $\boldsymbol{T}'\boldsymbol{l} \in \mathcal{E}_r \cap \mathcal{E}_s$, i.e. $\boldsymbol{l}'\boldsymbol{TV} = \boldsymbol{0}$. Therefore, $\mathcal{C}(\boldsymbol{TX})^{\perp} \subseteq \mathcal{C}(\boldsymbol{TV})^{\perp}$, i.e. $\mathcal{C}(\boldsymbol{TV}) \subseteq \mathcal{C}(\boldsymbol{TX})$. Conversely, assume that the latter condition holds and $\boldsymbol{l}'\boldsymbol{Ty}$ is any LZF. Then we have $\boldsymbol{l}'\boldsymbol{TX} = \boldsymbol{0}$, i.e. $\boldsymbol{l}'\boldsymbol{TV} = \boldsymbol{0}$, which implies that $\boldsymbol{l}'\boldsymbol{Ty}$ has zero variance. Therefore, $\boldsymbol{Ty}$ must be linearly complete.

Parts (c) and (d) follow from Propositions 11.24 and 11.25. □

11.2 Admissible, Bayes and minimax linear estimators

The general theory of admissible, Bayes and minimax estimators has been reviewed in Section B.3 of Appendix B. In this section we introduce linear versions of these in the context of the linear model.

11.2.1 *Admissible linear estimator*

Consider the problem of estimating an estimable vector LPF $\boldsymbol{A\beta}$ in the linear model $(\boldsymbol{y}, \boldsymbol{X\beta}, \sigma^2\boldsymbol{V})$. We compare estimators on the basis of the squared error loss function $L(\boldsymbol{\beta}, \boldsymbol{T}(\boldsymbol{y})) = \|\boldsymbol{T}(\boldsymbol{y}) - \boldsymbol{A\beta}\|^2$. An important result due to James and Stein (1961) implies that the BLUE of $\boldsymbol{A\beta}$ is *not* admissible within the class of *all* estimators with respect to the squared error loss function.

However, if we confine our attention only to linear estimators of the form $\boldsymbol{Ty}$, the question of admissibility should then be re-examined. An estimator which is admissible within the class of linear estimators is referred to as an *admissible linear estimator* (ALE). It can be shown that linear admissibility of an estimator with respect to the squared error loss function ensures its linear admissibility with respect to any quadratic loss function of the form $(\boldsymbol{Ty} - \boldsymbol{g}(\boldsymbol{\theta}))'\boldsymbol{B}(\boldsymbol{Ty} - \boldsymbol{g}(\boldsymbol{\theta}))$, where $\boldsymbol{B}$ is a nonnegative definite matrix (Exercise 11.8).

It seems rather natural that linearly complete and sufficient statistics play a central role in admissible linear estimation. The following proposition confirms this.

Proposition 11.28. *Any admissible linear estimator (with respect to the squared error loss function) of an estimable LPF* $\boldsymbol{A\beta}$ *in the linear model*

$(\boldsymbol{y}, \boldsymbol{X\beta}, \sigma^2\boldsymbol{V})$ is almost surely equal to a linear function of any linearly complete and sufficient statistic.

Proof. Let $\boldsymbol{Ty}$ be an admissible linear estimator of $\boldsymbol{A\beta}$ and $\boldsymbol{Sy}$ be a linearly complete and sufficient statistic. Let $\widehat{\boldsymbol{Ty}} = \widehat{E}(\boldsymbol{Ty}|\boldsymbol{Sy})$. According to Proposition 11.9, $\widehat{\boldsymbol{Ty}}$ must be the BLUE of $E(\boldsymbol{Ty})$. Then

$$E\|\boldsymbol{Ty} - \boldsymbol{A\beta}\|^2 = E\|\boldsymbol{Ty} - \widehat{\boldsymbol{Ty}}\|^2 + E\|\widehat{\boldsymbol{Ty}} - \boldsymbol{A\beta}\|^2 \geq E\|\widehat{\boldsymbol{Ty}} - \boldsymbol{A\beta}\|^2.$$

If this inequality is strict for some $\boldsymbol{\beta}$, then $\boldsymbol{Ty}$ would not be an admissible linear estimator of $\boldsymbol{A\beta}$. Therefore, $E\|\boldsymbol{Ty}-\widehat{\boldsymbol{Ty}}\|^2 = 0$, and the LZF $\boldsymbol{Ty}-\widehat{\boldsymbol{Ty}}$ is equal to $\boldsymbol{0}$ with probability 1. Thus, $\boldsymbol{Ty}$ is almost surely equal to $\widehat{\boldsymbol{Ty}}$, which is a linear function of $\boldsymbol{Sy}$. □

Since $\widehat{\boldsymbol{y}}$, the BLUE of $\boldsymbol{X\beta}$, is a linearly complete and sufficient statistic, the above proposition implies that every ALE is almost surely equal to a function of $\widehat{\boldsymbol{y}}$. In particular, if $\boldsymbol{Ty}$ is an ALE, it is almost surely equal to $\widehat{E}(\boldsymbol{Ty}|\widehat{\boldsymbol{y}}) = \boldsymbol{T}\widehat{\boldsymbol{y}}$.

Proposition 11.29. *The BLUE of $\boldsymbol{A\beta}$ in the model $(\boldsymbol{y}, \boldsymbol{X\beta}, \sigma^2\boldsymbol{V})$ is linearly admissible with respect to the squared error loss function.*

Proof. Let $\boldsymbol{Ty}$ have uniformly smaller risk than the risk of the BLUE of $\boldsymbol{A\beta}$. Without loss of generality we can replace $\boldsymbol{Ty}$ by $\boldsymbol{T}\widehat{\boldsymbol{y}}$. If $E(\boldsymbol{T}\widehat{\boldsymbol{y}}) = \boldsymbol{A\beta}$, then the uniqueness of the BLUE implies that $\boldsymbol{T}\widehat{\boldsymbol{y}}$ must be almost surely equal to the BLUE. Let us assume that $E(\boldsymbol{T}\widehat{\boldsymbol{y}}) = \boldsymbol{B\beta}$, such that $\boldsymbol{A\beta} - \boldsymbol{B\beta} \neq \boldsymbol{0}$. Since $\boldsymbol{T}\widehat{\boldsymbol{y}}$ has smaller mean squared error than the BLUE (denoted here by $\widehat{\boldsymbol{A\beta}}$), we have for all $\boldsymbol{\beta}$

$$\begin{aligned} 0 &\leq E\|\boldsymbol{A}\widehat{\boldsymbol{\beta}} - \boldsymbol{A\beta}\|^2 - E\|\boldsymbol{T}\widehat{\boldsymbol{y}} - \boldsymbol{A\beta}\|^2 \\ &= \mathrm{tr}[D(\boldsymbol{A}\widehat{\boldsymbol{\beta}}) - D(\boldsymbol{T}\widehat{\boldsymbol{y}})] - \|(\boldsymbol{A} - \boldsymbol{B})\boldsymbol{\beta}\|^2. \end{aligned}$$

The first term does not depend on $\boldsymbol{\beta}$, while $\|(\boldsymbol{A} - \boldsymbol{B})\boldsymbol{\beta}\|^2$ is an unbounded function of $\boldsymbol{\beta}$ that is positive for some value of $\boldsymbol{\beta}$. Letting the magnitude of $\boldsymbol{\beta}$ increase indefinitely we arrive at a contradiction, thus proving the result. □

The next natural question to ask is whether there are other admissible linear estimators besides the BLUE. The following proposition provides a characterization of all admissible linear estimators of an estimable vector LPF. This result is a special case of a theorem of Baksalary and Markiewicz

(1988) and is built upon a series of earlier results (see Cohen (1966), Shinozaki (1975), Rao (1976), Mathew et al. (1984), and Klonecki and Zontek (1988)). The proof is lengthy and is omitted.

Proposition 11.30. *The class of admissible linear estimators of an estimable LPF* $\boldsymbol{A\beta}$ *in the linear model* $(\boldsymbol{y}, \boldsymbol{X\beta}, \sigma^2\boldsymbol{V})$ *under the squared error loss function is the class of estimators* $\boldsymbol{Ty}$ *that satisfy the following four conditions.*

(a) $\mathcal{C}(\boldsymbol{VT}') \subseteq \mathcal{C}(\boldsymbol{X})$;
(b) $\boldsymbol{TVC}'$ *is symmetric;*
(c) $\boldsymbol{TVT}' \leq \boldsymbol{TVC}'$ *in the sense of the Löwner order;*
(d) $\mathcal{C}((\boldsymbol{T}-\boldsymbol{C})\boldsymbol{X}) = \mathcal{C}((\boldsymbol{T}-\boldsymbol{C})\boldsymbol{W})$;

where $\boldsymbol{C}$ *and* $\boldsymbol{W}$ *are matrices such that* $\boldsymbol{A}=\boldsymbol{CX}$ *and* $\mathcal{C}(\boldsymbol{W})=\mathcal{C}(\boldsymbol{V})\cap\mathcal{C}(\boldsymbol{X})$.

Remark 11.31. Some special cases of the above result are particularly interesting. When $\boldsymbol{A\beta}$ and $\boldsymbol{Ty}$ are scalars, condition (b) is redundant and condition (c) reduces to an algebraic inequality. When $\boldsymbol{V}$ is positive definite, condition (d) is redundant. When $\boldsymbol{A} = \boldsymbol{X}$, we can choose $\boldsymbol{C} = \boldsymbol{I}$. In such a case, admissibility of $\boldsymbol{Ty}$ as a linear estimator of $\boldsymbol{X\beta}$ implies that of $\boldsymbol{LTy}$ as a linear estimator of $\boldsymbol{LX\beta}$ for *any* $\boldsymbol{L}$ (Exercise 11.9). □

Example 11.32. If $\widehat{\boldsymbol{A\beta}}$ is the BLUE of $\boldsymbol{A\beta}$ in the linear model $(\boldsymbol{y}, \boldsymbol{X\beta}, \sigma^2\boldsymbol{V})$ where $\mathcal{C}(\boldsymbol{X}) \subseteq \mathcal{C}(\boldsymbol{V})$, then $c\widehat{\boldsymbol{A\beta}}$ is an ALE of $\boldsymbol{A\beta}$ for $0 \leq c \leq 1$ (see Exercise 11.7). In particular, $c\widehat{\boldsymbol{A\beta}}$ is an ALE of $\boldsymbol{A\beta}$ whenever $0 \leq c \leq 1$ and $\boldsymbol{V}$ is nonsingular. The condition of nonsingularity is unnecessary when $c = 1$. It transpires from these examples that the shrinkage estimator, considered in Section 5.6.3 for the special case $\boldsymbol{V} = \boldsymbol{I}$, is linearly admissible. □

A linear estimator of the form $\boldsymbol{Ty}$ is sometimes referred to as a *homogeneous* linear estimator, to distinguish it from an *inhomogeneous* linear estimator (also known as an *affine* estimator) of the form $\boldsymbol{Ty} + \boldsymbol{t}$, where $\boldsymbol{t}$ is a constant. If one looks for an estimator of an estimable parameter $\boldsymbol{A\beta}$ within this wider class of linear estimators, then a characterization similar to Proposition 11.30 can be given, with the additional condition $\boldsymbol{t} \in \mathcal{C}((\boldsymbol{T}-\boldsymbol{C})\boldsymbol{X})$. The BLUE is easily seen to be admissible within this class too.

Stepniak (1989), Fu and Tang (1993) and Wang and Li (2011) consider linear admissibility in the mixed linear model. Wu (1992) gives a summary of results on this topic as well as on admissible quadratic estimators of σ^2. Baksalary and Markiewicz (1990) extend the characterization of admissible linear estimators in the fixed effects linear model to the case of *non-identifiable* LPFs, although the usefulness of any estimator of non-identifiable LPFs is questionable. Baksalary et al. (1995) further extend this work to the case of a weighted quadratic risk function. Wu (2008) deals with admissibility of linear estimators under inequality constraints. Zhang et al. (2009) characterize admissible linear estimators in the multivariate linear model with inequality constraints on parameters. Markiewicz and Puntanen (2009) consider admissibility in the presence of nuisance parameters.

11.2.2 *Bayes linear estimator*

A *Bayes linear estimator* is similar to a Bayes estimator, when we restrict our attention to linear estimators. Specifically, suppose we have a prior $\pi(\cdot)$ on the vector parameter $\boldsymbol{\theta}$ and $\boldsymbol{y}$ is an observation vector which carries some information about the parametric function $\boldsymbol{g}(\boldsymbol{\theta})$. A *Bayes linear estimator* (BLE) of $\boldsymbol{g}(\boldsymbol{\theta})$ with respect to the prior π is defined as an estimator $\boldsymbol{T}(\boldsymbol{y})$ which minimizes the Bayes risk

$$r(\boldsymbol{T},\pi) = \int R(\boldsymbol{\theta},\boldsymbol{T})\, d\pi(\boldsymbol{\theta})$$

among the class of all *linear* estimators of the form $\boldsymbol{T}\boldsymbol{y}$. Rao (1976) defines such an estimator as a Bayes *homogeneous* linear estimator, as distinguished from an estimator which minimizes the Bayes risk among the class of inhomogeneous or affine estimators. We shall refer to the latter as a Bayes affine estimator.

A unique BLE must necessarily be linearly admissible. This follows from Proposition B.18 of Appendix B, the proof of which remains valid in the case of linear estimators.

Remark 11.33. If a quadratic loss function is used, then any BLE is almost surely a function of every linearly complete and sufficient statistic. To see this, let $\boldsymbol{T}\boldsymbol{y}$ be an estimator of $\boldsymbol{A}\boldsymbol{\beta}$ and $\widehat{\boldsymbol{y}}$ be the BLUE of $\boldsymbol{X}\boldsymbol{\beta}$ (which is almost surely a function of every linearly complete and sufficient statistic). Then for any symmetric and nonnegative definite matrix $\boldsymbol{B}$ we have

$$\begin{aligned}
&E[(\boldsymbol{T}\boldsymbol{y}-\boldsymbol{A}\boldsymbol{\beta})'\boldsymbol{B}(\boldsymbol{T}\boldsymbol{y}-\boldsymbol{A}\boldsymbol{\beta})]\\
&\quad = E[E\{(\boldsymbol{T}\boldsymbol{y}-\boldsymbol{A}\boldsymbol{\beta})'\boldsymbol{B}(\boldsymbol{T}\boldsymbol{y}-\boldsymbol{A}\boldsymbol{\beta})|\boldsymbol{\beta},\sigma^2\}]\\
&\quad - E[E\{(\boldsymbol{T}\widehat{\boldsymbol{y}}-\boldsymbol{A}\boldsymbol{\beta})'\boldsymbol{B}(\boldsymbol{T}\widehat{\boldsymbol{y}}-\boldsymbol{A}\boldsymbol{\beta})+(\boldsymbol{T}\boldsymbol{y}-\boldsymbol{T}\widehat{\boldsymbol{y}})'\boldsymbol{B}(\boldsymbol{T}\boldsymbol{y}-\boldsymbol{T}\widehat{\boldsymbol{y}})|\boldsymbol{\beta},\sigma^2\}].
\end{aligned}$$

Therefore,

$$\begin{aligned} E[(\boldsymbol{Ty}-\boldsymbol{A\beta})'\boldsymbol{B}(\boldsymbol{Ty}-\boldsymbol{A\beta})] &\geq E[E\{(\boldsymbol{T}\widehat{\boldsymbol{y}}-\boldsymbol{A\beta})'\boldsymbol{B}(\boldsymbol{T}\widehat{\boldsymbol{y}}-\boldsymbol{A\beta})|\boldsymbol{\beta},\sigma^2\}] \\ &= E[(\boldsymbol{T}\widehat{\boldsymbol{y}}-\boldsymbol{A\beta})'\boldsymbol{B}(\boldsymbol{T}\widehat{\boldsymbol{y}}-\boldsymbol{A\beta})]. \end{aligned}$$

Thus, for any estimator $\boldsymbol{Ty}$ (of $\boldsymbol{A\beta}$), we can find $\boldsymbol{T}\widehat{\boldsymbol{y}}$ which is a function of every linearly complete and sufficient statistic and has a smaller average risk. □

The next proposition provides a closed form expression of the BLE of an LPF in the general linear model under the squared error loss function, even when the LPF is not estimable.

Proposition 11.34. *Let the prior distribution of $\boldsymbol{\beta}$ and σ^2 in the linear model $(\boldsymbol{y},\boldsymbol{X\beta},\sigma^2\boldsymbol{V})$ be such that $E(\sigma^2)$ is positive and the matrix $E(\boldsymbol{\beta\beta}')$ finite. Let $\boldsymbol{U}=[E(\sigma^2)]^{-1}E(\boldsymbol{\beta\beta}')$. Then the unique BLE of the LPF $\boldsymbol{A\beta}$ with respect to the above prior and the squared error loss function can almost surely be represented as $\boldsymbol{A}\widehat{\boldsymbol{\beta}}_B$, where*

$$\widehat{\boldsymbol{\beta}}_B=\boldsymbol{UX}'(\boldsymbol{V}+\boldsymbol{XUX}')^{-}\boldsymbol{y}.$$

Proof. Let π be the prior distribution of $\boldsymbol{\beta}$ and σ^2. A BLE is obtained by minimizing, with respect to the matrix $\boldsymbol{T}$, the Bayes risk of the estimator $\boldsymbol{Ty}$:

$$\begin{aligned} r(\boldsymbol{T},\pi) &= E\left[E\left[\|\boldsymbol{Ty}-\boldsymbol{A\beta}\|^2 \,\middle|\, \boldsymbol{\beta},\sigma^2\right]\right] \\ &= E\left[E\left[\|(\boldsymbol{Ty}-\boldsymbol{TX\beta})+(\boldsymbol{TX}-\boldsymbol{A})\boldsymbol{\beta}\|^2 \,\middle|\, \boldsymbol{\beta},\sigma^2\right]\right] \\ &= E\left[\sigma^2\mathrm{tr}(\boldsymbol{TVT}')+\|(\boldsymbol{TX}-\boldsymbol{A})\boldsymbol{\beta}\|^2\right] \\ &= E(\sigma^2)\mathrm{tr}(\boldsymbol{TVT}')+\mathrm{tr}[(\boldsymbol{TX}-\boldsymbol{A})E(\boldsymbol{\beta\beta}')(\boldsymbol{TX}-\boldsymbol{A})'] \\ &= E(\sigma^2)\mathrm{tr}[\boldsymbol{TVT}'+(\boldsymbol{TX}-\boldsymbol{A})\boldsymbol{U}(\boldsymbol{TX}-\boldsymbol{A})']. \end{aligned}$$

Let $\boldsymbol{W}=\boldsymbol{V}+\boldsymbol{XUX}'$. It follows from Exercise 7.33 that $\mathcal{C}(\boldsymbol{XU})=\mathcal{C}(\boldsymbol{XUX}')\subseteq\mathcal{C}(\boldsymbol{W})$, so that we can write $\boldsymbol{XUA}'$ as $\boldsymbol{WT}_0'$ for some matrix $\boldsymbol{T}_0$. Therefore, a BLE of $\boldsymbol{A\beta}$ is $\boldsymbol{Ty}$ such that $\boldsymbol{T}$ minimizes

$$\begin{aligned} &\mathrm{tr}[\boldsymbol{TVT}'+(\boldsymbol{TX}-\boldsymbol{A})\boldsymbol{U}(\boldsymbol{TX}-\boldsymbol{A})'] \\ &= \mathrm{tr}[\boldsymbol{TWT}'-\boldsymbol{TWT}_0'-\boldsymbol{T}_0\boldsymbol{WT}'+\boldsymbol{AUA}'] \\ &= \mathrm{tr}[(\boldsymbol{T}-\boldsymbol{T}_0)\boldsymbol{W}(\boldsymbol{T}-\boldsymbol{T}_0)'+(\boldsymbol{AUA}'-\boldsymbol{T}_0\boldsymbol{WT}_0')]. \end{aligned}$$

The minimum value of the above is $\mathrm{tr}[\boldsymbol{AUA}'-\boldsymbol{T}_0\boldsymbol{WT}_0']$, which occurs when the trace of the nonnegative definite matrix $(\boldsymbol{T}-\boldsymbol{T}_0)\boldsymbol{W}(\boldsymbol{T}-\boldsymbol{T}_0)'$ is zero, i.e. when the matrix itself is $\mathbf{0}$. This happens if and only if $\boldsymbol{T} = \boldsymbol{T}_0 + \boldsymbol{F}$ where $\boldsymbol{F}$ is such that $\boldsymbol{FW} = \mathbf{0}$.

We now argue that $\boldsymbol{Fy} = \mathbf{0}$ almost surely. Indeed, Proposition 2.13(a) implies that

$$\boldsymbol{\beta} \in \mathcal{C}(E(\boldsymbol{\beta}) : D(\boldsymbol{\beta})) = \mathcal{C}(E(\boldsymbol{\beta})E(\boldsymbol{\beta})' + D(\boldsymbol{\beta})) = \mathcal{C}(\boldsymbol{U}),$$

and consequently $\boldsymbol{y} \in \mathcal{C}(\boldsymbol{X\beta} : \boldsymbol{V}) \subseteq \mathcal{C}(\boldsymbol{XUX}') + \mathcal{C}(\boldsymbol{V}) = \mathcal{C}(\boldsymbol{W})$. Therefore, the optimal $\boldsymbol{Ty}$ can almost surely be written as

$$\boldsymbol{Ty} = \boldsymbol{T}_0\boldsymbol{y} = \boldsymbol{AUX}'\boldsymbol{W}^-\boldsymbol{y} = \boldsymbol{AUX}'(\boldsymbol{V} + \boldsymbol{XUX}')^-\boldsymbol{y} = \boldsymbol{A}\widehat{\boldsymbol{\beta}}_B.$$

Since $\boldsymbol{y}$ and $\boldsymbol{XUA}'$ both belong to $\mathcal{C}(\boldsymbol{V} + \boldsymbol{XUX}')$, the above expression does not depend on the choice of the g-inverse. This proves the uniqueness of the BLE. □

The uniqueness of the BLE of $\boldsymbol{A\beta}$ implies that it must be linearly admissible. When $\boldsymbol{V}$ is positive definite, Rao (1976) proves that every ALE is either a BLE or the limit of a sequence of BLEs.

If the loss function is chosen to have the form $(\boldsymbol{Ty} - \boldsymbol{A\beta})'\boldsymbol{B}(\boldsymbol{Ty} - \boldsymbol{A\beta})$, where $\boldsymbol{B}$ is a nonnegative definite matrix, the estimator given in Proposition 11.34 is a BLE. However, the uniqueness holds only when $\boldsymbol{B}$ is positive definite. An important aspect of the BLE under a quadratic loss function is that it depends on the prior distribution of $\boldsymbol{\beta}$ and σ^2 only through $E(\boldsymbol{\beta\beta}')/E(\sigma^2)$.

If $\boldsymbol{V}$ is positive definite, then the g-inverse in the expression of the BLE can be replaced by an inverse. If $\boldsymbol{V}$ and $\boldsymbol{U}$ are both positive definite, the BLE simplifies to (Exercise 11.14)

$$\widehat{\boldsymbol{\beta}}_B = (\boldsymbol{X}'\boldsymbol{V}^{-1}\boldsymbol{X} + \boldsymbol{U}^{-1})^{-1}\boldsymbol{X}'\boldsymbol{V}^{-1}\boldsymbol{y}. \tag{11.5}$$

Recall from Proposition B.19(b) that a Bayes estimator is generally biased. The expression given in Proposition 11.34 suggests that the BLE is biased too. A formal proof of this fact is given below.

Proposition 11.35. *Given the set-up of Proposition 11.34, a Bayes linear estimator of an estimable LPF in a linear model cannot be unbiased unless it is almost surely equal to that LPF.*

Proof. Let $\boldsymbol{Ty}$ be the BLE of the estimable LPF $\boldsymbol{A\beta}$. If it is unbiased, then we have

$$E(\boldsymbol{Ty}) = \boldsymbol{A\beta} \qquad \text{for all permissible } \boldsymbol{\beta}.$$

Let $\boldsymbol{A} = \boldsymbol{C}\boldsymbol{X}$. We can express $\boldsymbol{A\beta}$ as $\boldsymbol{C}(\boldsymbol{V}+\boldsymbol{XUX}')(\boldsymbol{V}+\boldsymbol{XUX}')^-\boldsymbol{X\beta}$, where $\boldsymbol{U} = [E(\sigma^2)]^{-1}E(\boldsymbol{\beta\beta}')$, as in Proposition 11.34. Therefore, the above equation can be written as

$$\boldsymbol{A\beta} - \boldsymbol{TX\beta} = \boldsymbol{CV}(\boldsymbol{V}+\boldsymbol{XUX}')^-\boldsymbol{X\beta} = \boldsymbol{0} \qquad \text{for all permissible } \boldsymbol{\beta}.$$

It follows that

$$\begin{aligned}&E[\boldsymbol{CV}(\boldsymbol{V}+\boldsymbol{XUX}')^-\boldsymbol{X\beta\beta}'\boldsymbol{X}'(\boldsymbol{V}+\boldsymbol{XUX}')^-\boldsymbol{VC}']\\&= E(\sigma^2)\boldsymbol{CV}(\boldsymbol{V}+\boldsymbol{XUX}')^-\boldsymbol{XUX}'(\boldsymbol{V}+\boldsymbol{XUX}')^-\boldsymbol{VC}' = \boldsymbol{0},\end{aligned}$$

that is, $\boldsymbol{CV}(\boldsymbol{V}+\boldsymbol{XUX}')^-\boldsymbol{XUX}' = \boldsymbol{0}$. Consequently, the conditional covariance between $\boldsymbol{Ty}$ and $\boldsymbol{Cy}$ given $\boldsymbol{\beta}$ and σ^2 is zero. Note that *any* LUE of $\boldsymbol{A\beta}$ can almost surely be written as $\boldsymbol{Cy}$ for a suitable choice of $\boldsymbol{C}$ (see Proposition 7.3(a)). This implies that $\boldsymbol{Ty}$ is conditionally uncorrelated with every LUE of $\boldsymbol{A\beta}$, including $\boldsymbol{Ty}$ itself. Therefore, $\boldsymbol{Ty}$ must have zero dispersion and be almost surely equal to its conditional mean, $\boldsymbol{A\beta}$. □

Proposition 11.35 implies that the BLUE cannot be a BLE with respect to the squared error loss function.

An alternative characterization of the BLE in a somewhat more general set-up is given by Gnot (1983). Gruber (2010) provides a comparison of the MSEs of the BLE and the BLUE, conditional on $\boldsymbol{\beta}$, in the special case $\boldsymbol{V} = \boldsymbol{I}$. LaMotte (1978) considers the class of Bayes affine estimators in this special case. Gaffke and Heiligers (1989) deal with BLEs for the linear model with positive definite $\boldsymbol{V}$, subject to some linear restrictions on $\boldsymbol{\beta}$.

11.2.3 *Minimax linear estimator*

A *minimax linear estimator* minimizes the maximum risk among the class of linear estimators. In order to ensure that the maximum risk is finite, it is customary to impose an ellipsoidal (quadratic) restriction of the form $\boldsymbol{\theta}'\boldsymbol{H\theta} \le 1$ on the parameter space, where $\boldsymbol{H}$ is a nonnegative definite matrix. Thus a linear estimator $\boldsymbol{Ty}$ is formally defined to be a *minimax linear estimator* (MILE) of $\boldsymbol{\theta}$ if it minimizes the maximum risk

$$\sup_{\theta\in\Theta:\,\theta' H\theta\le 1} E[L(\boldsymbol{\theta}, \boldsymbol{Ty})].$$

Obviously a MILE would depend on the choice of the loss function as well as the matrix $\boldsymbol{H}$.

In the context of the linear model $(\boldsymbol{y}, \boldsymbol{X\beta}, \sigma^2\boldsymbol{V})$ and a quadratic loss function with weight matrix $\boldsymbol{B}$, a MILE of the estimable LPF $\boldsymbol{A\beta}$ is an estimator $\boldsymbol{Ty}$ which minimizes

$$\sup_{\beta:\,\beta' H\beta\le\sigma^2} E[(\boldsymbol{Ty}-\boldsymbol{A\beta})'\boldsymbol{B}(\boldsymbol{Ty}-\boldsymbol{A\beta})],$$

where $\boldsymbol{H}$ and $\boldsymbol{B}$ are both nonnegative definite matrices. The inclusion of σ^2 in the ellipsoidal restriction simplifies the mathematics, as we shall see.

If there is a prior distribution of $\boldsymbol{\beta}$ such that the average risk of the corresponding BLE is equal to its maximum risk, then the prior is least favourable and the BLE is a MILE. This interesting result, which follows from the proof of Proposition B.20 that continues to hold in the linear case, does not directly lead to the identification of a MILE though.

Let $\boldsymbol{FF}'$ be a rank-factorization of $\boldsymbol{B}$, and $\boldsymbol{C}$ be a matrix such that $\boldsymbol{A}=\boldsymbol{CX}$. We can then expand the risk function as

$$\begin{aligned} E[(\boldsymbol{Ty}-\boldsymbol{A\beta})'\boldsymbol{B}(\boldsymbol{Ty}-\boldsymbol{A\beta})] &= \mathrm{tr}E\left[\|\boldsymbol{F}'\boldsymbol{Ty}-\boldsymbol{F}'\boldsymbol{A\beta}\|^2\right] \\ &= \sigma^2\left[\mathrm{tr}(\boldsymbol{F}'\boldsymbol{TVT}'\boldsymbol{F})+\|\boldsymbol{F}'(\boldsymbol{T}-\boldsymbol{C})\boldsymbol{X\beta}\|^2/\sigma^2\right]. \end{aligned}$$

The problem of maximizing this with respect to $\boldsymbol{\beta}$ subject to the restriction $\boldsymbol{\beta}'\boldsymbol{H\beta}\le\sigma^2$ is somewhat simplified if we use the transformation $\boldsymbol{\gamma}=\boldsymbol{\beta}/\sigma$. The maximum risk corresponds to the maximum of $\|\boldsymbol{F}'(\boldsymbol{T}-\boldsymbol{C})\boldsymbol{X\gamma}\|^2$ with respect to $\boldsymbol{\gamma}$ subject to the restriction $\boldsymbol{\gamma}'\boldsymbol{H\gamma}\le 1$. It is easy to see that the quadratic function $\|\boldsymbol{F}'(\boldsymbol{T}-\boldsymbol{C})\boldsymbol{X\gamma}\|^2$ is unbounded if the matrix $\boldsymbol{H}$ is such that $\|\boldsymbol{F}'(\boldsymbol{T}-\boldsymbol{C})\boldsymbol{X\gamma}\|^2$ can be positive even when $\boldsymbol{\gamma}'\boldsymbol{H\gamma}=\boldsymbol{0}$. Thus, boundedness of the risk amounts to the condition '$\boldsymbol{H\gamma}=\boldsymbol{0}$ implies $\boldsymbol{F}'(\boldsymbol{T}-\boldsymbol{C})\boldsymbol{X\gamma}=\boldsymbol{0}$', that is,

$$\mathcal{C}(\boldsymbol{X}'(\boldsymbol{T}-\boldsymbol{C})'\boldsymbol{F})\subseteq\mathcal{C}(\boldsymbol{H}).$$

A simple sufficient condition for the above is $\mathcal{C}(\boldsymbol{X}')\subseteq\mathcal{C}(\boldsymbol{H})$. This condition is also necessary when $\boldsymbol{B}$ is positive definite (i.e. $\boldsymbol{B}$ is invertible) and the boundedness of the risk function of all linear estimators is required.

The condition $\mathcal{C}(\boldsymbol{X}')\subseteq\mathcal{C}(\boldsymbol{H})$ implies that the maximum risk associated with the estimator $\boldsymbol{Ty}$ of $\boldsymbol{A\beta}$ is

$$R_{max}(\boldsymbol{Ty},\boldsymbol{A\beta})=\sigma^2\left[\mathrm{tr}(\boldsymbol{F}'\boldsymbol{TVT}'\boldsymbol{F})+\|\boldsymbol{F}'(\boldsymbol{T}-\boldsymbol{C})\boldsymbol{XH}^-\boldsymbol{X}'(\boldsymbol{T}-\boldsymbol{C})'\boldsymbol{F}\|\right], \tag{11.6}$$

(see Exercise 11.10).

Obtaining a MILE by minimizing (11.6) with respect to $\boldsymbol{Ty}$ is usually a very difficult task in the general case. We present closed form solutions to this problem in the following special cases:

(a) $\boldsymbol{B}$ has rank one;

(b) $\boldsymbol{A\beta}$ is a scalar;

(c) $\boldsymbol{H}\propto\boldsymbol{I}$, $\boldsymbol{B}=\boldsymbol{I}$, $\boldsymbol{A}=\boldsymbol{I}$ and $\boldsymbol{V}$ nonsingular.

The following proposition, which is a generalization of a result due to Kuks and Olman (1972), provides the MILE in the case when $\boldsymbol{B}$ has rank 1.

Proposition 11.36. *Let $\boldsymbol{A\beta}$ be an estimable LPF in the linear model $(\boldsymbol{y}, \boldsymbol{X\beta}, \sigma^2\boldsymbol{V})$, and $\boldsymbol{H}$ be a nonnegative definite matrix with $\mathcal{C}(\boldsymbol{X}') \subseteq \mathcal{C}(\boldsymbol{H})$. A minimax linear estimator of $\boldsymbol{A\beta}$ subject to the restriction $\boldsymbol{\beta}'\boldsymbol{H\beta} \le \sigma^2$ and with respect to the loss function $L(\boldsymbol{Ty}, \boldsymbol{A\beta}) = E[\{(\boldsymbol{Ty} - \boldsymbol{A\beta})'\boldsymbol{f}\}^2]$ can almost surely be written as*

$$\widehat{\boldsymbol{A\beta}}_{m,f} = \boldsymbol{AH}^-\boldsymbol{X}'(\boldsymbol{V} + \boldsymbol{XH}^-\boldsymbol{X}')^-\boldsymbol{y} + (\boldsymbol{I} - \boldsymbol{P}_{\!f})\boldsymbol{a},$$

where $\boldsymbol{a}$ is an arbitrary vector, $\boldsymbol{P}_{\!f} = (\boldsymbol{f}'\boldsymbol{f})^{-1}\boldsymbol{ff}'$ and the two g-inverses are symmetric. Further, the linear estimator of $\boldsymbol{A\beta}$ which is minimax with respect to the above form of loss function for every $\boldsymbol{f}$, is unique and can almost surely be written as $\boldsymbol{AX}^-\widehat{\boldsymbol{X\beta}}_m$ where

$$\widehat{\boldsymbol{X\beta}}_m = \boldsymbol{XH}^-\boldsymbol{X}'(\boldsymbol{V} + \boldsymbol{XH}^-\boldsymbol{X}')^-\boldsymbol{y}.$$

Proof. We begin from (11.6) with $\boldsymbol{B} = \boldsymbol{ff}'$. It follows that a minimax estimator is one which minimizes

$$\boldsymbol{f}'\boldsymbol{TVT}'\boldsymbol{f} + \boldsymbol{f}'(\boldsymbol{T} - \boldsymbol{C})\boldsymbol{XH}^-\boldsymbol{X}'(\boldsymbol{T} - \boldsymbol{C})'\boldsymbol{f}.$$

Completing the square as in the proof of Proposition 11.34, we rewrite the above expression as

$$(\boldsymbol{T}'\boldsymbol{f} - \boldsymbol{QC}'\boldsymbol{f})'(\boldsymbol{V} + \boldsymbol{XH}^-\boldsymbol{X}')(\boldsymbol{T}'\boldsymbol{f} - \boldsymbol{QC}'\boldsymbol{f}) + \alpha,$$

where $\boldsymbol{Q} = (\boldsymbol{V} + \boldsymbol{XH}^-\boldsymbol{X}')^-\boldsymbol{XH}^-\boldsymbol{X}'$ and α is a scalar that does not depend on $\boldsymbol{T}$. Note that the above expression does not depend on the choice of the g-inverses. Therefore, the maximum risk is minimized when $\boldsymbol{T}'\boldsymbol{f}$ is equal to $\boldsymbol{QC}'\boldsymbol{f}$ plus a vector which is in the null space of $\mathcal{C}(\boldsymbol{V} + \boldsymbol{XH}^-\boldsymbol{X}')$. As we have seen in the proof of Proposition 11.34, we can ignore the latter vector in the representation of the corresponding estimator, $\boldsymbol{Ty}$. Thus, $\boldsymbol{Ty}$ is a MILE of $\boldsymbol{A\beta}$ only if $\boldsymbol{f}'\boldsymbol{Ty} = \boldsymbol{f}'\boldsymbol{CQ}'\boldsymbol{y}$ almost surely. This proves the first part of the proposition.

The second part is easily proved by observing that a MILE must satisfy $\boldsymbol{f}'(\boldsymbol{Ty} - \boldsymbol{CQ}'\boldsymbol{y}) = 0$ for all $\boldsymbol{f}$, i.e. $\boldsymbol{Ty} = \boldsymbol{CQ}'\boldsymbol{y}$, almost surely. □

Proposition 11.37. *Let $\boldsymbol{a}'\boldsymbol{\beta}$ be an estimable LPF in the linear model $(\boldsymbol{y}, \boldsymbol{X\beta}, \sigma^2\boldsymbol{V})$, and $\boldsymbol{H}$ be a nonnegative definite matrix with $\mathcal{C}(\boldsymbol{X}') \subseteq \mathcal{C}(\boldsymbol{H})$. The minimax linear estimator of $\boldsymbol{a}'\boldsymbol{\beta}$, subject to the restriction $\boldsymbol{\beta}'\boldsymbol{H\beta} \le \sigma^2$ and with respect to the loss function $L(\boldsymbol{t}'\boldsymbol{y}, \boldsymbol{a}'\boldsymbol{\beta}) = E[\|\boldsymbol{t}'\boldsymbol{y} - \boldsymbol{a}'\boldsymbol{\beta}\|^2]$, almost surely has the unique representation $\boldsymbol{c}'\widehat{\boldsymbol{X\beta}}_m$, where $\widehat{\boldsymbol{X\beta}}_m$ is as described in Proposition 11.36 and $\boldsymbol{c}$ is a vector satisfying $\boldsymbol{a} = \boldsymbol{X}'\boldsymbol{c}$.*

Proof. Since we have a single LPF, the matrix $\boldsymbol{B}$ of (11.6) reduces to a scalar. Hence, we can ignore its presence. Consequently $\boldsymbol{t}'\boldsymbol{y}$ is a minimax estimator of $\boldsymbol{a}'\boldsymbol{\beta}$ only if it minimizes

$$\boldsymbol{t}'\boldsymbol{V}\boldsymbol{t} + (\boldsymbol{t} - \boldsymbol{c})'\boldsymbol{X}\boldsymbol{H}^{-}\boldsymbol{X}'(\boldsymbol{t} - \boldsymbol{c}),$$

where $\boldsymbol{c}$ is a vector satisfying $\boldsymbol{a}'\boldsymbol{\beta} = \boldsymbol{c}'\boldsymbol{X}\boldsymbol{\beta}$. The rest of the proof follows along the lines of the proof of Proposition 11.36. □

The result of Proposition 11.36 can be derived from Proposition 11.37, by substituting $\boldsymbol{a} = \boldsymbol{A}'\boldsymbol{f}$, where $\boldsymbol{A}$ and $\boldsymbol{f}$ are as in the proof of Proposition 11.36.

The estimator $\widehat{\boldsymbol{X\beta}}_m$ described in Propositions 11.36 and 11.37 is called the Kuks-Olman estimator, in recognition of the early work by Kuks and Olman (1971, 1972). Gruber (2010) makes a detailed study of the maximum mean squared error of this estimator. This estimator has two interesting properties. Proposition 11.36 shows that a MILE of any estimable LPF with respect to a quadratic loss function with any rank-one weight matrix $\boldsymbol{B}$ can be obtained from $\widehat{\boldsymbol{X\beta}}_m$ by substitution. Proposition 11.37 shows that the unique MILE of any single estimable LPF with respect to the squared error loss function is obtained from $\widehat{\boldsymbol{X\beta}}_m$ by substitution. Thus, the Kuks-Olman estimator plays an important role in minimax linear estimation in the linear model. Before taking up the third special case mentioned on page 559, let us view this estimator from another angle. The form of this estimator is identical to that of $\boldsymbol{X}\widehat{\boldsymbol{\beta}}_B$, which is a BLE of $\boldsymbol{X\beta}$ with respect to any quadratic loss function, for $\boldsymbol{U} = \boldsymbol{H}^{-}$. See Exercise 11.15 for a formal relation between the two estimators.

An interesting property of $\boldsymbol{X}\widehat{\boldsymbol{\beta}}_m$, which follows from a result of Bunke (1975), is

$$\sup_{\beta:\beta' H\beta\le\sigma^2} E[(\boldsymbol{A}\boldsymbol{X}^{-}\boldsymbol{X}\widehat{\boldsymbol{\beta}}_m - \boldsymbol{A}\boldsymbol{\beta})(\boldsymbol{A}\boldsymbol{X}^{-}\boldsymbol{X}\widehat{\boldsymbol{\beta}}_m - \boldsymbol{A}\boldsymbol{\beta})']$$
$$\le \sup_{\beta:\beta' H\beta\le\sigma^2} E[(\boldsymbol{T}\boldsymbol{y} - \boldsymbol{A}\boldsymbol{\beta})(\boldsymbol{T}\boldsymbol{y} - \boldsymbol{A}\boldsymbol{\beta})'] \qquad (11.7)$$

for any estimable LPF $\boldsymbol{A\beta}$ and for any linear estimator $\boldsymbol{Ty}$ (see Exercise 11.11). In the above result, the supremum of a class of nonnegative definite matrices is the nonnegative definite matrix which is larger than or equal to every matrix of the class (in the sense of the Löwner order), such that no smaller matrix possesses this property.

When $\boldsymbol{V}$ is positive definite, the Kuks-Olman estimator simplifies to (Exercise 11.14)

$$\boldsymbol{X}\widehat{\boldsymbol{\beta}}_m = \boldsymbol{X}(\boldsymbol{X}'\boldsymbol{V}^{-1}\boldsymbol{X} + \boldsymbol{H})^{-}\boldsymbol{X}'\boldsymbol{V}^{-1}\boldsymbol{y}. \qquad (11.8)$$

A special case of the above estimator is the 'ridge estimator' discussed in Section 5.6.2. Gross and Markiewicz (2004) provide a justification of this estimator through a characterization of admissible linear estimators.

In spite of all the nice properties of $\widehat{\boldsymbol{X\beta}}_m$, it must be remembered that it is not necessarily a MILE of $\boldsymbol{X\beta}$ with respect to a general quadratic loss function in the case when the weight matrix $\boldsymbol{B}$ has arbitrary rank. This is illustrated by the next proposition which shows that the MILE of $\boldsymbol{\beta}$ in the special case $\boldsymbol{B} = \boldsymbol{I}$, $\boldsymbol{H} \propto \boldsymbol{I}$ and $\boldsymbol{V}$ nonsingular, is an entirely different estimator and is not a linear function of $\boldsymbol{X}\widehat{\boldsymbol{\beta}}_m$ (see also Exercise 11.12).

Proposition 11.38. *If $\boldsymbol{\beta}$ is estimable in the model $(\boldsymbol{y}, \boldsymbol{X\beta}, \sigma^2\boldsymbol{V})$ with nonsingular $\boldsymbol{V}$, then its minimax linear estimator subject to the restriction $\boldsymbol{\beta}'\boldsymbol{\beta} \le \sigma^2/h$ and with respect to the loss function $L(\boldsymbol{Ty}, \boldsymbol{\beta}) = E[\|\boldsymbol{Ty} - \boldsymbol{\beta}\|^2]$, almost surely has the unique representation*

$$\widehat{\boldsymbol{\beta}}_M = \frac{1}{1 + h \cdot \mathrm{tr}(\boldsymbol{X}'\boldsymbol{V}^{-1}\boldsymbol{X})^{-1}} (\boldsymbol{X}'\boldsymbol{V}^{-1}\boldsymbol{X})^{-1}\boldsymbol{X}'\boldsymbol{V}^{-1}\boldsymbol{y}.$$

Proof. Once again we begin with the expression of maximum risk given in (11.6). Substituting $\boldsymbol{A} = \boldsymbol{I}$, $\boldsymbol{B} = \boldsymbol{I}$ and $\boldsymbol{H} = h\boldsymbol{I}$ in this expression, we have

$$\sigma^{-2} R_{max}(\boldsymbol{Ty}, \boldsymbol{\beta}) = \mathrm{tr}(\boldsymbol{TVT}') + h^{-1}\|\boldsymbol{TX} - \boldsymbol{I}\|^2.$$

A minimax estimator has to minimize the right-hand side of the above equation. We shall simplify the problem by showing that

$$\begin{aligned} &\mathrm{tr}(\boldsymbol{TVT}') + h^{-1}\|\boldsymbol{TX} - \boldsymbol{I}\|^2 \\ &\ge \mathrm{tr}(\boldsymbol{TVT}') + \frac{\mathrm{tr}[(\boldsymbol{TX} - \boldsymbol{I})(\boldsymbol{X}'\boldsymbol{V}^{-1}\boldsymbol{X})^{-1}(\boldsymbol{TX} - \boldsymbol{I})']}{h\,\mathrm{tr}(\boldsymbol{X}'\boldsymbol{V}^{-1}\boldsymbol{X})^{-1}}. \end{aligned} \tag{11.9}$$

Note that the estimability of $\boldsymbol{\beta}$ implies that $\boldsymbol{X}$ has full column rank. Since $\boldsymbol{V}$ is nonsingular, $\mathcal{C}(\boldsymbol{X}') = \mathcal{C}(\boldsymbol{X}'\boldsymbol{V}^{-1}\boldsymbol{X})$ and therefore $\boldsymbol{X}'\boldsymbol{V}^{-1}\boldsymbol{X}$ is an invertible matrix. In order to prove (11.9), let $(\boldsymbol{X}'\boldsymbol{V}^{-1}\boldsymbol{X})^{-1}$ be factored as $\boldsymbol{LL}'$ where $\boldsymbol{L}$ is an invertible matrix. We have, for any vector $\boldsymbol{l}$ of appropriate dimension,

$$\|(\boldsymbol{TX} - \boldsymbol{I})\boldsymbol{Ll}\|^2 \le \|\boldsymbol{TX} - \boldsymbol{I}\|^2 \cdot \|\boldsymbol{Ll}\|^2.$$

Therefore, the matrix difference $\|\boldsymbol{TX} - \boldsymbol{I}\|^2\boldsymbol{L}'\boldsymbol{L} - \boldsymbol{L}'(\boldsymbol{TX} - \boldsymbol{I})'(\boldsymbol{TX} - \boldsymbol{I})\boldsymbol{L}$ is nonnegative definite, and it must have a nonnegative trace. It follows that

$$
\begin{aligned}
0 &\leq \operatorname{tr}\Big[\|\boldsymbol{TX}-\boldsymbol{I}\|^2\boldsymbol{L}'\boldsymbol{L}\Big]-\operatorname{tr}\Big[\boldsymbol{L}'(\boldsymbol{TX}-\boldsymbol{I})'(\boldsymbol{TX}-\boldsymbol{I})\boldsymbol{L}\Big]\\
&= \|\boldsymbol{TX}-\boldsymbol{I}\|^2\operatorname{tr}(\boldsymbol{LL}')-\operatorname{tr}\Big[(\boldsymbol{TX}-\boldsymbol{I})\boldsymbol{LL}'(\boldsymbol{TX}-\boldsymbol{I})'\Big]\\
&= \|\boldsymbol{TX}-\boldsymbol{I}\|^2\operatorname{tr}(\boldsymbol{X}'\boldsymbol{V}^{-1}\boldsymbol{X})^{-1}-\operatorname{tr}\Big[(\boldsymbol{TX}-\boldsymbol{I})(\boldsymbol{X}'\boldsymbol{V}^{-1}\boldsymbol{X})^{-1}(\boldsymbol{TX}-\boldsymbol{I})'\Big],
\end{aligned}
$$

and consequently

$$
\|\boldsymbol{TX}-\boldsymbol{I}\|^2 \geq \operatorname{tr}\Big[(\boldsymbol{TX}-\boldsymbol{I})(\boldsymbol{X}'\boldsymbol{V}^{-1}\boldsymbol{X})^{-1}(\boldsymbol{TX}-\boldsymbol{I})'\Big]/\operatorname{tr}(\boldsymbol{X}'\boldsymbol{V}^{-1}\boldsymbol{X})^{-1}.
$$

This proves (11.9).

If we can find a linear estimator $\boldsymbol{Ty}$ for which (11.9) holds with equality and the right-hand side is minimized at the same time, then $\boldsymbol{Ty}$ would be a MILE for the problem at hand. This minimization is a rather easy task. Let $\alpha = [h\cdot\operatorname{tr}(\boldsymbol{X}'\boldsymbol{V}^{-1}\boldsymbol{X})^{-1}]^{-1}$. Then the right-hand side of (11.9) can be written as

$$
\begin{aligned}
&\operatorname{tr}(\boldsymbol{TVT}') + \alpha\operatorname{tr}[(\boldsymbol{TX}-\boldsymbol{I})(\boldsymbol{X}'\boldsymbol{V}^{-1}\boldsymbol{X})^{-1}(\boldsymbol{TX}-\boldsymbol{I})']\\
&= \operatorname{tr}\Big[\boldsymbol{T}[\boldsymbol{V}+\alpha\boldsymbol{X}(\boldsymbol{X}'\boldsymbol{V}^{-1}\boldsymbol{X})^{-1}\boldsymbol{X}']\boldsymbol{T}' - \boldsymbol{T}[\alpha\boldsymbol{X}(\boldsymbol{X}'\boldsymbol{V}^{-1}\boldsymbol{X})^{-1}]\\
&\quad - [\alpha(\boldsymbol{X}'\boldsymbol{V}^{-1}\boldsymbol{X})^{-1}\boldsymbol{X}']\boldsymbol{T}' + \alpha(\boldsymbol{X}'\boldsymbol{V}^{-1}\boldsymbol{X})^{-1}\Big].
\end{aligned}
$$

By writing the $[\boldsymbol{V}+\alpha\boldsymbol{X}(\boldsymbol{X}'\boldsymbol{V}^{-1}\boldsymbol{X})^{-1}\boldsymbol{X}']$ as $\boldsymbol{W}$ and completing the squares, we can simplify the above expression to

$$
\operatorname{tr}\Big[(\boldsymbol{T}-\alpha(\boldsymbol{X}'\boldsymbol{V}^{-1}\boldsymbol{X})^{-1}\boldsymbol{X}'\boldsymbol{W}^{-1})\boldsymbol{W}(\boldsymbol{T}-\alpha(\boldsymbol{X}'\boldsymbol{V}^{-1}\boldsymbol{X})^{-1}\boldsymbol{X}'\boldsymbol{W}^{-1})'+\boldsymbol{K}\Big],
$$

where the matrix $\boldsymbol{K}$ does not depend on $\boldsymbol{T}$. Thus, the matrix

$$
\boldsymbol{T}_0 = \alpha(\boldsymbol{X}'\boldsymbol{V}^{-1}\boldsymbol{X})^{-1}\boldsymbol{X}'\boldsymbol{W}^{-1}
$$

is the unique minimizer of the right-hand side of (11.9). By expanding $\boldsymbol{W}^{-1}$ we have the following alternative expression of $\boldsymbol{T}_0$:

$$
\begin{aligned}
\boldsymbol{T}_0 &= \alpha(\boldsymbol{X}'\boldsymbol{V}^{-1}\boldsymbol{X})^{-1}\boldsymbol{X}'\boldsymbol{W}^{-1}\\
&= \alpha(\boldsymbol{X}'\boldsymbol{V}^{-1}\boldsymbol{X})^{-1}\boldsymbol{X}'[\boldsymbol{V}^{-1}\\
&\qquad\qquad -\boldsymbol{V}^{-1}\boldsymbol{X}(\alpha^{-1}\boldsymbol{X}'\boldsymbol{V}^{-1}\boldsymbol{X}+\boldsymbol{X}'\boldsymbol{V}^{-1}\boldsymbol{X})^{-1}\boldsymbol{X}'\boldsymbol{V}^{-1}]\\
&= \frac{\alpha}{1+\alpha}(\boldsymbol{X}'\boldsymbol{V}^{-1}\boldsymbol{X})^{-1}\boldsymbol{X}'\boldsymbol{V}^{-1}\\
&= \frac{1}{1+h\cdot\operatorname{tr}(\boldsymbol{X}'\boldsymbol{V}^{-1}\boldsymbol{X})^{-1}}(\boldsymbol{X}'\boldsymbol{V}^{-1}\boldsymbol{X})^{-1}\boldsymbol{X}'\boldsymbol{V}^{-1}.
\end{aligned}
$$

This simplification shows that the matrix $(\boldsymbol{T}_0\boldsymbol{X}-\boldsymbol{I})$ is proportional to the identity matrix of appropriate dimension. Consequently (11.9) holds with equality when $\boldsymbol{T}=\boldsymbol{T}_0$. This completes the proof of the proposition. □

The estimator $\widehat{\boldsymbol{\beta}}_M$ is linearly admissible with respect to the squared error loss function (see Example 11.32). An interesting fact is that $\boldsymbol{A}\widehat{\boldsymbol{\beta}}_M$ is not necessarily a MILE of $\boldsymbol{A\beta}$ under the conditions of Proposition 11.38 (see Exercise 11.13). Thus, the principle of substitution (see page 86) does not work here.

Apart from the closed form expressions for the MILE in the special cases considered in the preceding three propositions, finding the general solution to the problem of minimax linear estimation appears difficult. Läuter (1975) makes some progress for the special case when $\boldsymbol{V}$ and $\boldsymbol{H}$ are positive definite. Drygas (1985) provides a MILE in the special case of a single LPF, as in Proposition 11.37, but under the more general ellipsoidal restriction $(\boldsymbol{\beta} - \boldsymbol{\beta}_0)'\boldsymbol{H}(\boldsymbol{\beta} - \boldsymbol{\beta}_0) \le \sigma^2$. He also considers the problem of minimax linear *prediction* in this set-up. Stahlecker and Lauterbach (1989) proposes a numerical method of obtaining a MILE in the general case. Pilz (1986) considers a positive definite dispersion matrix but a more general restriction on $\boldsymbol{\beta}$: that it belongs to a compact set which is symmetric around a midpoint. He investigates minimax estimators in the class of *affine* (rather than linear) estimators and it turns out that such a minimax estimator under this set-up is a Bayes affine estimator corresponding to the least favourable prior. The search for the least favourable prior gives rise to an explicit expression of the minimax affine estimator in some special cases, including the case of linear inequality constraint on each parameter from both sides. Drygas (1996) attempts to solve the general problem with an ellipsoidal restriction on $\boldsymbol{\beta}$, using spectral decomposition of some matrices. It turns out that closed form solutions can only be found in some special cases.

A general ellipsoidal restriction on the parameter $\boldsymbol{\beta}$ appears frequently in the literature of minimax estimation. Although such a restriction is unlikely to arise naturally in a practical problem, it may very well be implied by other natural restrictions. Toutenburg (1982) shows how to construct the least restrictive ellipsoidal restriction from a set of finite and linear inequality constraints. In many practical situations it may be possible to construct a large enough ellipsoid so that the vector parameter is contained in it. Significantly, the BLUE becomes inadmissible — even among linear estimators — as soon as such a restriction is imposed. Hoffman (1996) identifies a class of MILEs that have smaller risk than the BLUE over the entire parameter ellipsoid, irrespective of the weight matrix of the quadratic risk function.

11.3 Other linear estimators

11.3.1 *Biased estimators revisited*

Biased estimators with smaller dispersion (i.e. the subset estimator, the principal components estimator, the ridge estimator and the shrinkage estimator) have already been discussed in the context of the homoscedastic linear model $(\boldsymbol{y}, \boldsymbol{X\beta}, \sigma^2\boldsymbol{I})$ in Sections 5.1 and 5.6. We now point out some inter-connections and generalizations.

In Exercise 7.10, the idea of principal components regression was generalized to the model $(\boldsymbol{y}, \boldsymbol{X\beta}, \sigma^2\boldsymbol{V})$, where both $\boldsymbol{X}$ and $\boldsymbol{V}$ have full column rank. The trade-off between bias and variance was also studied there.

The role of the matrix $r\boldsymbol{I}$ in (5.24) is to inflate the smaller eigenvalues of the matrix $\boldsymbol{X}'\boldsymbol{X}$. This can also be achieved by replacing $r\boldsymbol{I}$ by a positive definite matrix, $\boldsymbol{R}$. The corresponding ridge estimator is $(\boldsymbol{X}'\boldsymbol{X}+\boldsymbol{R})^{-1}\boldsymbol{X}'\boldsymbol{y}$. The obvious generalization of this estimator to the model $(\boldsymbol{y}, \boldsymbol{X\beta}, \sigma^2\boldsymbol{V})$ where $\boldsymbol{V}$ is a known positive definite matrix is

$$\widehat{\boldsymbol{\beta}}_R = (\boldsymbol{X}'\boldsymbol{V}^{-1}\boldsymbol{X} + \boldsymbol{R})^{-1}\boldsymbol{X}'\boldsymbol{V}^{-1}\boldsymbol{y}.$$

By comparing $\boldsymbol{X}\widehat{\boldsymbol{\beta}}_R$ with the expression of the Bayes Linear Estimator given in (11.5), we can identify the ridge estimator as the BLE corresponding to any prior such that $[E(\sigma^2)]^{-1}E(\boldsymbol{\beta\beta}') = \boldsymbol{R}^{-1}$. It can also be interpreted as the Kuks-Olman MILE (see (11.8)) with $\boldsymbol{H} = \boldsymbol{R}$. In view of these identifications, we can define the ridge estimator for singular $\boldsymbol{V}$ as

$$\widehat{\boldsymbol{\beta}}_R = \boldsymbol{R}^{-1}\boldsymbol{X}'(\boldsymbol{V} + \boldsymbol{X}\boldsymbol{R}^{-1}\boldsymbol{X}')^{-}\boldsymbol{y}.$$

The estimator does not depend on the choice of the g-inverse.

In the special case of full rank $\boldsymbol{X}$ and $\boldsymbol{V}$, the shrinkage estimator of $\boldsymbol{\beta}$ can be interpreted as the MILE under the conditions of Proposition 11.38. The choice of an s in the range $(0, 1)$ is equivalent to the choice of a positive h for the spherical restriction, $\boldsymbol{\beta}'\boldsymbol{\beta} \leq \sigma^2/h$. The shrinkage estimator is linearly admissible with respect to the squared error loss function (see Example 11.32).

11.3.2 *Best linear minimum bias estimator*

If one allows for bias, the class of linear estimators of an LPF $\boldsymbol{A\beta}$ becomes larger. In order to find a 'best' estimator in this class, we may consider the mean squared error matrix of the estimator $\boldsymbol{Ty}$ of $\boldsymbol{A\beta}$, given by

$$MSE(\boldsymbol{Ty}) = \sigma^2[\boldsymbol{TVT}' + (\boldsymbol{TX} - \boldsymbol{A})\boldsymbol{U}(\boldsymbol{TX} - \boldsymbol{A})'],$$

where $\boldsymbol{U} = \sigma^{-2}\boldsymbol{\beta}\boldsymbol{\beta}'$. It turns out that the matrix in the right-hand side of the above equation is minimized, in the sense of the Löwner order, when

$$\boldsymbol{T}\boldsymbol{y} = \boldsymbol{A}\boldsymbol{U}\boldsymbol{X}'(\boldsymbol{V} + \boldsymbol{X}\boldsymbol{U}\boldsymbol{X}')^{-}\boldsymbol{y} \tag{11.10}$$

(see the proof of Proposition 11.34). Following Lewis and Odell (1966), we shall call this estimator the best linear estimator (BLE) of $\boldsymbol{A}\boldsymbol{\beta}$. The best linear estimator of $\boldsymbol{A}\boldsymbol{\beta}$ exists *even if* $\boldsymbol{A}\boldsymbol{\beta}$ *is not estimable.* Like the best linear predictor, the best linear estimator cannot be used in practice, as $\boldsymbol{U}$ is not known. We can replace $\boldsymbol{U}$ by a prior guess, perhaps on the basis of a prior distribution of $\boldsymbol{\beta}$ and σ^2. We have already seen in Proposition 11.34 that a formal derivation of the Bayes linear estimator with respect to a prior distribution of $\boldsymbol{\beta}$ and σ^2 leads us to (11.10) with $\boldsymbol{U} = E(\boldsymbol{\beta}\boldsymbol{\beta}')/E(\sigma^2)$.

The BLE of $\boldsymbol{A}\boldsymbol{\beta}$ is obtained by minimizing $\boldsymbol{T}\boldsymbol{V}\boldsymbol{T}' + (\boldsymbol{T}\boldsymbol{X} - \boldsymbol{A})\boldsymbol{U}(\boldsymbol{T}\boldsymbol{X} - \boldsymbol{A})']$. If instead we minimize only the second term, representing the bias, the resulting estimator (obtained by completing the squares) is $\boldsymbol{A}\widehat{\boldsymbol{\beta}}_{limbe}$, where

$$\widehat{\boldsymbol{\beta}}_{limbe} = \boldsymbol{U}\boldsymbol{X}'(\boldsymbol{X}\boldsymbol{U}\boldsymbol{X}')^{-}\boldsymbol{y}.$$

This estimator is called a linear minimum bias estimator (LIMBE). In general it is not unique. The LIMBE with the minimum dispersion is called the best linear minimum bias estimator (BLIMBE). Chipman (1964) proposes this estimator specifically for non-estimable LPFs. If $\boldsymbol{U}$ and $\boldsymbol{V}$ are positive definite matrices, then the BLIMBE of $\boldsymbol{A}\boldsymbol{\beta}$ is $\boldsymbol{A}\widehat{\boldsymbol{\beta}}_{blimbe}$, where

$$\widehat{\boldsymbol{\beta}}_{blimbe} = \boldsymbol{U}\boldsymbol{X}'(\boldsymbol{X}\boldsymbol{U}\boldsymbol{X}'\boldsymbol{V}^{-1}\boldsymbol{X}\boldsymbol{U}\boldsymbol{X}')^{-}\boldsymbol{X}\boldsymbol{U}\boldsymbol{X}'\boldsymbol{V}^{-1}\boldsymbol{y}.$$

A brief derivation of this expression can be found in Rao (1973c).

Note that both the BLE and the BLIMBE depend on the choice of the matrix $\boldsymbol{U}$. It can be chosen by making use of extraneous information. Rao (1973c, p. 305) suggests an alternative consideration: to choose $\boldsymbol{U}$ as a relative weight given to the bias term as compared to the dispersion.

It was pointed out in Chapter 3 that a non-estimable parameter is not identifiable. Such a parameter can be meaningfully estimated only if extraneous information (such as a prior distribution) is judiciously used. The fact that the best linear estimator and the BLIMBE exist *even when the corresponding LPF is not identifiable* makes sense only when these estimator utilizes extraneous information via the matrix $\boldsymbol{U}$. If $\boldsymbol{U}$ is chosen without using such information, and $\boldsymbol{A}\boldsymbol{\beta}$ is not estimable, neither the best linear estimator nor the BLIMBE of $\boldsymbol{A}\boldsymbol{\beta}$ is meaningful.

The problem of identifying the 'best' estimator among various types of linear estimators continued to interest researchers over the years. Hallum et al. (1973) find the best linear estimator in a linear model with restrictions. Chaubey (1982) obtains the best linear estimator for a particular choice of the matrix $\boldsymbol{U}$, where the linear estimators are restricted to be LIMBE for another choice of $\boldsymbol{U}$. Schaffrin (1999) studies the best linear estimator as the condition of unbiasedness is gradually relaxed.

11.3.3 *'Consistent' estimator*

When the dispersion matrix $\boldsymbol{V}$ is singular, the response in the linear model $(\boldsymbol{y}, \boldsymbol{X\beta}, \sigma^2\boldsymbol{V})$ must be such that $\boldsymbol{y} - \boldsymbol{X\beta} \in \mathcal{C}(\boldsymbol{V})$ almost surely. This is a property of the model error. On the other hand, $\boldsymbol{X\beta}$ (the systematic part of $\boldsymbol{y}$) resides in $\mathcal{C}(\boldsymbol{X})$. Any estimator of $\boldsymbol{\beta}$ would lead to a decomposition of $\boldsymbol{y}$ into estimated 'systematic' and 'error' parts. If the estimator is reasonable, these two parts should belong to $\mathcal{C}(\boldsymbol{X})$ and $\mathcal{C}(\boldsymbol{V})$, respectively. The conditions

$$\widetilde{\boldsymbol{X\beta}} \in \mathcal{C}(\boldsymbol{X}), \qquad \boldsymbol{y} - \widetilde{\boldsymbol{X\beta}} \in \mathcal{C}(\boldsymbol{V})$$

are sometimes referred to as *consistency conditions* for an estimator $\widetilde{\boldsymbol{X\beta}}$ of $\boldsymbol{X\beta}$. Christensen (2011) refers to an LUE that satisfies the twin conditions by the name consistent LUE (CLUE). Remark 7.16 implies that the BLUE of $\boldsymbol{X\beta}$ is a CLUE. Christensen (2011, p. 229) obtains a CLUE that would minimize $\|\boldsymbol{y} - \widetilde{\boldsymbol{X\beta}}\|$, and called it the least squares CLUE. This estimator is not known to have any other optimal property and in general has a larger dispersion than the BLUE.

11.4 A geometric view of BLUE in the linear model

Consider the model equation

$$\boldsymbol{y} = \boldsymbol{X\beta} + \boldsymbol{\varepsilon}, \qquad E(\boldsymbol{\varepsilon}) = \boldsymbol{0}, \qquad D(\boldsymbol{\varepsilon}) = \sigma^2\boldsymbol{V}.$$

The term $\boldsymbol{X\beta}$ is the *systematic* or *signal* part of $\boldsymbol{y}$, while $\boldsymbol{\varepsilon}$ is the *error* or *noise*. By leaving $\boldsymbol{\beta}$ unspecified, the model postulates that the systematic part consists of an *unknown* linear combination of the columns of $\boldsymbol{X}$. The empirical equivalent of the model equation is

$$\boldsymbol{y} = \boldsymbol{X}\widehat{\boldsymbol{\beta}} + \boldsymbol{e} = \widehat{\boldsymbol{y}} + \boldsymbol{e},$$

where $\boldsymbol{X}\widehat{\boldsymbol{\beta}}$ is the vector of fitted values, which is an estimator of the systematic part. We can call $\widehat{\boldsymbol{y}}$ the *explained* part of $\boldsymbol{y}$ (through the model), while the residual $\boldsymbol{e}$ is the *unexplained* part.

An alternative way of interpreting the model is the following. The model postulates that the systematic part is *in the column space* $\mathcal{C}(\boldsymbol{X})$, while the error part has zero mean and dispersion proportional to $\boldsymbol{V}$. In this interpretation the emphasis is on the *vector space* specified as the 'systematic' part. The identity of the regressor variables is not important. A reparametrization preserves the vector spaces, and therefore it is expected to produce the same values of $\widehat{\boldsymbol{y}}$ and $\boldsymbol{e}$.

It turns out that there is much to learn from the vector space interpretation of best linear unbiased estimation. We have seen glimpses of the geometric view in Chapters 3, 4 and 7. The purpose of this section is to appreciate the BLUE from a purely geometric perspective.

11.4.1 *The homoscedastic case*

Let $\boldsymbol{V} = \boldsymbol{I}$. Figure 11.1 illustrates the decomposition $\boldsymbol{y} = \boldsymbol{X\beta} + \boldsymbol{\varepsilon}$. The vectors $\boldsymbol{y}$, $\boldsymbol{X\beta}$ and $\boldsymbol{\varepsilon}$ are represented by the line segments OA, OP and PA, respectively. The vertical axis represents $\mathcal{C}(\boldsymbol{X})^{\perp}$, while the horizontal plane represents $\mathcal{C}(\boldsymbol{X})$. In reality both of these spaces may have dimensions greater than two, and typically $\mathcal{C}(\boldsymbol{X})^{\perp}$ would have a larger dimension than $\mathcal{C}(\boldsymbol{X})$. We choose the dimensions 1 and 2 for $\mathcal{C}(\boldsymbol{X})^{\perp}$ and $\mathcal{C}(\boldsymbol{X})$ respectively, for the sake of visualization. The shaded area around the point P represents the region where the point A could possibly have appeared in another random experiment. The darker shade in the core of the region represents higher concentration of probability mass there.

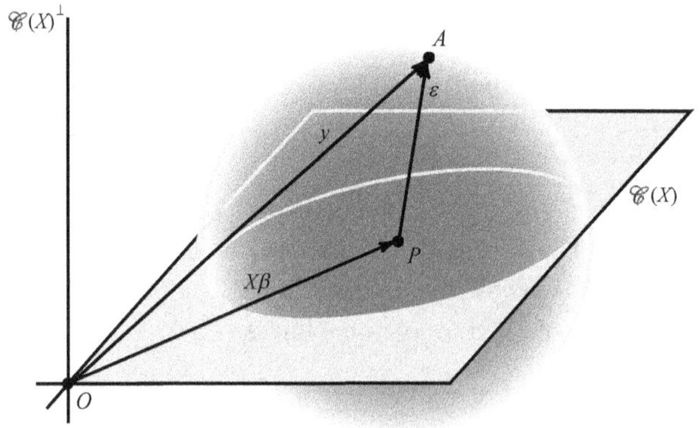

Fig. 11.1 A geometric view of the homoscedastic linear model

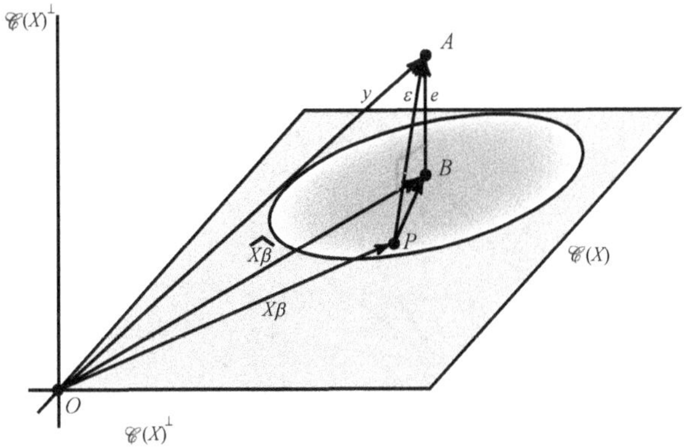

Fig. 11.2 A geometric view of BLUE in the homoscedastic linear model

The model specifies that OP lies somewhere on the horizontal plane. The estimation problem consists of identifying the vector OP. Figure 11.2 illustrates the synthesis of the BLUE of $\boldsymbol{X\beta}$, represented by the line OB, which is obtained by minimizing the length of the line BA over all possible locations of B in the plane $\mathcal{C}(\boldsymbol{X})$. The minimum length occurs when AB is perpendicular (orthogonal) to the horizontal plane. Thus, we have OB and BA corresponding to $\widehat{\boldsymbol{y}}$ and $\boldsymbol{e}$ in the decomposition $\boldsymbol{y} = \widehat{\boldsymbol{y}} + \boldsymbol{e}$. Clearly, $\widehat{\boldsymbol{y}}$ is the orthogonal projection of $\boldsymbol{y}$ on $\mathcal{C}(\boldsymbol{X})$, so that $\widehat{\boldsymbol{y}} \in \mathcal{C}(\boldsymbol{X})$ and $\boldsymbol{e} \in \mathcal{C}(\boldsymbol{X})^{\perp}$. The elliptical region around B is a typical confidence region for $\boldsymbol{X\beta}$. That the region lies entirely in the plane $\mathcal{C}(\boldsymbol{X})$ corresponds to the fact that $\mathcal{C}(D(\widehat{\boldsymbol{y}})) = \mathcal{C}(\boldsymbol{X})$.

11.4.2 *The effect of linear restrictions*

The effect of the restriction $\boldsymbol{A\beta} = \boldsymbol{\xi}$ in the homoscedastic case is illustrated in Figure 11.3, which is an extension of Figure 11.2. This diagram can be understood in the context of the 'equivalent' model $(\boldsymbol{y} - \boldsymbol{XA}'(\boldsymbol{AA}')^{-}\boldsymbol{\xi}, \boldsymbol{X}(\boldsymbol{I} - \boldsymbol{P}_{\boldsymbol{A}'}), \sigma^2\boldsymbol{I})$ (see the discussion preceding (3.21) on page 101). The vector $\boldsymbol{XA}'(\boldsymbol{AA}')^{-}\boldsymbol{\xi}$ is a part of $\boldsymbol{y}$ which is completely known because of the restrictions. This vector, represented by the line segment OO', lies in $\mathcal{C}(\boldsymbol{XP}_{\boldsymbol{A}'})$, which is represented by a bold line on the plane of $\mathcal{C}(\boldsymbol{X})$. The other bold line represents the locus of tips of all the vectors which can be written as $\boldsymbol{XA}'(\boldsymbol{AA}')^{-}\boldsymbol{\xi} + \boldsymbol{u}$, where $\boldsymbol{u} \in \mathcal{C}(\boldsymbol{X}(\boldsymbol{I} - \boldsymbol{P}_{\boldsymbol{A}'}))$.

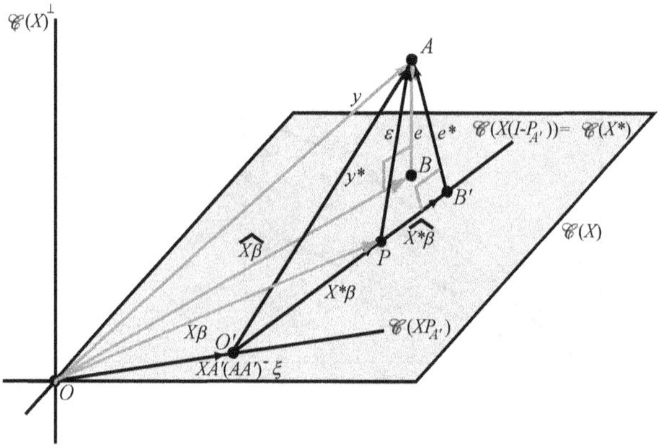

Fig. 11.3 A geometric view of restricted BLUE in the linear model

The point P (where OP is the unknown $\boldsymbol{X\beta}$) lies somewhere on this line. Since OO' is completely known, the estimation problem can be simplified by shifting the origin to O'. Consequent to this shift, the bold line passing through O' and P represents the vector space $\mathcal{C}(\boldsymbol{X}(\boldsymbol{I}-\boldsymbol{P}_{A'}))$. The estimation problem reduces to finding the line segment OP or the point P on this line. The 'restricted' BLUE is obtained by finding a point B' on this line so that the length of $B'A$ is the smallest. This is accomplished when $B'A$ is perpendicular to this line, and in particular, to $O'B'$. If we refer to the model $(\boldsymbol{y}-\boldsymbol{XA}'(\boldsymbol{AA}')^{-}\boldsymbol{\xi}, \boldsymbol{X}(\boldsymbol{I}-\boldsymbol{P}_{A'}), \sigma^2\boldsymbol{I})$ as $(\boldsymbol{y}^*, \boldsymbol{X}^*\beta, \sigma^2\boldsymbol{I})$ for brevity, then $\boldsymbol{y}^*$, $\widehat{\boldsymbol{X}^*\boldsymbol{\beta}}$ and $\boldsymbol{e}^*$ are represented by the line segments $O'A$, $O'B'$ and $B'A$, respectively. The vector $\widehat{\boldsymbol{X}^*\boldsymbol{\beta}}$ is the orthogonal projection of $\boldsymbol{y}^*$ on $\mathcal{C}(\boldsymbol{X}^*)$. The line segment OB' represents $\widehat{\boldsymbol{y}}_{rest}$, the fitted value of $\boldsymbol{y}$ under the restriction $\boldsymbol{A\beta}=\boldsymbol{\xi}$. The line segment $B'B$ can be seen as $\widehat{\boldsymbol{y}}_{rest}-\widehat{\boldsymbol{y}}$ or as $\boldsymbol{e}^*-\boldsymbol{e}$. The vectors OB' and $B'B$ are not shown explicitly in the figure.

11.4.3 *The general linear model*

In order to view the BLUE of $\boldsymbol{X\beta}$ in the general linear model as a projection, we need to use *oblique projections* rather than the orthogonal projection mentioned in Section A.4. Note that if $\boldsymbol{A}$ and $\boldsymbol{B}$ are matrices with the same number of rows and $\mathcal{C}(\boldsymbol{A})$ and $\mathcal{C}(\boldsymbol{B})$ are virtually disjoint, then any vector $\boldsymbol{l}$ in $\mathcal{C}(\boldsymbol{A}:\boldsymbol{B})$ has the *unique* representation $\boldsymbol{l}_1+\boldsymbol{l}_2$ where

$\boldsymbol{l}_1 \in \mathcal{C}(\boldsymbol{A})$ and $\boldsymbol{l}_2 \in \mathcal{C}(\boldsymbol{B})$. (If $\boldsymbol{l}_{1*} + \boldsymbol{l}_{2*}$ is another such representation, then $\boldsymbol{l}_1 - \boldsymbol{l}_{1*} = \boldsymbol{l}_{2*} - \boldsymbol{l}_2$ belongs to $\mathcal{C}(\boldsymbol{A})$ as well as $\mathcal{C}(\boldsymbol{B})$, which means that these column spaces are not virtually disjoint.) We need a projection matrix which will make this decomposition possible.

Definition 11.39. A matrix $\boldsymbol{P}_{A|B}$ is called a projector onto $\mathcal{C}(\boldsymbol{A})$ along $\mathcal{C}(\boldsymbol{B})$ if for all $\boldsymbol{l} \in \mathcal{C}(\boldsymbol{A} : \boldsymbol{B})$, $\boldsymbol{P}_{A|B}\boldsymbol{l} \in \mathcal{C}(\boldsymbol{A})$ and $(\boldsymbol{I} - \boldsymbol{P}_{A|B})\boldsymbol{l} \in \mathcal{C}(\boldsymbol{B})$. □

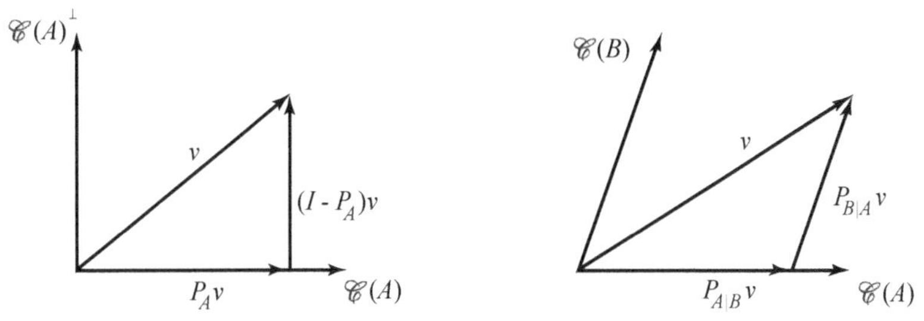

Fig. 11.4 Orthogonal projection (left) and oblique projection (right)

Figure 11.4 illustrates the contrast between the orthogonal projection onto a column space and the (oblique) projection onto that column space along another space, where both the spaces have dimension 1. The essential difference is that $\boldsymbol{P}_A\boldsymbol{l}$ and $(\boldsymbol{I} - \boldsymbol{P}_A)\boldsymbol{l}$ are orthogonal to one another, while $\boldsymbol{P}_{A|B}\boldsymbol{l}$ and $\boldsymbol{P}_{B|A}\boldsymbol{l}$ are not necessarily orthogonal.

The projection matrix $\boldsymbol{P}_{A|B}$ is unique and idempotent when $\mathcal{C}(\boldsymbol{A} : \boldsymbol{B})$ has full row rank. Otherwise it may be neither unique nor idempotent (see Exercise 11.16). In any case, the projection $\boldsymbol{P}_{A|B}\boldsymbol{l}$ for any $\boldsymbol{l} \in \mathcal{C}(\boldsymbol{A} : \boldsymbol{B})$ is unique. It can be verified that $\boldsymbol{I} - \boldsymbol{P}_{A|B}$ is a choice of $\boldsymbol{P}_{B|A}$. Also, $\boldsymbol{P}_A$ is the unique choice of $\boldsymbol{P}_{A|B}$ when $\boldsymbol{B}$ is $(\boldsymbol{I} - \boldsymbol{P}_A)$ or any other matrix spanning $\mathcal{C}(\boldsymbol{A})^\perp$. We now provide a useful choice of $\boldsymbol{P}_{A|B}$.

Proposition 11.40. *Let $\boldsymbol{A}$ and $\boldsymbol{B}$ be matrices with the same number of rows.*

(a) $\mathcal{C}(\boldsymbol{A})$ and $\mathcal{C}(\boldsymbol{B})$ are virtually disjoint if and only if $\mathcal{C}(\boldsymbol{A}') = \mathcal{C}(\boldsymbol{A}'(\boldsymbol{I} - \boldsymbol{P}_B))$.
(b) If $\mathcal{C}(\boldsymbol{A})$ and $\mathcal{C}(\boldsymbol{B})$ are virtually disjoint, then $\boldsymbol{A}[(\boldsymbol{I} - \boldsymbol{P}_B)\boldsymbol{A}]^-(\boldsymbol{I} - \boldsymbol{P}_B)$ is a projector onto $\mathcal{C}(\boldsymbol{A})$ along $\mathcal{C}(\boldsymbol{B})$.

Proof. Suppose $\mathcal{C}(\boldsymbol{A})$ and $\mathcal{C}(\boldsymbol{B})$ are virtually disjoint. It is clear that $\mathcal{C}(\boldsymbol{A}'(\boldsymbol{I}-\boldsymbol{P}_B)) \subseteq \mathcal{C}(\boldsymbol{A}')$. If the inclusion is *strict*, let $\boldsymbol{k}$ be a vector in $\mathcal{C}(\boldsymbol{A}')$ which is orthogonal to $\mathcal{C}(\boldsymbol{A}'(\boldsymbol{I}-\boldsymbol{P}_B))$. It follows that $\boldsymbol{Ak} \in \mathcal{C}(\boldsymbol{B})$. Since $\mathcal{C}(\boldsymbol{A})$ and $\mathcal{C}(\boldsymbol{B})$ are virtually disjoint, $\boldsymbol{Ak}$ must be $\boldsymbol{0}$. This implies that $\boldsymbol{k}$, which is of the form $\boldsymbol{A}'\boldsymbol{m}$ for some $\boldsymbol{m}$, is itself equal to $\boldsymbol{0}$. Conversely, if $\mathcal{C}(\boldsymbol{A}') = \mathcal{C}(\boldsymbol{A}'(\boldsymbol{I}-\boldsymbol{P}_B))$, let $\boldsymbol{A} = \boldsymbol{T}(\boldsymbol{I}-\boldsymbol{P}_B)\boldsymbol{A}$ for some $\boldsymbol{T}$. If $\boldsymbol{A}\boldsymbol{u}_1 = \boldsymbol{B}\boldsymbol{u}_2$ for some $\boldsymbol{u}_1$ and $\boldsymbol{u}_2$, we have

$$\boldsymbol{A}\boldsymbol{u}_1 = \boldsymbol{T}(\boldsymbol{I}-\boldsymbol{P}_B)\boldsymbol{A}\boldsymbol{u}_1 = \boldsymbol{T}(\boldsymbol{I}-\boldsymbol{P}_B)\boldsymbol{B}\boldsymbol{u}_2 = \boldsymbol{0}.$$

Thus, $\mathcal{C}(\boldsymbol{A})$ and $\mathcal{C}(\boldsymbol{B})$ are virtually disjoint. This proves part (a).

To prove part (b), let $\boldsymbol{P}_{A|B} = \boldsymbol{A}[(\boldsymbol{I}-\boldsymbol{P}_B)\boldsymbol{A}]^-(\boldsymbol{I}-\boldsymbol{P}_B)$ and let $\boldsymbol{l}$ be a vector in $\mathcal{C}(\boldsymbol{A}:\boldsymbol{B})$. Suppose $\boldsymbol{l}$ has the unique representation $\boldsymbol{l}_1+\boldsymbol{l}_2$ where $\boldsymbol{l}_1 \in \mathcal{C}(\boldsymbol{A})$ and $\boldsymbol{l}_2 \in \mathcal{C}(\boldsymbol{B})$. It is easy to see that $\boldsymbol{P}_{A|B}\boldsymbol{l} \in \mathcal{C}(\boldsymbol{A})$. Further, if $\boldsymbol{T}$ is a matrix such that $\boldsymbol{A}' = \boldsymbol{A}'(\boldsymbol{I}-\boldsymbol{P}_B)\boldsymbol{T}'$, we have

$$\begin{aligned}(\boldsymbol{I}-\boldsymbol{P}_{A|B})\boldsymbol{l} &= \boldsymbol{l} - \boldsymbol{A}[(\boldsymbol{I}-\boldsymbol{P}_B)\boldsymbol{A}]^-(\boldsymbol{I}-\boldsymbol{P}_B)\boldsymbol{l}\\ &= \boldsymbol{l} - \boldsymbol{T}(\boldsymbol{I}-\boldsymbol{P}_B)\boldsymbol{A}[(\boldsymbol{I}-\boldsymbol{P}_B)\boldsymbol{A}]^-(\boldsymbol{I}-\boldsymbol{P}_B)\boldsymbol{l}_1\\ &= \boldsymbol{l} - \boldsymbol{T}(\boldsymbol{I}-\boldsymbol{P}_B)\boldsymbol{l}_1 = \boldsymbol{l}-\boldsymbol{l}_1 = \boldsymbol{l}_2.\end{aligned}$$

Note that the vector $\boldsymbol{l}_2$ is in $\mathcal{C}(\boldsymbol{B})$. □

We now discuss the BLUE of $\boldsymbol{X\beta}$ in the general linear model in terms of an oblique projector.

Proposition 11.41. *Consider the linear model* $(\boldsymbol{y}, \boldsymbol{X\beta}, \sigma^2\boldsymbol{V})$.

(a) The response vector $\boldsymbol{y}$ *lies almost surely in* $\mathcal{C}(\boldsymbol{V}(\boldsymbol{I}-\boldsymbol{P}_X):\boldsymbol{X})$.
(b) $\mathcal{C}(\boldsymbol{V}(\boldsymbol{I}-\boldsymbol{P}_X))$ *and* $\mathcal{C}(\boldsymbol{X})$ *are virtually disjoint.*
(c) The BLUE of $\boldsymbol{X\beta}$ *is almost surely equal to* $\boldsymbol{P}_{X|V(I-P_X)}\boldsymbol{y}$.

Proof. Since $\boldsymbol{y} \in \mathcal{C}(\boldsymbol{V}:\boldsymbol{X})$ almost surely, it suffices to prove that $\mathcal{C}(\boldsymbol{V}:\boldsymbol{X}) = \mathcal{C}(\boldsymbol{V}(\boldsymbol{I}-\boldsymbol{P}_X):\boldsymbol{X})$. The inclusion of $\mathcal{C}(\boldsymbol{V}(\boldsymbol{I}-\boldsymbol{P}_X):\boldsymbol{X})$ in $\mathcal{C}(\boldsymbol{V}:\boldsymbol{X})$ is obvious. In order to prove the reverse inclusion, let $\boldsymbol{l} \in \mathcal{C}(\boldsymbol{V}(\boldsymbol{I}-\boldsymbol{P}_X):\boldsymbol{X})^\perp$. Since $\boldsymbol{X}'\boldsymbol{l} = \boldsymbol{0}$, we can write $\boldsymbol{l}$ as $(\boldsymbol{I}-\boldsymbol{P}_X)\boldsymbol{m}$. As $\boldsymbol{l}'\boldsymbol{V}(\boldsymbol{I}-\boldsymbol{P}_X) = \boldsymbol{0}$, we have $\boldsymbol{m}'(\boldsymbol{I}-\boldsymbol{P}_X)\boldsymbol{V}(\boldsymbol{I}-\boldsymbol{P}_X) = \boldsymbol{0}$, i.e. $\boldsymbol{m}'(\boldsymbol{I}-\boldsymbol{P}_X)\boldsymbol{V} = \boldsymbol{0}$. Hence, $\boldsymbol{l}'(\boldsymbol{V}:\boldsymbol{X}) = \boldsymbol{0}$. It follows that $\mathcal{C}(\boldsymbol{V}(\boldsymbol{I}-\boldsymbol{P}_X):\boldsymbol{X})^\perp \subseteq \mathcal{C}(\boldsymbol{V}:\boldsymbol{X})^\perp$.

Part (b) follows directly from part (a) of Proposition 11.40, by choosing $\boldsymbol{A} = \boldsymbol{V}(\boldsymbol{I}-\boldsymbol{P}_X)$ and $\boldsymbol{B} = \boldsymbol{X}$.

Using part (b) of Proposition 11.40, and comparing the resulting expression with (7.3), we have $\boldsymbol{e} = \boldsymbol{P}_{V(I-P_X)|X}\boldsymbol{y}$. Part (c) then follows from the fact that $\boldsymbol{I}-\boldsymbol{P}_{A|B}$ is a choice of $\boldsymbol{P}_{B|A}$. □

There is an interesting connection between the decomposition of the response as per Proposition 11.41 and the estimation and error spaces. According to this proposition, the response $\boldsymbol{y}$ can be uniquely decomposed as $\boldsymbol{y}_1 + \boldsymbol{y}_2$, where $\boldsymbol{y}_1 \in \mathcal{C}(\boldsymbol{X})$ and $\boldsymbol{y}_2 \in \mathcal{C}(\boldsymbol{V}(\boldsymbol{I} - \boldsymbol{P}_X))$. It follows from Proposition 11.25 that whenever a vector $\boldsymbol{l}$ is in the estimation space, $\boldsymbol{l}'\boldsymbol{y}$ is almost surely equal to $\boldsymbol{l}'\boldsymbol{y}_1$. Likewise, whenever $\boldsymbol{l}$ in the error space, $\boldsymbol{l}'\boldsymbol{y} = \boldsymbol{l}'\boldsymbol{y}_2$ almost surely.

See Rao (1974) for more information on oblique projectors, which was used by Baksalary and Trenkler (2009) to obtain different expressions of BLUE in the general linear model.

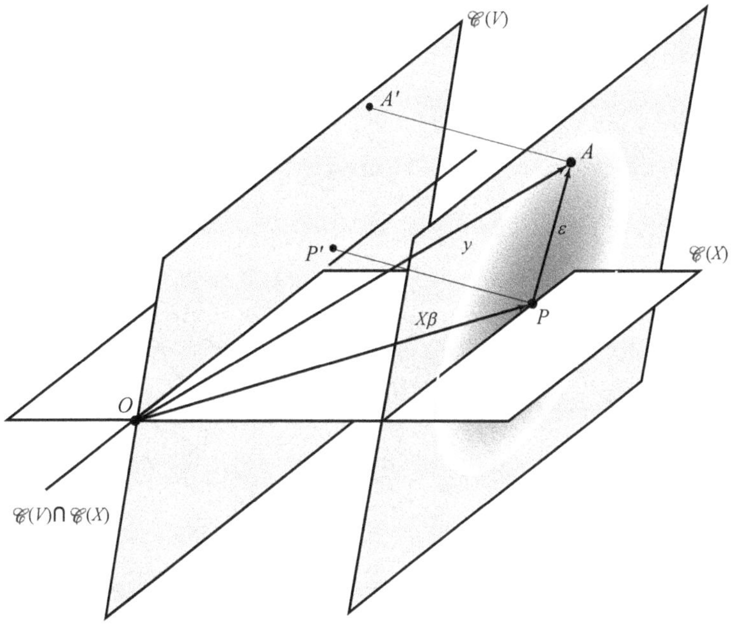

Fig. 11.5 A geometric view of the singular linear model

Figure 11.5 shows the synthesis of $\boldsymbol{y}$ in the general linear model $(\boldsymbol{y}, \boldsymbol{X\beta}, \sigma^2\boldsymbol{V})$ with possibly singular $\boldsymbol{V}$. The systematic part, $\boldsymbol{X\beta}$, is represented by the line OP, which lies in the plane representing $\mathcal{C}(\boldsymbol{X})$. If $\boldsymbol{V}$ is singular, then $\boldsymbol{\varepsilon}$ lies in the space $\mathcal{C}(\boldsymbol{V})$. The shaded area on this plane around the point P represents the region where the point A could possibly have appeared in another random sample.

Consider the plane of $\mathcal{C}(\boldsymbol{V})$ that passes through the point O. Since PA ($\boldsymbol{\varepsilon}$) is parallel to this plane, the perpendiculars from A and P on $\mathcal{C}(\boldsymbol{V})$, $A'A$ and $P'P$, must have the same length. These two vectors represent $(\boldsymbol{I} - \boldsymbol{P}_V)\boldsymbol{y}$ and $(\boldsymbol{I} - \boldsymbol{P}_V)\boldsymbol{X\beta}$, respectively. Thus, $P'P$ is the part of OP that is known exactly through $A'A$, because of the singularity of the model.

Figure 11.6 shows the construction of the BLUE in the general linear model. Note that the line of $\mathcal{C}(\boldsymbol{V}(\boldsymbol{I}-\boldsymbol{P}_X))$ is *not* perpendicular to the plane of $\mathcal{C}(\boldsymbol{X})$. This is in contrast with Figure 11.1, where the axis of $\mathcal{C}(\boldsymbol{X})^{\perp}$ is perpendicular to the plane of $\mathcal{C}(\boldsymbol{X})$.

The BLUE of $\boldsymbol{X\beta}$ is obtained by dropping the oblique projection of OA on the plane $\mathcal{C}(\boldsymbol{X})$ along $\mathcal{C}(\boldsymbol{V}(\boldsymbol{I} - \boldsymbol{P}_X))$. In other words, the point B is located by drawing a line parallel to $\mathcal{C}(\boldsymbol{V}(\boldsymbol{I} - \boldsymbol{P}_X))$, to intersect the

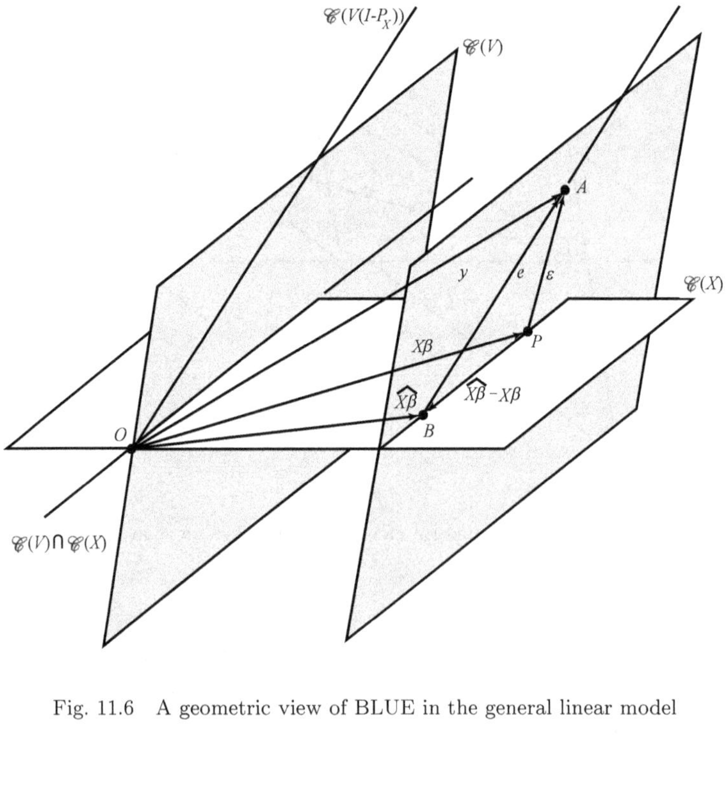

Fig. 11.6 A geometric view of BLUE in the general linear model

plane of $\mathcal{C}(\boldsymbol{X})$. Since $\mathcal{C}(\boldsymbol{V}(\boldsymbol{I}-\boldsymbol{P}_X))$ is included in $\mathcal{C}(\boldsymbol{V})$, the line BA (corresponding to the residual vector $\boldsymbol{e}$) is parallel to this plane. Therefore, the segment PB lies in the line through P that is parallel to $\mathcal{C}(\boldsymbol{V})\cap\mathcal{C}(\boldsymbol{X})$. PB corresponds to the error in the estimation of $\boldsymbol{X\beta}$, $\boldsymbol{X}\widehat{\boldsymbol{\beta}}-\boldsymbol{X\beta}$. This clearly shows why the space spanned by $D(\boldsymbol{X}\widehat{\boldsymbol{\beta}})$ is $\mathcal{C}(\boldsymbol{V})\cap\mathcal{C}(\boldsymbol{X})$, and the space spanned by $D(\boldsymbol{e})$ is $\mathcal{C}(\boldsymbol{V}(\boldsymbol{I}-\boldsymbol{P}_X))$ (see Proposition 7.15).

Figure 11.6 also illustrates that there is no need to separate the 'non-random' part of $\boldsymbol{y}$ to obtain the BLUE of $\boldsymbol{X\beta}$. The projections work much the same way as in the case of the homoscedastic linear model.

When $\boldsymbol{V}$ is singular, one can further decompose $\boldsymbol{X}\widehat{\boldsymbol{\beta}}$ into a deterministic and a stochastic part (see Nordström, 1985). The stochastic part is the orthogonal projection of OB on the line $\mathcal{C}(\boldsymbol{V})\cap\mathcal{C}(\boldsymbol{X})$, while the deterministic part is perpendicular drawn from O to the base of this projection.

Restrictions in the general linear model can be visualized in a similar manner. Drawing a diagram in the singular case is made difficult by the fact that one runs out of dimensions while tracking the transition from $\mathcal{C}(\boldsymbol{X})$ to $\mathcal{C}(\boldsymbol{X}(\boldsymbol{I}-\boldsymbol{P}_{A'}))$, and then to $\mathcal{C}(\boldsymbol{V})\cap\mathcal{C}(\boldsymbol{X}(\boldsymbol{I}-\boldsymbol{P}_{A'}))$!

11.5 Large sample properties of estimators

The assumption of normality of the response is crucial for the confidence regions and tests of hypotheses described in Chapters 4, 7 and 10. We now explore whether for large sample sizes, the inference can be carried out as described previously, even if the distributional assumption is replaced by weaker conditions.

We begin with the statement of a convergence result for the homoscedastic linear model. The proof of this result involves a series of results which are outside the purview of this book, and is omitted. We refer the reader to Sen and Singer (1993, Section 7.2) for a proof.

Proposition 11.42. *Suppose $\widehat{\boldsymbol{\beta}}_n$ is the least squares estimator of $\boldsymbol{\beta}$ in the linear model*

$$\boldsymbol{y}_n=\boldsymbol{X}_n\boldsymbol{\beta}+\boldsymbol{\varepsilon}_n,$$

where $\boldsymbol{\varepsilon}_n$ has independent and identically distributed components with mean 0 and variance σ^2. Let the matrix $\boldsymbol{X}_n$ have full column rank and satisfy the conditions:

(i) the elements of the matrix $n^{-1}\boldsymbol{X}_n'\boldsymbol{X}_n$ converge to those of a finite and positive definite matrix, $\boldsymbol{V}_*$, as the sample size n goes to ∞;

(*ii*) *the largest diagonal element of* $\boldsymbol{P}_{X_n}$ *goes to zero as* n *goes to* ∞.

Then $\sqrt{n}(\widehat{\boldsymbol{\beta}}_n - \boldsymbol{\beta})$ *converges in distribution to* $N(\boldsymbol{0}, \sigma^2\boldsymbol{V}_*^{-1})$. □

We now extend this theorem to the general linear model $(\boldsymbol{y}_n, \boldsymbol{X}_n\boldsymbol{\beta}, \sigma^2\boldsymbol{V}_n)$, where both $\boldsymbol{X}_n$ and $\boldsymbol{V}_n$ can be rank deficient. If $\boldsymbol{C}_n\boldsymbol{C}_n'$ is a rank factorization of $\boldsymbol{V}_n$, then $\boldsymbol{y}_n$ can be written as

$$\boldsymbol{y}_n = \boldsymbol{X}_n\boldsymbol{\beta} + \boldsymbol{C}_n\boldsymbol{\varepsilon}_n, \tag{11.11}$$

where $E(\boldsymbol{\varepsilon}_n) = \boldsymbol{0}$ and $D(\boldsymbol{\varepsilon}_n) = \sigma^2\boldsymbol{I}$. It is on the basis of this representation that the asymptotic normality of a BLUE is established.

Proposition 11.43. *Let* $\mathcal{M}_n$ *be the model (11.11) where* $\boldsymbol{\varepsilon}_n$ *has independent and identically distributed components with mean 0 and variance* σ^2. *Let the matrix* $\boldsymbol{C}_n$ *have full column rank and* $\boldsymbol{V}_n = \boldsymbol{C}_n\boldsymbol{C}_n'$. *Suppose the following conditions hold:*

(*i*) *the model* $\mathcal{M}_n$ *satisfies the consistency condition* $(\boldsymbol{I}-\boldsymbol{P}_{V_n})\boldsymbol{y}_n \in \mathcal{C}((\boldsymbol{I}-\boldsymbol{P}_{V_n})\boldsymbol{X}_n)$ *with probability 1, for every sample size* n;

(*ii*) $\rho(\boldsymbol{X}_n)$ *and* $\rho(\boldsymbol{V}_n : \boldsymbol{X}_n) - \rho(\boldsymbol{V}_n)$ *do not depend on* n;

(*iii*) *the matrix* $\boldsymbol{X}_n$ *has a rank factorization of the form*

$$\boldsymbol{X}_n = (\boldsymbol{X}_{1n} : \boldsymbol{X}_{2n})\begin{pmatrix}\boldsymbol{B}_1\\ \boldsymbol{B}_2\end{pmatrix},$$

where the matrix $\boldsymbol{B} = (\boldsymbol{B}_1' : \boldsymbol{B}_2')'$ *does not depend on* n *and* $\mathcal{C}(\boldsymbol{X}_{2n}) = \mathcal{C}(\boldsymbol{X}_n \cap \boldsymbol{V}_n)$;

(*iv*) *the elements of the matrix* $n^{-1}\boldsymbol{X}_{2n}'\boldsymbol{V}_n^-\boldsymbol{X}_{2n}$ *converge to those of a finite and positive definite matrix,* $\boldsymbol{V}_*$, *as the sample size* n *goes to* ∞;

(*v*) *the largest diagonal element of* $\boldsymbol{P}_{C_n^+X_{2n}}$ *goes to zero as* n *goes to* ∞.

If $\widehat{\boldsymbol{A\beta}}_n$ *is the BLUE of an LPF* $\boldsymbol{A\beta}$ *which is estimable under* $\mathcal{M}_n$ *for every* n, *then* $\sqrt{n}(\widehat{\boldsymbol{A\beta}}_n - \boldsymbol{A\beta})$ *converges in distribution to*

$$N\left(\boldsymbol{0}, \sigma^2\boldsymbol{A}\boldsymbol{B}^{-R}\begin{pmatrix}\boldsymbol{0} & \boldsymbol{0}\\ \boldsymbol{0} & \boldsymbol{V}_*^{-1}\end{pmatrix}\boldsymbol{B}^{-R'}\boldsymbol{A}'\right),$$

where $\boldsymbol{B}^{-R}$ *is any right-inverse of* $\boldsymbol{B}$. □

Proof. Note that $\boldsymbol{B}$ has linearly independent rows. Let $\boldsymbol{\gamma}_1 = \boldsymbol{B}_1\boldsymbol{\beta}$ and $\boldsymbol{\gamma}_2 = \boldsymbol{B}_2\boldsymbol{\beta}$. We shall show that

$$\widehat{\boldsymbol{\gamma}}_{1n} = [\boldsymbol{X}_{1n}'(\boldsymbol{I}-\boldsymbol{P}_{V_n})\boldsymbol{X}_{1n}]^{-1}\boldsymbol{X}_{1n}'(\boldsymbol{I}-\boldsymbol{P}_{V_n})\boldsymbol{y}_n$$
$$\text{and } \widehat{\boldsymbol{\gamma}}_{2n} = [\boldsymbol{X}_{2n}'\boldsymbol{V}_n^-\boldsymbol{X}_{2n}]^{-1}\boldsymbol{X}_{2n}'\boldsymbol{V}_n^-(\boldsymbol{y}_n - \boldsymbol{X}_{1n}\widehat{\boldsymbol{\gamma}}_{1n})$$

are the BLUEs of γ_1 and γ_2, respectively, under $\mathcal{M}_n$. To verify that the inverses exist, note that

$$\begin{aligned}\rho(\boldsymbol{X}_{1n}'(\boldsymbol{I}-\boldsymbol{P}_{V_n})\boldsymbol{X}_{1n}) &= \rho((\boldsymbol{I}-\boldsymbol{P}_{V_n})\boldsymbol{X}_n) = \rho(\boldsymbol{V}_n : \boldsymbol{X}_n) - \rho(\boldsymbol{V}_n)\\ &= \rho(\boldsymbol{X}_n) - \dim(\mathcal{C}(\boldsymbol{X}_n)\cap\mathcal{C}(\boldsymbol{V}_n)) \qquad \text{(see Table 11.1)}\\ &= \rho(\boldsymbol{X}_n) - \rho(\boldsymbol{X}_{2n})\\ &= \rho(\boldsymbol{X}_{1n}) \ \ \text{(from rank-factorization of } \boldsymbol{X}_n),\end{aligned}$$

which is the same as the number if columns of $\boldsymbol{X}_{1n}'(\boldsymbol{I}-\boldsymbol{P}_{V_n})\boldsymbol{X}_{1n}$. Likewise,

$$\rho(\boldsymbol{X}_{2n}'\boldsymbol{V}_n^-\boldsymbol{X}_{2n}) = \rho(\boldsymbol{X}_{2n}) \ \ (\text{as } \mathcal{C}(\boldsymbol{X}_{2n}) \subset \mathcal{C}(\boldsymbol{V}_n)),$$

which is the same as the number if columns of $\boldsymbol{X}_{2n}'\boldsymbol{V}_n^-\boldsymbol{X}_{2n}$. It is easy to verify that $E(\widehat{\gamma}_{1n}) = \gamma_{1n}$ and consequently $E(\widehat{\gamma}_{2n}) = \gamma_{2n}$. Thus, $\widehat{\gamma}_{1n}$ and $\widehat{\gamma}_{2n}$ are linear unbiased estimators of γ_1 and γ_2, respectively. Since $\widehat{\gamma}_{1n}$ has zero dispersion, it is the BLUE of γ_1. Further,

$$Cov(\widehat{\gamma}_{2n}, (\boldsymbol{I}-\boldsymbol{P}_{X_n})\boldsymbol{y}_n) = [\boldsymbol{X}_{2n}'\boldsymbol{V}_n^-\boldsymbol{X}_{2n}]^{-1}\boldsymbol{X}_{2n}'(\boldsymbol{I}-\boldsymbol{P}_{X_n}) = \boldsymbol{0}.$$

As $\widehat{\gamma}_{2n}$ is uncorrelated with every LZF of $\mathcal{M}_n$, it is the BLUE of γ_2.

The model $\mathcal{M}_n$ can be reparametrized as

$$\boldsymbol{y}_n = \boldsymbol{X}_{1n}\gamma_1 + \boldsymbol{X}_{2n}\gamma_2 + \boldsymbol{C}_n\varepsilon_n,$$

which is equivalent to the pair of equations

$$\begin{aligned}(\boldsymbol{I}-\boldsymbol{P}_{V_n})\boldsymbol{y}_n &= (\boldsymbol{I}-\boldsymbol{P}_{V_n})\boldsymbol{X}_{1n}\gamma_1,\\ \boldsymbol{C}_n^+(\boldsymbol{y}_n - \boldsymbol{X}_{1n}\widehat{\gamma}_{1n}) &= \boldsymbol{C}_n^+\boldsymbol{X}_{2n}\gamma_2 + \varepsilon_n.\end{aligned}$$

These equations correspond to the linear models

$$\begin{aligned}&\mathcal{M}_{1n} : ((\boldsymbol{I}-\boldsymbol{P}_{V_n})\boldsymbol{y}_n, (\boldsymbol{I}-\boldsymbol{P}_{V_n})\boldsymbol{X}_{1n}\gamma_1, \boldsymbol{0})\\ &\mathcal{M}_{2n} : (\boldsymbol{C}_n^+(\boldsymbol{y}_n - \boldsymbol{X}_{1n}\widehat{\gamma}_{1n}), \boldsymbol{C}_n^+\boldsymbol{X}_{2n}\gamma_2, \sigma^2\boldsymbol{I}).\end{aligned}$$

In these models, the parameters γ_1 and γ_2 are completely estimable. For $\mathcal{M}_1$, $\widehat{\gamma}_{1n}$ is the BLUE of γ_1 with zero dispersion. For $\mathcal{M}_2$, $\widehat{\gamma}_{1n}$ is the BLUE having dispersion

$$n^{-1}\boldsymbol{X}_{2n}'\boldsymbol{C}_n^{+\prime}\boldsymbol{C}_n^+\boldsymbol{X}_{2n} = n^{-1}\boldsymbol{X}_{2n}'\boldsymbol{V}^-\boldsymbol{X}_{2n}.$$

Using conditions (iv) and (v) and Proposition 11.42 for the model $\mathcal{M}_{2n}$, we have $\sqrt{n}(\widehat{\gamma}_{2n} - \gamma_2)$ converging in distribution to $N(\boldsymbol{0}, \sigma^2\boldsymbol{V}_*^{-1})$. Thus, we can conclude:

$$\sqrt{n}\begin{pmatrix}\widehat{\gamma}_{1n} - \gamma_1\\ \widehat{\gamma}_{2n} - \gamma_2\end{pmatrix} \text{ converges in distribution to } N\left(\boldsymbol{0}, \sigma^2\begin{pmatrix}\boldsymbol{0} & \boldsymbol{0}\\ \boldsymbol{0} & \boldsymbol{V}_*^{-1}\end{pmatrix}\right).$$

Using the fact that $\mathcal{C}(\boldsymbol{A}') \subset \mathcal{C}(\boldsymbol{X}_n') = \mathcal{C}(\boldsymbol{B}')$, we can write $\boldsymbol{A\beta} = \boldsymbol{AB}^{-R}\boldsymbol{B\beta} = \boldsymbol{AB}^{-R}\boldsymbol{\gamma}$ for any right-inverse of $\boldsymbol{B}$. Consequently, the BLUE of $\boldsymbol{A\beta}$ is $\boldsymbol{AB}^{-R}(\widehat{\boldsymbol{\gamma}}_{1n}' : \widehat{\boldsymbol{\gamma}}_{2n}')'$. The statement of the proposition follows. □

Remark 11.44. Conditions (ii) and (iii) of Proposition 11.43 essentially mean that the column space of $\boldsymbol{X}_n'$ remains the same as the sample size goes to ∞, and that the LPFs which can be estimated with zero error also remain the same. □

Remark 11.45. Under the conditions of Proposition 11.43, $\widehat{\boldsymbol{A\beta}}_n - \boldsymbol{A\beta}$ converges to zero almost surely as n goes to ∞. In this sense the BLUE can be said to be *strongly consistent.* □

When $\boldsymbol{V}_n$ is positive definite for every n, we have the following corollary to Proposition 11.43.

Proposition 11.46. *Let $\mathcal{M}_n$ be the model (11.11) where $\boldsymbol{\varepsilon}_n$ has independent and identically distributed components with mean 0 and variance σ^2. Let the square matrix $\boldsymbol{C}_n$ have full rank and $\boldsymbol{V}_n = \boldsymbol{C}_n\boldsymbol{C}_n'$. Suppose the following conditions hold:*

(i) the matrix $\boldsymbol{X}_n$ has a rank factorization of the form $\boldsymbol{X}_n = \boldsymbol{X}_{*n}\boldsymbol{B}$, where the matrix $\boldsymbol{B}$ does not depend on n;
(ii) the elements of the matrix $n^{-1}\boldsymbol{X}_{*n}'\boldsymbol{V}_n^{-1}\boldsymbol{X}_{*n}$ converge to those of a finite and positive definite matrix, $\boldsymbol{V}_*$, as the sample size n goes to ∞;
(iii) the largest diagonal element of $\boldsymbol{P}_{C_n^{-1}X_{*n}}$ goes to zero as n goes to ∞.

If $\widehat{\boldsymbol{A\beta}}_n$ is the BLUE of an LPF $\boldsymbol{A\beta}$ which is estimable under $\mathcal{M}_n$ for every n, then the limiting distribution of $\sqrt{n}(\widehat{\boldsymbol{A\beta}}_n - \boldsymbol{A\beta})$ is multivariate normal with mean $\boldsymbol{0}$ and dispersion $\sigma^2\boldsymbol{AB}^{-R}\boldsymbol{V}_*^{-1}\boldsymbol{B}^{-R'}\boldsymbol{A}'$, where $\boldsymbol{B}^{-R}$ is any right-inverse of $\boldsymbol{B}$. □

It can be shown that under the conditions of Proposition 11.42, the usual unbiased estimator of σ^2 under the model $(\boldsymbol{y}_n, \boldsymbol{X}_n\boldsymbol{\beta}, \sigma^2\boldsymbol{I})$ converges to σ^2 almost surely as n goes to ∞ (see Sen and Singer, 1993, p. 281). We can apply this result to the model $\mathcal{M}_{2n}$ described in the proof of Proposition 11.43. The usual estimator of σ^2 under $\mathcal{M}_{2n}$ is the same as that under $\mathcal{M}_n$. Thus, the estimator of σ^2 computed for $\mathcal{M}_n$ under the conditions of Proposition 11.43 is strongly consistent.

Similar arguments can be used to obtain large sample properties of the estimators for the multivariate linear model. We omit the details.

Nanayakkara and Cressie (1991) consider large-sample properties of the LSE when the model is heteroscedastic. Sen and Singer (1993) extend Proposition 11.46 (assuming that $\boldsymbol{X}_n$ has full column rank) to the case where $\boldsymbol{V}_n$ is estimated and the estimator satisfies certain conditions that ensure its closeness to $\boldsymbol{V}_n$ in the limit.

11.6 Complements/Exercises

Exercises with solutions given in Appendix C

11.1 If $\boldsymbol{y} \sim N(\boldsymbol{X\beta}, \sigma^2\boldsymbol{V})$, then show that the statistic $\boldsymbol{Ty}$ is linearly minimal sufficient for $\boldsymbol{\beta}$ only if it is complete and sufficient for $\boldsymbol{\beta}$, using the following steps.

- (a) Let $\boldsymbol{y}_1$ and $\boldsymbol{y}_2$ be as in Proposition 11.16. Assuming that there is no known restriction on the parameter space, explain why it is enough to show that $(\boldsymbol{y}_1' : \boldsymbol{y}_2')'$ is complete and sufficient for $\boldsymbol{\beta}$.
- (b) Show that the vector $(\boldsymbol{y}_1' : \boldsymbol{y}_2')'$ of part (a) is complete and sufficient for its expected value, provided there is no known restriction on the parameter space. Hence, prove that this vector is complete and sufficient for $\boldsymbol{\beta}$.
- (c) In the case of restricted parameter space, use the equivalent unrestricted model of Section 11.1.2 to complete the proof.

11.2 Obtain simpler expressions for the dimensions shown in Table 11.1 in the following special cases.

- (a) $\mathcal{C}(\boldsymbol{X}) = \mathcal{C}(\boldsymbol{V})$.
- (b) $\mathcal{C}(\boldsymbol{X}) \subset \mathcal{C}(\boldsymbol{V})$.
- (c) $\mathcal{C}(\boldsymbol{V}) \subset \mathcal{C}(\boldsymbol{X})$.
- (d) $\mathcal{C}(\boldsymbol{X}) = \mathcal{C}(\boldsymbol{V})^{\perp}$.
- (e) $\mathcal{C}(\boldsymbol{X}) \subset \mathcal{C}(\boldsymbol{V})^{\perp}$.
- (f) $\mathcal{C}(\boldsymbol{V})^{\perp} \subset \mathcal{C}(\boldsymbol{X})$.

11.3 Describe a linear analogue of the information inequality in the context of the linear model.

11.4 Prove Proposition 11.24.

11.5 Let $\boldsymbol{y}_{(i)} = \boldsymbol{L}^{(i)}\boldsymbol{L}_i\boldsymbol{y}$, where $\boldsymbol{L}_i$, $i = 1, 2, 3, 4$, are as in Proposition 11.16 and $(\boldsymbol{L}^{(1)} : \boldsymbol{L}^{(2)} : \boldsymbol{L}^{(3)} : \boldsymbol{L}^{(4)}) = \boldsymbol{L}^{-1}$. Show that

- (a) $\boldsymbol{y} = \boldsymbol{y}_{(1)} + \boldsymbol{y}_{(2)} + \boldsymbol{y}_{(3)} + \boldsymbol{y}_{(4)}$.
- (b) $\boldsymbol{y}_{(1)}$ and $\boldsymbol{y}_{(2)}$ are BLUEs, and their elements together constitute a generating set of BLUEs.

(c) $\boldsymbol{y}_{(3)}$ is an LZF whose elements constitute a generating set of LZFs.

(d) $D(\boldsymbol{y}_{(2)}) = \boldsymbol{0}$ and $\boldsymbol{y}_{(4)}$ is identically zero.

(e) $\boldsymbol{y}_{(1)} + \boldsymbol{y}_{(2)} = \boldsymbol{X}\widehat{\boldsymbol{\beta}}$ and $\boldsymbol{y}_{(3)} = \boldsymbol{e}$.

(f) $D(\boldsymbol{X}\widehat{\boldsymbol{\beta}}) = D(\boldsymbol{y}_{(1)})$ and $D(\boldsymbol{e}) = D(\boldsymbol{y}_{(3)})$.

11.6 Consider the linear models $\mathcal{M} = (\boldsymbol{y}, \boldsymbol{X\beta}, \sigma^2\boldsymbol{V})$ and $\mathcal{M}_D = (\boldsymbol{y}, \boldsymbol{V}(\boldsymbol{I} - \boldsymbol{P}_X)\gamma, \sigma^2\boldsymbol{V})$ with $\boldsymbol{V}$ positive definite. Bhimasankaram and Sengupta (1996) called $\mathcal{M}_D$ the *dual model* corresponding to $\mathcal{M}$. Show that

(a) the error space of $\mathcal{M}_D$ is the estimation space of $\mathcal{M}$, and vice versa;

(b) the class of LZFs of $\mathcal{M}_D$ coincides with the class of BLUEs of $\mathcal{M}$, and vice versa;

(c) the residual vector of $\mathcal{M}_D$ is almost surely equal to the vector of fitted values in $\mathcal{M}$, and vice versa;

(d) the dual of $\mathcal{M}_D$ is $\mathcal{M}$ or a reparametrization of it.

11.7 If $\widehat{\boldsymbol{y}}$ is the BLUE of $\boldsymbol{X\beta}$ in the linear model $(\boldsymbol{y}, \boldsymbol{X\beta}, \sigma^2\boldsymbol{V})$, then determine the conditions under which $c\boldsymbol{C}\widehat{\boldsymbol{y}}$ is an ALE of $\boldsymbol{CX\beta}$ for $0 \le c \le 1$.

11.8 Consider the problem of estimating the parametric function $\boldsymbol{g}(\boldsymbol{\theta})$ from the observation vector $\boldsymbol{y}$ using a linear estimator of the form $\boldsymbol{Ty}$. Let L_B indicate the loss function $(\boldsymbol{Ty} - \boldsymbol{g}(\boldsymbol{\theta}))'\boldsymbol{B}(\boldsymbol{Ty} - \boldsymbol{g}(\boldsymbol{\theta}))$, where $\boldsymbol{B}$ is a symmetric nonnegative definite matrix, and L_I be the loss function L_B for $\boldsymbol{B} = \boldsymbol{I}$.

(a) Let $\boldsymbol{Sy}$ be an admissible linear estimator of $\boldsymbol{g}(\boldsymbol{\theta})$ with respect to the loss function L_B, and let $\boldsymbol{Ty}$ be an inadmissible estimator whose risk function uniformly dominates that of $\boldsymbol{Sy}$. Show that $\boldsymbol{Ty}$ is inadmissible with respect to L_F, where $\boldsymbol{F} = \boldsymbol{B}/b$, b being the largest eigenvalue of $\boldsymbol{B}$.

(b) In the above set-up, prove that $\boldsymbol{Ty}$ cannot be linearly admissible for $\boldsymbol{g}(\boldsymbol{\theta})$ with respect to L_I.

(c) If $\boldsymbol{Ty}$ is an ALE of $\boldsymbol{g}(\boldsymbol{\theta})$ with respect to the loss function L_I, then show that it is an ALE with respect to the loss function L_B for any nonnegative definite $\boldsymbol{B}$.

11.9 Using the result of Exercise 11.8, show that whenever $\boldsymbol{Ty}$ is linearly admissible for $\boldsymbol{X\beta}$ in the model $(\boldsymbol{y}, \boldsymbol{X\beta}, \sigma^2\boldsymbol{V})$ with respect to the squared error loss function, $\boldsymbol{CTy}$ is linearly admissible for $\boldsymbol{CX\beta}$ with respect to the same loss function for any $\boldsymbol{C}$.

11.10 Show that the maximum risk of the estimator $\boldsymbol{Ty}$ of the estimable LPF $\boldsymbol{A\beta}$ in the linear model $(\boldsymbol{y}, \boldsymbol{X\beta}, \sigma^2\boldsymbol{V})$, with respect to the loss function $(\boldsymbol{Ty}-\boldsymbol{A\beta})'\boldsymbol{B}(\boldsymbol{Ty}-\boldsymbol{A\beta})$ and subject to the restriction $\boldsymbol{\beta}'\boldsymbol{H\beta} \le \sigma^2$, is given by (11.6). Assume that $\boldsymbol{B}$ and $\boldsymbol{H}$ are both nonnegative definite and $\mathcal{C}(\boldsymbol{X}') \subseteq \mathcal{C}(\boldsymbol{H})$.

11.11 Suppose $\boldsymbol{Ty}$ is a linear estimator of the estimable LPF $\boldsymbol{A\beta}$, where the parameter $\boldsymbol{\beta}$ satisfies the quadratic restriction $\boldsymbol{\beta}'\boldsymbol{H\beta} \le \sigma^2$, $\boldsymbol{H}$ being a nonnegative definite matrix such that $\mathcal{C}(\boldsymbol{X}') \subseteq \mathcal{C}(\boldsymbol{H})$.

(a) Show that for any vector $\boldsymbol{p}$ of suitable dimension,

$$\begin{aligned}&\boldsymbol{p}'E[(\boldsymbol{Ty}-\boldsymbol{A\beta})(\boldsymbol{Ty}-\boldsymbol{A\beta})']\boldsymbol{p}\\&\le \sigma^2[\boldsymbol{p}'\boldsymbol{TVT}'\boldsymbol{p}+\boldsymbol{p}'(\boldsymbol{T}-\boldsymbol{C})\boldsymbol{XH}^-\boldsymbol{X}'(\boldsymbol{T}-\boldsymbol{C})'\boldsymbol{p}],\end{aligned}$$

where $\boldsymbol{C}$ is a matrix such that $\boldsymbol{A} = \boldsymbol{CX}$.

(b) Show that

$$\begin{aligned}&\sup_{\boldsymbol{\beta}:\boldsymbol{\beta}'\boldsymbol{H\beta}\le\sigma^2} E[(\boldsymbol{Ty}-\boldsymbol{A\beta})(\boldsymbol{Ty}-\boldsymbol{A\beta})']\\&= \sigma^2[\boldsymbol{TVT}'+(\boldsymbol{T}-\boldsymbol{C})\boldsymbol{XH}^-\boldsymbol{X}'(\boldsymbol{T}-\boldsymbol{C})'],\end{aligned}$$

where the supremum is in the sense described on page 561.

(c) Using the fact that the maximum mean squared error of $\boldsymbol{p}'\boldsymbol{Ty}$ for estimating $\boldsymbol{p}'\boldsymbol{A\beta}$ is minimized when $\boldsymbol{p}'\boldsymbol{Ty}$ is chosen as $\boldsymbol{p}'\boldsymbol{AX}^-\boldsymbol{X}\widehat{\boldsymbol{\beta}}_m$, prove (11.7).

11.12 Consider the linear model $(\boldsymbol{y}, \boldsymbol{X\beta}, \sigma^2\boldsymbol{V})$ where $\boldsymbol{X}$ and $\boldsymbol{V}$ have full column rank and $\rho(\boldsymbol{X}) > 1$. Consider the problem of minimax linear estimation of $\boldsymbol{\beta}$ with respect to the loss function $(\boldsymbol{Ty}-\boldsymbol{\beta})'\boldsymbol{B}(\boldsymbol{Ty}-\boldsymbol{\beta})$ and the restriction $\boldsymbol{\beta}'\boldsymbol{\beta} = \sigma^2/h$. Show that the MILEs for the cases (a) $\boldsymbol{B} = \boldsymbol{I}$ and (b) $\boldsymbol{B}$ is an arbitrary positive semidefinite matrix of rank 1, are almost surely different.

11.13 Consider the linear model $(\boldsymbol{y}, \boldsymbol{X\beta}, \sigma^2\boldsymbol{V})$ where $\boldsymbol{X}$ and $\boldsymbol{V}$ have full column rank and $\rho(\boldsymbol{X}) > 1$. Show that the MILE of $\boldsymbol{a}'\boldsymbol{\beta}$ with respect to the loss function $|\boldsymbol{t}'\boldsymbol{y} - \boldsymbol{a}'\boldsymbol{\beta}|^2$ and the restriction $\boldsymbol{\beta}'\boldsymbol{\beta} = \sigma^2/h$, is almost surely different from $\boldsymbol{a}'\widehat{\boldsymbol{\beta}}_M$, where $\widehat{\boldsymbol{\beta}}_M$ is as defined in Proposition 11.38.

11.14 Consider the model $(\boldsymbol{y}, \boldsymbol{X\beta}, \sigma^2\boldsymbol{V})$ where $\boldsymbol{V}$ is positive definite.

(a) If $\boldsymbol{H}$ is a matrix such that $\mathcal{C}(\boldsymbol{X}') \subseteq \mathcal{C}(\boldsymbol{H})$, then show that the Kuks-Olman estimator of $\boldsymbol{X\beta}$ for the quadratic restriction $\boldsymbol{\beta}'\boldsymbol{H\beta} \le \sigma^2$ can almost surely be written as $\boldsymbol{X}\widehat{\boldsymbol{\beta}}_m = \boldsymbol{X}(\boldsymbol{X}'\boldsymbol{V}^{-1}\boldsymbol{X}+\boldsymbol{H})^-\boldsymbol{X}'\boldsymbol{V}^{-1}\boldsymbol{y}$.

(b) If the prior distribution of $\boldsymbol{\beta}$ and σ^2 is such that

$$[E(\sigma^2)]^{-1}E(\boldsymbol{\beta}\boldsymbol{\beta}') = \boldsymbol{U},$$

where $\boldsymbol{U}$ is a positive definite matrix, then show that the BLE of $\boldsymbol{\beta}$ is $\widehat{\boldsymbol{\beta}}_B = (\boldsymbol{X}'\boldsymbol{V}^{-1}\boldsymbol{X} + \boldsymbol{U}^{-1})^{-1}\boldsymbol{X}'\boldsymbol{V}^{-1}\boldsymbol{y}$.

11.15 Consider the linear model $(\boldsymbol{y}, \boldsymbol{X\beta}, \sigma^2\boldsymbol{V})$ where the prior distribution of $\boldsymbol{\beta}$ given σ^2 is such that $\gamma'\boldsymbol{H}\gamma \leq 1$ and $E(\gamma\gamma') = \boldsymbol{U}$, where $\gamma = \boldsymbol{\beta}/\sigma$ and $\boldsymbol{H}$ and $\boldsymbol{U}$ are nonnegative definite matrices and $\mathcal{C}(\boldsymbol{X}') \subseteq \mathcal{C}(\boldsymbol{H})$. Suppose the squared error loss function is used to obtain the MILE and BLE of the estimable LPF $\boldsymbol{a}'\boldsymbol{\beta}$. Show that the least favourable prior for γ (as far as the BLE of $\boldsymbol{a}'\boldsymbol{\beta}$ is concerned) is one for which $\boldsymbol{U} = \boldsymbol{H}^-$ for some g-inverse of $\boldsymbol{H}$. Also show that the MILE and BLE of $\boldsymbol{a}'\boldsymbol{\beta}$ and coincide.

11.16 Suppose $\mathcal{C}(\boldsymbol{A})$ and $\mathcal{C}(\boldsymbol{B})$ are virtually disjoint. Prove the following facts about the oblique projection matrix $\boldsymbol{P}_{A|B}$.

(a) $\boldsymbol{P}_{A|B}$ is uniquely defined when $(\boldsymbol{A} : \boldsymbol{B})$ has full row rank.
(b) $\boldsymbol{P}_{A|B}$ is idempotent when $(\boldsymbol{A} : \boldsymbol{B})$ has full row rank.
(c) $\boldsymbol{P}_{A|B}$ is neither unique nor idempotent when $(\boldsymbol{A} : \boldsymbol{B})$ does not have full row rank.

Additional exercises

11.17 Let the best linear predictor (BLP) of $\boldsymbol{y}$ given $\boldsymbol{x}$ be defined as in Exercise 2.10. Given the linear model $(\boldsymbol{y}, \boldsymbol{X\beta}, \sigma^2\boldsymbol{V})$, show that the BLP of $\boldsymbol{y}$ given $\boldsymbol{Ty}$ is a function of $\boldsymbol{Ty}$ alone (irrespective of $\boldsymbol{\beta}$) if and only if $\boldsymbol{Ty}$ is linearly sufficient for $\boldsymbol{\beta}$.

11.18 Given the model $\mathcal{M} = (\boldsymbol{y}, \boldsymbol{X\beta}, \sigma^2\boldsymbol{V})$ for the response $\boldsymbol{y}$, consider the model $\mathcal{M}_T = (\boldsymbol{Ty}, \boldsymbol{TX\beta}, \sigma^2\boldsymbol{TVT}')$ for the linearly transformed response $\boldsymbol{Ty}$. Show that all the BLUEs of $\mathcal{M}$ are BLUEs of $\mathcal{M}_T$ if and only if $\boldsymbol{Ty}$ is linearly sufficient for $\boldsymbol{\beta}$.

11.19 Modify the statement of Proposition 11.20 for the case when $\boldsymbol{z}$ is *any* basis set of BLUEs and prove the result.

Appendix A

Matrix and Vector Preliminaries

This appendix provides a brief summary of the concepts and results of linear algebra that have been used in the book. Related results are grouped into sections and their proofs, when considered lengthy and inessential for understanding the results, omitted. Our limited purpose here is to acquaint the reader with essential facts in order to make the treatment self-contained. No attempt is made at comprehensive coverage or at stating the results in their most general form or even in conventional order. Additional information may be found from e.g. Rao and Bhimasankaram (2000), Banerjee and Roy (2014) and Searle and Khuri (2017).

Matrix notations introduced in this appendix and used in the chapters are summarized in the *Glossary of matrix notations* given at the beginning of the book.

A.1 Matrices and vectors

A *matrix* is a rectangular array of numbers arranged in *rows* and *columns*. If a matrix has m rows and n columns, then it is said to be of *order* $m \times n$. We denote matrices by bold and uppercase Roman or Greek letters, such as $\boldsymbol{A}$, and occasionally specify the order explicitly as a subscript, as in $\boldsymbol{A}_{m\times n}$. The entry in the ith row and the jth column of a matrix is called its (i,j)th *element*. We denote an element of a matrix by the corresponding lowercase letter, with the location specified as subscript. For instance, the (i,j)th element of the matrix $\boldsymbol{A}$ is $a_{i,j}$. We also use the simplified notation a_{ij} where there is no scope of ambiguity. Sometimes we describe a matrix by its typical elements: $((a_{i,j}))$ represents the matrix whose (i,j)th element is $a_{i,j}$, that is,

$$\boldsymbol{A} = ((a_{i,j})) = ((a_{ij})).$$

We only deal with matrices whose elements are real numbers, i.e. take values in $\mathbb{R}$, the real line. An $m \times n$ matrix assumes values in $\mathbb{R}^{mn}$, the mn-fold Cartesian product of the real line.

When two matrices have identical orders, one can define their sum. The sum or addition of the two matrices $\boldsymbol{A}_{m\times n}$ and $\boldsymbol{B}_{m\times n}$ is defined as

$$\boldsymbol{A}+\boldsymbol{B} = ((a_{ij}+b_{ij})).$$

The scalar product of a matrix $\boldsymbol{A}$ with a real number c is defined as

$$c\boldsymbol{A} = ((c\,a_{ij})).$$

The difference of $\boldsymbol{A}_{m\times n}$ and $\boldsymbol{B}_{m\times n}$ is defined as $\boldsymbol{A}+(-1)\boldsymbol{B}$. Thus,

$$\boldsymbol{A}-\boldsymbol{B} = ((a_{ij}-b_{ij})).$$

The product of the matrix $\boldsymbol{A}_{m\times n}$ with the matrix $\boldsymbol{B}_{n\times k}$, denoted by $\boldsymbol{AB}$, is defined as

$$\boldsymbol{AB} = \left(\left(\sum_{l=1}^{n} a_{il}b_{lj}\right)\right).$$

The product matrix is of order $m \times k$. The product is defined only when the number of columns of $\boldsymbol{A}$ is the same as the number of rows of $\boldsymbol{B}$. In general, $\boldsymbol{AB} \neq \boldsymbol{BA}$ even if both the products are defined and are of the same order. To emphasize the importance of the order of the multiplication, the operation of obtaining $\boldsymbol{AB}$ is referred to as 'the post-multiplication of $\boldsymbol{A}$ by $\boldsymbol{B}$' or 'the pre-multiplication of $\boldsymbol{B}$ by $\boldsymbol{A}$.'

A series of additions and subtractions (such as $\boldsymbol{A}+\boldsymbol{B}-\boldsymbol{C}$) and a series of multiplications (such as $\boldsymbol{ABC}$) may be defined likewise, irrespective of the sequence of the operations. Whenever we carry out these operations without mentioning the orders explicitly, it is to be understood that the matrices involved have orders that are appropriate for the operations.

The elements occurring in the (i,i)th position of a matrix $(i = 1, 2, \ldots)$ are called *diagonal elements*, while the others are called non-diagonal or off-diagonal elements. A *diagonal matrix* is a matrix with all off-diagonal elements equal to zero.

If $\boldsymbol{A} = ((a_{ij}))$, the *transpose* of $\boldsymbol{A}$ is defined as

$$\boldsymbol{A}' = ((a_{ji})).$$

It is easy to verify that $(\boldsymbol{AB})' = \boldsymbol{B}'\boldsymbol{A}'$. A *square* matrix is one with the number of rows equal to the number of columns. A square matrix $\boldsymbol{A}$ is called *symmetric* if $\boldsymbol{A}' = \boldsymbol{A}$, that is, if $a_{ij} = a_{ji}$ for all i and j. The sum of all the diagonal elements of a square matrix is called the *trace* of the matrix. We denote the trace of the matrix $\boldsymbol{A}$ by $\mathrm{tr}(\boldsymbol{A})$. It can be verified that

$$\mathrm{tr}(\boldsymbol{A}_{m\times n}\boldsymbol{B}_{n\times m}) = \mathrm{tr}(\boldsymbol{B}_{n\times m}\boldsymbol{A}_{m\times n}) = \sum_{i=1}^{m}\sum_{j=1}^{n} a_{ij}b_{ji}.$$

The *determinant* $|\boldsymbol{A}|$ of an $n \times n$ square matrix $\boldsymbol{A}$ is defined through the following recursive relation, for successively larger n:

$$|\boldsymbol{A}| = \begin{cases} a_{11} & \text{if } n = 1, \\ \sum_{j=1}^{n}(-1)^{1+j}a_{1j}|\boldsymbol{A}_{-1,-j}| & \text{if } n > 1, \end{cases}$$

where $\boldsymbol{A}_{-i,-j}$ is the $(n-1)\times(n-1)$ matrix obtained from $\boldsymbol{A}$ by removing its ith row and jth column. It can be shown that

$$\begin{aligned} |\boldsymbol{A}| = |\boldsymbol{A}'| &= \sum_{j=1}^{n}(-1)^{i+j}a_{ij}|\boldsymbol{A}_{-i,-j}|, \quad i = 1,\ldots,n \\ &= \sum_{i=1}^{n}(-1)^{i+j}a_{ij}|\boldsymbol{A}_{-i,-j}|, \quad j = 1,\ldots,n, \end{aligned}$$

i.e. the sum can be computed across the elements of any single row or column. Further, if $\boldsymbol{A}$ and $\boldsymbol{B}$ are square matrices of the same order, then $|\boldsymbol{AB}| = |\boldsymbol{A}|\cdot|\boldsymbol{B}|$.

A matrix with a single row is called a *row vector*, while a matrix with a single column is called a *column vector*, or simply a *vector*. We denote a vector, with a bold and lowercase Roman or Greek letter, such as $\boldsymbol{a}$ or $\boldsymbol{\alpha}$. We use the corresponding lowercase (non-bold) letter to represent an element of a vector, with the location specified as subscript. Thus, a_i and α_i are the ith elements of the vectors $\boldsymbol{a}$ and $\boldsymbol{\alpha}$, respectively. If the order of a vector is $n \times 1$, then we call it a vector of *order* n for brevity. A matrix with a single row and a single column is a *scalar*, which we denote by a lowercase Roman or Greek letter, such as a and α.

We use special notations for a few frequently used matrices. A matrix having all the elements equal to zero is denoted by $\mathbf{0}$, regardless of the order. Therefore, a vector of 0s is also denoted by $\mathbf{0}$. A *nontrivial* vector or matrix is one which is not identically equal to $\mathbf{0}$. The notation bold $\mathbf{1}$ represents a vector of 1s (every element equal to 1). A square, diagonal matrix with all the diagonal elements equal to 1, is called an *identity* matrix, and is denoted by $\boldsymbol{I}$. It can be verified that

$$\boldsymbol{A} + \mathbf{0} = \boldsymbol{A}, \quad \boldsymbol{A}\mathbf{0} = \mathbf{0}\boldsymbol{A} = \mathbf{0}, \quad \text{and} \quad \boldsymbol{AI} = \boldsymbol{IA} = \boldsymbol{A}$$

for any matrix $\boldsymbol{A}$ and for matrices $\mathbf{0}$ and $\boldsymbol{I}$ of appropriate order.

Often a few contiguous rows and/or columns of a matrix are identified as *blocks*. For instance, we can partition $\boldsymbol{I}_{5\times 5}$ into four blocks as

$$\boldsymbol{I}_{5\times 5} = \begin{pmatrix} \boldsymbol{I}_{3\times 3} & \boldsymbol{0}_{3\times 2} \\ \boldsymbol{0}_{2\times 3} & \boldsymbol{I}_{2\times 2} \end{pmatrix}.$$

The blocks of a matrix can sometimes be handled as single elements. For instance, it can be easily verified that

$$(\boldsymbol{A}_{m\times n_1}\ \boldsymbol{B}_{m\times n_2}\ \boldsymbol{C}_{m\times n_3}) \begin{pmatrix} \boldsymbol{u}_{n_1\times 1} \\ \boldsymbol{v}_{n_2\times 1} \\ \boldsymbol{w}_{n_3\times 1} \end{pmatrix} = \boldsymbol{A}\boldsymbol{u} + \boldsymbol{B}\boldsymbol{v} + \boldsymbol{C}\boldsymbol{w}.$$

A set of vectors $\{\boldsymbol{v}_1, \ldots, \boldsymbol{v}_k\}$ is called *linearly dependent* if there is a set of real numbers $\{a_1, \ldots, a_k\}$, not all zero, such that $\sum_{i=1}^k a_i \boldsymbol{v}_i = \boldsymbol{0}$. If a set of vectors is not linearly dependent, it is called *linearly independent*. Thus, all the columns of a matrix $\boldsymbol{A}$ are linearly independent if there is no nontrivial vector $\boldsymbol{b}$ such that the linear combination of the columns $\boldsymbol{A}\boldsymbol{b} = \boldsymbol{0}$. All the rows of $\boldsymbol{A}$ are linearly independent if there is no nontrivial vector $\boldsymbol{c}$ such that the linear combination of the rows $\boldsymbol{c}'\boldsymbol{A} = \boldsymbol{0}$.

The *column rank* of a matrix $\boldsymbol{A}$ is the maximum number of linearly independent columns of $\boldsymbol{A}$. Likewise, the *row rank* is the maximum number of its rows that are linearly independent. If the column rank of a matrix $\boldsymbol{A}_{m\times n}$ is equal to n, the matrix is called *full column rank*, and it is called *full row rank* if the row rank equals m. A matrix which is neither full row rank nor full column rank is called *rank-deficient*. An important result of matrix theory is that the row rank of any matrix is equal to its column rank (see e.g. Rao and Bhimasankaram (2000, p. 109) for a proof). This number is called the *rank* of the corresponding matrix. We denote the rank of the matrix $\boldsymbol{A}$ by $\rho(\boldsymbol{A})$. Obviously, $\rho(\boldsymbol{A}) \le \min\{m, n\}$. A square matrix $\boldsymbol{B}_{n\times n}$ is called *full rank* or *nonsingular* if $\rho(\boldsymbol{B}) = n$. If $\rho(\boldsymbol{B}_{n\times n}) < n$, then $\boldsymbol{B}$ is called a *singular* matrix. Thus, a singular matrix is a square matrix which is rank-deficient. A square matrix is singular if and only if its determinant is 0.

For every nonsingular matrix $\boldsymbol{B}$, there is a matrix $\boldsymbol{C}$ such that $\boldsymbol{C}\boldsymbol{B} = \boldsymbol{B}\boldsymbol{C} = \boldsymbol{I}$. For this reason, the matrix $\boldsymbol{B}$ is also called an *invertible* matrix, and $\boldsymbol{C}$ is called the *inverse* of $\boldsymbol{B}$, denoted by $\boldsymbol{B}^{-1}$. If $\boldsymbol{A}$ and $\boldsymbol{B}$ are both nonsingular with the same order, then $(\boldsymbol{A}\boldsymbol{B})^{-1} = \boldsymbol{B}^{-1}\boldsymbol{A}^{-1}$.

Example A.1. (Basic matrix operations) Let us begin with the matrices

$$\boldsymbol{M}_1 = \begin{pmatrix} 1 & 4 & 9 \\ 2 & 5 & 7 \\ 3 & 6 & 8 \end{pmatrix}, \qquad \boldsymbol{M}_2 = \begin{pmatrix} 1 & 4 \\ 2 & 5 \\ 3 & 6 \end{pmatrix}, \qquad \boldsymbol{M}_3 = \begin{pmatrix} 6 & 3 \\ 5 & 2 \\ 4 & 1 \end{pmatrix}.$$

Some examples of sum, difference, scalar product and matrix product, obtained from the R commands

```
M1 <- cbind(c(1,2,3),c(4,5,6),c(9,7,8))
M2 <- matrix(1:6, ncol = 2)
M3 <- matrix(6:1, ncol = 2)
M2+M3; M2-M3; 2 * M2; M1 %*% M2
```

are given below.

$$\boldsymbol{M}_2 + \boldsymbol{M}_3 = \begin{pmatrix} 7 & 7 \\ 7 & 7 \\ 7 & 7 \end{pmatrix}, \quad \boldsymbol{M}_2 - \boldsymbol{M}_3 = \begin{pmatrix} -5 & 1 \\ -3 & 3 \\ -1 & 5 \end{pmatrix},$$

$$2\boldsymbol{M}_2 = \begin{pmatrix} 2 & 8 \\ 4 & 10 \\ 6 & 12 \end{pmatrix}, \quad \boldsymbol{M}_1\boldsymbol{M}_2 = \begin{pmatrix} 36 & 78 \\ 33 & 75 \\ 39 & 90 \end{pmatrix}.$$

The following code gives computations of an identity matrix of a specified order and the trace, transpose and rank of a given matrix.

```
M4 <- diag(1,3); M4                    # identity matrix of order 3x3
library(lmreg)
tr(M1)                                 # trace of M1
det(M1)                                # determinant of M1
t(M2)                                  # transpose of M2
qr(M2+M3)$rank                         # rank of M2+M3
```

The above lines of code produce the computed values

$$\boldsymbol{M}_4 = \begin{pmatrix} 1 & 0 & 0 \\ 0 & 1 & 0 \\ 0 & 0 & 1 \end{pmatrix}, \ \text{tr}(\boldsymbol{M}_1) = 14, \ |\boldsymbol{M}_1| = -9, \ \boldsymbol{M}_2' = \begin{pmatrix} 1 & 2 & 3 \\ 4 & 5 & 6 \end{pmatrix}, \ \rho(\boldsymbol{M}_2 + \boldsymbol{M}_3) = 1.$$

The R command `qr(M1)$rank` produces the value 3, which indicates that $\boldsymbol{M}_1$ is nonsingular and therefore invertible. The inverse of $\boldsymbol{M}_1$, obtained through the command `solve(M1)`, is

$$\boldsymbol{M}_1^{-1} = \begin{pmatrix} \frac{2}{9} & -\frac{22}{9} & \frac{17}{9} \\ -\frac{5}{9} & \frac{19}{9} & -\frac{11}{9} \\ \frac{3}{9} & -\frac{6}{9} & \frac{3}{9} \end{pmatrix}.$$

All these results may be verified through manual computation. □

There can be a practical difficulty in the determination of the rank of a matrix, which is linked to linear dependence of rows or columns. A computer's ability to determine whether a linear combination of vectors is indeed zero is limited by various factors such as the machine precision and the method of computation.[1]

The *inner product* of two vectors $\boldsymbol{a}$ and $\boldsymbol{b}$, having the same order n, is defined as the matrix product $\boldsymbol{a}'\boldsymbol{b} = \sum_{i=1}^{n} a_i b_i$. This happens to be a scalar, and is identical to $\boldsymbol{b}'\boldsymbol{a}$. We define the *norm* of a vector $\boldsymbol{a}$ as $\|\boldsymbol{a}\| = (\boldsymbol{a}'\boldsymbol{a})^{1/2}$. If $\|\boldsymbol{a}\| = 1$, then $\boldsymbol{a}$ is called a vector with *unit norm*, or simply a *unit vector*.

A useful reorganization of a matrix $\boldsymbol{A}$ is the vector formed by stacking its columns consecutively. We denote this vector by $\mathrm{vec}(\boldsymbol{A})$. It is easy to see that $\mathrm{tr}(\boldsymbol{AB}) = \mathrm{vec}(\boldsymbol{A}')'\mathrm{vec}(\boldsymbol{B})$. The number $\|\mathrm{vec}(\boldsymbol{A})\|$ is called the Frobenius norm of the matrix $\boldsymbol{A}$, and is denoted by $\|\boldsymbol{A}\|_F$. The sum of squares of all the elements of the matrix $\boldsymbol{A}$ is $\|\boldsymbol{A}\|_F^2$. The Frobenius norm is also referred to as the 'Euclidean norm' in statistical literature. In the special case of a vector $\boldsymbol{a}$, $\|\boldsymbol{a}\|_F = \|\boldsymbol{a}\|$.

The *Kronecker product* of two matrices $\boldsymbol{A}_{m\times n}$ and $\boldsymbol{B}_{p\times q}$, denoted by

$$\boldsymbol{A} \otimes \boldsymbol{B} = ((a_{ij}\boldsymbol{B})),$$

is a partitioned $mp \times nq$ matrix with $a_{ij}\boldsymbol{B}$ as its (i,j)th block.

The Kronecker product is found to be very useful in the manipulation of matrices with special block structure. It follows from the definition of the Kronecker product that

(a) $(\boldsymbol{A}_1 + \boldsymbol{A}_2) \otimes \boldsymbol{B} = \boldsymbol{A}_1 \otimes \boldsymbol{B} + \boldsymbol{A}_2 \otimes \boldsymbol{B}$;
(b) $\boldsymbol{A} \otimes (\boldsymbol{B}_1 + \boldsymbol{B}_2) = \boldsymbol{A} \otimes \boldsymbol{B}_1 + \boldsymbol{A} \otimes \boldsymbol{B}_2$;
(c) $(\boldsymbol{A}_1\boldsymbol{A}_2) \otimes (\boldsymbol{B}_1\boldsymbol{B}_2) = (\boldsymbol{A}_1 \otimes \boldsymbol{B}_1)(\boldsymbol{A}_2 \otimes \boldsymbol{B}_2)$;
(d) $(\boldsymbol{A} \otimes \boldsymbol{B})' = \boldsymbol{A}' \otimes \boldsymbol{B}'$;
(e) $\boldsymbol{A}_{m\times n}\boldsymbol{b} = (\boldsymbol{b}' \otimes \boldsymbol{I}_{m\times m})\mathrm{vec}(\boldsymbol{A})$.

Example A.2. (Basic matrix operations, continued) We now provide an R code for computing the long vector form, the Frobenius norm and the Kronecker product of some matrices defined in Example A.1.

```
as.vector(M2)                                  # vec of M2
library(lmreg)
frob(M2)                                       # Frobenius norm of M2
kronecker(M1, M2)                  # Kronecker product of M1 with M2
```

[1]The computation in R shown in the above example is based on a particular implementation of QR decomposition of matrices (Rao and Bhimasankaram, 2000), where one can choose to specify a threshold for deciding how small a number should be regarded as zero.

The function `frob` is also readily available from the R package `lmreg`. The quantities computed through the above lines of code are

$$\mathrm{vec}(\boldsymbol{M}_2) = \begin{pmatrix} 1 \\ 2 \\ 3 \\ 4 \\ 5 \\ 6 \end{pmatrix}, \qquad \boldsymbol{M}_1 \otimes \boldsymbol{M}_2 = \left(\begin{array}{cc|cc|cc} 1 & 4 & 4 & 16 & 9 & 36 \\ 2 & 5 & 8 & 20 & 18 & 45 \\ 3 & 6 & 12 & 24 & 27 & 54 \\ \hline 2 & 8 & 5 & 20 & 7 & 28 \\ 4 & 10 & 10 & 25 & 14 & 35 \\ 6 & 12 & 15 & 30 & 21 & 42 \\ \hline 3 & 12 & 6 & 24 & 8 & 32 \\ 6 & 15 & 12 & 30 & 16 & 40 \\ 9 & 18 & 18 & 36 & 24 & 48 \end{array}\right).$$

$$\|\boldsymbol{M}_2\|_F = 9.539,$$

□

For a vector $\boldsymbol{v}_{n\times 1}$ and a matrix $\boldsymbol{A}_{n\times n}$, the scalar quantity

$$\boldsymbol{v}'\boldsymbol{A}\boldsymbol{v} = \sum_{i=1}^{n}\sum_{j=1}^{n} a_{ij}v_i v_j$$

is called a *quadratic form* in $\boldsymbol{v}$. Note that $\boldsymbol{v}'\boldsymbol{A}\boldsymbol{v} = \boldsymbol{v}'(\frac{1}{2}(\boldsymbol{A}+\boldsymbol{A}'))\boldsymbol{v}$. Properties of the quadratic form $\boldsymbol{v}'\boldsymbol{A}\boldsymbol{v}$ can be studied after assuming $\boldsymbol{A}$ to be symmetric, without loss of generality. (This is because of the fact that even if $\boldsymbol{A}$ is asymmetric, $\boldsymbol{v}'\boldsymbol{A}\boldsymbol{v}$ can be written as $\boldsymbol{v}'(\frac{1}{2}(\boldsymbol{A}+\boldsymbol{A}'))\boldsymbol{v}$, and $\frac{1}{2}(\boldsymbol{A}+\boldsymbol{A}')$ is a symmetric matrix.) The quadratic form $\boldsymbol{v}'\boldsymbol{A}\boldsymbol{v}$ is characterized by the symmetric matrix $\boldsymbol{A}$, which is called the matrix of the quadratic form. Such a matrix is called

(a) *positive definite* if $\boldsymbol{v}'\boldsymbol{A}\boldsymbol{v} > 0$ for all $\boldsymbol{v} \neq \boldsymbol{0}$,
(b) *negative definite* if $\boldsymbol{v}'\boldsymbol{A}\boldsymbol{v} < 0$ for all $\boldsymbol{v} \neq \boldsymbol{0}$,
(c) *nonnegative definite* if $\boldsymbol{v}'\boldsymbol{A}\boldsymbol{v} \geq 0$ for all $\boldsymbol{v}$,
(d) *positive semidefinite* if $\boldsymbol{v}'\boldsymbol{A}\boldsymbol{v} \geq 0$ for all $\boldsymbol{v}$ and $\boldsymbol{v}'\boldsymbol{A}\boldsymbol{v} = 0$ for some $\boldsymbol{v} \neq \boldsymbol{0}$, and
(e) *indefinite* if $\boldsymbol{v}'\boldsymbol{A}\boldsymbol{v} > 0$ for some $\boldsymbol{v}$ and $\boldsymbol{v}'\boldsymbol{A}\boldsymbol{v} < 0$ for some other $\boldsymbol{v}$.

A positive definite matrix is nonsingular, while a positive semidefinite matrix is singular (see Exercise A.3). Saying that a matrix is nonnegative definite is equivalent to saying that it is either positive definite or positive semidefinite. *Negative definite* and *nonpositive definite* matrices can be defined likewise.

Example A.3. Suppose

$$\boldsymbol{A} = \begin{pmatrix} 21 & -6 & 12 \\ -6 & 12 & -6 \\ 12 & -6 & 21 \end{pmatrix}, \ \boldsymbol{B} = \begin{pmatrix} 12 & 0 & 6 \\ 0 & 6 & -6 \\ 6 & -6 & 9 \end{pmatrix}, \ \boldsymbol{C} = \begin{pmatrix} 11 & 2 & 8 \\ 2 & 2 & -10 \\ 8 & -10 & 5 \end{pmatrix}, \ \boldsymbol{v} = \begin{pmatrix} v_1 \\ v_2 \\ v_3 \end{pmatrix}.$$

It can be verified that the quadratic form $\boldsymbol{v}'\boldsymbol{A}\boldsymbol{v}$ is identical to

$$9(2v_1 + 2v_2 - v_3)^2 + 36(2v_1 - v_2 + 2v_3)^2 + 9(v_1 - 2v_2 - 2v_3)^2,$$

which is nonnegative. For this expression to be zero, one must have

$$\begin{aligned} 2v_1 + 2v_2 - v_3 &= 0, \\ 2v_1 - v_2 + 2v_3 &= 0, \\ v_1 - 2v_2 - 2v_3 &= 0. \end{aligned}$$

The unique solution to these three equations turns out to be $v_1 = v_2 = v_3 = 0$. In other words, the quadratic form $\boldsymbol{v}'\boldsymbol{A}\boldsymbol{v}$ cannot be zero unless $\boldsymbol{v}$ itself is zero. Therefore, the matrix $\boldsymbol{A}$ is positive definite. It follows that the matrix $-\boldsymbol{A}$ is negative definite.

Likewise, the quadratic form $\boldsymbol{v}'\boldsymbol{B}\boldsymbol{v}$ can be written as

$$9(2v_1 + 2v_2 - v_3)^2 + 18(2v_1 - v_2 + 2v_3)^2,$$

which is nonnegative. It is equal to zero when $\boldsymbol{v}$ is any multiple of the vector $(-1 : 2 : 2)'$. Therefore, $\boldsymbol{B}$ is positive semidefinite. Both $\boldsymbol{A}$ and $\boldsymbol{B}$ can be said to be nonnegative definite.

The quadratic form $\boldsymbol{v}'\boldsymbol{C}\boldsymbol{v}$ can be positive or negative, depending on the choice of the vector $\boldsymbol{v}$. Two contrasting examples are $\boldsymbol{v}_1 = (-1 : 2 : 2)'$ and $\boldsymbol{v}_2 = (2 : -1 : 2)'$. As $\boldsymbol{v}_1'\boldsymbol{C}\boldsymbol{v}_1 = -9$ and $\boldsymbol{v}_2'\boldsymbol{C}\boldsymbol{v}_2 = 18$, $\boldsymbol{C}$ is an *indefinite* matrix. □

If $\boldsymbol{A}_{n\times n}$ is a positive definite matrix, then one can define a general inner product between the pair of order-n vectors $\boldsymbol{a}$ and $\boldsymbol{b}$ as $\boldsymbol{a}'\boldsymbol{A}\boldsymbol{b}$. The corresponding generalized norm of $\boldsymbol{a}$ would be $(\boldsymbol{a}'\boldsymbol{A}\boldsymbol{a})^{1/2}$. Since $\boldsymbol{A}$ is a positive definite matrix, $\boldsymbol{a}'\boldsymbol{A}\boldsymbol{a}$ is always positive for $\boldsymbol{a} \neq \boldsymbol{0}$.

A.2 Generalized inverse

If $\boldsymbol{AB} = \boldsymbol{I}$, then $\boldsymbol{B}$ is called a *right-inverse* of $\boldsymbol{A}$, and $\boldsymbol{A}$ is called a *left-inverse* of $\boldsymbol{B}$. We denote a right-inverse of $\boldsymbol{A}$ by $\boldsymbol{A}^{-R}$. It exists only when $\boldsymbol{A}$ is of full row rank. Likewise, we denote a left-inverse of $\boldsymbol{B}$, which exists only when $\boldsymbol{B}$ is of full column rank, by $\boldsymbol{B}^{-L}$. Even when a right-inverse or a left-inverse exists, it may not be unique. For a rectangular matrix

$A_{m\times n}$, the rank condition indicates that there cannot be a right-inverse when $m > n$, and there cannot be a left-inverse when $m < n$. As a matter of fact, both the inverses of a matrix would exist if and only if it is square and full rank. In such a case, $\boldsymbol{A}^{-L}$ and $\boldsymbol{A}^{-R}$ happen to be unique and equal to each other (this follows from Theorem 2.1.1 of Rao and Mitra, 1971). This special matrix is none other than the *inverse* of the matrix $\boldsymbol{A}$. By definition, the inverse exists and is unique if and only if $\boldsymbol{A}$ is nonsingular, and $\boldsymbol{A}\boldsymbol{A}^{-1} = \boldsymbol{A}^{-1}\boldsymbol{A} = \boldsymbol{I}$. It is easy to see that for a nonsingular matrix $\boldsymbol{A}$, $|\boldsymbol{A}^{-1}| = 1/|\boldsymbol{A}|$.

A matrix $\boldsymbol{B}$ is called a *generalized inverse* or *g-inverse* of $\boldsymbol{A}$ if $\boldsymbol{ABA} = \boldsymbol{A}$. A g-inverse of $\boldsymbol{A}$ is denoted by $\boldsymbol{A}^{-}$. Obviously, if $\boldsymbol{A}$ is of the order $m \times n$, then $\boldsymbol{A}^{-}$ must be of the order $n \times m$. Every matrix has at least one g-inverse. Every symmetric matrix has at least one symmetric g-inverse (see Exercise A.5). If $\boldsymbol{A}$ has a left-inverse then that is easily seen to be a g-inverse of $\boldsymbol{A}$. This holds for a right-inverse too. In general, $\boldsymbol{A}^{-}$ is not uniquely defined. It is unique if and only if $\boldsymbol{A}$ is nonsingular, in which case $\boldsymbol{A}^{-} = \boldsymbol{A}^{-1}$.

Even though the inverses $\boldsymbol{A}^{-}$, $\boldsymbol{A}^{-L}$ and $\boldsymbol{A}^{-R}$ are not uniquely defined in general, we often work with these notations anyway, particularly in those expressions where the specific choice of $\boldsymbol{A}^{-}$, $\boldsymbol{A}^{-L}$ or $\boldsymbol{A}^{-R}$ does not matter.

We have just noted that the matrix $\boldsymbol{A}$ has an inverse if and only if it is square and nonsingular. Every other matrix has a g-inverse that is necessarily nonunique. However, it can be shown that for every matrix $\boldsymbol{A}$ there is a unique matrix $\boldsymbol{B}$ having the properties

(a) $\boldsymbol{ABA} = \boldsymbol{A}$,
(b) $\boldsymbol{BAB} = \boldsymbol{B}$,
(c) $\boldsymbol{AB} = (\boldsymbol{AB})'$,
(d) $\boldsymbol{BA} = (\boldsymbol{BA})'$.

Property (a) indicates that $\boldsymbol{B}$ is a g-inverse of $\boldsymbol{A}$. This special g-inverse is called the *Moore-Penrose inverse* of $\boldsymbol{A}$, and is denoted by $\boldsymbol{A}^{+}$. When $\boldsymbol{A}$ is invertible, $\boldsymbol{A}^{+} = \boldsymbol{A}^{-1}$. When $\boldsymbol{A}$ is a square and diagonal matrix, $\boldsymbol{A}^{+}$ is obtained by replacing the nonzero diagonal elements of $\boldsymbol{A}$ by their respective reciprocals.

Example A.4. Let

$$\boldsymbol{A} = \begin{pmatrix} 2 & 3 \\ 1 & 1 \\ -2 & -1 \end{pmatrix}, \quad \boldsymbol{B} = \begin{pmatrix} -\frac{5}{18} & \frac{1}{9} & -\frac{13}{18} \\ \frac{1}{2} & 0 & \frac{1}{2} \end{pmatrix}, \quad \boldsymbol{C} = \begin{pmatrix} -\frac{8}{9} & \frac{23}{9} & -\frac{1}{9} \\ 1 & -2 & 0 \end{pmatrix}.$$

Then it can be verified that $\boldsymbol{B}$ and $\boldsymbol{C}$ are distinct choices of $\boldsymbol{A}^{-L}$. Likewise, $\boldsymbol{B}'$ and $\boldsymbol{C}'$ are right-inverses of $\boldsymbol{A}'$. While $\boldsymbol{B}$ is the Moore-Penrose inverse of $\boldsymbol{A}$, $\boldsymbol{C}$ is not, since $\boldsymbol{AC}$ is not a symmetric matrix.

The Moore-Penrose inverse of a matrix, which is uniquely defined even when other g-inverses are there, can be computed by using the R function `ginv()`, which is a part of the package `MASS`. □

If $\boldsymbol{A}$ is invertible and $\boldsymbol{A}^{-1} = \boldsymbol{A}'$, then $\boldsymbol{A}$ is called an *orthogonal* matrix. If $\boldsymbol{A}$ has full column rank and $\boldsymbol{A}'$ is a left-inverse of $\boldsymbol{A}$, then $\boldsymbol{A}$ is said to be *semi-orthogonal.* If $\boldsymbol{a}_1, \ldots, \boldsymbol{a}_n$ are the columns of a semi-orthogonal matrix, then $\boldsymbol{a}_i'\boldsymbol{a}_j = 0$ for $i \neq j$, while $\boldsymbol{a}_i'\boldsymbol{a}_i = 1$. A semi-orthogonal matrix happens to be orthogonal if it is square.

The following inversion formulae are useful for small-scale computations.

$$\begin{aligned}
a^+ &= \begin{cases} \frac{1}{a} & \text{if } a \neq 0, \\ 0 & \text{if } a = 0; \end{cases} \\
\boldsymbol{a}^+ &= \begin{cases} (\boldsymbol{a}'\boldsymbol{a})^{-1}\boldsymbol{a}' & \text{if } \|\boldsymbol{a}\| > 0, \\ \boldsymbol{0} & \text{if } \|\boldsymbol{a}\| = 0; \end{cases} \\
\boldsymbol{A}^+ &= \lim_{\delta \to 0} (\boldsymbol{A}'\boldsymbol{A} + \delta^2 \boldsymbol{I})^{-1}\boldsymbol{A}' = \lim_{\delta \to 0} \boldsymbol{A}'(\boldsymbol{A}\boldsymbol{A}' + \delta^2 \boldsymbol{I})^{-1}; \\
(\boldsymbol{A}'\boldsymbol{A})^+ &= \boldsymbol{A}^+(\boldsymbol{A}^+)'.
\end{aligned}$$

The third formula is proved in Albert (1972, p. 19). The other formulae are proved by direct verification. Two other formulae are given in Proposition A.18. See Golub and Van Loan (2013) for numerically stable methods for computing the Moore-Penrose inverse.

Possible choices of the right- and left-inverses, when they exist, are

$$\begin{aligned}
\boldsymbol{A}^{-L} &= (\boldsymbol{A}'\boldsymbol{A})^{-1}\boldsymbol{A}'; \\
\boldsymbol{A}^{-R} &= \boldsymbol{A}'(\boldsymbol{A}\boldsymbol{A}')^{-1}.
\end{aligned}$$

In fact, these choices of left- and right-inverses are Moore-Penrose inverses.

If $\boldsymbol{A}^-$ is a particular g-inverse of $\boldsymbol{A}$, other g-inverses can be expressed as

$$\boldsymbol{A}^- + \boldsymbol{B} - \boldsymbol{A}^-\boldsymbol{A}\boldsymbol{B}\boldsymbol{A}\boldsymbol{A}^-,$$

where $\boldsymbol{B}$ is an arbitrary matrix of appropriate order. This is a characterization of *all* g-inverses of $\boldsymbol{A}$ (see Rao, 1973c, p. 25).

We conclude this section with inversion formulae for matrices with some special structure.

It follows from the definition and properties of the Kronecker product of matrices (see Section A.1) that a generalized inverse of $\boldsymbol{A}\otimes\boldsymbol{B}$ is $\boldsymbol{A}^-\otimes\boldsymbol{B}^-$, where $\boldsymbol{A}^-$ and $\boldsymbol{B}^-$ are *any* g-inverse of $\boldsymbol{A}$ and $\boldsymbol{B}$, respectively.

It can be verified by direct substitution that if $\boldsymbol{A}$, $\boldsymbol{C}$ and $\boldsymbol{A}+\boldsymbol{BCD}$ are nonsingular matrices, then $\boldsymbol{C}^{-1}+\boldsymbol{DA}^{-1}\boldsymbol{B}$ is also nonsingular and

$$(\boldsymbol{A}+\boldsymbol{BCD})^{-1}=\boldsymbol{A}^{-1}-\boldsymbol{A}^{-1}\boldsymbol{B}(\boldsymbol{C}^{-1}+\boldsymbol{DA}^{-1}\boldsymbol{B})^{-1}\boldsymbol{DA}^{-1}. \tag{A.1}$$

Consider the square matrix

$$\boldsymbol{M}=\begin{pmatrix}\boldsymbol{A} & \boldsymbol{B}\\ \boldsymbol{C} & \boldsymbol{D}\end{pmatrix}.$$

If $\boldsymbol{M}$ and $\boldsymbol{A}$ are both nonsingular, then (see Rao and Bhimasankaram, 2000, p. 138)

$$\boldsymbol{M}^{-1}=\begin{pmatrix}\boldsymbol{A}^{-1}+\boldsymbol{A}^{-1}\boldsymbol{BT}^{-1}\boldsymbol{CA}^{-1} & -\boldsymbol{A}^{-1}\boldsymbol{BT}^{-1}\\ -\boldsymbol{T}^{-1}\boldsymbol{CA}^{-1} & \boldsymbol{T}^{-1}\end{pmatrix} \tag{A.2}$$

$$=\begin{pmatrix}\boldsymbol{A}^{-1} & \boldsymbol{0}\\ \boldsymbol{0} & \boldsymbol{0}\end{pmatrix}+\begin{pmatrix}\boldsymbol{A}^{-1}\boldsymbol{B}\\ -\boldsymbol{I}\end{pmatrix}\boldsymbol{T}^{-1}\left(\boldsymbol{CA}^{-1}\ -\boldsymbol{I}\right), \tag{A.3}$$

where $\boldsymbol{T}=\boldsymbol{D}-\boldsymbol{CA}^{-1}\boldsymbol{B}$, which must be a nonsingular matrix (see Exercise A.7). This matrix is called the Schur complement (Zhang, 2005) of the diagonal block $\boldsymbol{D}$ in the matrix $\boldsymbol{M}$, and is found to be useful in many ways for multivariate computations (see, for instance, (2.6) and Proposition 2.25). If the matrix $\boldsymbol{M}$ defined above is a symmetric and nonnegative definite matrix (in which case $\boldsymbol{C}=\boldsymbol{B}'$), then a g-inverse of $\boldsymbol{M}$ is

$$\boldsymbol{M}^-=\begin{pmatrix}\boldsymbol{A}^-+\boldsymbol{A}^-\boldsymbol{BT}^-\boldsymbol{B}'\boldsymbol{A}^- & -\boldsymbol{A}^-\boldsymbol{BT}^-\\ -\boldsymbol{T}^-\boldsymbol{B}'\boldsymbol{A}^- & \boldsymbol{T}^-\end{pmatrix}$$

$$=\begin{pmatrix}\boldsymbol{A}^- & \boldsymbol{0}\\ \boldsymbol{0} & \boldsymbol{0}\end{pmatrix}+\begin{pmatrix}\boldsymbol{A}^-\boldsymbol{B}\\ -\boldsymbol{I}\end{pmatrix}\boldsymbol{T}^-\left(\boldsymbol{B}'\boldsymbol{A}^-\ -\boldsymbol{I}\right), \tag{A.4}$$

where $\boldsymbol{T}=\boldsymbol{D}-\boldsymbol{B}'\boldsymbol{A}^-\boldsymbol{B}$, as can be proved by direct verification (Exercise A.8). The matrix $\boldsymbol{T}$ is a nonnegative definite matrix too (see Exercise A.20).

A.3 Vector space and projection

For our purpose, a *vector space* is a nonempty set $\mathcal{S}$ of vectors of fixed order such that if $\boldsymbol{u}\in\mathcal{S}$ and $\boldsymbol{v}\in\mathcal{S}$, then $a\boldsymbol{u}+b\boldsymbol{v}\in\mathcal{S}$ for any pair of real numbers a and b. If the vectors in $\mathcal{S}$ have order n, then $\mathcal{S}\subseteq\mathbb{R}^n$.

If $\mathcal{S}_1$ and $\mathcal{S}_2$ are two vector spaces containing vectors of the same order, then the intersection $\mathcal{S}_1\cap\mathcal{S}_2$ contains all the vectors that belong to both the spaces. Every vector space contains the vector $\mathbf{0}$. If $\mathcal{S}_1 \cap \mathcal{S}_2 = \{\mathbf{0}\}$, then $\mathcal{S}_1$ and $\mathcal{S}_2$ are said to be *virtually disjoint*. It is easy to see that $\mathcal{S}_1 \cap \mathcal{S}_2$ is itself a vector space. However, the union $\mathcal{S}_1 \cup \mathcal{S}_2$ is not necessarily a vector space. The smallest vector space that contains the set $\mathcal{S}_1 \cup \mathcal{S}_2$ is called the *sum* of the two spaces, and is denoted by $\mathcal{S}_1 + \mathcal{S}_2$. It consists of all the vectors of the form $\boldsymbol{u} + \boldsymbol{v}$ where $\boldsymbol{u} \in \mathcal{S}_1$ and $\boldsymbol{v} \in \mathcal{S}_2$.

A vector $\boldsymbol{u}$ is said to be *orthogonal to* another vector $\boldsymbol{v}$ of the same order if $\boldsymbol{u}'\boldsymbol{v} = 0$. If a vector is orthogonal to *all* the vectors in the vector space $\mathcal{S}$, then it is said to be *orthogonal to* $\mathcal{S}$. If $\mathcal{S}_1$ and $\mathcal{S}_2$ are two vector spaces such that each vector in $\mathcal{S}_1$ is orthogonal to every vector in $\mathcal{S}_2$, then the two spaces are said to be *orthogonal to each other*. Two vector spaces that are orthogonal to each other must be virtually disjoint, but the converse is not true. The sum of two spaces that are orthogonal to each other is called the *direct sum*, for which we use the special symbol '$\oplus$.' Thus, when $\mathcal{S}_1$ and $\mathcal{S}_2$ are orthogonal to each other, $\mathcal{S}_1 + \mathcal{S}_2$ is written as $\mathcal{S}_1 \oplus \mathcal{S}_2$. If $\mathcal{S}_1 \oplus \mathcal{S}_2 = \mathbb{R}^n$ for a suitable integer n, then $\mathcal{S}_1$ and $\mathcal{S}_2$ are called *orthogonal complements* of each other. We then write $\mathcal{S}_1 = \mathcal{S}_2^\perp$ and $\mathcal{S}_2 = \mathcal{S}_1^\perp$. Clearly, $(\mathcal{S}^\perp)^\perp = \mathcal{S}$.

A set of vectors $\{\boldsymbol{u}_1, \ldots, \boldsymbol{u}_k\}$ is called a *basis* of the vector space $\mathcal{S}$ if (a) $\boldsymbol{u}_i \in \mathcal{S}$ for $i = 1, \ldots, k$, (b) the set $\{\boldsymbol{u}_1, \ldots, \boldsymbol{u}_k\}$ is linearly independent and (c) every member of $\mathcal{S}$ is a linear combination of $\boldsymbol{u}_1, \ldots, \boldsymbol{u}_k$. Every vector space has a basis, which is in general not unique. However, the number of vectors in any two bases of $\mathcal{S}$ is the same (see Exercise A.9). Thus, the number of basis vectors is a uniquely defined attribute of any given vector space. This number is called the *dimension* of the vector space. The dimension of the vector space $\mathcal{S}$ is denoted by $\dim(\mathcal{S})$. Two different vector spaces may have the same dimension. If $\mathcal{S}$ consists of vectors of order n, then $\dim(\mathcal{S}) \le n$ (see Exercise A.11).

Example A.5. Let

$$\boldsymbol{u}_1 = \begin{pmatrix}1\\0\\0\end{pmatrix}, \quad \boldsymbol{u}_2 = \begin{pmatrix}1\\1\\0\end{pmatrix}, \quad \boldsymbol{u}_3 = \begin{pmatrix}0\\1\\0\end{pmatrix}, \quad \boldsymbol{u}_4 = \begin{pmatrix}0\\0\\1\end{pmatrix}.$$

Define

$$\begin{aligned}
\mathcal{S}_1 &= \{\boldsymbol{u} : \boldsymbol{u} = a\boldsymbol{u}_1 + b\boldsymbol{u}_2 \text{ for any real } a \text{ and } b\},\\
\mathcal{S}_2 &= \{\boldsymbol{u} : \boldsymbol{u} = a\boldsymbol{u}_1 + b\boldsymbol{u}_4 \text{ for any real } a \text{ and } b\},\\
\mathcal{S}_3 &= \{\boldsymbol{u} : \boldsymbol{u} = a\boldsymbol{u}_4 \text{ for any real } a\},\\
\mathcal{S}_4 &= \{\boldsymbol{u} : \boldsymbol{u} = a\boldsymbol{u}_1 \text{ for any real } a\},\\
\mathcal{S}_5 &= \{\boldsymbol{u} : \boldsymbol{u} = a\boldsymbol{u}_2 \text{ for any real } a\}.
\end{aligned}$$

It is easy to see that $\mathcal{S}_1, \ldots, \mathcal{S}_5$ are vector spaces. A basis of $\mathcal{S}_1$ is $\{\boldsymbol{u}_1, \boldsymbol{u}_2\}$. An alternative basis of $\mathcal{S}_1$ is $\{\boldsymbol{u}_1, \boldsymbol{u}_3\}$. The pair of vector spaces $\mathcal{S}_4$ and $\mathcal{S}_5$ constitute an example of virtually disjoint spaces which are not orthogonal to each other. The spaces $\mathcal{S}_1$ and $\mathcal{S}_3$ are orthogonal to each other. In fact, $\mathcal{S}_1 \oplus \mathcal{S}_3 = \mathbb{R}^3$, so that $\mathcal{S}_3 = \mathcal{S}_1^\perp$. The intersection between $\mathcal{S}_1$ and $\mathcal{S}_2$ consists of all the vectors which are scalar multiples of $\boldsymbol{u}_1$, i.e. $\mathcal{S}_1 \cap \mathcal{S}_2 = \mathcal{S}_4$. In this case, $\mathcal{S}_1 \cup \mathcal{S}_2$ is not a vector space. For instance, $\boldsymbol{u}_2 + \boldsymbol{u}_4$ is not a member of $\mathcal{S}_1 \cup \mathcal{S}_2$, even though $\boldsymbol{u}_2$ and $\boldsymbol{u}_4$ are. The sum, $\mathcal{S}_1 + \mathcal{S}_2$ is equal to $\mathbb{R}^3$, which is a vector space. Even so, $\mathcal{S}_1$ and $\mathcal{S}_2$ are not orthogonal, let alone being orthogonal complements of one another. □

Note that a set of pairwise orthogonal vectors are linearly independent, but the converse does not hold. If the vectors in a basis set are orthogonal to each other, this special basis set is called an *orthogonal basis*. If in addition, the vectors have unit norm, then the basis is called an *orthonormal basis*. For instance, in Example A.5, $\{\boldsymbol{u}_1, \boldsymbol{u}_3\}$ is an orthonormal basis for $\mathcal{S}_1$. Given any basis set, one can always construct an orthogonal or orthonormal basis out of it, such that the new basis spans the same vector space. Gram-Schmidt orthogonalization (see Golub and Van Loan, 2013) is a sequential method for such a conversion.

A few important properties of vector spaces are given below.

Proposition A.6. Suppose $\mathcal{S}_1$ and $\mathcal{S}_2$ are two vector spaces.

(a) $\dim(\mathcal{S}_1 \cap \mathcal{S}_2) + \dim(\mathcal{S}_1 + \mathcal{S}_2) = \dim(\mathcal{S}_1) + \dim(\mathcal{S}_2)$.
(b) $(\mathcal{S}_1 + \mathcal{S}_2)^\perp = \mathcal{S}_1^\perp \cap \mathcal{S}_2^\perp$.
(c) If $\mathcal{S}_1 \subseteq \mathcal{S}_2$ and $\dim(\mathcal{S}_1) = \dim(\mathcal{S}_2)$, then $\mathcal{S}_1 = \mathcal{S}_2$.

Proof. See Exercise A.10. □

Note that part (b) of the above proposition also implies that $(\mathcal{S}_1 \cap \mathcal{S}_2)^\perp = \mathcal{S}_1^\perp + \mathcal{S}_2^\perp$.

For any vector space $\mathcal{S}$ containing vectors of order n, we have $\mathcal{S} \oplus \mathcal{S}^\perp = \mathbb{R}^n$. Hence, every vector $\boldsymbol{v}$ of order n can be decomposed as

$$\boldsymbol{v} = \boldsymbol{v}_1 + \boldsymbol{v}_2,$$

where $\boldsymbol{v}_1 \in \mathcal{S}$ and $\boldsymbol{v}_2 \in \mathcal{S}^\perp$. As the two parts belong to mutually orthogonal spaces, they are orthogonal to each other. This is called an *orthogonal decomposition* of the vector $\boldsymbol{v}$. The vector $\boldsymbol{v}_1$ is called the *projection* of $\boldsymbol{v}$ on $\mathcal{S}$. The projection of a vector on a vector space is uniquely defined (see Exercise A.12). See Section 11.4.3 for another kind of projection called oblique projection.

A matrix $\boldsymbol{P}$ is called a *projection matrix* for the vector space $\mathcal{S}$ if $\boldsymbol{Pv} = \boldsymbol{v}$ for all $\boldsymbol{v} \in \mathcal{S}$ and $\boldsymbol{Pv} \in \mathcal{S}$ for all $\boldsymbol{v}$ of appropriate order. In such a case, $\boldsymbol{Pv}$ is the projection of the vector $\boldsymbol{v}$ on $\mathcal{S}$. Since $\boldsymbol{PPv} = \boldsymbol{Pv}$ for any $\boldsymbol{v}$, the matrix $\boldsymbol{P}$ satisfies the property $\boldsymbol{P}^2 = \boldsymbol{P}$. Square matrices having this property are called *idempotent* matrices. Every projection matrix is necessarily an idempotent matrix. If $\boldsymbol{P}$ is an idempotent matrix, it is easy to see that $\boldsymbol{I} - \boldsymbol{P}$ is also idempotent.

If $\boldsymbol{P}$ is a projection matrix of the vector space $\mathcal{S}$ such that $\boldsymbol{I} - \boldsymbol{P}$ is a projection matrix of $\mathcal{S}^\perp$, then $\boldsymbol{P}$ is called the *orthogonal projection matrix* of $\mathcal{S}$. Every vector space has a unique *orthogonal* projection matrix, although it may have other projection matrices (see Exercise A.13). We denote the orthogonal projection matrix of $\mathcal{S}$ by $\boldsymbol{P}_{\mathcal{S}}$. An orthogonal projection matrix is not only idempotent but also symmetric. In fact, every symmetric and idempotent matrix is the orthogonal projection matrix of some vector space (see Exercise A.14).

Example A.7. Consider the vector space $\mathcal{S}_1$ of Example A.5, and the matrices

$$\boldsymbol{P}_1 = \begin{pmatrix} 1 & 0 & 0 \\ 0 & 1 & 0 \\ 0 & 0 & 0 \end{pmatrix} \quad \text{and} \quad \boldsymbol{P}_2 = \begin{pmatrix} 1 & 0 & 1 \\ 0 & 1 & 1 \\ 0 & 0 & 0 \end{pmatrix}.$$

Notice that $\boldsymbol{P}_i\boldsymbol{u}_j = \boldsymbol{u}_j$ for $i = 1, 2$, $j = 1, 2$. Therefore, $\boldsymbol{P}_i\boldsymbol{v} = \boldsymbol{v}$ for any $\boldsymbol{v} \in \mathcal{S}_1$ and $i = 1, 2$. Further, $\boldsymbol{P}_i = (\boldsymbol{u}_1 : \boldsymbol{u}_2)\boldsymbol{T}_i$, $i = 1, 2$, where

$$\boldsymbol{T}_1 = \begin{pmatrix} 1 & -1 & 0 \\ 0 & 1 & 0 \end{pmatrix}, \quad \boldsymbol{T}_2 = \begin{pmatrix} 1 & -1 & 0 \\ 0 & 1 & 1 \end{pmatrix}.$$

Therefore, for any $\boldsymbol{v}$, $\boldsymbol{P}_i\boldsymbol{v} = (\boldsymbol{u}_1 : \boldsymbol{u}_2)(\boldsymbol{T}_i\boldsymbol{v})$. The latter is a linear combination of $\boldsymbol{u}_1$ and $\boldsymbol{u}_2$ and hence is in $\mathcal{S}_1$. Thus, $\boldsymbol{P}_1$ and $\boldsymbol{P}_2$ are both projection matrices of $\mathcal{S}_1$. It can be verified that both are idempotent matrices.

Notice that $\boldsymbol{u}_4 \in \mathcal{S}_3 = \mathcal{S}_1^\perp$. Further, $(\boldsymbol{I} - \boldsymbol{P}_1)\boldsymbol{u}_4 = \boldsymbol{u}_4$, but $(\boldsymbol{I} - \boldsymbol{P}_2)\boldsymbol{u}_4 \neq \boldsymbol{u}_4$. Also, $(\boldsymbol{I} - \boldsymbol{P}_1)\boldsymbol{v}$ is in $\mathcal{S}_3$ for all $\boldsymbol{v}$. Therefore, $\boldsymbol{P}_1$ is the orthogonal projection matrix for $\mathcal{S}_1$, while $\boldsymbol{P}_2$ is not. □

Proposition A.8. *If the vectors $\boldsymbol{u}_1, \ldots, \boldsymbol{u}_k$ constitute an orthonormal basis of a vector space $\mathcal{S}$, then $\boldsymbol{P}_{\mathcal{S}} = \sum_{i=1}^k \boldsymbol{u}_i\boldsymbol{u}_i'$.*

Proof. Let $\boldsymbol{P} = \sum_{i=1}^{k} \boldsymbol{u}_i\boldsymbol{u}_i'$. Since any vector $\boldsymbol{v}$ in $\mathcal{S}$ is of the form $\sum_{i=1}^{k} \alpha_i \boldsymbol{u}_i$, it follows that

$$\boldsymbol{P}\boldsymbol{v} = \sum_{i=1}^{k}\sum_{j=1}^{k} \boldsymbol{u}_i\boldsymbol{u}_i'\boldsymbol{u}_j\alpha_j = \sum_{i=1}^{k} \alpha_i\boldsymbol{u}_i = \boldsymbol{v}.$$

One the other hand, for a general vector $\boldsymbol{v}$, $\boldsymbol{P}\boldsymbol{v} = \sum_{i=1}^{k}\sum_{j=1}^{k}(\boldsymbol{u}_i'\boldsymbol{v})\boldsymbol{u}_i$, which is evidently in $\mathcal{S}$. Therefore, $\boldsymbol{P}$ is indeed a projection matrix for $\mathcal{S}$.

We now have to show that $\boldsymbol{I} - \boldsymbol{P}$ is a projection matrix of $\mathcal{S}^\perp$. Let $\boldsymbol{v} \in \mathcal{S}^\perp$, so that $\boldsymbol{v}'\boldsymbol{u}_j = 0$ for $j = 1, \ldots, k$. Then

$$(\boldsymbol{I} - \boldsymbol{P})\boldsymbol{v} = \boldsymbol{v} - \sum_{j=1}^{k} \boldsymbol{u}_j(\boldsymbol{u}_j'\boldsymbol{v}) = \boldsymbol{v}.$$

Since $\boldsymbol{u}_j'\boldsymbol{P} = \boldsymbol{u}_j'$, we have for any vector $\boldsymbol{v}$ of appropriate order,

$$\boldsymbol{u}_j'(\boldsymbol{I} - \boldsymbol{P})\boldsymbol{v} = 0, \qquad j = 1, \ldots, k.$$

Therefore, $(\boldsymbol{I} - \boldsymbol{P})\boldsymbol{v}$ is orthogonal to $\mathcal{S}$, and is indeed a member of $\mathcal{S}^\perp$. Combining these results, and using the fact that the orthogonal projection matrix of a vector space is unique (see Exercise A.13), we have $\boldsymbol{P}_{\mathcal{S}} = \boldsymbol{P}$. □

A.4 Column space

Let the matrix $\boldsymbol{A}$ have the columns $\boldsymbol{a}_1, \boldsymbol{a}_2, \ldots, \boldsymbol{a}_n$. A linear combination of these columns may be written as

$$\boldsymbol{A}\boldsymbol{x} = x_1\boldsymbol{a}_1 + x_2\boldsymbol{a}_2 + \cdots + x_n\boldsymbol{a}_n,$$

$\boldsymbol{x}$ being a vector with elements $x_1, x_2, \ldots, x_n$. The set of all vectors, which may be expressed as such a linear combination, is a vector space and is called the *column space* or *range space* of $\boldsymbol{A}$. We denote it by $\mathcal{C}(\boldsymbol{A})$. The vector space $\mathcal{C}(\boldsymbol{A})$ is said to be *spanned by* the columns of $\boldsymbol{A}$. The statement $\boldsymbol{u} \in \mathcal{C}(\boldsymbol{A})$ is equivalent to saying that the vector $\boldsymbol{u}$ is of the form $\boldsymbol{A}\boldsymbol{x}$, where $\boldsymbol{x}$ is another vector. The *row space* of $\boldsymbol{A}$ is defined as $\mathcal{C}(\boldsymbol{A}')$. The *null space* of a matrix $\boldsymbol{A}$ is the space of vectors $\boldsymbol{u}$ that are orthogonal to the columns of $\boldsymbol{A}$, which may described as $\mathcal{C}(\boldsymbol{A}')^\perp$ as per the notations already used.

Example A.9. For the matrix $\boldsymbol{A}$ of Example A.4, we show below how the function `basis` of the R package `lmreg` may be used to obtain a semi-orthogonal matrix with columns forming an orthonormal basis of $\mathcal{C}(\boldsymbol{A})$.

```
library(lmreg)
A <- cbind(c(2,1,-2),c(3,1,-1)); basis(A)
```

This produces the basis vectors $(-0.817646 : -0.323475 : 0.476255)'$ and $(0.525261 : -0.080467 : 0.847128)'$. The column space of the matrix $\boldsymbol{B}'$ of Example A.4 is found to have the same set of basis vectors, obtained through the additional code

```
B = rbind(c(-5/18,1/9,-13/18),c(1/2,0,1/2)); basis(t(B)).
```
□

We now list a few useful results.

Proposition A.10.

(a) $\mathcal{C}(\boldsymbol{A} : \boldsymbol{B}) = \mathcal{C}(\boldsymbol{A}) + \mathcal{C}(\boldsymbol{B})$.
(b) $\mathcal{C}(\boldsymbol{AB}) \subseteq \mathcal{C}(\boldsymbol{A})$.
(c) $\mathcal{C}(\boldsymbol{AA}') = \mathcal{C}(\boldsymbol{A})$. *Consequently,* $\rho(\boldsymbol{AA}') = \rho(\boldsymbol{A})$.
(d) $\mathcal{C}(\boldsymbol{C}) \subseteq \mathcal{C}(\boldsymbol{A})$ *only if* $\boldsymbol{C}$ *is of the form* $\boldsymbol{AB}$ *for a suitable matrix* $\boldsymbol{B}$.
(e) If $\mathcal{C}(\boldsymbol{B}) \subseteq \mathcal{C}(\boldsymbol{A})$, *then* $\boldsymbol{AA}^-\boldsymbol{B} = \boldsymbol{B}$, *irrespective of the choice of the g-inverse. Similarly,* $\mathcal{C}(\boldsymbol{B}') \subseteq \mathcal{C}(\boldsymbol{A}')$ *implies* $\boldsymbol{BA}^-\boldsymbol{A} = \boldsymbol{B}$.
(f) $\mathcal{C}(\boldsymbol{B}') \subseteq \mathcal{C}(\boldsymbol{A}')$ *and* $\mathcal{C}(\boldsymbol{C}) \subseteq \mathcal{C}(\boldsymbol{A})$ *if and only if* $\boldsymbol{BA}^-\boldsymbol{C}$ *is invariant under the choice of the g-inverse.*
(g) $\boldsymbol{B}'\boldsymbol{A} = \boldsymbol{0}$ *if and only if* $\mathcal{C}(\boldsymbol{B}) \subseteq \mathcal{C}(\boldsymbol{A})^\perp$.
(h) $dim(\mathcal{C}(\boldsymbol{A})) = \rho(\boldsymbol{A})$.
(i) If $\boldsymbol{A}$ *has* n *rows, then* $dim(\mathcal{C}(\boldsymbol{A})^\perp) = n - \rho(\boldsymbol{A})$.
(j) If $\mathcal{C}(\boldsymbol{A}) \subseteq \mathcal{C}(\boldsymbol{B})$ *and* $\rho(\boldsymbol{A}) = \rho(\boldsymbol{B})$, *then* $\mathcal{C}(\boldsymbol{A}) = \mathcal{C}(\boldsymbol{B})$. *In particular,* $\mathcal{C}(\boldsymbol{I}_{n\times n}) = \mathbb{R}^n$.
(k) $\rho(\boldsymbol{AB}) \le \min\{\rho(\boldsymbol{A}), \rho(\boldsymbol{B})\}$.
(l) $\rho(\boldsymbol{A} + \boldsymbol{B}) \le \rho(\boldsymbol{A}) + \rho(\boldsymbol{B})$.

Proof. Part (a) follows easily from definition.

Every vector belonging to $\mathcal{C}(\boldsymbol{AB})$ is of the form $\boldsymbol{ABl}$ or $\boldsymbol{A}(\boldsymbol{Bl})$, which is clearly in $\mathcal{C}(\boldsymbol{A})$. This proves part (b).

To prove that $\mathcal{C}(\boldsymbol{AA}') = \mathcal{C}(\boldsymbol{A})$, note that

$$\boldsymbol{l} \in \mathcal{C}(\boldsymbol{AA}')^\perp \Rightarrow \boldsymbol{l}'\boldsymbol{AA}' = \boldsymbol{0} \quad \Rightarrow \quad \boldsymbol{l}'\boldsymbol{AA}'\boldsymbol{l} = 0 \quad \Rightarrow \boldsymbol{A}'\boldsymbol{l} = \boldsymbol{0} \quad \Rightarrow \quad \boldsymbol{l} \in \mathcal{C}(\boldsymbol{A})^\perp.$$

Thus $\mathcal{C}(\boldsymbol{AA}')^\perp \subseteq \mathcal{C}(\boldsymbol{A})^\perp$, and consequently, $\mathcal{C}(\boldsymbol{A}) \subseteq \mathcal{C}(\boldsymbol{AA}')$. The reverse inclusion follows from part (b). By equating the dimensions (see part (h), proved below), we have $\rho(\boldsymbol{AA}') = \rho(\boldsymbol{A})$.

To prove part (d), let $\boldsymbol{C} = (\boldsymbol{c}_1 : \cdots : \boldsymbol{c}_k)$. Since $\mathcal{C}(\boldsymbol{C}) \subseteq \mathcal{C}(\boldsymbol{A})$, $\boldsymbol{c}_j \in \mathcal{C}(\boldsymbol{A})$ for $j = 1, \ldots, k$. Therefore, for each j between 1 and k, there is a vector $\boldsymbol{b}_j$ such that $\boldsymbol{c}_j = \boldsymbol{Ab}_j$. It follows that $\boldsymbol{C} = \boldsymbol{AB}$ where $\boldsymbol{B} = (\boldsymbol{b}_1 : \cdots : \boldsymbol{b}_k)$.

If $\mathcal{C}(\boldsymbol{B}) \subseteq \mathcal{C}(\boldsymbol{A})$, then there is a matrix $\boldsymbol{T}$ such that $\boldsymbol{B} = \boldsymbol{AT}$. Hence, $\boldsymbol{AA}^-\boldsymbol{B} = \boldsymbol{AA}^-\boldsymbol{AT} = \boldsymbol{AT} = \boldsymbol{B}$. The other statement of part (e) is proved in a similar manner.

In order to prove part (f), let $\mathcal{C}(\boldsymbol{B}') \subseteq \mathcal{C}(\boldsymbol{A}')$ and $\mathcal{C}(\boldsymbol{C}) \subseteq \mathcal{C}(\boldsymbol{A})$. There are matrices $\boldsymbol{T}_1$ and $\boldsymbol{T}_2$ such that $\boldsymbol{B} = \boldsymbol{T}_1\boldsymbol{A}$ and $\boldsymbol{C} = \boldsymbol{A}\boldsymbol{T}_2$. If $\boldsymbol{A}_1^-$ and $\boldsymbol{A}_2^-$ are two g-inverses of $\boldsymbol{A}$, then

$$\boldsymbol{B}\boldsymbol{A}_1^-\boldsymbol{C} - \boldsymbol{B}\boldsymbol{A}_2^-\boldsymbol{C} = \boldsymbol{T}_1(\boldsymbol{A}\boldsymbol{A}_1^-\boldsymbol{A} - \boldsymbol{A}\boldsymbol{A}_2^-\boldsymbol{A})\boldsymbol{T}_2 = \boldsymbol{T}_1(\boldsymbol{A} - \boldsymbol{A})\boldsymbol{T}_2 = \boldsymbol{0}.$$

This proves the invariance of $\boldsymbol{B}\boldsymbol{A}^-\boldsymbol{C}$ under the choice of the g-inverse. In order to prove the converse, consider the g-inverses $\boldsymbol{A}_1^- = \boldsymbol{A}^+$ and $\boldsymbol{A}_2^- = \boldsymbol{A}^+ + \boldsymbol{K} - \boldsymbol{A}^+\boldsymbol{A}\boldsymbol{K}\boldsymbol{A}\boldsymbol{A}^+$, where $\boldsymbol{K}$ is an arbitrary matrix of appropriate dimension. Then the invariance of $\boldsymbol{B}\boldsymbol{A}^-\boldsymbol{C}$ implies

$$\boldsymbol{0} = \boldsymbol{B}\boldsymbol{A}_2^-\boldsymbol{C} - \boldsymbol{B}\boldsymbol{A}_1^-\boldsymbol{C} = \boldsymbol{B}\boldsymbol{K}\boldsymbol{C} - (\boldsymbol{B}\boldsymbol{A}^+\boldsymbol{A})\boldsymbol{K}(\boldsymbol{A}\boldsymbol{A}^+\boldsymbol{C})$$

for all $\boldsymbol{K}$. By choosing $\boldsymbol{K} = \boldsymbol{u}_i\boldsymbol{v}_j'$, where $\boldsymbol{u}_i$ is the ith column of an appropriate identity matrix and $\boldsymbol{v}_j$ is the jth row of another identity matrix, we conclude that

$$(\boldsymbol{B}\boldsymbol{u}_i)(\boldsymbol{v}_j'\boldsymbol{C}) = (\boldsymbol{B}\boldsymbol{A}^+\boldsymbol{A}\boldsymbol{u}_i)(\boldsymbol{v}_j'\boldsymbol{A}\boldsymbol{A}^+\boldsymbol{C}) \qquad \text{for all } i, j.$$

Therefore, $\boldsymbol{B} = \alpha\boldsymbol{B}\boldsymbol{A}^+\boldsymbol{A}$ and $\boldsymbol{C} = \alpha^{-1}\boldsymbol{A}\boldsymbol{A}^+\boldsymbol{C}$ for some $\alpha \neq 0$. (In fact, using the first identity repeatedly, we can show that $\alpha = 1$.) Therefore, $\mathcal{C}(\boldsymbol{B}') \subseteq \mathcal{C}(\boldsymbol{A}')$ and $\mathcal{C}(\boldsymbol{C}) \subseteq \mathcal{C}(\boldsymbol{A})$.

Part (g) is proved by noting that $\boldsymbol{l} \in \mathcal{C}(\boldsymbol{B})$ implies $\boldsymbol{l} = \boldsymbol{B}\boldsymbol{m}$ for some vector $\boldsymbol{m}$, and consequently $\boldsymbol{l}'\boldsymbol{A} = \boldsymbol{m}'\boldsymbol{B}'\boldsymbol{A} = \boldsymbol{0}$ or $\boldsymbol{l} \in \mathcal{C}(\boldsymbol{A})^\perp$.

To prove part (h), let $k = \rho(\boldsymbol{A})$, and $\boldsymbol{a}_1, \ldots, \boldsymbol{a}_k$ be linearly independent columns of $\boldsymbol{A}$. By definition, any column of $\boldsymbol{A}$ outside this list is a linear combination of these columns. Therefore, any vector in $\mathcal{C}(\boldsymbol{A})$ is also a linear combination of these vectors. Hence, these vectors constitute a basis set of $\mathcal{C}(\boldsymbol{A})$, and $\dim(\mathcal{C}(\boldsymbol{A})) = k = \rho(\boldsymbol{A})$.

Part (i) follows from part (h) above and part (a) of Proposition A.6.

Part (j) is a direct consequence of part (g) above and part (c) of Proposition A.6.

Parts (b) and (h) imply that $\rho(\boldsymbol{A}\boldsymbol{B}) \leq \rho(\boldsymbol{A})$ and $\rho(\boldsymbol{A}\boldsymbol{B}) = \rho(\boldsymbol{B}'\boldsymbol{A}') \leq \rho(\boldsymbol{B}') = \rho(\boldsymbol{B})$. Combining these two, we have the result of part (k).

In order to prove part (l), observe that

$$\begin{aligned}\rho(\boldsymbol{A}+\boldsymbol{B}) = \dim(\mathcal{C}(\boldsymbol{A}+\boldsymbol{B})) &\leq \dim(\mathcal{C}(\boldsymbol{A}:\boldsymbol{B})) \\ \leq \dim(\mathcal{C}(\boldsymbol{A})) + \dim(\mathcal{C}(\boldsymbol{B})) &= \rho(\boldsymbol{A}) + \rho(\boldsymbol{B}),\end{aligned}$$

where the second inequality follows part (a) of Proposition A.6. □

It follows from part (h) of proposition A.10 that the dimension of the null space $\mathcal{C}(\boldsymbol{A}')^\perp$ of an $m \times n$ matrix $\boldsymbol{A}$ is $n - \rho(\boldsymbol{A})$.

A few additional results on column spaces will be presented in the next section. We now examine the projection matrices corresponding to a column space.

Proposition A.11. *For any matrix* $\boldsymbol{A}$, *the matrix* $\boldsymbol{A}\boldsymbol{A}^-$ *is a projection matrix for* $\mathcal{C}(\boldsymbol{A})$. *Further, the orthogonal projection matrix for* $\mathcal{C}(\boldsymbol{A})$ *is* $\boldsymbol{P}_{\mathcal{C}(A)} = \boldsymbol{A}(\boldsymbol{A}'\boldsymbol{A})^-\boldsymbol{A}'$.

Proof. For any $\boldsymbol{v}$ of appropriate order, $(\boldsymbol{A}\boldsymbol{A}^-)\boldsymbol{v}$ is obviously in $\mathcal{C}(\boldsymbol{A})$. If $\boldsymbol{v} \in \mathcal{C}(\boldsymbol{A})$, it is of the form $\boldsymbol{A}\boldsymbol{t}$. In such a case, $(\boldsymbol{A}\boldsymbol{A}^-)\boldsymbol{v} = \boldsymbol{A}\boldsymbol{A}^-\boldsymbol{A}\boldsymbol{t} = \boldsymbol{A}\boldsymbol{t} = \boldsymbol{v}$. Therefore, $\boldsymbol{A}\boldsymbol{A}^-$ is a projection matrix for $\mathcal{C}(\boldsymbol{A})$.

Let $\boldsymbol{P} = \boldsymbol{A}(\boldsymbol{A}'\boldsymbol{A})^-\boldsymbol{A}'$. Parts (c) and (e) of Proposition A.10 imply that $\boldsymbol{A}(\boldsymbol{A}'\boldsymbol{A})^-\boldsymbol{A}'\boldsymbol{A} = \boldsymbol{A}$. Thus, $(\boldsymbol{A}'\boldsymbol{A})^-\boldsymbol{A}'$ is a g-inverse of $\boldsymbol{A}$, and consequently $\boldsymbol{P}$ is a projection matrix for $\mathcal{C}(\boldsymbol{A})$. Part (f) of Proposition A.10 ensures that $\boldsymbol{P}$ is defined uniquely, irrespective of the choice of $(\boldsymbol{A}'\boldsymbol{A})^-$ used in its definition.

Now suppose $\boldsymbol{l} \in \mathcal{C}(\boldsymbol{A})^\perp$, so that $\boldsymbol{A}'\boldsymbol{l} = \boldsymbol{0}$. Then $\boldsymbol{P}\boldsymbol{l} = \boldsymbol{0}$ and $(\boldsymbol{I}-\boldsymbol{P})\boldsymbol{l} = \boldsymbol{l}$. Further, for any general $\boldsymbol{l}$, $(\boldsymbol{I}-\boldsymbol{P})\boldsymbol{l} \in \mathcal{C}(\boldsymbol{A})^\perp$ since $\boldsymbol{A}'(\boldsymbol{I}-\boldsymbol{P})\boldsymbol{l} = \boldsymbol{0}$. Therefore, $\boldsymbol{I}-\boldsymbol{P}$ is a projection matrix for $\mathcal{C}(\boldsymbol{A})^\perp$. The conclusion follows. □

We abbreviate $\boldsymbol{P}_{\mathcal{C}(A)}$ by $\boldsymbol{P}_A$. The above proposition implies an explicit form of $\boldsymbol{P}_{\mathcal{C}(A)^\perp}$, which is $\boldsymbol{I} - \boldsymbol{P}_A$. It is easy to see that $\mathcal{C}(\boldsymbol{P}_A) = \mathcal{C}(\boldsymbol{A})$ and $\mathcal{C}(\boldsymbol{I} - \boldsymbol{P}_A) = \mathcal{C}(\boldsymbol{A})^\perp$.

Example A.12. The orthogonal projection matrix for the column space of a given matrix can be computed by the function `projector` of the R package `lmreg`. The same package contains another function, `compbasis`, which returns a semi-orthogonal matrix with columns forming a basis of $\mathcal{C}(M)^\perp$ any given matrix $\boldsymbol{M}$. The following code uses these functions to obtain $\boldsymbol{P}_A$, basis of $\mathcal{C}(\boldsymbol{A})^\perp$ and $\boldsymbol{I} - \boldsymbol{P}_A$, where the matrix $\boldsymbol{A}$ is as in Example A.4.

```
A <- cbind(c(2,1,-2),c(3,1,-1))
library(lmreg)
projector(A)
compbasis(A)
diag(1,dim(A)[1]) - projector(A)
```

The three resulting matrices are

$$\frac{1}{18}\begin{pmatrix} 17 & 4 & 1 \\ 4 & 2 & -4 \\ 1 & -4 & 17 \end{pmatrix}, \quad \begin{pmatrix} -0.235702 \\ 0.942809 \\ 0.235702 \end{pmatrix}, \quad \frac{1}{18}\begin{pmatrix} 1 & -4 & -1 \\ -4 & 16 & 4 \\ -1 & 4 & 1 \end{pmatrix}.$$

One can check whether one column space is a subset of another, using the logical function `is.included` of the R package `lmreg`. We now use this function to compare the column spaces of $\boldsymbol{A}$, $\boldsymbol{I}$ and $\boldsymbol{P}_A$, as follows.

```
I <- diag(1,3)
is.included(A,I); is.included(I,A)
is.included(projector(A),A); is.included(A,projector(A))
```

The conclusion is that among the statements $\mathcal{C}(\boldsymbol{A}) \subseteq \mathcal{C}(\boldsymbol{I})$, $\mathcal{C}(\boldsymbol{I}) \subseteq \mathcal{C}(\boldsymbol{A})$, $\mathcal{C}(\boldsymbol{P}_A) \subseteq \mathcal{C}(\boldsymbol{A})$ and $\mathcal{C}(\boldsymbol{A}) \subseteq \mathcal{C}(\boldsymbol{P}_A)$, only the second one is false. □

The column space of a single non-null vector, $\boldsymbol{u}$, has dimension 1. The corresponding orthogonal projection matrix is $\boldsymbol{P}_u = (\boldsymbol{u}'\boldsymbol{u})^{-1}\boldsymbol{u}\boldsymbol{u}'$. If $\boldsymbol{u}$ has unit norm, then $\boldsymbol{P}_u$ reduces to $\boldsymbol{u}\boldsymbol{u}'$. (This fact can also be seen as a corollary to Proposition A.8.) For a given pair of vectors $\boldsymbol{u}$ and $\boldsymbol{v}$ having the same order, $\boldsymbol{u}'\boldsymbol{v}/\boldsymbol{u}'\boldsymbol{u}$ is the projection of $\boldsymbol{v}$ on $\mathcal{C}(\boldsymbol{u})$. We refer to it as the *component* of $\boldsymbol{v}$ along $\boldsymbol{u}$. An element of a vector is an example of the notion of 'component'. Indeed, if $\boldsymbol{u}_i$ is the vector consisting of zero's except for a 1 in the ith position, then the component of $\boldsymbol{v}$ along $\boldsymbol{u}_i$ is the ith component (or element) of $\boldsymbol{v}$.

Remark A.13. If $\boldsymbol{u}$ and $\boldsymbol{v}$ are two vectors of the same order, it follows from the above discussion that $(\boldsymbol{u}'\boldsymbol{v})^2/(\boldsymbol{u}'\boldsymbol{u}) = \boldsymbol{v}'\boldsymbol{P}_u\boldsymbol{v} \le \boldsymbol{v}'\boldsymbol{v}$. The result

$$(\boldsymbol{u}'\boldsymbol{v})^2 \le \|\boldsymbol{u}\|^2 \cdot \|\boldsymbol{v}\|^2 \tag{A.5}$$

is the well-known *Cauchy-Schwarz inequality.* □

Proposition A.14. *Suppose* $\boldsymbol{A}$ *and* $\boldsymbol{B}$ *are matrices having the same number of rows.*

(a) $\mathcal{C}(\boldsymbol{A}:\boldsymbol{B}) = \mathcal{C}(\boldsymbol{A}) \oplus \mathcal{C}((\boldsymbol{I}-\boldsymbol{P}_A)\boldsymbol{B})$.
(b) $\boldsymbol{P}_{(A:B)} = \boldsymbol{P}_A + \boldsymbol{P}_{(I-P_A)B}$.
(c) $\mathcal{C}(\boldsymbol{A}) \cap \mathcal{C}(\boldsymbol{B}) = \mathcal{C}(\boldsymbol{A}\boldsymbol{A}'(\boldsymbol{A}\boldsymbol{A}'+\boldsymbol{B}\boldsymbol{B}')^-\boldsymbol{B}\boldsymbol{B}')$.

Proof. The spaces $\mathcal{C}(\boldsymbol{A})$ and $\mathcal{C}((\boldsymbol{I}-\boldsymbol{P}_A)\boldsymbol{B})$ are easily seen to be mutually orthogonal. Let $\boldsymbol{l} \in \mathcal{C}(\boldsymbol{A}:\boldsymbol{B})$. Then $\boldsymbol{l}$ can be written as $\boldsymbol{A}\boldsymbol{u}+\boldsymbol{B}\boldsymbol{v}$ for some vectors $\boldsymbol{u}$ and $\boldsymbol{v}$. Therefore,

$$\boldsymbol{l} = \boldsymbol{P}_A(\boldsymbol{A}\boldsymbol{u}+\boldsymbol{B}\boldsymbol{v}) + (\boldsymbol{I}-\boldsymbol{P}_A)(\boldsymbol{A}\boldsymbol{u}+\boldsymbol{B}\boldsymbol{v}) = \boldsymbol{P}_A(\boldsymbol{A}\boldsymbol{u}+\boldsymbol{B}\boldsymbol{v}) + (\boldsymbol{I}-\boldsymbol{P}_A)\boldsymbol{B}\boldsymbol{v}.$$

The first vector, $\boldsymbol{P}_A(\boldsymbol{A}\boldsymbol{u}+\boldsymbol{B}\boldsymbol{v})$ is in $\mathcal{C}(\boldsymbol{A})$, while the second is in $\mathcal{C}((\boldsymbol{I}-\boldsymbol{P}_A)\boldsymbol{B})$. Thus, $\boldsymbol{l} \in \mathcal{C}(\boldsymbol{A}) \oplus \mathcal{C}((\boldsymbol{I}-\boldsymbol{P}_A)\boldsymbol{B})$. Reversing this sequence of arguments, we have $\boldsymbol{l} \in \mathcal{C}(\boldsymbol{A}) \oplus \mathcal{C}((\boldsymbol{I}-\boldsymbol{P}_A)\boldsymbol{B}) \Rightarrow \boldsymbol{l} \in \mathcal{C}(\boldsymbol{A}:\boldsymbol{B})$. The result of part (a) is obtained by combining these two implications.

Part (b) is a direct consequence of part (a) and the fact that

$$P_{\mathcal{S}_1 \oplus \mathcal{S}_2} = P_{\mathcal{S}_1} + P_{\mathcal{S}_2}.$$

whenever $\mathcal{S}_1$ and $\mathcal{S}_2$ are mutually orthogonal vector spaces (see Exercise A.15).

Part (c) follows from the facts $\mathcal{C}(\boldsymbol{A}) = \mathcal{C}(\boldsymbol{A}\boldsymbol{A}')$ and $\mathcal{C}(\boldsymbol{B}) = \mathcal{C}(\boldsymbol{B}\boldsymbol{B}')$ (see part (c) of Proposition A.10) and Exercise A.21. □

Example A.15. Part (a) of Proposition A.14 provides us a way of supplementing the basis of the column space of a matrix to a larger basis of the column space of a column-augmented matrix. This computation is done by the function `supplbasis` of the R package `lmreg`, which takes as input two matrices $\boldsymbol{A}$ and $\boldsymbol{B}$ with equal number of rows and returns a semi-orthogonal matrix with columns that supplement an orthonormal basis of $\mathcal{C}(\boldsymbol{A})$ to form an orthonormal basis of $\mathcal{C}(\boldsymbol{A} : \boldsymbol{B})$. The usage of this function is illustrated through the following code, where $\boldsymbol{A}$ is as in Example A.4 and $\boldsymbol{B}$ is the diagonal matrix with diagonal elements 1, 1 and 0.

```
A <- cbind(c(2,1,-2),c(3,1,-1)); B <- diag(c(1,1,0))
supplbasis(A,B)
```

The resulting basis vector is $(-0.235702 : 0.942809 : 0.235702)'$.

Note that in this case, $\mathcal{C}(\boldsymbol{A} : \boldsymbol{B})$ is the space of all real vectors of order 3, and a basis for $\mathcal{C}(\boldsymbol{A})$ had been obtained in Example A.9. By putting together that basis with the above vector, we have

$$\begin{pmatrix} -.817646 & 0.525261 & -0.235702 \\ -0.323475 & -0.080467 & 0.942809 \\ 0.476255 & 0.847128 & 0.235702 \end{pmatrix},$$

which is an orthogonal matrix with columns spanning the space of all real vectors of order 3.

One can choose a linear combination of the two columns of $\boldsymbol{A}$ such that the last element is 0, which means the vector is in $\mathcal{C}(\boldsymbol{B})$. A particular choice is the vector $(4 : 1 : 0)'$. Scalar multiples of this vector should constitute $\mathcal{C}(A) \cap \mathcal{C}(B)$. For general computation of the basis of the intersection of two column spaces, we can use part (c) of Proposition A.14. This is accomplished by the function `intsectbasis` of the R package `lmreg`. If this function is used for the matrices $\boldsymbol{A}$ and $\boldsymbol{B}$ described above, through the command `intsectbasis(A,B)`, a basis vector of $\mathcal{C}(\boldsymbol{A}) \cap \mathcal{C}(\boldsymbol{B})$ is obtained as $(-0.97014 : -0.24254 : 4.88 \times 10^{-16})'$. This unit vector is close to $\frac{1}{\sqrt{17}}(-4 : -1 : 0)'$, which is a multiple of the vector $(4 : 1 : 0)'$ obtained above through manual calculations. □

A.5 Matrix decompositions

A number of decompositions of matrices are found to be useful for numerical computations as well as for theoretical developments. We mention a few of them here.

Any non-null matrix $\boldsymbol{A}_{m\times n}$ of rank r can be written as $\boldsymbol{B}_{m\times r}\boldsymbol{C}_{r\times n}$, where $\boldsymbol{B}$ has full column rank and $\boldsymbol{C}$ has full row rank. This is called a *rank-factorization.*

Any matrix $\boldsymbol{A}_{m\times n}$ can be written as $\boldsymbol{UDV}'$, where $\boldsymbol{U}_{m\times m}$ and $\boldsymbol{V}_{n\times n}$ are orthogonal matrices and $\boldsymbol{D}_{m\times n}$ is a diagonal matrix with nonnegative diagonal elements. This is called a *singular value decomposition* (SVD) of the matrix $\boldsymbol{A}$. The nonzero diagonal elements of $\boldsymbol{D}$ are referred to as the *singular values* of the matrix $\boldsymbol{A}$. The columns of $\boldsymbol{U}$ and $\boldsymbol{V}$ corresponding to the singular values are called the *left* and *right singular vectors* of $\boldsymbol{A}$, respectively.

It can be seen that $\rho(\boldsymbol{A}) = \rho(\boldsymbol{D})$ (see Exercise A.17). Therefore, the number of nonzero (positive) singular values of a matrix is equal to its rank. The diagonal elements of $\boldsymbol{D}$ can be permuted in any way, provided the columns of $\boldsymbol{U}$ and $\boldsymbol{V}$ are also permuted accordingly. A combination of such permuted versions of $\boldsymbol{D}$, $\boldsymbol{U}$ and $\boldsymbol{V}$ would constitute another SVD of $\boldsymbol{A}$ (see Exercise A.2). If the singular values are arranged so that the positive elements occur in the first few diagonal positions, then we can write $\boldsymbol{A} = \sum_{i=1}^{r} d_i\boldsymbol{u}_i\boldsymbol{v}_i'$, where $r = \rho(\boldsymbol{A})$, $d_1, \ldots, d_r$ are the nonzero singular values, while $\boldsymbol{u}_1, \ldots, \boldsymbol{u}_r$ and $\boldsymbol{v}_1, \ldots, \boldsymbol{v}_r$ are the corresponding left and right singular vectors. This is an alternative form of the SVD. This sum can also be written as $\boldsymbol{U}_1\boldsymbol{D}_1\boldsymbol{V}_1'$, where $\boldsymbol{U}_1 = \{\boldsymbol{u}_1 : \cdots : \boldsymbol{u}_r\}$, $\boldsymbol{V}_1 = \{\boldsymbol{v}_1 : \cdots : \boldsymbol{v}_r\}$ and $\boldsymbol{D}_1$ is a diagonal matrix with d_i in the (i,i)th location, $i = 1, \ldots, r$.

Example A.16. Consider the matrix

$$\boldsymbol{A} = \begin{pmatrix} 4 & 5 & 2 \\ 0 & 3 & 6 \\ 4 & 5 & 2 \\ 0 & 3 & 6 \end{pmatrix}.$$

The rank of $\boldsymbol{A}$ is 2. An SVD of $\boldsymbol{A}$ is $\boldsymbol{UDV}'$, where

$$\boldsymbol{U} = \begin{pmatrix} \frac{1}{2} & \frac{1}{2} & \frac{1}{2} & \frac{1}{2} \\ \frac{1}{2} & -\frac{1}{2} & \frac{1}{2} & -\frac{1}{2} \\ \frac{1}{2} & \frac{1}{2} & -\frac{1}{2} & -\frac{1}{2} \\ \frac{1}{2} & -\frac{1}{2} & -\frac{1}{2} & \frac{1}{2} \end{pmatrix}, \quad \boldsymbol{D} = \begin{pmatrix} 12 & 0 & 0 \\ 0 & 6 & 0 \\ 0 & 0 & 0 \\ 0 & 0 & 0 \end{pmatrix}, \quad \boldsymbol{V} = \begin{pmatrix} \frac{1}{3} & \frac{2}{3} & \frac{2}{3} \\ \frac{2}{3} & \frac{1}{3} & -\frac{2}{3} \\ \frac{2}{3} & -\frac{2}{3} & \frac{1}{3} \end{pmatrix}.$$

This decomposition is not unique. We can have another decomposition by reversing the signs of the first columns of $\boldsymbol{U}$ and $\boldsymbol{V}$. Yet another SVD is obtained by replacing the last two columns of $\boldsymbol{U}$ by $\left(\frac{1}{\sqrt{2}} : 0 : -\frac{1}{\sqrt{2}} : 0\right)'$ and $\left(0 : \frac{1}{\sqrt{2}} : 0 : -\frac{1}{\sqrt{2}}\right)'$.

The R function `svd` may be used as follows to obtain a version of singular value decomposition.

```
A <- cbind(c(4,0,4,0),c(5,3,5,3),c(2,6,2,6))
svd(A)
```

The above code produces three singular values, 12, 6 and 0, and the corresponding left and right singular vectors in matrix form:

$$(\boldsymbol{u}_1 : \boldsymbol{u}_2 : \boldsymbol{u}_3) = \begin{pmatrix} -\frac{1}{2} & \frac{1}{2} & -\frac{1}{\sqrt{2}} \\ -\frac{1}{2} & -\frac{1}{2} & 0 \\ -\frac{1}{2} & \frac{1}{2} & \frac{1}{\sqrt{2}} \\ -\frac{1}{2} & -\frac{1}{2} & 0 \end{pmatrix}, \quad (\boldsymbol{v}_1 : \boldsymbol{v}_2 : \boldsymbol{v}_3) = \begin{pmatrix} -\frac{1}{3} & \frac{2}{3} & -\frac{2}{3} \\ -\frac{2}{3} & \frac{1}{3} & \frac{2}{3} \\ -\frac{2}{3} & -\frac{2}{3} & -\frac{1}{3} \end{pmatrix}.$$

Two alternative forms of SVD of $\boldsymbol{A}$ are given below:

$$d_1\boldsymbol{u}_1\boldsymbol{v}_1' + d_2\boldsymbol{u}_2\boldsymbol{v}_2' = 12\begin{pmatrix} \frac{1}{2} \\ \frac{1}{2} \\ \frac{1}{2} \\ \frac{1}{2} \end{pmatrix}\left(\tfrac{1}{3}\ \tfrac{2}{3}\ \tfrac{2}{3}\right) + 6\begin{pmatrix} \frac{1}{2} \\ -\frac{1}{2} \\ \frac{1}{2} \\ -\frac{1}{2} \end{pmatrix}\left(\tfrac{2}{3}\ \tfrac{1}{3}\ -\tfrac{2}{3}\right),$$

$$\boldsymbol{U}_1\boldsymbol{D}_1\boldsymbol{V}_1' = \begin{pmatrix} \frac{1}{2} & \frac{1}{2} \\ \frac{1}{2} & -\frac{1}{2} \\ \frac{1}{2} & \frac{1}{2} \\ \frac{1}{2} & -\frac{1}{2} \end{pmatrix}\begin{pmatrix} 12 & 0 \\ 0 & 6 \end{pmatrix}\begin{pmatrix} \frac{1}{3} & \frac{2}{3} & \frac{2}{3} \\ \frac{2}{3} & \frac{1}{3} & -\frac{2}{3} \end{pmatrix}.$$

Two rank-factorizations of $\boldsymbol{A}$ are $(\boldsymbol{U}_1\boldsymbol{D}_1)(\boldsymbol{V}_1')$ and $(\boldsymbol{U}_1)(\boldsymbol{D}_1\boldsymbol{V}_1')$. □

If $\boldsymbol{A}$ is a symmetric matrix, it can be decomposed as $\boldsymbol{V\Lambda V}'$, where $\boldsymbol{V}$ is an orthogonal matrix and $\boldsymbol{\Lambda}$ is a square and diagonal matrix. The diagonal elements of $\boldsymbol{\Lambda}$ are real, but these need not be nonnegative (see Proposition A.18 below). The set of the distinct diagonal elements of $\boldsymbol{\Lambda}$ is called the *spectrum* of $\boldsymbol{A}$. We refer to $\boldsymbol{V\Lambda V}'$ as a *spectral decomposition* of the symmetric matrix $\boldsymbol{A}$. The diagonal elements of $\boldsymbol{\Lambda}$ and the columns of $\boldsymbol{V}$ have the property

$$\boldsymbol{A}\boldsymbol{v}_i = \lambda_i\boldsymbol{v}_i, \qquad i = 1, \ldots, n,$$

λ_i and $\boldsymbol{v}_i$ being the ith diagonal element of $\boldsymbol{\Lambda}$ and the ith column of $\boldsymbol{V}$, respectively. Combinations of scalars and vectors satisfying this property are generally called *eigenvalues* and *eigenvectors* of $\boldsymbol{A}$, respectively. Thus, every λ_i is an eigenvalue of $\boldsymbol{A}$, while $\boldsymbol{v}_i$ is an eigenvector of $\boldsymbol{A}$ corresponding to the eigenvalue λ_i.

There are several connections among the three decompositions mentioned so far. If $\boldsymbol{A}$ is a general matrix with SVD $\boldsymbol{UDV}'$, a spectral decomposition of the nonnegative definite matrix $\boldsymbol{A}'\boldsymbol{A}$ is $\boldsymbol{VD}^2\boldsymbol{V}'$. If $\boldsymbol{A}$ is itself a nonnegative definite matrix, any SVD of $\boldsymbol{A}$ is a spectral decomposition, and vice versa. An alternative form of spectral decomposition of a symmetric nonnegative definite matrix $\boldsymbol{A}$ is $\boldsymbol{V}_1\boldsymbol{\Lambda}_1\boldsymbol{V}_1'$ where $\boldsymbol{V}_1$ is semi-orthogonal and $\boldsymbol{\Lambda}_1$ is a nonsingular, diagonal matrix. If $\rho(\boldsymbol{A}) = r$, then $\boldsymbol{\Lambda}_1$ has r positive diagonal elements, and can be written as $\boldsymbol{D}_1^2$, $\boldsymbol{D}_1$ being another diagonal matrix. Thus, $\boldsymbol{A}$ can be factored as $(\boldsymbol{V}_1\boldsymbol{D}_1)(\boldsymbol{V}_1\boldsymbol{D}_1)'$. This construction shows that any nonnegative definite matrix can be rank-factorized as $\boldsymbol{BB}'$ where $\boldsymbol{B}$ has full column rank. The rank-factorization we use for nonnegative definite matrices is generally of this form (see Rao and Bhimasankaram, 2000, p. 361 for an algorithm for this decomposition). We have already seen in Example A.16 how an SVD leads to a rank-factorization of a general matrix (not necessarily square).

Although the SVD is not unique, the set of singular values of any matrix is unique. Likewise, a symmetric matrix can have many spectral decompositions, but a unique set of eigenvalues.

Example A.17. Consider the symmetric matrix

$$\boldsymbol{B} = \begin{pmatrix} 32 & 40 & 16 \\ 40 & 68 & 56 \\ 16 & 56 & 80 \end{pmatrix}.$$

Note that $\boldsymbol{B} = \boldsymbol{A}'\boldsymbol{A}$, where $\boldsymbol{A}$ is as in Example A.16. One can obtain the spectral decomposition of $\boldsymbol{B}$ through the R code `B = t(A)%*%A; eigen(B)`. It produces three eigenvalues, 144, 36 and 1.152×10^{-14} and the matrix of eigenvectors

$$(\boldsymbol{v}_1 : \boldsymbol{v}_2 : \boldsymbol{v}_3) = \begin{pmatrix} -\frac{1}{3} & \frac{2}{3} & \frac{2}{3} \\ -\frac{2}{3} & \frac{1}{3} & -\frac{2}{3} \\ -\frac{2}{3} & -\frac{2}{3} & \frac{1}{3} \end{pmatrix}.$$

This matrix may be recognized as the matrix of right singular vector obtained by `svd(A)` in Example A.16, with an inconsequential change of sign in the last column. The eigenvalues are squares of the singular values of $\boldsymbol{A}$, except that the last eigenvalue is slightly different from the anticipated value, 0. The departure results from computational inaccuracy. Interestingly, the R command `svd(B)` produces the singular values 144, 36 and 7.259×10^{-15}, the last one being marginally closer to the correct value, zero. The corresponding matrices of the left and right singular vector are both equal to the matrix of eigenvectors reported above. □

Rank-factorization, singular value decomposition and spectral decomposition help us better understand the concepts introduced in the preceding sections. We now present a few characterizations based on these decompositions.

Proposition A.18. *Suppose $\boldsymbol{U}_1\boldsymbol{D}_1\boldsymbol{V}_1'$ is an SVD of the matrix $\boldsymbol{A}$, such that $\boldsymbol{D}_1$ is full rank. Suppose, further, that $\boldsymbol{B}$ is a symmetric matrix with spectral decomposition $\boldsymbol{V\Lambda V}'$, $\boldsymbol{\Lambda}$ having the same order as $\boldsymbol{B}$.*

(a) $\boldsymbol{P}_{\!\!A} = \boldsymbol{U}_1\boldsymbol{U}_1'$.
(b) $\boldsymbol{A}^+ = \boldsymbol{V}_1\boldsymbol{D}_1^{-1}\boldsymbol{U}_1'$.
(c) $\boldsymbol{P}_{\!\!A} = \boldsymbol{A}\boldsymbol{A}^+$.
(d) *$\boldsymbol{B}$ is nonnegative (or positive) definite if and only if all the elements of $\boldsymbol{\Lambda}$ are nonnegative (or positive).*
(e) *If $\boldsymbol{B}$ is nonnegative definite, then $\boldsymbol{B}^+ = \boldsymbol{V\Lambda}^+\boldsymbol{V}'$*
(f) *$\boldsymbol{B}$ is idempotent if and only if all the elements of $\boldsymbol{\Lambda}$ are either 0 or 1.*
(g) *If $\boldsymbol{CD}$ is a rank-factorization of $\boldsymbol{A}$, then the Moore-Penrose inverse of $\boldsymbol{A}$ is given by*

$$\boldsymbol{A}^+ = \boldsymbol{D}'(\boldsymbol{DD}')^{-1}(\boldsymbol{C}'\boldsymbol{C})^{-1}\boldsymbol{C}'.$$

(h) $\mathrm{tr}(\boldsymbol{B}) = \mathrm{tr}(\boldsymbol{\Lambda})$, *the sum of the eigenvalues.*
(i) $|\boldsymbol{B}| = |\boldsymbol{\Lambda}|$, *the product of the eigenvalues.*

Proof. Note that $\boldsymbol{U}_1$ and $\boldsymbol{V}_1$ are semi-orthogonal matrices. Further,

$$\mathcal{C}(\boldsymbol{A}) = \mathcal{C}(\boldsymbol{AA}') = \mathcal{C}(\boldsymbol{U}_1\boldsymbol{D}_1\boldsymbol{D}_1\boldsymbol{U}_1') = \mathcal{C}(\boldsymbol{U}_1\boldsymbol{D}_1) = \mathcal{C}(\boldsymbol{U}_1).$$

The last equality holds because $\boldsymbol{D}_1$ is invertible. It follows from Proposition A.11 that $\boldsymbol{P}_{\!\!A} = \boldsymbol{P}_{\!\!U_1} = \boldsymbol{U}_1(\boldsymbol{U}_1'\boldsymbol{U}_1)^-\boldsymbol{U}_1' = \boldsymbol{U}_1\boldsymbol{U}_1'$.

Part (b) is proved by verifying the four conditions that the Moore-Penrose inverse must satisfy (see Section A.2).

Part (c) follows directly from parts (a) and (b).

Suppose the elements of $\boldsymbol{\Lambda}$ are $\lambda_1, \ldots, \lambda_n$ and the columns of $\boldsymbol{V}$ are $\boldsymbol{v}_1, \ldots, \boldsymbol{v}_n$. Then, for any vector $\boldsymbol{l}$ of order n,

$$\boldsymbol{l}'\boldsymbol{B}\boldsymbol{l} = \boldsymbol{l}'\left(\sum_{i=1}^{n} \lambda_i \boldsymbol{v}_i \boldsymbol{v}_i'\right)\boldsymbol{l} = \sum_{i=1}^{n} \lambda_i (\boldsymbol{l}'\boldsymbol{v}_i)^2.$$

If $\lambda_1, \ldots, \lambda_n$ are all nonnegative, $\boldsymbol{l}'\boldsymbol{B}\boldsymbol{l}$ is nonnegative for all $\boldsymbol{l}$, indicating that $\boldsymbol{B}$ is nonnegative definite. Otherwise, if $\lambda_j < 0$ for some j, we have $\boldsymbol{v}_j'\boldsymbol{B}\boldsymbol{v}_j = \lambda_j < 0$, and $\boldsymbol{B}$ is not nonnegative definite. Thus, $\boldsymbol{B}$ is nonnegative definite if and only if the elements of $\boldsymbol{\Lambda}$ are nonnegative. If the word 'nonnegative' is replaced by 'positive,' the statement is proved in a similar manner. This proves part (d).

As mentioned on page 591, the Moore-Penrose inverse of a square and diagonal matrix is obtained by replacing the nonzero elements of the matrix by their respective reciprocals. Therefore, $\boldsymbol{\Lambda}^+$ is obtained from $\boldsymbol{\Lambda}$ by this process. The matrix $\boldsymbol{V}\boldsymbol{\Lambda}^+\boldsymbol{V}'$ is easily seen to satisfy the four properties of a Moore-Penrose inverse given on page 591, using the fact that $\boldsymbol{V}$ is an orthogonal matrix. This proves part (e).

In order to prove part (f), note that $\boldsymbol{B}^2 = \boldsymbol{B}$ if and only if $\boldsymbol{V}\boldsymbol{\Lambda}^2\boldsymbol{V}' = \boldsymbol{V}\boldsymbol{\Lambda}\boldsymbol{V}'$, which is equivalent to $\boldsymbol{\Lambda}^2 = \boldsymbol{\Lambda}$. Since $\boldsymbol{\Lambda}$ is a diagonal matrix, this is possible if and only if each diagonal element of $\boldsymbol{\Lambda}$ is equal to its square. The statement follows.

Let $\boldsymbol{F} = \boldsymbol{D}'(\boldsymbol{D}\boldsymbol{D}')^{-1}(\boldsymbol{C}'\boldsymbol{C})^{-1}\boldsymbol{C}'$, where $\boldsymbol{C}$ and $\boldsymbol{D}$ are as in part (g). The conditions $\boldsymbol{A}\boldsymbol{F}\boldsymbol{A} = \boldsymbol{A}$, $\boldsymbol{F}\boldsymbol{A}\boldsymbol{F}$, $\boldsymbol{A}\boldsymbol{F} = (\boldsymbol{A}\boldsymbol{F})'$ and $\boldsymbol{F}\boldsymbol{A} = (\boldsymbol{F}\boldsymbol{A})'$ are easily verified. Hence, $\boldsymbol{F}$ must be the Moore-Penrose inverse of $\boldsymbol{A}$.

Part (h) follows from the fact that $\text{tr}(\boldsymbol{V}\boldsymbol{\Lambda}\boldsymbol{V}') = \text{tr}(\boldsymbol{\Lambda}\boldsymbol{V}'\boldsymbol{V}) = \text{tr}(\boldsymbol{\Lambda})$.

Part (i) is proved by observing $|\boldsymbol{V}\boldsymbol{\Lambda}\boldsymbol{V}'| = |\boldsymbol{\Lambda}\boldsymbol{V}'\boldsymbol{V}| = |\boldsymbol{\Lambda}| \cdot |\boldsymbol{V}|^2 = |\boldsymbol{\Lambda}|$. □

In view of Proposition A.11, part (c) of Proposition A.18 describes how a projection matrix $\boldsymbol{A}\boldsymbol{A}^-$ can be made an orthogonal projection matrix by choosing the g-inverse suitably. Part (d) implies that a nonnegative definite matrix is singular if and only if it has at least one zero eigenvalue. Part (f) characterizes the eigenvalues of orthogonal projection matrices (see Exercise A.14). Parts (f) and (h) imply that whenever $\boldsymbol{B}$ is an orthogonal projection matrix, $\rho(\boldsymbol{B}) = \text{tr}(\boldsymbol{B})$. According to part (d) of Proposition A.18, $\boldsymbol{B}$ is nonnegative definite only if $|\boldsymbol{B}| \geq 0$, positive definite only if $|\boldsymbol{B}| > 0$ and positive semidefinite (singular) only if $|\boldsymbol{B}| = 0$.

The decompositions described above also serve as tools to prove some theoretical results that may be stated without reference to the decompositions. We illustrate the utility of rank-factorization by proving a few more results on column spaces.

Proposition A.19.

(a) If $\boldsymbol{B}$ *is nonnegative definite, then* $\mathcal{C}(\boldsymbol{ABA'}) = \mathcal{C}(\boldsymbol{AB})$, *and* $\rho(\boldsymbol{ABA'}) = \rho(\boldsymbol{AB}) = \rho(\boldsymbol{BA'})$.

(b) If $\begin{pmatrix} \boldsymbol{A} & \boldsymbol{B} \\ \boldsymbol{B'} & \boldsymbol{C} \end{pmatrix}$ *is a nonnegative definite matrix, then* $\mathcal{C}(\boldsymbol{B}) \subseteq \mathcal{C}(\boldsymbol{A})$ *and* $\mathcal{C}(\boldsymbol{B'}) \subseteq \mathcal{C}(\boldsymbol{C})$.

Proof. Suppose $\boldsymbol{CC'}$ is a rank-factorization of $\boldsymbol{B}$. Then

$$\mathcal{C}(\boldsymbol{ABA'}) = \mathcal{C}(\boldsymbol{ACC'A'}) \subseteq \mathcal{C}(\boldsymbol{ACC'}) \subseteq \mathcal{C}(\boldsymbol{AC}).$$

However, $\mathcal{C}(\boldsymbol{AC}) = \mathcal{C}((\boldsymbol{AC})(\boldsymbol{AC})') = \mathcal{C}(\boldsymbol{ABA'})$. Thus, all the above column spaces are identical. In particular, $\mathcal{C}(\boldsymbol{AB}) = \mathcal{C}(\boldsymbol{ACC'}) = \mathcal{C}(\boldsymbol{ABA'})$. Consequently, $\rho(\boldsymbol{ABA'}) = \rho(\boldsymbol{AB}) = \rho((\boldsymbol{AB})') = \rho(\boldsymbol{BA'})$.

In order to prove part (b), let $\boldsymbol{TT'}$ be a rank-factorization of the given nonnegative definite matrix, and let $\begin{pmatrix} \boldsymbol{T}_1 \\ \boldsymbol{T}_2 \end{pmatrix}$ be a partition of $\boldsymbol{T}$ such that the block $\boldsymbol{T}_1$ has the same number of rows as $\boldsymbol{A}$. Then we have

$$\boldsymbol{TT'} = \begin{pmatrix} \boldsymbol{T}_1\boldsymbol{T}_1' & \boldsymbol{T}_1\boldsymbol{T}_2' \\ \boldsymbol{T}_2\boldsymbol{T}_1' & \boldsymbol{T}_2\boldsymbol{T}_2' \end{pmatrix} = \begin{pmatrix} \boldsymbol{A} & \boldsymbol{B} \\ \boldsymbol{B'} & \boldsymbol{C} \end{pmatrix}.$$

Comparing the blocks, we have $\boldsymbol{A} = \boldsymbol{T}_1\boldsymbol{T}_1'$ and $\boldsymbol{B} = \boldsymbol{T}_1\boldsymbol{T}_2'$. Further, $\mathcal{C}(\boldsymbol{B}) = \mathcal{C}(\boldsymbol{T}_1\boldsymbol{T}_2') \subseteq \mathcal{C}(\boldsymbol{T}_1) = \mathcal{C}(\boldsymbol{T}_1\boldsymbol{T}_1') = \mathcal{C}(\boldsymbol{A})$. Repeating this argument on the transposed matrix, we have $\mathcal{C}(\boldsymbol{B'}) \subseteq \mathcal{C}(\boldsymbol{C})$. □

An easily verifiable decomposition of a symmetric and nonnegative definite partitioned matrix is

$$\begin{pmatrix} \boldsymbol{A} & \boldsymbol{B} \\ \boldsymbol{B'} & \boldsymbol{C} \end{pmatrix} = \begin{pmatrix} \boldsymbol{I} & \boldsymbol{0} \\ \boldsymbol{B'A^-} & \boldsymbol{I} \end{pmatrix} \begin{pmatrix} \boldsymbol{A} & \boldsymbol{0} \\ \boldsymbol{0} & \boldsymbol{C} - \boldsymbol{B'A^-B} \end{pmatrix} \begin{pmatrix} \boldsymbol{I} & \boldsymbol{A^-B} \\ \boldsymbol{0} & \boldsymbol{I} \end{pmatrix}, \tag{A.6}$$

where $\boldsymbol{A}^-$ is any g-inverse of $\boldsymbol{A}$. Note that the matrix at the center of the right-hand side is block diagonal, and the bottom right block happens to be the of $\boldsymbol{D}$ in the matrix of the left-hand side. One can also re-write the above identity as

$$\begin{pmatrix} \boldsymbol{I} & \boldsymbol{0} \\ -\boldsymbol{B'A^-} & \boldsymbol{I} \end{pmatrix} \begin{pmatrix} \boldsymbol{A} & \boldsymbol{B} \\ \boldsymbol{B'} & \boldsymbol{C} \end{pmatrix} \begin{pmatrix} \boldsymbol{I} & -\boldsymbol{A^-B} \\ \boldsymbol{0} & \boldsymbol{I} \end{pmatrix} = \begin{pmatrix} \boldsymbol{A} & \boldsymbol{0} \\ \boldsymbol{0} & \boldsymbol{C} - \boldsymbol{B'A^-B} \end{pmatrix}, \tag{A.7}$$

which shows how the original matrix can be reduced to a block diagonal matrix. These identities are useful in proving many theoretical results (see Exercises A.7, A.8, A.23).

A.6 Löwner order

Nonnegative definite matrices are often arranged by a partial order called the Löwner order, defined below.

Definition A.20. If $\boldsymbol{A}$ and $\boldsymbol{B}$ are nonnegative definite matrices of the same order, then $\boldsymbol{A}$ is said to be *smaller than* $\boldsymbol{B}$ *in the sense of the Löwner order* (written as $\boldsymbol{A} \leq \boldsymbol{B}$ or $\boldsymbol{B} \geq \boldsymbol{A}$) if the difference $\boldsymbol{B} - \boldsymbol{A}$ is nonnegative definite. If the difference is positive definite, then $\boldsymbol{A}$ is said to be strictly smaller than $\boldsymbol{B}$ (written as $\boldsymbol{A} < \boldsymbol{B}$ or $\boldsymbol{B} > \boldsymbol{A}$). □

It is easy to see that whenever $\boldsymbol{A} \leq \boldsymbol{B}$, every diagonal element of $\boldsymbol{A}$ is less than or equal to the corresponding diagonal element of $\boldsymbol{B}$. Apart from the diagonal elements, several other real-valued functions of the matrix elements happen to be algebraically ordered whenever the corresponding matrices are Löwner ordered.

Proposition A.21. *Let* $\boldsymbol{A}$ *and* $\boldsymbol{B}$ *be symmetric and nonnegative definite matrices having the same order and let* $\boldsymbol{A} \leq \boldsymbol{B}$. *Then*

(a) $\mathrm{tr}(\boldsymbol{A}) \leq \mathrm{tr}(\boldsymbol{B})$;
(b) the largest eigenvalue of $\boldsymbol{A}$ *is less than or equal to that of* $\boldsymbol{B}$;
(c) the smallest eigenvalue of $\boldsymbol{A}$ *is less than or equal to that of* $\boldsymbol{B}$;
(d) $|\boldsymbol{A}| \leq |\boldsymbol{B}|$.

Proof. Part (a) follows from the fact that $\boldsymbol{B} - \boldsymbol{A}$ is a symmetric and nonnegative definite matrix, and the sum of the eigenvalues of this matrix is $\mathrm{tr}(\boldsymbol{B}) - \mathrm{tr}(\boldsymbol{A})$. Notice that $\boldsymbol{u}'\boldsymbol{A}\boldsymbol{u} \leq \boldsymbol{u}'\boldsymbol{B}\boldsymbol{u}$ for every $\boldsymbol{u}$, and that the inequality continues to hold after both sides are maximized or minimized with respect to $\boldsymbol{u}$. Part (b) follows from this fact and Proposition A.26, we part (c) follows from application of that proposition to $-\boldsymbol{A}$. In order to prove part (d), note that the proof is nontrivial only when $|\boldsymbol{A}| > 0$. Let $\boldsymbol{A}$ be positive definite and $\boldsymbol{C}\boldsymbol{C}'$ be a rank-factorization of $\boldsymbol{A}$. It follows that $\boldsymbol{I} \leq \boldsymbol{C}^{-1}\boldsymbol{B}(\boldsymbol{C}')^{-1}$. By part (c), the smallest eigenvalue (and hence, every eigenvalue) of $\boldsymbol{C}^{-1}\boldsymbol{B}(\boldsymbol{C}')^{-1}$ is greater than or equal to 1. Therefore, $|\boldsymbol{C}^{-1}\boldsymbol{B}(\boldsymbol{C}')^{-1}| \geq 1$. The stated result follows from the identities $|\boldsymbol{C}^{-1}\boldsymbol{B}(\boldsymbol{C}')^{-1}| = |\boldsymbol{C}^{-1}| \cdot |\boldsymbol{B}| \cdot |(\boldsymbol{C}')^{-1}| = |\boldsymbol{B}| \cdot |\boldsymbol{A}|^{-1}$. □

Note that the matrix functions considered in Proposition A.22 are in fact functions of the eigenvalues. It can be shown that whenever $\boldsymbol{A} \leq \boldsymbol{B}$, all the ordered eigenvalues of $\boldsymbol{A}$ are smaller than the corresponding eigenvalues of $\boldsymbol{B}$ (see Zhang, 2013, p. 227). Thus, the Löwner order implies algebraic order of *any* increasing function of the ordered eigenvalues. The four parts of Proposition A.21 are special cases of this stronger result.

There is a direct relation between the Löwner order and the column spaces of the corresponding matrices.

Proposition A.22. *Let $\boldsymbol{A}$ and $\boldsymbol{B}$ be matrices having the same number of rows.*

(a) If $\boldsymbol{A}$ and $\boldsymbol{B}$ are both symmetric and nonnegative definite, then $\boldsymbol{A} \le \boldsymbol{B}$ implies $\mathcal{C}(\boldsymbol{A}) \subseteq \mathcal{C}(\boldsymbol{B})$.
(b) $\mathcal{C}(\boldsymbol{A}) \subseteq \mathcal{C}(\boldsymbol{B})$ if and only if $\boldsymbol{P}_{A} \le \boldsymbol{P}_{B}$ and $\mathcal{C}(\boldsymbol{A}) \subset \mathcal{C}(\boldsymbol{B})$ if and only if $\boldsymbol{P}_{A} < \boldsymbol{P}_{B}$.

Proof. Whenever $\boldsymbol{A} \le \boldsymbol{B}$, we can write $\boldsymbol{B} = \boldsymbol{A}+\boldsymbol{C}$ where $\boldsymbol{C}$ is nonnegative definite. Let $\boldsymbol{A}_1\boldsymbol{A}_1'$ and $\boldsymbol{C}_1\boldsymbol{C}_1'$ be the rank-factorizations of $\boldsymbol{A}$ and $\boldsymbol{C}$, respectively. Then $\boldsymbol{B} = \boldsymbol{A}_1\boldsymbol{A}_1' + \boldsymbol{C}_1\boldsymbol{C}_1' = (\boldsymbol{A}_1 : \boldsymbol{C}_1)(\boldsymbol{A}_1 : \boldsymbol{C}_1)'$, so that $\mathcal{C}(\boldsymbol{A}) = \mathcal{C}(\boldsymbol{A}_1) \subseteq \mathcal{C}(\boldsymbol{A}_1 : \boldsymbol{C}_1) = \mathcal{C}(\boldsymbol{B})$. This proves part (a).

In order to prove part (b), let $\mathcal{C}(\boldsymbol{A}) \subseteq \mathcal{C}(\boldsymbol{B})$. Note that $\mathcal{C}(\boldsymbol{B}) = \mathcal{C}(\boldsymbol{A} : \boldsymbol{B})$. From Proposition A.14(b) we have

$$\boldsymbol{P}_{B} = \boldsymbol{P}_{A:B} = \boldsymbol{P}_{A} + \boldsymbol{P}_{(I-P_A)B} \ge \boldsymbol{P}_{A}.$$

In particular, if $\mathcal{C}(\boldsymbol{A}) \subset \mathcal{C}(\boldsymbol{B})$, then $\mathcal{C}((\boldsymbol{I} - \boldsymbol{P}_{A})\boldsymbol{B})$ cannot be identically zero, which leads to the strict order $\boldsymbol{P}_{A} < \boldsymbol{P}_{B}$. On the other hand, when $\boldsymbol{P}_{A} \le \boldsymbol{P}_{B}$, part (a) implies that $\mathcal{C}(\boldsymbol{A}) \subseteq \mathcal{C}(\boldsymbol{B})$. If $\boldsymbol{P}_{A} < \boldsymbol{P}_{B}$, there is a vector $\boldsymbol{l}$ such that $\boldsymbol{A}'\boldsymbol{l} = \boldsymbol{0}$ but $\boldsymbol{B}'\boldsymbol{l} \ne \boldsymbol{0}$. Therefore, $\mathcal{C}(\boldsymbol{B})^{\perp} \subset \mathcal{C}(\boldsymbol{A}')^{\perp}$, i.e. $\mathcal{C}(\boldsymbol{A}) \subset \mathcal{C}(\boldsymbol{B})$. □

A.7 Solutions of linear equations

Consider a set of linear equations written in the matrix-vector form as $\boldsymbol{A}\boldsymbol{x} = \boldsymbol{b}$, where $\boldsymbol{x}$ is unknown. Proposition A.23 below provides answers to the following questions:

(a) When do the equations have a solution?
(b) If there is a solution, when is it unique?
(c) When there is a solution, how can we characterize all the solutions?

Proposition A.23. *Suppose $\boldsymbol{A}_{m\times n}$ and $\boldsymbol{b}_{m\times 1}$ are known.*

(a) The equations $\boldsymbol{A}\boldsymbol{x} = \boldsymbol{b}$ have a solution if and only if $\boldsymbol{b} \in \mathcal{C}(\boldsymbol{A})$.

(b) *The equations* $\boldsymbol{Ax} = \boldsymbol{b}$ *have a unique solution if and only if* $\boldsymbol{b} \in \mathcal{C}(\boldsymbol{A})$ *and* $\rho(\boldsymbol{A}) = n$.

(c) *If* $\boldsymbol{b} \in \mathcal{C}(\boldsymbol{A})$, *every solution to the equations* $\boldsymbol{Ax} = \boldsymbol{b}$ *is of the form* $\boldsymbol{A}^{-}\boldsymbol{b} + (\boldsymbol{I} - \boldsymbol{A}^{-}\boldsymbol{A})\boldsymbol{c}$ *where* $\boldsymbol{A}^{-}$ *is any fixed g-inverse of* $\boldsymbol{A}$ *and* $\mathbf{c}$ *is an arbitrary vector.*

Proof. Part (a) follows directly from parts (b) and (d) of Proposition A.10.

Part (b) is proved by observing that $\boldsymbol{b}$ can be expressed as a unique linear combination of the columns of $\boldsymbol{A}$ if and only if $\boldsymbol{b} \in \mathcal{C}(\boldsymbol{A})$ and the columns of $\boldsymbol{A}$ are linearly independent.

It is easy to see that whenever $\boldsymbol{b} \in \mathcal{C}(\boldsymbol{A})$, $\boldsymbol{A}^{-}\boldsymbol{b}$ is a solution to $\boldsymbol{Ax} = \boldsymbol{b}$. If $\boldsymbol{x}_0$ is another solution, then $\boldsymbol{x}_0 - \boldsymbol{A}^{-}\boldsymbol{b}$ must be in $\mathcal{C}(\boldsymbol{A}')^{\perp}$. Since $\boldsymbol{Al} = \boldsymbol{0}$ if and only if $(\boldsymbol{I} - \boldsymbol{A}^{-}\boldsymbol{A})\boldsymbol{l} = \boldsymbol{l}$, $\mathcal{C}(\boldsymbol{A}')^{\perp}$ must be the same as $\mathcal{C}(\boldsymbol{I} - \boldsymbol{A}^{-}\boldsymbol{A})$. Hence $\boldsymbol{x}_0$ must be of the form $\boldsymbol{A}^{-}\boldsymbol{b} + (\boldsymbol{I} - \boldsymbol{A}^{-}\boldsymbol{A})\boldsymbol{c}$ for some $\boldsymbol{c}$. □

Remark A.24. If $\boldsymbol{b}$ is a non-null vector contained in $\mathcal{C}(\boldsymbol{A})$, every solution of the equations $\boldsymbol{Ax} = \boldsymbol{b}$ can be shown to have the form $\boldsymbol{A}^{-}\boldsymbol{b}$ where $\boldsymbol{A}^{-}$ is *some* g-inverse of $\boldsymbol{A}$. (See Corollary 1, p. 27 of Rao and Mitra, 1971). □

Since the equations $\boldsymbol{Ax} = \boldsymbol{b}$ have no solution unless $\boldsymbol{b} \in \mathcal{C}(\boldsymbol{A})$, this condition is often called the *consistency condition.* If this condition is violated, the equations have an inherent contradiction.

If $\boldsymbol{A}$ is a square and nonsingular matrix, then the conditions of parts (a) and (b) are automatically satisfied. In such a case, $\boldsymbol{Ax} = \boldsymbol{b}$ has a unique solution given by $\boldsymbol{x} = \boldsymbol{A}^{-1}\boldsymbol{b}$.

If $\boldsymbol{b} \in \mathcal{C}(\boldsymbol{A})$, a general form of the solution of $\boldsymbol{Ax} = \boldsymbol{b}$ is $\boldsymbol{A}^{+}\boldsymbol{b} + (\boldsymbol{I} - \boldsymbol{P}_{A'})\boldsymbol{c}$. This is obtained by choosing the g-inverse in part (c) as $\boldsymbol{A}^{+}$.

A.8 Optimization of quadratic forms and functions

Consider a quadratic function $q(\boldsymbol{x}) = \boldsymbol{x}'\boldsymbol{Ax} + \boldsymbol{b}'\boldsymbol{x} + c$ of a vector variable $\boldsymbol{x}$, where we assume $\boldsymbol{A}$ to be symmetric without loss of generality. In order to minimize or maximize $q(\boldsymbol{x})$ with respect to $\boldsymbol{x}$, we can differentiate $q(\boldsymbol{x})$ with respect to the components of $\boldsymbol{x}$, one at a time, and set the derivatives equal to zero. The solution(s) of these simultaneous equations are candidates for the optimizing value of $\boldsymbol{x}$. This algebra can be carried out in a neater way using vector calculus.

Let $\boldsymbol{x} = (x_1, \ldots, x_n)'$. The *gradient vector* and the *Hessian matrix* of a real-valued function $f(\boldsymbol{x})$ is defined as the vector of first derivatives and the matrix of second derivatives, respectively:

$$\frac{\partial f(\boldsymbol{x})}{\partial \boldsymbol{x}} = \begin{pmatrix} \frac{\partial f(\boldsymbol{x})}{\partial x_1} \\ \frac{\partial f(\boldsymbol{x})}{\partial x_2} \\ \vdots \\ \frac{\partial f(\boldsymbol{x})}{\partial x_n} \end{pmatrix}, \quad \frac{\partial^2 f(\boldsymbol{x})}{\partial \boldsymbol{x} \partial \boldsymbol{x}'} = \begin{pmatrix} \frac{\partial^2 f(\boldsymbol{x})}{\partial x_1^2} & \frac{\partial^2 f(\boldsymbol{x})}{\partial x_1 \partial x_2} & \cdots & \frac{\partial^2 f(\boldsymbol{x})}{\partial x_1 \partial x_n} \\ \frac{\partial^2 f(\boldsymbol{x})}{\partial x_2 \partial x_1} & \frac{\partial^2 f(\boldsymbol{x})}{\partial x_2^2} & \cdots & \frac{\partial^2 f(\boldsymbol{x})}{\partial x_2 \partial x_n} \\ \vdots & \vdots & \ddots & \vdots \\ \frac{\partial^2 f(\boldsymbol{x})}{\partial x_n \partial x_1} & \frac{\partial^2 f(\boldsymbol{x})}{\partial x_n \partial x_2} & \cdots & \frac{\partial^2 f(\boldsymbol{x})}{\partial x_n^2} \end{pmatrix}.$$

A differentiable function has a maximum or a minimum at the point $\boldsymbol{x}_0$ only if its gradient is zero at $\boldsymbol{x}_0$. If the gradient is zero at $\boldsymbol{x}_0$, it is a minimum if the Hessian at $\boldsymbol{x}_0$ is nonnegative definite, and maximum if the Hessian is nonpositive definite.

Proposition A.25. *Let $q(\boldsymbol{x}) = \boldsymbol{x}'\boldsymbol{A}\boldsymbol{x} + \boldsymbol{b}'\boldsymbol{x} + c$, where $\boldsymbol{A}$ is a symmetric matrix.*

(a) $\dfrac{\partial(\boldsymbol{x}'\boldsymbol{A}\boldsymbol{x})}{\partial \boldsymbol{x}} = 2\boldsymbol{A}\boldsymbol{x}, \ \dfrac{\partial(\boldsymbol{b}'\boldsymbol{x})}{\partial \boldsymbol{x}} = \boldsymbol{b}, \ \dfrac{\partial c}{\partial \boldsymbol{x}} = \boldsymbol{0}.$

(b) $\dfrac{\partial^2(\boldsymbol{x}'\boldsymbol{A}\boldsymbol{x})}{\partial \boldsymbol{x}\partial \boldsymbol{x}'} = 2\boldsymbol{A}, \ \dfrac{\partial^2(\boldsymbol{b}'\boldsymbol{x})}{\partial \boldsymbol{x}\partial \boldsymbol{x}'} = \boldsymbol{0}, \ \dfrac{\partial^2 c}{\partial \boldsymbol{x}\partial \boldsymbol{x}'} = \boldsymbol{0}.$

(c) $q(\boldsymbol{x})$ has a maximum if and only if $\boldsymbol{b} \in \mathcal{C}(\boldsymbol{A})$ and $-\boldsymbol{A}$ is nonnegative definite. In such a case, a maximizer of $q(\boldsymbol{x})$ is of the form $-\frac{1}{2}\boldsymbol{A}^-\boldsymbol{b} + (\boldsymbol{I} - \boldsymbol{A}^-\boldsymbol{A})\boldsymbol{x}_0$, where $\boldsymbol{x}_0$ is arbitrary.

(d) $q(\boldsymbol{x})$ has a minimum if and only if $\boldsymbol{b} \in \mathcal{C}(\boldsymbol{A})$ and $\boldsymbol{A}$ is nonnegative definite. In such a case, a minimizer of $q(\boldsymbol{x})$ is of the form $-\frac{1}{2}\boldsymbol{A}^-\boldsymbol{b} + (\boldsymbol{I} - \boldsymbol{A}^-\boldsymbol{A})\boldsymbol{x}_0$, where $\boldsymbol{x}_0$ is arbitrary.

Proof. The proposition is proved by direct verification of the expressions and the conditions stated above, and by making use of part (c) of Proposition A.23. □

Most of the time it is easier to maximize or minimize a quadratic function by 'completing squares', rather than by using vector calculus. To see this, assume that $\boldsymbol{b} \in \mathcal{C}(\boldsymbol{A})$ are rewrite $q(\boldsymbol{x})$ as

$$\left(\boldsymbol{x} + \frac{1}{2}\boldsymbol{A}^-\boldsymbol{b}\right)' \boldsymbol{A} \left(\boldsymbol{x} + \frac{1}{2}\boldsymbol{A}^-\boldsymbol{b}\right) + \left(c - \frac{1}{4}\boldsymbol{b}'\boldsymbol{A}^-\boldsymbol{b}\right).$$

If $\boldsymbol{A} \geq \boldsymbol{0}$, then $q(\boldsymbol{x})$ is minimized when $\boldsymbol{x} = -\frac{1}{2}\boldsymbol{A}^-\boldsymbol{b} + (\boldsymbol{I} - \boldsymbol{A}^-\boldsymbol{A})\boldsymbol{x}_0$ for arbitrary $\boldsymbol{x}_0$. The minimum value of $q(\boldsymbol{x})$ is $\boldsymbol{c} - \frac{1}{4}\boldsymbol{b}'\boldsymbol{A}^-\boldsymbol{b}$. If $\boldsymbol{A} \leq \boldsymbol{0}$, then $q(\boldsymbol{x})$ is maximized at this value of $\boldsymbol{x}$, and the maximum value is $\boldsymbol{c} - \frac{1}{4}\boldsymbol{b}'\boldsymbol{A}^-\boldsymbol{b}$.

The quadratic function $q(\boldsymbol{x})$ may be maximized or minimized subject to the *linear constraint* $\boldsymbol{D}\boldsymbol{x} = \boldsymbol{e}$ using the Lagrange multiplier method. This is accomplished by adding the term $2\boldsymbol{y}'(\boldsymbol{D}\boldsymbol{x} - \boldsymbol{e})$ to $q(\boldsymbol{x})$ and optimizing the sum with respect to $\boldsymbol{x}$ and $\boldsymbol{y}$. Thus, the task is to optimize

$$\begin{pmatrix} \boldsymbol{x} \\ \boldsymbol{y} \end{pmatrix}' \begin{pmatrix} \boldsymbol{A} & \boldsymbol{D}' \\ \boldsymbol{D} & \boldsymbol{0} \end{pmatrix} \begin{pmatrix} \boldsymbol{x} \\ \boldsymbol{y} \end{pmatrix} + \begin{pmatrix} \boldsymbol{b} \\ -2\boldsymbol{e} \end{pmatrix}' \begin{pmatrix} \boldsymbol{x} \\ \boldsymbol{y} \end{pmatrix} + c$$

with respect to $(\boldsymbol{x}' : \boldsymbol{y}')'$. This is clearly covered by the results given in Proposition A.25.

The next proposition deals with maximization of a quadratic form under a *quadratic constraint.*

Proposition A.26. *Let $\boldsymbol{A}$ be a symmetric matrix, and $\boldsymbol{b}$ be a vector such that $\boldsymbol{b}'\boldsymbol{b} = 1$. Then $\boldsymbol{b}'\boldsymbol{A}\boldsymbol{b}$ is maximized with respect to $\boldsymbol{b}$ when $\boldsymbol{b}$ is a unit-norm eigenvector of $\boldsymbol{A}$ corresponding to its largest eigenvalue, and the corresponding maximum value of $\boldsymbol{A}$ is equal to the largest eigenvalue.*

Proof. Let $\boldsymbol{V}\boldsymbol{\Lambda}\boldsymbol{V}'$ be a spectral decomposition of $\boldsymbol{A}$, and let $\lambda_1, \ldots, \lambda_n$, the diagonal elements of $\boldsymbol{\Lambda}$, be in decreasing order. Suppose $\boldsymbol{a} = \boldsymbol{V}\boldsymbol{b}$. It follows that the optimization problem at hand is equivalent to the task of maximizing $\sum_{i=1}^n \lambda_i a_i^2$ subject to the constraint $\sum_{i=1}^n a_i^2 = 1$. It is easy to see that the weighted sum of λ_is is maximized when $a_1 = 1$ and $a_i = 0$ for $i = 2, \ldots, n$. This choice ensures the solution stated in the proposition. □

Note that if $\boldsymbol{b}_0$ maximizes $\boldsymbol{b}'\boldsymbol{A}\boldsymbol{b}$ subject to the unit-norm condition, so does $-\boldsymbol{b}_0$. Other solutions can be found if $\lambda_1 = \lambda_2$. If $\lambda_1 > 0$, then the statement of the above proposition can be strengthened by replacing the constraint $\boldsymbol{b}'\boldsymbol{b}$ with the inequality constraint $\boldsymbol{b}'\boldsymbol{b} \leq 1$.

An equivalent statement to Proposition A.26 is the following: *The ratio $\boldsymbol{b}'\boldsymbol{A}\boldsymbol{b}/\boldsymbol{b}'\boldsymbol{b}$ is maximized over all $\boldsymbol{b} \neq \boldsymbol{0}$ when $\boldsymbol{b}$ is an eigenvector of $\boldsymbol{A}$ corresponding to its largest eigenvalue. The corresponding maximum value of $\boldsymbol{b}'\boldsymbol{A}\boldsymbol{b}/\boldsymbol{b}'\boldsymbol{b}$ is equal to the largest eigenvalue of $\boldsymbol{A}$.*

Similarly it may be noted that $\boldsymbol{b}'\boldsymbol{A}\boldsymbol{b}$ is *minimized* with respect to $\boldsymbol{b}$ subject to the condition $\boldsymbol{b}'\boldsymbol{b} = 1$ when $\boldsymbol{b}$ is a unit-norm eigenvector of $\boldsymbol{A}$ corresponding to its smallest eigenvalue. The corresponding minimum value of $\boldsymbol{b}'\boldsymbol{A}\boldsymbol{b}$ is equal to the smallest eigenvalue of $\boldsymbol{A}$. This statement can be proved along the lines of Proposition A.26. An equivalent statement in terms of the minimization of the ratio $\boldsymbol{b}'\boldsymbol{A}\boldsymbol{b}/\boldsymbol{b}'\boldsymbol{b}$ can also be made.

We define the *norm* of any rectangular matrix $\boldsymbol{A}$ as the largest value of the ratio

$$\frac{\|\boldsymbol{Ab}\|}{\|\boldsymbol{b}\|} = \left(\frac{\boldsymbol{b}'\boldsymbol{A}'\boldsymbol{Ab}}{\boldsymbol{b}'\boldsymbol{b}}\right)^{1/2},$$

and denote it by $\|\boldsymbol{A}\|$. Proposition A.26 and the preceding discussion imply that $\|\boldsymbol{A}\|$ must be equal to the square-root of the largest eigenvalue of $\boldsymbol{A}'\boldsymbol{A}$, which is equal to the largest singular value of $\boldsymbol{A}$ (see the discussion of page 605). It also follows that the vector $\boldsymbol{b}$ that maximizes the above ratio is proportional to a right singular vector of $\boldsymbol{A}$ corresponding to its largest singular value. The norm defined here is different from the Frobenius norm defined on page 588.

A.9 Complements/Exercises

A.1 Find a matrix $\boldsymbol{P}_{n\times n}$ such that for any matrix $\boldsymbol{A}_{m\times n}$, $\boldsymbol{AP}$ is a modification of $\boldsymbol{A}$ with the first two columns interchanged. Can you find a matrix $\boldsymbol{Q}$ with suitable order such that $\boldsymbol{QA}$ is another modification of $\boldsymbol{A}$ with the first two rows interchanged?

A.2 Obtain the inverses of the matrices $\boldsymbol{P}$ and $\boldsymbol{Q}$ of Exercise A.1.

A.3 Let $\boldsymbol{A}$ be a matrix of order $n \times n$.

(a) Show that if $\boldsymbol{A}$ is positive definite, then it is nonsingular.

(b) Show that if $\boldsymbol{A}$ is symmetric and positive semidefinite, then it is singular.

(c) If $\boldsymbol{A}$ is positive semidefinite but not necessarily symmetric, does it follow that it is singular?

A.4 Show that

$$\begin{pmatrix} \boldsymbol{A}^-_{n_1\times m_1} & \boldsymbol{0}_{n_1\times m_2} \\ \boldsymbol{0}_{n_2\times m_1} & \boldsymbol{B}^-_{n_2\times m_2} \end{pmatrix}$$

is a g-inverse of

$$\begin{pmatrix} \boldsymbol{A}_{m_1\times n_1} & \boldsymbol{0}_{m_1\times n_2} \\ \boldsymbol{0}_{m_2\times n_1} & \boldsymbol{B}_{m_2\times n_2} \end{pmatrix}.$$

A.5 Is $(\boldsymbol{A}^-)'$ a g-inverse of $\boldsymbol{A}'$? Show that a symmetric matrix always has a symmetric g-inverse.

A.6 If $\boldsymbol{A}$ has full column rank, show that every g-inverse of $\boldsymbol{A}$ is also a left-inverse.

A.7 If $\boldsymbol{A}$ is nonsingular, show that the matrix $\boldsymbol{M} = \begin{pmatrix} \boldsymbol{A} & \boldsymbol{B} \\ \boldsymbol{C} & \boldsymbol{D} \end{pmatrix}$ is nonsingular if and only if $\boldsymbol{D} - \boldsymbol{CA}^{-1}\boldsymbol{B}$ is nonsingular.

A.8 Prove (A.4).

A.9 Show that any two bases of a given vector space must have the same number of vectors.

A.10 Prove Proposition A.6.

A.11 Prove that the dimension of a vector space is no more than the order of the vectors it contains.

A.12 Show that the projection of a vector on a vector space is uniquely defined.

A.13 Prove that the orthogonal projection matrix for a given vector space is unique.

A.14 (a) Prove that every idempotent matrix is a projection matrix.

(b) Prove that a matrix is an orthogonal projection matrix if and only if it is symmetric and idempotent.

A.15 If $\mathcal{S}_1$ and $\mathcal{S}_2$ are mutually orthogonal vector spaces, show that

$$\boldsymbol{P}_{\mathcal{S}_1 \oplus \mathcal{S}_2} = \boldsymbol{P}_{\mathcal{S}_1} + \boldsymbol{P}_{\mathcal{S}_2}.$$

A.16 Show that $\boldsymbol{p} \in \mathcal{C}(\boldsymbol{A}')$ if and only if $\boldsymbol{Ax} = \boldsymbol{0}$ implies $\boldsymbol{p}'\boldsymbol{x} = 0$.

A.17 Prove that $\rho(\boldsymbol{AB}) = \min\{\rho(\boldsymbol{A}), \rho(\boldsymbol{B})\}$ if either $\boldsymbol{A}$ or $\boldsymbol{B}$ is nonsingular. Also show that if $\boldsymbol{UDV}'$ is an SVD of $\boldsymbol{A}$ where $\boldsymbol{U}$ and $\boldsymbol{V}$ are orthogonal matrices, then $\rho(\boldsymbol{A}) = \rho(\boldsymbol{D})$.

A.18 If $\boldsymbol{BC}$ is a rank-factorization of $\boldsymbol{A}$, show that $\mathcal{C}(\boldsymbol{A}) = \mathcal{C}(\boldsymbol{B})$.

A.19 If $\boldsymbol{B}$ and $\boldsymbol{C}$ are non-null matrices and $\boldsymbol{A}$ is another matrix such that the product $\boldsymbol{BA}^-\boldsymbol{C}$ is well-defined and does not depend on the choice of $\boldsymbol{A}^-$, then show that $\mathcal{C}(\boldsymbol{C}) \subseteq \mathcal{C}(\boldsymbol{A})$ and $\mathcal{C}(\boldsymbol{B}') \subseteq \mathcal{C}(\boldsymbol{A}')$. [This result is the converse of part (f) of Proposition A.10; see Rao, Mitra and Bhimasankaram, 1972 for related results.]

A.20 (a) Show that the symmetric matrix $\begin{pmatrix} \boldsymbol{A} & \boldsymbol{B} \\ \boldsymbol{B}' & \boldsymbol{C} \end{pmatrix}$ is nonnegative definite if and only if $\boldsymbol{A}$ and $\boldsymbol{C} - \boldsymbol{B}'\boldsymbol{A}^-\boldsymbol{B}$ are both nonnegative definite and the latter matrix does not depend on the choice of $\boldsymbol{A}^-$.

(b) If the symmetric matrices $\boldsymbol{A}$ and $\boldsymbol{C} - \boldsymbol{B}'\boldsymbol{A}^-\boldsymbol{B}$ are both nonnegative definite and $\mathcal{C}(\boldsymbol{B}) \subseteq \mathcal{C}(\boldsymbol{A})$, show that $\mathcal{C}(\boldsymbol{B}') \subseteq \mathcal{C}(\boldsymbol{C})$ and $\boldsymbol{A} - \boldsymbol{BC}^-\boldsymbol{B}'$ is nonnegative definite.

A.21 If $\boldsymbol{V}_1$ and $\boldsymbol{V}_2$ are symmetric and nonnegative definite matrices, show that their *parallel sum* given by $\boldsymbol{V}_1(\boldsymbol{V}_1 + \boldsymbol{V}_2)^-\boldsymbol{V}_2$ (see Rao and Mitra, 1971, p. 188) has the following properties.

(a) The parallel sum does not depend on the choice of $(\boldsymbol{V}_1 + \boldsymbol{V}_2)^-$.

(b) The parallel sum is symmetric and nonnegative definite.

(c) $\mathcal{C}(\boldsymbol{V}_1(\boldsymbol{V}_1 + \boldsymbol{V}_2)^-\boldsymbol{V}_2) = \mathcal{C}(\boldsymbol{V}_1) \cap \mathcal{C}(\boldsymbol{V}_2)$.

A.22 Show that the dimension of $\mathcal{C}(\boldsymbol{A}) \cap \mathcal{C}(\boldsymbol{B})$ is less than or equal to the rank of $\boldsymbol{A}'\boldsymbol{B}$, and that the inequality can be strict.

A.23 If $\boldsymbol{A}$ is a nonsingular matrix and $\boldsymbol{D}$ is a square matrix, show that

$$\begin{vmatrix} \boldsymbol{A} & \boldsymbol{B} \\ \boldsymbol{C} & \boldsymbol{D} \end{vmatrix} = |\boldsymbol{A}| \cdot |\boldsymbol{D} - \boldsymbol{C}\boldsymbol{A}^{-1}\boldsymbol{B}|.$$

A.24 Let $\boldsymbol{A}$ and $\boldsymbol{B}$ be symmetric matrices such that $\boldsymbol{A} \leq \boldsymbol{B}$.

(a) If $\boldsymbol{A}$ and $\boldsymbol{B}$ are positive definite, show that $\boldsymbol{B}^{-1} \leq \boldsymbol{A}^{-1}$.

(b) If $\boldsymbol{A}$ and $\boldsymbol{B}$ are nonnegative definite, show that $\boldsymbol{A}\boldsymbol{B}^{-}\boldsymbol{A} \leq \boldsymbol{A}$. Does $\boldsymbol{A}\boldsymbol{B}^{-}\boldsymbol{A}$ depend on the choice of the g-inverse?

A.25 Prove that the converse of part (a) of Proposition A.22 does not hold, that is, for symmetric and nonnegative definite matrices $\boldsymbol{A}$ and $\boldsymbol{B}$ satisfying the condition $\mathcal{C}(\boldsymbol{A}) \subseteq \mathcal{C}(\boldsymbol{B})$, one does not necessarily have $\boldsymbol{A} \leq \boldsymbol{B}$.

A.26 Show the Cramer-Rao lower bound on the variance of an unbiased estimator (Proposition B.14) is smaller whenever the information matrix larger in the sense of the Löwner order.

A.27 Prove the following results for the Kronecker product of two matrices $\boldsymbol{A}$ and $\boldsymbol{B}$.

(a) $\boldsymbol{P}_{A \otimes B} = \boldsymbol{P}_{A} \otimes \boldsymbol{P}_{B}$.

(b) If $\boldsymbol{A}$ and $\boldsymbol{B}$ have full column rank, so does $\boldsymbol{A} \otimes \boldsymbol{B}$.

(c) $\rho(\boldsymbol{A} \otimes \boldsymbol{B}) = \rho(\boldsymbol{A})\rho(\boldsymbol{B})$.

(d) If $\boldsymbol{A}_1\boldsymbol{A}_2$ and $\boldsymbol{B}_1\boldsymbol{B}_2$ are rank-factorizations of $\boldsymbol{A}$ and $\boldsymbol{B}$, respectively, then $(\boldsymbol{A}_1 \otimes \boldsymbol{B}_1)(\boldsymbol{A}_2 \otimes \boldsymbol{B}_2)$ is a rank-factorization of $\boldsymbol{A} \otimes \boldsymbol{B}$.

A.28 If $\boldsymbol{A}$ and $\boldsymbol{B}$ are symmetric and positive definite matrices, show that $|\boldsymbol{A} \otimes \boldsymbol{B}| = |\boldsymbol{A}|^{\rho(\boldsymbol{B})} \cdot |\boldsymbol{B}|^{\rho(\boldsymbol{A})}$.

A.29 Show that $\text{vec}(\boldsymbol{A}\boldsymbol{B}\boldsymbol{C}) = (\boldsymbol{C}' \otimes \boldsymbol{A})\text{vec}(\boldsymbol{B})$.

A.30 Show that the system of equations $\boldsymbol{A}\boldsymbol{x} = \boldsymbol{b}$ is consistent (that, is, there is a solution for $\boldsymbol{x}$) if and only if $\boldsymbol{l}'\boldsymbol{A} = \boldsymbol{0}$ implies $\boldsymbol{l}'\boldsymbol{b} = 0$.

A.31 If $\boldsymbol{B}$ is a symmetric matrix such that $\boldsymbol{A}\boldsymbol{B}\boldsymbol{A}$ is well-defined, then show that $\boldsymbol{A}\boldsymbol{B}\boldsymbol{A} = \boldsymbol{0}$ if and only if $\boldsymbol{B}$ is of the form $\boldsymbol{C} - \boldsymbol{P}_{A}\boldsymbol{C}\boldsymbol{P}_{A}$ for some symmetric matrix $\boldsymbol{C}$.

A.32 (a) If $\boldsymbol{A}$ is a nonnegative definite matrix and $\boldsymbol{a} \in \mathcal{C}(\boldsymbol{A})$, show that $(\boldsymbol{l}'\boldsymbol{a})^2/\boldsymbol{l}'\boldsymbol{A}\boldsymbol{l} \leq \boldsymbol{a}'\boldsymbol{A}^{-}\boldsymbol{a}$ for all non-null vectors $\boldsymbol{l}$ of appropriate order.

(b) If $\boldsymbol{A}$ is a nonnegative definite matrix and $\mathcal{C}(\boldsymbol{B}) \subseteq \mathcal{C}(\boldsymbol{A})$, show that $\boldsymbol{l}'\boldsymbol{B}\boldsymbol{B}'\boldsymbol{l}/\boldsymbol{l}'\boldsymbol{A}\boldsymbol{l} \leq \|\boldsymbol{B}'\boldsymbol{A}^{-}\boldsymbol{B}\|$ for all non-null vectors $\boldsymbol{l}$ of appropriate order.

Appendix B

Review of Statistical Theory

In this appendix we summarize the statistical theory which serves as the background for the various chapters in the book. The aim is to present the results in a coherent and self-contained manner. In order to cover only the essential facts, we sometimes use weaker versions of some standard results. As mentioned on page 29, we do not make a notational distinction between a random vector and a particular realization of it.

B.1 Basic concepts of inference

Suppose the random vector $\boldsymbol{y}$ has distribution $\boldsymbol{F}_\theta$, which involves a vector parameter $\boldsymbol{\theta}$ that can assume any value from a set $\boldsymbol{\Theta}$. If one has to draw inference about $\boldsymbol{\theta}$ from $\boldsymbol{y}$, a reasonable approach is to work with a vector-valued function $\boldsymbol{t}$ of $\boldsymbol{y}$ that has all the information which is relevant for $\boldsymbol{\theta}$. The concept of *sufficiency* is useful for this purpose. A statistic $\boldsymbol{t}(\boldsymbol{y})$ is called *sufficient* for the parameter $\boldsymbol{\theta}$ if the conditional distribution of $\boldsymbol{y}$ given $\boldsymbol{t}(\boldsymbol{y}) = \boldsymbol{t}_0$ does not involve $\boldsymbol{\theta}$. The idea of summarizing information through sufficient statistic is more meaningful when the summary is as brief as possible. A sufficient statistic $\boldsymbol{t}(\boldsymbol{y})$ is called *minimal* if it is a function of any other sufficient statistic almost surely for all $\boldsymbol{\theta}$. If we have a minimal sufficient statistic, we have no more than what we need to know from $\boldsymbol{y}$ about $\boldsymbol{\theta}$.

On the other hand, we can also identify the information that is *not* relevant for inference about $\boldsymbol{\theta}$. A statistic $\boldsymbol{z}(\boldsymbol{y})$ is called *ancillary* for $\boldsymbol{\theta}$ if the marginal distribution of $\boldsymbol{z}(\boldsymbol{y})$ does not depend on $\boldsymbol{\theta}$. An ancillary statistic is called *maximal* if every other ancillary statistic is almost surely equal to a function of it. Note that the value of a distribution function at any given point can be expressed as the expected value of an indicator function. Therefore, we can characterize a statistic $\boldsymbol{z}(\boldsymbol{y})$ as ancillary for the parameter $\boldsymbol{\theta}$ if the expectation of any function of $\boldsymbol{z}(\boldsymbol{y})$ does not involve $\boldsymbol{\theta}$. By the same token, we can characterize a statistic $\boldsymbol{t}(\boldsymbol{y})$ as sufficient for the parameter $\boldsymbol{\theta}$ if the conditional expectation of any function of $\boldsymbol{y}$ given $\boldsymbol{t}(\boldsymbol{y})$ is almost surely a function of $\boldsymbol{t}(\boldsymbol{y})$ and does not depend on $\boldsymbol{\theta}$.

Example B.1. Suppose the order-n vector $\boldsymbol{y}$ has the distribution $N(\mu\mathbf{1}, \boldsymbol{I})$. It is easy to see that the conditional distribution of $\boldsymbol{y}$ given $\mathbf{1}'\boldsymbol{y} = t_0$ is $N((t_0/n)\mathbf{1}, (\boldsymbol{I} - n^{-1}\mathbf{1}\mathbf{1}'))$, which does not depend on μ. Hence, $t(\boldsymbol{y}) = \mathbf{1}'\boldsymbol{y}$ is a sufficient statistic for μ. (This can also be proved via the factorization theorem given below.) The vector $\boldsymbol{y}$ is also sufficient. The statistic $\mathbf{1}'\boldsymbol{y}$ is minimal sufficient, but $\boldsymbol{y}$ is not.

The distribution of $\boldsymbol{z}(\boldsymbol{y}) = (\boldsymbol{I} - n^{-1}\mathbf{1}\mathbf{1}')\boldsymbol{y}$ does not depend on μ. Hence, any function of this vector is ancillary for μ. In particular, $\|(\boldsymbol{I} - n^{-1}\mathbf{1}\mathbf{1}')\boldsymbol{y}\|^2$ is ancillary, and has χ^2_{n-1} distribution, irrespective of μ. □

Sometimes even a minimal sufficient statistic contains redundant information in the sense that a function of it is ancillary. A sufficient statistic is most useful in summarizing the data if no nontrivial function of it is ancillary. A sufficient statistic $\boldsymbol{t}(\boldsymbol{y})$ is called *complete* if $E[g(\boldsymbol{t}(\boldsymbol{y}))] = \mathbf{0}$ for all $\boldsymbol{\theta} \in \boldsymbol{\Theta}$ implies that the function g is zero almost everywhere (i.e. over a set having probability 1) for all $\boldsymbol{\theta}$. A complete sufficient statistic may not always exist. Bahadur (1957) showed that if it does, then it must be minimal too (see Schervish, 1995, p. 94).

Example B.2. In Example B.1, where $\boldsymbol{y} \sim N(\mu\mathbf{1}, \sigma^2\boldsymbol{I})$, it can be shown that $\mathbf{1}'\boldsymbol{y}$ is complete, though the proof is beyond the scope of the present discussion. Since the statistic is also sufficient for μ, it is minimal. □

Example B.3. Suppose $y_1, \ldots, y_n$ are independent samples from the uniform distribution over the interval $(\theta - \frac{1}{2}, \theta + \frac{1}{2})$, $-\infty < \theta < \infty$. It can be seen that a minimal sufficient statistic for θ is

$$(y_{min}, y_{max}),$$

where y_{min} and y_{max} are the smallest and largest of the y_is, respectively. However, it is not complete, since

$$E\left(y_{max} - y_{min} - \frac{n-1}{n+1}\right) = 0 \quad \text{for all } \theta,$$

thus exhibiting a nontrivial function with zero expectation. □

The relation between a complete sufficient statistic and an ancillary statistic is brought out by the following result (Basu, 1958).

Proposition B.4. (Basu's Theorem) *If $\boldsymbol{t}(\boldsymbol{y})$ is a complete sufficient statistic for $\boldsymbol{\theta}$, it is independent of any ancillary statistic $\boldsymbol{z}(\boldsymbol{y})$.*

Proof. Note that $P(\boldsymbol{z}(\boldsymbol{y}) \in A)$ is independent of $\boldsymbol{\theta}$ whenever A is a set for which the probability is defined. Denoting $P(\boldsymbol{z}(\boldsymbol{y}) \in A|\boldsymbol{t}(\boldsymbol{y}) = \boldsymbol{t}_0) - P(\boldsymbol{z}(\boldsymbol{y}) \in A)$ by $g_A(\boldsymbol{t}_0)$, we have $E(g_A(\boldsymbol{t}(\boldsymbol{y}))) = 0$ for all $\boldsymbol{\theta}$. By completeness, g_A must be zero almost everywhere. Therefore, $\boldsymbol{t}(\boldsymbol{y})$ must be independent of $\boldsymbol{z}(\boldsymbol{y})$. □

See Schervish (1995) for a stronger version of the above theorem.

Example B.5. In Examples B.1 and B.2, the complete sufficient statistic $\boldsymbol{1}'\boldsymbol{y}$ and the ancillary $\|(\boldsymbol{I} - n^{-1}\boldsymbol{1}\boldsymbol{1}')\boldsymbol{y}\|^2$ are independent. □

A simple way of deriving a sufficient statistic is given in the following proposition.

Proposition B.6. (Factorization Theorem) *Let $f_{\boldsymbol{\theta}}$ be the probability density function or the probability mass function of the random vector $\boldsymbol{y}$, where $\boldsymbol{\theta}$ is a vector parameter which can assume any value from a set $\boldsymbol{\Theta}$. Then a statistic $\boldsymbol{t}(\boldsymbol{y})$ is sufficient for $\boldsymbol{\theta}$ if and only if $f_{\boldsymbol{\theta}}$ can be factorized as*

$$f_{\boldsymbol{\theta}}(\boldsymbol{y}) = g_{\boldsymbol{\theta}}(\boldsymbol{t}(\boldsymbol{y})) \cdot h(\boldsymbol{y}),$$

where $g_{\boldsymbol{\theta}}$ and h are nonnegative functions and h does not depend on $\boldsymbol{\theta}$.

Proof. We shall prove the result in the continuous case; the proof in the discrete case is similar. Suppose $f_{\boldsymbol{\theta}}$ can be factorized as stated in the proposition. Then the probability density function of $\boldsymbol{t}(\boldsymbol{y})$ at the point $\boldsymbol{t}_0$ is given by

$$p_{\boldsymbol{\theta}}(\boldsymbol{t}_0) = \int_{\boldsymbol{t}(\boldsymbol{y}) = \boldsymbol{t}_0} f_{\boldsymbol{\theta}}(\boldsymbol{y})d\boldsymbol{y} = g_{\boldsymbol{\theta}}(\boldsymbol{t}_0) \int_{\boldsymbol{t}(\boldsymbol{y}) = \boldsymbol{t}_0} h(\boldsymbol{y})d\boldsymbol{y} = g_{\boldsymbol{\theta}}(\boldsymbol{t}_0)H(\boldsymbol{t}_0),$$

for some function H. Thus, the conditional density of $\boldsymbol{y}$ given $\boldsymbol{t}(\boldsymbol{y}) = \boldsymbol{t}_0$ is

$$\frac{f_{\boldsymbol{\theta}}(\boldsymbol{y})}{p_{\boldsymbol{\theta}}(\boldsymbol{t}_0)} = \frac{g_{\boldsymbol{\theta}}(\boldsymbol{t}_0)h(\boldsymbol{y})}{g_{\boldsymbol{\theta}}(\boldsymbol{t}_0)H(\boldsymbol{t}_0)} = \frac{h(\boldsymbol{y})}{H(\boldsymbol{t}_0)},$$

which does not depend on $\boldsymbol{\theta}$. Therefore, $\boldsymbol{t}(\boldsymbol{y})$ is sufficient for $\boldsymbol{\theta}$.

In order to prove the converse, let $\boldsymbol{t}(\boldsymbol{y})$ be sufficient for $\boldsymbol{\theta}$. Then the conditional density of $\boldsymbol{y}$ given $\boldsymbol{t}(\boldsymbol{y}) = \boldsymbol{t}_0$,

$$\frac{f_{\boldsymbol{\theta}}(\boldsymbol{y})}{p_{\boldsymbol{\theta}}(\boldsymbol{t}_0)},$$

does not depend on $\boldsymbol{\theta}$. If we denote this ratio by $k(\boldsymbol{y}, \boldsymbol{t}_0)$, then we have $f_\theta(\boldsymbol{y}) = p_\theta(\boldsymbol{t}_0) \cdot k(\boldsymbol{y}, \boldsymbol{t}_0)$ for all $\boldsymbol{t}_0$. In particular, we have

$$f_\theta(\boldsymbol{y}) = p_\theta(\boldsymbol{t}(\boldsymbol{y})) \cdot k(\boldsymbol{y}, \boldsymbol{t}(\boldsymbol{y})),$$

which is of the form stated in the proposition. □

A family $\mathcal{P} = \{f_\theta, \boldsymbol{\theta}_{k\times 1} \in \boldsymbol{\Theta}\}$ of distributions of $\boldsymbol{y}$ is said to form a k-dimensional exponential family if the density (or probability mass function) has the form

$$f_\theta(\boldsymbol{y}) = c(\boldsymbol{\theta}) \exp\left[\sum_{j=1}^{k} q_j(\boldsymbol{\theta}) t_j(\boldsymbol{y})\right] \cdot h(\boldsymbol{y}), \tag{B.1}$$

where $q_1(\boldsymbol{\theta}), \ldots, q_k(\boldsymbol{\theta})$ and $c(\boldsymbol{\theta})$ are real-valued functions of the parameter $\boldsymbol{\theta}$ and $t_1(\boldsymbol{y}), \ldots, t_k(\boldsymbol{y})$ and $h(\boldsymbol{y})$ are real-valued statistics. The quantities $q_1(\boldsymbol{\theta}), \ldots, q_k(\boldsymbol{\theta})$ are called the *natural parameters* of the exponential family. Most common families of distributions like the binomial, gamma, normal and multivariate normal can be shown to belong to such an exponential family.

The following result shows that exponential families admit sufficient statistics for natural parameters which, under general conditions, are also minimal and complete.

Proposition B.7. *If $\boldsymbol{y}_1, \ldots, \boldsymbol{y}_n$ are samples from the distribution (B.1), and the set $\{(q_1(\boldsymbol{\theta}), q_2(\boldsymbol{\theta}), \ldots, q_k(\boldsymbol{\theta})), \boldsymbol{\theta} \in \boldsymbol{\Theta}\}$ contains a k-dimensional rectangle, then the vector statistic*

$$\boldsymbol{t}(\boldsymbol{y}_1, \ldots, \boldsymbol{y}_n) = \left(\sum_{i=1}^{n} t_1(\boldsymbol{y}_i) : \sum_{i=1}^{n} t_2(\boldsymbol{y}_i) : \cdots : \sum_{i=1}^{n} t_k(\boldsymbol{y}_i)\right)'$$

is complete and sufficient for the natural parameters $q_1(\boldsymbol{\theta}), \ldots, q_k(\boldsymbol{\theta})$.

Proof. Sufficiency follows directly from the factorization theorem. For proof of completeness, we refer the reader to Lehmann and Casella (1998). □

Example B.8. Let the p-dimensional random vectors $\boldsymbol{y}_1, \ldots, \boldsymbol{y}_n$ be samples from $N(\boldsymbol{\mu}, \boldsymbol{\Sigma})$, where $\boldsymbol{\Sigma}$ is positive definite. Here, $\boldsymbol{\theta}$ consists of the elements of $\boldsymbol{\mu}$ and $\boldsymbol{\Sigma}$. Define the sample mean vector and sample variance-covariance matrix as

$$\bar{\boldsymbol{y}} = n^{-1} \sum_{i=1}^{n} \boldsymbol{y}_i, \qquad \boldsymbol{S} = n^{-1} \sum_{i=1}^{n} (\boldsymbol{y}_i - \bar{\boldsymbol{y}})(\boldsymbol{y}_i - \bar{\boldsymbol{y}})'.$$

Then the joint density of $\boldsymbol{y}_1, \ldots, \boldsymbol{y}_n$ can be written as

$$\begin{aligned}
\prod_{i=1}^{n} f_\theta(\boldsymbol{y}_i) &= (2\pi|\boldsymbol{\Sigma}|)^{-n/2} \exp\left[-\frac{1}{2}\sum_{i=1}^{n}(\boldsymbol{y}_i-\boldsymbol{\mu})'\boldsymbol{\Sigma}^{-1}(\boldsymbol{y}_i-\boldsymbol{\mu})\right] \\
&\propto |\boldsymbol{\Sigma}|^{-n/2}\exp\left[-\frac{1}{2}\sum_{i=1}^{n}(\boldsymbol{y}_i-\bar{\boldsymbol{y}}+\bar{\boldsymbol{y}}-\boldsymbol{\mu})'\boldsymbol{\Sigma}^{-1}(\boldsymbol{y}_i-\bar{\boldsymbol{y}}+\bar{\boldsymbol{y}}-\boldsymbol{\mu})\right] \\
&= |\boldsymbol{\Sigma}|^{-n/2}\exp\left[-\frac{1}{2}\sum_{i=1}^{n}(\boldsymbol{y}_i-\bar{\boldsymbol{y}})'\boldsymbol{\Sigma}^{-1}(\boldsymbol{y}_i-\bar{\boldsymbol{y}})+n(\bar{\boldsymbol{y}}-\boldsymbol{\mu})'\boldsymbol{\Sigma}^{-1}(\bar{\boldsymbol{y}}-\boldsymbol{\mu})\right] \\
&= |\boldsymbol{\Sigma}|^{-n/2}\exp\left[-\frac{n}{2}\left(\mathrm{tr}(\boldsymbol{\Sigma}^{-1}\boldsymbol{S})+\bar{\boldsymbol{y}}'\boldsymbol{\Sigma}^{-1}\bar{\boldsymbol{y}}-2\bar{\boldsymbol{y}}'\boldsymbol{\Sigma}^{-1}\boldsymbol{\mu}+\boldsymbol{\mu}'\boldsymbol{\Sigma}^{-1}\boldsymbol{\mu}\right)\right] \\
&= |\boldsymbol{\Sigma}|^{-n/2}\exp\left[-\frac{n}{2}\boldsymbol{\mu}'\boldsymbol{\Sigma}^{-1}\boldsymbol{\mu}\right] \\
&\quad\cdot\exp\left[-\frac{1}{2}\left(\mathrm{tr}(\boldsymbol{\Sigma}^{-1}(\boldsymbol{S}+\bar{\boldsymbol{y}}\bar{\boldsymbol{y}}'))-2\bar{\boldsymbol{y}}'\boldsymbol{\Sigma}^{-1}\boldsymbol{\mu}\right)\right].
\end{aligned}$$

Since the last expression is of the form (B.1), $\bar{\boldsymbol{y}}$ and $\boldsymbol{S}+\bar{\boldsymbol{y}}\bar{\boldsymbol{y}}'$ must be complete and sufficient for the elements of $\boldsymbol{\Sigma}^{-1}\boldsymbol{\mu}$ and $\boldsymbol{\Sigma}$. Therefore, $\bar{\boldsymbol{y}}$ and $\boldsymbol{S}$ are complete and sufficient for $\boldsymbol{\mu}$ and $\boldsymbol{\Sigma}$. □

B.2 Point estimation

Suppose $\boldsymbol{t}(\boldsymbol{y})$ is used to estimate $\boldsymbol{g}(\boldsymbol{\theta})$, a function of $\boldsymbol{\theta}$. It cannot be a good estimator if it is systematically away from $\boldsymbol{g}(\boldsymbol{\theta})$. The quantity $E[\boldsymbol{t}(\boldsymbol{y})]-\boldsymbol{g}(\boldsymbol{\theta})$ is called the *bias* of $\boldsymbol{t}(\boldsymbol{y})$. If the bias is zero for all $\boldsymbol{\theta}\in\boldsymbol{\Theta}$, the estimator is called *unbiased*.

The bias is only one criterion for judging the quality of an estimator. The ill-effects of the deviation of $\boldsymbol{t}(\boldsymbol{y})$ from $\boldsymbol{g}(\boldsymbol{\theta})$ is generally expressed in terms of a function $L(\boldsymbol{\theta},\boldsymbol{t}(\boldsymbol{y}))$, called the *loss-function*, which is nonnegative everywhere and zero at $\boldsymbol{t}(\boldsymbol{y})=\boldsymbol{g}(\boldsymbol{\theta})$. Often the loss function is also assumed to be convex in the second argument. The *risk function* of the estimator $\boldsymbol{t}$ is defined as $R(\boldsymbol{\theta},\boldsymbol{t})=E[L(\boldsymbol{\theta},\boldsymbol{t}(\boldsymbol{y}))]$. An important example in the case of a real-valued g (and a scalar t) is the squared error loss function, defined as $L(\boldsymbol{\theta},t(\boldsymbol{y}))=(t(\boldsymbol{y})-g(\boldsymbol{\theta}))^2$. For this loss function, the risk of t, $E[(t(\boldsymbol{y})-g(\boldsymbol{\theta}))^2]$ is called the *mean squared error* (MSE). It is easy to see that

$$E[(t(\boldsymbol{y})-g(\boldsymbol{\theta}))^2]=Var(t(\boldsymbol{y}))+[E(t(\boldsymbol{y}))-g(\boldsymbol{\theta})]^2,$$

that is, the mean squared error of $t(\boldsymbol{y})$ is the sum of its variance and squared bias. In particular, the risk of an unbiased estimator with respect to the squared error loss function is just its variance.

If $\boldsymbol{g}$ is a vector-valued function of $\boldsymbol{\theta}$, the *MSE matrix* of an estimator $\boldsymbol{t}(\boldsymbol{y})$ is defined as $E[(\boldsymbol{t}(\boldsymbol{y}) - \boldsymbol{g}(\boldsymbol{\theta}))(\boldsymbol{t}(\boldsymbol{y}) - \boldsymbol{g}(\boldsymbol{\theta}))']$. The MSE matrix of $\boldsymbol{t}(\boldsymbol{y})$ can be decomposed as

$$\begin{aligned} &E[(\boldsymbol{t}(\boldsymbol{y}) - \boldsymbol{g}(\boldsymbol{\theta}))(\boldsymbol{t}(\boldsymbol{y}) - \boldsymbol{g}(\boldsymbol{\theta}))'] \\ &= D(\boldsymbol{t}(\boldsymbol{y})) + [E(\boldsymbol{t}(\boldsymbol{y})) - \boldsymbol{g}(\boldsymbol{\theta})][E(\boldsymbol{t}(\boldsymbol{y})) - \boldsymbol{g}(\boldsymbol{\theta})]'. \end{aligned}$$

In the above, the first term is the dispersion of $\boldsymbol{t}(\boldsymbol{y})$, while the second term is the bias vector times its transpose.

Returning to the estimation of the real-valued functions of $\boldsymbol{\theta}$, the following result underscores the importance of a sufficient statistic in improving estimators by reducing their risk functions.

Proposition B.9. (Rao-Blackwell theorem) *In the above set-up, let* $\boldsymbol{t}(\boldsymbol{y})$ *be sufficient for* $\boldsymbol{\theta} \in \boldsymbol{\Theta}$, $s(\boldsymbol{y})$ *be an estimator of a real-valued function* $g(\boldsymbol{\theta})$ *and* L *be a loss function which is convex in the second argument. If* $s(\boldsymbol{y})$ *has a finite expectation, then the risk function (with respect to* L*) of the revised estimator* $E[s(\boldsymbol{y})|\boldsymbol{t}(\boldsymbol{y})]$ *is at most as large as that of* $s(\boldsymbol{y})$.

Proof. Let $h(\boldsymbol{t}_0) = E[s(\boldsymbol{y})|\boldsymbol{t}(\boldsymbol{y}) = \boldsymbol{t}_0]$. According to the Jensen's equality, a convex function of the expected value of a random variable is less than or equal to the expectation of that convex function of the random variable. Choosing the random variable as $s(\boldsymbol{y})$ and taking all the expectations with respect to the conditional distribution of $\boldsymbol{y}$ given $\boldsymbol{t}(\boldsymbol{y}) = \boldsymbol{t}_0$, we have for all $\boldsymbol{\theta}$

$$L(\boldsymbol{\theta}, h(\boldsymbol{t}_0)) \leq E[L(\boldsymbol{\theta}, s(\boldsymbol{y}))|\boldsymbol{t}(\boldsymbol{y}) = \boldsymbol{t}_0].$$

Integrating both sides with respect to the distribution of $\boldsymbol{t}(\boldsymbol{y})$, we obtain $R(\boldsymbol{\theta}, h(\boldsymbol{t})) \leq R(\boldsymbol{\theta}, s)$. □

If we choose to work with unbiased estimators and the squared error loss function, then the ideal choice would be an estimator that has the minimum risk, which corresponds to the minimum variance. An unbiased estimator of $g(\boldsymbol{\theta})$ that has uniformly (in $\boldsymbol{\theta}$) smaller variance than all other unbiased estimators is called the *uniformly minimum variance unbiased estimator* (UMVUE). The UMVUE need not always exist. However, if it exists then it is unique. We shall prove the uniqueness with the help of an interesting characterization of UMVUEs, provided by the following proposition.

Proposition B.10. *In the above set-up, let* $t(\boldsymbol{y})$ *be an unbiased estimator of* $g(\boldsymbol{\theta})$ *with finite variance for all* $\boldsymbol{\theta} \in \boldsymbol{\Theta}$. *It is a UMVUE of* $g(\boldsymbol{\theta})$ *if and* *only if it is uncorrelated with every unbiased estimator of zero having finite variance for all* $\boldsymbol{\theta} \in \boldsymbol{\Theta}$.

Proof. Let $t(\boldsymbol{y})$ be uncorrelated with every unbiased estimator of zero having finite variance, and let $s(\boldsymbol{y})$ be another unbiased estimator of $g(\boldsymbol{\theta})$. There is nothing to prove if $s(\boldsymbol{y})$ has infinite variance. Otherwise, $t(\boldsymbol{y})$ must be uncorrelated with $s(\boldsymbol{y}) - t(\boldsymbol{y})$. It follows that

$$\begin{aligned} Var(s(\boldsymbol{y})) &= Var(t(\boldsymbol{y}) + (s(\boldsymbol{y}) - t(\boldsymbol{y}))) \\ &= Var(t(\boldsymbol{y})) + Var((s(\boldsymbol{y}) - t(\boldsymbol{y}))) \geq Var(t(\boldsymbol{y})). \end{aligned}$$

Therefore, $t(\boldsymbol{y})$ must be a UMVUE.

To prove the converse, let $t(\boldsymbol{y})$ be correlated with $z(\boldsymbol{y})$, an unbiased estimator of zero with finite and positive variance. Using the principle of decorrelation (see Proposition 2.28), we can construct another unbiased estimator of $g(\boldsymbol{\theta})$,

$$s(\boldsymbol{y}) = t(\boldsymbol{y}) - Cov(t(\boldsymbol{y}), z(\boldsymbol{y}))[Var(z(\boldsymbol{y}))]^{-1} z(\boldsymbol{y}),$$

which is uncorrelated with $z(\boldsymbol{y})$. Thus, $t(\boldsymbol{y})$ is the sum of two uncorrelated random variables one of which is $s(\boldsymbol{y})$. It is easy to see that $t(\boldsymbol{y})$ has larger variance than $s(\boldsymbol{y})$, i.e. $t(\boldsymbol{y})$ cannot be a UMVUE. □

A consequence of the above proposition is that if $t_1(\boldsymbol{y})$ and $t_2(\boldsymbol{y})$ are two UMVUEs, both must be uncorrelated with $t_1(\boldsymbol{y}) - t_2(\boldsymbol{y})$. It follows that

$$\begin{aligned} & Var(t_1(\boldsymbol{y}) - t_2(\boldsymbol{y})) \\ & = Cov(t_1(\boldsymbol{y}), t_1(\boldsymbol{y}) - t_2(\boldsymbol{y})) - Cov(t_2(\boldsymbol{y}), t_1(\boldsymbol{y}) - t_2(\boldsymbol{y})) \quad = \quad 0, \end{aligned}$$

that is, $t_1(\boldsymbol{y}) = t_2(\boldsymbol{y})$ almost surely. This proves the uniqueness of the UMVUE whenever it exists.

Given an unbiased estimator of $g(\boldsymbol{\theta})$ and a complete sufficient statistic for $\boldsymbol{\theta}$, the UMVUE can be determined by the following extension of Proposition B.9. It says in essence, that any function of a complete sufficient statistic is the unique UMVUE of its own expectation.

Proposition B.11. (Lehmann-Scheffé theorem) *In the above set-up, let* $g(\boldsymbol{\theta})$ *have an unbiased estimator* $s(\boldsymbol{y})$*, and* $t(\boldsymbol{y})$ *be a complete sufficient statistic for* $\boldsymbol{\theta}$*. Then* $E(s(\boldsymbol{y})|t(\boldsymbol{y}))$ *is the (almost surely) unique UMVUE of* $g(\boldsymbol{\theta})$.

Proof. Let $U_1(\boldsymbol{y}) = E(s(\boldsymbol{y})|t(\boldsymbol{y}))$. It is easy to see that $U_1(\boldsymbol{y})$ is a function of $t(\boldsymbol{y})$, and is unbiased for $g(\boldsymbol{\theta})$. To prove that it is the UMVUE, let $U_2(\boldsymbol{y})$ be another unbiased estimator of $g(\boldsymbol{\theta})$ with smaller variance than $U_1(\boldsymbol{y})$. We can assume without loss of generality that $U_2(\boldsymbol{y})$ is a function of t also (if not, we can reduce its variance by conditioning on $t(\boldsymbol{y})$, while preserving unbiasedness). Note that $E[U_1(t(\boldsymbol{y})) - U_2(t(\boldsymbol{y}))] = 0$ for all $\boldsymbol{\theta}$. Because of the completeness of $t(\boldsymbol{y})$, we must have $U_1(t(\boldsymbol{y})) - U_2(t(\boldsymbol{y})) = 0$ with probability 1 for all $\boldsymbol{\theta}$. Therefore, $U_2(\boldsymbol{y})$ cannot have smaller variance than $U_1(\boldsymbol{y})$. □

Example B.12. Let $\boldsymbol{y} \sim N(\mu\mathbf{1}, \sigma^2\boldsymbol{I})$ as in Example B.1. The statistic $t(\boldsymbol{y}) = \mathbf{1}'\boldsymbol{y}$ is complete and sufficient for μ. Any component of $\boldsymbol{y}$ is an unbiased estimator of μ. We can find the unique UMVUE of μ by taking the conditional expectation of any of these given $t(\boldsymbol{y})$. The result turns out to be $n^{-1}\mathbf{1}'\boldsymbol{y}$, the sample mean (see Exercise B.6).

Further, using the result of Example B.8 for $p = 1$, we conclude that $n^{-1}\mathbf{1}'\boldsymbol{y}$ and $n^{-1}\|\boldsymbol{y}-(n^{-1}\mathbf{1}'\boldsymbol{y})\mathbf{1}\|^2$ are complete and sufficient statistics for μ and σ^2. As $n^{-1}\mathbf{1}'\boldsymbol{y}$ and $(n-1)^{-1}\|\boldsymbol{y}-(n^{-1}\mathbf{1}'\boldsymbol{y})\mathbf{1}\|^2$ are unbiased estimators of μ and σ^2, respectively, and are functions of the complete and sufficient statistics, these must be UMVUEs. □

Apart from the UMVUE (which may not always exist), there are many formal methods of point estimation including the method of moments, the method of maximum likelihood, and several distance based methods. We shall briefly describe the method of maximum likelihood (ML) here.

Suppose a given observation $\boldsymbol{y}$ has a probability density function (or probability mass function — in the discrete case) $f_{\boldsymbol{\theta}}(\boldsymbol{y})$, for a given parameter value $\boldsymbol{\theta}$. One can also interpret $f_{\boldsymbol{\theta}}(\boldsymbol{y})$ as a function of $\boldsymbol{\theta}$ for a given/observed value of $\boldsymbol{y}$. In the latter sense, it represents the likelihood of the parameter $\boldsymbol{\theta}$ to have generated the observed vector $\boldsymbol{y}$. When $f_{\boldsymbol{\theta}}(\boldsymbol{y})$ is viewed as a function of $\boldsymbol{\theta}$ for fixed $\boldsymbol{y}$, it is called the *likelihood function* of $\boldsymbol{\theta}$. If we know $\boldsymbol{y}$ and would like to figure out which value of $\boldsymbol{\theta}$ is most likely to have generated this $\boldsymbol{y}$, we should then ask for what $\boldsymbol{\theta}$ is $f_{\boldsymbol{\theta}}(\boldsymbol{y})$ a maximum. A value $\widehat{\boldsymbol{\theta}}$ satisfying

$$f_{\widehat{\boldsymbol{\theta}}}(\boldsymbol{y}) \geq f_{\boldsymbol{\theta}}(\boldsymbol{y}) \quad \forall\, \boldsymbol{\theta}$$

is called the maximum likelihood estimator (MLE) of $\boldsymbol{\theta}$. Provided a number of regularity conditions hold and the derivatives exist, such a point can be obtained by methods of calculus. Since $\log p$ is a monotonically increasing function of p, maximizing $f_{\boldsymbol{\theta}}(\boldsymbol{y})$ is equivalent to maximizing $\log f_{\boldsymbol{\theta}}(\boldsymbol{y})$ with respect to $\boldsymbol{\theta}$, which is often easier (e.g. when $f_{\boldsymbol{\theta}}(\boldsymbol{y})$ is in the exponential family). The maximum occurs at a point where the gradient vector satisfies the likelihood equation

$$\frac{\partial \log f_{\boldsymbol{\theta}}(\boldsymbol{y})}{\partial \boldsymbol{\theta}} = \mathbf{0},$$

and the matrix of second derivatives (Hessian matrix)

$$\frac{\partial^2 \log f_{\boldsymbol{\theta}}(\boldsymbol{y})}{\partial \boldsymbol{\theta} \partial \boldsymbol{\theta}'}$$

is negative definite.

Example B.13. Let $\boldsymbol{y}_{n \times 1} \sim N(\mu \mathbf{1}, \sigma^2 \boldsymbol{I})$. Here, $\boldsymbol{\theta} = (\mu : \sigma^2)'$. It can be easily seen that

$$\log f_{\boldsymbol{\theta}}(\boldsymbol{y}) = -(n/2)\log(2\pi\sigma^2) - (\boldsymbol{y} - \mu\mathbf{1})'(\boldsymbol{y} - \mu\mathbf{1})/(2\sigma^2).$$

Consequently

$$\frac{\partial \log f_{\boldsymbol{\theta}}(\boldsymbol{y})}{\partial \boldsymbol{\theta}} = \begin{pmatrix} -\dfrac{n\mu - \mathbf{1}'\boldsymbol{y}}{\sigma^2} \\ -\dfrac{n}{2\sigma^2} + \dfrac{(\boldsymbol{y} - \mu\mathbf{1})'(\boldsymbol{y} - \mu\mathbf{1})}{2(\sigma^2)^2} \end{pmatrix}.$$

Equating this vector to zero, we obtain

$$\widehat{\mu} = n^{-1}\mathbf{1}'\boldsymbol{y},$$
$$\text{and } \widehat{\sigma^2} = n^{-1}(\boldsymbol{y} - \widehat{\mu}\mathbf{1})'(\boldsymbol{y} - \widehat{\mu}\mathbf{1})$$

as the unique solution. Note that $\widehat{\mu}$ and $\widehat{\sigma^2}$ are the sample mean and sample variance, respectively. These would be the respective MLEs of μ and σ^2 if the Hessian matrix is negative definite. Indeed,

$$\left.\frac{\partial^2 \log f_{\boldsymbol{\theta}}(\boldsymbol{y})}{\partial \boldsymbol{\theta} \partial \boldsymbol{\theta}'}\right|_{\boldsymbol{\theta} = \widehat{\boldsymbol{\theta}}} = \begin{pmatrix} -\dfrac{n}{\widehat{\sigma^2}} & \dfrac{n\widehat{\mu} - \mathbf{1}'\boldsymbol{y}}{(\widehat{\sigma^2})^2} \\ \dfrac{n\widehat{\mu} - \mathbf{1}'\boldsymbol{y}}{(\widehat{\sigma^2})^2} & -\dfrac{\|\boldsymbol{y} - \widehat{\mu}\mathbf{1}\|^2}{(\widehat{\sigma^2})^3} + \dfrac{n}{2(\widehat{\sigma^2})^2} \end{pmatrix}$$
$$= -\begin{pmatrix} n/\widehat{\sigma^2} & 0 \\ 0 & n/(2(\widehat{\sigma^2})^2) \end{pmatrix},$$

which is obviously negative definite. □

Recall that, when a sufficient statistic $\boldsymbol{t}(\boldsymbol{y})$ is available, the density of $\boldsymbol{y}$ can be factored as

$$f_{\boldsymbol{\theta}}(\boldsymbol{y}) = g_{\boldsymbol{\theta}}(\boldsymbol{t}(\boldsymbol{y})) \cdot h(\boldsymbol{y})$$

in view of the factorization theorem (Proposition B.6). Therefore, maximizing the log-likelihood is equivalent to maximizing $\log g_{\boldsymbol{\theta}}(\boldsymbol{t}(\boldsymbol{y}))$. The value of $\boldsymbol{\theta}$ which maximizes this quantity must depend on $\boldsymbol{y}$, only through $\boldsymbol{t}(\boldsymbol{y})$. Thus, the MLE is a function of every sufficient statistic.

It can be shown that under some regularity conditions, the bias of the MLE goes to zero as the sample size goes to infinity. Thus, it is said to be *asymptotically unbiased.* On the other hand, a UMVUE is always unbiased.

We now discuss a theoretical limit on the dispersion of an unbiased estimator, regardless of the method of estimation. Let $f_{\boldsymbol{\theta}}(\boldsymbol{y})$ be the likelihood function of the r-dimensional vector parameter $\boldsymbol{\theta}$ corresponding to observation $\boldsymbol{y}$. Let

$$\mathcal{I}(\boldsymbol{\theta}) = E\left(\left(-\frac{\partial^2 \log f_{\boldsymbol{\theta}}(\boldsymbol{y})}{\partial\theta_i\partial\theta_j}\right)\right), \tag{B.2}$$

assuming that the derivatives and the expectation exist. The matrix $\mathcal{I}(\boldsymbol{\theta})$ is called the (Fisher) *information matrix* for $\boldsymbol{\theta}$. The information matrix can be shown to be an indicator of sensitivity of the distribution of $\boldsymbol{y}$ to changes in the value of $\boldsymbol{\theta}$ (larger sensitivity implies greater potential of knowing $\boldsymbol{\theta}$ from the observation $\boldsymbol{y}$).

Proposition B.14. *Under the above set-up, let $\boldsymbol{t}(\boldsymbol{y})$ be an unbiased estimator of the k-dimensional vector parameter $\boldsymbol{g}(\boldsymbol{\theta})$, and let*

$$\frac{\partial g_i(\boldsymbol{\theta})}{\partial\theta_j} = E\left[t_i(\boldsymbol{y})\frac{\partial \log f_{\boldsymbol{\theta}}(\boldsymbol{y})}{\partial\theta_j}\right],\ i,j=1,\ldots,r;\quad \boldsymbol{G}(\boldsymbol{\theta}) = \left(\left(\frac{\partial g_i(\theta)}{\partial\theta_j}\right)\right).$$

Then

$$D(\boldsymbol{t}(\boldsymbol{y})) \geq \boldsymbol{G}(\boldsymbol{\theta})\mathcal{I}^-(\boldsymbol{\theta})\boldsymbol{G}'(\boldsymbol{\theta})$$

in the sense of the Löwner order, and $\boldsymbol{G}(\boldsymbol{\theta})\mathcal{I}^-(\boldsymbol{\theta})\boldsymbol{G}(\boldsymbol{\theta})$ does not depend on the choice of the g-inverse.

Proof. Let $\boldsymbol{s}(\boldsymbol{y}) = \dfrac{\partial \log f_{\boldsymbol{\theta}}(\boldsymbol{y})}{\partial\boldsymbol{\theta}}$. It is easy to see that $E[\boldsymbol{s}(\boldsymbol{y})] = \boldsymbol{0}$, and

$$E\left[\frac{\partial^2 \log f_{\boldsymbol{\theta}}(\boldsymbol{y})}{\partial\theta_i\partial\theta_j}\right] = E\left[\frac{\dfrac{\partial^2 f_{\boldsymbol{\theta}}(\boldsymbol{y})}{\partial\theta_i\partial\theta_j}}{f_{\boldsymbol{\theta}}(\boldsymbol{y})}\right] - E\left[\left(\frac{\dfrac{\partial f_{\boldsymbol{\theta}}(\boldsymbol{y})}{\partial\theta_i}}{f_{\boldsymbol{\theta}}(\boldsymbol{y})}\right)\left(\frac{\dfrac{\partial f_{\boldsymbol{\theta}}(\boldsymbol{y})}{\partial\theta_j}}{f_{\boldsymbol{\theta}}(\boldsymbol{y})}\right)\right]$$
$$= 0 - Cov(s_i(\boldsymbol{y}), s_j(\boldsymbol{y})),$$

that is, $D(\boldsymbol{s}(\boldsymbol{y})) = \mathcal{I}(\boldsymbol{\theta})$. Further $Cov(\boldsymbol{t}(\boldsymbol{y}), \boldsymbol{s}(\boldsymbol{y})) = \boldsymbol{G}(\boldsymbol{\theta})$. Hence, the dispersion matrix

$$D\begin{pmatrix}\boldsymbol{t}(\boldsymbol{y})\\ \boldsymbol{s}(\boldsymbol{y})\end{pmatrix} = \begin{pmatrix}D(\boldsymbol{t}(\boldsymbol{y})) & \boldsymbol{G}(\boldsymbol{\theta})\\ \boldsymbol{G}'(\boldsymbol{\theta}) & \mathcal{I}(\boldsymbol{\theta})\end{pmatrix}$$

must be nonnegative definite. The result of Exercise A.20(a) indicates that $D(\boldsymbol{t}(\boldsymbol{y})) - \boldsymbol{G}(\boldsymbol{\theta})\mathcal{I}^{-}(\boldsymbol{\theta})\boldsymbol{G}'(\boldsymbol{\theta})$ is nonnegative definite. The inequality follows. The invariance of $\boldsymbol{G}(\boldsymbol{\theta})\mathcal{I}^{-}(\boldsymbol{\theta})\boldsymbol{G}(\boldsymbol{\theta})'$ on the choice of $\mathcal{I}^{-}(\boldsymbol{\theta})$ is a consequence of Propositions 2.13(b) and A.10(f). □

The proof of Proposition B.14 reveals that the information matrix has the following alternative expressions

$$\mathcal{I}(\boldsymbol{\theta}) = -E\left(\frac{\partial^2 \log f_{\boldsymbol{\theta}}(\boldsymbol{y})}{\partial\boldsymbol{\theta}\partial\boldsymbol{\theta}'}\right) = E\left[\left(\frac{\partial \log f_{\boldsymbol{\theta}}(\boldsymbol{y})}{\partial\boldsymbol{\theta}}\right)\left(\frac{\partial \log f_{\boldsymbol{\theta}}(\boldsymbol{y})}{\partial\boldsymbol{\theta}}\right)'\right].$$

The lower bound on $D(\boldsymbol{t}(\boldsymbol{y}))$ given in Proposition B.14 depends only on the distribution of $\boldsymbol{y}$, and the result holds for any unbiased estimator, irrespective of the method of estimation. This result is known as the *information inequality* or *Cramer-Rao inequality.* The Cramer-Rao lower bound holds even if there is no UMVUE for $\boldsymbol{g}(\boldsymbol{\theta})$. If $\boldsymbol{t}(\boldsymbol{y})$ is an unbiased estimator of $\boldsymbol{\theta}$ itself, then the information inequality simplifies to $D(\boldsymbol{t}(\boldsymbol{y})) \geq \mathcal{I}^{-1}(\boldsymbol{\theta})$.

Example B.15. Let $\boldsymbol{y}_{n\times 1} \sim N(\mu\mathbf{1}, \sigma^2\boldsymbol{I})$ and $\boldsymbol{\theta} = (\mu : \sigma^2)'$. It follows from the calculations of Example B.13 that

$$\mathcal{I}(\boldsymbol{\theta}) = \begin{pmatrix} n/\sigma^2 & 0 \\ 0 & n/(2\sigma^4) \end{pmatrix}.$$

The information matrix is proportional to the sample size. The Cramer-Rao lower bound on the variance of any unbiased estimator of μ and σ^2 are σ^2/n and $2\sigma^4/n$, respectively. The bound σ^2/n is *achieved* by the sample mean, which is the UMVUE as well as the MLE of μ. The variance of the UMVUE of σ^2 (given in Example B.12) is $2\sigma^4/(n-1)$, and therefore this estimator does not achieve the Cramer-Rao lower bound. The variance of the MLE of σ^2 (given in Example B.13) is $2(n-1)\sigma^4/n^2$, which is *smaller* than the Cramer-Rao lower bound. However, the information inequality is not applicable to this estimator, as it is biased. □

If $t(\boldsymbol{y})$ is an unbiased estimator of the parameter $g(\boldsymbol{\theta})$ and b_g is the corresponding Cramer-Rao lower bound described in Proposition B.14, then the ratio $b_g/Var(t(\boldsymbol{y}))$ is called the *efficiency* of $\boldsymbol{t}(\boldsymbol{y})$.

The Cramer-Rao lower bound has a special significance for maximum likelihood estimators. Let $\boldsymbol{\theta}_0$ be the 'true' value of $\boldsymbol{\theta}$, and $\mathcal{I}(\boldsymbol{\theta})$ be the corresponding information matrix. It can be shown under some regularity conditions that, (a) the likelihood equation for $\boldsymbol{\theta}$ has at least one *consistent* solution $\widehat{\boldsymbol{\theta}}$ (that is, for all $\delta > 0$, the probability $P[\|\widehat{\boldsymbol{\theta}} - \boldsymbol{\theta}_0\| > \delta]$ goes to 0 as the sample size n goes to infinity), (b) the distribution function of $n^{1/2}(\widehat{\boldsymbol{\theta}} - \boldsymbol{\theta})$ converges pointwise to that of $N(\mathbf{0}, \boldsymbol{G}(\boldsymbol{\theta})\mathcal{I}^{-}(\boldsymbol{\theta}_0)\boldsymbol{G}'(\boldsymbol{\theta}))$, and (c) the consistent MLE is asymptotically unique in the sense that if $\widehat{\boldsymbol{\theta}}_1$ and $\widehat{\boldsymbol{\theta}}_2$ are distinct roots of the likelihood equation which are both consistent, then $n^{1/2}(\widehat{\boldsymbol{\theta}}_1 - \widehat{\boldsymbol{\theta}}_2)$ goes to $\mathbf{0}$ with probability 1 as n goes to infinity.

We refer the reader to Schervish (1995) for more discussion of Fisher information and other measures of information.

B.3 Bayesian estimation

Sometimes certain knowledge about the parameter $\boldsymbol{\theta}$ may be available prior to one's access to the vector of observations $\boldsymbol{y}$. Such knowledge may be subjective or based on past experience in similar experiments. Bayesian inference consists of making appropriate use of this prior knowledge. This knowledge is often expressed in terms of a *prior distribution* (or simply a *prior*) of $\boldsymbol{\theta}$, denoted by $\pi(\boldsymbol{\theta})$. Once a prior is attached to $\boldsymbol{\theta}$, the 'distribution' of $\boldsymbol{y}$ mentioned in the foregoing discussion has to be interpreted as the conditional distribution of $\boldsymbol{y}$ given $\boldsymbol{\theta}$. The average risk of the estimator $\boldsymbol{t}(\boldsymbol{y})$ with respect to the prior $\pi(\boldsymbol{\theta})$ is

$$r(\boldsymbol{t}, \pi) = \int R(\boldsymbol{\theta}, \boldsymbol{t})\, d\pi(\boldsymbol{\theta}),$$

where $R(\boldsymbol{\theta}, \boldsymbol{t})$ is the risk function, defined in Section B.2.

Definition B.16. An estimator which minimizes the average risk (also known as the *Bayes risk*) $r(\boldsymbol{t}, \pi)$ is called the *Bayes estimator* of $g(\boldsymbol{\theta})$ with respect to the prior π.

A Bayes estimator $\boldsymbol{t}$ of $g(\boldsymbol{\theta})$ is said to be *unique* if for any other Bayes estimator $\boldsymbol{s}$, $r(\boldsymbol{s}, \pi) \leq r(\boldsymbol{t}, \pi)$ implies that $P_{\theta}(\boldsymbol{t}(\boldsymbol{y}) \neq \boldsymbol{s}(\boldsymbol{y})) = 0$ for all $\boldsymbol{\theta} \in \boldsymbol{\Theta}$.

The comparison of estimators with respect to a risk function sometimes reveals the unsuitability of some estimators. For instance, if the risk function of one estimator is larger than that of another estimator for all values of the parameter, the former estimator should not be considered a competitor. Such an estimator is called an *inadmissible* estimator.

Definition B.17. An estimator t belonging to a class of estimators $\mathcal{A}$ is called *admissible* for the parameter $g(\boldsymbol{\theta})$ in the class $\mathcal{A}$ with respect to the loss function L if there is no estimator s in $\mathcal{A}$ such that $R(\boldsymbol{\theta}, s) \leq R(\boldsymbol{\theta}, t)$ for all $\boldsymbol{\theta} \in \boldsymbol{\Theta}$, with strict inequality for at least one $\boldsymbol{\theta} \in \boldsymbol{\Theta}$. □

The above definition can be used even when the scalar function g and the scalar statistic t are replaced by vector-valued $\boldsymbol{g}$ and $\boldsymbol{t}$. The risk continues to be defined as the expected loss, while the loss is a function of $\boldsymbol{\theta}$ and $\boldsymbol{t}$. The squared error loss function in the vector case is $\|\boldsymbol{t}(\boldsymbol{y})-\boldsymbol{g}(\boldsymbol{\theta})\|^2$.

Proposition B.18. *If a Bayes estimator is unique, then it is admissible.*

Proof. Let $\boldsymbol{t}$ be an inadmissible but unique Bayes estimator of $\boldsymbol{g}(\boldsymbol{\theta})$ with respect to the prior $\pi(\boldsymbol{\theta})$. Let $\boldsymbol{s}$ be another estimator such that $R(\boldsymbol{\theta},\boldsymbol{s}) \le R(\boldsymbol{\theta},\boldsymbol{t})$ for all $\boldsymbol{\theta}$ with strict inequality for some $\boldsymbol{\theta}$. It follows that $r(\boldsymbol{s},\pi) \le r(\boldsymbol{t},\pi)$, that is, $\boldsymbol{s}$ is another Bayes estimator. The uniqueness of $\boldsymbol{t}$ implies that $P_{\theta}(\boldsymbol{t}(\boldsymbol{y}) \ne \boldsymbol{s}(\boldsymbol{y})) = 0$ for all $\boldsymbol{\theta} \in \boldsymbol{\Theta}$. This contradicts the assumption that $R(\boldsymbol{\theta},\boldsymbol{s})$ is strictly less than $R(\boldsymbol{\theta},\boldsymbol{t})$ for some $\boldsymbol{\theta}$. □

We now obtain an explicit expression of the Bayes estimator in the case of the squared error loss function, and prove that it is essentially a biased estimator.

Proposition B.19. *In the above set up, let L be the squared error loss function.*

(a) The Bayes estimator of $\boldsymbol{g}(\boldsymbol{\theta})$ is $\mathbf{t}(\boldsymbol{y}) = E(\boldsymbol{g}(\boldsymbol{\theta})|\boldsymbol{y})$, where the expectation is taken with respect to the conditional distribution of $\boldsymbol{\theta}$ given $\boldsymbol{y}$.
(b) The Bayes estimator $\mathbf{t}(\boldsymbol{y})$ cannot be unbiased unless $\mathbf{t}(\boldsymbol{y})$ is almost surely equal to $\boldsymbol{g}(\boldsymbol{\theta})$.

Proof. It is easy to see that $\boldsymbol{t}(\boldsymbol{y})$, as defined in part (a), is the unique minimizer of $E[L(\boldsymbol{\theta},\boldsymbol{t}(\boldsymbol{y}))|\boldsymbol{y}]$. Therefore,

$$E[L(\boldsymbol{\theta},\boldsymbol{t}(\boldsymbol{y}))|\boldsymbol{y}] \le E[L(\boldsymbol{\theta},\boldsymbol{s}(\boldsymbol{y}))|\boldsymbol{y}]$$

for any other estimator $\boldsymbol{s}$ of $\boldsymbol{g}(\boldsymbol{\theta})$. By taking the expectation of both sides with respect to the distribution of $\boldsymbol{y}$, it follows that $\boldsymbol{t}(\boldsymbol{y})$ minimizes the Bayes risk.

In order to prove part (b), assume that $\boldsymbol{t}(\boldsymbol{y})$ is unbiased for $\boldsymbol{g}(\boldsymbol{\theta})$. Therefore, we have

$$E(\boldsymbol{t}(\boldsymbol{y})|\boldsymbol{\theta}) = \boldsymbol{g}(\boldsymbol{\theta}) \qquad \text{for all } \boldsymbol{\theta} \in \boldsymbol{\Theta}.$$

Therefore,

$$\begin{aligned} E[\|\boldsymbol{g}(\boldsymbol{\theta})\|^2] = E[(\boldsymbol{g}(\boldsymbol{\theta}))'E(\boldsymbol{t}(\boldsymbol{y})|\boldsymbol{\theta})] &= E[(\boldsymbol{g}(\boldsymbol{\theta}))'\boldsymbol{t}(\boldsymbol{y})] \\ = E[(\boldsymbol{t}(\boldsymbol{y}))'E(\boldsymbol{g}(\boldsymbol{\theta})|\boldsymbol{y})] &= E[\|\boldsymbol{t}(\boldsymbol{y})\|^2]. \end{aligned}$$

Consequently

$$E[\|\boldsymbol{t}(\boldsymbol{y}) - \boldsymbol{g}(\boldsymbol{\theta})\|^2] = E[\|\boldsymbol{t}(\boldsymbol{y})\|^2] + E[\|\boldsymbol{g}(\boldsymbol{\theta})\|^2] - 2E[(\boldsymbol{g}(\boldsymbol{\theta}))'\boldsymbol{t}(\boldsymbol{y})] = 0.$$

This implies that $E(\|\boldsymbol{t}(\boldsymbol{y}) - \boldsymbol{g}(\boldsymbol{\theta})\|^2) = 0$, where the expectation is taken over the distributions of $\boldsymbol{y}$ and $\boldsymbol{\theta}$. Therefore, $\|\boldsymbol{t}(\boldsymbol{y}) - \boldsymbol{g}(\boldsymbol{\theta})\|^2 = 0$ with probability 1. □

It can be shown that the above proposition also holds when L is any quadratic loss function of the form $(\boldsymbol{t}(\boldsymbol{y}) - \boldsymbol{g}(\boldsymbol{\theta}))'\boldsymbol{B}(\boldsymbol{t}(\boldsymbol{y}) - \boldsymbol{g}(\boldsymbol{\theta}))$, where $\boldsymbol{B}$ is a positive definite matrix.

Minimizing the average or Bayes risk does not ensure that the risk will be as small as possible for a specific value of the parameter $\boldsymbol{\theta}$. Indeed, it does not make sense to choose an estimator which minimizes $R(\boldsymbol{\theta}, \boldsymbol{t})$ for a specific $\boldsymbol{\theta}$, because $\boldsymbol{\theta}$ is unknown. A conservative strategy would be to choose an estimator which minimizes $R(\boldsymbol{\theta}, \boldsymbol{t})$ in the worst possible case, that is, which minimizes $\sup_{\theta \in \Theta} R(\boldsymbol{\theta}, \boldsymbol{t})$. Such an estimator is called a *minimax* estimator.

It is usually very difficult to find a minimax estimator. However, a solution can often be found in the form of a Bayes estimator. Specifically, we shall show that if we can find a prior such that the average risk of a corresponding Bayes estimator is equal to its maximum risk, then that Bayes estimator is also a minimax estimator. The prior which maximizes the average risk (of the corresponding Bayes estimator) over all possible priors is called a *least favourable* prior.

Proposition B.20. *Suppose a distribution π on $\boldsymbol{\Theta}$ and a corresponding Bayes estimator $\mathbf{t}$ of $\boldsymbol{g}(\boldsymbol{\theta})$, are such that*

$$r(\boldsymbol{t}, \pi) = \sup_{\theta \in \Theta} R(\boldsymbol{\theta}, \boldsymbol{t}).$$

Then π is a least favourable prior and $\mathbf{t}$ is a minimax estimator of $\boldsymbol{g}(\boldsymbol{\theta})$. Further, if $\mathbf{t}$ is the unique Bayes estimator of $\boldsymbol{g}(\boldsymbol{\theta})$ (corresponding to π), then it is the unique minimax estimator.

Proof. Let π_* be another distribution on $\boldsymbol{\Theta}$, and $\boldsymbol{t}_*$ be the corresponding Bayes estimator. Then

$$\begin{aligned} r(\boldsymbol{t}_*, \pi_*) = \int R(\boldsymbol{\theta}, \boldsymbol{t}_*)\, d\pi_*(\boldsymbol{\theta}) \quad &\leq \quad \int R(\boldsymbol{\theta}, \boldsymbol{t})\, d\pi_*(\boldsymbol{\theta}) \\ \leq \sup_{\theta \in \Theta} R(\boldsymbol{\theta}, \boldsymbol{t}) \quad &= \quad r(\boldsymbol{t}, \pi), \end{aligned}$$

which shows that π is a least favourable prior.

Let $\boldsymbol{s}$ be another estimator. It follows that

$$\sup_{\theta\in\Theta} R(\boldsymbol{\theta}, \boldsymbol{t}) = \int R(\boldsymbol{\theta}, \boldsymbol{t})\, d\pi(\boldsymbol{\theta}) \leq \int R(\boldsymbol{\theta}, \boldsymbol{s})\, d\pi(\boldsymbol{\theta}) \leq \sup_{\theta\in\Theta} R(\boldsymbol{\theta}, \boldsymbol{s}).$$

Consequently, $\boldsymbol{t}$ is a minimax estimator.

If $\boldsymbol{t}$ is the unique Bayes estimator and $\boldsymbol{s}$ is not a Bayes estimator, then $\int R(\boldsymbol{\theta}, \boldsymbol{t})\, d\pi(\boldsymbol{\theta})$ must be *strictly* smaller than $\int R(\boldsymbol{\theta}, \boldsymbol{s})\, d\pi(\boldsymbol{\theta})$. Therefore, $\sup_{\theta\in\Theta} R(\boldsymbol{\theta}, \boldsymbol{t}) < \sup_{\theta\in\Theta} R(\boldsymbol{\theta}, \boldsymbol{s})$, which implies that $\boldsymbol{t}$ is the unique minimax estimator. □

If a minimax estimator is not admissible, then there must be another estimator with smaller risk, which must also be minimax. Therefore, a minimax estimator is admissible whenever it is unique. Note that a Bayes estimator has a similar property (see Proposition B.18).

B.4 Tests of hypotheses

An important aspect of inference is to test the validity (truth or credibility) of a certain statement (hypothesis) about an unknown parameter $\boldsymbol{\theta}$, which may have any value from a set $\boldsymbol{\Theta}$, by making use of a random sample $\boldsymbol{y}$ from a probability distribution controlled by $\boldsymbol{\theta}$. If $\boldsymbol{\Theta}_0$ and $\boldsymbol{\Theta}_1$ denote disjoint subsets of $\boldsymbol{\Theta}$, one may wish to test the *null hypothesis* $\mathcal{H}_0 : \boldsymbol{\theta} \in \boldsymbol{\Theta}_0$ versus the *alternative hypothesis* $\mathcal{H}_1 : \boldsymbol{\theta} \in \boldsymbol{\Theta}_1$. If $\boldsymbol{\Theta}_i$, $i = 0, 1$, contains just one parameter value, it is called a *simple hypothesis* and otherwise, a *composite hypothesis*. For any given sample $\boldsymbol{y}$, the testing is accomplished by constructing a test function $\varphi(\boldsymbol{y})$, taking values in $[0, 1]$, which denotes the probability of rejecting the null hypothesis for the given sample. The null hypothesis is rejected if $\varphi(\boldsymbol{y}) = 1$ and accepted if $\varphi(\boldsymbol{y}) = 0$. If $0 < \varphi(\boldsymbol{y}) < 1$, the null hypothesis is rejected or accepted on the basis of a random experiment (independent of $\boldsymbol{y}$) so that the probability of rejection of $\mathcal{H}_0$ is exactly equal to $\varphi(\boldsymbol{y})$. The set $\{\boldsymbol{y} : \varphi(\boldsymbol{y}) = 1\}$ is called the *rejection region* of the test, while the *acceptance region* is the set $\{\boldsymbol{y} : \varphi(\boldsymbol{y}) = 0\}$.

A test can have two types of errors: (i) *type I* — the error of rejecting $\mathcal{H}_0$ when it is correct, and (ii) *type II* — the error of accepting $\mathcal{H}_0$ when it is wrong. Therefore, the probability of type I error is $E[\varphi(\boldsymbol{y})]$ when $\boldsymbol{\theta} \in \boldsymbol{\Theta}_0$, and the probability of type II error is $E[1 - \varphi(\boldsymbol{y})]$ when $\boldsymbol{\theta} \in \boldsymbol{\Theta}_1$. The *power* of the test is the probability of correct decision, $E[\varphi(\boldsymbol{y})]$, when $\boldsymbol{\theta} \in \boldsymbol{\Theta}_1$. Since simultaneous minimization of both of these error probabilities cannot be accomplished, classical testing methods try to maximize the power of the test (i.e. minimize the probability of type II error) over all tests φ satisfying an upper bound on the probability of type I error, that is,

$$\sup_{\boldsymbol{\theta} \in \boldsymbol{\Theta}_0} E[\varphi(\boldsymbol{y})] \leq \alpha. \tag{B.3}$$

Here, $\alpha \in [0,1]$ is a predetermined number called the *level of significance*. The left-hand side of (B.3) is called the *size* (or minimum level of significance) of the test. For a given data set, the p-value of a test is the minimum level of significance at which the null hypotheses is rejected. A small p-value indicates greater credibility of the alternative hypothesis. A test is said to be *most powerful* test of level α, for a specific $\boldsymbol{\theta} \in \boldsymbol{\Theta}_1$, if it has the largest power subject to (B.3). A *uniformly most powerful* (UMP) test is one which maximizes the power $E[\varphi(\boldsymbol{y})]$ for all $\boldsymbol{\theta} \in \boldsymbol{\Theta}_1$ subject to (B.3). A test is said to be an *unbiased test* if its power never falls below its size, that is,

$$\inf_{\boldsymbol{\theta} \in \boldsymbol{\Theta}_1} E[\varphi(\boldsymbol{y})] \geq \sup_{\boldsymbol{\theta} \in \boldsymbol{\Theta}_0} E[\varphi(\boldsymbol{y})].$$

A family of probability distributions having density (or probability mass function) $f_\theta(\boldsymbol{y})$, and indexed by the real-valued parameter $\theta \in \Theta$, is said to have *monotone likelihood ratio* (MLR) in a statistic $t(\boldsymbol{y})$ if for $\theta_1 < \theta_2$, $f_{\theta_1}(\boldsymbol{y})/f_{\theta_2}(\boldsymbol{y})$ is a monotone function in $t(\boldsymbol{y})$. One-parameter exponential families can be shown to have the MLR property.

The following result presents a most powerful test when both $\mathcal{H}_0$ and $\mathcal{H}_1$ are simple hypotheses.

Proposition B.21. (Neyman-Pearson lemma) *For testing* $\mathcal{H}_0 : \boldsymbol{\theta} = \boldsymbol{\theta}_0$ *versus* $\mathcal{H}_1 : \boldsymbol{\theta} = \boldsymbol{\theta}_1$, *the test*

$$\varphi_c(\boldsymbol{y}) = \begin{cases} 1 & \text{if } f_{\theta_1}(\boldsymbol{y}) > c \cdot f_{\theta_0}(\boldsymbol{y}), \\ 0 & \text{if } f_{\theta_1}(\boldsymbol{y}) < c \cdot f_{\theta_0}(\boldsymbol{y}), \end{cases}$$

where c satisfies the level condition $E[\varphi(\boldsymbol{y})] = \alpha$ for $\theta = \theta_0$, is the most powerful test of level α.

Proof. Let E_i denote expectation when $\boldsymbol{\theta} = \boldsymbol{\theta}_i$, $i = 0, 1$. Let $\varphi(\boldsymbol{y})$ be any level α test. Then $E_0(\varphi_c(\boldsymbol{y})) = \alpha \geq E_0(\varphi(\boldsymbol{y}))$. Further,

$$\begin{aligned}
&E_1[\varphi_c(\boldsymbol{y}) - \varphi(\boldsymbol{y})] \\
&= \int [\varphi_c(\boldsymbol{y}) - \varphi(\boldsymbol{y})] f_{\theta_1}(\boldsymbol{y}) d\boldsymbol{y} \\
&= \int [\varphi_c(\boldsymbol{y}) - \varphi(\boldsymbol{y})][f_{\theta_1}(\boldsymbol{y}) - c f_{\theta_0}(\boldsymbol{y})] d\boldsymbol{y} + c E_0[\varphi_c(\boldsymbol{y}) - \varphi(\boldsymbol{y})] \\
&\geq \int [\varphi_c(\boldsymbol{y}) - \varphi(\boldsymbol{y})][f_{\theta_1}(\boldsymbol{y}) - c f_{\theta_0}(\boldsymbol{y})] d\boldsymbol{y}.
\end{aligned}$$

Note that the second factor of the integrand is positive if and only if $\varphi_c(\boldsymbol{y}) = 1$, in which case the first factor is nonnegative. The second factor is negative if and only if $\varphi_c(\boldsymbol{y}) = 0$, in which case the first factor is nonpositive. It follows that the product of the two factors of the integrand is always nonnegative, and hence, $E_1[\varphi_c(\boldsymbol{y}) - \varphi(\boldsymbol{y})] \geq 0$. □

The decision mechanism of the most powerful test described in the Neyman-Pearson lemma can alternatively be expressed in terms of the likelihood ratio $f_{\theta_1}(\boldsymbol{y})/f_{\theta_0}(\boldsymbol{y})$. For this reason, this test is also called the *likelihood ratio test* (LRT). The threshold c is called the *critical value* of the test.

When $\boldsymbol{\theta}$ is a scaler (θ), the critical value often depends only on the sign of $\theta_1 - \theta_0$. This happens typically when the family of distributions indexed by the parameter θ has a monotone likelihood ratio in some statistic (for instance, in a one-parameter exponential family). In such a case, whenever $\mathcal{H}_1$ is of the form $\theta > \theta_0$ (one-sided alternative), the likelihood ratio test is UMP. The same holds for the other one-sided alternative hypothesis, $\theta < \theta_0$. However, there is no UMP test for a two-sided alternative hypothesis such as $\theta \neq \theta_0$. In this case one can usually find a UMP unbiased (UMPU) test.

Returning to the case of vector parameters, suppose $\boldsymbol{\Theta}$ is a vector space of dimension k and $\boldsymbol{\Theta}_0$ is a subspace of $\boldsymbol{\Theta}$, having dimension l ($l < k$). Then in order to test the null hypothesis $\mathcal{H}_0 : \boldsymbol{\theta} \in \boldsymbol{\Theta}_0$ versus the alternative $\mathcal{H}_1 : \boldsymbol{\theta} \notin \boldsymbol{\Theta}_0$, one can use the *generalized likelihood ratio test* (GLRT), based on the ratio

$$\ell(\boldsymbol{y}) = \frac{\sup\limits_{\boldsymbol{\theta} \in \boldsymbol{\Theta}_0} f_{\boldsymbol{\theta}}(\boldsymbol{y})}{\sup\limits_{\boldsymbol{\theta} \in \boldsymbol{\Theta}} f_{\boldsymbol{\theta}}(\boldsymbol{y})}. \tag{B.4}$$

Clearly, $\ell(\boldsymbol{y})$ is in the range [0,1]. The closer it is to zero, the less credible is the null hypothesis. Thus, the GLRT rejects $\mathcal{H}_0$ when $\ell \leq c$, where c is determined by the level condition. It can be shown that subject to some regularity conditions, $-2\log\ell$ has an asymptotic χ^2_{k-l} distribution as the sample size goes to infinity, under the null hypothesis. Excessively large values of $-2\log\ell$ would indicate rejection of $\mathcal{H}_0$. The GLRT often leads one to such optimal tests as the UMP or the UMPU tests, when these exist. A detailed discussion of testing of hypotheses, including various optimal tests and the regularity conditions required for the above asymptotic result can be found in Lehmann and Romano (2005).

B.5 Confidence region

Suppose one is interested in constructing a set of values where the unknown parameter may lie, with a certain probability. In frequentist terminology such a set of possible values is called a *confidence region or set*, while the analogous Bayesian concept is referred to as a *credible set.* Given a sample $\boldsymbol{y}$ from $f_\theta(\boldsymbol{y})$, $\boldsymbol{\theta} \in \boldsymbol{\Theta}$, the goal is to construct a set $C(\boldsymbol{y}) \subset \boldsymbol{\Theta}$ with the property

$$P_\theta[\boldsymbol{\theta} \in C(\boldsymbol{y})] \geq 1 - \alpha \quad \forall\, \boldsymbol{\theta} \in \boldsymbol{\Theta}, \tag{B.5}$$

for a given confidence level $1-\alpha$. In the above, P_θ is probability computed on the basis of the density f_θ. In the frequentist sense, randomness of the event $\boldsymbol{\theta} \in C(\boldsymbol{y})$ is not because of the parameter $\boldsymbol{\theta}$, but due to the set $C(\boldsymbol{y})$ which depends on $\boldsymbol{y}$ and varies from sample to sample. This random set $C(\boldsymbol{y})$, called a level $(1-\alpha)$ confidence set or region, contains an unknown but fixed $\boldsymbol{\theta}$ with probability $(1-\alpha)$ or more. Such a set should be small so that the chances of containing a 'wrong' $\boldsymbol{\theta}$ is as small as possible (without this restriction, $\boldsymbol{\Theta}$ would be an excellent choice). We call a set $C(\boldsymbol{y})$ *uniformly most accurate* (UMA) confidence region of level $(1-\alpha)$ if it minimizes

$$P_\theta[\boldsymbol{\theta}_* \in C(\boldsymbol{y})] \quad \forall\, \boldsymbol{\theta}_* \neq \boldsymbol{\theta}$$

among all sets satisfying (B.5). We also call a confidence region *unbiased* if it has a better chance of containing the 'correct' $\boldsymbol{\theta}$ than any incorrect $\boldsymbol{\theta}_*$, that is, if

$$P_\theta[\boldsymbol{\theta} \in C(\boldsymbol{y})] \geq P_\theta[\boldsymbol{\theta}_* \in C(\boldsymbol{y})] \quad \forall\, \boldsymbol{\theta}_* \neq \boldsymbol{\theta}. \tag{B.6}$$

A UMA confidence region among those satisfying (B.6) is called a *uniformly most accurate unbiased* (UMAU) confidence region of level α.

One way of obtaining a UMA confidence region is to choose

$$C(\boldsymbol{y}) = \{\boldsymbol{\theta}_0 \,:\, \boldsymbol{y} \in A(\boldsymbol{\theta}_0)\},$$

where $A(\boldsymbol{\theta}_0)$ is the acceptance region of the corresponding uniformly most powerful test for $\mathcal{H}_0 \,:\, \boldsymbol{\theta} = \boldsymbol{\theta}_0$, when this test exists. A UMAU confidence region can be found from a uniformly most powerful unbiased test in a similar manner. Thus, there is a duality between hypothesis testing and confidence regions. We can also construct confidence regions from the generalized likelihood ratio test.

Example B.22. Consider testing $\mathcal{H}_0 \,:\, \mu = \mu_0$ versus $\mathcal{H}_1 \,:\, \mu \neq \mu_0$ from observation $\boldsymbol{y}_{n\times 1} \sim N(\mu\mathbf{1}, \sigma^2\boldsymbol{I})$. The uniformly most powerful unbiased level α test has the acceptance region (see Lehmann and Romano, 2005, p. 156)

$$A(\mu_0) = \left\{ \boldsymbol{y} : \frac{|\bar{y} - \mu_0|}{\sqrt{\widehat{\sigma^2}/n}} \leq t_{n-1,\frac{\alpha}{2}} \right\},$$

where $\bar{y} = n^{-1}\mathbf{1}'\boldsymbol{y}$ and $t_{n-1,\frac{\alpha}{2}}$ is the $(1 - \frac{\alpha}{2})$ quantile of the t-distribution with n degrees of freedom. Thus, a UMAU confidence set for μ (in this case, an interval) is given by

$$C(\boldsymbol{y}) = \left\{ \mu_0 : \frac{|\bar{y} - \mu_0|}{\sqrt{\widehat{\sigma^2}/n}} \leq t_{n-1,\frac{\alpha}{2}} \right\}. \qquad \square$$

From the Bayesian point of view, the parameter $\boldsymbol{\theta}$ itself is random with a prior distribution $\pi(\boldsymbol{\theta})$. The posterior distribution of $\boldsymbol{\theta}$ given the data $\boldsymbol{y}$ is

$$\pi(\boldsymbol{\theta}|\boldsymbol{y}) = \frac{f_\theta(\boldsymbol{y})\pi(\boldsymbol{\theta})}{\int_{\boldsymbol{\Theta}} f_\theta(\boldsymbol{y})\pi(\boldsymbol{\alpha})d\boldsymbol{\alpha}}.$$

A set $C_*(\boldsymbol{y}) \subset \boldsymbol{\Theta}$ with the property

$$\int_{C_*} \pi(\boldsymbol{\theta}|\boldsymbol{y})d\boldsymbol{\theta} \geq 1 - \alpha$$

is called a $(1-\alpha)$ level *credible set*. In order to make such a set the smallest possible, we look for a region $C_*(\boldsymbol{y})$ where the posterior is large, that is,

$$C_*(\boldsymbol{y}) = \{\boldsymbol{\theta} : \pi(\boldsymbol{\theta}|\boldsymbol{y}) \geq c\},$$

where the threshold c is determined by the level condition. Such a set is called the *highest posterior density* (HPD) credible set.

B.6 Complements/Exercises

B.1 *Conditional sufficiency.* Let z have the uniform distribution over the interval [1,2]. Let $y_1, \ldots, y_n$ be independently distributed as $N(\theta, z)$ for given z, θ being a real-valued parameter. The observation consists of $\boldsymbol{y} = (y_1 : \ldots : y_n)$ and z. Show that the vector $\left(n^{-1}\mathbf{1}'\boldsymbol{y} : z\right)'$ is minimal sufficient, even though z is ancillary (i.e. the vector is not complete sufficient). In such a case, $n^{-1}\mathbf{1}'\boldsymbol{y}$ is said to be conditionally sufficient given z. Verify that given z, $n^{-1}\mathbf{1}'\boldsymbol{y}$ is indeed sufficient for θ.

B.2 Let $x_1, \ldots, x_n$ be independent and identically distributed with density $f_\theta(x) = g(x - \theta)$ for some function g which is free of the parameter θ. Show that the range $\max_{1 \leq i \leq n} x_i - \min_{1 \leq i \leq n} x_i$ is ancillary. Show that this statistic is not maximal ancillary for $n \geq 3$.

B.3 Show that the information inequality of Proposition B.14 holds with equality only if $\boldsymbol{t}(\boldsymbol{y})$ is sufficient for $\boldsymbol{\theta}$. Is the converse true?

B.4 If the parameter $\boldsymbol{\theta}$ of Proposition B.14 is transformed to $\boldsymbol{\eta}$ by a one-to-one mapping $\boldsymbol{\eta} = \boldsymbol{h}(\boldsymbol{\theta})$ such that the matrix $\partial\boldsymbol{\eta}/\partial\boldsymbol{\theta}$ exists and is invertible, show that the Cramer-Rao lower bound is unaffected by this reparametrization.

B.5 Show that the UMVUE described in Proposition B.11 uniformly minimizes the risk of an unbiased estimator with respect to *any* loss function which is convex in its second argument.

B.6 If $y_1, \ldots, y_n$ are samples from $N(\theta, 1)$ and $\bar{y}$ is the sample mean, show that the conditional distribution of y_1 given $\bar{y}$ is $N(\bar{y}, (1-1/n))$. Relate the finding with Proposition B.9 (Rao-Blackwell theorem).

B.7 If $y_1, \ldots, y_n$ are samples from $N(\mu, 1)$ and the prior of μ is $N(\theta, \tau)$, then show that the Bayes estimator of μ with respect to the squared error loss function is $\alpha\theta + (1-\alpha)n^{-1}\sum_{i=1}^{n} y_i$, where $\alpha = 1/(1+n\tau)$.

B.8 *Jeffreys' prior.* Given the scalar parameter θ, suppose the random variable y has the probability density function $f_\theta(y)$ and the Fisher information for θ based on the observation y is $\mathcal{I}(\theta)$. If $\int \sqrt{\mathcal{I}(\theta)}d\theta$ exists and is equal to a constant $1/c$, then one can choose the prior distribution with density $\pi(\theta) = c\sqrt{\mathcal{I}(\theta)}$. This special prior gives more weight to those values of θ for which the distribution of y is more informative about θ. Such a prior distribution is called Jeffreys' prior.

(a) Let h be a one-to-one differentiable function with differentiable inverse, and $\eta = h(\theta)$. Obtain the Fisher information for η.

(b) Obtain the density of Jeffreys' prior for η.

(c) If θ has Jeffreys' prior distribution, what is the density of η? Compare it with the answer of part (b).

B.9 If y has probability density function $\theta^{-1}\exp(-y/\theta)$, $y \geq 0$, $\theta > 0$, then show that the estimator y is unbiased for θ but inadmissible with respect to the squared error loss function. Find an admissible estimator.

B.10 Let $\boldsymbol{y} \sim N(\mu\mathbf{1}, \boldsymbol{I})$, $\mu \in (-\infty, \infty)$. Find the UMP test for the null hypothesis $\mathcal{H}_0 : \mu = 0$ against the alternative $\mathcal{H}_1 : \mu > 0$. Find the GLRT for this problem. Which test has greater power for a given size? What happens when the alternative is two-sided, i.e. $\mathcal{H}_1 : \mu \neq 0$?

B.11 Let $\boldsymbol{y} \sim N(\mu\mathbf{1}, \boldsymbol{I})$, $\mu \in (-\infty, \infty)$. Find the level $(1-\alpha)$ UMA confidence region for μ when it is known that $\mu \geq 0$. Find the level $(1-\alpha)$ UMAU confidence region for μ when it is only known that $\mu \in (-\infty, \infty)$.

Appendix C

Solutions to Selected Exercises

Chapter 1

1.1(a) The variable y is the highest temperature of the day, x is the temperature at 6:00 am. One can look for a linear prediction formula for y in terms of x, using paired data on both variables for many days of the year.

(b) The variable y is the actual speed of a vehicle, x is the speed shown on the speedometer; the relation between them has to be found. This relationship is specific to a vehicle. The vehicle has to be driven at various speeds through the target area of a speed detector and the speed-dial data have to be matched with the speed detector data.

(c) The variable y is the age at death recorded at the mortuary, x is the length of the life-line on his/her palm. The task is to determine whether the lifeline has any effect whatsoever on the lifetime. Data should be recorded whenever any dead body arrives, for several days.

(d) The variable y is the grade point average (GPA) obtained by a student in an undergraduate program, x_1 is their gender and x_2 is the score used for selection to that program. The problem is to check whether female students do significantly better at college than males with comparable score at the selection stage, i.e., whether gender has a significant effect on grades (even though score used for selection may also explain a part of the variation in GPA). The data may be sampled from the academic records held by the college.

1.2 The model is $y = \alpha_0 + \alpha_1 x_1 + \beta_1 x_2 + \gamma x_3 + \varepsilon$, where

$$x_1 = (1 - x_3)x, \quad x_2 = x_3 x, \quad x_3 = \begin{cases} 1 & \text{if } x > x_0, \\ 0 & \text{if } x \le x_0, \end{cases}, \quad \gamma = \beta_0 - \alpha_0.$$

1.3 If $E(\varepsilon) = E(\delta) = 0$, then

$$E(v)E(1/v) = (\beta_0 + \beta_1 x) \cdot \frac{\kappa_0 s}{\kappa_1 + s} = \left(\frac{1}{\kappa_0} + \frac{\kappa_1}{\kappa_0 s}\right) \cdot \frac{\kappa_0 s}{\kappa_1 + s} = 1.$$

Further, $E(v\cdot(1/v)) = 1$. Thus, v and $1/v$ must be uncorrelated, even though these are functions of one another.

If v and $1/v$ are uncorrelated, and x and y are independent and have the same distribution as v, then

$$E(v)E(1/v) = E(x/y) = E[(x/y)I(x < y)] + E[(x/y)I(x \geq y)],$$

which can be written either as $E[(x/y)I(x < y)] + E[(y/x)I(x \leq y)]$ or as $E[(y/x)I(x > y)] + E[(x/y)I(x \geq y)]$. Therefore,

$$\begin{aligned} E(v)E(1/v) &= \frac{1}{2}[E\{(x/y)I(x < y)\} + E\{(y/x)I(x \leq y)\} \\ &\quad + E\{(y/x)I(x > y)\} + E\{(x/y)I(x \geq y)\}] \\ &= \frac{1}{2}[E(x/y) + E(y/x)] = E[(x^2 + y^2)/(2xy)] \\ &= E[(x - y)^2/(2xy)] + 1. \end{aligned}$$

Thus, the covariance between v and $1/v$ is $-E[(x-y)^2/(2xy)]$. This is strictly negative when v is a nonnegative random variable, such as the rate of reaction mentioned in Example 1.13.

1.4 Since $E(\log u) = 0$, we have (conditionally on l and k)

$$Var(\varepsilon) = Var(q - al^\alpha k^\beta) = Var(al^\alpha k^\beta u - al^\alpha k^\beta) = (al^\alpha k^\beta)^2 Var(u - 1).$$

This quantity is large whenever $\log(al^\alpha k^\beta)$ (i.e. mean of $\log q$) is large.

1.5 (a) The model error is $\varepsilon - \beta_1\delta$.

$$E((\varepsilon - \beta_1\delta)x_o) = E((\varepsilon - \beta_1\delta)(x + \delta)) = -\beta_1 Var(\delta).$$

In the case of random regressors, the correlation between model error and any regressor of model (1.1) should be zero.

(b) It is a special case of the simultaneous equations model of Example 1.18.

1.6 The δ_is should be random, not necessarily with zero mean. The model is a special case of the mixed effects model. Let $\alpha_i = E(\delta_i)$ and $\beta_i = \delta_i - \alpha_i$. Then the model is

$$y_i = \mu + \alpha_i + (\beta_i + \varepsilon_{ij}), \quad i, j = 1, \ldots, 10.$$

The average 'improvement in status' is

$$\frac{1}{100}\sum_{i=1}^{10}\sum_{j=1}^{10}(\mu + \alpha_i) = \mu + \frac{1}{10}\sum_{i=1}^{10}\alpha_i,$$

which should be the focus of inference. (The dispersion matrix of the model errors $\beta_i+\varepsilon_{ij}$, $i, j = 1, \ldots, 10$, has a special structure, discussed in Chapter 8.)

Chapter 2

2.1 (a) Suppose Σ is nonsingular, and factored as CC', where C is also a nonsingular matrix. Let $z = C^{-1}y$. Since $y \sim N(\mu, \Sigma)$, if follows that $z \sim N(C^{-1}\mu, I)$. Therefore, we have from (2.2)

$$f(z) = (2\pi)^{-n/2} \exp[-\tfrac{1}{2}(z - C^{-1}\mu)'(z - C^{-1}\mu)].$$

The vector y is obtained from z through the linear transformation $y = Cz$, which has Jacobian $|C|$ of $|\Sigma|^{1/2}$. Therefore, the density of y is

$$\begin{aligned} f(y) &= (2\pi)^{-n/2}|C|^{-1} \exp[-\tfrac{1}{2}(C^{-1}y - C^{-1}\mu)'(C^{-1}y - C^{-1}\mu)] \\ &= (2\pi)^{-n/2}|\Sigma|^{-1/2} \exp[-\tfrac{1}{2}(y - \mu)'\Sigma^{-1}(y - \mu)], \end{aligned}$$

which coincides with (2.3).

(b) Suppose Σ is singular, and has a spectral decomposition $V\Lambda V'$. Suppose further Λ has diagonal elements $\lambda_1, \ldots, \lambda_{\rho(\Sigma)}, 0, \ldots, 0$. Also, let $z = V'(y - \mu)$. It follows that $z \sim N(0, \Lambda)$. If z is written as $(z_1 : \cdots : z_n)'$, then these elements are independent, $z_1, \ldots, z_{\rho(\Sigma)}$ are normal with zero mean and variance $\lambda_1, \ldots, \lambda_{\rho(\Sigma)}$, respectively, and $z_{\rho(\Sigma)+1}, \ldots, z_n$ are identically zero with probability 1. Therefore,

$$\begin{aligned} f(z) &= \prod_{i=1}^{\rho(\Sigma)} \left\{(2\pi\lambda_i)^{-1/2} \exp[-\tfrac{1}{2}z_i^2/\lambda_i]\right\}, \quad z_{\rho(\Sigma)+1} = \cdots = z_n = 0 \\ &= (2\pi)^{-\rho(\Sigma)/2}|\Lambda_1|^{-1/2} \exp[-\tfrac{1}{2}z'\Lambda^+ z], \quad z_2 = 0, \end{aligned}$$

where Λ_1 is the diagonal matrix with elements $\lambda_1, \ldots, \lambda_{\rho(\Sigma)}$ and $z_2 = (z_{\rho(\Sigma)+1} : \cdots : z_n)'$. We have to specify the density of y by making use of the reverse transformation $y = Vz + \mu$. The Jacobian of this transformation is $|V| = 1$, as V is an orthogonal matrix. Therefore,

$$\begin{aligned} f(y) &= (2\pi)^{-\rho(\Sigma)/2}|\Lambda_1|^{-1/2} \exp[-\tfrac{1}{2}(y - \mu)'V\Lambda^+V'(y - \mu)], \quad V_2'y = 0 \\ &= (2\pi)^{-\rho(\Sigma)/2}|\Lambda_1|^{-1/2} \exp[-\tfrac{1}{2}(y - \mu)'\Sigma^+(y - \mu)], \quad V_2V_2'y = 0, \end{aligned}$$

where V_2 consists of the last $n - \rho(\Sigma)$ columns of V. If V is written as $(V_1{:}V_2)$, it is seen that $\mathcal{C}(V_1) = \mathcal{C}(\Sigma)$ and $V_1V_1' = P_\Sigma$. Thus, $V_2V_2' = I - P_\Sigma$, and hence the constraint $V_2V_2'y = 0$ can be written as $(I - P_\Sigma)y = 0$. Further, Proposition 2.13 implies that Σ^+ in the expression of $f(y)$ can be replaced by any Σ^-. Finally, if Σ is rank-factored as CC', then $|C'C| = |C'V_1V_1'C| = |V_1'CC'V_1| = |V_1'\Sigma V_1| = |\Lambda_1|$.
Therefore, $f(y)$ is given by (2.11).

2.2 Let CC' be a rank-factorization of Σ and C^{-L} be a left-inverse of C. From Proposition 2.13 we know that $z \in \mathcal{C}(\Sigma) = \mathcal{C}(C)$ with probability 1. Let

$\boldsymbol{l} = \boldsymbol{C}^{-L}\boldsymbol{z}$ such that $\boldsymbol{C}\boldsymbol{l} = \boldsymbol{z}$ with probability 1. Then $\boldsymbol{z}'\boldsymbol{\Sigma}^{-}\boldsymbol{z} = \boldsymbol{l}'\boldsymbol{P}_{C'}\boldsymbol{l} = \boldsymbol{l}'\boldsymbol{l}$ for every choice of $\boldsymbol{\Sigma}^{-}$. Further, $\boldsymbol{l} \sim N(\boldsymbol{0}, \boldsymbol{I}_{\rho(\Sigma)\times\rho(\Sigma)})$. The result follows.

2.3 (a) The result follows from the Fisher-Cochran theorem, with $r = 2$, $\boldsymbol{A}_1 = \boldsymbol{A}$ and $\boldsymbol{A}_2 = \boldsymbol{I} - \boldsymbol{A}$.

(b) If $\boldsymbol{AB} = \boldsymbol{0}$, then $\boldsymbol{I} - \boldsymbol{A} - \boldsymbol{B}$ is idempotent, and $\rho(\boldsymbol{A}) + \rho(\boldsymbol{B}) + \rho(\boldsymbol{I} - \boldsymbol{A} - \boldsymbol{B}) = n$. It follows from the Fisher-Cochran theorem that $\boldsymbol{y}'\boldsymbol{A}\boldsymbol{y}$ and $\boldsymbol{y}'\boldsymbol{B}\boldsymbol{y}$ are independent. Conversely, if these are independent, then $\boldsymbol{y}'\boldsymbol{A}\boldsymbol{y} + \boldsymbol{y}'\boldsymbol{B}\boldsymbol{y}$ is chi-square distributed (this follows from part (a) and the definition of the chi-square distribution). The result of Exercise 2.4 implies that $\boldsymbol{A} + \boldsymbol{B}$ must be idempotent, and hence, $\boldsymbol{AB} = \boldsymbol{0}$.

(c) Let $\boldsymbol{U}_A$ and $\boldsymbol{U}_C$ be semi-orthogonal matrices so that $\boldsymbol{A} = \boldsymbol{U}_A\boldsymbol{U}_A'$ and $\mathcal{C}(\boldsymbol{U}_C) = \mathcal{C}(\boldsymbol{C}')$. The condition $\boldsymbol{CA} = \boldsymbol{0}$ implies that $\boldsymbol{U}_C'\boldsymbol{U}_A = \boldsymbol{0}$, i.e. $\boldsymbol{U}_C'\boldsymbol{y}$ and $\boldsymbol{U}_A'\boldsymbol{y}$ are independent and hence $\boldsymbol{C}\boldsymbol{y}$ and $\boldsymbol{y}'\boldsymbol{A}\boldsymbol{y}$ are independent. Conversely, if $\boldsymbol{C}\boldsymbol{y}$ and $\boldsymbol{y}'\boldsymbol{A}\boldsymbol{y}$ are independent then $\boldsymbol{y}'\boldsymbol{A}\boldsymbol{y}$ is independent of $\boldsymbol{U}_C'\boldsymbol{y}$, and hence, of $\boldsymbol{y}'(\boldsymbol{U}_C\boldsymbol{U}_C')\boldsymbol{y}$. Using part (b) we have $\boldsymbol{U}_C\boldsymbol{U}_C'\boldsymbol{A} = \boldsymbol{0}$, which implies that $\boldsymbol{U}_C'\boldsymbol{A}$ and $\boldsymbol{CA}$ are both null matrices.

2.4 Let $\boldsymbol{V}\boldsymbol{\Lambda}\boldsymbol{V}'$ be a spectral decomposition of $\boldsymbol{A}$, and let $\boldsymbol{x}_{n\times 1} = \boldsymbol{V}'\boldsymbol{y}$. Then $\boldsymbol{y}'\boldsymbol{A}\boldsymbol{y} = \boldsymbol{x}'\boldsymbol{\Lambda}\boldsymbol{x}$ and $\boldsymbol{x} \sim N(\boldsymbol{\theta}, \boldsymbol{I})$, where $\boldsymbol{\theta} = \boldsymbol{V}'\boldsymbol{\mu}$. The moment generating function of $\boldsymbol{x}'\boldsymbol{\Lambda}\boldsymbol{x}$ is $E[\exp(t\boldsymbol{x}'\boldsymbol{\Lambda}\boldsymbol{x})]$, which simplifies to

$$\exp\left[\sum_{i=1}^{n} \frac{\lambda_i t\theta_i^2}{1 - 2\lambda_i t}\right] \prod_{i=1}^{n} (1 - 2\lambda_i t)^{-1/2}, \quad 0 \le t < \min_{1\le i\le n} \lambda_i,$$

where $\lambda_1, \ldots, \lambda_n$ are the diagonal elements of $\boldsymbol{\Lambda}$ and $\boldsymbol{\theta} = (\theta_1 : \cdots : \theta_n)'$. The moment generating function of $\chi_r^2(c)$ is $\exp[ct/(1-2t)](1-2t)^{-r/2}$, $t \in [0, 1)$. These two functions are identical only if each λ_i is either 0 or 1, r is the number of nonzero λ_i's and $c = \sum_{i=1}^n \lambda_i\theta_i^2 = \boldsymbol{\theta}'\boldsymbol{\Lambda}\boldsymbol{\theta} = \boldsymbol{\mu}'\boldsymbol{A}\boldsymbol{\mu}$.

2.5 If $\boldsymbol{AB} = \boldsymbol{0}$, we can rank-factorize $\boldsymbol{A}$ and $\boldsymbol{B}$ as $\boldsymbol{A}_1\boldsymbol{A}_1'$ and $\boldsymbol{B}_1\boldsymbol{B}_1'$ and prove that $\boldsymbol{A}_1'\boldsymbol{y}$ and $\boldsymbol{B}_1'\boldsymbol{y}$ are independent, and hence their squared norms are independent. To prove the converse, note that the moment generating function of $\boldsymbol{y}'\boldsymbol{A}\boldsymbol{y}$ and $\boldsymbol{y}'\boldsymbol{B}\boldsymbol{y}$ is proportional to $|\boldsymbol{I} - 2t_1\boldsymbol{A} - 2t_2\boldsymbol{B}|^{-1/2}$. If the quadratic forms are independent, then this can be factored into $g(t_1)$ and $h(t_2)$. Putting $t_1 = 0$, we have $h(t_2)$ proportional to $|\boldsymbol{I} - 2t_2\boldsymbol{B}|^{-1/2}$. Likewise, $g(t_1)$ is proportional to $|\boldsymbol{I} - 2t_1\boldsymbol{A}|^{-1/2}$. Consequently $|\boldsymbol{I} - 2t_1\boldsymbol{A} - 2t_2\boldsymbol{B}|$ can be written as $|\boldsymbol{I} - 2t_1\boldsymbol{A}| \cdot |\boldsymbol{I} - 2t_2\boldsymbol{B}|$ or $|\boldsymbol{I} - 2t_1\boldsymbol{A} - 2t_2\boldsymbol{B} + 4t_1t_2\boldsymbol{AB}|$, for all t_1 and t_2 over a rectangle. It follows that $\boldsymbol{AB} = \boldsymbol{0}$.

2.6 As in the proof of Proposition 2.21, we can argue that it is sufficient to prove that $E[L_{g_\tau}(y, \boldsymbol{x}; \tau)|\boldsymbol{x}] \le L_g(y, \boldsymbol{x}; \tau)|\boldsymbol{x}]$ for any fixed $\boldsymbol{x}$, where $g(\boldsymbol{x})$ is any function of $\boldsymbol{x}$. This inequality, in turn, would follow if we can show that for any distribution of y having τ-quantile q,

$$\begin{aligned} &E[(1-\tau)(q-y)I(y \le q) + \tau(y-q)I(y > q)] \\ &\le E[(1-\tau)(c-y)I(y \le c) + \tau(y-c)I(y > c)] \end{aligned}$$

for any constant c. In particular, for any $c > q$, we have

$$\begin{aligned}
&[(1-\tau)(c-y)I(y \le c) + \tau(y-c)I(y > c)] \\
&\qquad - [(1-\tau)(q-y)I(y \le q) + \tau(y-q)I(y > q)] \\
&= (1-\tau)(c-q)I(y \le q) + \tau(q-c)I(y > c) \\
&\quad + [(1-\tau)(c-y) - \tau(y-q)]I(q < y \le c) \\
&= (1-\tau)(c-q)I(y \le q) + \tau(q-c)I(y > c) \\
&\quad + [\tau(q-c) + (c-y)]I(q < y \le c) \\
&= (1-\tau)(c-q)I(y \le q) + \tau(q-c)I(y > q) + (c-y)I(q < y \le c) \\
&\ge (1-\tau)(c-q)I(y \le q) + \tau(q-c)I(y > q).
\end{aligned}$$

On the other hand, for any $c < q$, we have

$$\begin{aligned}
&[(1-\tau)(c-y)I(y \le c) + \tau(y-c)I(y > c)] \\
&\qquad - [(1-\tau)(q-y)I(y \le q) + \tau(y-q)I(y > q)] \\
&= (1-\tau)(c-q)I(y \le c) + \tau(q-c)I(y > q) \\
&\quad + [\tau(y-c) - (1-\tau)(q-y)]I(c < y \le q) \\
&= (1-\tau)(c-q)I(y \le c) + \tau(q-c)I(y > q) \\
&\quad + [(1-\tau)(c-q) + (y-c)]I(c < y \le q) \\
&= (1-\tau)(c-q)I(y \le q) + \tau(q-c)I(y > q) + (y-c)I(c < y \le q) \\
&\ge (1-\tau)(c-q)I(y \le q) + \tau(q-c)I(y > q).
\end{aligned}$$

Thus, we have the same inequality for all values of c. By taking expected values of the two sides, we obtain

$$\begin{aligned}
&E[(1-\tau)(c-y)I(y \le c) + \tau(y-c)I(y > c)] \\
&\qquad - E[(1-\tau)(q-y)I(y \le q) + \tau(y-q)I(y > q)] \\
&\ge (1-\tau)(c-q)P(y \le q) + \tau(q-c)P(y > q) \\
&\ge (1-\tau)\tau(c-q) + \tau(1-\tau)(q-c) = 0.
\end{aligned}$$

It follows that $E[L_{g_\tau}(y, \boldsymbol{x}; \tau)] \le E[L_g(y, \boldsymbol{x}; \tau)]$ for any function $g(\boldsymbol{x})$.

2.7 Let the dispersion matrix of y, x_1 and $\boldsymbol{x}_2$ be factored into standard deviation and correlation matrices as

$$\begin{aligned}
\boldsymbol{\Sigma}_{yx_1x_2} &= \begin{pmatrix} \sigma_y^2 & \sigma_{x_1y} & \boldsymbol{\sigma}'_{x_2y} \\ \sigma_{x_1y} & \sigma_{x_1}^2 & \boldsymbol{\sigma}'_{x_2x_1} \\ \boldsymbol{\sigma}_{x_2y} & \boldsymbol{\sigma}_{x_2x_1} & \boldsymbol{\Sigma}_{x_2x_2} \end{pmatrix} \\
&= \begin{pmatrix} \sigma_y & 0 & \mathbf{0} \\ 0 & \sigma_{x_1} & \mathbf{0} \\ \mathbf{0} & \mathbf{0} & \boldsymbol{\Delta}_{x_2x_2}^{1/2} \end{pmatrix} \begin{pmatrix} 1 & r_{x_1y} & \boldsymbol{r}'_{x_2y} \\ r_{x_1y} & 1 & \boldsymbol{r}'_{x_2x_1} \\ \boldsymbol{r}_{x_2y} & \boldsymbol{r}_{x_2x_1} & \boldsymbol{R}_{x_2x_2} \end{pmatrix} \begin{pmatrix} \sigma_y & 0 & \mathbf{0} \\ 0 & \sigma_{x_1} & \mathbf{0} \\ \mathbf{0} & \mathbf{0} & \boldsymbol{\Delta}_{x_2x_2}^{1/2} \end{pmatrix}.
\end{aligned}$$

Therefore, we can write

$$\begin{aligned}
\boldsymbol{\Sigma}_{yx_1\cdot x_2} &= \begin{pmatrix} \sigma_y^2 & \sigma_{x_1y} \\ \sigma_{x_1y} & \sigma_{x_1}^2 \end{pmatrix} - \begin{pmatrix} \boldsymbol{\sigma}'_{x_2y} \\ \boldsymbol{\sigma}'_{x_2x_1} \end{pmatrix} \boldsymbol{\Sigma}_{x_2x_2}^{-1} (\boldsymbol{\sigma}_{x_2y}\ \boldsymbol{\sigma}_{x_2x_1}) \\
&= \begin{pmatrix} \sigma_y^2 - \boldsymbol{\sigma}'_{x_2y}\boldsymbol{\Sigma}_{x_2x_2}^{-1}\boldsymbol{\sigma}_{x_2y} & \sigma_{x_1y} - \boldsymbol{\sigma}'_{x_2y}\boldsymbol{\Sigma}_{x_2x_2}^{-1}\boldsymbol{\sigma}_{x_2x_1} \\ \sigma_{x_1y} - \boldsymbol{\sigma}'_{x_2x_1}\boldsymbol{\Sigma}_{x_2x_2}^{-1}\boldsymbol{\sigma}_{x_2y} & \sigma_{x_1}^2 - \boldsymbol{\sigma}'_{x_2x_1}\boldsymbol{\Sigma}_{x_2x_2}^{-1}\boldsymbol{\sigma}_{x_2x_1} \end{pmatrix} \\
&= \begin{pmatrix} \sigma_y^2(1 - \boldsymbol{r}'_{x_2y}\boldsymbol{R}_{x_2x_2}^{-1}\boldsymbol{r}_{x_2y}) & \sigma_y\sigma_{x_1}(r_{x_1y} - \boldsymbol{r}'_{x_2y}\boldsymbol{R}_{x_2x_2}^{-1}\boldsymbol{r}_{x_2x_1}) \\ \sigma_{x_1}\sigma_y(r_{x_1y} - \boldsymbol{r}'_{x_2x_1}\boldsymbol{R}_{x_2x_2}^{-1}\boldsymbol{r}_{x_2y}) & \sigma_{x_1}^2(1 - \boldsymbol{r}'_{x_2x_1}\boldsymbol{R}_{x_2x_2}^{-1}\boldsymbol{r}_{x_2x_1}) \end{pmatrix} \\
&= \begin{pmatrix} \sigma_{y\cdot x_2}^2 & \sigma_{y\cdot x_2}\sigma_{x_1\cdot x_2}\rho_{yx_1\cdot x_2} \\ \sigma_{y\cdot x_2}\sigma_{x_1\cdot x_2}\rho_{yx_1\cdot x_2} & \sigma_{x_1\cdot x_2}^2 \end{pmatrix},
\end{aligned}$$

where

$$\begin{aligned}
\sigma_{y\cdot x_2}^2 &= \sigma_y^2(1 - \boldsymbol{r}'_{x_2y}\boldsymbol{R}_{x_2x_2}^{-1}\boldsymbol{r}_{x_2y}), \\
\sigma_{x_1\cdot x_2}^2 &= \sigma_{x_1}^2(1 - \boldsymbol{r}'_{x_2x_1}\boldsymbol{R}_{x_2x_2}^{-1}\boldsymbol{r}_{x_2x_1}), \\
\rho_{yx_1\cdot x_2} &= \frac{r_{x_1y} - \boldsymbol{r}'_{x_2y}\boldsymbol{R}_{x_2x_2}^{-1}\boldsymbol{r}_{x_2x_1}}{\sqrt{(1 - \boldsymbol{r}'_{x_2y}\boldsymbol{R}_{x_2x_2}^{-1}\boldsymbol{r}_{x_2y})(1 - \boldsymbol{r}'_{x_2x_1}\boldsymbol{R}_{x_2x_2}^{-1}\boldsymbol{r}_{x_2x_1})}}.
\end{aligned}$$

Using formulae (A.4) and (A.1) for matrix inversion, we have from (2.17),

$$\begin{aligned}
\begin{pmatrix} \beta_1 \\ \vdots \\ \beta_k \end{pmatrix} &= \begin{pmatrix} \sigma_{x_1}^2 & \boldsymbol{\sigma}'_{x_2x_1} \\ \boldsymbol{\sigma}_{x_2x_1} & \boldsymbol{\Sigma}_{x_2x_2} \end{pmatrix}^{-1} \begin{pmatrix} \sigma_{x_1y} \\ \boldsymbol{\sigma}_{x_2y} \end{pmatrix} \\
&= \begin{pmatrix} \sigma_{x_1}^{-2} + \sigma_{x_1}^{-4}\boldsymbol{\sigma}'_{x_2x_1}\boldsymbol{T}\boldsymbol{\sigma}_{x_2x_1} & -\sigma_{x_1}^{-2}\boldsymbol{\sigma}'_{x_2x_1}\boldsymbol{T} \\ \sigma_{x_1}^{-2}\boldsymbol{T}\boldsymbol{\sigma}_{x_2x_1} & \boldsymbol{T} \end{pmatrix} \begin{pmatrix} \sigma_{x_1y} \\ \boldsymbol{\sigma}_{x_2y} \end{pmatrix}, \\
\text{where } \boldsymbol{T} &= (\boldsymbol{\Sigma}_{x_2x_2} - \sigma_{x_1}^{-2}\boldsymbol{\sigma}_{x_2x_1}\boldsymbol{\sigma}'_{x_2x_1})^{-1} \\
&= \boldsymbol{\Sigma}_{x_2x_2}^{-1} + \boldsymbol{\Sigma}_{x_2x_2}^{-1}\boldsymbol{\sigma}_{x_2x_1}\boldsymbol{\sigma}'_{x_2x_1}\boldsymbol{\Sigma}_{x_2x_2}^{-1}/(\sigma_{x_1}^2 - \boldsymbol{\sigma}'_{x_2x_1}\boldsymbol{\Sigma}_{x_2x_2}^{-1}\boldsymbol{\sigma}_{x_2x_1}).
\end{aligned}$$

Therefore

$$\begin{aligned}
\beta_1 &= \frac{\sigma_{x_1y}}{\sigma_{x_1}^2} + \frac{\sigma_{x_1y}\boldsymbol{\sigma}'_{x_2x_1}\boldsymbol{T}\boldsymbol{\sigma}_{x_2x_1}}{\sigma_{x_1}^4} - \frac{\boldsymbol{\sigma}'_{x_2x_1}\boldsymbol{T}\boldsymbol{\sigma}_{x_2y}}{\sigma_{x_1}^2} \\
&= \frac{\sigma_{x_1y}}{\sigma_{x_1}^2} + \frac{\sigma_{x_1y}\boldsymbol{\sigma}'_{x_2x_1}\boldsymbol{\Sigma}_{x_2x_2}^{-1}\boldsymbol{\sigma}_{x_2x_1}}{\sigma_{x_1}^4} - \frac{\boldsymbol{\sigma}'_{x_2x_1}\boldsymbol{\Sigma}_{x_2x_2}^{-1}\boldsymbol{\sigma}_{x_2y}}{\sigma_{x_1}^2} \\
&\quad + \frac{\sigma_{x_1y}(\boldsymbol{\sigma}'_{x_2x_1}\boldsymbol{\Sigma}_{x_2x_2}^{-1}\boldsymbol{\sigma}_{x_2x_1})^2}{\sigma_{x_1}^4(\sigma_{x_1}^2 - \boldsymbol{\sigma}'_{x_2x_1}\boldsymbol{\Sigma}_{x_2x_2}^{-1}\boldsymbol{\sigma}_{x_2x_1})} - \frac{\boldsymbol{\sigma}'_{x_2x_1}\boldsymbol{\Sigma}_{x_2x_2}^{-1}\boldsymbol{\sigma}_{x_2x_1}\boldsymbol{\sigma}'_{x_2x_1}\boldsymbol{\Sigma}_{x_2x_2}^{-1}\boldsymbol{\sigma}_{x_2y}}{\sigma_{x_1}^2(\sigma_{x_1}^2 - \boldsymbol{\sigma}'_{x_2x_1}\boldsymbol{\Sigma}_{x_2x_2}^{-1}\boldsymbol{\sigma}_{x_2x_1})} \\
&= \frac{\sigma_y r_{x_1y}}{\sigma_{x_1}} + \frac{\sigma_y r_{x_1y}\boldsymbol{r}'_{x_2x_1}\boldsymbol{R}_{x_2x_2}^{-1}\boldsymbol{r}_{x_2x_1}}{\sigma_{x_1}} - \frac{\sigma_y\boldsymbol{r}'_{x_2x_1}\boldsymbol{R}_{x_2x_2}^{-1}\boldsymbol{r}_{x_2y}}{\sigma_{x_1}} \\
&\quad + \frac{\sigma_y r_{x_1y}(\boldsymbol{r}'_{x_2x_1}\boldsymbol{R}_{x_2x_2}^{-1}\boldsymbol{r}_{x_2x_1})^2}{\sigma_{x_1}(1 - \boldsymbol{r}'_{x_2x_1}\boldsymbol{R}_{x_2x_2}^{-1}\boldsymbol{r}_{x_2x_1})} - \frac{\sigma_y\boldsymbol{r}'_{x_2x_1}\boldsymbol{R}_{x_2x_2}^{-1}\boldsymbol{r}_{x_2x_1}\boldsymbol{r}'_{x_2x_1}\boldsymbol{R}_{x_2x_2}^{-1}\boldsymbol{r}_{x_2y}}{\sigma_{x_1}(1 - \boldsymbol{r}'_{x_2x_1}\boldsymbol{R}_{x_2x_2}^{-1}\boldsymbol{r}_{x_2x_1})}
\end{aligned}$$

$$= \frac{\sigma_y(r_{x_1y} - \boldsymbol{r}'_{x_2y}\boldsymbol{R}^{-1}_{x_2x_2}\boldsymbol{r}_{x_2x_1})}{\sigma_{x_1}(1 - \boldsymbol{r}'_{x_2x_1}\boldsymbol{R}^{-1}_{x_2x_2}\boldsymbol{r}_{x_2x_1})} = \rho_{yx_1\cdot x_2}\frac{\sigma_{y\cdot x_2}}{\sigma_{x_1\cdot x_2}}.$$

2.8 (a) By conditioning the quadratic form on $\boldsymbol{x}$, we have

$$\begin{aligned}
&E[(\boldsymbol{y} - \boldsymbol{g}(\boldsymbol{x}))'\boldsymbol{W}(\boldsymbol{x})(\boldsymbol{y} - \boldsymbol{g}(\boldsymbol{x}))] \\
&\quad = E[E\{(\boldsymbol{y} - \boldsymbol{g}(\boldsymbol{x}))'\boldsymbol{W}(\boldsymbol{x})(\boldsymbol{y} - \boldsymbol{g}(\boldsymbol{x}))|\boldsymbol{x}\}] \\
&\quad = E[E\{(\boldsymbol{y} - E(\boldsymbol{y}|\boldsymbol{x}) + E(\boldsymbol{y}|\boldsymbol{x}) - \boldsymbol{g}(\boldsymbol{x}))'\boldsymbol{W}(\boldsymbol{x}) \\
&\qquad\qquad (\boldsymbol{y} - E(\boldsymbol{y}|\boldsymbol{x}) + E(\boldsymbol{y}|\boldsymbol{x}) - \boldsymbol{g}(\boldsymbol{x}))|\boldsymbol{x}\}] \\
&\quad = E[E\{(\boldsymbol{y} - E(\boldsymbol{y}|\boldsymbol{x}))'\boldsymbol{W}(\boldsymbol{x})(\boldsymbol{y} - E(\boldsymbol{y}|\boldsymbol{x}))|\boldsymbol{x}\}] \\
&\qquad + E[E\{(E(\boldsymbol{y}|\boldsymbol{x}) - \boldsymbol{g}(\boldsymbol{x}))'\boldsymbol{W}(\boldsymbol{x})(E(\boldsymbol{y}|\boldsymbol{x}) - \boldsymbol{g}(\boldsymbol{x}))|\boldsymbol{x}\}] \\
&\qquad + 2E[(E(\boldsymbol{y}|\boldsymbol{x}) - \boldsymbol{g}(\boldsymbol{x}))'\boldsymbol{W}(\boldsymbol{x})E\{(\boldsymbol{y} - E(\boldsymbol{y}|\boldsymbol{x}))|\boldsymbol{x}\}] \\
&\quad = E[(\boldsymbol{y} - E(\boldsymbol{y}|\boldsymbol{x}))'\boldsymbol{W}(\boldsymbol{x})(\boldsymbol{y} - E(\boldsymbol{y}|\boldsymbol{x}))] \\
&\qquad + E[(E(\boldsymbol{y}|\boldsymbol{x}) - \boldsymbol{g}(\boldsymbol{x}))'\boldsymbol{W}(\boldsymbol{x})(E(\boldsymbol{y}|\boldsymbol{x}) - \boldsymbol{g}(\boldsymbol{x}))] \\
&\quad \geq E[(\boldsymbol{y} - E(\boldsymbol{y}|\boldsymbol{x})'\boldsymbol{W}(\boldsymbol{x})(\boldsymbol{y} - E(\boldsymbol{y}|\boldsymbol{x}))].
\end{aligned}$$

The equality holds if and only if the second quadratic form is zero, i.e. $E(\boldsymbol{y}|\boldsymbol{x}) - \boldsymbol{g}(\boldsymbol{x}) = \boldsymbol{0}$ almost surely.

(b) The inequality of part (a) holds with equality if and only if $E[(E(\boldsymbol{y}|\boldsymbol{x}) - \boldsymbol{g}(\boldsymbol{x}))'\boldsymbol{W}(\boldsymbol{x})(E(\boldsymbol{y}|\boldsymbol{x}) - \boldsymbol{g}(\boldsymbol{x}))] = \boldsymbol{0}$. When $\boldsymbol{W}(\boldsymbol{x})$ is positive semidefinite, a necessary and sufficient condition for this is that $\boldsymbol{g}(\boldsymbol{x}) = E(\boldsymbol{y}|\boldsymbol{x}) + \boldsymbol{w}(\boldsymbol{x})$ almost surely, where $\boldsymbol{w}(\boldsymbol{x})$ is any vector satisfying $\boldsymbol{W}(\boldsymbol{x})\boldsymbol{w}(\boldsymbol{x}) = \boldsymbol{0}$.

2.9 (a) Note that for any linear predictor $\boldsymbol{Lx} + \boldsymbol{c}$,

$$\begin{aligned}
&E\left(\{\boldsymbol{y} - \boldsymbol{Lx} - \boldsymbol{c}\}'\boldsymbol{W}(\boldsymbol{x})\{\boldsymbol{y} - \boldsymbol{Lx} - \boldsymbol{c}\}\right) \\
&\quad = E[\{(\boldsymbol{y} - \boldsymbol{L}(\boldsymbol{x} - \boldsymbol{\mu}_x) - \boldsymbol{\mu}_y) + (\boldsymbol{\mu}_y - \boldsymbol{L\mu}_x - \boldsymbol{c})\}'\boldsymbol{W}(\boldsymbol{x}) \\
&\qquad\qquad \{(\boldsymbol{y} - \boldsymbol{L}(\boldsymbol{x} - \boldsymbol{\mu}_x) - \boldsymbol{\mu}_y) + (\boldsymbol{\mu}_y - \boldsymbol{L\mu}_x - \boldsymbol{c})\}] \\
&\quad = E[\{\boldsymbol{y} - \boldsymbol{L}(\boldsymbol{x} - \boldsymbol{\mu}_x) - \boldsymbol{\mu}_y\}'\boldsymbol{W}(\boldsymbol{x})\{\boldsymbol{y} - \boldsymbol{L}(\boldsymbol{x} - \boldsymbol{\mu}_x) - \boldsymbol{\mu}_y\}] \\
&\qquad + 2E[\{\boldsymbol{y} - \boldsymbol{L}(\boldsymbol{x} - \boldsymbol{\mu}_x) - \boldsymbol{\mu}_y\}'\boldsymbol{W}(\boldsymbol{x})\{\boldsymbol{\mu}_y - \boldsymbol{L\mu}_x - \boldsymbol{c}\}] \\
&\qquad + \{\boldsymbol{\mu}_y - \boldsymbol{L\mu}_x - \boldsymbol{c}\}'\{\boldsymbol{\mu}_y - \boldsymbol{L\mu}_x - \boldsymbol{c}\} \\
&\quad = E[\{\boldsymbol{y} - \boldsymbol{L}(\boldsymbol{x} - \boldsymbol{\mu}_x) - \boldsymbol{\mu}_y\}'\boldsymbol{W}(\boldsymbol{x})\{\boldsymbol{y} - \boldsymbol{L}(\boldsymbol{x} - \boldsymbol{\mu}_x) - \boldsymbol{\mu}_y\}] \\
&\qquad + \{\boldsymbol{\mu}_y - \boldsymbol{L\mu}_x - \boldsymbol{c}\}'\boldsymbol{W}(\boldsymbol{x})\{\boldsymbol{\mu}_y - \boldsymbol{L\mu}_x - \boldsymbol{c}\} \\
&\quad \geq E[\{\boldsymbol{y} - \boldsymbol{L}(\boldsymbol{x} - \boldsymbol{\mu}_x) - \boldsymbol{\mu}_y\}'\boldsymbol{W}(\boldsymbol{x})\{\boldsymbol{y} - \boldsymbol{L}(\boldsymbol{x} - \boldsymbol{\mu}_x) - \boldsymbol{\mu}_y\}] \\
&\quad = \mathrm{tr}(\boldsymbol{W}(\boldsymbol{x})E[\{\boldsymbol{y} - \boldsymbol{L}(\boldsymbol{x} - \boldsymbol{\mu}_x) - \boldsymbol{\mu}_y\}\{\boldsymbol{y} - \boldsymbol{L}(\boldsymbol{x} - \boldsymbol{\mu}_x) - \boldsymbol{\mu}_y\}']) \\
&\quad = \mathrm{tr}(\boldsymbol{W}(\boldsymbol{x})D(\boldsymbol{y} - \boldsymbol{L}(\boldsymbol{x} - \boldsymbol{\mu}_x) - \boldsymbol{\mu}_y)).
\end{aligned}$$

This shows that the value of the criterion for the predictor $\boldsymbol{Lx} + \boldsymbol{c}$ is at least as large as that for its unbiased version, $\boldsymbol{L}(\boldsymbol{x}-\boldsymbol{\mu}_x)+\boldsymbol{\mu}_y$. Further,

$$\begin{aligned}
&D(\boldsymbol{y}-\boldsymbol{L}(\boldsymbol{x}-\boldsymbol{\mu}_x)-\boldsymbol{\mu}_y)\\
&\quad= D(\{\boldsymbol{y}-\widehat{E}(\boldsymbol{y}|\boldsymbol{x})\}+\{\widehat{E}(\boldsymbol{y}|\boldsymbol{x})-\boldsymbol{L}(\boldsymbol{x}-\boldsymbol{\mu}_x)-\boldsymbol{\mu}_y\})\\
&\quad= D(\boldsymbol{y}-\widehat{E}(\boldsymbol{y}|\boldsymbol{x}))+D(\widehat{E}(\boldsymbol{y}|\boldsymbol{x})-\boldsymbol{L}(\boldsymbol{x}-\boldsymbol{\mu}_x)-\boldsymbol{\mu}_y)\\
&\qquad+Cov(\boldsymbol{y}-\widehat{E}(\boldsymbol{y}|\boldsymbol{x}),\widehat{E}(\boldsymbol{y}|\boldsymbol{x})-\boldsymbol{L}(\boldsymbol{x}-\boldsymbol{\mu}_x)-\boldsymbol{\mu}_y)\\
&\qquad+Cov(\widehat{E}(\boldsymbol{y}|\boldsymbol{x})-\boldsymbol{L}(\boldsymbol{x}-\boldsymbol{\mu}_x)-\boldsymbol{\mu}_y,\boldsymbol{y}-\widehat{E}(\boldsymbol{y}|\boldsymbol{x})).
\end{aligned}$$

The last two terms vanish because of part (b) of Proposition 2.25. Therefore,

$$\begin{aligned}
&\mathrm{tr}(\boldsymbol{W}(\boldsymbol{x})D(\boldsymbol{y}-\boldsymbol{L}(\boldsymbol{x}-\boldsymbol{\mu}_x)-\boldsymbol{\mu}_y))\\
&\quad=\mathrm{tr}(\boldsymbol{W}(\boldsymbol{x})D(\boldsymbol{y}-\widehat{E}(\boldsymbol{y}|\boldsymbol{x})))+\mathrm{tr}(\boldsymbol{W}(\boldsymbol{x})D(\widehat{E}(\boldsymbol{y}|\boldsymbol{x})-\boldsymbol{L}(\boldsymbol{x}-\boldsymbol{\mu}_x)-\boldsymbol{\mu}_y))\\
&\quad=E(\{\boldsymbol{y}-\widehat{E}(\boldsymbol{y}|\boldsymbol{x})\}'\boldsymbol{W}(\boldsymbol{x})\{\boldsymbol{y}-\widehat{E}(\boldsymbol{y}|\boldsymbol{x})\})\\
&\qquad+E(\{\widehat{E}(\boldsymbol{y}|\boldsymbol{x})-\boldsymbol{L}(\boldsymbol{x}-\boldsymbol{\mu}_x)-\boldsymbol{\mu}_y\}'\boldsymbol{W}(\boldsymbol{x})\{\widehat{E}(\boldsymbol{y}|\boldsymbol{x})-\boldsymbol{L}(\boldsymbol{x}-\boldsymbol{\mu}_x)-\boldsymbol{\mu}_y\})\\
&\quad\ge E\left(\{\boldsymbol{y}-\widehat{E}(\boldsymbol{y}|\boldsymbol{x})\}'\boldsymbol{W}(\boldsymbol{x})\{\boldsymbol{y}-\widehat{E}(\boldsymbol{y}|\boldsymbol{x})\}\right).
\end{aligned}$$

This proves the result of part (a).

(b) When $\boldsymbol{W}(\boldsymbol{x})$ is positive semidefinite, the optimal predictor would not be unique. This is because of the fact that if $\boldsymbol{v}(\boldsymbol{x})$ is a vector belonging to $\mathcal{C}(\boldsymbol{W}(\boldsymbol{x}))^{\perp}$, then $\widehat{E}(\boldsymbol{y}|\boldsymbol{x})+\boldsymbol{v}(\boldsymbol{x})$ produces the same value of the criterion as $\widehat{E}(\boldsymbol{y}|\boldsymbol{x})$.

2.10 We observe from the principle of decorrelation (see Proposition 2.28) that the zero-mean vector $\boldsymbol{y}-\boldsymbol{\mu}_y-\boldsymbol{V}_{yx}\boldsymbol{V}_{xx}^-(\boldsymbol{x}-\boldsymbol{\mu}_x)$ is uncorrelated with $\boldsymbol{x}-\boldsymbol{\mu}_x$. Therefore,

$$\begin{aligned}
&E[(\boldsymbol{y}-\boldsymbol{L}\boldsymbol{x}-\boldsymbol{c})(\boldsymbol{y}-\boldsymbol{L}\boldsymbol{x}-\boldsymbol{c})']\\
&\quad=E[(\boldsymbol{y}-\boldsymbol{\mu}_y-\boldsymbol{V}_{yx}\boldsymbol{V}_{xx}^-(\boldsymbol{x}-\boldsymbol{\mu}_x))(\boldsymbol{y}-\boldsymbol{\mu}_y-\boldsymbol{V}_{yx}\boldsymbol{V}_{xx}^-(\boldsymbol{x}-\boldsymbol{\mu}_x))']\\
&\qquad+E[(\boldsymbol{\mu}_y+\boldsymbol{V}_{yx}\boldsymbol{V}_{xx}^-(\boldsymbol{x}-\boldsymbol{\mu}_x)-\boldsymbol{L}\boldsymbol{x}-\boldsymbol{c})(\boldsymbol{\mu}_y+\boldsymbol{V}_{yx}\boldsymbol{V}_{xx}^-(\boldsymbol{x}-\boldsymbol{\mu}_x)-\boldsymbol{L}\boldsymbol{x}-\boldsymbol{c})'].
\end{aligned}$$

This expression is minimized when the second term is zero, which happens only if $E[\|\boldsymbol{\mu}_y+\boldsymbol{V}_{yx}\boldsymbol{V}_{xx}^-(\boldsymbol{x}-\boldsymbol{\mu}_x)-\boldsymbol{L}\boldsymbol{x}-\mathbf{c}\|^2]$ is zero, that is, $\boldsymbol{L}\boldsymbol{x}+c$ is almost surely equal to $\boldsymbol{\mu}_y+\boldsymbol{V}_{yx}\boldsymbol{V}_{xx}^-(\boldsymbol{x}-\boldsymbol{\mu}_x)$ or $\widehat{E}(\boldsymbol{y}|\boldsymbol{x})$. The sufficiency of this condition is obvious.

The mean squared prediction error matrix for the BLP is

$$E[(\boldsymbol{y}-\boldsymbol{\mu}_y-\boldsymbol{V}_{yx}\boldsymbol{V}_{xx}^-(\boldsymbol{x}-\boldsymbol{\mu}_x))(\boldsymbol{y}-\boldsymbol{\mu}_y-\boldsymbol{V}_{yx}\boldsymbol{V}_{xx}^-(\boldsymbol{x}-\boldsymbol{\mu}_x))']=\boldsymbol{V}_{yy}-\boldsymbol{V}_{yx}\boldsymbol{V}_{xx}^-\boldsymbol{V}_{xy}.$$

2.11 Let $\boldsymbol{x}=\mathrm{vec}(\boldsymbol{X})$ and

$$\boldsymbol{\varepsilon}=\boldsymbol{y}-E(\boldsymbol{y})-Cov(\boldsymbol{y},\boldsymbol{x})[D(\boldsymbol{x})]^-(\boldsymbol{x}-E(\boldsymbol{x})).$$

It follows from the principle of decorrelation (see Proposition 2.28) that $\boldsymbol{\varepsilon}$ is uncorrelated with $\boldsymbol{x}$. It is easily seen to have zero mean. We only need to show that $\boldsymbol{y} - \boldsymbol{\varepsilon}$ can be written in the form $(\mathbf{1} : \boldsymbol{X})\boldsymbol{\beta}$. This reduction has been shown in the proof of Proposition 2.20.

The decomposition is similar to (1.4), but here $\boldsymbol{X}$ is random. The model (1.4)–(1.5) may not even hold conditionally on $\boldsymbol{X}$, as $D(\boldsymbol{y}|\boldsymbol{X})$ may not be the same as $D(\boldsymbol{\varepsilon})$ and may depend on $\boldsymbol{X}$.

If $\boldsymbol{y}$ and $\boldsymbol{X}$ are jointly normal, then $(\mathbf{1} : \boldsymbol{X})\boldsymbol{\beta}$ is the conditional mean of $\boldsymbol{y}$ given $\boldsymbol{X}$ and $\sigma^2\boldsymbol{V}$ is the conditional dispersion (see Proposition 2.20). In such a case the model (1.4) is applicable here, conditionally on $\boldsymbol{X}$.

2.12 (a) Since $\boldsymbol{u}-\boldsymbol{B}\boldsymbol{v}$ is uncorrelated with $\boldsymbol{v}$, we have $D(\boldsymbol{u}) = D(\boldsymbol{u}-\boldsymbol{B}\boldsymbol{v}+\boldsymbol{B}\boldsymbol{v}) = D(\boldsymbol{u}-\boldsymbol{B}\boldsymbol{v}) + D(\boldsymbol{B}\boldsymbol{v}) \geq D(\boldsymbol{u}-\boldsymbol{B}\boldsymbol{v})$.

(b) Adjusting for the covariance of $\boldsymbol{u}-\boldsymbol{B}_1\boldsymbol{v}_1$ with $\boldsymbol{v}$, we have a random vector of the form $\boldsymbol{u}-\boldsymbol{C}\boldsymbol{v}$. The latter must coincide with $\boldsymbol{u}-\boldsymbol{B}\boldsymbol{v}$ because of Proposition 2.28. The stated result follows from part (a) with $\boldsymbol{u}-\boldsymbol{B}_1\boldsymbol{v}_1$ playing the role of $\boldsymbol{u}$.

Chapter 3

3.1 An LUE in a saturated model cannot be improved by removing correlation with LZFs, as there is no LZF.

3.2 Assuming that $\boldsymbol{X}$ has p columns, let $\boldsymbol{I}_{p\times p} = (\boldsymbol{u}_1 : \cdots : \boldsymbol{u}_p)$. All the components of $\boldsymbol{\beta}$ are estimable if and only if $\boldsymbol{u}_j'\boldsymbol{\beta}$ is estimable for $j = 1,\ldots,p$, i.e. $\boldsymbol{u}_j \in \mathcal{C}(\boldsymbol{X}')$ for $j = 1,\ldots,p$. The latter condition is equivalent to $\mathcal{C}(\boldsymbol{I}_{p\times p}) \subseteq \mathcal{C}(\boldsymbol{X}')$, i.e. $\rho(\boldsymbol{X}) = \dim(\mathcal{C}(\boldsymbol{X})) = \dim(\mathcal{C}(\boldsymbol{I}_{p\times p})) = p$. If this condition holds, then for all $\boldsymbol{p}_{p\times 1}$ we have $\boldsymbol{p} \in \mathcal{C}(\boldsymbol{X}')$ and hence $\boldsymbol{p}'\boldsymbol{\beta}$ is estimable.

3.3 If $\boldsymbol{A\beta}$ is non-estimable, then it follows from Proposition 3.27 that it is not identifiable. Thus, by definition there are $\boldsymbol{\beta}_1$ and $\boldsymbol{\beta}_2$ such that $\boldsymbol{A\beta}_1 \neq \boldsymbol{A\beta}_2$ and yet the density of $\boldsymbol{y}$ is the same for $\boldsymbol{\beta} = \boldsymbol{\beta}_1$ and $\boldsymbol{\beta} = \boldsymbol{\beta}_2$. If $\boldsymbol{T}(\boldsymbol{y})$ is any statistic, then the congruence of the densities implies that $E(\boldsymbol{T}(\boldsymbol{y}))$ has the same value for $\boldsymbol{\beta} = \boldsymbol{\beta}_1$ and $\boldsymbol{\beta} = \boldsymbol{\beta}_2$. For $\boldsymbol{T}(\boldsymbol{y})$ to be an unbiased estimator of $\boldsymbol{A\beta}$, we should have $\boldsymbol{A\beta}_1 = \boldsymbol{A\beta}_2$, which is a contradiction.

3.4 Let $\boldsymbol{u}_1$ be the first column of $\boldsymbol{I}_{p\times p}$. If $\boldsymbol{x}_1$ has an exact linear relationship with the other columns of $\boldsymbol{X}$, then there is a $p\times 1$ vector $\boldsymbol{l}$ such that $\boldsymbol{Xl} = \mathbf{0}$ and $\boldsymbol{u}_1'\boldsymbol{l} \neq 0$. This is impossible when $\boldsymbol{u}_1$ is of the form $\boldsymbol{X}'\boldsymbol{m}$. Therefore, $\boldsymbol{u}_1 \notin \mathcal{C}(\boldsymbol{X}')$, and hence the coefficient of $\boldsymbol{x}_1$ is not estimable.

To prove the converse, let $\boldsymbol{u}_1 \notin \mathcal{C}(\boldsymbol{X}')$. It follows that $\boldsymbol{u}_1'(\boldsymbol{I} - \boldsymbol{P}_{\boldsymbol{X}'})\boldsymbol{u}_1 > 0$, i.e. the first element of the vector $(\boldsymbol{I} - \boldsymbol{P}_{\boldsymbol{X}'})\boldsymbol{u}_1$ is nonzero. Let $\boldsymbol{l}$ be a multiple of the latter vector such that its first element is equal to 1. It follows that $\boldsymbol{Xl} = \mathbf{0}$, i.e. $\boldsymbol{x}_1$ can be written as a linear combination of the other columns of $\boldsymbol{X}$.

3.5 Since $\mathcal{C}(\boldsymbol{X}') \subseteq \mathcal{C}(\boldsymbol{X}' : \boldsymbol{A}')$, these two column spaces coincide if and only if their dimensions are identical, i.e. $\rho(\boldsymbol{X}' : \boldsymbol{A}') = \rho(\boldsymbol{A})$. Conversely, $\mathcal{C}(\boldsymbol{X}') = \mathcal{C}(\boldsymbol{X}' : \boldsymbol{A}')$ if and only if $\mathcal{C}(\boldsymbol{A}') \subseteq \mathcal{C}(\boldsymbol{X}')$, i.e. $\boldsymbol{A\beta}$ is estimable.

3.6 The 'if' part is obvious. To prove the 'only if' part, note that $\boldsymbol{l}'\boldsymbol{y} + c$ is unbiased for $\boldsymbol{p}'\boldsymbol{\beta}$ only if $\boldsymbol{l}'\boldsymbol{X\beta} + c = \boldsymbol{p}'\boldsymbol{\beta}$ for all $\boldsymbol{\beta}$. Putting $\boldsymbol{\beta} = \boldsymbol{0}$ into this identity, we have $c = 0$ and hence, $\boldsymbol{l}'\boldsymbol{X\beta} = \boldsymbol{p}'\boldsymbol{\beta}$ for all $\boldsymbol{\beta}$. The latter identity implies $\boldsymbol{X}'\boldsymbol{l} = \boldsymbol{p}$.

3.7 The linear function $\boldsymbol{l}'\boldsymbol{y}$ is the BLUE of its expectation if and only if it is uncorrelated with $(\boldsymbol{I} - \boldsymbol{P}_X)\boldsymbol{y}$, i.e. $(\boldsymbol{I} - \boldsymbol{P}_X)\boldsymbol{l} = \boldsymbol{0}$. The latter condition is equivalent to $\boldsymbol{l} \in \mathcal{C}(\boldsymbol{X})$.

3.8 (a) The likelihood of the data is proportional to $g\left(\|\boldsymbol{y} - \boldsymbol{X\beta}\|^2\right)$. Since g is a nondecreasing function, an MLE minimizes $\|\boldsymbol{y} - \boldsymbol{X\beta}\|^2$, and hence it is an LSE.
(b) The MLE is unique if and only if $\boldsymbol{X}$ has full column rank.

3.9 The LSE can be interpreted as a weighted average of all the LSEs of $\boldsymbol{\beta}$ obtained from the $\binom{n}{r}$ sub-models. Note that r is the smallest number of observations in a sub-model so that $\boldsymbol{\beta}$ can possibly be estimated from it, and that the weight is zero for any sub-model where $\boldsymbol{\beta}$ is not estimable. In the special case of simple linear regression, let $\widehat{\boldsymbol{\beta}}_{ij}$ denote the 'LSE' from the i and jth observations (i.e. from (x_i, y_i) and (x_j, y_j)). Let $\boldsymbol{x} = (x_1 : \cdots : x_n)'$. It follows from (3.3) that whenever $x_i \neq x_j$,

$$\widehat{\boldsymbol{\beta}}_{ij} = \begin{pmatrix} \frac{x_i y_j - x_j y_i}{x_i - x_j} \\ \frac{y_i - y_j}{x_i - x_j} \end{pmatrix}.$$

Defining the weight w_{ij} as $(x_i - x_j)^2/(2n\boldsymbol{x}'\boldsymbol{x} - 2n^2\bar{x}^2)$, we have

$$\sum_{i=1}^{n}\sum_{j=1}^{n} w_{ij}\widehat{\boldsymbol{\beta}}_{ij} = \frac{1}{2n\boldsymbol{x}'\boldsymbol{x} - 2n^2\bar{x}^2}\begin{pmatrix} 2n\bar{y}\boldsymbol{x}'\boldsymbol{x} - 2n\bar{x}\boldsymbol{x}'\boldsymbol{y} \\ 2n\boldsymbol{x}'\boldsymbol{y} - 2n^2\bar{x}\bar{y} \end{pmatrix},$$

which simplifies to $\widehat{\boldsymbol{\beta}}$. Note that the set of weights constitutes a special case of the given weights for general r, and it satisfies the condition $\sum_{i=1}^{n}\sum_{j=1}^{n} w_{ij} = 1$. Thus, the LSE of $\boldsymbol{\beta}$ is a weighted sum of the slopes and intercepts of lines passing through pairs of points, and larger weights are given to pairs of points having x-values far from one another.

3.10 The validity of the g-inverses can be verified directly from definition. For *any* $\boldsymbol{X}^-$, $\boldsymbol{X}^-\widehat{\boldsymbol{y}} = \boldsymbol{X}^-\boldsymbol{P}_X\boldsymbol{y} = [\boldsymbol{X}^-\boldsymbol{X}(\boldsymbol{X}'\boldsymbol{X})^-]\boldsymbol{X}'\boldsymbol{y}$, which is a special choice of $\widehat{\boldsymbol{\beta}}_{LS}$ given by (3.1) with $\boldsymbol{X}^-\boldsymbol{X}(\boldsymbol{X}'\boldsymbol{X})^-$ serving as $(\boldsymbol{X}'\boldsymbol{X})^-$. On the other hand, for *any* $(\boldsymbol{X}'\boldsymbol{X})^-$, we can rewrite (3.1) as $\widehat{\boldsymbol{\beta}}_{LS} = (\boldsymbol{X}'\boldsymbol{X})^-\boldsymbol{X}'\boldsymbol{y} = [(\boldsymbol{X}'\boldsymbol{X})^-\boldsymbol{X}']\boldsymbol{P}_X\boldsymbol{y}$, which is of the form $\boldsymbol{X}^-\widehat{\boldsymbol{y}}$ with $[(\boldsymbol{X}'\boldsymbol{X})^-\boldsymbol{X}']$ serving as $\boldsymbol{X}^-$.

3.11 Suppose $\boldsymbol{l}'\boldsymbol{y}$ is any LZF with nonzero variance. Then it must be correlated with some LZF of $\mathcal{A}$. Let $\boldsymbol{Ly}$ be a vector of all the members of $\mathcal{A}$. After adjusting for the covariance of $\boldsymbol{l}'\boldsymbol{y}$ with $\boldsymbol{Ly}$, we obtain the new random variable $\boldsymbol{m}'\boldsymbol{y} = \boldsymbol{l}'\boldsymbol{y} - Cov(\boldsymbol{l}'\boldsymbol{y}, \boldsymbol{L}\boldsymbol{y})[D(\boldsymbol{L}\boldsymbol{y})]^{-}\boldsymbol{L}\boldsymbol{y}$, which is uncorrelated with the members of $\mathcal{A}$. Since $\boldsymbol{m}'\boldsymbol{y}$ is itself an LZF, by definition of $\mathcal{A}$ we have $Var(\boldsymbol{m}'\boldsymbol{y}) = 0$. Therefore, $\boldsymbol{m}'\boldsymbol{y} = 0$ with probability 1, that is, $\boldsymbol{l}'\boldsymbol{y}$ is almost surely equal to a linear function of the elements of $\mathcal{A}$.

3.12 Let $\boldsymbol{U}_1$ and $\boldsymbol{U}_2$ be semi-orthogonal matrices whose columns form bases of $\mathcal{C}(\boldsymbol{X})$ and $\mathcal{C}(\boldsymbol{I} - \boldsymbol{P}_X)$, respectively. (These can be matrices of left singular vectors of $\boldsymbol{X}$ and $\boldsymbol{I} - \boldsymbol{P}_X$ corresponding to their respective sets of positive singular values.) Clearly $\rho(\boldsymbol{U}_1) = \rho(\boldsymbol{X})$, $\rho(\boldsymbol{U}_2) = n - \rho(\boldsymbol{X})$, and $\boldsymbol{U}_1'\boldsymbol{U}_2 = \boldsymbol{0}$. Choose $\boldsymbol{L}$ as the orthogonal matrix $(\boldsymbol{U}_1 : \boldsymbol{U}_2)'$. It is easy to see that $\boldsymbol{L}\boldsymbol{y}$ satisfies condition (a), that is, all the elements of $\boldsymbol{L}\boldsymbol{y}$ are uncorrelated and have variance σ^2. The elements of $\boldsymbol{U}_1'\boldsymbol{y}$ are BLUE, because $Cov(\boldsymbol{U}_1'\boldsymbol{y}, (\boldsymbol{I} - \boldsymbol{P}_X)\boldsymbol{y}) = \sigma^2\boldsymbol{U}_1'(\boldsymbol{I} - \boldsymbol{P}_X) = \boldsymbol{0}$. Also, there is a matrix $\boldsymbol{T}$ such that $\boldsymbol{P}_X = \boldsymbol{U}_1\boldsymbol{T}$; so $\boldsymbol{T}'\boldsymbol{U}_1'\boldsymbol{y}$ is the BLUE of $\boldsymbol{X}\boldsymbol{\beta}$. Every other BLUE is a linear function of it. Thus, condition (b) is satisfied by $\boldsymbol{L}\boldsymbol{y}$. The elements of $\boldsymbol{U}_2\boldsymbol{y}$ are LZFs, since $\boldsymbol{U}_2'\boldsymbol{X} = \boldsymbol{0}$. There is a matrix $\boldsymbol{K}$ such that $\boldsymbol{I} - \boldsymbol{P}_X = \boldsymbol{U}_2\boldsymbol{K}$, and hence $(\boldsymbol{I} - \boldsymbol{P}_X)\boldsymbol{y} = \boldsymbol{K}'\boldsymbol{U}_2'\boldsymbol{y}$ almost surely. Therefore, every LZF is a linear function of $\boldsymbol{U}_2'\boldsymbol{y}$. This proves that $\boldsymbol{L}\boldsymbol{y}$ satisfies condition (c).

3.13 Let $\boldsymbol{z}$ be as in Remark 3.48, and $\boldsymbol{C}\boldsymbol{C}'$ be a rank-factorization of $\sigma^{-2}D(\boldsymbol{z})$. Suppose $\boldsymbol{v} = \boldsymbol{C}^{-L}\boldsymbol{z}$, where $\boldsymbol{C}^{-L}$ is any left-inverse of $\boldsymbol{C}$. It is easy to see that the elements of $\boldsymbol{v}$ are LZFs, these are uncorrelated and have variance σ^2. Further, as $\boldsymbol{z} \in \mathcal{C}(\boldsymbol{C})$ with probability 1 (because of Proposition 2.13), we can write $\boldsymbol{z}$ as $\boldsymbol{C}\boldsymbol{v}$ almost surely. Therefore, the elements of $\boldsymbol{v}$ form a basis set of LZFs. The conclusions follow from Definition 3.47, Proposition 3.33 and (3.19).

3.14 The proof proceeds along the lines of that of Proposition 3.45.

3.15 Let $\boldsymbol{z}$ be a vector whose elements constitute a standardized basis set of LZFs. Then $Var(\boldsymbol{z}'\boldsymbol{z}) = 2(n-r)\sigma^4$, where $r = \rho(\boldsymbol{X})$. Hence $E[(cR_0^2 - \sigma^2)^2] = [E(cR_0^2 - \sigma^2)]^2 + Var(cR_0^2 - \sigma^2) = [((n-r)c - 1)^2 + 2(n-r)c^2]\sigma^4$.

(a) For $c = 1/(n-r)$, we have $E[(\widehat{\sigma^2} - \sigma^2)^2] = 2\sigma^4/(n-r)$. For $c = 1/n$, we have $E[(\widehat{\sigma^2}_{ML} - \sigma^2)^2] = \sigma^4(2n - 2r + r^2)/n^2$. The MSE of $\widehat{\sigma^2}$ is smaller if and only if $r^2 - (n+2)r + 4n < 0$. The roots of the quadratic function in r are $\frac{1}{2}[n + 2 \pm ((n+2)^2 - 16n)^{1/2}]$. The inequality never holds when $n < 12$. When $n \geq 12$, the MSE of $\widehat{\sigma^2}$ is smaller if and only if r is between the above two roots (e.g. when $n = 12$, $r = 7$).

(b) The MSE of cR_0^2 is minimized when $c = 1/(n-r+2)$. The biased estimator $R_0^2/(n-r+2)$ is strictly smaller than $\widehat{\sigma^2}$, and it coincides with $\widehat{\sigma^2}_{ML}$ only in the special case $r = 2$.

(c) The smallest MSE is $[1 - (n-r)(n-r+2)]\sigma^4$.

3.16 $\boldsymbol{X}\widehat{\boldsymbol{\beta}} = \boldsymbol{Z}\widehat{\boldsymbol{\theta}}$, $\widehat{\boldsymbol{\theta}} = (\boldsymbol{Z}'\boldsymbol{Z})^{-1}\boldsymbol{Z}'\boldsymbol{X}\widehat{\boldsymbol{\beta}}$.

3.17 When the restriction $\tau_1 = \tau_2$ is imposed, the BLUE $\widehat{\tau}_1 - \widehat{\tau}_2$ turns into an LZF. The restrictions $\beta_1 + \beta_2 = 0$ and $\tau_1 + \tau_2 = 0$ amount to a reparametrization. The sets of BLUEs and LZFs remain unchanged.

3.18 The rank condition ensures $\rho(\boldsymbol{X}') = \rho((\boldsymbol{I}-\boldsymbol{P}_{A'})\boldsymbol{X}')$ (see Proposition A.14), and hence $\mathcal{C}(\boldsymbol{X}) = \mathcal{C}(\boldsymbol{X}(\boldsymbol{I}-\boldsymbol{P}_{A'}))$. Let $\boldsymbol{Z} = \boldsymbol{X}(\boldsymbol{I}-\boldsymbol{P}_{A'})$, choose $\boldsymbol{T}_1$ as a matrix such that $\boldsymbol{Z}\boldsymbol{T}_1 = \boldsymbol{X}$ and define $\boldsymbol{\theta}_0 = -\boldsymbol{T}_1\boldsymbol{A}'(\boldsymbol{A}\boldsymbol{A}')^-\boldsymbol{\xi}$. Then the 'equivalent model' mentioned on page 101 simplifies to $(\boldsymbol{y}+\boldsymbol{Z}\boldsymbol{\theta}_0, \boldsymbol{Z}\boldsymbol{\theta}, \sigma^2\boldsymbol{I})$, which fits the description of a general reparametrization given on page 95.

3.19 (a) The model equation is

$$\log q = \log a + \alpha \log l + \beta \log k + \log u,$$

which is of the form $y = \beta_0 + \alpha x_1 + \beta x_2 + \varepsilon$. Under the restriction $\alpha + \beta = 1$, the model can be written as

$$\log(q/k) = \log a + \alpha \log(l/k) + \varepsilon,$$

which is of the form $y = \beta_0 + \alpha x + \varepsilon$.

(b) Following the proof of Proposition 3.52(c), the decrease in $D(\boldsymbol{X}\widehat{\boldsymbol{\beta}})$ is $\sigma^2(\boldsymbol{P}_X - \boldsymbol{P}_{X(I-P_{A'})})$. Here, $\boldsymbol{A} = (0:1:1)$, so $\mathcal{C}(\boldsymbol{X}(\boldsymbol{I}-\boldsymbol{P}_{A'}))$ is spanned by the vectors $\mathbf{1}$ and $\boldsymbol{x}_1 - \boldsymbol{x}_2$. In contrast, $\mathcal{C}(\boldsymbol{X})$ is spanned by $\mathbf{1}$, $\boldsymbol{x}_1$ and $\boldsymbol{x}_2$. If $\boldsymbol{v}$ is a vector in $\mathcal{C}(\boldsymbol{X})$ which is orthogonal to $\mathcal{C}(\boldsymbol{X}(\boldsymbol{I}-\boldsymbol{P}_{A'}))$, then

$$\sigma^2(\boldsymbol{P}_X - \boldsymbol{P}_{X(I-P_{A'})}) = \sigma^2\boldsymbol{P}_v.$$

Writing $\boldsymbol{v}$ as $g_1\mathbf{1} + g_2\boldsymbol{x}_1 + g_3\boldsymbol{x}_2$, and using its orthogonality with $\mathbf{1}$ and $\boldsymbol{x}_1 - \boldsymbol{x}_2$, we have a set of possible choices $g_1 = (\bar{x}_2\boldsymbol{x}_1 - \bar{x}_1\boldsymbol{x}_2)'(\boldsymbol{x}_1 - \boldsymbol{x}_2)$, $g_2 = (\boldsymbol{x}_2 - \bar{x}_2\mathbf{1})'(\boldsymbol{x}_1 - \boldsymbol{x}_2)$ and $g_3 = -(\boldsymbol{x}_1 - \bar{x}_1\mathbf{1})'(\boldsymbol{x}_1 - \boldsymbol{x}_2)$. The decrease in $D(\widehat{\boldsymbol{\beta}})$ is $\sigma^2(\boldsymbol{X}'\boldsymbol{X})^{-1}\boldsymbol{X}'\boldsymbol{P}_v\boldsymbol{X}(\boldsymbol{X}'\boldsymbol{X})^{-1}$.

3.20 Let $\boldsymbol{X}_2 = (\mathbf{1} : \boldsymbol{Z})$. The sample dispersion matrix of the response and the explanatory variables is

$$\begin{aligned}\widehat{\boldsymbol{\Sigma}}_{yx_1Z} &= \frac{1}{n}(\boldsymbol{y}:\boldsymbol{x}_1:\boldsymbol{Z})'(\boldsymbol{I}-\boldsymbol{P}_1)(\boldsymbol{y}:\boldsymbol{x}_1:\boldsymbol{Z})\\ &= \frac{1}{n}\begin{pmatrix}(\boldsymbol{y}:\boldsymbol{x}_1)'(\boldsymbol{I}-\boldsymbol{P}_1)(\boldsymbol{y}:\boldsymbol{x}_1) & (\boldsymbol{y}:\boldsymbol{x}_1)'(\boldsymbol{I}-\boldsymbol{P}_1)\boldsymbol{Z}\\ \boldsymbol{Z}'(\boldsymbol{I}-\boldsymbol{P}_1)(\boldsymbol{y}:\boldsymbol{x}_1) & \boldsymbol{Z}'(\boldsymbol{I}-\boldsymbol{P}_1)\boldsymbol{Z}\end{pmatrix}.\end{aligned}$$

Therefore, the dispersion matrix of the response and the first explanatory variable, corrected for the other variables, is

$$\begin{aligned}\widehat{\boldsymbol{\Sigma}}_{yx_1\cdot z} &= \frac{1}{n}(\boldsymbol{y}:\boldsymbol{x}_1)'(\boldsymbol{I}-\boldsymbol{P}_1)(\boldsymbol{y}:\boldsymbol{x}_1)\\ &\quad -\frac{1}{n}(\boldsymbol{y}:\boldsymbol{x}_1)'(\boldsymbol{I}-\boldsymbol{P}_1)\boldsymbol{Z}(\boldsymbol{Z}'(\boldsymbol{I}-\boldsymbol{P}_1)\boldsymbol{Z})^-\boldsymbol{Z}'(\boldsymbol{I}-\boldsymbol{P}_1)(\boldsymbol{y}:\boldsymbol{x}_1)\\ &= \frac{1}{n}(\boldsymbol{y}:\boldsymbol{x}_1)'(\boldsymbol{I}-\boldsymbol{P}_1-\boldsymbol{P}_{(I-P_1)Z})(\boldsymbol{y}:\boldsymbol{x}_1)\\ &= \frac{1}{n}(\boldsymbol{y}:\boldsymbol{x}_1)'(\boldsymbol{I}-\boldsymbol{P}_{X_2})(\boldsymbol{y}:\boldsymbol{x}_1) = \frac{1}{n}\begin{pmatrix}\boldsymbol{y}'(\boldsymbol{I}-\boldsymbol{P}_{X_2})\boldsymbol{y} & \boldsymbol{y}'(\boldsymbol{I}-\boldsymbol{P}_{X_2})\boldsymbol{x}_1\\ \boldsymbol{x}_1'(\boldsymbol{I}-\boldsymbol{P}_{X_2})\boldsymbol{y} & \boldsymbol{x}_1'(\boldsymbol{I}-\boldsymbol{P}_{X_2})\boldsymbol{x}_1\end{pmatrix}.\end{aligned}$$

Thus, the requisite sample partial correlation is

$$\begin{aligned}\widehat{\rho}_{yx_1\cdot z} &= \frac{\boldsymbol{y}'(\boldsymbol{I}-\boldsymbol{P}_{X_2})\boldsymbol{x}_1}{\sqrt{\boldsymbol{y}'(\boldsymbol{I}-\boldsymbol{P}_{X_2})\boldsymbol{y}\cdot\boldsymbol{x}_1'(\boldsymbol{I}-\boldsymbol{P}_{X_2})\boldsymbol{x}_1}}\\ &= \frac{\boldsymbol{y}'(\boldsymbol{I}-\boldsymbol{P}_{X_2})(\boldsymbol{I}-\boldsymbol{P}_1)(\boldsymbol{I}-\boldsymbol{P}_{X_2})\boldsymbol{x}_1}{\sqrt{\boldsymbol{y}'(\boldsymbol{I}-\boldsymbol{P}_{X_2})(\boldsymbol{I}-\boldsymbol{P}_1)(\boldsymbol{I}-\boldsymbol{P}_{X_2})\boldsymbol{y}\cdot\boldsymbol{x}_1'(\boldsymbol{I}-\boldsymbol{P}_{X_2})(\boldsymbol{I}-\boldsymbol{P}_1)(\boldsymbol{I}-\boldsymbol{P}_{X_2})\boldsymbol{x}_1}},\end{aligned}$$

since $\mathbf{1}\in\mathcal{C}(\boldsymbol{X}_2)$. The last expression coincides with the sample correlation between $(\boldsymbol{I}-\boldsymbol{P}_{X_2})\boldsymbol{y}$ and $(\boldsymbol{I}-\boldsymbol{P}_{X_2})\boldsymbol{x}_1$.

The slope of the LS fitted line through the scatter plot of $(\boldsymbol{I}-\boldsymbol{P}_{X_2})\boldsymbol{y}$ vs. $(\boldsymbol{I}-\boldsymbol{P}_{X_2})\boldsymbol{x}_1$ is

$$\begin{aligned}&\frac{\boldsymbol{y}'(\boldsymbol{I}-\boldsymbol{P}_{X_2})(\boldsymbol{I}-\boldsymbol{P}_1)(\boldsymbol{I}-\boldsymbol{P}_{X_2})\boldsymbol{x}_1}{\boldsymbol{x}_1'(\boldsymbol{I}-\boldsymbol{P}_{X_2})(\boldsymbol{I}-\boldsymbol{P}_1)(\boldsymbol{I}-\boldsymbol{P}_{X_2})\boldsymbol{x}_1}\\ &\quad= \frac{\boldsymbol{y}^{*\prime}(\boldsymbol{I}-\boldsymbol{P}_1)\boldsymbol{x}_1^*}{\boldsymbol{x}_1^{*\prime}(\boldsymbol{I}-\boldsymbol{P}_1)\boldsymbol{x}_1^*}\end{aligned}$$

where $\boldsymbol{y}^*=(\boldsymbol{I}-\boldsymbol{P}_{X_2})\boldsymbol{y}$, $\boldsymbol{x}_1^*=(\boldsymbol{I}-\boldsymbol{P}_{X_2})\boldsymbol{x}_1)$. Thus, the sample correlation is

$$\begin{aligned}&\frac{\boldsymbol{y}^{*\prime}(\boldsymbol{I}-\boldsymbol{P}_1)\boldsymbol{x}_1^*}{\sqrt{\boldsymbol{y}^{*\prime}(\boldsymbol{I}-\boldsymbol{P}_1)\boldsymbol{y}^*\cdot\boldsymbol{x}_1^{*\prime}(\boldsymbol{I}-\boldsymbol{P}_1)\boldsymbol{x}_1^*}}\cdot\sqrt{\frac{\boldsymbol{y}^{*\prime}(\boldsymbol{I}-\boldsymbol{P}_1)\boldsymbol{y}^*}{\boldsymbol{x}_1^{*\prime}(\boldsymbol{I}-\boldsymbol{P}_1)\boldsymbol{x}_1^*}}\\ &\quad=\widehat{\rho}_{yx_1\cdot z}\cdot\sqrt{\frac{\boldsymbol{y}'(\boldsymbol{I}-\boldsymbol{P}_{X_2})\boldsymbol{y}}{\boldsymbol{x}_1'(\boldsymbol{I}-\boldsymbol{P}_{X_2})\boldsymbol{x}_1}}\\ &\quad=\widehat{\rho}_{yx_1\cdot z}\cdot\frac{\widehat{\sigma}_{y\cdot z}}{\widehat{\sigma}_{x_1\cdot z}}.\end{aligned}$$

The last expression is similar to (2.19).

3.21 The information matrix is $\sigma^{-2}\boldsymbol{Z}'\boldsymbol{Z}$ or $\sigma^{-2}\boldsymbol{T}_2'\boldsymbol{X}'\boldsymbol{X}\boldsymbol{T}_2$, where $\boldsymbol{Z}$ and $\boldsymbol{T}_2$ are as described in Example 3.49. We can write

$$\boldsymbol{Z}=\boldsymbol{X}\boldsymbol{T}_2=\begin{pmatrix}\mathbf{1} & \frac{1}{3}\mathbf{1} & \frac{1}{3}\mathbf{1} & \frac{1}{3}\mathbf{1} & \frac{1}{3}\mathbf{1}\\ \mathbf{1} & \frac{1}{3}\mathbf{1} & \frac{1}{3}\mathbf{1} & -\frac{2}{3}\mathbf{1} & \frac{1}{3}\mathbf{1}\\ [.5ex]\mathbf{1} & \frac{1}{3}\mathbf{1} & \frac{1}{3}\mathbf{1} & \frac{1}{3}\mathbf{1} & -\frac{2}{3}\mathbf{1}\\ [.5ex]\mathbf{1} & -\frac{2}{3}\mathbf{1} & \frac{1}{3}\mathbf{1} & \frac{1}{3}\mathbf{1} & \frac{1}{3}\mathbf{1}\\ [.5ex]\mathbf{1} & -\frac{2}{3}\mathbf{1} & \frac{1}{3}\mathbf{1} & -\frac{2}{3}\mathbf{1} & \frac{1}{3}\mathbf{1}\\ \mathbf{1} & -\frac{2}{3}\mathbf{1} & \frac{1}{3}\mathbf{1} & \frac{1}{3}\mathbf{1} & -\frac{2}{3}\mathbf{1}\\ \mathbf{1} & \frac{1}{3}\mathbf{1} & -\frac{2}{3}\mathbf{1} & \frac{1}{3}\mathbf{1} & \frac{1}{3}\mathbf{1}\\ [.5ex]\mathbf{1} & \frac{1}{3}\mathbf{1} & -\frac{2}{3}\mathbf{1} & -\frac{2}{3}\mathbf{1} & \frac{1}{3}\mathbf{1}\\ \mathbf{1} & \frac{1}{3}\mathbf{1} & -\frac{2}{3}\mathbf{1} & \frac{1}{3}\mathbf{1} & -\frac{2}{3}\mathbf{1}\end{pmatrix}.$$

Thus,

$$\sigma^{-2}\boldsymbol{T}_2'\boldsymbol{X}'\boldsymbol{X}\boldsymbol{T}_2 = \sigma^{-2}\begin{pmatrix} 90 & 0 & 0 & 0 & 0 \\ 0 & 20 & -10 & 0 & 0 \\ 0 & -10 & 20 & 0 & 0 \\ 0 & 0 & 0 & 20 & -10 \\ 0 & 0 & 0 & -10 & 20 \end{pmatrix},$$

and its inverse is

$$\sigma^2(\boldsymbol{Z}'\boldsymbol{Z})^{-1} = \sigma^2\begin{pmatrix} \frac{1}{90} & 0 & 0 & 0 & 0 \\ 0 & \frac{1}{15} & \frac{1}{30} & 0 & 0 \\ 0 & \frac{1}{30} & \frac{1}{15} & 0 & 0 \\ 0 & 0 & 0 & \frac{1}{15} & \frac{1}{30} \\ 0 & 0 & 0 & \frac{1}{30} & \frac{1}{15} \end{pmatrix},$$

which is block diagonal. Cramer-Rao bound for θ_4 is $\sigma^2/15$. This matches with the bound ($\sigma^2/15$) for $\tau_1 - \tau_2$ obtained in Example 3.56, as $\theta_5 = \tau_1 - \tau_2$.

3.22 The information matrix is $2\sigma^{-2}\boldsymbol{I}$ for the model of Exercise 3.35 and $2\sigma^{-2}\boldsymbol{I} + 4\boldsymbol{1}\boldsymbol{1}'$ for the model of Exercise 3.36. The latter information matrix is larger in the sense of the Löwner order.

3.23 Let n_i be the number of measurements involving object i, $i = 1\ldots,k$. For $k = 1$, the information matrix is $\sigma^{-2}\begin{pmatrix} n & n_1 \\ n_1 & n_1 \end{pmatrix}$, and

$$Var(\widehat{\beta}_1) = \frac{\sigma^2 n}{nn_1 - n_1^2} = \frac{\sigma^2}{n}\cdot\frac{1}{(n_1/n)(1-n_1/n)} \geq \frac{\sigma^2}{n/4}.$$

The bound is achieved when $n_1 = n/2$. When $k > 1$, '$n_i = n/2$ for all i' continues to be a necessary condition, but the other weights act as nuisance parameters and may increase the variance (see Section 3.12). It follows from the discussion of that section that the presence of the nuisance parameters does not make a difference in the variance of the BLUE of $\boldsymbol{t}'(\boldsymbol{I} - \boldsymbol{P}_{X_2})\boldsymbol{X}_1\boldsymbol{\beta}_1$ if and only if $\|\boldsymbol{P}_{X_1}(\boldsymbol{I} - \boldsymbol{P}_{X_2})\boldsymbol{t}\|^2 = \|\boldsymbol{P}_X(\boldsymbol{I} - \boldsymbol{P}_{X_2})\boldsymbol{t}\|^2$, i.e. $\|\boldsymbol{P}_{(I-P_{X_1})X_2}(\boldsymbol{I} - \boldsymbol{P}_{X_2})\boldsymbol{t}\|^2 = 0$. The latter condition is equivalent to $\boldsymbol{X}_2'(\boldsymbol{I}-\boldsymbol{P}_{X_1})(\boldsymbol{I}-\boldsymbol{P}_{X_2})\boldsymbol{t} = \boldsymbol{0}$, or $\boldsymbol{X}_2'\boldsymbol{P}_{X_1}(\boldsymbol{I} - \boldsymbol{P}_{X_2})\boldsymbol{t} = \boldsymbol{0}$. If we are concerned with the LPF β_1, then we can assume without loss of generality

$$\boldsymbol{X}_1 = \begin{pmatrix} \boldsymbol{1}_{\frac{n}{2}\times 1} & \boldsymbol{1}_{\frac{n}{2}\times 1} \\ \boldsymbol{1}_{\frac{n}{2}\times 1} & \boldsymbol{0}_{\frac{n}{2}\times 1} \end{pmatrix},$$

and expect $\boldsymbol{X}_2$ to be such that all the parameters are estimable. Writing $\boldsymbol{\beta}_1$ as $(\beta_0 : \beta_1)'$ and β_1 as $\boldsymbol{t}'(\boldsymbol{I} - \boldsymbol{P}_{X_2})\boldsymbol{X}_1\boldsymbol{\beta}_1$, we observe that

$$\boldsymbol{X}_1'(\boldsymbol{I} - \boldsymbol{P}_{X_2})\boldsymbol{t} = \frac{2}{n}\boldsymbol{X}_1'\begin{pmatrix} \boldsymbol{1}_{\frac{n}{2}} \\ -\boldsymbol{1}_{\frac{n}{2}} \end{pmatrix}.$$

Therefore, the condition $X_2' P_{X_1}(I - P_{X_2})t = 0$ further simplifies to

$$X_2' \begin{pmatrix} \mathbf{1}_{\frac{n}{2}} \\ -\mathbf{1}_{\frac{n}{2}} \end{pmatrix} = \mathbf{0},$$

that is, *each of the objects* $2, 3, \ldots, k$ *must be weighed with and without object 1 for an equal number of times.* When this condition is applied to all the objects, we obtain the conditions (i) every single object occurs in $n/2$ rows of the matrix X and (ii) every pair of objects occurs in $n/4$ rows. Then

$$X'X = \begin{pmatrix} n & n/2 & n/2 & \cdots & n/2 \\ n/2 & n/2 & n/4 & \cdots & n/4 \\ n/2 & n/4 & n/2 & \cdots & n/4 \\ \vdots & \vdots & \vdots & \ddots & \vdots \\ n/2 & n/4 & n/4 & \cdots & n/2 \end{pmatrix} = \frac{n}{4} \begin{pmatrix} 4 & 2 \cdot \mathbf{1}' \\ 2 \cdot \mathbf{1} & I + \mathbf{1}\mathbf{1}' \end{pmatrix}.$$

It is easy to see that the above condition is also sufficient.

3.24 Since x_{ij} can only be 0, 1 or -1, any diagonal element of the information matrix is less than or equal to n/σ^2. When β_i is estimable, the ith diagonal element of $(X'X)^-$ is uniquely defined, and is larger than the reciprocal of the corresponding diagonal element of $X'X$ (see Section A.2). Hence, the ith diagonal element of $\sigma^2(X'X)^-$ is at least σ^2/n. This proves the first part. In order that this inequality holds with equality for all i, (i) there should be no zero in the matrix X, and (ii) all its columns should be orthogonal. This can happen only if n is a multiple of 2^k. The conditions (i) and (ii) are easily seen to be sufficient. When there is an intercept term (β_0), this can be treated as an additional weight which is present with a positive sign in all the measurements, and the conditions (i) and (ii) are still necessary and sufficient. However, n should be a multiple of 2^{k+1}.

3.25 (a) The result follows from the definition of the Cramer-Rao lower bound and the block matrix inversion formula of Section A.2.

(b) Let $X = (x_1 : X_2)$. When β_1 is non-estimable, we have $x_1 \in \mathcal{C}(X_2)$ (see Exercise 3.4), i.e. $\|(I - P_{X_2})x_1\|^2 = \mathbf{0}$. It is easy to see that $\mathcal{I}_{11.2} = \|(I - P_{X_2})x_1\|^2$.

(c) The quantity $\mathcal{I}_{11.2}$ can be interpreted as the information for β_1, adjusted for the other parameters. When β_1 is non-estimable, the information is zero.

(d) Essentially the same argument holds, after reparametization. Let $p'\beta$ be any LPF (not necessarily estimable), with $\|p\| = 1$, and let P be such that the matrix $(p : P)$ is orthogonal. It follows that the information for $p'\beta$ is $\mathcal{I}_\mu p'X'(I - P_{XP})Xp$ or $\mathcal{I}_\mu p'X'(I - P_{X(I-pp')})Xp$. When $\|p\|$ not necessarily equal to 1, the information for $p'\beta$ is

$$\mathcal{I}_{p'\beta} = \mathcal{I}_\mu (p'p)^{-2} p'X'(I - P_{X(I-P_p)})Xp.$$

3.26 (a) The probability density function of y is $\frac{1}{\sigma}h\left(\frac{y-\mu}{\sigma}\right)$. It can be shown through simple calculations that

$$\frac{\partial \log \frac{1}{\sigma}h\left(\frac{y-\mu}{\sigma}\right)}{\partial \mu} = -\frac{1}{\sigma} \cdot \frac{\partial \log h(u)}{\partial u},$$
$$\frac{\partial \log \frac{1}{\sigma}h\left(\frac{y-\mu}{\sigma}\right)}{\partial \sigma^2} = -\frac{1}{2\sigma^2} - \frac{u}{2\sigma^2}\frac{\partial \log h(u)}{\partial u},$$

where $u = (y-\mu)/\sigma$. The stated result follows by simplifying the information matrix,

$$\int_{-\infty}^{\infty} \left(\frac{\partial \log \frac{1}{\sigma}h\left(\frac{y-\mu}{\sigma}\right)}{\partial \boldsymbol{\theta}}\right)\left(\frac{\partial \log \frac{1}{\sigma}h\left(\frac{y-\mu}{\sigma}\right)}{\partial \boldsymbol{\theta}}\right)' \frac{1}{\sigma}\, h\Big(\frac{y-\mu}{\sigma}\Big)dy,$$

and making use of the fact that the integrand of the off-diagonal term is an odd function of u. Simplification of the expression of the bottom diagonal term is aided by the identity

$$\int_{-\infty}^{\infty} u\left(\frac{\partial h(u)}{\partial u}\right) du = -1.$$

(b) Let $s(u) = \frac{1}{\sigma} \cdot \frac{\partial \log h(u)}{\partial u}$. Then $s\left(\frac{y-\mu}{\sigma}\right)$ has mean 0 and variance I_μ. Further,

$$Cov\left(s\left(\frac{y-\mu}{\sigma}\right), y\right) = \int_{-\infty}^{\infty} \left(\frac{\partial h(u)}{\partial u}\right)\Bigg|_{u=\frac{y-\mu}{\sigma}} \frac{y-\mu}{\sigma^2}dy$$
$$= \sigma^2 \int_{-\infty}^{\infty} u\left(\frac{\partial h(u)}{\partial u}\right) du \;=\; -1.$$

The stated result follows from the fact that the largest value of the squared correlation between two random variables is equal to 1.

(c) The squared correlation is equal to 1 if and only if the two random variables are almost surely linear functions of one another. This condition simplifies to $s(u) = au + b$. Integrating the two sides with respect to u, we conclude that $\log h(u)$ must be a quadratic function of u which is symmetric around $u = 0$. The conclusion follows in view of the condition $Var(u) = 1$.

We have $I_\mu \geq 1/\sigma^2$ with equality holding only in the case of the normal distribution. Thus, whenever y has mean μ, variance σ^2 and a symmetric and differentiable distribution around μ, and the information matrix for these parameters exists, the information for μ is the smallest when the distribution of y is normal.

Table C.1 ANOVA for Exercise 4.1

Source	Sum of Squares	Degrees of Freedom	Mean Square
Deviation from $\mathcal{H}_0$	$R_H^2 - R_0^2 = \|\widehat{\boldsymbol{y}} - \boldsymbol{X\xi}\|^2$	$r = \rho(\boldsymbol{X})$	$\dfrac{\|\widehat{\boldsymbol{y}} - \boldsymbol{X\xi}\|^2}{r}$
Error	$R_0^2 = \|\boldsymbol{e}\|^2$	$n-r$	$\widehat{\sigma^2} = \dfrac{\|\boldsymbol{e}\|^2}{n-r}$
Total	$R_H^2 = \|\boldsymbol{y} - \boldsymbol{X\xi}\|^2$	n	

Chapter 4

4.1 Here, $\boldsymbol{A} = \boldsymbol{I}$. As $\boldsymbol{\beta}$ may not be testable, we can ignore the top row of Table 4.3 (see footnote there). If we work with the other two columns and simplify them using the fact $\|\widehat{\boldsymbol{y}} + \boldsymbol{e} - \boldsymbol{\xi}\|^2 = \|\widehat{\boldsymbol{y}} - \boldsymbol{\xi}\|^2 + \|\boldsymbol{e}\|^2$, we obtain the ANOVA table given in Table C.1. The GLRT is to reject $\mathcal{H}_0$ if $\|\widehat{\boldsymbol{y}} - \boldsymbol{X\xi}\|^2/r\widehat{\sigma^2} > F_{r,n-r,\alpha}$.

4.2 (a) Number of linearly independent hypotheses, i.e., number of parameters is 16. Number of linearly independent testable hypotheses is $\rho(\boldsymbol{X}) = 9$. Hence, the maximum number of linearly independent hypotheses (considered together) that are completely untestable is $16 - 9 = 7$.

(b) By part (c) of Proposition 4.12, no hypothesis involving a single linear combination of the parameters can be partially testable; it has to be either testable or completely untestable. Using the other parts of that proposition, the hypothesis (i) is found to be completely untestable and the hypotheses (ii) and (iii) are found to be testable.

4.3 Using Proposition 4.13 we can decompose the hypothesis $\boldsymbol{A\beta} = \boldsymbol{\xi}$ into two hypothesis one of which is completely testable and the other, completely untestable. The completely untestable hypothesis only amounts to a reparametrization (see Exercise 3.18), while the completely testable hypothesis is of the form $\boldsymbol{A}_*\boldsymbol{\beta} = \boldsymbol{\xi}_*$ where $\rho(\boldsymbol{A}_*) = \dim(\mathcal{C}(\boldsymbol{A}') \cap \mathcal{C}(\boldsymbol{X}'))$. It is clear that the constraints $\boldsymbol{A\beta} = \boldsymbol{\xi}$ and $\boldsymbol{A}_*\boldsymbol{\beta} = \boldsymbol{\xi}_*$ lead to the same value of R_H^2. Therefore, the GLRT for the testable part of $\boldsymbol{A\beta} = \boldsymbol{\xi}$ is the test described in Proposition 4.21 with $m = \rho(\boldsymbol{A}_*)$. It follows from Proposition A.6 that the latter number is the same as $\rho(\boldsymbol{A}') + \rho(\boldsymbol{X}') - \rho(\boldsymbol{X}' : \boldsymbol{A}')$.

Suppose $\rho(\boldsymbol{A})$ is used in place of $\rho(\boldsymbol{A}_*)$, and let R_c^2 be the sum of squares of $\rho(\boldsymbol{A}) - \rho(\boldsymbol{A}_*)$ samples from $N(0, \sigma^2)$ which are independent of $\boldsymbol{y}$. Then under the null hypothesis

$$P\left[\frac{R_H^2 - R_0^2}{R_0^2} \cdot \frac{\rho(\boldsymbol{A})}{n-r} > F_{\rho(A),n-r,\alpha}\right] < P\left[\frac{R_H^2 - R_0^2 + R_c^2}{R_0^2} \cdot \frac{\rho(\boldsymbol{A})}{n-r} > F_{\rho(A),n-r,\alpha}\right] = \alpha.$$

Therefore, whenever $\rho(\boldsymbol{A})$ is used instead of $\rho(\boldsymbol{A}_*)$, the size of the test is smaller than α. Another way of interpreting the incorrect test is that the appropriate test statistic is compared to a cut-off value which is too large for size α. Hence, the test would have unnecessarily small power.

4.4 (a) Consider the model

$$\left(\begin{pmatrix}\boldsymbol{y}_1\\ \vdots\\ \boldsymbol{y}_m\end{pmatrix}, \begin{pmatrix}\boldsymbol{1}_{n_1\times 1}\otimes \boldsymbol{u}_1'\\ \vdots\\ \boldsymbol{1}_{n_m\times 1}\otimes \boldsymbol{u}_m'\end{pmatrix}\begin{pmatrix}\mu_1\\ \vdots\\ \mu_m\end{pmatrix}, \sigma^2\boldsymbol{I}\right),$$

where $(\boldsymbol{u}_1:\cdots:\boldsymbol{u}_m)=\boldsymbol{I}_{m\times m}$. Let $\boldsymbol{\mu}=(\mu_1:\cdots:\mu_m)'$ and $\boldsymbol{Z}=(\boldsymbol{x}_1:\cdots:\boldsymbol{x}_m)'$. Then the restriction $\boldsymbol{\mu}=\boldsymbol{Z\beta}$ reduces the above model to $(\boldsymbol{y}, \boldsymbol{X\beta}, \sigma^2\boldsymbol{I})$. A more standard (but equivalent) form of the restriction is $(\boldsymbol{I}-\boldsymbol{P}_{\!Z})\boldsymbol{\mu}=\boldsymbol{0}$.

(b) The pure error sum of squares is $R^2_{(0)}=\sum_{i=1}^m \|\boldsymbol{y}_i-\bar{y}_i\boldsymbol{1}\|^2$.

(c) The lack of fit sum of squares is $R^2_{(0)}-R^2_0$, where $R^2_0=\sum_{i=1}^m\|\boldsymbol{y}_i-\boldsymbol{x}_i'\widehat{\boldsymbol{\beta}}\boldsymbol{1}\|^2$ the SSE under the model $(\boldsymbol{y}, \boldsymbol{X\beta}, \sigma^2\boldsymbol{I})$.

(d) The ANOVA is given in Table C.2.

Table C.2 ANOVA for Exercise 4.4

Source	Sum of Squares	Degrees of Freedom	Mean Square
Lack of fit	$R^2_{(0)}-R^2_0$	$m-r$	$\dfrac{R^2_{(0)}-R^2_0}{m-r}$
Pure error	$R^2_{(0)}=\sum_{i=1}^m\|\boldsymbol{y}_i-\bar{y}_i\boldsymbol{1}\|^2$	$n-m$	$\dfrac{R^2_{(0)}}{n-m}$
Total	$R^2_0=\sum_{i=1}^m\|\boldsymbol{y}_i-\boldsymbol{x}_i'\widehat{\boldsymbol{\beta}}\boldsymbol{1}\|^2$	$n-r$	

(e) The GLRT is to reject the hypothesis of adequate fit when $[(R^2_{(0)}-R^2_0)/R^2_{(0)}]\times(n-m)/(m-r)>F_{m-r,n-m,\alpha}$.

4.5 In this case R^2_H is easier to compute than $R^2_H-R^2_0$. The hypothesis can be written as $\beta_1/b_1=\beta_2/b_2=\cdots=\beta_k/b_k$. Under $\mathcal{H}_0$, an unrestricted, reparametrized model is $(\boldsymbol{y}, (\boldsymbol{Xb})\theta, \sigma^2\boldsymbol{I})$. The ANOVA is given in Table C.3. The GLRT is to reject $\mathcal{H}_0$ when $\|(\boldsymbol{P}_{\!X}-\boldsymbol{P}_{\!Xb})\boldsymbol{y}\|^2/(k-1)\widehat{\sigma^2}>F_{k-1,n-k,\alpha}$.

4.6 (a) The conditional mean of $\boldsymbol{A}(\boldsymbol{X}\widehat{\boldsymbol{\beta}})\boldsymbol{e}$ given $\boldsymbol{X}\widehat{\boldsymbol{\beta}}$ is $\boldsymbol{0}$.

(b) $D(\boldsymbol{A}(\boldsymbol{X}\widehat{\boldsymbol{\beta}})\boldsymbol{e})=\sigma^2E[\boldsymbol{A}(\boldsymbol{X}\widehat{\boldsymbol{\beta}})(\boldsymbol{I}-\boldsymbol{P}_{\!X})\boldsymbol{A}'(\boldsymbol{X}\widehat{\boldsymbol{\beta}})]$.

(c) A vector of transformed GZFs with the required properties is $\boldsymbol{LA}(\boldsymbol{X}\widehat{\boldsymbol{\beta}})\boldsymbol{e}$, where $\boldsymbol{L}$ is a left-inverse of $\boldsymbol{C}$ and $\boldsymbol{C}$ is a rank-factorization of $\boldsymbol{A}(\boldsymbol{X}\widehat{\boldsymbol{\beta}})(\boldsymbol{I}-\boldsymbol{P}_{\!X})\boldsymbol{A}'(\boldsymbol{X}\widehat{\boldsymbol{\beta}})$. Note that the dispersion of the conditional expectation of this vector is $\boldsymbol{0}$, and hence its dispersion is just the expected value of the conditional dispersion.

Table C.3 ANOVA for Exercise 4.5

Source	Sum of Squares	Degrees of Freedom	Mean Square
Deviation from $\mathcal{H}_0$	$R_H^2 - R_0^2 =$ $\|(\boldsymbol{P_X} - \boldsymbol{P_{Xb}})\boldsymbol{y}\|^2$	$k-1$	$\dfrac{\|(\boldsymbol{P_X} - \boldsymbol{P_{Xb}})\boldsymbol{y}\|^2}{k-1}$
Error	$R_0^2 = \|\boldsymbol{e}\|^2$	$n{-}k$	$\widehat{\sigma^2} = \dfrac{\|\boldsymbol{e}\|^2}{n{-}k}$
Total	$R_H^2 = \|(\boldsymbol{I} - \boldsymbol{P_{Xb}})\boldsymbol{y}\|^2$	$n-1$	

(d) Each component of the GZF of part (c) has to be divided by an estimator of σ which does not depend on the transformed GZFs (for given $\boldsymbol{X}\widehat{\boldsymbol{\beta}}$). We can use a set of additional GZFs which, together with the present set, constitutes a basis set of LZFs (for given $\boldsymbol{X}\widehat{\boldsymbol{\beta}}$). The sum of squares of the latter GZFs is $R_0^2 - \|\boldsymbol{LA}(\boldsymbol{X}\widehat{\boldsymbol{\beta}})\boldsymbol{e}\|^2$, and the number of these GZFs is

$$n - \rho(\boldsymbol{X}) - \rho(\boldsymbol{A}(\boldsymbol{X}\widehat{\boldsymbol{\beta}})(\boldsymbol{I} - \boldsymbol{P_X})\boldsymbol{A}'(\boldsymbol{X}\widehat{\boldsymbol{\beta}})) = n - \rho(\boldsymbol{X}{:}\boldsymbol{A}'(\boldsymbol{X}\widehat{\boldsymbol{\beta}})).$$

Hence, a natural choice of the requisite estimator of σ is $[(R_0^2 - \|\boldsymbol{LA}(\boldsymbol{X}\widehat{\boldsymbol{\beta}})\boldsymbol{e}\|^2)/(n - \rho(\boldsymbol{X} : \boldsymbol{A}'(\boldsymbol{X}\widehat{\boldsymbol{\beta}})))]^{1/2}$.

4.7 The GLRT is to reject the null hypothesis if

$$\frac{\boldsymbol{e}'\boldsymbol{A}'[\boldsymbol{A}(\boldsymbol{I} - \boldsymbol{P_X})\boldsymbol{A}']^-\boldsymbol{Ae}}{\|\boldsymbol{e}\|^2 - \boldsymbol{e}'\boldsymbol{A}'[\boldsymbol{A}(\boldsymbol{I} - \boldsymbol{P_X})\boldsymbol{A}']^-\boldsymbol{Ae}} \cdot \frac{n - \rho(\boldsymbol{X} : \boldsymbol{A}')}{\rho(\boldsymbol{X} : \boldsymbol{A}') - \rho(\boldsymbol{X})}$$
$$> F_{\rho(X:A')-\rho(X),n-\rho(X:A'),\alpha},$$

where $\boldsymbol{e} = (\boldsymbol{I} - \boldsymbol{P_X})\boldsymbol{y}$. When the elements of $\boldsymbol{A}$ are functions of $\boldsymbol{X\beta}$ and the latter is replaced by $\boldsymbol{X}\widehat{\boldsymbol{\beta}}$ in the above test statistic, the null distribution of the statistic does not change, thanks to the result of Exercise 4.6.

4.8 Since $\boldsymbol{p}_1'\boldsymbol{\beta}$ and $\boldsymbol{p}_2'\boldsymbol{\beta}$ are not multiples of one another, their BLUEs, $\boldsymbol{p}_1'\widehat{\boldsymbol{\beta}}$ and $\boldsymbol{p}_2'\widehat{\boldsymbol{\beta}}$, have an invertible variance-covariance matrix ($\sigma^2\boldsymbol{K}$). Thus,

$$D\begin{pmatrix} \boldsymbol{p}_1'\widehat{\boldsymbol{\beta}} \\ \boldsymbol{p}_2'\widehat{\boldsymbol{\beta}} \\ (\boldsymbol{p}_1 + \boldsymbol{p}_2)'\widehat{\boldsymbol{\beta}} \end{pmatrix} = \sigma^2 \begin{pmatrix} \boldsymbol{K} & \boldsymbol{K}\begin{pmatrix}1\\1\end{pmatrix} \\ (1:1)\boldsymbol{K} & (1:1)\boldsymbol{K}\begin{pmatrix}1\\1\end{pmatrix} \end{pmatrix}.$$

According to the inversion formula of page 593, a possible choice of the g-inverse of this dispersion matrix is $\begin{pmatrix} \sigma^{-2}\boldsymbol{K}^{-1} & \boldsymbol{0} \\ \boldsymbol{0} & 0 \end{pmatrix}$. Hence, a $100(1-\alpha)\%$

elliptical confidence region of $(\boldsymbol{p}_1'\boldsymbol{\beta} : \boldsymbol{p}_2'\boldsymbol{\beta} : (\boldsymbol{p}_1+\boldsymbol{p}_2)'\boldsymbol{\beta})'$ is

$$\left\{\begin{pmatrix} x\\ y\\ z\end{pmatrix} : \begin{pmatrix} x-\boldsymbol{p}_1'\widehat{\boldsymbol{\beta}}\\ y-\boldsymbol{p}_2'\widehat{\boldsymbol{\beta}}\\ z-(\boldsymbol{p}_1+\boldsymbol{p}_2)'\widehat{\boldsymbol{\beta}}\end{pmatrix}' \begin{pmatrix} \boldsymbol{K}^{-1} & \boldsymbol{0}\\ \boldsymbol{0} & 0\end{pmatrix} \begin{pmatrix} x-\boldsymbol{p}_1'\widehat{\boldsymbol{\beta}}\\ y-\boldsymbol{p}_2'\widehat{\boldsymbol{\beta}}\\ z-(\boldsymbol{p}_1+\boldsymbol{p}_2)'\widehat{\boldsymbol{\beta}}\end{pmatrix} \le 2\widehat{\sigma^2}F_{2,n-r,\alpha}\right\}.$$

This simplifies to

$$\left\{\begin{pmatrix} x\\ y\\ z\end{pmatrix} : \begin{pmatrix} x-\boldsymbol{p}_1'\widehat{\boldsymbol{\beta}}\\ y-\boldsymbol{p}_2'\widehat{\boldsymbol{\beta}}\end{pmatrix}' \boldsymbol{K}^{-1} \begin{pmatrix} x-\boldsymbol{p}_1'\widehat{\boldsymbol{\beta}}\\ y-\boldsymbol{p}_2'\widehat{\boldsymbol{\beta}}\end{pmatrix} \le 2\widehat{\sigma^2}F_{2,n-r,\alpha}\right\}.$$

The latter is a $100(1-\alpha)\%$ elliptical confidence region of $(\boldsymbol{p}_1'\boldsymbol{\beta} : \boldsymbol{p}_2'\boldsymbol{\beta})'$.

4.9 The maximum modulus-t confidence intervals cannot be used as the fitted values are correlated. The Bonferroni confidence intervals should not be used, because these are too wide. The half-width of each of these intervals is of the order of $t_{n-r,\alpha/2n}$, which is an increasing function of n for large n (the degrees of freedom ceases to matter when $n-r$ is large, as the t-distribution converges to the normal distribution). The half-width of the Scheffé interval is of the order of $(mF_{m,n-r,\alpha})^{1/2}$, which gradually reduces with n. These confidence intervals are by far the best choice. The conclusion generally holds when confidence intervals of many linearly dependent LPFs are needed.

4.10 (a) (i) Write the hyperplane equation as $\boldsymbol{a}'(\boldsymbol{\theta}-\boldsymbol{\theta}_0)=d$. Let $\boldsymbol{F}\boldsymbol{F}'$ be a rank factorization of $\boldsymbol{M}$. By writing a point $\boldsymbol{\theta}_*$ common to the ellipsoid and the hyperplane as $\boldsymbol{\theta}_0+\boldsymbol{M}\boldsymbol{t}$, we have from the Cauchy-Schwartz inequality

$$\begin{aligned} d^2 = [\boldsymbol{a}'(\boldsymbol{\theta}_*-\boldsymbol{\theta}_0)]^2 &= [\boldsymbol{a}'\boldsymbol{M}\boldsymbol{t}]^2 = [\boldsymbol{a}'\boldsymbol{F}\boldsymbol{F}'\boldsymbol{t}]^2\\ \le \|\boldsymbol{F}'\boldsymbol{a}\|^2\cdot\|\boldsymbol{F}'\boldsymbol{t}\|^2 &= (\boldsymbol{a}'\boldsymbol{M}\boldsymbol{a})(\boldsymbol{t}'\boldsymbol{M}\boldsymbol{t}) \le \boldsymbol{a}'\boldsymbol{M}\boldsymbol{a}.\end{aligned}$$

The last step follows from the fact that $\boldsymbol{t}'\boldsymbol{M}\boldsymbol{t} = (\boldsymbol{\theta}_*-\boldsymbol{\theta}_0)'\boldsymbol{M}^-(\boldsymbol{\theta}-\boldsymbol{\theta}_0) \le 1$. Thus, a common solution does not exist if $d^2 > \boldsymbol{a}'\boldsymbol{M}\boldsymbol{a}$.
(ii) If $d^2 = \boldsymbol{a}'\boldsymbol{M}\boldsymbol{a}$, both the inequalities must hold with equality. The second of these implies that $\boldsymbol{\theta}_*$ must lie on the boundary of the elliptical region. The Cauchy-Schwartz inequality holds with equality if and only if $\boldsymbol{F}'\boldsymbol{t} = \psi\boldsymbol{F}'\boldsymbol{a}$, i.e. $\boldsymbol{\theta}_* = \boldsymbol{\theta}_0 + \psi\boldsymbol{M}\boldsymbol{a}$ for some constant ψ. This constant must be $d/(\boldsymbol{a}'\boldsymbol{M}\boldsymbol{a})$, so that $\boldsymbol{\theta}_*$ lies on the hyperplane. Thus, the choices $c = \boldsymbol{a}'\boldsymbol{\theta}_0 \pm (\boldsymbol{a}'\boldsymbol{M}\boldsymbol{a})^{1/2}$ lead to a unique point being common to the ellipsoidal region and the hyperplane (its tangent).
(iii) If $d^2 < \boldsymbol{a}'\boldsymbol{M}\boldsymbol{a}$ and $\boldsymbol{\theta}_*$ lies in the intersection, then we can construct $\boldsymbol{\theta}_\dagger = \boldsymbol{\theta}_* + \boldsymbol{g}$, where $\boldsymbol{g}$ is in $\mathcal{C}(\boldsymbol{M})\cap\mathcal{C}(\boldsymbol{a})^\perp$ and is small enough to ensure that $\boldsymbol{\theta}_\dagger$ satisfies the inequality. Since $\boldsymbol{\theta}_\dagger$ also lies on the hyperplane, any convex combination of $\boldsymbol{\theta}_*$ and $\boldsymbol{\theta}_\dagger$ lies in the intersection of the hyperplane and the ellipsoidal region.

(b) Put $\boldsymbol{\theta}=\boldsymbol{A}\boldsymbol{\beta}$, $\boldsymbol{\theta}_0=\boldsymbol{A}\widehat{\boldsymbol{\beta}}$, $\boldsymbol{M}=m\widehat{\sigma^2}F_{m,n-r,\alpha}\boldsymbol{A}(\boldsymbol{X}'\boldsymbol{X})^-\boldsymbol{A}$ in part (a) and choose $\boldsymbol{a}$ as the jth column of the $q\times q$ identity matrix.

4.11 (a) The mean is $E(a) = 0$, and the variance is

$$Var(a) = \sigma^2[\boldsymbol{p}_1'(\boldsymbol{X}'\boldsymbol{X})^-\boldsymbol{p}_1 - 2\lambda\boldsymbol{p}_1'(\boldsymbol{X}'\boldsymbol{X})^-\boldsymbol{p}_2 + \lambda^2\boldsymbol{P}_2'(\boldsymbol{X}'\boldsymbol{X})^-\boldsymbol{p}_2].$$

However, a is not an LZF, as it depends on the unknown λ. In fact, it is a function of BLUEs.

(b) $[a^2/Var(a)]/[\widehat{\sigma^2}/\sigma^2] \sim F_{1,n-r}$.

(c) $[a^2/Var(a)]/[\widehat{\sigma^2}/\sigma^2] < c$ if and only if $(\boldsymbol{p}_1'\widehat{\boldsymbol{\beta}} - \boldsymbol{p}_2'\widehat{\boldsymbol{\beta}})^2$ is less than $cVar(a)\widehat{\sigma^2}/\sigma^2$. The latter inequality can be rewritten as

$$\lambda^2[(\boldsymbol{p}_1'\widehat{\boldsymbol{\beta}})^2 - c\widehat{\sigma^2}\boldsymbol{p}_2'(\boldsymbol{X}'\boldsymbol{X})^-\boldsymbol{p}_2] - 2\lambda[(\boldsymbol{p}_1'\widehat{\boldsymbol{\beta}})(\boldsymbol{p}_2'\widehat{\boldsymbol{\beta}}) - c\widehat{\sigma^2}\boldsymbol{p}_1'(\boldsymbol{X}'\boldsymbol{X})^-\boldsymbol{p}_2] + [(\boldsymbol{p}_1'\widehat{\boldsymbol{\beta}})^2 - c\widehat{\sigma^2}\boldsymbol{p}_1'(\boldsymbol{X}'\boldsymbol{X})^-\boldsymbol{p}_1] < 0.$$

If $\boldsymbol{p}_2'\boldsymbol{\beta}$ is insignificant, the question of estimating $\boldsymbol{p}_1'\boldsymbol{\beta}/\boldsymbol{p}_2'\boldsymbol{\beta}$ does not arise. Let us assume that $\boldsymbol{p}_2'\boldsymbol{\beta}$ is significant. Then the coefficient of λ^2 is negative and the discriminant of the quadratic function is positive. In such a case, the above inequality holds if and only if λ lies between the roots of the quadratic function. We can choose $c = F_{1,n-r,\alpha}$, so that the interval between the corresponding roots is a $100\alpha(1-\alpha)\%$ confidence interval of λ.

4.12 $\beta_0 + \beta_1 x + \beta_2 x^2$ is minimized when $x = -\beta_1/(2\beta_2)$. A confidence interval can be found if β_2 is significant at $\alpha = 0.05$. Putting $\boldsymbol{p}_1'\boldsymbol{\beta} = \beta_1$ and $\boldsymbol{p}_2'\boldsymbol{\beta} = -2\beta_2$ in Exercise 4.11, we have the confidence interval

$$\Big[2\widehat{\beta}_1\widehat{\beta}_2 - F_{1,n-3,\alpha}\widehat{\sigma^2}q_{12} \pm [(2\widehat{\beta}_1\widehat{\beta}_2 - F_{1,n-3,\alpha}\widehat{\sigma^2}q_{12})^2 - (\widehat{\beta}_1^2 - F_{1,n-3,\alpha}\widehat{\sigma^2}q_{11})(4\widehat{\beta}_2^2 - F_{1,n-3,\alpha}\widehat{\sigma^2}q_{22})]^{1/2}\Big] /[4\widehat{\beta}_2^2 - F_{1,n-3,\alpha}\widehat{\sigma^2}q_{22}],$$

where

$$\begin{pmatrix} q_{11} & q_{12} \\ q_{12} & q_{22} \end{pmatrix} = D\begin{pmatrix} \widehat{\beta}_1 \\ \widehat{\beta}_2 \end{pmatrix}.$$

4.13 The result follows from Proposition 4.34 after simplifying the term $\boldsymbol{x}'(\boldsymbol{X}'\boldsymbol{X})^-\boldsymbol{x}$ to the expression given within the parentheses. The width of the confidence band is a monotonically increasing function of $(x-\bar{x})^2/(\overline{x^2}-\bar{x}^2)$, which is the smallest at $x = \bar{x}$.

4.14 The prediction error of the BLUP $\widehat{\boldsymbol{y}}_0$ can be decomposed into two uncorrelated parts:

$$\widehat{\boldsymbol{y}}_0 - \boldsymbol{y}_0 = (\boldsymbol{X}_0\widehat{\boldsymbol{\beta}} - \boldsymbol{X}_0\boldsymbol{\beta}) - (\boldsymbol{y}_0 - \boldsymbol{X}_0\boldsymbol{\beta}).$$

Hence, $D(\widehat{\boldsymbol{y}}_0 - \boldsymbol{y}_0) = \sigma^2[\boldsymbol{X}_0(\boldsymbol{X}'\boldsymbol{X})^-\boldsymbol{X}_0' + \boldsymbol{I}]$, which has rank q. The result of part (a) follows from the fact that $(\boldsymbol{y}_0 - \widehat{\boldsymbol{y}}_0)'[\sigma^{-2}D(\widehat{\boldsymbol{y}}_0 - \boldsymbol{y}_0)]^{-1}(\boldsymbol{y}_0 - \widehat{\boldsymbol{y}}_0)/q\widehat{\sigma^2} \sim F_{q,n-r}$. Part (b) follows from part (a) and Exercise 4.10.

Chapter 5

5.1 For the models of either example, $y|x_1, x_2 \sim N(20 - x_1 - x_2, 1)$.
For Example 5.3, $x_2|x_1 \sim N(0.999x_1, 0.05^2)$. Therefore,

$$\begin{aligned}
E(y|x_1) &= 20 - x_1 - E(x_2|x_1) = 20 - x_1 - (0.999x_1) = 20 - 1.999x_1. \\
Var(y|x_1) &= E_{x_2|x_1}[Var(y|x_1, x_2) + Var_{x_2|x_1}[E(y|x_1, x_2)] \\
&= 1 + Var_{x_2|x_1}(20 - x_1 - x_2) \\
&= 1 + Var_{x_2|x_1}(x_2) = 1 + 0.05^2 = 1.0025.
\end{aligned}$$

In deriving the latter expression, we have made use of the conditional (on x_1) version of the fact $Var(y) = E_{x_2}(Var(y|x_2)) + Var_{x_2}(E(y|x_2))$. The estimated regression of y on x_1 is reported in the example as $18.6 - 2.119x_1$, while the corresponding error variance is estimated as 0.616^2. These estimates are not far from the theoretical values, $20 - 1.999x_1$ and 1.0025, respectively, considering that the sample size is only 10.

For Example 5.4, $x_2|x_1 \sim N(0.5x_1, 1.5^2)$. Therefore,

$$\begin{aligned}
E(y|x_1) &= 20 - x_1 - E(x_2|x_1) = 20 - x_1 - (0.5x_1) = 20 - 1.5x_1. \\
Var(y|x_1) &= 1 + Var_{x_2|x_1}(20 - x_1 - x_2) \\
&= 1 + Var_{x_2|x_1}(x_2) = 1 + 1.5^2 = 3.25.
\end{aligned}$$

The estimates of the two quantities reported in the example are $18.785 - 1.529x_1$ and 2.01^2, respectively, which are reasonable considering the sample size.

5.2 (a) $\boldsymbol{p}'\boldsymbol{\beta}$ and $\boldsymbol{p}_2'\boldsymbol{\beta}_2$ are both estimable under the full model. Hence $\boldsymbol{p}_1'\boldsymbol{\beta}_1 = \boldsymbol{p}'\boldsymbol{\beta} - \boldsymbol{p}_2'\boldsymbol{\beta}_2$ is also estimable in the full model. It follows that it is estimable in the subset model too.

(b) The result follows from the fact that $\sigma^{-2}D(\widehat{\boldsymbol{\beta}}_2)$ is the lower right block of $(\boldsymbol{X}'\boldsymbol{X})^{-1}$, which simplifies to $[\boldsymbol{X}_2'(\boldsymbol{I} - \boldsymbol{P}_{X_1})\boldsymbol{X}_2]^{-1}$.

(c) $Cov(\boldsymbol{p}'\widehat{\boldsymbol{\beta}}, \widehat{\boldsymbol{\beta}}_2) = \sigma^2\boldsymbol{p}'(\boldsymbol{X}'\boldsymbol{X})^{-1}(\boldsymbol{0} : \boldsymbol{I})'$; the result follows using the block matric inversion formula.

(d) According to (7.18), $MSE(\widehat{\boldsymbol{p}'\boldsymbol{\beta}}) - MSE(\widehat{\boldsymbol{p}'\boldsymbol{\beta}_s}) = \boldsymbol{c}'\boldsymbol{D}^{-1}[\boldsymbol{D} - \boldsymbol{\beta}_2\boldsymbol{\beta}_2)']\boldsymbol{D}^{-1}\boldsymbol{c}$, where $\boldsymbol{D} = D(\widehat{\boldsymbol{\beta}}_2) = \sigma^2[\boldsymbol{X}_2'(\boldsymbol{I} - \boldsymbol{P}_{X_1})\boldsymbol{X}_2]^{-1}$ and $\boldsymbol{c}' = Cov(\widehat{\boldsymbol{p}'\boldsymbol{\beta}}) = \boldsymbol{q}'\boldsymbol{D}$ (using parts (b) and (c)). The difference is nonnegative if and only if $\boldsymbol{q}'\boldsymbol{D}\boldsymbol{q} \geq (\boldsymbol{q}'\boldsymbol{\beta}_2)^2$, which simplifies to the stated condition.

(e) If $\boldsymbol{p}_2'$ is considered an additional observation in the multivariate linear model $(\boldsymbol{X}_2, (\boldsymbol{I} \otimes \boldsymbol{X}_1)\text{vec}(\boldsymbol{B}), \boldsymbol{\Sigma} \otimes \boldsymbol{I})$, and $\boldsymbol{p}_1'$ is the corresponding row vector of explanatory variables, then the BLUP of $\boldsymbol{p}_2'$ is $\boldsymbol{p}_1'(\boldsymbol{X}_1'\boldsymbol{X}_1)^-\boldsymbol{X}_1'\boldsymbol{X}_2$ (see Chapter 10). The corresponding prediction error is $\boldsymbol{q}'$. The matrix $\boldsymbol{X}_2'(\boldsymbol{I} - \boldsymbol{P}_{X_1})\boldsymbol{X}_2$ is the matrix of error sums and products for the multivariate linear model.

5.3 Using the expression for adjusted R-square, we can write

$$\begin{aligned}
1 - R_a^2 &= \frac{\frac{1}{n-p}\sum_{i=1}^n (y_i - \widehat{y}_i)^2}{\frac{1}{n-1}\sum_{i=1}^n (y_i - \bar{y})^2} = \frac{n-1}{n-p} \cdot \frac{\|(\boldsymbol{I} - \boldsymbol{P}_X)\boldsymbol{y}\|^2}{\|(\boldsymbol{I} - \boldsymbol{P}_1)\boldsymbol{y}\|^2} \\
&= \frac{n-1}{n-p} \cdot \frac{\|(\boldsymbol{I} - \boldsymbol{P}_X)\boldsymbol{y}\|^2}{\|(\boldsymbol{I} - \boldsymbol{P}_X)\boldsymbol{y}\|^2 + \|(\boldsymbol{P}_X - \boldsymbol{P}_1)\boldsymbol{y}\|^2} \\
&= \frac{n-1}{n-p} \cdot \frac{1}{1 + \dfrac{p-1}{n-p} \cdot \dfrac{n-p}{p-1} \cdot \dfrac{\|(\boldsymbol{P}_X - \boldsymbol{P}_1)\boldsymbol{y}\|^2}{\|(\boldsymbol{I} - \boldsymbol{P}_X)\boldsymbol{y}\|^2}} \\
&= \frac{n-1}{n-p} \cdot \frac{1}{1 + \frac{n-p}{p-1} F_{p-1,n-p}(\lambda)},
\end{aligned}$$

where λ is the non-centrality parameter of the numerator sum of squares of the ratio $F_{p-1,n-p}(\lambda)$. According to Proposition 2.10 (Fisher-Cochran theorem), this sum of squares is independent of the denominator sum of squares (under the assumption of normality), and the non-centrality parameter is

$$\lambda = \frac{\|(\boldsymbol{P}_X - \boldsymbol{P}_1)\boldsymbol{X\beta}\|^2}{\sigma^2} = \frac{\|(\boldsymbol{I} - \boldsymbol{P}_1)\boldsymbol{X\beta}\|^2}{\sigma^2}.$$

Therefore, $P(1 - R_a^2 < 0)$ simplifies to $P(F_{p-1,n-p}(\lambda) < 1)$. Since

$$E\left[\frac{\|(\boldsymbol{P}_X - \boldsymbol{P}_1)\boldsymbol{y}\|^2}{(p-1)}\right] = \left(1 + \frac{\lambda}{p-1}\right)\sigma^2$$

and $E\left[\|(\boldsymbol{I} - \boldsymbol{P}_X)\boldsymbol{y}\|^2/(n-p)\right] = \sigma^2$, the distribution of

$$F_{p-1,n-p}(\lambda) = \frac{\|(\boldsymbol{P}_X - \boldsymbol{P}_1)\boldsymbol{y}\|^2/(p-1)}{\|(\boldsymbol{I} - \boldsymbol{P}_X)\boldsymbol{y}\|^2/(n-p)}$$

would have a lot of mass around $1 + \lambda/(p-1)$. Thus, the probability of adjusted R-square being negative is small unless $\lambda = \|(\boldsymbol{I} - \boldsymbol{P}_1)\boldsymbol{X\beta}\|^2/\sigma^2$ is small.

5.4 It follows from the definition of C_p that if $(\boldsymbol{y}, \boldsymbol{X}_1\boldsymbol{\beta}_1, \sigma^2\boldsymbol{I})$ is the correct model,

$$\begin{aligned}
E(\widehat{\sigma^2 C_p}) &= E(\|(\boldsymbol{I} - \boldsymbol{P}_{X_1})\boldsymbol{Y}\|^2) - (n+2p)E(\widehat{\sigma^2}) \\
&= E(\|(\boldsymbol{I} - \boldsymbol{P}_{X_1})\boldsymbol{\varepsilon}\|^2) - \frac{n+2p}{n - \rho(\boldsymbol{X})} E(\|(\boldsymbol{I} - \boldsymbol{P}_X)\boldsymbol{\varepsilon}\|^2) \\
&= (n-p)\sigma^2 + \frac{n+2p}{n-\rho(\boldsymbol{X})} \times (n - \rho(\boldsymbol{X}))\sigma^2 = p\sigma^2.
\end{aligned}$$

5.5 Assuming without loss of generality the variables to be linearly independent. Let A be the best subset according to R_a^2, and B be a subset of larger size, the sizes (i.e. the number of variables in the two subsets) being p_A and p_B, respectively. Then $p_A \le p_B$ and $\widehat{\sigma_A^2} \le \widehat{\sigma_B^2}$. Hence,

$$\begin{aligned} C_p(B) - C_p(A) &= 2(p_B - p_A) + [(n - p_B)\widehat{\sigma_B^2} - (n - p_A)\widehat{\sigma_A^2}]/\widehat{\sigma^2} \\ &= 2(p_B - p_A) + (n - p_B)(\widehat{\sigma_B^2} - \widehat{\sigma_A^2})/\widehat{\sigma^2} - (p_B - p_A)\widehat{\sigma_A^2}/\widehat{\sigma^2} \\ &\ge 2(p_B - p_A) - (p_B - p_A)\widehat{\sigma_A^2}/\widehat{\sigma^2} \\ &\ge 2(p_B - p_A) - (p_B - p_A) = p_B - p_A \ge 0. \end{aligned}$$

Thus, B cannot be the 'best' subset according to Mallows's C_p.

5.6 (a) The AIC simplifies as

$$\begin{aligned} &2p - 2\log(\widehat{L}_p) \\ &= \left[2p + n\log(2\pi\widehat{\sigma^2}_{ML}) + \frac{1}{\widehat{\sigma^2}_{ML}}\sum_{i=1}^{n}(y_i - \widehat{y}_i)^2\right]\Bigg|_{\text{subset model}} \\ &= 2p + n\log\left(\frac{2\pi}{n}\sum_{i=1}^{n}(y_i - \widehat{y}_i)^2\Big|_{\text{subset model}}\right) + n \\ &= n\log\left(\frac{1}{n}\sum_{i=1}^{n}(y_i - \widehat{y}_i)^2\Big|_{\text{subset model}}\right) + 2p + n + n\log(2\pi). \end{aligned}$$

(b) The maximized value of the criterion for a given subset model is

$$\begin{aligned} &\max_{\text{subset }\boldsymbol{\beta}}[2p - 2\log(L_p)] \\ &= \max_{\text{subset }\boldsymbol{\beta}}\left[2p + n\log(2\pi\sigma^2) + \frac{1}{\sigma^2}\sum_{i=1}^{n}(y_i - \boldsymbol{x}_i'\boldsymbol{\beta})^2\right] \\ &= 2p + n\log(2\pi\sigma^2) + \frac{1}{\sigma^2}\sum_{i=1}^{n}(y_i - \widehat{y}_i)^2\Big|_{\text{subset model}}. \end{aligned}$$

Maximizing this quantity with respect to the choice of the subset, while keeping σ^2 fixed at $\widehat{\sigma^2}$ (irrespective of its value) is equivalent to maximizing

$$C_p = \frac{\sum_{i=1}^{n}(y_i - \widehat{y}_i)^2\Big|_{\text{subset model}}}{\widehat{\sigma^2}} - n + 2p.$$

5.7 Let $\boldsymbol{u}_i$ be the ith column of the $n \times n$ identity matrix. Then $h_i = \|\boldsymbol{H}\boldsymbol{u}_i\|^2$. Thus, $h_i = 0$ implies $\boldsymbol{H}\boldsymbol{u}_i = \boldsymbol{0}$, i.e., $E(y_i) = \boldsymbol{u}_i'\boldsymbol{X}\boldsymbol{\beta} = \boldsymbol{u}_i'\boldsymbol{H}\boldsymbol{X}\boldsymbol{\beta} = 0$ for all $\boldsymbol{\beta}$. Conversely, $E(y_i) = 0$ for all $\boldsymbol{\beta}$ implies $\boldsymbol{u}_i'\boldsymbol{X} = \boldsymbol{0}$, which in turn implies $h_i = \boldsymbol{u}_i'\boldsymbol{X}(\boldsymbol{X}'\boldsymbol{X})^{-1}\boldsymbol{X}\boldsymbol{u}_i = 0$. Thus, $h_i = 0$ is equivalent to y_i being an LZF.

5.8 Let $\boldsymbol{u}_i$ be the ith column of the $n \times n$ identity matrix. The covariance of $y_i = \boldsymbol{u}_i'\boldsymbol{y}$ with the residual vector $(\boldsymbol{I} - \boldsymbol{H})\boldsymbol{y}$ is $\sigma^2\boldsymbol{u}_i'(\boldsymbol{I} - \boldsymbol{H})$, which is zero if and only if $\|(\boldsymbol{I}-\boldsymbol{H})\boldsymbol{u}_i\|^2 = 1-h_i = 0$. Thus, the y_i is itself the BLUE of $E(y_i)$ if and only if $h_i = 1$.

Alternative argument: BLUE of $E(y_i)$ is $\widehat{y}_i$. For $\widehat{y}_i$ to coincide with y_i, one has to have $e_i = 0$. Since e_i is already zero, the requisite condition is for the variance of e_i, or $(1-h_i)\sigma^2$, to be zero. The last condition is equivalent to $h_i = 1$.

5.9 Let $\boldsymbol{u}_i$ be the ith column of $\boldsymbol{I}_{n\times n}$. The ith row of $\boldsymbol{X}$ is not a linear combination of the other rows if and only if the following condition holds: there is a vector $\boldsymbol{l}$ such that $\boldsymbol{X}'\boldsymbol{l} = \boldsymbol{0}$ but $\boldsymbol{x}'\boldsymbol{u}_i \neq 0$. The negation of this condition is: for all $\boldsymbol{l}$ such that $\boldsymbol{X}'\boldsymbol{l} = \boldsymbol{0}$ we must have $\boldsymbol{l}'\boldsymbol{u}_i = 0$, which holds if and only if $\boldsymbol{u}_i$ is orthogonal to $\mathcal{C}(\boldsymbol{X})^{\perp}$, i.e. $\boldsymbol{u}_i \in \mathcal{C}(\boldsymbol{X})$. The last condition is equivalent to $\boldsymbol{u}_i'\boldsymbol{H}\boldsymbol{u}_i = 1$, i.e. $h_i = 1$.

5.10 Let us write $\boldsymbol{X}$ as $(\boldsymbol{1} : \boldsymbol{Z})$, where $\boldsymbol{Z} = (\boldsymbol{x}_1 : \cdots : \boldsymbol{x}_n)'$. The crucial identity needed here is

$$\boldsymbol{P}_X = \boldsymbol{P}_1 + \boldsymbol{P}_{(I-P_1)Z},$$

which follows from Proposition A.14(b). By comparing the ith diagonal elements of the two sides, we have

$$h_i = \frac{1}{n} + \boldsymbol{u}_i'\boldsymbol{P}_{(I-P_1)Z}\boldsymbol{u}_i,$$

where $\boldsymbol{u}_i$ is the ith column of $\boldsymbol{I}_{n\times n}$. Further, $(\boldsymbol{I}-\boldsymbol{P}_1)\boldsymbol{Z} = \boldsymbol{Z} - \boldsymbol{1}\bar{\boldsymbol{x}}'$. It follows that $\boldsymbol{u}_i'(\boldsymbol{I}-\boldsymbol{P}_1)\boldsymbol{Z} = \boldsymbol{x}_i' - \bar{\boldsymbol{x}}'$ and $\boldsymbol{Z}'(\boldsymbol{I}-\boldsymbol{P}_1)\boldsymbol{Z} = \sum_{j=1}^{n}(\boldsymbol{x}_j-\bar{\boldsymbol{x}})(\boldsymbol{x}_i-\bar{\boldsymbol{x}})' = \boldsymbol{S}$. Therefore,

$$\begin{aligned}\boldsymbol{u}_i'\boldsymbol{P}_{(I-P_1)Z}\boldsymbol{u}_i &= \boldsymbol{u}_i'(\boldsymbol{I}-\boldsymbol{P}_1)\boldsymbol{Z}[\boldsymbol{Z}'(\boldsymbol{I}-\boldsymbol{P}_1)\boldsymbol{Z}]^-\boldsymbol{Z}'(\boldsymbol{I}-\boldsymbol{P}_1)\boldsymbol{u}_i\\ &= (\boldsymbol{x}_i-\bar{\boldsymbol{x}})'\boldsymbol{S}^-(\boldsymbol{x}_i-\bar{\boldsymbol{x}}) = m_i.\end{aligned}$$

The result follows.

5.11 (a) $\frac{1}{n}\sum_{i=1}^{n} h_i = \frac{1}{n}\text{tr}(\boldsymbol{H}) = \rho(\boldsymbol{X})/n = (k+1)/n$.

(b) For any $n\times 1$ vector $\boldsymbol{u}$, $(\boldsymbol{I}-\frac{1}{n}\boldsymbol{1}\boldsymbol{1}')\boldsymbol{u} = \boldsymbol{u}-\bar{u}\boldsymbol{1}$, where $\bar{u}$ is the average value of the elements of $\boldsymbol{u}$. Thus, $(\boldsymbol{I}-\frac{1}{n}\boldsymbol{1}\boldsymbol{1}')\boldsymbol{u}$ is the mean-subtracted or 'centered' version of $\boldsymbol{u}$. Hence, $\boldsymbol{X}_c = (\boldsymbol{I}-\frac{1}{n}\boldsymbol{1}\boldsymbol{1}')\boldsymbol{X}$ consists of centered versions of the columns of $\boldsymbol{X}$. Its ith row consists of the deviations of the elements from their respective column means. Let this vector be $\boldsymbol{x}_{ci}$. Then from the decomposition $\boldsymbol{H} = \boldsymbol{P}_X = \boldsymbol{P}_1 + \boldsymbol{P}_{(I-\frac{1}{n}11')X}$, we conclude that $h_i = 1/n + \boldsymbol{x}_{ci}'(\boldsymbol{X}_c'\boldsymbol{X}_c)^-\boldsymbol{x}_{ci}$, which is of the described form.

(c) Let $\boldsymbol{X}_* = (\boldsymbol{X} : \boldsymbol{y})$. Then

$$\boldsymbol{P}_{X_*} = \boldsymbol{P}_X + \boldsymbol{P}_{(I-P_X)y} = \boldsymbol{H} + \boldsymbol{P}_e.$$

Since $\boldsymbol{P}_{X_*}$ is an orthogonal projection matrix, its ith diagonal element is in the range [0,1]. Hence we have the required inequality.

5.12 Suppose, after inclusion of the additional observation, the new model matrix is $\boldsymbol{X}_* = (\boldsymbol{X}' : \boldsymbol{z})'$, where $\boldsymbol{X}$ is the model matrix in the absence of the additional observation and $\boldsymbol{z}$ is the appended row. Therefore, $\boldsymbol{X}_*'\boldsymbol{X}_* = \boldsymbol{X}'\boldsymbol{X}+\boldsymbol{z}\boldsymbol{z}'$. Since $\boldsymbol{X}'\boldsymbol{X} \le \boldsymbol{X}_*'\boldsymbol{X}_*$ in the sense of Löwner order, it follows from Exercise A.24(a) that $(\boldsymbol{X}_*'\boldsymbol{X}_*)^{-1} \le (\boldsymbol{X}'\boldsymbol{X})^{-1}$. Therefore, if $\boldsymbol{z}_i'$ is the ith row of $\boldsymbol{X}$, we have $\boldsymbol{z}_i'(\boldsymbol{X}_*'\boldsymbol{X}_*)^{-1}\boldsymbol{z}_i \le \boldsymbol{z}_i(\boldsymbol{X}'\boldsymbol{X})^{-1}\boldsymbol{z}_i$. The left and right sides of the inequality my be recognized as the leverages of the ith observation after and before inclusion of the additional observation, respectively.

5.13 Let the indices of the r identical (or sign-reversed) rows of the model matrix $\boldsymbol{X}$ be $i_1, \ldots, i_r$. Let $\boldsymbol{U}$ be the matrix formed with columns $i_1, \ldots, i_r$ of the $n \times n$ identity matrix, with the columns sign-reversed in those cases where the replicated rows of $\boldsymbol{X}$ are sign-reversed. Let $\boldsymbol{z}_i$ be the ith row of $\boldsymbol{X}$. It is easy to see that $h_{i_1} = \cdots = h_{i_r}$. Further,

$$rh_{i_1} = \sum_{j=1}^{r} h_{i_j} = \operatorname{tr}(\boldsymbol{U}'\boldsymbol{P}_{\boldsymbol{X}}\boldsymbol{U}) = \operatorname{tr}[(\boldsymbol{X}\boldsymbol{U})'(\boldsymbol{X}'\boldsymbol{X})^{-1}(\boldsymbol{X}\boldsymbol{U})].$$

Since

$$\boldsymbol{U}'\boldsymbol{X}'\boldsymbol{X}\boldsymbol{U} = \sum_{j=1}^{r} \boldsymbol{z}_{i_j}\boldsymbol{z}_{i_j}' \le \sum_{i=1}^{n} z_i z_i' = \boldsymbol{X}'\boldsymbol{X},$$

we have, by Exercise A.24(a)), $(\boldsymbol{X}'\boldsymbol{X})^{-1} \le (\boldsymbol{U}'\boldsymbol{X}'\boldsymbol{X}\boldsymbol{U})^{-1}$, which implies $(\boldsymbol{X}\boldsymbol{U})'(\boldsymbol{X}'\boldsymbol{X})^{-1}(\boldsymbol{X}\boldsymbol{U}) \le \boldsymbol{P}_{\boldsymbol{X}\boldsymbol{U}}$. Therefore,

$$rh_{i_1} = \operatorname{tr}[(\boldsymbol{X}\boldsymbol{U})'(\boldsymbol{X}'\boldsymbol{X})^{-1}(\boldsymbol{X}\boldsymbol{U})] \le \operatorname{tr}(\boldsymbol{P}_{\boldsymbol{X}\boldsymbol{U}}) = \rho(\boldsymbol{X}\boldsymbol{U}) = \rho(\boldsymbol{z}_{i_1}) = 1.$$

It follows that $h_{i_1} \le 1/r$.

5.14 (a) Using the subscript $(-i)$ to represent computations without the ith observation, we can write

$$\begin{aligned}\boldsymbol{X}_{(-i)}'\boldsymbol{X}_{(-i)} &= \boldsymbol{X}'\boldsymbol{X} - \boldsymbol{x}_i\boldsymbol{x}_i',\\ \boldsymbol{X}_{(-i)}'\boldsymbol{y}_{(-i)} &= \boldsymbol{X}'\boldsymbol{y} - \boldsymbol{x}_i y_i.\end{aligned}$$

Thus, by making use of the inversion formula (A.1), we obtain

$$\begin{aligned}e_{i(-i)} &= y_i - \boldsymbol{x}_i'\widehat{\boldsymbol{\beta}}_{(-i)}\\ &= y_i - \boldsymbol{x}_i'(\boldsymbol{X}'\boldsymbol{X} - \boldsymbol{x}_i\boldsymbol{x}_i')^{-1}(\boldsymbol{X}'\boldsymbol{y} - \boldsymbol{x}_i y_i)\\ &= y_i - \boldsymbol{x}_i'\left[(\boldsymbol{X}'\boldsymbol{X})^{-1} + \frac{1}{1-h_i}(\boldsymbol{X}'\boldsymbol{X})^{-1}\boldsymbol{x}_i\boldsymbol{x}_i'(\boldsymbol{X}'\boldsymbol{X})^{-1}\right](\boldsymbol{X}'\boldsymbol{y} - \boldsymbol{x}_i y_i)\\ &= y_i - \boldsymbol{x}_i'\widehat{\boldsymbol{\beta}} + h_i y_i - \frac{1}{1-h_i}(h_i\boldsymbol{x}_i'\widehat{\boldsymbol{\beta}} - h_i^2 y_i)\\ &= \frac{y_i - \boldsymbol{x}_i'\widehat{\boldsymbol{\beta}}}{1-h_i} = \frac{e_i}{1-h_i}.\end{aligned}$$

(b) The deleted studentized residual is

$$\left.\frac{e_{i(-i)}}{\sqrt{var\left(e_{i(-i)}\right)}}\right|_{\sigma^2=\widehat{\sigma^2}_{(-i)}} = \left.\frac{\frac{e_i}{1-h_i}}{\sqrt{var\left(\frac{e_i}{1-h_i}\right)}}\right|_{\sigma^2=\widehat{\sigma^2}_{(-i)}}$$

$$= \left.\frac{e_i}{\sqrt{var\left(e_i\right)}}\right|_{\sigma^2=\widehat{\sigma^2}_{(-i)}} = \frac{e_i}{\sqrt{\widehat{\sigma^2}_{(-i)}(1-h_i)}} = t_i.$$

5.15 (a) The slope of the least squares fitted line through the component plus residual plot for the last regressor is

$$\frac{\boldsymbol{x}_k'(\boldsymbol{I}-\boldsymbol{P}_1)(\boldsymbol{e}+\widehat{\beta}_k\boldsymbol{x}_k)}{\boldsymbol{x}_k'(\boldsymbol{I}-\boldsymbol{P}_1)\boldsymbol{x}_k} = \frac{\boldsymbol{x}_k'\boldsymbol{e}}{\boldsymbol{x}_k'(\boldsymbol{I}-\boldsymbol{P}_1)\boldsymbol{x}_k}+\widehat{\beta}_k$$
$$= \frac{\boldsymbol{x}_k'(\boldsymbol{I}-\boldsymbol{P}_X)\boldsymbol{e}}{\boldsymbol{x}_k'(\boldsymbol{I}-\boldsymbol{P}_1)\boldsymbol{x}_k}+\widehat{\beta}_k = \widehat{\beta}_k.$$

The intercept is $\frac{1}{n}\boldsymbol{1}'(\boldsymbol{e}+\widehat{\beta}_k\boldsymbol{x}_k)-\widehat{\beta}_k\times\frac{1}{n}\boldsymbol{1}'\boldsymbol{x}_k=0$.

(b) The residual vector for the least squares fitted line through the component plus residual plot is $(\boldsymbol{e}+\widehat{\beta}_k\boldsymbol{x}_k)-\widehat{\beta}_k\boldsymbol{x}_k=\boldsymbol{e}$, which is the residual vector for the model $(\boldsymbol{y},\boldsymbol{X\beta},\sigma^2\boldsymbol{I})$.

(c) Although the error sum of squares for the two models are identical, the error degrees of freedom are $n-1$ and $n-\rho(\boldsymbol{X})$, respectively. The discrepancy is because of the fact that the model $(\boldsymbol{e}+\widehat{\beta}_k\boldsymbol{x}_k,\boldsymbol{x}_k\beta_k,\sigma^2\boldsymbol{I})$ is too simplistic a model. The dispersion matrix of $\boldsymbol{e}+\widehat{\beta}_k\boldsymbol{x}_k$ is not $\sigma^2\boldsymbol{I}$, but is equal to $\sigma^2(\boldsymbol{I}-\boldsymbol{P}_{X_{(k-1)}})$. If the correct dispersion matrix is used (by utilizing the theory developed in Chapter 7), then the resulting estimator of σ^2 would be the same as that from the model $(\boldsymbol{y},\boldsymbol{X\beta},\sigma^2\boldsymbol{I})$.

5.16 (a) Since $\boldsymbol{1}'\boldsymbol{y}_{res}=0$ and $\boldsymbol{1}'\boldsymbol{x}_{k,res}=0$, the least squares fitted line through the added variable plot has intercept equal to 0. The slope is equal to the LSE of β_k from the model $(\boldsymbol{y}_{res},\boldsymbol{x}_{k,res}\beta_k,\sigma^2\boldsymbol{I})$. Starting from the other end, we get the LSE of β_k in the model $(\boldsymbol{y},\boldsymbol{X\beta},\sigma^2\boldsymbol{I})$, written in terms of the last column $\boldsymbol{u}_{k+1}$ of the $(k+1)\times(k+1)$ identity matrix, as

$$\boldsymbol{u}_{k+1}'(\boldsymbol{X}'\boldsymbol{X})^{-1}\boldsymbol{X}'\boldsymbol{y}$$
$$=\boldsymbol{u}_{k+1}'\begin{pmatrix}\boldsymbol{X}_{k-1}'\boldsymbol{X}_{k-1} & \boldsymbol{X}_{k-1}'\boldsymbol{x}_k\\ \boldsymbol{x}_k'\boldsymbol{X}_{k-1} & \boldsymbol{x}_k'\boldsymbol{x}_k\end{pmatrix}^{-1}\begin{pmatrix}\boldsymbol{X}_{k-1}'\\ \boldsymbol{x}_k'\end{pmatrix}\boldsymbol{y}$$
$$=\frac{1}{\boldsymbol{x}_{k,res}'(\boldsymbol{I}-\boldsymbol{P}_{X_{(k-1)}})\boldsymbol{x}_{k,res}}\left(-\boldsymbol{x}_k'\boldsymbol{X}_{k-1}(\boldsymbol{X}_{k-1}'\boldsymbol{X}_{k-1})^{-1}\ :\ 1\right)\begin{pmatrix}\boldsymbol{X}_{k-1}'\\ \boldsymbol{x}_k'\end{pmatrix}\boldsymbol{y}$$
$$=\frac{\boldsymbol{x}_k'(\boldsymbol{I}-\boldsymbol{P}_{X_{(k-1)}})\boldsymbol{y}}{\boldsymbol{x}_k'(\boldsymbol{I}-\boldsymbol{P}_{X_{(k-1)}})\boldsymbol{x}_k}$$

$$= \frac{\boldsymbol{x}_k'(\boldsymbol{I} - \boldsymbol{P}_{X_{(k-1)}})(\boldsymbol{I} - \boldsymbol{P}_1)(\boldsymbol{I} - \boldsymbol{P}_{X_{(k-1)}})\boldsymbol{y}}{\boldsymbol{x}_k'(\boldsymbol{I} - \boldsymbol{P}_{X_{(k-1)}})(\boldsymbol{I} - \boldsymbol{P}_1)(\boldsymbol{I} - \boldsymbol{P}_{X_{(k-1)}})\boldsymbol{x}_k} = \frac{\boldsymbol{x}_{k,res}'(\boldsymbol{I} - \boldsymbol{P}_1)\boldsymbol{y}_{res}}{\boldsymbol{x}_{k,res}'(\boldsymbol{I} - \boldsymbol{P}_1)\boldsymbol{x}_{k,res}},$$

which is the LSE of β_k from the model $(\boldsymbol{y}_{res}, \boldsymbol{x}_{k,res}\beta_k, \sigma^2\boldsymbol{I})$.

(b) The residual vector for the model $(\boldsymbol{y}, \boldsymbol{X\beta}, \sigma^2\boldsymbol{I})$ is

$$\begin{aligned}(\boldsymbol{I} - \boldsymbol{P}_X)\boldsymbol{y} &= (\boldsymbol{I} - \boldsymbol{P}_{X_{(k-1)}} - \boldsymbol{P}_{(I-P_{X_{(k-1)}})x_k})\boldsymbol{y} \\ &= (\boldsymbol{I} - \boldsymbol{P}_{(I-P_{X_{(k-1)}})x_k})(\boldsymbol{I} - \boldsymbol{P}_{X_{(k-1)}})\boldsymbol{y} = (\boldsymbol{I} - \boldsymbol{P}_{x_{k,res}})\boldsymbol{y}_{res},\end{aligned}$$

which is the residual vector of the model $(\boldsymbol{y}_{res}, \boldsymbol{x}_{k,res}\beta_k, \sigma^2\boldsymbol{I})$.

(c) The answer is no; the explanation is the same as in part (c) of Exercise 5.15 above.

5.17 The vector of fitted values obtained from the WLSE $\widehat{\boldsymbol{\beta}}_{WLS}$ can be written as $\boldsymbol{X}\widehat{\boldsymbol{\beta}}_{WLS}$. Consider a general vector $\boldsymbol{Xb} = b_0\boldsymbol{1} + \boldsymbol{Zl}$. The sample correlation between this vector and $\boldsymbol{y}$ is

$$\begin{aligned}corr(\boldsymbol{Zl} + b_0\boldsymbol{1}, \boldsymbol{y}) &= \frac{\sum_{i=1}^n (y_i - \bar{y})(\boldsymbol{l}'\boldsymbol{z}_i + b_0 - \boldsymbol{l}'\bar{\boldsymbol{z}} - b_0)}{\sqrt{\sum_{i=1}^n (y_i - \bar{y})^2}\sqrt{\sum_{i=1}^n (\boldsymbol{l}'\boldsymbol{z}_i - \boldsymbol{l}'\bar{\boldsymbol{z}})^2}} \\ &= \frac{\boldsymbol{y}'(\boldsymbol{I} - \frac{1}{n}\boldsymbol{11}')\boldsymbol{Zl}}{\sqrt{\boldsymbol{y}'(\boldsymbol{I} - \frac{1}{n}\boldsymbol{11}')\boldsymbol{y}}\sqrt{\boldsymbol{l}'\boldsymbol{Z}'(\boldsymbol{I} - \frac{1}{n}\boldsymbol{11}')\boldsymbol{Zl}}} \\ &\le \sqrt{\frac{(\boldsymbol{l}'\boldsymbol{Z}'(\boldsymbol{I} - \frac{1}{n}\boldsymbol{11}')\boldsymbol{y})^2}{\boldsymbol{y}'(\boldsymbol{I} - \frac{1}{n}\boldsymbol{11}')\boldsymbol{y} \cdot \boldsymbol{l}'\boldsymbol{Z}'(\boldsymbol{I} - \frac{1}{n}\boldsymbol{11}')\boldsymbol{Zl}}}.\end{aligned}$$

Suppose $\boldsymbol{Z}'(\boldsymbol{I} - \frac{1}{n}\boldsymbol{11}')\boldsymbol{Z} = \boldsymbol{BB}'$, where $\boldsymbol{B}$ is a nonsingular matrix. Then we have, by Cauchy-Scwartz inequality,

$$\begin{aligned}\widehat{corr}(\boldsymbol{l}'\boldsymbol{x}, y) &\le \sqrt{\frac{(\boldsymbol{l}'\boldsymbol{BB}^{-1}\boldsymbol{Z}'(\boldsymbol{I} - \frac{1}{n}\boldsymbol{11}')\boldsymbol{y})^2}{\boldsymbol{y}'(\boldsymbol{I} - \frac{1}{n}\boldsymbol{11}')\boldsymbol{y} \cdot \boldsymbol{l}'\boldsymbol{BB}'\boldsymbol{l}}} \\ &\le \sqrt{\frac{\boldsymbol{l}'\boldsymbol{BB}'\boldsymbol{l} \cdot \boldsymbol{y}'(\boldsymbol{I} - \frac{1}{n}\boldsymbol{11}')\boldsymbol{Z}(\boldsymbol{B}^{-1})'\boldsymbol{B}^{-1}\boldsymbol{Z}'(\boldsymbol{I} - \frac{1}{n}\boldsymbol{11}')\boldsymbol{y}}{\boldsymbol{y}'(\boldsymbol{I} - \frac{1}{n}\boldsymbol{11}')\boldsymbol{y} \cdot \boldsymbol{l}'\boldsymbol{BB}'\boldsymbol{l}}} \\ &= \sqrt{\frac{\boldsymbol{y}'(\boldsymbol{I} - \frac{1}{n}\boldsymbol{11}')\boldsymbol{Z}(\boldsymbol{Z}'(\boldsymbol{I} - \frac{1}{n}\boldsymbol{11}')\boldsymbol{Z})^{-1}\boldsymbol{Z}'(\boldsymbol{I} - \frac{1}{n}\boldsymbol{11}')\boldsymbol{y}}{\boldsymbol{y}'(\boldsymbol{I} - \frac{1}{n}\boldsymbol{11}')\boldsymbol{y}}} \\ &= \sqrt{\frac{\boldsymbol{y}'\boldsymbol{P}_{(I-P_1)Z}\boldsymbol{y}}{\boldsymbol{y}'(\boldsymbol{I} - \boldsymbol{P}_1)\boldsymbol{y}}} = \sqrt{\frac{\boldsymbol{y}'(\boldsymbol{P}_X - \boldsymbol{P}_1)\boldsymbol{y}}{\boldsymbol{y}'(\boldsymbol{I} - \boldsymbol{P}_1)\boldsymbol{y}}} \\ &= \sqrt{1 - \frac{\boldsymbol{y}'(\boldsymbol{I} - \boldsymbol{P}_X)\boldsymbol{y}}{\boldsymbol{y}'(\boldsymbol{I} - \boldsymbol{P}_1)\boldsymbol{y}}} = R = corr(\widehat{\boldsymbol{y}}, \boldsymbol{y}),\end{aligned}$$

$\widehat{\boldsymbol{y}}$ being the vector of fitted values obtained from the LSE.

5.18 The value of R^2 defined in (5.11), as obtained from the WLS analysis is

$$1-\frac{\|\boldsymbol{y}-\boldsymbol{X}\widehat{\boldsymbol{\beta}}_{WLS}\|^2}{\|\boldsymbol{y}-\bar{y}\mathbf{1}\|^2}\le 1-\frac{\min_{\beta}\|\boldsymbol{y}-\boldsymbol{X}\boldsymbol{\beta}\|^2}{\|\boldsymbol{y}-\bar{y}\mathbf{1}\|^2}=1-\frac{\|\boldsymbol{y}-\boldsymbol{X}\widehat{\boldsymbol{\beta}}_{OLS}\|^2}{\|\boldsymbol{y}-\bar{y}\mathbf{1}\|^2},$$

the last quantity being the value of R^2 defined in (5.11), as obtained from the OLS analysis.

5.19 We shall use the notation ϕ instead of ϕ_1 for simplicity.

(a) Writing ε_{i+1} as $\phi\varepsilon_i+\delta_{i+1}$ and using the fact that δ_{i+1} is uncorrelated with ε_i, we have $E[(\varepsilon_{i+1}-\varepsilon_i)^2]=2Var(\varepsilon_i)(1-\phi)$. It follows that the probability limit of DW is $2(1-\phi)$. The limit is equal to 2 for $\phi=0$. The extreme values of DW, 0 and 4, correspond to $\phi=1$ and $\phi=-1$, respectively.

(b) Note that $DW=\|\boldsymbol{A}\boldsymbol{e}\|^2/\|\boldsymbol{e}\|^2$, where

$$\boldsymbol{A}=\begin{pmatrix}1&-1&0&\cdots&0\\0&1&-1&\cdots&0\\ \vdots&\ddots&\ddots&\ddots&\vdots\\0&\cdots&0&1&-1\end{pmatrix}.$$

Write the residual vector $\boldsymbol{e}$ as $(\boldsymbol{I}-\boldsymbol{H})\boldsymbol{\varepsilon}$. Since $\boldsymbol{A}\boldsymbol{e}$ and $\boldsymbol{e}$ have zero mean, the probability limit of DW is

$$\frac{\mathrm{tr}(\boldsymbol{A}D(\boldsymbol{e})\boldsymbol{A}')}{\mathrm{tr}(D(\boldsymbol{e}))}=\frac{\mathrm{tr}(\boldsymbol{A}(\boldsymbol{I}-\boldsymbol{H})\boldsymbol{V}(\boldsymbol{I}-\boldsymbol{H})\boldsymbol{A}')}{\mathrm{tr}((\boldsymbol{I}-\boldsymbol{H})\boldsymbol{V}(\boldsymbol{I}-\boldsymbol{H}))},$$

where $\boldsymbol{V}$ is the dispersion matrix of the model error, which depends on σ^2 and ϕ. The numerator can be expanded as

$$\mathrm{tr}(\boldsymbol{A}\boldsymbol{V}\boldsymbol{A}')-2\mathrm{tr}(\boldsymbol{A}\boldsymbol{H}\boldsymbol{V}\boldsymbol{A}')+2\mathrm{tr}(\boldsymbol{A}\boldsymbol{H}\boldsymbol{V}\boldsymbol{H}\boldsymbol{A}').$$

Using the explicit expression of $\boldsymbol{V}$ given in Example 8.20, one can simplify the first term of the right-hand to $2(n-1)\sigma^2(1-\phi)$, as in part (a). The magnitude of the (i,j)th element of $\boldsymbol{H}\boldsymbol{V}$ is bounded from above as

$$\left|\sigma^2\sum_{l=1}^{n}h_{i,l}\phi^{|l-j|}\right|<\frac{c\sigma^2}{n}\sum_{l=1}^{n}|\phi|^{|l-j|}<\frac{2c\sigma^2}{n(1-|\phi|)}.$$

Therefore, each diagonal element of $\boldsymbol{A}\boldsymbol{H}\boldsymbol{V}\boldsymbol{A}$ is bounded from above by $8c\sigma^2/n(1-|\phi|)$, and the trace has smaller magnitude than $8c\sigma^2/(1-|\phi|)$. Thus, $2\mathrm{tr}(\boldsymbol{A}\boldsymbol{H}\boldsymbol{V}\boldsymbol{A}')$ is negligible in comparison to $\mathrm{tr}(\boldsymbol{A}\boldsymbol{V}\boldsymbol{A}')$ for large n. Likewise, the magnitude of the (i,j)th element of $\boldsymbol{H}\boldsymbol{V}\boldsymbol{H}$ is bounded from above as

$$\begin{aligned}\left|\sigma^2\sum_{l=1}^{n}\sum_{m=1}^{n} h_{i,l}\phi^{|l-m|}h_{m,j}\right| &\le \frac{c^2\sigma^2}{n^2}\sum_{l=1}^{n}\sum_{m=1}^{n}|\phi|^{|l-m|}\\ = \frac{c^2\sigma^2}{n^2}\sum_{s=0}^{n-1}|\phi|^s(n-s) &\le \frac{c^2\sigma^2}{n}\sum_{s=0}^{n-1}|\phi|^s \le \frac{c^2\sigma^2}{n(1-|\phi|)}.\end{aligned}$$

Therefore, the trace of $\boldsymbol{AHVHA}$ has smaller magnitude than $4c^2\sigma^2/(1-|\phi|)$, which is negligible in comparison to $\text{tr}(\boldsymbol{AVA}')$ for large n. Thus, $\text{tr}(\boldsymbol{A}(\boldsymbol{I}-\boldsymbol{H})\boldsymbol{V}(\boldsymbol{I}-\boldsymbol{H})\boldsymbol{A}')/n$ converges to $2\sigma^2(1-\phi)$. Using a similar argument, $\text{tr}((\boldsymbol{I}-\boldsymbol{H})\boldsymbol{V}(\boldsymbol{I}-\boldsymbol{H}))/n$ can be shown to converge to σ^2. Hence, the probability limit of DW is $2(1-\phi)$, as in part (a).

5.20 Following the solution to Exercise 5.14(b), we can write

$$\begin{aligned}DFFITS_i &= \frac{\widehat{y}_i-\widehat{y}_{i(-i)}}{\sqrt{\widehat{\sigma^2}_{(-i)}h_i}} = \frac{e_{i(-i)}-e_i}{\sqrt{\widehat{\sigma^2}_{(-i)}h_i}} = \frac{e_i/(1-h_i)-e_i}{\sqrt{\widehat{\sigma^2}_{(-i)}h_i}}\\ &= \frac{e_i}{\sqrt{\widehat{\sigma^2}_{(-i)}}}\times\frac{\sqrt{h_i}}{(1-h_i)} = \frac{t_i\sqrt{(1-h_i)h_i}}{(1-h_i)} = \left(\frac{h_i}{1-h_i}\right)^{1/2}t_i.\end{aligned}$$

5.21 Following the solution to Exercise 5.14(a), we can write

$$\begin{aligned}\widehat{\boldsymbol{y}}_{(-i)} &= \boldsymbol{X}(\boldsymbol{X}'_{(-i)}\boldsymbol{X}_{(-i)})^{-1}\boldsymbol{X}'_{(-i)}\boldsymbol{y}_{(-i)} = \boldsymbol{X}(\boldsymbol{X}'\boldsymbol{X}-\boldsymbol{x}_i\boldsymbol{x}_i')^{-1}(\boldsymbol{X}'\boldsymbol{y}-\boldsymbol{x}_iy_i)\\ &= \boldsymbol{X}\left[(\boldsymbol{X}'\boldsymbol{X})^{-1}+\frac{1}{1-h_i}(\boldsymbol{X}'\boldsymbol{X})^{-1}\boldsymbol{x}_i\boldsymbol{x}_i'(\boldsymbol{X}'\boldsymbol{X})^{-1}\right](\boldsymbol{X}'\boldsymbol{y}-\boldsymbol{x}_iy_i)\\ &= \widehat{\boldsymbol{y}}+\frac{1}{1-h_i}\boldsymbol{X}(\boldsymbol{X}'\boldsymbol{X})^{-1}\boldsymbol{x}_i\boldsymbol{x}_i'\widehat{\boldsymbol{\beta}}-\boldsymbol{X}(\boldsymbol{X}'\boldsymbol{X})^{-1}\boldsymbol{x}_iy_i\\ &\quad -\frac{h_i}{1-h_i}\boldsymbol{X}(\boldsymbol{X}'\boldsymbol{X})^{-1}\boldsymbol{x}_iy_i\\ &= \widehat{\boldsymbol{y}}+\frac{1}{1-h_i}\boldsymbol{X}(\boldsymbol{X}'\boldsymbol{X})^{-1}\boldsymbol{x}_i[\boldsymbol{x}_i'\widehat{\boldsymbol{\beta}}-(1-h_i)y_i-h_iy_i]\\ &= \widehat{\boldsymbol{y}}-\frac{e_i}{1-h_i}\boldsymbol{X}(\boldsymbol{X}'\boldsymbol{X})^{-1}\boldsymbol{x}_i.\end{aligned}$$

Therefore,

$$COOKD_i = \frac{\|\widehat{\boldsymbol{y}}-\widehat{\boldsymbol{y}}_{(-i)}\|^2}{(k+1)\widehat{\sigma^2}} = \frac{e_i^2h_i}{(k+1)\widehat{\sigma^2}(1-h_i)^2} = \frac{1}{k+1}\left(\frac{h_i}{1-h_i}\right)r_i^2.$$

5.22 (a) Let $\boldsymbol{u}_j$ be the jth column of $\boldsymbol{I}_{p\times p}$. Then

$$\begin{aligned}IVIF_j &= \boldsymbol{u}_j'(\boldsymbol{X}'\boldsymbol{X})^{-1}\boldsymbol{u}_j\cdot\boldsymbol{u}_j'(\boldsymbol{X}'\boldsymbol{X})\boldsymbol{u}_j\\ &= \boldsymbol{u}_j'(\boldsymbol{D}\boldsymbol{X}_s'\boldsymbol{X}_s\boldsymbol{D})^{-1}\boldsymbol{u}_j\cdot\boldsymbol{u}_j'(\boldsymbol{D}\boldsymbol{X}_s'\boldsymbol{X}_s\boldsymbol{D})\boldsymbol{u}_j\end{aligned}$$

$$= \boldsymbol{u}_j' \boldsymbol{D}^{-1}(\boldsymbol{X}_s'\boldsymbol{X}_s)^{-1}\boldsymbol{D}^{-1}\boldsymbol{u}_j \cdot \boldsymbol{u}_j'\boldsymbol{D}(\boldsymbol{X}_s'\boldsymbol{X}_s)\boldsymbol{D}\boldsymbol{u}_j$$
$$= \|\boldsymbol{x}_{(j)}\|^{-2}\boldsymbol{u}_j'(\boldsymbol{X}_s'\boldsymbol{X}_s)^{-1}\boldsymbol{u}_j \cdot \|\boldsymbol{x}_{(j)}\|^2\boldsymbol{u}_j'(\boldsymbol{X}_s'\boldsymbol{X}_s)\boldsymbol{u}_j$$
$$= \boldsymbol{u}_j(\boldsymbol{X}_s'\boldsymbol{X}_s)^{-1}\boldsymbol{u}_j.$$

(b) If $\boldsymbol{X}_s'\boldsymbol{X}_s = \begin{pmatrix} \boldsymbol{A} & \boldsymbol{a} \\ \boldsymbol{a}' & 1 \end{pmatrix}$ then it follows from part (a) that $IVIF_k = 1/(1 - \boldsymbol{a}'\boldsymbol{A}^{-1}\boldsymbol{a})$. While $\boldsymbol{a}'\boldsymbol{A}^{-1}\boldsymbol{a}$ is nonnegative, it cannot be greater than 1, since $IVIF_k$ is a diagonal element of a nonnegative definite matrix. Thus, $1 - \boldsymbol{a}'\boldsymbol{A}^{-1}\boldsymbol{a} \leq 1$ and so $IVIF_k \geq 1$. Likewise, the other VIFs are also greater than or equal to 1.

(c) The result follows from part (a).

5.23 (a) Note that the largest eingenvalue of $\boldsymbol{X}_s'\boldsymbol{X}_s$ is no smaller than the average of the eigenvalues, which is $\text{tr}(\boldsymbol{X}_s'\boldsymbol{X}_s)/(k+1)$ or 1. Hence, $\pi_{1j} = (v_{1j}^2/\lambda_1)/IVIF_{j-1} \leq 1/IVIF_{j-1}$.

(b) As noted in above, $\lambda_1 \geq 1$. Thus, we have

$$IVIF_{j-1} = \sum_{i=1}^{k+1} \frac{v_{ij}^2}{\lambda_i} \leq \sum_{i=1}^{k+1} \frac{v_{ij}^2}{\lambda_{k+1}} = \frac{1}{\lambda_{k+1}} \leq \frac{\lambda_1}{\lambda_{k+1}} = \kappa^2.$$

On the other hand,

$$\sum_{j=1}^{k+1} IVIF_{j-1} = \sum_{j=1}^{k+1}\sum_{i=1}^{k+1} \frac{v_{ij}^2}{\lambda_i} = \sum_{i=1}^{k+1} \frac{1}{\lambda_i} \geq \frac{1}{\lambda_{k+1}} \geq \frac{\lambda_1/(k+1)}{\lambda_{k+1}} = \frac{\kappa^2}{k+1}.$$

5.24 $\|\widehat{\boldsymbol{\beta}}_{pc}\|^2 = \|\boldsymbol{\Lambda}_1^{-1}\boldsymbol{Z}_1'\boldsymbol{y}\|^2 \leq \|\boldsymbol{\Lambda}_1^{-1}\boldsymbol{Z}_1'\boldsymbol{y}\|^2 + \|\boldsymbol{\Lambda}_2^{-1}\boldsymbol{Z}_2'\boldsymbol{y}\|^2 = \|\widehat{\boldsymbol{\beta}}\|^2$.

5.25 $D_r = \sigma^2(\boldsymbol{X}'\boldsymbol{X} + r\boldsymbol{I})^{-1}\boldsymbol{X}'\boldsymbol{X}(\boldsymbol{X}'\boldsymbol{X} + r\boldsymbol{I})^{-1}$. If $\lambda_1 \geq \cdots \geq \lambda_{k+1}$ are the eigenvalues of $\boldsymbol{X}'\boldsymbol{X}$, then $\sigma^2\lambda_j/(\lambda_j + r)^2$, $j = 1, \ldots, k+1$ are the eigenvalues of D_r. Each eigenvalue is a decreasing function of r. Hence, every eigenvalue of D_{r_1} is strictly larger than the corresponding eigenvalue of D_{r_2} if $r_1 < r_2$.

5.26 (a) Using the method of Lagrange multipliers minimize $\|\boldsymbol{y} - \boldsymbol{X\beta}\|^2 + r\left(\|\boldsymbol{\beta}\|^2 - b^2\right)$ with respect to $\boldsymbol{\beta}$ and r. Differentiating the expression with respect to $\boldsymbol{\beta}$ and setting it equal to zero we have the solution $\widehat{\boldsymbol{\beta}}_r = (\boldsymbol{X}'\boldsymbol{X} + r\boldsymbol{I})^{-1}\boldsymbol{X}'\boldsymbol{y}$, while differentiation with respect to r leads one to the equation $\|\widehat{\boldsymbol{\beta}}_r\|^2 = b^2$.

(b) If $\sum_{i=1}^{k+1} \lambda_i \boldsymbol{v}_i \boldsymbol{v}_i'$ is a spectral decomposition of $\boldsymbol{X}'\boldsymbol{X}$, then

$$\|\boldsymbol{y} - \boldsymbol{X}\widehat{\boldsymbol{\beta}}_r\|^2 = \|\boldsymbol{y} - \boldsymbol{P}_X\boldsymbol{y}\|^2 + \|\boldsymbol{P}_X\boldsymbol{y} - \boldsymbol{X}\widehat{\boldsymbol{\beta}}_r\|^2$$
$$= R_0^2 + \|[(\boldsymbol{X}'\boldsymbol{X})^{-1} - (\boldsymbol{X}'\boldsymbol{X} + r\boldsymbol{I})^{-1}]\boldsymbol{X}'\boldsymbol{y}\|^2$$
$$= R_0^2 + \boldsymbol{y}'\boldsymbol{X}[(\boldsymbol{X}'\boldsymbol{X})^{-1} - (\boldsymbol{X}'\boldsymbol{X} + r\boldsymbol{I})^{-1}]^2\boldsymbol{X}'\boldsymbol{y}$$

$$= R_0^2 + \boldsymbol{y}'\boldsymbol{X}\left[\sum_{i=1}^{k+1}\left(\frac{1}{\lambda_i} - \frac{1}{\lambda_i + r}\right)\boldsymbol{v}_i\boldsymbol{v}_i'\right]^2 \boldsymbol{X}'\boldsymbol{y}$$

$$= R_0^2 + \sum_{i=1}^{k+1}\left(\frac{1}{\lambda_i} - \frac{1}{\lambda_i + r}\right)^2 (\boldsymbol{v}_i'\boldsymbol{X}'\boldsymbol{y})^2,$$

which is clearly an increasing function of r.

(c) All the eigenvalues of $(\boldsymbol{X}'\boldsymbol{X} + r\boldsymbol{I})^{-2}$ are decreasing functions of r, and $\widehat{\boldsymbol{\beta}}_r'\widehat{\boldsymbol{\beta}}_r$ is a quadratic form in this matrix.

(d) It follows from parts (b) and (c) that $\|\boldsymbol{y} - \boldsymbol{X}\widehat{\boldsymbol{\beta}}_r\|^2$ is a decreasing function of b. Hence, we have

$$\min_{\boldsymbol{\beta}\,:\,\|\boldsymbol{\beta}\|^2 = a^2} \|\boldsymbol{y} - \boldsymbol{X}\boldsymbol{\beta}\|^2 \ge \min_{\boldsymbol{\beta}\,:\,\|\boldsymbol{\beta}\|^2 = b^2} \|\boldsymbol{y} - \boldsymbol{X}\boldsymbol{\beta}\|^2$$

whenever $a < b$. The result follows.

5.27 (a) The inequality (5.26) holds for all $r > 0$ if and only if $\inf_{r>0}\frac{1}{r} > (\|\boldsymbol{X}\boldsymbol{\beta}\|^2/\sigma^2 - 1)/(2\lambda)$, i.e. $\|\boldsymbol{X}\boldsymbol{\beta}\|^2/\sigma^2 - 1 < 0$ or $\|\boldsymbol{X}\boldsymbol{\beta}\|^2 < \sigma^2$.

(b) The inequality (5.28) holds for all $s > 0$ if and only if

$$\inf_{s>0} s > \frac{\|\boldsymbol{X}\boldsymbol{\beta}\|^2/\sigma^2 - 1}{\|\boldsymbol{X}\boldsymbol{\beta}\|^2/\sigma^2 + 1},$$

i.e., $\|\boldsymbol{X}\boldsymbol{\beta}\|^2/\sigma^2 - 1 < 0$ or $\|\boldsymbol{X}\boldsymbol{\beta}\|^2 < \sigma^2$.

(c) The requisite condition is that the matrix difference

$$MSE(\widehat{\boldsymbol{\beta}}) - MSE(\boldsymbol{0}) = \sigma^2(\boldsymbol{X}'\boldsymbol{X})^{-1} - \boldsymbol{\beta}\boldsymbol{\beta}'$$

is positive definite. An equivalent condition is $\boldsymbol{\beta}'\sigma^{-2}\boldsymbol{X}'\boldsymbol{X}\boldsymbol{\beta} < 1$, or $\|\boldsymbol{X}\boldsymbol{\beta}\|^2 < \sigma^2$.

(d) Since the conditions of parts (a), (b) and (c) are equivalent, it can be said that the ridge or the shrinkage estimator would have smaller MSE than the BLUE for *all* choices of the parameter r or s only in a pathological case. This case arises when the squared magnitude of the systematic part of the linear model, $\|\boldsymbol{X}\boldsymbol{\beta}\|^2$, is weaker than $1/n$th fraction of the expected squared error part, $E\|\boldsymbol{\varepsilon}\|^2 = n\sigma^2$. In such a case, even the trivial estimator $\boldsymbol{0}$ beats the BLUE in terms of MSE!

5.28 Condition for smaller MSE of the shrinkage estimator is

$$s > \frac{\|\boldsymbol{X}(\boldsymbol{\beta}_0 - \boldsymbol{\beta})\|^2/\sigma^2 - 1}{\|\boldsymbol{X}(\boldsymbol{\beta}_0 - \boldsymbol{\beta})\|^2/\sigma^2 + 1}.$$

This holds for all $s \in (0,1)$ if and only if $\|\boldsymbol{X}(\boldsymbol{\beta}_0 - \boldsymbol{\beta})\|^2 < \sigma^2$. Thus, $\boldsymbol{\beta}_0$ has to be sufficiently close to the 'true' value of $\boldsymbol{\beta}$ in order that the shrinkage estimator has smaller MSE irrespective of the value of s.

5.29 (a) $s > [\boldsymbol{\beta}'\boldsymbol{A}'[D(\boldsymbol{A}\widehat{\boldsymbol{\beta}})]^{-}\boldsymbol{A}\boldsymbol{\beta} - 1]/[\boldsymbol{\beta}'\boldsymbol{A}'[D(\boldsymbol{A}\widehat{\boldsymbol{\beta}})]^{-}\boldsymbol{A}\boldsymbol{\beta} + 1]$.

(b) $\sigma^2 > \boldsymbol{\beta}'\boldsymbol{A}'[\sigma^{-2}D(\boldsymbol{A}\widehat{\boldsymbol{\beta}})]^{-}\boldsymbol{A}\boldsymbol{\beta}$.

(c) $s > [\boldsymbol{\beta}'\boldsymbol{X}'[D(\boldsymbol{X}\widehat{\boldsymbol{\beta}})]^{-}\boldsymbol{X}\boldsymbol{\beta} - 1]/[\boldsymbol{\beta}'\boldsymbol{X}'[D(\boldsymbol{X}\widehat{\boldsymbol{\beta}})]^{-}\boldsymbol{X}\boldsymbol{\beta} + 1]$, where $D(\boldsymbol{X}\widehat{\boldsymbol{\beta}}) = \sigma^2[\boldsymbol{V} - \boldsymbol{V}(\boldsymbol{I} - \boldsymbol{P}_X)\{(\boldsymbol{I} - \boldsymbol{P}_X)\boldsymbol{V}(\boldsymbol{I} - \boldsymbol{P}_X)\}^{-}(\boldsymbol{I} - \boldsymbol{P}_X)\boldsymbol{V}]$.

(d) The simplified conditions for the three parts are

$$\begin{aligned} s &> \frac{\boldsymbol{\beta}'\boldsymbol{A}'[\sigma^2\boldsymbol{A}(\boldsymbol{X}'\boldsymbol{X})^{-}\boldsymbol{A}']^{-}\boldsymbol{A}\boldsymbol{\beta} - 1}{\boldsymbol{\beta}'\boldsymbol{A}'[\sigma^2\boldsymbol{A}(\boldsymbol{X}'\boldsymbol{X})^{-}\boldsymbol{A}']^{-}\boldsymbol{A}\boldsymbol{\beta} + 1}, \\ \sigma^2 &> \boldsymbol{\beta}'\boldsymbol{A}'(\boldsymbol{X}'\boldsymbol{X})^{-}\boldsymbol{A}\boldsymbol{\beta}, \\ s &> \frac{\|\boldsymbol{X}\boldsymbol{\beta}\|^2/\sigma^2 - 1}{\|\boldsymbol{X}\boldsymbol{\beta}\|^2/\sigma^2 + 1} \end{aligned}$$

5.30 According to the logistic regression model (see Example 5.7.2),

$$P(y = 1|x) = \frac{\exp(\beta_0 + \beta_1 x)}{1 + \exp(\beta_0 + \beta_1 x)} = \begin{cases} \frac{\exp(\beta_0)}{1+\exp(\beta_0)} & \text{if } x = 0, \\ \frac{\exp(\beta_0+\beta_1)}{1+\exp(\beta_0+\beta_1)} & \text{if } x = 1. \end{cases}$$

According to the probit regression model (see Example 5.7.2),

$$P(y = 1|x) = \Phi(\alpha_0 + \alpha_1 x) = \begin{cases} \Phi(\alpha_0) & \text{if } x = 0, \\ \Phi(\alpha_0 + \alpha_1) & \text{if } x = 1. \end{cases}$$

The two models are reparametrizations of one another, with

$$\begin{aligned} \beta_0 &= \text{logit}(\Phi(\alpha_0)), \quad \beta_1 = \text{logit}(\Phi(\alpha_0 + \alpha_1)) - \text{logit}(\Phi(\alpha_0)); \\ \alpha_0 &= \Phi^{-1}\left(\frac{\exp(\beta_0)}{1 + \exp(\beta_0)}\right), \\ \alpha_1 &= \Phi^{-1}\left(\frac{\exp(\beta_0 + \beta_1)}{1 + \exp(\beta_0 + \beta_1)}\right) - \Phi^{-1}\left(\frac{\exp(\beta_0)}{1 + \exp(\beta_0)}\right). \end{aligned}$$

It is easier to express the model and the likelihood in terms of a third reparametrization, $p_0 = \Phi(\alpha_0)$, $p_1 = \Phi(\alpha_0 + \alpha_1)$. The null hypothesis that x has no effect (either $\alpha_1 = 0$ or $\beta_1 = 0$), can be expressed as the restriction $p_0 = p_1$. Since maximization of the likelihood, with and without the restriction, should not depend on a particular parametrization, the likelihood ratio test would produce the same statistic, irrespective of the choice of the link function. However, the results of tests based on the normal approximation of the estimated regression coefficients would generally depend on that choice.

Chapter 6

6.1 $E\|(P_X - P_1)y\|^2 = E[\mathrm{tr}\{(P_X - P_1)yy'(P_X - P_1)\}]$ can be written as the sum of a dispersion and a bias term. Consequently MS_g simplifies to $\sigma^2 + (t-1)^{-1}\sum_{i=1}^t n_i(\tau_i - \bar{\tau})^2$.

6.2 The reparametrized model is $(\boldsymbol{y}, \boldsymbol{Z}\boldsymbol{\eta}, \sigma^2\boldsymbol{I})$, where

$$\boldsymbol{Z} = (\mathbf{1}_{n\times 1} : (\boldsymbol{I} - t^{-1}\mathbf{1}\mathbf{1}') \otimes \mathbf{1} : \mathbf{1} \otimes (\boldsymbol{I} - b^{-1}\mathbf{1}\mathbf{1}'))$$

and $\boldsymbol{\eta} = (\eta_0 : \boldsymbol{\eta}_1' : \boldsymbol{\eta}_2')'$, with $\eta_0 = \mu + \frac{1}{t}\sum_{i=1}^t \tau_i + \frac{1}{b}\sum_{j=1}^b \beta_j$, $\boldsymbol{\eta}_1 = (\tau_1 : \cdots : \tau_t)'$ and $\boldsymbol{\eta}_2 = (\beta_1 : \cdots : \beta_b)'$.

6.3 Bonferroni and Scheffé confidence intervals are conservative. Maximum modulus-t intervals are not applicable here because the BLUEs of the treatment differences are dependent. However, Tukey's honestly significant difference method can be used, as $\mu + \tau_i + \bar{\beta}$ is estimable for each i and their BLUEs $(\bar{y}_{1\cdot}, \ldots, \bar{y}_{t\cdot})$ are uncorrelated. The confidence intervals are

$$(\bar{y}_{i\cdot} - \bar{y}_{j\cdot} - HSD, \bar{y}_{i\cdot} - \bar{y}_{j\cdot} + HSD), \quad i, j = 1, \ldots, t,$$

where HSD is as in Section 6.2.4 with $n_1 = b$ and $\widehat{\sigma^2} = MS_e$.

6.4 For the model $y_{i*} = \lambda x_{i*} + \varepsilon_{i*}$, $i = 1, \ldots, n$ with uncorrelated errors having variance σ^2, it is easy to see that the BLUE of λ is $\widehat{\lambda} = \sum_i (y_{i*}x_{i*}) / \left(\sum_i x_{i*}^2\right)$. The variance of the BLUE is $\sigma^2 / \sum_i x_{i*}^2$. Hence, the sum of squares due to deviation from the hypothesis $\lambda = 0$ is $\widehat{\lambda}^2/[Var(\widehat{\lambda})/\sigma^2]$, which simplifies to $\widehat{\lambda}^2 \sum_i x_{i*}^2$, i.e. $\left(\sum_i y_{i*}x_{i*}\right)^2 / \left(\sum_i x_{i*}^2\right)$. The model (6.25) is a special case of the above model, for which the expressions of $\widehat{\lambda}$ and the 'sum of squares due to deviation from the hypothesis $\lambda = 0$' simplify to (6.26) and (6.27), respectively.

6.5 The underlying model is (6.29) with γ_{ij} replaced by $\lambda(\tau_i - \bar{\tau})(\beta_j - \bar{\beta})$. The model can be written as $(\boldsymbol{y}, \boldsymbol{X}\boldsymbol{\beta} + \boldsymbol{A}'\lambda, \sigma^2\boldsymbol{I})$, where

$$\begin{aligned}
\boldsymbol{X} &= (\mathbf{1}_{t\times 1} \otimes \mathbf{1}_{b\times 1} : \boldsymbol{I}_{t\times t} \otimes \mathbf{1}_{b\times 1} : \mathbf{1}_{t\times 1} \otimes \boldsymbol{I}_{b\times b}) \otimes \mathbf{1}_{m\times 1},\\
\boldsymbol{\beta} &= (\mu : (\tau_1 : \cdots : \tau_t) : (\beta_1 : \cdots : \beta_b))',\\
\boldsymbol{A}' &= (\boldsymbol{\tau} - \bar{\tau}\mathbf{1}) \otimes (\boldsymbol{\beta} - \bar{\beta}\mathbf{1}) \otimes \mathbf{1}_{m\times 1}.
\end{aligned}$$

A generalization of Tukey's test for nonadditivity would be to test if $\lambda = 0$, using the statistic of Exercise 4.7 (see also Exercise 6.33). When the unknown parameters are replaced by their respective BLUEs, the test reduces to rejecting the hypothesis of no interaction when $(n-t-b)N/D > F_{1,n-t-b}$, where

$$N = \left(\sum_{i=1}^{t} \sum_{j=1}^{b} \sum_{k=1}^{m} e_{ijk} (\overline{y}_{i..} - \overline{y}_{...})(\overline{y}_{.j.} - \overline{y}_{...}) \right)^2,$$

$$D = mR_0^2 \sum_{i=1}^{t} \sum_{j=1}^{b} (\overline{y}_{i..} - \overline{y}_{...})^2 (\overline{y}_{.j.} - \overline{y}_{...})^2 - N.$$

6.6 Let $\sum_i c_i \tau_i$ have an LUE of the form $\sum_i \sum_j \sum_k l_{ijk} y_{ijk}$. Then

$$\sum_{i=1}^{t} \sum_{j=1}^{b} \sum_{k=1}^{m} l_{ijk} (\mu + \tau_i + \beta_j + \gamma_{ij}) = \sum_{i=1}^{t} c_i \tau_i,$$

for *all* values of the parameters. By putting $\gamma_{1j} = 1$ for all j and all other parameters equal to 0 in the above equation, we have $\sum_j \sum_k l_{1jk} = 0$. On the other hand, by putting $\tau_1 = 1$ and all other parameters equal to 0, we have $\sum_j \sum_k l_{1jk} = c_1$. Hence we must have $c_1 = 0$. Likewise, $c_2 = \cdots = c_t = 0$.

6.7 Here,

$$\boldsymbol{I} - \boldsymbol{P}_X = \boldsymbol{I} - \boldsymbol{I}_{t\times t} \otimes \boldsymbol{I}_{b\times b} \otimes \boldsymbol{P}_{1_{m\times 1}} = \boldsymbol{I}_{t\times t} \otimes \boldsymbol{I}_{b\times b} \otimes (\boldsymbol{I} - \boldsymbol{P}_{1_{m\times 1}}).$$

This implies that $(\boldsymbol{I}-\boldsymbol{P}_X)\boldsymbol{P}_\mu = \boldsymbol{0}$, $(\boldsymbol{I}-\boldsymbol{P}_X)\boldsymbol{P}_\tau = \boldsymbol{0}$, $(\boldsymbol{I}-\boldsymbol{P}_X)\boldsymbol{P}_\beta = \boldsymbol{0}$ and $(\boldsymbol{I}-\boldsymbol{P}_X)\boldsymbol{P}_\gamma = \boldsymbol{0}$, where $\boldsymbol{P}_\mu$, $\boldsymbol{P}_\tau$, $\boldsymbol{P}_\beta$ and $\boldsymbol{P}_\gamma$ are as in (6.30). Thus, the four components shown in (6.31) are uncorrelated with all LZFs, and must be the BLUEs of their respective expected values. The expression of the error sum of squares, given in (6.34) follows from the fact that the element of $(\boldsymbol{I}-\boldsymbol{P}_X)\boldsymbol{y}$ corresponding to y_{ijk} is $(y_{ijk} - \bar{y}_{ij\cdot})$.

6.8 We use Proposition 4.12. Here, $\boldsymbol{A} = (\boldsymbol{0}_{tb\times 1} : \boldsymbol{0}_{tb\times t} : \boldsymbol{0}_{tb\times b} : \boldsymbol{I}_{tb\times tb})$ and $\boldsymbol{\xi} = \boldsymbol{0}_{tb\times 1}$. A vector $\boldsymbol{l}$ is in $\mathcal{C}(\boldsymbol{A}')$ if and only if it is of the form $(0 : \boldsymbol{0}_{1\times t} : \boldsymbol{0}_{1\times b} : \boldsymbol{u}')'$ where $\boldsymbol{u}$ is an arbitrary $tb \times 1$ vector. Note that

$$\mathcal{C}(\boldsymbol{X}') = \mathcal{C}((\boldsymbol{1}_{t\times 1} \otimes \boldsymbol{1}_{b\times 1} : \boldsymbol{I}_{t\times t} \otimes \boldsymbol{1}_{b\times 1} : \boldsymbol{1}_{t\times 1} \otimes \boldsymbol{I}_{b\times b} : \boldsymbol{I}_{t\times t} \otimes \boldsymbol{I}_{b\times b})').$$

Therefore, if $\boldsymbol{l} \in \mathcal{C}(\boldsymbol{A}') \cap \mathcal{C}(\boldsymbol{X}')$, then we must have a $tb \times 1$ vector k such that

$$\begin{pmatrix} \boldsymbol{1}'_{tb\times 1} \\ \boldsymbol{I}_{t\times t} \otimes \boldsymbol{1}'_{b\times 1} \\ \boldsymbol{1}'_{t\times 1} \otimes \boldsymbol{I}_{b\times b} \\ \boldsymbol{I}_{t\times t} \otimes \boldsymbol{I}_{b\times b} \end{pmatrix} \boldsymbol{k} = \boldsymbol{l} = \begin{pmatrix} 0 \\ \boldsymbol{0}_{t\times 1} \\ \boldsymbol{0}_{b\times 1} \\ \boldsymbol{u}_{tb\times 1} \end{pmatrix}.$$

The bottom part of the equation gives $\boldsymbol{k} = \boldsymbol{u}$, while the top parts give three conditions which are equivalent to $\boldsymbol{u} \in \mathcal{C}((\boldsymbol{I} - \boldsymbol{P}_{1_{t\times 1}}) \otimes (\boldsymbol{I} - \boldsymbol{P}_{1_{b\times 1}}))$. Thus, we can choose

$$\boldsymbol{A}'\boldsymbol{T}' = (\boldsymbol{0}_{tb\times 1} : \boldsymbol{0}_{tb\times t} : \boldsymbol{0}_{tb\times b} : (\boldsymbol{I} - \boldsymbol{P}_{1_{t\times 1}}) \otimes (\boldsymbol{I} - \boldsymbol{P}_{1_{b\times 1}}))',$$

which is ensured by the choice $\boldsymbol{T} = (\boldsymbol{I} - \boldsymbol{P}_{1_{t\times 1}}) \otimes (\boldsymbol{I} - \boldsymbol{P}_{1_{b\times 1}})$. The condition $\boldsymbol{TA\beta} = \boldsymbol{T\xi}$ reduces to $\gamma_{ij} - \bar{\gamma}_{i\cdot} - \bar{\gamma}_{\cdot j} + \bar{\gamma}_{\cdot\cdot} = 0$ for all i and j. Thus, the testable part of the hypothesis of 'no interaction effect' is that all the LPFs of type (d) mentioned on page 311 are zero. The sum of squares for deviation from this hypothesis is S_γ, which is the sum of squares of the BLUEs of all these LPFs, with $(t-1)(b-1)$ degrees of freedom.

Since $\boldsymbol{T}$ is a projection matrix, the untestable part of $\boldsymbol{A\beta} = \boldsymbol{\xi}$ must be $(\boldsymbol{I} - \boldsymbol{T})\boldsymbol{A\beta} = (\boldsymbol{I} - \boldsymbol{T})\boldsymbol{\xi}$. This simplifies to $\bar{\gamma}_{i\cdot} + \bar{\gamma}_{\cdot j} - \bar{\gamma}_{\cdot\cdot} = 0$ for all i and j, which is equivalent to the side conditions $\bar{\gamma}_{i\cdot} = \bar{\gamma}_{\cdot j} = \bar{\gamma}_{\cdot\cdot} = 0$ for all i and j.

6.9 As $\boldsymbol{a} \in \mathcal{C}(\boldsymbol{A})$ and $\boldsymbol{b} \in \mathcal{C}(\boldsymbol{B})$, we can write $\boldsymbol{P}_X$ as $\boldsymbol{P}_\mu + \boldsymbol{P}_\tau + \boldsymbol{P}_\beta + \boldsymbol{P}\gamma$, where

$$\begin{aligned}
\boldsymbol{P}_\mu &= \boldsymbol{P}_a \otimes \boldsymbol{P}_b,\\
\boldsymbol{P}_\tau &= (\boldsymbol{P}_A - \boldsymbol{P}_a) \otimes \boldsymbol{P}_b,\\
\boldsymbol{P}_\beta &= \boldsymbol{P}_a \otimes (\boldsymbol{P}_B - \boldsymbol{P}_b),\\
\boldsymbol{P}_\gamma &= (\boldsymbol{P}_A - \boldsymbol{P}_a) \otimes (\boldsymbol{P}_B - \boldsymbol{P}_b).
\end{aligned}$$

Thus, $\boldsymbol{P}_X = \boldsymbol{P}_A \otimes \boldsymbol{P}_B$ and $\boldsymbol{I} - \boldsymbol{P}_X = (\boldsymbol{I} - \boldsymbol{P}_A) \otimes (\boldsymbol{I} - \boldsymbol{P}_B)$. It is easy to see that the column spaces of $\boldsymbol{I} - \boldsymbol{P}_X$, $\boldsymbol{P}_\mu$, $\boldsymbol{P}_\tau$, $\boldsymbol{P}_\beta$ and $\boldsymbol{P}_\gamma$ are orthogonal to one another. Thus, $\boldsymbol{P}_\mu\boldsymbol{y}$, $\boldsymbol{P}_\tau\boldsymbol{y}$, $\boldsymbol{P}_\beta\boldsymbol{y}$ and $\boldsymbol{P}_\gamma\boldsymbol{y}$ are uncorrelated with all LZFs, and must be the BLUEs of their respective expected values. The vector of fitted values can be decomposed into the uncorrelated BLUEs

$$\boldsymbol{P}_X\boldsymbol{y} = \boldsymbol{P}_\mu\boldsymbol{y} + \boldsymbol{P}_\tau\boldsymbol{y} + \boldsymbol{P}_\beta\boldsymbol{y} + \boldsymbol{P}_\gamma\boldsymbol{y}.$$

This decomposition would lead to an ANOVA table. In order to obtain simple expressions of the constituent terms, we decompose the element of $\boldsymbol{P}_X\boldsymbol{y}$ corresponding to $y_{ik_1jk_2}$ as

$$\widehat{y}_{ik_1jk_2} = \overline{y}_{....} + (\overline{y}_{i...} - \overline{y}_{....}) + (\overline{y}_{..j.} - \overline{y}_{....}) + (\overline{y}_{i\cdot j\cdot} - \overline{y}_{i...} - \overline{y}_{..j.} + \overline{y}_{....}).$$

The corresponding residual is

$$e_{ik_1jk_2} = y_{ik_1jk_2} - \widehat{y}_{ik_1jk_2} = y_{ik_1jk_2} - \overline{y}_{i\cdot j\cdot}.$$

Note that averaging over k_1 and k_2 always occur together. We can merge these two indices and go back to the arrangement of observations given in (6.37). In summary, we have,

$$\begin{aligned}
\widehat{y}_{ijk} &= \overline{y}_{...} + (\overline{y}_{i..} - \overline{y}_{...}) + (\overline{y}_{.j.} - \overline{y}_{...}) + (\overline{y}_{ij.} - \overline{y}_{i..} - \overline{y}_{.j.} + \overline{y}_{...}),\\
e_{ijk} &= y_{ijk} - \overline{y}_{ij.}.
\end{aligned}$$

as per the notation of (6.37). The four terms in the decomposition of $\widehat{y}_{ijk}$

have the same interpretation as those in (6.31), with

$$\bar{\tau} = \sum_i m_i\tau_i / \sum_i m_i,$$
$$\bar{\beta} = \sum_j n_j\beta_j / \sum_j n_j,$$
$$\bar{\gamma}_{\cdot i} = \sum_j n_j\gamma_{ij} / \sum_j n_j,$$
$$\bar{\gamma}_{j\cdot} = \sum_i m_i\gamma_{ij} / \sum_i m_i,$$
$$\bar{\gamma}_{\cdot\cdot} = \sum_i\sum_j m_i n_j\gamma_{ij} / \sum_i\sum_j m_i n_j.$$

The sum of squares are as follows:

Between treatments, $S_\tau = \sum_{i=1}^{t}\sum_{j=1}^{b} m_i n_j (\overline{y}_{i\cdot\cdot} - \overline{y}_{\cdot\cdot\cdot})^2,$

Between blocks, $S_\beta = \sum_{i=1}^{t}\sum_{j=1}^{b} m_i n_j (\overline{y}_{\cdot j\cdot} - \overline{y}_{\cdot\cdot\cdot})^2,$

Interaction, $S_\gamma = \sum_{i=1}^{t}\sum_{j=1}^{b} m_i n_j (\overline{y}_{ij\cdot} - \overline{y}_{i\cdot\cdot} - \overline{y}_{\cdot j\cdot} + \overline{y}_{\cdot\cdot\cdot})^2,$

Error, $R_0^2 = \sum_{i=1}^{t}\sum_{j=1}^{b}\sum_{k=1}^{m_i n_j} (y_{ijk} - \overline{y}_{ij\cdot})^2,$

Total, $S_t = \sum_{i=1}^{t}\sum_{j=1}^{b}\sum_{k=1}^{m_i n_j} (y_{ijk} - \overline{y}_{\cdot\cdot\cdot})^2.$

The ANOVA of Table 6.8 continues to hold.

6.10 (a) y_a satisfies the equation $y_{kl} - \overline{y}_{k\cdot} - \overline{y}_{\cdot l} + \overline{y}_{\cdot\cdot} = 0$, which leads us to

$$y_a = \{(b-1)(t-1)\}^{-1}\left[\sum_{i\neq k} y_{il} + \sum_{j\neq l} y_{kj} - \sum\sum_{(i,j)\neq(k,l)} y_{ij}\right].$$

(b) y_b satisfies the equation $y_{kl} - \overline{y}_{\cdot l} = 0$, which leads us to

$$y_b = (t-1)^{-1}\sum_{i\neq k} y_{il}.$$

(c) The degrees of freedom for the above sums of squares decrease by 1 because of the missing observation. Using $R_0^2|_{y_{kl}=y_a}$ and $R_H^2|_{y_{kl}=y_b}$ in the expression of the GLRT, we have the F-statistic

$$\frac{\sum_i\sum_j(y_{ij}-\overline{y}_{.j})^2\Big|_{y_{kl}=y_b} - \sum_i\sum_j(y_{ij}-\overline{y}_{i.}-\overline{y}_{.j}+\overline{y}_{..})^2\Big|_{y_{kl}=y_a}}{\sum_i\sum_j(y_{ij}-\overline{y}_{i.}-\overline{y}_{.j}+\overline{y}_{..})^2\Big|_{y_{kl}=y_a}} \times \frac{n-t-b}{t-1}$$

with $t-1$ and $n-t-b$ degrees of freedom.

6.11 Here we have for $i=1,\ldots,t$, $j=1,\ldots,h$ and $k=1,\ldots,b$,

$$y_{ijk} = \mu + \tau_i + \theta_j + \beta_k + \varepsilon_{ijk}.$$

If we let $\boldsymbol{\beta} = (\mu : \tau_1 : \cdots : \tau_t : \theta_1 : \cdots : \theta_h : \beta_1 : \cdots : \beta_b)'$, and arrange the data so that k changes faster than j which changes faster than i, then the design matrix is

$$\boldsymbol{X} = (\mathbf{1}_t \otimes \mathbf{1}_h \otimes \mathbf{1}_b : \boldsymbol{I}_{t\times t} \otimes \mathbf{1}_h \otimes \mathbf{1}_b : \mathbf{1}_t \otimes \boldsymbol{I}_{h\times h} \otimes \mathbf{1}_b : \mathbf{1}_t \otimes \mathbf{1}_h \otimes \boldsymbol{I}_{b\times b}).$$

(We write $\mathbf{1}_{t\times 1}$ as $\mathbf{1}_t$ for brevity.) The relevant projection matrices are

$$\begin{aligned}
\boldsymbol{P}_\mu &= \boldsymbol{P}_{1_t} \otimes \boldsymbol{P}_{1_h} \otimes \boldsymbol{P}_{1_b},\\
\boldsymbol{P}_\tau &= (\boldsymbol{I} - \boldsymbol{P}_{1_t}) \otimes \boldsymbol{P}_{1_h} \otimes \boldsymbol{P}_{1_b},\\
\boldsymbol{P}_\theta &= \boldsymbol{P}_{1_t} \otimes (\boldsymbol{I} - \boldsymbol{P}_{1_h}) \otimes \boldsymbol{P}_{1_b},\\
\boldsymbol{P}_\mu &= \boldsymbol{P}_{1_t} \otimes \boldsymbol{P}_{1_h} \otimes (\boldsymbol{I} - \boldsymbol{P}_{1_b}),\\
\boldsymbol{P}_e &= \boldsymbol{I} - \boldsymbol{P}_\mu - \boldsymbol{P}_\tau - \boldsymbol{P}_\theta - \boldsymbol{P}_\beta.
\end{aligned}$$

The sum of squares are

$$\begin{aligned}
S_\tau &= hb\sum_{i=1}^{t}(\overline{y}_{i..} - \overline{y}_{...})^2,\\
S_\theta &= tb\sum_{j=1}^{t}(\overline{y}_{.j.} - \overline{y}_{...})^2,\\
S_\tau &= th\sum_{k=1}^{b}(\overline{y}_{..k} - \overline{y}_{...})^2,\\
R_0^2 &= \sum_{i=1}^{t}\sum_{j=1}^{t}\sum_{k=1}^{b}(y_{ijk} - \overline{y}_{i..} - \overline{y}_{.j.} - \overline{y}_{..k} + 2\overline{y}_{...})^2,\\
S_t &= \sum_{i=1}^{t}\sum_{j=1}^{t}\sum_{k=1}^{b}(y_{ijk} - \overline{y}_{...})^2.
\end{aligned}$$

The ANOVA is given in Table C.4.

Table C.4 ANOVA for Exercise 6.11

Source	Sum of Squares	Degrees of Freedom	Mean Square
Between treatments	$S_\mathcal{T}$	$t-1$	$MS_\mathcal{T} = \dfrac{S_\mathcal{T}}{t-1}$
Between type I blocks	S_θ	$h-1$	$MS_\theta = \dfrac{S_\theta}{h-1}$
Between type II blocks	S_β	$b-1$	$MS_\beta = \dfrac{S_\beta}{b-1}$
Error	R_0^2	ν *	$MS_e = \dfrac{R_0^2}{\nu}$
Total	S_t	$thb-1$	

6.12 As the index i is completely determined by the indices j and k, we can ignore it and arrange the observations by the latter indices as

$$\boldsymbol{y} = (y_{111}:\cdots:y_{b1b} : y_{221}:\cdots:y_{12b} : \cdots\cdots : y_{bb1}:\cdots:y_{(b-1)bb})'.$$

If $\boldsymbol{\beta} = (\mu_0 : \tau_1 : \cdots : \tau_b : \beta_1 : \cdots : \beta_b : \gamma_1 : \cdots : \gamma_b)'$, then the corresponding $\boldsymbol{X}$ matrix has the form specified in part (a). Part (b) is easily verified. To prove part (c), decompose $\boldsymbol{P}_X$ as $\boldsymbol{P}_\mu + \boldsymbol{P}_\tau + \boldsymbol{P}_\beta + \boldsymbol{P}_\gamma$, where

$$\begin{aligned}
\boldsymbol{P}_\mu &= \boldsymbol{P}_{1_{b\times b}} \otimes \boldsymbol{P}_{1_{b\times b}},\\
\boldsymbol{P}_\tau &= \boldsymbol{P}_{Z-b^{-1}1_{b\times 1}\otimes 1_{b\times 1}1'_{b\times 1}},\\
\boldsymbol{P}_\beta &= (\boldsymbol{I}_{b\times b} - \boldsymbol{P}_{1_{b\times b}}) \otimes \boldsymbol{P}_{1_{b\times b}},\\
\boldsymbol{P}_\gamma &= \boldsymbol{P}_{1_{b\times b}} \otimes (\boldsymbol{I}_{b\times b} - \boldsymbol{P}_{1_{b\times b}}).
\end{aligned}$$

The sums of squares for the two block effects are

$$S_\beta = \|\boldsymbol{P}_\beta \boldsymbol{y}\|^2 = b\sum_{j=1}^{b}(\overline{y}_{\cdot j \cdot} - \overline{y}_{\dots})^2,$$

$$S_\gamma = \|\boldsymbol{P}_\gamma \boldsymbol{y}\|^2 = b\sum_{k=1}^{b}(\overline{y}_{\cdot\cdot k} - \overline{y}_{\dots})^2,$$

By symmetry of the design in the three factors, the treatment sum of squares is

$$S_\tau = b\sum_{i=1}^{b}(\overline{y}_{i\cdot\cdot} - \overline{y}_{\dots})^2,$$

with $b-1$ degrees of freedom. This leads us to the ANOVA of Table C.5.

Table C.5 ANOVA for Exercise 6.12

Source	Sum of Squares	Degrees of Freedom	Mean Square
Between treatments	$S_\tau = b\sum_{i=1}^{b}(\overline{y}_{i..} - \overline{y}_{...})^2$	$b-1$	$MS_\tau = \dfrac{S_\tau}{b-1}$
Between blocks type I	$S_\beta = b\sum_{j=1}^{b}(\overline{y}_{.j.} - \overline{y}_{...})^2$	$b-1$	$MS_\beta = \dfrac{S_\beta}{b-1}$
Between blocks type II	$S_\gamma = b\sum_{k=1}^{b}(\overline{y}_{..k} - \overline{y}_{...})^2$	$b-1$	$MS_\gamma = \dfrac{S_\gamma}{b-1}$
Error	$R_0^2 = S_t - S_\tau - S_\beta - S_\gamma$	$(b-1) \times (b-2)$	$MS_e = \dfrac{S_e}{(b-1)(b-2)}$
Total	$S_t = \sum_{j=1}^{b}\sum_{k=1}^{b}(y_{ijk} - \overline{y}_{...})^2$	b^2-1	

6.13 The model is

$$y_{ijkl} = \mu + \tau_i + \beta_j + \gamma_{ik} + \varepsilon_{ijkl},$$

for $i = 1, \ldots, t$, $j = 1, \ldots, b$, $k = 1, \ldots, d$ and $l = 1, \ldots, m$, where γ_{ik} is the effect of the kth dose level of the ith drug.

If $\boldsymbol{\beta} = (\mu : \tau_1 : \cdots : \tau_t : \beta_1 : \cdots : \beta_b : \gamma_{11} : \cdots \gamma_{1d} : \cdots : \gamma_{t1} : \cdots : \gamma_{td})'$, and the indices i, k, j and l change successively faster, then the design matrix can be written as

$$\boldsymbol{X} = (\mathbf{1}_t \otimes \mathbf{1}_d \otimes \mathbf{1}_b : \boldsymbol{I}_{t\times t} \otimes \mathbf{1}_d \otimes \mathbf{1}_b : \mathbf{1}_t \otimes \mathbf{1}_d \otimes \boldsymbol{I}_{b\times b} : \boldsymbol{I}_{t\times t} \otimes \boldsymbol{I}_{d\times d} \otimes \mathbf{1}_b) \otimes \mathbf{1}_m.$$

(We write $\mathbf{1}_{t\times 1}$ as $\mathbf{1}_t$ here for the sake of brevity.) The projection matrices are

$$\boldsymbol{P}_\mu = \boldsymbol{P}_{\mathbf{1}_t} \otimes \boldsymbol{P}_{\mathbf{1}_d} \otimes \boldsymbol{P}_{\mathbf{1}_b} \otimes \boldsymbol{P}_{\mathbf{1}_m},$$

$$\boldsymbol{P}_\tau = (\boldsymbol{I} - \boldsymbol{P}_{\mathbf{1}_t}) \otimes \boldsymbol{P}_{\mathbf{1}_d} \otimes \boldsymbol{P}_{\mathbf{1}_b} \otimes \boldsymbol{P}_{\mathbf{1}_m},$$

$$\boldsymbol{P}_\beta = \boldsymbol{P}_{\mathbf{1}_t} \otimes \boldsymbol{P}_{\mathbf{1}_d} \otimes (\boldsymbol{I} - \boldsymbol{P}_{\mathbf{1}_b}) \otimes \boldsymbol{P}_{\mathbf{1}_m},$$

$$\boldsymbol{P}_\gamma = \boldsymbol{I}_{t\times t} \otimes (\boldsymbol{I} - \boldsymbol{P}_{\mathbf{1}_d}) \otimes \boldsymbol{P}_{\mathbf{1}_b} \otimes \boldsymbol{P}_{\mathbf{1}_m},$$

$$\boldsymbol{P}_e = \boldsymbol{I} - [\boldsymbol{I}_{t\times t} \otimes \boldsymbol{I}_{d\times d} \otimes \boldsymbol{P}_{\mathbf{1}_b} + \boldsymbol{P}_{\mathbf{1}_t} \otimes \boldsymbol{P}_{\mathbf{1}_d} \otimes (\boldsymbol{I} - \boldsymbol{P}_{\mathbf{1}_b})] \otimes \boldsymbol{P}_{\mathbf{1}_m}.$$

Table C.6 ANOVA for Exercise 6.13

Source	Sum of Squares	Degrees of Freedom	Mean Square
Between drugs	S_τ	$t-1$	$MS_\tau = \dfrac{S_\tau}{t-1}$
Between doses	S_γ	$t(d-1)$	$MS_\gamma = \dfrac{S_\gamma}{t(d-1)}$
Between blocks	S_β	$b-1$	$MS_\beta = \dfrac{S_\beta}{b-1}$
Error	R_0^2	$tdbm - td - b + 1$	$MS_e = \dfrac{R_0^2}{tdbm - td - b + 1}$
Total	S_t	$tdbm-1$	

The sum of squares are

$$S_\tau = dbm\sum_{i=1}^{t}(\overline{y}_{i\cdots} - \overline{y}_{\cdots\cdot})^2,$$

$$S_\gamma = bm\sum_{i=1}^{t}\sum_{k=1}^{d}(\overline{y}_{i\cdot k\cdot} - \overline{y}_{i\cdots})^2,$$

$$S_\beta = tdm\sum_{j=1}^{b}(\overline{y}_{\cdot j\cdot\cdot} - \overline{y}_{\cdots\cdot})^2,$$

$$R_0^2 = \sum_{i=1}^{t}\sum_{j=1}^{b}\sum_{k=1}^{d}\sum_{l=1}^{m}(y_{ijkl} - \overline{y}_{\cdot j\cdot\cdot} - \overline{y}_{i\cdot k\cdot} + \overline{y}_{i\cdots})^2,$$

$$S_t = \sum_{i=1}^{t}\sum_{j=1}^{b}\sum_{k=1}^{d}\sum_{l=1}^{m}(y_{ijkl} - \overline{y}_{\cdots\cdot})^2$$

The ANOVA is given in Table C.6.

6.14 From (6.43) we have $\widehat{\eta} = \boldsymbol{z}'(\boldsymbol{I} - \boldsymbol{P}_X)\boldsymbol{y}/\boldsymbol{z}'(\boldsymbol{I} - \boldsymbol{P}_X)\boldsymbol{z}$, that is,

$$\widehat{\eta} = \frac{\sum_i\sum_j(c_{ij} - \bar{z}_{i\cdot} - \bar{z}_{\cdot j} + \bar{z}_{\cdot\cdot})(y_{ij} - \overline{y}_{i\cdot} - \overline{y}_{\cdot j} + \overline{y}_{\cdot\cdot})}{\sum_i\sum_j(z_{ij} - \bar{z}_{i\cdot} - \bar{z}_{\cdot j} + \bar{z}_{\cdot\cdot})^2}.$$

It follows from Remark 6.14 that $\boldsymbol{X}\widehat{\boldsymbol{\beta}} = \boldsymbol{X}\widehat{\boldsymbol{\beta}}_0 - \widehat{\eta}\widehat{\boldsymbol{X}\boldsymbol{\alpha}}$, where the elements of $\boldsymbol{X}\widehat{\boldsymbol{\beta}}_0$ and $\widehat{\boldsymbol{X}\boldsymbol{\alpha}}$ corresponding to y_{ij} are $\overline{y}_{i\cdot} + \overline{y}_{\cdot j} - \overline{y}_{\cdot\cdot}$ and $\bar{z}_{i\cdot} + \bar{z}_{\cdot j} - \bar{z}_{\cdot\cdot}$, respectively. Thus, the fitted value of y_{ij} is $(\overline{y}_{i\cdot}+\overline{y}_{\cdot j}-\overline{y}_{\cdot\cdot})+\widehat{\eta}(z_{ij}-\bar{z}_{i\cdot}-\bar{z}_{\cdot j}+\bar{z}_{\cdot\cdot})$.

The variance of $\widehat{\eta}$ is

$$Var(\widehat{\eta}) = \frac{\sigma^2}{\boldsymbol{z}'(\boldsymbol{I}-\boldsymbol{P}_X)\boldsymbol{z}} = \frac{\sigma^2}{\sum_i\sum_j(z_{ij}-\bar{z}_{i\cdot}-\bar{z}_{\cdot j}+\bar{z}_{\cdot\cdot})^2}.$$

As $\boldsymbol{X}\widehat{\boldsymbol{\beta}}_0$ and $\widehat{\eta}$ are uncorrelated, we have

$$\begin{aligned} D(\boldsymbol{X}\widehat{\boldsymbol{\beta}}) &= D(\boldsymbol{X}\widehat{\boldsymbol{\beta}}_0) + D(\widehat{\boldsymbol{X}\boldsymbol{\alpha}\eta}) \\ &= \sigma^2\left[\boldsymbol{P}_X + \frac{\widehat{\boldsymbol{X}\boldsymbol{\alpha}}\widehat{\boldsymbol{X}\boldsymbol{\alpha}}'}{\boldsymbol{z}'(\boldsymbol{I}-\boldsymbol{P}_X)\boldsymbol{z}}\right]. \end{aligned}$$

The element of this matrix corresponding to the pair y_{ij} and y_{kl} is σ^2 times

$$\frac{1}{n} + \left(\delta_{ik}-\frac{1}{t}\right)\frac{1}{b} + \left(\delta_{jl}-\frac{1}{b}\right)\frac{1}{t} + \frac{(\bar{z}_{i\cdot}+\bar{z}_{\cdot j}-\bar{z}_{\cdot\cdot})(\bar{z}_{k\cdot}+\bar{z}_{\cdot l}-\bar{z}_{\cdot\cdot})}{\sum_i\sum_j(z_{ij}-\bar{z}_{i\cdot}-\bar{z}_{\cdot j}+\bar{z}_{\cdot\cdot})^2},$$

where $\delta_{ij} = 1$ when $i = j$ and 0 otherwise.

6.15 Following (6.42), we have

$$\begin{pmatrix} R^2_{0\beta} & \boldsymbol{r}' \\ \boldsymbol{r} & \boldsymbol{R} \end{pmatrix} = \begin{pmatrix} \boldsymbol{y}'(\boldsymbol{I}-\boldsymbol{P}_X)\boldsymbol{y} & \boldsymbol{y}'(\boldsymbol{I}-\boldsymbol{P}_X)\boldsymbol{z} \\ \boldsymbol{z}'(\boldsymbol{I}-\boldsymbol{P}_X)\boldsymbol{y} & \boldsymbol{z}'(\boldsymbol{I}-\boldsymbol{P}_X)\boldsymbol{z} \end{pmatrix},$$

where $\boldsymbol{I}-\boldsymbol{P}_X = (\boldsymbol{I}-\boldsymbol{P}_{1_{t\times1}})\otimes(\boldsymbol{I}-\boldsymbol{P}_{1_{b\times1}})$. Under the null hypothesis we can ignore the effect of the treatments, so that $\boldsymbol{I}-\boldsymbol{P}_{X(I-P_{A'})} = (\boldsymbol{I}-\boldsymbol{P}_{1_{t\times1}})\otimes\boldsymbol{I}_{b\times b}$. We have from (6.49)

$$\begin{pmatrix} R^2_{H\beta} & \boldsymbol{r}'_H \\ \boldsymbol{r}_H & \boldsymbol{R}_H \end{pmatrix} = \begin{pmatrix} \boldsymbol{y}'(\boldsymbol{I}-\boldsymbol{P}_{X(I-P_{A'})})\boldsymbol{y} & \boldsymbol{y}'(\boldsymbol{I}-\boldsymbol{P}_{X(I-P_{A'})})\boldsymbol{z} \\ \boldsymbol{z}'(\boldsymbol{I}-\boldsymbol{P}_{X(I-P_{A'})})\boldsymbol{y} & \boldsymbol{z}'(\boldsymbol{I}-\boldsymbol{P}_{X(I-P_{A'})})\boldsymbol{z} \end{pmatrix}.$$

Further, from (6.47) and (6.48) the sums of squares corrected for covariates are

$$\begin{aligned} R_0^2 &= \boldsymbol{y}'(\boldsymbol{I}-\boldsymbol{P}_X)\boldsymbol{y} - \frac{[\boldsymbol{y}'(\boldsymbol{I}-\boldsymbol{P}_X)\boldsymbol{z}]^2}{\boldsymbol{z}'(\boldsymbol{I}-\boldsymbol{P}_X)\boldsymbol{z}} \\ &= \sum_i\sum_j(y_{ij}-\bar{y}_{i\cdot}-\bar{y}_{\cdot j}+\bar{y}_{\cdot\cdot})^2 \\ &\quad - \frac{\left[\sum_i\sum_j(z_{ij}-\bar{z}_{i\cdot}-\bar{z}_{\cdot j}+\bar{z}_{\cdot\cdot})(y_{ij}-\bar{y}_{i\cdot}-\bar{y}_{\cdot j}+\bar{y}_{\cdot\cdot})\right]^2}{\sum_i\sum_j(z_{ij}-\bar{z}_{i\cdot}-\bar{z}_{\cdot j}+\bar{z}_{\cdot\cdot})^2}, \end{aligned}$$

$$R_H^2 = y'(I - P_{X(I-P_{A'})})y - \frac{[y'(I - P_{X(I-P_{A'})})z]^2}{z'(I - P_{X(I-P_{A'})})z}$$
$$= \sum_i \sum_j (y_{ij} - \bar{y}_{\cdot j})^2 - \frac{\left[\sum_i \sum_j (z_{ij} - \bar{z}_{\cdot j})(y_{ij} - \bar{y}_{\cdot j})\right]^2}{\sum_i \sum_j (z_{ij} - \bar{z}_{\cdot j})^2}.$$

It is clear that in this case $\rho(X : z) = \rho(X) + \rho(z)$. Hence, the degrees of freedom associated with R_0^2 and R_H^2 are $n-t-b$ and $n-b-1$, respectively. The GLRT would reject the null hypothesis for large values of the statistic $\frac{R_H^2 - R_0^2}{R_0^2} \cdot \frac{n-t-b}{t-1}$, whose null distribution is $F_{t-1,n-t-b}$.

6.16 Suppose the matrices S_τ, S_β, S_e and S_t are obtained from the matrix

$$\begin{pmatrix} y'Py & y'Pz \\ z'Py & z'Pz \end{pmatrix},$$

by replacing P with $P_\tau = (I - P_{1_{t\times 1}}) \otimes P_{1_{b\times 1}}$, $P_\beta = P_{1_{t\times 1}} \otimes (I - P_{1_{b\times 1}})$, $P_e = (I - P_{1_{t\times 1}}) \otimes (I - P_{1_{b\times 1}})$ and $P_t = I - P_{1_{t\times 1}} \otimes P_{1_{b\times 1}}$, respectively. Then the ANCOVA is given in Table C.7.

Table C.7 ANCOVA of Exercise 6.16

Source	Sum of Squares and products	Degrees of Freedom
Between treatments	$S_\tau = (y : z)'P_\tau(y : z)$	$t-1$
Between blocks	$S_\beta = (y : z)'P_\beta(y : z)$	$b-1$
Error	$S_e = (y : z)'P_e(y : z)$	$(t-1)(b-1)$
Total	$S_t = (y : z)'P_t(y : z)$	$n-1$

6.17 We only have to simplify the GLRT described in the solution of Exercise 6.15. Here,

$$z_{ij} = \begin{cases} 1 & \text{if } i = k,\ j = l, \\ 0 & \text{otherwise,} \end{cases} \quad \bar{z}_{i\cdot} = \begin{cases} \frac{1}{b} & \text{if } i = k, \\ 0 & \text{otherwise,} \end{cases}$$

$$\bar{z}_{\cdot j} = \begin{cases} \frac{1}{t} & \text{if } j = l, \\ 0 & \text{otherwise,} \end{cases} \quad \bar{z}_{\cdot\cdot} = \frac{1}{tb}.$$

Therefore, we have the simplifications

$$R_0^2 = \sum_i \sum_j (y_{ij} - \overline{y}_{i.} - \overline{y}_{.j} + \overline{y}_{..})^2 - \frac{tb(y_{kl} - \overline{y}_{k.} - \overline{y}_{.l} + \overline{y}_{..})^2}{(t-1)(b-1)},$$

$$R_H^2 = \sum_i \sum_j (y_{ij} - \overline{y}_{.j})^2 - \frac{t(y_{kl} - \overline{y}_{.l})^2}{t-1}.$$

The GLRT statistic is $\frac{R_H^2 - R_0^2}{R_0^2} \cdot \frac{n-t-b}{t-1}$, which simplifies to

$$\frac{b\sum_{i=1}^{t}(\overline{y}_{i.} - \overline{y}_{..})^2 + \frac{tb(y_{kl}-\overline{y}_{k.}-\overline{y}_{.l}+\overline{y}_{..})^2}{(t-1)(b-1)} - \frac{t(y_{kl}-\overline{y}_{.l})^2}{t-1}}{\sum_i\sum_j(y_{ij}-\overline{y}_{i.}-\overline{y}_{.j}+\overline{y}_{..})^2 - \frac{tb(y_{kl}-\overline{y}_{k.}-\overline{y}_{.l}+\overline{y}_{..})^2}{(t-1)(b-1)}} \cdot \frac{n-t-b}{t-1},$$

and its null distribution is $F_{t-1,n-t-b}$.

6.18 The derivative of the GLRT with respect to y_{kl} turns out to be 0, so it does not matter which value of y_{kl} is used. This is only to be expected, since the covariate effectively removes the observation y_{kl} — as mentioned in Section 6.3.4. This test is in fact the GLRT for the hypothesis of 'no difference of treatment effects' in the case of unbalanced data, the lack of balance being only due to the unavailability of y_{kl}.

6.19 (a) When $y_{kl} = y_a$, the covariate correction term vanishes.
(b) The covariate-corrected R_H^2 at $y_{kl} = y_a$ simplifies as follows.

$$\begin{aligned}
&\sum_i\sum_j (y_{ij} - \overline{y}_{.j})^2 - t(y_a - \overline{y}_{.l})^2/(t-1) \\
&= \sum_i\sum_{j\neq l}(y_{ij} - \overline{y}_{.j})^2 + \sum_{i\neq k}\left(y_{il} - \frac{(t-1)y_b + y_a}{t}\right)^2 \\
&\quad - (t-1)^{-1}\left(y_a - \frac{(t-1)y_b + y_a}{t}\right)^2 \\
&= \sum_i\sum_{j\neq l}(y_{ij} - \overline{y}_{.j})^2 + \sum_{i\neq k}(y_{il} - y_b)^2 = \sum_i\sum_j (y_{ij} - \overline{y}_{.j})^2 \,|_{y_{kl}=y_b}\,.
\end{aligned}$$

(c) It is clear from parts (a) and (b) that the value of the test statistic of Exercise 6.17 at $y_{kl} = y_a$ is the same as the test statistic of Exercise 6.10. However, it was shown in Exercise 6.18 that the test statistic of Exercise 6.17 does not depend on y_{kl}. This proves the result.

Chapter 7

7.1 It was shown after (7.1) that the BLUE of an estimable LPF $\boldsymbol{A\beta}$ is $\boldsymbol{AX}^{-}\widehat{\boldsymbol{y}}$. Further, any LZF $\boldsymbol{B}(\boldsymbol{I}-\boldsymbol{P}_X)\boldsymbol{y}$ can be written as $\boldsymbol{B}(\boldsymbol{I}-\boldsymbol{P}_X)\boldsymbol{e}$; see (7.3).

7.2 Let $\boldsymbol{CC}'$ be a rank-factorization of $\boldsymbol{V}$ and $\boldsymbol{G}$ be a left-inverse of $\boldsymbol{C}$. Consider the model equations

$$\begin{aligned}\boldsymbol{y} &= \boldsymbol{X\beta}+\boldsymbol{\varepsilon},\\ \boldsymbol{Gy} &= \boldsymbol{GX\beta}+\boldsymbol{G\varepsilon}.\end{aligned}$$

As $\mathcal{C}(\boldsymbol{X})\subseteq\mathcal{C}(\boldsymbol{V})$, all the terms of the first equation are in $\mathcal{C}(\boldsymbol{C})$. Hence, the first equation is obtained from the second by premultiplying all the terms by $\boldsymbol{C}$. Thus the two model equations are equivalent. Let $\boldsymbol{y}_*=\boldsymbol{Gy}$, $\boldsymbol{X}_*=\boldsymbol{GX}$ and $\boldsymbol{\varepsilon}_*=\boldsymbol{G\varepsilon}$. It is clear that $E(\boldsymbol{\varepsilon}_*)=\boldsymbol{0}$ and $D(\boldsymbol{\varepsilon}_*)=\sigma^2\boldsymbol{I}$, and the given model holds for $\boldsymbol{y}_*$.

7.3 If $(\boldsymbol{y},\boldsymbol{X\beta},\sigma^2\boldsymbol{V})$ is the model for $\boldsymbol{y}$, then $(\boldsymbol{C}^{-1}\boldsymbol{y},\boldsymbol{C}^{-1}\boldsymbol{X\beta},\sigma^2\boldsymbol{I})$ is the equivalent model for $\boldsymbol{C}^{-1}\boldsymbol{y}$. The BLUE of $\boldsymbol{A\beta}$ obtained from the latter (homoscedastic) model is

$$\begin{aligned}\widehat{\boldsymbol{A\beta}} &= \boldsymbol{A}[(\boldsymbol{C}^{-1}\boldsymbol{X})'(\boldsymbol{C}^{-1}\boldsymbol{X})]^{-}(\boldsymbol{C}^{-1}\boldsymbol{X})'(\boldsymbol{C}^{-1}\boldsymbol{y})\\ &= \boldsymbol{A}(\boldsymbol{X}'\boldsymbol{V}^{-1}\boldsymbol{X})^{-}\boldsymbol{X}'\boldsymbol{V}^{-1}\boldsymbol{y},\end{aligned}$$

and its dispersion is

$$\sigma^2\boldsymbol{A}[(\boldsymbol{C}^{-1}\boldsymbol{X})'(\boldsymbol{C}^{-1}\boldsymbol{X})]^{-}\boldsymbol{A}'=\sigma^2\boldsymbol{A}(\boldsymbol{X}'\boldsymbol{V}^{-1}\boldsymbol{X})^{-}\boldsymbol{A}'.$$

7.4 The result holds trivially when $Var(\widehat{\boldsymbol{p}'\boldsymbol{\beta}_{LU}})=0$, i.e. when $\widehat{\boldsymbol{p}'\boldsymbol{\beta}_{LU}}$ is almost surely a constant. Let $Var(\widehat{\boldsymbol{p}'\boldsymbol{\beta}_{LU}})>0$. Let $\boldsymbol{By}$ be a vector whose elements constitute a generating set of LZFs, and write $\widehat{\boldsymbol{p}'\boldsymbol{\beta}_{LU}}$ as $\boldsymbol{p}'\widehat{\boldsymbol{\beta}}+\boldsymbol{l}'\boldsymbol{By}$. Then

$$\begin{aligned}1-\eta_p &= 1-\frac{Var(\boldsymbol{p}'\widehat{\boldsymbol{\beta}})}{Var(\boldsymbol{p}'\widehat{\boldsymbol{\beta}})+Var(\boldsymbol{l}'\boldsymbol{By})}=\frac{Var(\boldsymbol{l}'\boldsymbol{By})}{Var(\widehat{\boldsymbol{p}'\boldsymbol{\beta}_{LU}})}\\ &= \frac{Cov(\boldsymbol{l}'\boldsymbol{By},\boldsymbol{By})[D(\boldsymbol{By})]^{-}Cov(\boldsymbol{By},\boldsymbol{l}'\boldsymbol{By})}{Var(\widehat{\boldsymbol{p}'\boldsymbol{\beta}_{LU}})}\\ &= \frac{Cov(\widehat{\boldsymbol{p}'\boldsymbol{\beta}_{LU}},\boldsymbol{By})[D(\boldsymbol{By})]^{-}Cov(\boldsymbol{By},\widehat{\boldsymbol{p}'\boldsymbol{\beta}_{LU}})}{Var(\widehat{\boldsymbol{p}'\boldsymbol{\beta}_{LU}})},\end{aligned}$$

which is the squared multiple correlation coefficient of $\widehat{\boldsymbol{p}'\boldsymbol{\beta}_{LU}}$ with $\boldsymbol{By}$ (see (2.21)). The notion of efficiency used here is equivalent to the definition given on page 627, when the error is normally distributed. If the error has a symmetric non-normal distribution satisfying the conditions of Exercise 7.14, then the correct expression for efficiency is equal to the given expression times $\sigma^2\mathcal{I}_\mu$, where $\mathcal{I}_\mu$ is as defined in Exercise 3.26.

7.5 The expression for $D(\widehat{\boldsymbol{y}}_*)$ follows from Proposition 7.32. The relation $D(\widehat{\boldsymbol{y}}) \le D(\widehat{\boldsymbol{y}}_*)$ follows from Proposition 7.30(b). As $D(\widehat{\boldsymbol{y}}_*) - D(\widehat{\boldsymbol{y}}) = \sigma^2 \boldsymbol{XUX}'$, equality holds if and only if $\boldsymbol{XUX}' = \boldsymbol{0}$, i.e. $\mathcal{C}(\boldsymbol{X}) \subseteq \mathcal{C}(\boldsymbol{V})$.

7.6 If $\boldsymbol{z}$ is a vector of LZFs whose elements constitute a generating set, and $\boldsymbol{CC}'$ is a rank-factorization of $\sigma^{-2}D(\boldsymbol{z})$, then for every left-inverse C^{-L} of $\boldsymbol{C}$, the elements of the vector $\boldsymbol{C}^{-L}\boldsymbol{z}$ constitutes a standardized basis set of LZFs. This fact follows from the arguments of Exercise 3.13. Hence, $R_0^2 = \boldsymbol{z}'(\boldsymbol{C}^{-L})'\boldsymbol{C}^{-L}\boldsymbol{z} = \boldsymbol{z}[\sigma^{-2}D(\boldsymbol{z})]^-\boldsymbol{z}$ for any choice of the g-inverse in the latter expression.

7.7 Let $\boldsymbol{W} = \boldsymbol{V} + \boldsymbol{XUX}'$ where $\boldsymbol{U}$ is an arbitrary matrix of appropriate order. It is easy to see that the matrix $\boldsymbol{V}$ in the expression of $\boldsymbol{e}$ in (7.3) can be replaced by $\boldsymbol{W}$. Substituting this in $\boldsymbol{e}'\boldsymbol{Me}$, we have after simplification

$$\begin{aligned}\boldsymbol{e}'\boldsymbol{Me} &= \boldsymbol{y}'(\boldsymbol{I}-\boldsymbol{P_X})\{(\boldsymbol{I}-\boldsymbol{P_X})\boldsymbol{W}(\boldsymbol{I}-\boldsymbol{P_X})\}^-(\boldsymbol{I}-\boldsymbol{P_X})\boldsymbol{y}\\ &= \boldsymbol{y}'(\boldsymbol{I}-\boldsymbol{P_X})\{(\boldsymbol{I}-\boldsymbol{P_X})\boldsymbol{V}(\boldsymbol{I}-\boldsymbol{P_X})\}^-(\boldsymbol{I}-\boldsymbol{P_X})\boldsymbol{y},\end{aligned}$$

which is identical to the expression of R_0^2 given in (7.7).

7.8 Rank factorize $\boldsymbol{V}$ as $\boldsymbol{CC}'$ and $\boldsymbol{U}$ as $\boldsymbol{KK}'$. Then $\mathcal{C}(\boldsymbol{C}) \subseteq \mathcal{C}(\boldsymbol{C} : \boldsymbol{XK}) \subseteq \mathcal{C}(\boldsymbol{C} : \boldsymbol{X})$. This is equivalent to $\mathcal{C}(\boldsymbol{V}) \subseteq \mathcal{C}(\boldsymbol{V} + \boldsymbol{XUX}') \subseteq \mathcal{C}(\boldsymbol{V} : \boldsymbol{X})$.

7.9 From the result of Exercise 7.8, we have $\mathcal{C}(\boldsymbol{V}) \subseteq \mathcal{C}(\boldsymbol{W}) \subseteq \mathcal{C}(\boldsymbol{V} : \boldsymbol{X})$. Hence, the condition $\mathcal{C}(\boldsymbol{X}) \subseteq \mathcal{C}(\boldsymbol{W})$ implies $\mathcal{C}(\boldsymbol{V} : \boldsymbol{X}) = \mathcal{C}(\boldsymbol{W})$. The reverse implication is obvious. This proves the equivalence of (a) and (b). The equivalence of (a) and (c) follows from the inclusion $\mathcal{C}(\boldsymbol{W}) \subseteq \mathcal{C}(\boldsymbol{V} : \boldsymbol{X})$.

7.10 Let $\boldsymbol{U\Lambda U}'$ be a spectral decomposition of $\boldsymbol{X}'\boldsymbol{V}^{-1}\boldsymbol{X}$. Arrange the eigenvalues of $\boldsymbol{X}'\boldsymbol{V}^{-1}\boldsymbol{X}$ in the decreasing order, and partition the matrices $\boldsymbol{U}$ and $\boldsymbol{\Lambda}$ suitably so that

$$\boldsymbol{U\Lambda U}' = (\boldsymbol{U}_1 : \boldsymbol{U}_2)\begin{pmatrix}\boldsymbol{\Lambda}_1 & \boldsymbol{0}\\ \boldsymbol{0} & \boldsymbol{\Lambda}_2\end{pmatrix}\begin{pmatrix}\boldsymbol{U}_1'\\ \boldsymbol{U}_2'\end{pmatrix} = \boldsymbol{U}_1\boldsymbol{\Lambda}_1\boldsymbol{U}_1' + \boldsymbol{U}_2\boldsymbol{\Lambda}_2\boldsymbol{U}_2',$$

where the diagonal elements of $\boldsymbol{\Lambda}_2$ are small. Thus we have

$$\widehat{\boldsymbol{\gamma}}_{pc} = \begin{pmatrix}\boldsymbol{\Lambda}_1^{-1}\boldsymbol{Z}_1'\boldsymbol{V}^{-1}\boldsymbol{y}\\ \boldsymbol{0}\end{pmatrix}; \qquad \widehat{\boldsymbol{\beta}}_{pc} = \boldsymbol{U}\widehat{\boldsymbol{\gamma}}_{pc} = (\boldsymbol{U}_1\boldsymbol{\Lambda}_1^{-1}\boldsymbol{U}_1')\boldsymbol{X}'\boldsymbol{V}^{-1}\boldsymbol{y}.$$

This leads us to difference of MSEs similar to that given in page 257 and the similar conditions for superiority of the principal components estimator.

7.11 Let $\boldsymbol{u}_1 = \boldsymbol{P}_1'\boldsymbol{u}$ and $\boldsymbol{u}_2 = \boldsymbol{P}_2'\boldsymbol{u}$. Then $\boldsymbol{u}$ is the sum of the orthogonal vectors $\boldsymbol{P}_1\boldsymbol{u}_1$ and $\boldsymbol{P}_2\boldsymbol{u}_2$. The constraint $\boldsymbol{X\beta} + \boldsymbol{Fu} = \boldsymbol{y}$ is equivalent to $\boldsymbol{QX\beta} + \boldsymbol{QFu} = \boldsymbol{Qy}$, which can be rewritten as

$$\begin{pmatrix}\boldsymbol{Q}_1\boldsymbol{FP}_1 & \boldsymbol{0}\\ \boldsymbol{Q}_2\boldsymbol{FP}_1 & \boldsymbol{Q}_2\boldsymbol{X}\end{pmatrix}\begin{pmatrix}\boldsymbol{u}_1\\ \boldsymbol{\beta}\end{pmatrix} = \begin{pmatrix}\boldsymbol{Q}_1\boldsymbol{y}\\ \boldsymbol{Q}_2\boldsymbol{y} - \boldsymbol{Q}_2\boldsymbol{FP}_2\boldsymbol{u}_2\end{pmatrix},$$

in view of the facts $Q_1X = 0$ and $Q_1FP_2 = 0$. The matrix on the left-hand side has full column rank, and the equation is consistent (as $X\beta + Fu = y$ is consistent). Hence there is a solution to the above equation for every y and u_2. As Q_1FP_1 has full column rank, u_1 is uniquely determined by the first of the above two equations, $Q_1FP_1u_1 = Q_1y$. The objective function $\|u\|^2 = \|u_1\|^2 + \|u_2\|^2$ is thus minimized by setting $\|u_2\|^2 = 0$. Note that the matrix equations given above always have a solution, irrespective of the choice of u_2, as long as u_1 satisfies the first equation.

Comparing the dispersions of $Q_1FP_1\widehat{u}_1$ and Q_1y, we have

$$\begin{aligned} Q_1FP_1D(\widehat{u}_1)P_1'F'Q_1' &= \sigma^2Q_1FF'Q_1' = \sigma^2Q_1FPP'F'Q_1' \\ &= \sigma^2Q_1FP_1P_1'F'Q_1', \end{aligned}$$

as $Q_1FP_2 = 0$. Since Q_1FP_1 has a left-inverse, we have $D(\widehat{u}_1) = \sigma^2I$. Further, $\widehat{u}_1$ must be an LZF, as

$$E[(Q_1FP_1)^{-1}Q_1y] = (Q_1FP_1)^{-1}Q_1X\beta = 0.$$

$\widehat{u}_1$ has $\rho(V : X) - \rho(X)$ elements. Therefore, its elements must constitute a standardized basis set of LZFs.

Comparing the dispersions of the two sides of the equation $Q_2FP_1\widehat{u}_1 + Q_2X\widehat{\beta} = Q_2y$, we have

$$\sigma^2Q_2FP_1P_1'F'Q_2' + Q_2D(X\widehat{\beta})Q_2' = \sigma^2Q_2FPP'F'Q_2'.$$

Thus, $Q_2D(X\widehat{\beta})Q_2' = \sigma^2Q_2FP_2P_2'F'Q_2'$. This matrix has a left-inverse, since Q_2 has linearly independent columns. Hence, $D(X\widehat{\beta}) = \sigma^2FP_2P_2'F'$.

7.12 The condition $\mathcal{C}(W) = \mathcal{C}(V : X)$ ensures that the expressions of Proposition 7.30 do not depend on the choice of any of the g-inverses. It is easy to check that $E(X\widehat{\beta}_{WLS}) = X\beta$. The unbiased estimator $X\widehat{\beta}_{WLS}$ is uncorrelated with all LZFs, as

$$\begin{aligned} &Cov(X\widehat{\beta}_{WLS}, (I-P_X)y) \\ &= \sigma^2X(X'W^-X)^-X'W^-V(I-P_X) \\ &= \sigma^2X(X'W^-X)^-X'W^-W(I-P_X) = \sigma^2X(I-P_X) = 0. \end{aligned}$$

This proves part (a). To prove part (b), note that

$$\begin{aligned} &D(X\widehat{\beta}_{WLS}) \\ &= \sigma^2X(X'W^-X)^-X'W^-VW^-X(X'W^-X)^-X' \\ &= \sigma^2X(X'W^-X)^-X'W^-[W - XUX']W^-X(X'W^-X)^-X' \\ &= \sigma^2[X(X'W^-X)^-X' - XUX']. \end{aligned}$$

Parts (c) and (d) follow from Proposition 7.22.

7.13 Let CC' be a rank-factorization of V, C^{-L} be a left-inverse of C and F be a matrix such that $FV = 0$ and $\rho(F) = n - \rho(V)$. Then

$$\begin{pmatrix} C^{-L}y \\ Fy \end{pmatrix} \sim N\left(\begin{pmatrix} C^{-L}X\beta \\ 0 \end{pmatrix}, \sigma^2 \begin{pmatrix} I & 0 \\ 0 & 0 \end{pmatrix}\right).$$

As $y \in \mathcal{C}(V : X) = \mathcal{C}(V)$, one can retrieve y from the above vector by premultiplying the latter with $(C : 0)$. Since $C^{-L}y$ and Fy are independent and the distribution of the latter is free of β and σ^2, we can ignore it for consideration of the information matrix. It follows from the discussion of Section 3.12 that the information matrix for θ is

$$\begin{pmatrix} \frac{1}{\sigma^2}(C^{-L}X)'C^{-L}X & 0 \\ 0 & \frac{\rho(V)}{2\sigma^4} \end{pmatrix} = \begin{pmatrix} \frac{1}{\sigma^2}X'V^{-}X & 0 \\ 0 & \frac{\rho(V)}{2\sigma^4} \end{pmatrix}.$$

As $\mathcal{C}(X) \subseteq \mathcal{C}(V)$, the expression does not depend on the choice of the g-inverse. The expressions for the Cramer-Rao lower bounds follow.

7.14 It follows along lines of the proof of Proposition 7.38 that the Cramer-Rao lower bound for the dispersion of an unbiased estimator of the LPF $A\beta$ is

$$\mathcal{I}_\mu^{-1} AX^{-}[V - V(I - P_X)\{(I - P_X)V(I - P_X)\}^{-}(I - P_X)V](AX^{-})',$$

where $\mathcal{I}_\mu$ is as in Exercise 3.26. This bound, which does not depend on the choice of the g-inverses, is smaller than the bound given in Proposition 7.38, since $\sigma^2\mathcal{I}_\mu \geq 1$ (according to the result of Exercise 3.26).

7.15 (a) $\mathcal{M}_R$ is equivalent to the unrestricted model

$$\mathcal{M}_r = (y - XA'(AA')^{-}\xi, X(I - P_{A'})\theta, \sigma^2 V),$$

where $\beta = (I - P_{A'})\theta + XA'(AA')^{-}\xi$. Therefore, $X\widehat{\beta}$ is the BLUE of $X\beta$ under $\mathcal{M}_R$ if and only if it is uncorrelated with the LZFs of $\mathcal{M}_r$. The algebraic form of this condition simplifies to orthogonality of the columns of $D(X\widehat{\beta})$ and $I - P_{X(I-P_{A'})}$. Since the column space of the latter matrix is $\mathcal{C}(X(I - P_{A'}))^{\perp}$, the condition is equivalent to $\mathcal{C}(D(X\widehat{\beta})) \subseteq \mathcal{C}(X(I - P_{A'}))$. The result follows from Proposition 7.15.

(b) If V is nonsingular, $\mathcal{C}(V) \cap \mathcal{C}(X)$ simplifies to $\mathcal{C}(X)$. Hence, the condition of part (a) reduces to $\mathcal{C}(X) = \mathcal{C}(X(I - P_{A'}))$, i.e. $\rho(X') = \rho((I - P_{A'})X') = \rho(X' : A') - \rho(A')$. The rank condition $\rho(X' : A') = \rho(X') + \rho(A')$ holds if and only if and only if $\mathcal{C}(X')$ and $\mathcal{C}(A')$ are virtually disjoint, or $A\beta = \xi$ is a completely untestable hypothesis in $\mathcal{M}$.

7.16 It follows from (7.18) that $MSE(X\widehat{\beta}) - MSE(X\widehat{\beta}_R)$ is nonnegative definite whenever $D - (A\beta - \xi)(A\beta - \xi)'$ is nonnegative definite. The result of Exercise A.20 implies that a sufficient condition for the latter is (7.19).

7.17 Using an argument similar to the one leading to (7.18), we have that $MSE(\boldsymbol{X}\widehat{\boldsymbol{\beta}}) - MSE(\boldsymbol{X}\widehat{\boldsymbol{\beta}}_R)$ is nonnegative definite whenever $D(\widehat{\boldsymbol{A\beta}}) + \sigma^2\boldsymbol{W} - (\boldsymbol{A\beta} - \boldsymbol{\xi})(\boldsymbol{A\beta} - \boldsymbol{\xi})'$ is nonnegative definite. It follows from Exercise A.20 that a sufficient condition for the latter is $(\boldsymbol{A\beta} - \boldsymbol{\xi})'[D(\widehat{\boldsymbol{A\beta}}) + \sigma^2\boldsymbol{W}]^-(\boldsymbol{A\beta} - \boldsymbol{\xi}) \le 1$.

7.18 Since $\boldsymbol{p}'\boldsymbol{\beta}$ is estimable, there is a reparametrization of the given model where $\boldsymbol{p}'\boldsymbol{\beta}$ is the first component of the parameter vector. Using the arguments of Example 7.44 for the transformed model, the inequality-constrained LSE is

$$\boldsymbol{X}\widehat{\boldsymbol{\beta}}_{constrained} = \begin{cases} \text{BLUE of } \boldsymbol{X\beta} \text{ in } (\boldsymbol{y}, \boldsymbol{X\beta}, \sigma^2\boldsymbol{V}), & \text{if } \widehat{\boldsymbol{p}'\boldsymbol{\beta}} \le b, \\ \text{BLUE of } \boldsymbol{X\beta} \text{ in } (\boldsymbol{y}, \boldsymbol{X\beta}, \sigma^2\boldsymbol{V}) & \\ \text{subject to } \boldsymbol{p}'\boldsymbol{\beta} = b, & \text{otherwise.} \end{cases}$$

7.19 Suppose $\boldsymbol{l}'\boldsymbol{y}$ is an LUE of $\boldsymbol{p}'\boldsymbol{\beta}_1$. From Proposition 7.3, $\boldsymbol{l}'\boldsymbol{y}$ is almost surely equal to $\boldsymbol{k}'\boldsymbol{y}$ where $\boldsymbol{k}'\boldsymbol{X}_1\boldsymbol{\beta}_1 + \boldsymbol{k}'\boldsymbol{X}_2\boldsymbol{\beta}_2 = \boldsymbol{p}'\boldsymbol{\beta}_1$ for all $\boldsymbol{\beta}_1$ and $\boldsymbol{\beta}_2$. Therefore $\boldsymbol{X}_1'\boldsymbol{k} = \boldsymbol{p}$ and $\boldsymbol{X}_2'\boldsymbol{k} = \boldsymbol{0}$. It follows that $\boldsymbol{k} \in \mathcal{C}(\boldsymbol{X}_2)^\perp$, i.e. $\boldsymbol{k} = (\boldsymbol{I} - \boldsymbol{P}_{X_2})\boldsymbol{m}$ for some vector $\boldsymbol{m}$. Consequently $\boldsymbol{p} = \boldsymbol{X}_1'(\boldsymbol{I} - \boldsymbol{P}_{X_2})\boldsymbol{m}$, i.e. $\boldsymbol{p} \in \mathcal{C}(\boldsymbol{X}_1'(\boldsymbol{I} - \boldsymbol{P}_{X_2}))$. Conversely, if $\boldsymbol{p} \in \mathcal{C}(\boldsymbol{X}_1'(\boldsymbol{I} - \boldsymbol{P}_{X_2}))$, then there is a vector $\boldsymbol{m}$ such that $\boldsymbol{p} = \boldsymbol{X}_1'(\boldsymbol{I} - \boldsymbol{P}_{X_2})\boldsymbol{m}$. Then $\boldsymbol{m}'(\boldsymbol{I} - \boldsymbol{P}_{X_2})\boldsymbol{y}$ is an LUE of $\boldsymbol{p}'\boldsymbol{\beta}_1$.

7.20 Using the result of Remark 7.46, we have

$$(\boldsymbol{I} - \boldsymbol{P}_{X_2})\boldsymbol{X}_1\widehat{\boldsymbol{\beta}}_1 \Big|_{\mathcal{M}} = \boldsymbol{P}_{(I-P_{X_2})X_1}\boldsymbol{y} = (\boldsymbol{I} - \boldsymbol{P}_{X_2})\boldsymbol{X}_1\widehat{\boldsymbol{\beta}}_1 \Big|_{\mathcal{M}^*}.$$

Likewise, the dispersions of the two estimators are also identical. However,

$$R_0^2 \Big|_{\mathcal{M}^*} = \|(\boldsymbol{I} - \boldsymbol{P}_{(I-P_{X_2})X_1})\boldsymbol{y}\|^2 = R_0^2 \Big|_{\mathcal{M}} + \|\boldsymbol{P}_{X_2}\boldsymbol{y}\|^2.$$

The error degrees of freedom under the two models are $\nu_{\mathcal{M}} = n - \rho(\boldsymbol{X}_1 : \boldsymbol{X}_2)$ and $\nu_{\mathcal{M}} = n - \rho((\boldsymbol{I} - \boldsymbol{P}_{X_2})\boldsymbol{X}_1) = \nu_{\mathcal{M}} + \rho(\boldsymbol{X}_2)$. Hence,

$$\widehat{\sigma^2}_{\mathcal{M}} = R_0^2 \Big|_{\mathcal{M}} \Big/ \nu_{\mathcal{M}},$$

$$\text{whereas } \widehat{\sigma^2}_{\mathcal{M}^*} = \left(R_0^2 \Big|_{\mathcal{M}} + \|\boldsymbol{P}_{X_2}\boldsymbol{y}\|^2\right) \Big/ (\nu_{\mathcal{M}} + \rho(\boldsymbol{X}_2)).$$

Thus, $\mathcal{M}^*$ cannot serve as a reduced model for $\mathcal{M}$.

7.21 The numerator and denominator of the GLRT statistic are maximized when the respective exponents are minimized. The minimized values are $R_H^2/(2\sigma^2)$ and $R_0^2/(2\sigma^2)$, respectively. Hence, the GLRT statistic is

$$\ell = \frac{\max\limits_{\sigma^2}(2\pi\sigma^2)^{-\frac{\rho(V:X)}{2}}|\boldsymbol{C}'\boldsymbol{C}|^{-\frac{1}{2}}\exp[-R_H^2/(2\sigma^2)]}{\max\limits_{\sigma^2}(2\pi\sigma^2)^{-\frac{\rho(V:X)}{2}}|\boldsymbol{C}'\boldsymbol{C}|^{-\frac{1}{2}}\exp[-R_0^2/(2\sigma^2)]},$$

where CC' is a rank-factorization of V. The numerator is maximized when $\sigma^2 = R_H^2/\rho(V{:}X)$, while the denominator is maximized when $\sigma^2 = R_0^2/\rho(V{:}X)$. Substituting these values, we have $\ell = (R_H^2/R_0^2)^{-\frac{\rho(V:X)}{2}}$, which is a monotonically decreasing function of the ratio given in Proposition 7.48. The null hypothesis is rejected for small values of ℓ, and hence, for large values of this ratio. It follows from Proposition 7.41 and the subsequent discussion that the latter is the ratio of averages of squares of two sets of independent LZFs of variance σ^2, whenever the null hypothesis holds. The number of LZFs in the two sets are m and $n'-r$, respectively. Hence, the ratio has $F_{m,n'-r}$ distribution under $\mathcal{H}_0$. The result follows.

7.22 It is clear that $\widehat{y}_0 = (\widehat{y}_{01}, \ldots, \widehat{y}_{0q})'$, where $\widehat{y}_{0i}$ is the BLUP of y_{0i} as per Proposition 7.49, $i = 1, \ldots, q$. The prediction error of the BLUP vector $\widehat{y}_0$ can be decomposed as

$$\begin{aligned}\widehat{y}_0 - y_0 &= X_0\widehat{\beta} + V_0'V^-e - y_0 = (X_0\widehat{\beta} - V_0'V^-X\widehat{\beta}) - (y_0 - V_0'V^-y)\\ &= [X_0(\widehat{\beta} - \beta) - V_0'V^-(X\widehat{\beta} - X\beta)]\\ &\quad - [(y_0 - X_0\beta) - V_0'V^-(y - X\beta)].\end{aligned}$$

The second term in the last expression is $(y_0 - X_0\beta)$ with adjustment for covariance with $y - X\beta$, while the first term is a linear function of y. The two terms must be uncorrelated. Hence, $D(\widehat{y}_0 - y_0)$ is the sum of the dispersions of the two terms, which simplifies to

$$(X_0X^- - V_0'V^-)D(X\widehat{\beta})(X_0X^- - V_0'V^-)' + \sigma^2(V_{00} - V_0'V^-V_0).$$

The rank of this matrix is m. The result of part (a) follows from the fact that $(y_0 - \widehat{y}_0)'[\sigma^{-2}D(\widehat{y}_0 - y_0)]^-(y_0 - \widehat{y}_0)/m\widehat{\sigma^2} \sim F_{m,n'-r}$. Part (b) follows from part (a) and Exercise 4.10.

7.23 (a) As $y_0 - X_0\beta - V_0'V^-(y - X\beta) \sim N(0, \sigma^2(V_{00} - V_0'V^-V_0))$, the inequality

$$\begin{aligned}&(y_0 - X_0\beta - V_0'V^-(y - X\beta))'[\sigma^2(V_{00} - V_0'V^-V_0)]^-\\ &(y_0 - X_0\beta - V_0'V^-(y - X\beta)) \;<\; \chi^2_{s,\gamma}\end{aligned}$$

holds with probability $1 - \gamma$. The result follows from Exercise 4.10.

(b) Simultaneous confidence intervals for $x_{0j}'\beta - v_{0j}'V^-X\beta$, $j = 1, \ldots, q$, with confidence coefficient $1 - \alpha/2$ are given by the Scheffé confidence intervals of Section 7.12 with $x_{0j} - X'V^-v_{0j}$, m' and $\alpha/2$ replacing a_j, m and α, respectively. These are

$$\left[(x_{0j}'X^- - v_{0j}'V^-)X\widehat{\beta} - \sqrt{m'F_{m',n'-r,\alpha/2}c_i\widehat{\sigma^2}},\right.$$
$$\left.(x_{0j}'X^- - v_{0j}'V^-)X\widehat{\beta} + \sqrt{m'F_{m',n'-r,\alpha/2}c_i\widehat{\sigma^2}}\right],$$

$j = 1, \ldots, q$. A $100(1-\alpha/2)\%$ upper confidence limit for σ^2 is

$$\left[0, \widehat{\sigma^2}/\chi^2_{n'-r,1-\alpha/2}\right].$$

Because of the Bonferroni inequality, $\boldsymbol{x}_{0j}'\boldsymbol{\beta} - \boldsymbol{v}_{0j}'\boldsymbol{V}^-\boldsymbol{X}\boldsymbol{\beta}$, $j = 1, \ldots, q$, and σ^2 simultaneously belong to their respective confidence intervals with probability at least $1-\alpha$. The worst-case combination of these inequalities, together with part (a) gives the requisite simultaneous tolerance intervals.

(c) When $\boldsymbol{V}_{00} - \boldsymbol{V}_0'\boldsymbol{V}^-\boldsymbol{V}_0$ is a diagonal matrix, the components of $\boldsymbol{y}_0 - \boldsymbol{X}_0\boldsymbol{\beta} - \boldsymbol{V}_0'\boldsymbol{V}^-(\boldsymbol{y}-\boldsymbol{X}\boldsymbol{\beta})$ are independently distributed as $N(0, \sigma^2(v_{0i} - \boldsymbol{v}_{0i}'\boldsymbol{V}^-\boldsymbol{v}_{0i}))$, $i = 1, \ldots, q$. Hence, each of the inequalities

$$|y_{0i} - \boldsymbol{x}_{0i}'\boldsymbol{\beta} - \boldsymbol{v}_{0i}'\boldsymbol{V}^-(\boldsymbol{y} - \boldsymbol{X}\boldsymbol{\beta})| < z_{\gamma/2}\sigma\sqrt{v_{0i} - \boldsymbol{v}_{0i}'\boldsymbol{V}^-\boldsymbol{v}_{0i}},$$

$i = 1, \ldots, q$, holds with probability $1-\gamma$. When there are arbitrary number of independent replicates of any combination of $y_{01}, \ldots, y_{0q}$, these inequalities are satisfied by $100(1-\gamma)\%$ of these (on the average). The stated result is obtained from the above using the worst-case combination of the $100(1-\alpha/2)\%$ Scheffé confidence intervals of $\boldsymbol{x}_{0i}'\boldsymbol{\beta} - \boldsymbol{v}_{0i}'\boldsymbol{V}^-\boldsymbol{X}\boldsymbol{\beta}$, $i = 1, \ldots, q$, and $100(1-\alpha/2)\%$ upper confidence limit for σ^2 given in part (b), together with the Bonferroni inequality.

7.24 Since each stratum has a specific mean, the one-way classification model is appropriate here. The BLUP for each stratum total turns out to be the usual expansion estimator for that stratum (see Example 7.50), and the BLUP of the population total is the sum of these over all strata. The MSEP is also the sum of the MSEP of the stratum-specific expansion estimators.

7.25 As the strata are uncorrelated, we can consider one stratum at a time. The model for the ith stratum is

$$E\begin{pmatrix}\boldsymbol{y}_s\\ \boldsymbol{y}_r\end{pmatrix} = \mu_i\boldsymbol{1}, \quad D\begin{pmatrix}\boldsymbol{y}_s\\ \boldsymbol{y}_r\end{pmatrix} = \sigma_i^2[(1-\rho_i)\boldsymbol{I} + \rho_i\boldsymbol{1}\boldsymbol{1}'].$$

We have

$$\boldsymbol{V}_{ss}^{-1} = [(1-\rho_i)\boldsymbol{I} + \rho_i\boldsymbol{1}\boldsymbol{1}']^{-1} = \frac{1}{1-\rho_i}\left[\boldsymbol{I} - \frac{\rho}{1+(n_i-1)\rho_i}\boldsymbol{1}\boldsymbol{1}'\right],$$

n_i being the number of sampled units from the ith stratum. Since $\boldsymbol{X}_s = \boldsymbol{1}$, $\boldsymbol{X}_s'\boldsymbol{V}_{ss}^{-1}\boldsymbol{X}_s$ simplifies to $n_i/[1+(n_i-1)\rho_i]$, and $\boldsymbol{X}_s'\boldsymbol{V}_{ss}^{-1}\boldsymbol{y}_s$ simplifies to $n_i\bar{y}_{si}/[1+(n_i-1)\rho_i]$, where $\bar{y}_{si}$ is the sample average within the ith stratum. Hence, the BULE of μ_i is

$$\hat{\mu}_i = (\boldsymbol{X}_s'\boldsymbol{V}_{ss}^{-1}\boldsymbol{X}_s)^{-1}\boldsymbol{X}_s'\boldsymbol{V}_{ss}^{-1}\boldsymbol{y}_s = \bar{y}_{si}.$$

It follows from (7.22) that the BLUP of the population total in ith stratum is

$$\begin{aligned}
&\mathbf{1}'\boldsymbol{y}_s + \mathbf{1}'[\boldsymbol{X}_r\hat{\mu}_i + \boldsymbol{V}_{rs}\boldsymbol{V}_{ss}^{-1}(\boldsymbol{y}_s - \mathbf{1}\hat{\mu}_i)] \\
&= n_i\bar{y}_{si} + (N_i - n_i)\bar{y}_{si} + \frac{\rho_i}{1-\rho_i}\mathbf{1}'\mathbf{1}\mathbf{1}'\left[\boldsymbol{I} - \frac{\rho}{1+(n_i-1)\rho_i}\mathbf{1}\mathbf{1}'\right](\boldsymbol{y}_s - \mathbf{1}\hat{\mu}_i) \\
&= N_i\bar{y}_{si},
\end{aligned}$$

where N_i is the population size in the ith stratum. This is just the expansion estimator, which remains the BLUP in spite of the within-strata correlation. The MSEP of the BLUP is

$$\sigma_i^2\mathbf{1}'(\boldsymbol{V}_{rr} - \boldsymbol{V}_{rs}\boldsymbol{V}_{ss}^-\boldsymbol{V}_{sr})\mathbf{1} + \sigma_i^2\frac{[\mathbf{1}'(\boldsymbol{X}_r\boldsymbol{X}_s^- - \boldsymbol{V}_{rs}\boldsymbol{V}_{ss}^-)\boldsymbol{X}_s]^2}{\boldsymbol{X}_s'\boldsymbol{V}_{ss}^{-1}\boldsymbol{X}_s}.$$

This expression simplifies to $\sigma_i^2(1-\rho_i)N_i(N_i-n_i)/n_i$.

Chapter 8

8.1 Let $\boldsymbol{H} = \boldsymbol{P}_X$ and use Proposition 8.2(b). In order that $\boldsymbol{HV}$ is symmetric, we must have $h_{i,j}v_{j,j} = (\boldsymbol{HV})_{i,j} = (\boldsymbol{HV})_{j,i} = h_{j,i}v_{i,i}$ for all i,j. Since the $v_{i,i}$s are unequal and $h_{i,j} = h_{j,i}$, we must have $h_{i,j} = 0$ for $i \neq j$. Thus, $\boldsymbol{H}$ is a diagonal matrix. Then the rank of $\boldsymbol{P}_X$ is equal to the number of nonzero leverages. Since $\mathbf{1} \in \mathcal{C}(\boldsymbol{X})$, all the leverages are nonzero (see Exercise 3.11, part (b)). Therefore, the rank of the hat matrix is equal to n, but it should have been equal to k.

8.2 (a) It is easy to see that $\boldsymbol{VP}_X = \alpha\boldsymbol{P}_X$, which is symmetric. Hence, the LSE of $\boldsymbol{X\beta}$ is its BLUE. The estimator of $D(\boldsymbol{X}\widehat{\boldsymbol{\beta}})$ under the wrong model is

$$\frac{\boldsymbol{y}'(\boldsymbol{I}-\boldsymbol{P}_X)\boldsymbol{y}}{n-\rho(\boldsymbol{X})}\boldsymbol{P}_X = \frac{\boldsymbol{\delta}'\boldsymbol{CC}'\boldsymbol{\delta}}{n-\rho(\boldsymbol{X})}\boldsymbol{P}_X,$$

where $\boldsymbol{\delta}$ is such that $\boldsymbol{y} = \boldsymbol{X\beta}+\boldsymbol{V\delta}$. In contrast, the estimator of $D(\boldsymbol{X}\widehat{\boldsymbol{\beta}})$ under the correct model is

$$\begin{aligned}
&\frac{\boldsymbol{y}'(\boldsymbol{I}-\boldsymbol{P}_X)\{(\boldsymbol{I}-\boldsymbol{P}_X)\boldsymbol{V}(\boldsymbol{I}-\boldsymbol{P}_X)\}^-(\boldsymbol{I}-\boldsymbol{P}_X)\boldsymbol{y}}{\rho(\boldsymbol{X}:\boldsymbol{V})-\rho(\boldsymbol{X})}\cdot\boldsymbol{P}_X\boldsymbol{VP}_X \\
&= \frac{\boldsymbol{y}'(\boldsymbol{I}-\boldsymbol{P}_X)\{\boldsymbol{CC}'\}^-(\boldsymbol{I}-\boldsymbol{P}_X)\boldsymbol{y}}{\rho(\boldsymbol{V})-\rho(\boldsymbol{X})}\cdot\alpha\boldsymbol{P}_X \\
&= \frac{\boldsymbol{\delta}'\boldsymbol{CC}'\{\boldsymbol{CC}'\}^-\boldsymbol{CC}'\boldsymbol{\delta}}{\rho(\boldsymbol{X})+\rho(\boldsymbol{C})-\rho(\boldsymbol{X})}\cdot\alpha\boldsymbol{P}_X = \frac{\boldsymbol{\delta}'\boldsymbol{CC}'\boldsymbol{\delta}}{\rho(\boldsymbol{C})}\cdot\alpha\boldsymbol{P}_X = \frac{\boldsymbol{\delta}'\boldsymbol{CC}'\boldsymbol{\delta}}{n-\rho(\boldsymbol{X})}\cdot\boldsymbol{P}_X.
\end{aligned}$$

(b) Proposition 8.9 is not applicable, as $\rho(\boldsymbol{X}:\boldsymbol{V})$ or $\rho(\boldsymbol{V})$ is not necessarily equal to n. If $\rho(\boldsymbol{V}) = n$, then $\rho(\boldsymbol{C}) = n - \rho(\boldsymbol{X})$, so that $\boldsymbol{CC}' = \boldsymbol{I} - \boldsymbol{P}_X$ and $\alpha = 1$. In such a case $\boldsymbol{V} = \boldsymbol{I}$, so there is no contradiction.

(c) Yes.

(d) If $\rho(\boldsymbol{C}) < n - \rho(\boldsymbol{X})$, the answer is no. If $\rho(\boldsymbol{C}) = n - \rho(\boldsymbol{X})$, the 'wrong' model is right!

8.3 Let $\boldsymbol{y} = (\boldsymbol{y}_1' : \cdots : \boldsymbol{y}_p')'$, $\boldsymbol{\eta} = (\boldsymbol{\eta}_1' : \cdots : \boldsymbol{\eta}_p')'$ and $\boldsymbol{\varepsilon} = (\boldsymbol{\varepsilon}_1' : \cdots : \boldsymbol{\varepsilon}_p')'$. Then

$$\boldsymbol{y} = (\boldsymbol{1}_p \otimes \boldsymbol{X})\boldsymbol{\beta} + [(\boldsymbol{I}_{p\times p} \otimes \boldsymbol{X})\boldsymbol{\eta} + \boldsymbol{\varepsilon}].$$

The dispersion matrix of the error (shown in square brackets) is $\boldsymbol{V} = \boldsymbol{I}_{p\times p} \otimes (\boldsymbol{X\Sigma X}' + \sigma^2\boldsymbol{I})$. Since

$$\boldsymbol{V}(\boldsymbol{1}_p \otimes \boldsymbol{X}) = \boldsymbol{1}_p \otimes (\boldsymbol{X\Sigma X}'\boldsymbol{X} + \sigma^2\boldsymbol{X}) = (\boldsymbol{1}_p \otimes \boldsymbol{X})(\boldsymbol{I}_{p\times p} \otimes (\boldsymbol{\Sigma X}'\boldsymbol{X} + \sigma^2\boldsymbol{I})),$$

the conclusion follows from Proposition 8.2(a).

8.4 Let $\boldsymbol{l}'\boldsymbol{P}_X\boldsymbol{y}$ be an LSE with zero variance, so that $\boldsymbol{l}\boldsymbol{P}_X\boldsymbol{V}\boldsymbol{P}_X\boldsymbol{l} = 0$. It follows that $\boldsymbol{V}\boldsymbol{P}_X\boldsymbol{l} = \boldsymbol{0}$, i.e. $\boldsymbol{P}_X\boldsymbol{l} \in \mathcal{C}(\boldsymbol{V})^\perp \cap \mathcal{C}(\boldsymbol{X})$. Hence, $\mathcal{C}(\boldsymbol{V})^\perp$ and $\mathcal{C}(\boldsymbol{X})$ are not virtually disjoint. Conversely, if these two column spaces are not virtually disjoint, then there is a nontrivial vector $\boldsymbol{m}$ lying in the intersection such that $\boldsymbol{P}_X\boldsymbol{m} = \boldsymbol{m}$, and $\boldsymbol{m}'\boldsymbol{y}$ is easily seen to be an LSE with zero variance.

If $\boldsymbol{l}'\boldsymbol{P}_X\boldsymbol{y}$ is an LSE with zero variance, then overestimation of its variance means $\boldsymbol{l}'\boldsymbol{P}_X\boldsymbol{l} > \boldsymbol{0}$. This generally holds, except when $\boldsymbol{l}'\boldsymbol{P}_X\boldsymbol{l} = 0$, i.e. $\boldsymbol{P}_X\boldsymbol{l} = \boldsymbol{0}$, i.e. $\boldsymbol{l}'\boldsymbol{P}_X\boldsymbol{y}$ is zero with probability 1.

8.5 Write the model error as $\widehat{\boldsymbol{V}}\boldsymbol{l}$. Then

$$\begin{aligned}\widehat{\boldsymbol{X\beta}}_{pi} &= [\boldsymbol{I} - \widehat{\boldsymbol{V}}(\boldsymbol{I}-\boldsymbol{P}_X)\{(\boldsymbol{I}-\boldsymbol{P}_X)\widehat{\boldsymbol{V}}(\boldsymbol{I}-\boldsymbol{P}_X)\}^-(\boldsymbol{I}-\boldsymbol{P}_X)](\boldsymbol{X\beta} + \widehat{\boldsymbol{V}}\boldsymbol{l})\\ &= \boldsymbol{X\beta} + [\widehat{\boldsymbol{V}} - \widehat{\boldsymbol{V}}(\boldsymbol{I}-\boldsymbol{P}_X)\{(\boldsymbol{I}-\boldsymbol{P}_X)\widehat{\boldsymbol{V}}(\boldsymbol{I}-\boldsymbol{P}_X)\}^-(\boldsymbol{I}-\boldsymbol{P}_X)\widehat{\boldsymbol{V}}]\boldsymbol{l}.\end{aligned}$$

The proof of Proposition 7.15 implies that the column space of the matrix in front of $\boldsymbol{l}$ in the last expression is $\mathcal{C}(\boldsymbol{X}) \cap \mathcal{C}(\widehat{\boldsymbol{V}})$. The conclusion follows.

8.6 (a) The result follows from Proposition 8.18.
(b) The dispersion matrix is

$$\begin{aligned}D(\boldsymbol{X}\widehat{\boldsymbol{\beta}}_{pia}) = \sigma^2 E_V&[\boldsymbol{I} - \boldsymbol{V}(\boldsymbol{I}-\boldsymbol{P}_X)\{(\boldsymbol{I}-\boldsymbol{P}_X)\boldsymbol{V}(\boldsymbol{I}-\boldsymbol{P}_X)\}^-(\boldsymbol{I}-\boldsymbol{P}_X)]\boldsymbol{V}\\ E_V&[\boldsymbol{I} - (\boldsymbol{I}-\boldsymbol{P}_X)\{(\boldsymbol{I}-\boldsymbol{P}_X)\boldsymbol{V}(\boldsymbol{I}-\boldsymbol{P}_X)\}^-(\boldsymbol{I}-\boldsymbol{P}_X)\boldsymbol{V}].\end{aligned}$$

8.7 The argument given for $(\boldsymbol{I} - \boldsymbol{P}_X)\boldsymbol{y}$ in Section 8.2.3 goes through for $\boldsymbol{By}$. Hence, the MLE of $\boldsymbol{\theta}$ obtained from the model $(\boldsymbol{By}, \boldsymbol{0}, \boldsymbol{BV}(\boldsymbol{\theta})\boldsymbol{B}')$ coincides with the REML of $\boldsymbol{\theta}$ in the original model. As the REML is free of $\boldsymbol{B}$, the MLE does not depend on the choice of $\boldsymbol{B}$.

8.8 The first part follows from derivative calculations such as $\frac{\partial \log|A|}{\partial A} = \boldsymbol{A}^{-1}$. The REML estimating equation is obtained from the ML estimating equation by replacing $\boldsymbol{e}$ and $\boldsymbol{V}(\theta)$ by $\boldsymbol{U}'\boldsymbol{e}$ and $\boldsymbol{U}'\boldsymbol{V}(\theta)\boldsymbol{U}$, respectively, where $\boldsymbol{UU}'$ is a rank-factorization of $\boldsymbol{I} - \boldsymbol{P}_X$.

8.9 If $\boldsymbol{y}'\boldsymbol{Qy}$ is a quadratic and unbiased estimator of $\boldsymbol{p}'\boldsymbol{\theta}$, then $\boldsymbol{\beta}'\boldsymbol{X}'\boldsymbol{QX\beta} + \mathrm{tr}(\boldsymbol{QV}(\boldsymbol{\theta})) = \boldsymbol{p}'\boldsymbol{\theta}$ for all $\boldsymbol{\theta}$. If $\boldsymbol{p}'\boldsymbol{\theta}_1 \neq \boldsymbol{p}'\boldsymbol{\theta}_2$, then $\mathrm{tr}(\boldsymbol{QV}(\boldsymbol{\theta}_1)) \neq \mathrm{tr}(\boldsymbol{QV}(\boldsymbol{\theta}_2))$, which means that $\boldsymbol{V}(\boldsymbol{\theta}_1) \neq \boldsymbol{V}(\boldsymbol{\theta}_2)$. Hence, $\boldsymbol{p}'\boldsymbol{\theta}$ is identifiable. The other implication is obvious from the definition.

8.10 Let $\boldsymbol{Q}_\dagger = \frac{1}{2}(\boldsymbol{Q}+\boldsymbol{Q}')$ so that $\boldsymbol{y}'\boldsymbol{Q}_\dagger\boldsymbol{y} = \boldsymbol{y}'\boldsymbol{Q}\boldsymbol{y}$ and $\boldsymbol{Q}_\dagger$ is symmetric. Let $\boldsymbol{U\Lambda U}'$ be a spectral decomposition of $\boldsymbol{Q}_\dagger$, $\boldsymbol{\Lambda}$ being a nonsingular diagonal matrix of nonzero eigenvalues. From the proof of Proposition 8.27(b), we have $\boldsymbol{\beta}'\boldsymbol{X}'\boldsymbol{Q}_\dagger\boldsymbol{X\beta} = 0$ for all $\boldsymbol{\beta}$ such that $\left(I - \boldsymbol{P}_{V(\theta)}\right)\boldsymbol{X\beta} = \left(I - \boldsymbol{P}_{V(\theta)}\right)\boldsymbol{y}$, as a necessary condition of unbiasedness. The condition $\boldsymbol{\beta}'\boldsymbol{X}'\boldsymbol{Q}_\dagger\boldsymbol{X\beta} = 0$ is equivalent to $\boldsymbol{U}'\boldsymbol{X\beta} = 0$. Hence, the above necessary condition is equivalent to $\boldsymbol{U}'\boldsymbol{y}$ being an LZF. From Proposition 7.3, there is a matrix $\boldsymbol{U}_*$ such that $\boldsymbol{U}\boldsymbol{y} = \boldsymbol{U}_*\boldsymbol{y}$ almost surely and $\boldsymbol{U}_*\boldsymbol{X} = \boldsymbol{0}$. Define $\boldsymbol{Q}_* = \boldsymbol{U}_*\boldsymbol{\Lambda}\boldsymbol{U}_*'$. This matrix satisfies the requisite conditions.

8.11 If $\boldsymbol{C}_i\boldsymbol{C}_i'$ is a rank-factorization of $\boldsymbol{V}_i$, $i = 1, \ldots, k$, then

$$\mathcal{C}(\boldsymbol{V}(\boldsymbol{\theta})) = \mathcal{C}(\sigma_1\boldsymbol{C}_1 : \cdots : \sigma_k\boldsymbol{C}_k) = \mathcal{C}(\boldsymbol{C}_1 : \cdots : \boldsymbol{C}_k) = \mathcal{C}(\boldsymbol{V}_1 : \cdots : \boldsymbol{V}_k).$$

8.12 The statement of Remark 7.17 is proved easily using the form of the BLUE for nonsingular dispersion matrix given is Remark 7.17. The REML estimating equation is obtained by replacing $\boldsymbol{V}_j$, $\boldsymbol{V}(\boldsymbol{\theta})$ and $\boldsymbol{e}(\boldsymbol{\theta})$ by $\boldsymbol{U}'\boldsymbol{V}_j\boldsymbol{U}$, $\boldsymbol{U}'\boldsymbol{V}(\boldsymbol{\theta})\boldsymbol{U}$ and $\boldsymbol{U}'\boldsymbol{e}(\boldsymbol{\theta})$, respectively, where $\boldsymbol{UU}'$ is a rank-factorization of $\boldsymbol{I} - \boldsymbol{P}_X$.

8.13 In the balanced case the MINQUE does not depend on the choice of $\boldsymbol{w}$, so the MINQUE is the same as the REML estimator, mentioned in Example 8.38. In the unbalanced case, we have $\boldsymbol{V}(\boldsymbol{w}) = \boldsymbol{I}$, $\boldsymbol{V}^-(\boldsymbol{w}) = \boldsymbol{I}$, $\boldsymbol{W}_2 = \boldsymbol{I} - n^{-1}\boldsymbol{1}\boldsymbol{1}'$, where $n = \sum_i m_i$. $\boldsymbol{W}_1$ turns out to be $\boldsymbol{V}_1 - (((\frac{m_i+m_j}{n} - \sum_l \frac{m_l^2}{n^2})\boldsymbol{1}_{m_i}\boldsymbol{1}_{m_j}'))$. Hence,

$$\begin{aligned}
\operatorname{tr}(\boldsymbol{W}^-(\boldsymbol{w})^-\boldsymbol{W}_1\boldsymbol{W}^-(\boldsymbol{w})\boldsymbol{W}_1) &= \sum_i m_i^2 - \frac{2}{n}\sum_i m_i^3 + \frac{1}{n^2}\left(\sum_i m_i^2\right)^2,\\
\operatorname{tr}(\boldsymbol{W}^-(\boldsymbol{w})^-\boldsymbol{W}_1\boldsymbol{W}^-(\boldsymbol{w})\boldsymbol{W}_2) &= n - \frac{1}{n}\sum_i m_i^2,\\
\operatorname{tr}(\boldsymbol{W}^-(\boldsymbol{w})^-\boldsymbol{W}_2\boldsymbol{W}^-(\boldsymbol{w})\boldsymbol{W}_2) &= n-1.
\end{aligned}$$

After simplifying the expressions of $\boldsymbol{b}(\boldsymbol{\theta})'\boldsymbol{W}_1\boldsymbol{b}(\boldsymbol{\theta})$ and $\boldsymbol{b}(\boldsymbol{\theta})'\boldsymbol{W}_2\boldsymbol{b}(\boldsymbol{\theta})$ given in Example 8.38 for $\sigma_1^2 = 0$ and $\sigma_2^2 = 1$, we have the equations

$$\sigma_1^2\left[\sum_i m_i^2 - \frac{2}{n}\sum_i m_i^3 + \frac{1}{n^2}\left(\sum_i m_i^2\right)^2\right] + \sigma_2^2\left[n - \frac{1}{n}\sum_i m_i^2\right] = \sum_i m_i^2(\bar{y}_i - \bar{y})^2,$$

$$\sigma_1^2\left[n - \frac{1}{n}\sum_i m_i^2\right] + \sigma_2^2(n-1) = \sum_{i,j}(y_{ij} - \bar{y})^2.$$

The MINQUE(0) estimators of σ_1^2 and σ_2^2 are the solutions to the above equations. These reduce to (8.8) when $m_1 = \cdots = m_t = m$.

8.14 Expand the right-hand side of (8.15) as

$$2\mathrm{tr}\left(\widetilde{\boldsymbol{Q}}\sum_{i=1}^{k}\sigma_i^2\boldsymbol{U}_i\boldsymbol{U}_i'\widetilde{\boldsymbol{Q}}\sum_{j=1}^{k}\sigma_j^2\boldsymbol{U}_j\boldsymbol{U}_j'\right) = 2\sum_{i=1}^{k}\sum_{j=1}^{k}\sigma_i^2\sigma_j^2\|\boldsymbol{U}_i'\widetilde{\boldsymbol{Q}}\boldsymbol{U}_j\|_F^2.$$

For fixed $\boldsymbol{\theta}$, this is similar to the objective function (8.11) which is minimized by the MINQUE under the same conditions of unbiasedness and translation invariance. Therefore, by Proposition 8.36, the MIVQUE must have the stated form. The argument holds similarly when $\boldsymbol{\theta}$ is replaced by an approximation, $\boldsymbol{w}$. However, if $\boldsymbol{w}$ is a function of $\boldsymbol{y}$, then the approximate MIVQUE may not be a quadratic or unbiased estimator.

8.15 The BLUE can be written as

$$\begin{aligned}\widehat{\boldsymbol{\beta}} = (\boldsymbol{X}'\boldsymbol{V}^{-1}\boldsymbol{X})^{-1}\boldsymbol{X}'\boldsymbol{V}^{-1}\boldsymbol{y} &= \left(\sum_{j=1}^{m}\sigma_j^{-2}\boldsymbol{X}_j'\boldsymbol{X}_j\right)^{-1}\left(\sum_{j=1}^{m}\sigma_j^{-2}\boldsymbol{X}_j'\boldsymbol{y}_j\right)\\ &= \left(\sum_{j=1}^{m}(D(\widehat{\boldsymbol{\beta}}_{(j)}))^{-1}\right)^{-1}\left(\sum_{j=1}^{m}(D(\widehat{\boldsymbol{\beta}}_{(j)}))^{-1}\widehat{\boldsymbol{\beta}}_{(j)}\right).\end{aligned}$$

This proves the first part. The proof of the second part is similar.

8.16 (a) The BLUE is

$$\widehat{\boldsymbol{\beta}} = \left(\sum_{j=1}^{m}\widehat{\sigma_j^2}(\widehat{D}(\widehat{\boldsymbol{\beta}}_{(j)}))^{-1}\right)^{-1}\left(\sum_{j=1}^{m}\widehat{\sigma_j^2}(\widehat{D}(\widehat{\boldsymbol{\beta}}_{(j)}))^{-1}\widehat{\boldsymbol{\beta}}_{(j)}\right).$$

(b) The dispersion of the BLUE is

$$D(\widehat{\boldsymbol{\beta}}) = \sigma_1^2\left(\sum_{j=1}^{m}\widehat{\sigma_j^2}(\widehat{D}(\widehat{\boldsymbol{\beta}}_{(j)}))^{-1}\right)^{-1}.$$

(c) Since $\boldsymbol{y}_j - \boldsymbol{X}_j'\widehat{\boldsymbol{\beta}}$ is an LZF in the jth submodel as well as the full model, it is uncorrelated with $\widehat{\boldsymbol{\beta}}_{(j)}$ and $\widehat{\boldsymbol{\beta}}$. Hence,

$$\begin{aligned}\widehat{\sigma^2} &= \left(\sum_{j=1}^{m}n_j - k\right)^{-1}\sum_{j=1}^{m}\|\boldsymbol{y}_j - \boldsymbol{X}_j'\widehat{\boldsymbol{\beta}}\|^2\\ &= \left(\sum_{j=1}^{m}n_j - k\right)^{-1}\sum_{j=1}^{m}\left[\|\boldsymbol{y}_j - \boldsymbol{X}_j'\widehat{\boldsymbol{\beta}}_{(j)}\|^2 + \|\boldsymbol{X}_j'\widehat{\boldsymbol{\beta}}_{(j)} - \boldsymbol{X}_j'\widehat{\boldsymbol{\beta}}\|^2\right]\\ &= \left(\sum_{j=1}^{m}n_j - k\right)^{-1}\sum_{j=1}^{m}\widehat{\sigma_j^2}\left[(n_j - k) + (\widehat{\boldsymbol{\beta}}_{(j)}-\widehat{\boldsymbol{\beta}})'(\widehat{D}(\widehat{\boldsymbol{\beta}}_{(j)}))^{-1}(\widehat{\boldsymbol{\beta}}_{(j)}-\widehat{\boldsymbol{\beta}})\right].\end{aligned}$$

8.17 The given statistic is always translation invariant, as it is a function of the group-specific LZFs which are also LZFs of the grand model. Setting the expected value of $q(w_0, w_1, w_2)$ equal to σ_1^2 and comparing coefficients, we have the equations

$$w_0 + w_1 + w_2 = 1,$$
$$w_0\bar{\psi}_0 + w_1\bar{\psi}_1 + w_2\bar{\psi}_2 = 0,$$

where $\bar{\psi}_0$, $\bar{\psi}_1$ and $\bar{\psi}_2$ are the average values of ψ_i in groups G_{0a} and G_{0b} (combined), G_1 and G_2, respectively. If $\bar{\psi}_1 \neq \bar{\psi}_2$, then $w_1 = w_2$ implies $w_1 = w_2 = 0$, i.e. the weights must unequal if nonzero. If $\bar{\psi}_1 = \bar{\psi}_2$, then $w_1 + w_2$ should be equal to $\bar{\psi}_0/(\bar{\psi}_0 - \bar{\psi}_2)$ (which is also equal to $1 - w_0$), and the choice of w_2 does not matter.

Chapter 9

9.1 It is enough to prove that there are additional estimable LPFs in the augmented model if and only if $\rho(\boldsymbol{X}_n) - \rho(\boldsymbol{X}_m) > 0$, and that there are additional LZFs if and only if $l_* > \rho(\boldsymbol{X}_n) - \rho(\boldsymbol{X}_m)$. The first statement follows from the fact that there is a $\boldsymbol{p}'\boldsymbol{\beta}$ such that $\boldsymbol{p} \in \mathcal{C}(\boldsymbol{X}_n')$ but $\boldsymbol{p} \notin \mathcal{C}(\boldsymbol{X}_m')$ if and only if $\rho(\boldsymbol{X}_n) > \rho(\boldsymbol{X}_m)$. The second statement is a consequence of the representation

$$l_* - \rho(\boldsymbol{X}_n) + \rho(\boldsymbol{X}_m) = [\rho(\boldsymbol{X}_n : \boldsymbol{V}_n) - \rho(\boldsymbol{X}_n)] - [\rho(\boldsymbol{X}_m : \boldsymbol{V}_m) - \rho(\boldsymbol{X}_m)],$$

and the fact that the two bracketed terms in the last expression represent the number of elements in a standardized basis set of LZFs for $\mathcal{M}_n$ and $\mathcal{M}_m$, respectively (see Proposition 7.19).

9.2 The condition of case (c) implies that there is an $l \times m$ matrix $\boldsymbol{B}$ such that $(\boldsymbol{X}_l : \boldsymbol{V}_{lm} : \boldsymbol{V}_l) = \boldsymbol{B}(\boldsymbol{X}_m : \boldsymbol{V}_m : \boldsymbol{V}_{ml})$. Thus, $\boldsymbol{X}_l = \boldsymbol{B}\boldsymbol{X}_m$ and $\boldsymbol{V}_l = \boldsymbol{B}\boldsymbol{V}_m\boldsymbol{B}'$. Writing the model equation for the augmented model as

$$\begin{matrix} \boldsymbol{y}_m = \boldsymbol{X}_m\boldsymbol{\beta} + \boldsymbol{\varepsilon}_m \\ \boldsymbol{y}_l = \boldsymbol{X}_l\boldsymbol{\beta} + \boldsymbol{\varepsilon}_l \end{matrix},$$

we can see that whenever $l_* = 0$, $E[(\boldsymbol{\varepsilon}_l - \boldsymbol{B}\boldsymbol{\varepsilon}_m)(\boldsymbol{\varepsilon}_l - \boldsymbol{B}\boldsymbol{\varepsilon}_m)'] = \boldsymbol{0}$ and $\boldsymbol{X}_l\boldsymbol{\beta} = \boldsymbol{B}\boldsymbol{X}_m\boldsymbol{\beta}$. Thus, the second equation can almost surely be obtained by premultiplying the first equation with $\boldsymbol{B}$. Thus, *the models $\mathcal{M}_m$ and $\mathcal{M}_n$ are equivalent.*

9.3 Let $\widetilde{\boldsymbol{\beta}}_m$ be such that for any LPF $\boldsymbol{p}'\boldsymbol{\beta}$ which is estimable under $\mathcal{M}_m$, $\boldsymbol{p}'\widetilde{\boldsymbol{\beta}}_m$ is its restricted BLUE from this model. Note that

$$\boldsymbol{X}_m\widetilde{\boldsymbol{\beta}}_m = \boldsymbol{X}_m\widehat{\boldsymbol{\beta}}_m - Cov(\boldsymbol{X}_m\widehat{\boldsymbol{\beta}}_m, \boldsymbol{A}\widehat{\boldsymbol{\beta}}_m)[D(\boldsymbol{A}\widehat{\boldsymbol{\beta}}_m)]^-(\boldsymbol{A}\widehat{\boldsymbol{\beta}}_m - \boldsymbol{\xi}).$$

It follows that the BLUP of $\boldsymbol{y}_l$ from restricted $\mathcal{M}_m$ is

$$\begin{aligned}
\widetilde{\boldsymbol{y}}_l &= \boldsymbol{X}_l\widetilde{\boldsymbol{\beta}}_m + \boldsymbol{V}_{ml}'\boldsymbol{V}_m^-(\boldsymbol{y}_m - \boldsymbol{X}_m\widetilde{\boldsymbol{\beta}}_m) \\
&= \boldsymbol{X}_l\widehat{\boldsymbol{\beta}}_m - Cov(\boldsymbol{X}_l\widehat{\boldsymbol{\beta}}_m, \boldsymbol{A}\widehat{\boldsymbol{\beta}}_m)[D(\boldsymbol{A}\widehat{\boldsymbol{\beta}}_m)]^-(\boldsymbol{A}\widehat{\boldsymbol{\beta}}_m - \boldsymbol{\xi}) \\
&\quad + \boldsymbol{V}_{ml}'\boldsymbol{V}_m^-(\boldsymbol{y}_m - \boldsymbol{X}_m\widehat{\boldsymbol{\beta}}_m + Cov(\boldsymbol{X}_m\widehat{\boldsymbol{\beta}}_m, \boldsymbol{A}\widehat{\boldsymbol{\beta}}_m)[D(\boldsymbol{A}\widehat{\boldsymbol{\beta}}_m)]^-(\boldsymbol{A}\widehat{\boldsymbol{\beta}}_m - \boldsymbol{\xi})) \\
&= (\boldsymbol{y}_l - \boldsymbol{w}_l) \\
&\quad - Cov(\boldsymbol{X}_l\widehat{\boldsymbol{\beta}}_m - \boldsymbol{V}_{ml}'\boldsymbol{V}_m^-\boldsymbol{X}_m\widehat{\boldsymbol{\beta}}_m, \boldsymbol{A}\widehat{\boldsymbol{\beta}}_m)[D(\boldsymbol{A}\widehat{\boldsymbol{\beta}}_m)]^-(\boldsymbol{A}\widehat{\boldsymbol{\beta}}_m - \boldsymbol{\xi})) \\
&= (\boldsymbol{y}_l - \boldsymbol{w}_l) + Cov(\boldsymbol{d}_l(\widehat{\boldsymbol{\beta}}_m) - \boldsymbol{d}_l(\boldsymbol{\beta}), \boldsymbol{A}\widehat{\boldsymbol{\beta}}_m)[D(\boldsymbol{A}\widehat{\boldsymbol{\beta}}_m)]^-(\boldsymbol{A}\widehat{\boldsymbol{\beta}}_m - \boldsymbol{\xi})) \\
&= (\boldsymbol{y}_l - \boldsymbol{w}_l) + Cov(\boldsymbol{w}_l, \boldsymbol{A}\widehat{\boldsymbol{\beta}}_m)[D(\boldsymbol{A}\widehat{\boldsymbol{\beta}}_m)]^-(\boldsymbol{A}\widehat{\boldsymbol{\beta}}_m - \boldsymbol{\xi})) = \boldsymbol{y}_l - \boldsymbol{w}_{l*}.
\end{aligned}$$

In the above simplification we have used the fact that $\boldsymbol{d}_l(\boldsymbol{\beta})$ is uncorrelated with $\boldsymbol{y}_m$, and hence, with $\boldsymbol{A}\widehat{\boldsymbol{\beta}}_m$. The result follows.

9.4 Make the following identifications: $\boldsymbol{x}_{t-1}$ is $\boldsymbol{X}_m\boldsymbol{\beta}$, $\boldsymbol{B}_t$ is $\boldsymbol{I}$, $\boldsymbol{H}_t$ is $\boldsymbol{X}_l\boldsymbol{X}_m^-$, $\boldsymbol{u}_t$ is $\boldsymbol{0}$, $\boldsymbol{v}_t = \boldsymbol{\varepsilon}_l$ and $\boldsymbol{z}_t$ is $\boldsymbol{y}_l$. Then equations (9.14)–(9.15) signify no change. Equations (9.18)–(9.19) simplify to

$$\begin{aligned}
\boldsymbol{X}_m\widehat{\boldsymbol{\beta}}_n &= \boldsymbol{X}_m\widehat{\boldsymbol{\beta}}_m + D(\boldsymbol{X}_m\widehat{\boldsymbol{\beta}}_m)(\boldsymbol{X}_l\boldsymbol{X}_m^-)'[\sigma^2\boldsymbol{V}_l + D(\boldsymbol{X}_m\widehat{\boldsymbol{\beta}}_m)]^-(\boldsymbol{y}_l - \boldsymbol{X}_l\widehat{\boldsymbol{\beta}}_m), \\
D(\boldsymbol{X}_m\widehat{\boldsymbol{\beta}}_n) &= D(\boldsymbol{X}_m\widehat{\boldsymbol{\beta}}_m) \\
&\quad - D(\boldsymbol{X}_m\widehat{\boldsymbol{\beta}}_m)(\boldsymbol{X}_l\boldsymbol{X}_m^-)'[\sigma^2\boldsymbol{V}_l + D(\boldsymbol{X}_m\widehat{\boldsymbol{\beta}}_m)]^-(\boldsymbol{X}_l\boldsymbol{X}_m^-)D(\boldsymbol{X}_m\widehat{\boldsymbol{\beta}}_m).
\end{aligned}$$

If we let $\boldsymbol{w}_l = \boldsymbol{y}_l - \boldsymbol{X}_l\widehat{\boldsymbol{\beta}}_m$ (as in (9.4)), then $D(\boldsymbol{w}_l) = \sigma^2\boldsymbol{V}_l + D(\boldsymbol{X}_m\widehat{\boldsymbol{\beta}}_m)$ and $Cov(\boldsymbol{X}_m\widehat{\boldsymbol{\beta}}_m, \boldsymbol{w}_l) = -D(\boldsymbol{X}_m\widehat{\boldsymbol{\beta}}_m)(\boldsymbol{X}_l\boldsymbol{X}_m^-)'$. Thus, the above update equations are equivalent to parts (a) and (b) of Proposition 9.8(a).

9.5 Note that $\varepsilon_t = \phi_1\varepsilon_{t-1} + v_{1,t-1} + \delta_t$, $v_{k,t} = \phi_{k+1}\varepsilon_{t-1} + v_{k+1,t-1} + \theta_k\delta_t$ for $k = 1, \ldots, r-2$ and $v_{r-1,t} = \phi_r\varepsilon_{t-1} + \theta_{r-1}\delta_t$. Thus, we have the state-space model (9.7)–(9.8) with

$$\boldsymbol{B}_t = \begin{pmatrix} \boldsymbol{I} & \boldsymbol{0} & 0\,0 \cdots 0 \\ \boldsymbol{0} & \phi_1 & 1\,0 \cdots 0 \\ \boldsymbol{0} & \phi_2 & 0\,1 \cdots 0 \\ \vdots & \vdots & \vdots\;\vdots \ddots \vdots \\ \boldsymbol{0} & \phi_{r-1} & 0\,0 \cdots 1 \\ \boldsymbol{0} & \phi_r & 0\,0 \cdots 0 \end{pmatrix}, \quad \boldsymbol{u}_t = \begin{pmatrix} 0 \\ 1 \\ \theta_1 \\ \vdots \\ \theta_{r-2} \\ \theta_{r-1} \end{pmatrix}\delta_t, \quad \boldsymbol{H}_t' = \begin{pmatrix} \boldsymbol{\alpha}_t \\ 1 \\ \boldsymbol{0} \end{pmatrix},$$

and $\boldsymbol{v}_t = \boldsymbol{0}$. The update equations (9.14)–(9.19) simplify to the recursions

$$\begin{aligned}
\boldsymbol{P}_{t|t-1} &= \boldsymbol{B}_t\boldsymbol{P}_{t-1}\boldsymbol{B}_t', \\
\widehat{\boldsymbol{x}}_t &= \widehat{\boldsymbol{x}}_{t|t-1} + \boldsymbol{P}_{t|t-1}\boldsymbol{H}_t' \cdot \frac{y_t - \alpha_t'\widehat{\boldsymbol{\beta}}_{t-1}}{\boldsymbol{H}_t\boldsymbol{P}_{t|t-1}\boldsymbol{H}_t'},
\end{aligned}$$

$$\boldsymbol{P}_t = \boldsymbol{P}_{t|t-1} - \boldsymbol{P}_{t|t-1}\boldsymbol{H}_t'\boldsymbol{H}_t\boldsymbol{P}_{t|t-1} \cdot \frac{1}{\boldsymbol{H}_t\boldsymbol{P}_{t|t-1}\boldsymbol{H}_t'},$$

$\widehat{\boldsymbol{\beta}}_t$ being obtained from the top part of $\widehat{\boldsymbol{x}}_t$, and $D(\widehat{\boldsymbol{\beta}}_t)$ from the top left block of $\boldsymbol{P}_t$.

9.6 It follows from the result of Exercise A.8 that the minimum mean squared error predictor of $\boldsymbol{Cx}$ in the set-up of Proposition 9.18 is $E(\boldsymbol{Cx}|\boldsymbol{z}, \boldsymbol{h})$, which must be a linear (affine) function of $\boldsymbol{z}$ and $\boldsymbol{h}$ because of the multivariate normaliy of the errors. Thus, the problem reduces to that of finding the best *linear* predictor. Proposition 9.18 and the subsequent theory of Section 9.1.6 applies.

9.7 It is clear that

$$\begin{aligned}\boldsymbol{r}_l &= \boldsymbol{w}_l + \boldsymbol{d}_l(\widehat{\boldsymbol{\beta}}_n) - \boldsymbol{d}_l(\widehat{\boldsymbol{\beta}}_m)\\ &= \boldsymbol{w}_l + (-\boldsymbol{V}_{lm}\boldsymbol{V}_m^- : \boldsymbol{I})(\boldsymbol{X}_n\widehat{\boldsymbol{\beta}}_m - \boldsymbol{X}_n\widehat{\boldsymbol{\beta}}_n)\\ &= \boldsymbol{w}_l + (-\boldsymbol{V}_{lm}\boldsymbol{V}_m^- : \boldsymbol{I})Cov(\boldsymbol{X}_n\widehat{\boldsymbol{\beta}}_m, \boldsymbol{w}_l)[D(\boldsymbol{w}_l)]^-\boldsymbol{w}_l,\end{aligned}$$

by making use of part (a) of Proposition 9.8. The converse (i.e. $\boldsymbol{w}_l$ being a function of $\boldsymbol{r}_l$) holds only if $\rho(D(\boldsymbol{r}_l)) = l_* - [\rho(\boldsymbol{X}_n) - \rho(\boldsymbol{X}_m)]$.

9.8 Since $\boldsymbol{x}_{(k)} \notin \mathcal{C}(\boldsymbol{X}_{(k-1)})$, we have $\rho(\boldsymbol{X}_{(k-1)}) = \rho(\boldsymbol{X}_{(k)}) - 1$. Hence, the number of LZFs constituting a standardized basis set for the larger model, $n - \rho(\boldsymbol{X}_{(k)})$, is one less than $n - \rho(\boldsymbol{X}_{(k-1)})$, the corresponding number for the smaller model. This accounts for the increase in degrees of freedom of R_0^2. As far as the restricted model is concerned, the role of $\boldsymbol{X}$ is assumed by $\boldsymbol{X}(\boldsymbol{I} - \boldsymbol{P}_{A'})$ (see page 101). If $\boldsymbol{B} = (\boldsymbol{A} : \boldsymbol{0})$ so that $\boldsymbol{A\beta}_{(k-1)} = \boldsymbol{B\beta}_{(k)}$, then

$$\begin{aligned}\rho(\boldsymbol{X}_{(k)}(\boldsymbol{I} - \boldsymbol{P}_{B'})) &= \rho(\boldsymbol{B}' : \boldsymbol{X}_{(k)}') - \rho(\boldsymbol{B}') = \rho(\boldsymbol{X}_{(k-1)}) + 1 - \rho(\boldsymbol{A})\\ &= \rho(\boldsymbol{X}_{(k-1)}(\boldsymbol{I} - \boldsymbol{P}_{A'})) - 1.\end{aligned}$$

Thus, the degrees of freedom of R_H^2 also decreases by 1.

9.9 We can write the hypothesis as $\boldsymbol{TA\beta} = \boldsymbol{0}$, where $\boldsymbol{A} = (\boldsymbol{0} : \boldsymbol{I})$ and $\boldsymbol{T} = (\boldsymbol{I} - \boldsymbol{P}_{X_{(h)}})\boldsymbol{X}_{(j)}$. We only have to verify that the matrix $\boldsymbol{T}$ satisfies the condition of Proposition 4.13(a), i.e. $\mathcal{C}(\boldsymbol{A}'\boldsymbol{T}') = \mathcal{C}(\boldsymbol{A}') \cap \mathcal{C}(\boldsymbol{X}_{(k)}')$. It is easy to see that $\boldsymbol{A}'\boldsymbol{T}' = \boldsymbol{X}_{(k)}'(\boldsymbol{I} - \boldsymbol{P}_{X_{(h)}})$, so that $\mathcal{C}(\boldsymbol{A}'\boldsymbol{T}') \subseteq \mathcal{C}(\boldsymbol{A}') \cap \mathcal{C}(\boldsymbol{X}_{(k)}')$. To complete the proof, we have to establish the equality of the dimensions of the two vector spaces. It follows from Proposition A.6(a) that

$$\begin{aligned}\dim(\mathcal{C}(\boldsymbol{A}') \cap \mathcal{C}(\boldsymbol{X}_{(k)}')) &= \rho(\boldsymbol{A}') + \rho(\boldsymbol{X}_{(k)}') - \rho(\boldsymbol{A}' : \boldsymbol{X}_{(k)}')\\ &= j + \rho(\boldsymbol{X}_{(k)}) - [j + \rho(\boldsymbol{X}_{(h)})]\\ &= \rho(\boldsymbol{X}_{(k)}) - \rho(\boldsymbol{X}_{(h)}) = \rho(\boldsymbol{TA}).\end{aligned}$$

9.10 Both sides of the first equation are BLUEs of $(\boldsymbol{I}-\boldsymbol{P}_{X_{(h)}})\boldsymbol{X}_{(j)}\boldsymbol{\beta}_{(j)}$, while both sides of the second equation are BLUEs of

$$\boldsymbol{X}'_{(j)}(\boldsymbol{I}-\boldsymbol{P}_{X_{(h)}})\{(\boldsymbol{I}-\boldsymbol{P}_{X_{(h)}})\boldsymbol{V}(\boldsymbol{I}-\boldsymbol{P}_{X_{(h)}})\}^{-}(\boldsymbol{I}-\boldsymbol{P}_{X_{(h)}})\boldsymbol{X}_{(j)}\boldsymbol{\beta}_{(j)}.$$

The equivalence follows from the uniqueness of the BLUE.

9.11 The expected values of $\boldsymbol{\nu}$ and $\boldsymbol{t}$ are $(\boldsymbol{I}-\boldsymbol{P}_{X_{(h)}})\boldsymbol{X}_{(j)}\boldsymbol{\beta}_{(j)}$ and $\boldsymbol{X}'_{(j)}(\boldsymbol{I}-\boldsymbol{P}_{X_{(h)}})\{(\boldsymbol{I}-\boldsymbol{P}_{X_{(h)}})\boldsymbol{V}(\boldsymbol{I}-\boldsymbol{P}_{X_{(h)}})\}^{-}(\boldsymbol{I}-\boldsymbol{P}_{X_{(h)}})\boldsymbol{X}_{(j)}\boldsymbol{\beta}_{(j)}$, respectively. These are estimable in the residual model, since we can write these as $(\boldsymbol{I}-\boldsymbol{P}_{X_{(h)}})\boldsymbol{X}_{(j)res}\boldsymbol{\beta}_{(j)}$ and $\boldsymbol{X}'_{(j)}(\boldsymbol{I}-\boldsymbol{P}_{X_{(h)}})\{\boldsymbol{V}(\boldsymbol{I}-\boldsymbol{P}_{X_{(h)}})\}^{-}\boldsymbol{X}_{(j)res}\boldsymbol{\beta}_{(j)}$, respectively. Since $\mathcal{C}(\boldsymbol{X}_{(j)res})\subseteq\mathcal{C}(\boldsymbol{V})$, we conclude from Remark 7.27 that the BLUE of the expected value of $\boldsymbol{t}$ is obtained by replacing $\boldsymbol{\beta}_{(j)}$ with $(\boldsymbol{X}'_{(j)res}\boldsymbol{V}^{-}\boldsymbol{X}_{(j)res})^{-}\boldsymbol{X}'_{(j)res}\boldsymbol{V}^{-}\boldsymbol{y}_{res}$ in its expression. In view of Remark 9.35, this expression simplifies to $D(\boldsymbol{t})[D(\boldsymbol{t})]^{-}\boldsymbol{t}$ or $\boldsymbol{t}$. The fact that $\boldsymbol{\nu}$ is the BLUE of its expectation follows from the result of Exercise 9.10.

9.12 (a) When the jth block is deleted, the corresponding block mean becomes non-estimable and the error degrees of freedom reduces by $t-1$. Note that the LZF $\boldsymbol{r}_l$ defined in Proposition 9.21 consists $e_{1j},\ldots,e_{tj}$, defined in (6.17). It follows from the form of the corresponding projection matrix that $\boldsymbol{r}_l[\sigma^{-2}D(\boldsymbol{r}_l)]^{-}\boldsymbol{r}_l$ is just the sum of squares of these residuals. Thus, the error sum of squares reduces by $\sum_{i=1}^{t}e_{ij}^2$. The reduction factor $1-\sum_{i=1}^{t}e_{ij}^2/R_0^2$ can be regarded as a measure of influence of the jth block on the error sum of squares.

(b) The change in the between treatments sum of squares can be obtained from change in the error sum of squares under the restriction that all blocks are equivalent, as per Proposition 9.22. However, an easier way is to calculate the change in the constituent terms of S_τ, given in Table 6.4. The value of S_τ changes by the factor $(b/S_\tau)\sum_{i=1}^{t}[(\bar{y}_{i\cdot}-\bar{y}_{\cdot\cdot})-e_{ij}/(b-1)]^2$, which can be called a measure of influence of the jth block on the between treatments sum of squares.

(c) The GLRT statistic is altered by the factor

$$\frac{S_\tau\left(1-\sum_{i=1}^{t}e_{ij}^2\right)/R_0^2}{(b-1)\sum_{i=1}^{t}[(\bar{y}_{i\cdot}-\bar{y}_{\cdot\cdot})-e_{ij}/(b-1)]^2},$$

the revised null distribution being $F_{t-1,(b-2)(t-1)}$. The above factor is a measure of influence of the jth block on the GLRT.

9.13 The missing plot substitution technique can be used. If y_{ijk} is the missing observation, then it should be replaced by its BLUP, $(m-1)^{-1}\sum_{k'\neq k}y_{ijk'}$, for the computation of R_0^2. The BLUP of y_{ijk} (to be used for substitution) in the case of various restricted sums of squares are as follows:

(a) BLUP for the hypothesis of no difference of treatment effects:

$$(tm-1)^{-1}\sum_{i'}\sum_{\substack{k'\\(i',k')\neq(i,k)}} y_{i'jk'};$$

(b) BLUP for the hypothesis of no difference of treatment effects:

$$(bm-1)^{-1}\sum_{j'}\sum_{\substack{k'\\(j',k')\neq(j,k)}} y_{ij'k'};$$

(c) BLUP for the hypothesis of no interaction effects:

$$\frac{t\displaystyle\sum_{j'}\sum_{\substack{k'\\(j',k')\neq(j,k)}} y_{ij'k'} + b\sum_{i'}\sum_{\substack{k'\\(i',k')\neq(i,k)}} y_{i'jk'} - \sum_{i'}\sum_{j'}\sum_{k'} y_{i'j'k'}}{tbm-t-b+1}.$$

The degrees of freedom for each of the above sums of squares reduce by 1 because of the missing observations. These sums of squares can be used to obtain the GLRTs using standard theory.

Chapter 10

10.1 The vector $\mathrm{vec}(\boldsymbol{E})$ belongs almost surely to the column space of its own dispersion matrix, given in (10.5). Use the fact that $\boldsymbol{P}_{A\otimes B} = \boldsymbol{P}_A \otimes \boldsymbol{P}_B$, where

$$\boldsymbol{A}=\boldsymbol{\Sigma},\quad \boldsymbol{B}=\boldsymbol{V}\left(\boldsymbol{I}-\boldsymbol{P}_X\right)\left\{\left(\boldsymbol{I}-\boldsymbol{P}_X\right)\boldsymbol{V}\left(\boldsymbol{I}-\boldsymbol{P}_X\right)\right\}^{-}\left(\boldsymbol{I}-\boldsymbol{P}_X\right)\boldsymbol{V}.$$

According to Proposition 7.15, $\boldsymbol{P}_B = \boldsymbol{P}_{V(I-P_X)}$. Therefore, there is a matrix $\boldsymbol{K}_{n\times q}$ such that

$$\mathrm{vec}(\boldsymbol{E}) = \left[\boldsymbol{P}_\Sigma \otimes \boldsymbol{P}_{V(I-P_X)}\right]\mathrm{vec}(\boldsymbol{K}) = \mathrm{vec}\left(\boldsymbol{P}_{V(I-P_X)}\boldsymbol{K}\boldsymbol{P}_\Sigma\right)$$

almost surely. Since $\boldsymbol{P}_{V(I-P_X)}$ can be written as $\boldsymbol{V}(\boldsymbol{I}-\boldsymbol{P}_X)\boldsymbol{K}_1$ and $\boldsymbol{P}_\Sigma$ can be written as $\boldsymbol{K}_2\boldsymbol{\Sigma}$ for some $\boldsymbol{K}_1$ and $\boldsymbol{K}_2$, we have with probability 1

$$\mathrm{vec}(\boldsymbol{E}) = \mathrm{vec}\left(\boldsymbol{V}\left(\boldsymbol{I}-\boldsymbol{P}_X\right)\boldsymbol{K}_1\boldsymbol{K}\boldsymbol{K}_2\boldsymbol{\Sigma}\right).$$

Writing $\boldsymbol{K}_1\boldsymbol{K}\boldsymbol{K}_2$ as $\boldsymbol{L}$, we have by virtue of Exercise A.29

$$\mathrm{vec}(\boldsymbol{E}) = \mathrm{vec}\left(\boldsymbol{V}\left(\boldsymbol{I}-\boldsymbol{P}_X\right)\boldsymbol{L}\boldsymbol{\Sigma}\right) = \left[\boldsymbol{\Sigma}\otimes\boldsymbol{V}\left(\boldsymbol{I}-\boldsymbol{P}_X\right)\right]\mathrm{vec}(\boldsymbol{L})$$

with probability 1. The representation given in Remark 10.7 follows.

10.2 Let the random matrices $\boldsymbol{Y}_{n\times q}$ and $\boldsymbol{X}_{n\times(p+1)}$ be such that $\boldsymbol{X} = (\mathbf{1} : \boldsymbol{Z})$,

$$\mathrm{vec}(\boldsymbol{Y} : \boldsymbol{Z}) \sim N\left(\begin{pmatrix}\boldsymbol{\mu}_y\\ \boldsymbol{\mu}_x\end{pmatrix}_{(p+q)\times 1} \otimes \mathbf{1}_{n\times 1},\ \ \boldsymbol{\Sigma}_{(p+q)\times(p+q)} \otimes \boldsymbol{V}_{n\times n}\right).$$

It follows along the lines of the proof of Proposition 2.20 that

$$E(\boldsymbol{Y}|\boldsymbol{X}) = (\mathbf{1} : \boldsymbol{Z})\mathcal{B},$$
$$D(\mathrm{vec}(\boldsymbol{Y})|\boldsymbol{X}) = \boldsymbol{\Sigma} \otimes \boldsymbol{V},$$

where

$$\mathcal{B} = \begin{pmatrix}\boldsymbol{\mu}_y + \boldsymbol{\Sigma}_{yx}\boldsymbol{\Sigma}_{xx}^{-}\boldsymbol{\mu}_x\\ \boldsymbol{\Sigma}_{xx}^{-}\boldsymbol{\Sigma}_{xy}\end{pmatrix},$$
$$\boldsymbol{\Sigma} = (\boldsymbol{\Sigma}_{yy} - \boldsymbol{\Sigma}_{yx}\boldsymbol{\Sigma}_{xx}^{-}\boldsymbol{\Sigma}_{xy}).$$

10.3 It follows from Proposition 10.1 that the elements of $(\boldsymbol{I} - \boldsymbol{P}_X)\boldsymbol{Y}$ constitute a generating set of all LZFs. According to (10.5), the rows of this matrix are NLZFs. It remains to be shown that every single NLZF is a linear combination of the *rows* of $(\boldsymbol{I} - \boldsymbol{P}_X)\boldsymbol{Y}$. Let $\sum_{l=1}^{q} \boldsymbol{a}_{li}'(\boldsymbol{I} - \boldsymbol{P}_X)\boldsymbol{Y}\boldsymbol{u}_l$, $i =, \ldots, q$ be a set of LZFs constituting an NLZF. Then the covariance between its ith and jth components,

$$Cov\left(\sum_{l=1}^{q} \boldsymbol{a}_{li}'(\boldsymbol{I} - \boldsymbol{P}_X)\boldsymbol{Y}\boldsymbol{u}_l, \sum_{l=1}^{q} \boldsymbol{a}_{lj}'(\boldsymbol{I} - \boldsymbol{P}_X)\boldsymbol{Y}\boldsymbol{u}_l\right)$$
$$= \sum_{l=1}^{q}\sum_{l'=1}^{q} \boldsymbol{a}_{li}'(\boldsymbol{I} - \boldsymbol{P}_X)\boldsymbol{V}(\boldsymbol{I} - \boldsymbol{P}_X)\boldsymbol{a}_{l'j}\sigma_{l,l'},$$

must be proportional to $\sigma_{i,j}$. This can happen only if $\boldsymbol{a}_{li} = \boldsymbol{a}$ for $i = l$ and $\mathbf{0}$ otherwise. Therefore the chosen NLZF can be written as the row vector $\boldsymbol{a}'(\boldsymbol{I} - \boldsymbol{P}_X)\boldsymbol{Y}(\boldsymbol{u}_1 : \cdots \boldsymbol{u}_q)$ or $\boldsymbol{a}'(\boldsymbol{I} - \boldsymbol{P}_X)\boldsymbol{Y}$.
The fact that the rows of $\boldsymbol{E}$ also constitute a generating set of NLZFs follows from the identification $(\boldsymbol{I} - \boldsymbol{P}_X)\boldsymbol{Y} = (\boldsymbol{I} - \boldsymbol{P}_X)\boldsymbol{E}$.

10.4 Let $\boldsymbol{Z} = \boldsymbol{L}\boldsymbol{Y}$. Then

$$\begin{aligned}D(\mathrm{vec}(\boldsymbol{Z})) &= D((\boldsymbol{I} \otimes \boldsymbol{L})\mathrm{vec}(\boldsymbol{Y}))\\ &= (\boldsymbol{I} \otimes \boldsymbol{L})(\boldsymbol{\Sigma} \otimes \boldsymbol{V})(\boldsymbol{I} \otimes \boldsymbol{L}')\\ &= \boldsymbol{\Sigma} \otimes \boldsymbol{L}\boldsymbol{V}\boldsymbol{L}',\end{aligned}$$

which is of the required form. If $\boldsymbol{C}\boldsymbol{C}'$ is a rank-factorization of $\boldsymbol{A} = \boldsymbol{L}\boldsymbol{V}\boldsymbol{L}'$, then $\boldsymbol{C}^{-L}\boldsymbol{Z}$ is also a generating set of NLZFs (as $\boldsymbol{L}\boldsymbol{Y} = \boldsymbol{C}\boldsymbol{C}^{-L}\boldsymbol{L}\boldsymbol{Y}$ almost surely). Further, $D(\mathrm{vec}(\boldsymbol{C}^{-L}\boldsymbol{Z})) = \boldsymbol{\Sigma} \otimes \boldsymbol{I}$. Hence, by definition $\boldsymbol{R}_0 = (\boldsymbol{C}^{-L}\boldsymbol{Z})'(\boldsymbol{C}^{-L}\boldsymbol{Z}) = \boldsymbol{Z}'\boldsymbol{A}^{-}\boldsymbol{Z}$, irrespective of the g-inverse.

10.5 (a) *Parallelity of lines* ($\boldsymbol{A}\mathcal{B}\boldsymbol{C} = \mathbf{0}$):

$$\boldsymbol{R}_0 = \begin{pmatrix} r_{2,2} & \cdots & r_{2,k_1} \\ \vdots & \ddots & \vdots \\ r_{k_1,2} & \cdots & r_{k_1,k_1} \end{pmatrix}, \quad \text{where}$$

$$r_{l,k} = \sum_{j=1}^{2}\sum_{i=1}^{n_j}(y_{ij1}-y_{ijl}-\bar{y}_{\cdot j1}+\bar{y}_{\cdot jl})(y_{ij1}-y_{ijk}-\bar{y}_{\cdot j1}+\bar{y}_{\cdot jk}),$$

$$\boldsymbol{R}_H = \begin{pmatrix} s_{2,2} & \cdots & s_{2,k_1} \\ \vdots & \ddots & \vdots \\ s_{k_1,2} & \cdots & s_{k_1,k_1} \end{pmatrix}, \quad \text{where}$$

$$s_{l,k} = \sum_{j=1}^{2}\sum_{i=1}^{n_j}(y_{ij1}-y_{ijl}-\bar{y}_{\cdot\cdot 1}+\bar{y}_{\cdot\cdot l})(y_{ij1}-y_{ijk}-\bar{y}_{\cdot\cdot 1}+\bar{y}_{\cdot\cdot k}).$$

The GLRT is equivalent to the statistic $(n_1+n_2-k_1)(|\boldsymbol{R}_H|-|\boldsymbol{R}_0|)/[(k_1-1)|\boldsymbol{R}_0|]$, whose null distribution is $F_{k_1-1,n_1+n_2-k_1}$.

(b) *Equality of lines* ($\boldsymbol{A}\mathcal{B} = \mathbf{0}$):

$$\boldsymbol{R}_0 = \begin{pmatrix} r_{1,1} & \cdots & r_{1,k_1} \\ \vdots & \ddots & \vdots \\ r_{k_1,1} & \cdots & r_{k_1,k_1} \end{pmatrix}, \quad \text{where}$$

$$r_{l,k} = \sum_{j=1}^{2}\sum_{i=1}^{n_j}(y_{ijl}-\bar{y}_{\cdot jl})(y_{ijk}-\bar{y}_{\cdot jk}),$$

$$\boldsymbol{R}_H = \begin{pmatrix} s_{1,1} & \cdots & s_{1,k_1} \\ \vdots & \ddots & \vdots \\ s_{k_1,1} & \cdots & s_{k_1,k_1} \end{pmatrix}, \quad \text{where}$$

$$s_{l,k} = \sum_{j=1}^{2}\sum_{i=1}^{n_j}(y_{ijl}-\bar{y}_{\cdot\cdot l})(y_{ijk}-\bar{y}_{\cdot\cdot k}),$$

The GLRT is equivalent to the statistic $(n_1 + n_2 - k_1 - 1)(|\boldsymbol{R}_H| - |\boldsymbol{R}_0|)/(k_1|\boldsymbol{R}_0|)$, whose null distribution is $F_{k_1,n_1+n_2-k_1-1}$.

(c) *Horizontality of lines* ($\mathcal{B}\boldsymbol{C} = \mathbf{0}$): $\boldsymbol{R}_0$ is as in part (a),

$$\boldsymbol{R}_H = \begin{pmatrix} s_{2,2} & \cdots & s_{2,k_1} \\ \vdots & \ddots & \vdots \\ s_{k_1,2} & \cdots & s_{k_1,k_1} \end{pmatrix}, \quad \text{where}$$

$$s_{l,k} = \sum_{j=1}^{2}\sum_{i=1}^{n_j}(y_{ij1}-y_{ijl})(y_{ij1}-y_{ijk}).$$

The GLRT reduces to the Wilks' lambda statistic $\Lambda = |\boldsymbol{R}_0|/|\boldsymbol{R}_H|$ with parameters k_1-1, n_1+n_2-2 and 2. The null distribution of $\frac{n_1+n_2-k_1-1}{2} \cdot \frac{1-\sqrt{\Lambda}}{\sqrt{\Lambda}}$ is $F_{4,2n_1+2n_2-2k_1-2}$ (see Rao, 1973c, p. 556).

10.6 The test may be carried out under the model $\text{vec}(\boldsymbol{Y}_*) \sim N((\boldsymbol{I}\otimes\boldsymbol{1})\boldsymbol{\beta}, \boldsymbol{\Sigma}\otimes\boldsymbol{I})$, where $\boldsymbol{Y}_*$ and $\boldsymbol{\Sigma}_*$ are as in Example 10.22, and $\boldsymbol{\beta}' = \frac{1}{2}(1 : 1)\mathcal{B}\boldsymbol{C}$. The hypothesis $\mathcal{H}_p$ is built into this model, while $\mathcal{H}_c$ amounts to $\boldsymbol{\beta} = \boldsymbol{0}$. Here, $\boldsymbol{R}_0$ is the same as $\boldsymbol{R}_H$ of part (a) of Exercise 10.5, while $\boldsymbol{R}_H$ is the same as that of part (c). The GLRT is equivalent to the statistic $(n_1+n_2-k_1+1)(|\boldsymbol{R}_H| - |\boldsymbol{R}_0|)/[(k_1-1)|\boldsymbol{R}_0|]$, whose null distribution is $F_{k_1-1,n_1+n_2-k_1+1}$.

Chapter 11

11.1 (a) If $\boldsymbol{Ty}$ is linearly minimal sufficient for $\boldsymbol{\beta}$, then according to Proposition 11.16, $\boldsymbol{Ty}$ and $(\boldsymbol{y}_1' : \boldsymbol{y}_2')'$ are linear functions of one another. Hence, it is enough to work with the latter statistic.

(b) If $\boldsymbol{L}_1$ and $\boldsymbol{L}_2$ are as in the proof of Proposition 11.16, then

$$\begin{pmatrix}\boldsymbol{y}_1\\ \boldsymbol{y}_2\end{pmatrix} \sim N\left(\begin{pmatrix}\boldsymbol{\mu}_1\\ \boldsymbol{\mu}_2\end{pmatrix},\ \sigma^2\begin{pmatrix}\boldsymbol{I} & \boldsymbol{0}\\ \boldsymbol{0} & \boldsymbol{0}\end{pmatrix}\right),$$

where $\boldsymbol{\mu}_i = \boldsymbol{L}_i\boldsymbol{X}\boldsymbol{\beta}$, $i = 1,2$. If $\boldsymbol{ZK}$ is a rank-factorization of $\boldsymbol{X}$ and $\boldsymbol{K\beta} = \boldsymbol{\theta}$, then $(\boldsymbol{y}, \boldsymbol{Z\theta}, \sigma^2\boldsymbol{V})$ is a reparametrization of the original model. Further,

$$\begin{pmatrix}\boldsymbol{\mu}_1\\ \boldsymbol{\mu}_2\end{pmatrix} = \begin{pmatrix}\boldsymbol{L}_1\boldsymbol{Z}\\ \boldsymbol{L}_2\boldsymbol{Z}\end{pmatrix}\boldsymbol{\theta} = \boldsymbol{H\theta}.$$

The $\rho(\boldsymbol{X}) \times \rho(\boldsymbol{X})$ matrix $\boldsymbol{H}$ is invertible, since

$$\begin{aligned}
\rho(\boldsymbol{H}) &= \rho\begin{pmatrix}\boldsymbol{L}_1\boldsymbol{Z}\\ \boldsymbol{L}_2\boldsymbol{Z}\end{pmatrix} = \rho\begin{pmatrix}\boldsymbol{L}_1\boldsymbol{X}\\ \boldsymbol{L}_2\boldsymbol{X}\end{pmatrix}\\
&= \rho(\boldsymbol{L}_1\boldsymbol{X}) + \rho(\boldsymbol{L}_2\boldsymbol{X}) = \rho(\boldsymbol{U}_1'\boldsymbol{\Lambda}^{-1/2}\boldsymbol{U}'\boldsymbol{X}) + \rho(\boldsymbol{U}_2'\boldsymbol{X})\\
&= \rho(\boldsymbol{\Lambda}^{-1/2}\boldsymbol{U}'\boldsymbol{X}) + \rho(\boldsymbol{U}_2\boldsymbol{U}_2'\boldsymbol{X})\\
&= \dim(\mathcal{C}(\boldsymbol{V}) \cap \mathcal{C}(\boldsymbol{X})) + \rho((\boldsymbol{I} - \boldsymbol{P}_{\boldsymbol{V}})\boldsymbol{X}) = \rho(\boldsymbol{X}).
\end{aligned}$$

In the absence of any known constraint on the parameters, $(\boldsymbol{y}_1' : \boldsymbol{y}_2')'$ is complete and sufficient for $(\boldsymbol{\mu}_1' : \boldsymbol{\mu}_2')'$, according to Proposition B.7. Therefore, it is complete and sufficient for $\boldsymbol{\theta}$, and consequently for $\boldsymbol{\beta}$.

(c) If there is a known restriction on the parameters, then we can consider the decomposition of the response in the equivalent unrestricted model of Section 11.1.2, as per Proposition 11.16. Thus, any linearly minimal sufficient $\boldsymbol{Ty}$ is equivalent to $(\boldsymbol{y}_1' : \boldsymbol{y}_2')$ for the equivalent unrestricted model. The result of part (b) can then be used.

11.2 It is enough to identify $r_{b1} = \dim(\mathcal{C}(\boldsymbol{X}) \cap \mathcal{C}(\boldsymbol{V}))$, $r_{b0} = \rho(\boldsymbol{V} : \boldsymbol{X}) - \rho(\boldsymbol{V})$, $r_{z1} = \rho(\boldsymbol{V} : \boldsymbol{X}) - \rho(\boldsymbol{X})$ and $r_{z0} = n - \rho(\boldsymbol{V} : \boldsymbol{X})$ in the various special cases; the other numbers can be obtained by addition. These are given in Table C.8.

Table C.8 Dimensions of various spaces of Exercise 11.2

Case	r_{b1}	r_{b0}	r_{z1}	r_{z0}
(a)	$\rho(\boldsymbol{X})$	0	0	$n-\rho(\boldsymbol{X})$
(b)	$\rho(\boldsymbol{X})$	0	$\rho(\boldsymbol{V})-\rho(\boldsymbol{X})$	$n-\rho(\boldsymbol{V})$
(c)	$\rho(\boldsymbol{V})$	$\rho(\boldsymbol{X})-\rho(\boldsymbol{V})$	0	$n-\rho(\boldsymbol{X})$
(d)	0	$\rho(\boldsymbol{X})$	$\rho(\boldsymbol{V})$	0
(e)	0	$\rho(\boldsymbol{X})$	$\rho(\boldsymbol{V})$	$n-\rho(\boldsymbol{X})-\rho(\boldsymbol{V})$
(f)	$\rho(\boldsymbol{X})+\rho(\boldsymbol{V})-n$	$n-\rho(\boldsymbol{V})$	$n-\rho(\boldsymbol{X})$	0

11.3 If $\boldsymbol{Ty}$ is a linear unbiased estimator of $\boldsymbol{A\beta}$ under the linear model $(\boldsymbol{y}, \boldsymbol{X\beta}, \sigma^2\boldsymbol{V})$, then

$$D(\boldsymbol{Ty}) \geq \sigma^2 \boldsymbol{T}[\boldsymbol{V} - \boldsymbol{V}(\boldsymbol{I}-\boldsymbol{P}_X)\{(\boldsymbol{I}-\boldsymbol{P}_X)\boldsymbol{V}^-(\boldsymbol{I}-\boldsymbol{P}_X)\}^-(\boldsymbol{I}-\boldsymbol{P}_X)\boldsymbol{V}]\boldsymbol{T}'$$

in the sense of the Löwner order. The bound is achieved by the BLUE, $\boldsymbol{T}\widehat{\boldsymbol{y}}$.

11.4 Part (a) follows from the definitions of linearly ancillary statistic, linearly maximal ancillary and error space. In order to prove part (b), note that $\boldsymbol{l}'\boldsymbol{y}$ is a linearly ancillary statistic *and* a function of $\boldsymbol{Ty}$ if and only if $\boldsymbol{l} \in \mathcal{C}(\boldsymbol{T}') \cap \mathcal{E}_r$. Further, from Remark 11.23, we find that $\boldsymbol{l}'\boldsymbol{y}$ is almost surely equal to 0 if and only if $\boldsymbol{l} \in \mathcal{C}(\boldsymbol{L}_4') = \mathcal{E}_s \cap \mathcal{E}_r$. The statement follows from the definition of a linearly complete statistic. Part (c) follows from Proposition 11.12. According to Proposition 11.11 (Bahadur's theorem), no linear function of a linearly minimal sufficient statistic can be a linear ancillary. In other words, every linear function of such a statistic is almost surely equal to a BLUE or is identically $\boldsymbol{0}$. Thus, $\boldsymbol{Ty}$ is linearly minimal sufficient only if $\mathcal{C}(\boldsymbol{T}') \subseteq \mathcal{E}_s$. The other inclusion follows from part (c). This proves the necessity of the condition given in part (d). Sufficiency follows from parts (b) and (c).

11.5 Part (a) follows from the fact that $\boldsymbol{y}_{(1)} + \boldsymbol{y}_{(2)} + \boldsymbol{y}_{(3)} + \boldsymbol{y}_{(4)} = \boldsymbol{L}^{-1}\boldsymbol{Ly}$. The columns of $\boldsymbol{L}^{-1}$ must be linearly independent. Hence, $\boldsymbol{L}^{(i)}$, $i = 1,2,3,4$ have left-inverses. Therefore, $\boldsymbol{y}_1$, $\boldsymbol{y}_2$, $\boldsymbol{y}_3$ and $\boldsymbol{y}_4$ can be retrieved via linear transformation of $\boldsymbol{y}_{(1)}$, $\boldsymbol{y}_{(2)}$, $\boldsymbol{y}_{(3)}$ and $\boldsymbol{y}_{(4)}$, respectively. Proposition 11.16 implies that $\boldsymbol{y}_{(1)}$ and $\boldsymbol{y}_{(2)}$ are BLUEs. As $\boldsymbol{y}_1$ and $\boldsymbol{y}_2$ are functions of these, part (b) is proved. Part (c) is proved similarly. Part (d) is obvious. Part (e) follows from the fact that $\boldsymbol{y}_{(1)} + \boldsymbol{y}_{(2)}$ is a BLUE with expectation $\boldsymbol{X\beta}$, and $\boldsymbol{y}_{(4)}$ is identically zero. Part (f) is a consequence of parts (d) and (e).

11.6 (a) The error space of $\mathcal{M}_D$ is $\mathcal{C}(\boldsymbol{V}(\boldsymbol{I}-\boldsymbol{P}_X))^\perp$, which coincides with the estimation space of $\mathcal{M}$, as per Proposition 11.25. The estimation space of $\mathcal{M}_D$ is

$$\mathcal{C}(\boldsymbol{V}(\boldsymbol{I}-\boldsymbol{P}_{V(I-P_X)}))^\perp = \mathcal{C}(\boldsymbol{V}^{-1}(\boldsymbol{V}(\boldsymbol{I}-\boldsymbol{P}_X))) = \mathcal{C}(\boldsymbol{X})^\perp,$$

which coincides with the error space of $\mathcal{M}$.

(b) This result follows from part (a).

(c) Let $\boldsymbol{X}_* = \boldsymbol{V}(\boldsymbol{I} - \boldsymbol{P}_X)$. Then $\boldsymbol{V}^{-1}\boldsymbol{X}_* = (\boldsymbol{I} - \boldsymbol{P}_X)$. Hence, the vector of fitted values of $\mathcal{M}_D$ is

$$\begin{aligned}&\boldsymbol{X}_*(\boldsymbol{X}_*'\boldsymbol{V}^{-1}\boldsymbol{X}_*)^-\boldsymbol{X}_*'\boldsymbol{V}^{-1}\boldsymbol{y}\\&\quad= \boldsymbol{V}(\boldsymbol{I} - \boldsymbol{P}_X)[(\boldsymbol{I} - \boldsymbol{P}_X)\boldsymbol{V}(\boldsymbol{I} - \boldsymbol{P}_X)]^-(\boldsymbol{I} - \boldsymbol{P}_X)\boldsymbol{y},\end{aligned}$$

which is the residual vector in $\mathcal{M}$. It follows that the vector of residuals of $\mathcal{M}_D$ is the vector of fitted values of $\mathcal{M}$.

(d) The dual of $\mathcal{M}_D$ is $(\boldsymbol{y}, \boldsymbol{V}(\boldsymbol{I} - \boldsymbol{P}_{X_*})\boldsymbol{\theta}, \sigma^2\boldsymbol{V})$. However,

$$\mathcal{C}(\boldsymbol{V}(\boldsymbol{I} - \boldsymbol{P}_{X_*})) = \mathcal{C}(\boldsymbol{V}^{-1}\boldsymbol{X}_*)^\perp = \mathcal{C}(\boldsymbol{I} - \boldsymbol{P}_X)^\perp = \mathcal{C}(\boldsymbol{X}).$$

Therefore, the dual of the dual model is at most a reparametrization of the original model.

11.7 Let $\boldsymbol{L} = \boldsymbol{I} - \boldsymbol{V}(\boldsymbol{I} - \boldsymbol{P}_X)\{(\boldsymbol{I} - \boldsymbol{P}_X)\boldsymbol{V}(\boldsymbol{I} - \boldsymbol{P}_X)\}^-(\boldsymbol{I} - \boldsymbol{P}_X)$ and $\boldsymbol{T} = c\boldsymbol{C}\boldsymbol{L}$ where $0 \le c \le 1$. Then $\mathcal{C}(\boldsymbol{V}\boldsymbol{T}') \subseteq \mathcal{C}(\boldsymbol{V}\boldsymbol{L}') \subseteq \mathcal{C}(\boldsymbol{X})$ according to Proposition 7.15(a). Therefore, the matrix $\boldsymbol{T}$ satisfies conditions (a) of Proposition 11.30. Since $\boldsymbol{T}\boldsymbol{V}\boldsymbol{C}' = c\boldsymbol{C}(\boldsymbol{L}\boldsymbol{V})\boldsymbol{C}'$ and $\boldsymbol{L}\boldsymbol{V}$ is symmetric, condition (b) is also satisfied. Condition (c) is satisfied, as $\boldsymbol{T}\boldsymbol{V}\boldsymbol{T}' = c^2\boldsymbol{C}(\boldsymbol{L}\boldsymbol{V})\boldsymbol{C}'$ and $\boldsymbol{T}\boldsymbol{V}\boldsymbol{C}' = c\boldsymbol{C}(\boldsymbol{L}\boldsymbol{V})\boldsymbol{C}'$. In order to check condition (d), let $\boldsymbol{W} = \boldsymbol{V}\boldsymbol{L}' = \boldsymbol{L}\boldsymbol{V}\boldsymbol{L}$. Then $\mathcal{C}((\boldsymbol{T} - \boldsymbol{C})\boldsymbol{X}) = \mathcal{C}((1-c)\boldsymbol{C}\boldsymbol{X})$ and $\mathcal{C}((\boldsymbol{T} - \boldsymbol{C})\boldsymbol{W}) = \mathcal{C}((1-c)\boldsymbol{C}\boldsymbol{V}\boldsymbol{L}')$. The condition is satisfied trivially when $c = 1$. If $c < 1$, then $\mathcal{C}((\boldsymbol{T}-\boldsymbol{C})\boldsymbol{W}) = \mathcal{C}(\boldsymbol{C}\boldsymbol{X}) \cap \mathcal{C}(\boldsymbol{C}\boldsymbol{V}) \subseteq \mathcal{C}(\boldsymbol{C}\boldsymbol{X}) = \mathcal{C}((\boldsymbol{T} - \boldsymbol{C})\boldsymbol{X})$, and the two column spaces are identical if and only if $\mathcal{C}(\boldsymbol{C}\boldsymbol{X}) \subseteq \mathcal{C}(\boldsymbol{C}\boldsymbol{V})$. A sufficient condition for this is $\mathcal{C}(\boldsymbol{X}) \subseteq \mathcal{C}(\boldsymbol{V})$, which obviously holds when $\boldsymbol{V}$ is positive definite.

11.8 (a) The inequality $E[(\boldsymbol{S}\boldsymbol{y} - \boldsymbol{g}(\boldsymbol{\theta}))'\boldsymbol{B}(\boldsymbol{S}\boldsymbol{y} - \boldsymbol{g}(\boldsymbol{\theta}))] \le E[(\boldsymbol{T}\boldsymbol{y} - \boldsymbol{g}(\boldsymbol{\theta}))'\,\boldsymbol{B}(\boldsymbol{T}\boldsymbol{y} - \boldsymbol{g}(\boldsymbol{\theta}))]$ is preserved when $\boldsymbol{B}$ is replaced by $\boldsymbol{F} = \boldsymbol{B}/b$.

(b) Let $\boldsymbol{R}\boldsymbol{y} = \boldsymbol{T}\boldsymbol{y} + \boldsymbol{F}(\boldsymbol{S}\boldsymbol{y} - \boldsymbol{T}\boldsymbol{y})$. Using the fact that $\boldsymbol{F}^2 \le \boldsymbol{F}$, we have

$$\begin{aligned}&E[(\boldsymbol{R}\boldsymbol{y} - \boldsymbol{g}(\boldsymbol{\theta}))'(\boldsymbol{R}\boldsymbol{y} - \boldsymbol{g}(\boldsymbol{\theta}))]\\&\quad= E[(\boldsymbol{T}\boldsymbol{y} - \boldsymbol{g}(\boldsymbol{\theta}))'(\boldsymbol{T}\boldsymbol{y} - \boldsymbol{g}(\boldsymbol{\theta}))] + 2E[(\boldsymbol{T}\boldsymbol{y} - \boldsymbol{g}(\boldsymbol{\theta}))'\boldsymbol{F}(\boldsymbol{S}\boldsymbol{y} - \boldsymbol{T}\boldsymbol{y})]\\&\qquad+ E[(\boldsymbol{S}\boldsymbol{y} - \boldsymbol{T}\boldsymbol{y})'\boldsymbol{F}^2(\boldsymbol{S}\boldsymbol{y} - \boldsymbol{T}\boldsymbol{y})]\\&\quad\le E[(\boldsymbol{T}\boldsymbol{y} - \boldsymbol{g}(\boldsymbol{\theta}))'(\boldsymbol{T}\boldsymbol{y} - \boldsymbol{g}(\boldsymbol{\theta}))] + E[(\boldsymbol{S}\boldsymbol{y} - \boldsymbol{g}(\boldsymbol{\theta}))'\boldsymbol{F}(\boldsymbol{S}\boldsymbol{y} - \boldsymbol{g}(\boldsymbol{\theta}))]\\&\qquad- E[(\boldsymbol{T}\boldsymbol{y} - \boldsymbol{g}(\boldsymbol{\theta}))'\boldsymbol{F}(\boldsymbol{T}\boldsymbol{y} - \boldsymbol{g}(\boldsymbol{\theta}))]\\&\quad\le E[(\boldsymbol{T}\boldsymbol{y} - \boldsymbol{g}(\boldsymbol{\theta}))'(\boldsymbol{T}\boldsymbol{y} - \boldsymbol{g}(\boldsymbol{\theta}))].\end{aligned}$$

Thus, $\boldsymbol{T}\boldsymbol{y}$ is linearly inadmissible.

(c) The result is proved by contradiction using part (b).

11.9 The risk of $\boldsymbol{C}\boldsymbol{T}\boldsymbol{y}$ with respect to the squared error loss function (L_I) is equal to the risk of $\boldsymbol{T}\boldsymbol{y}$ with respect to the loss function L_B, where $\boldsymbol{B} = \boldsymbol{C}'\boldsymbol{C}$. The result follows from Exercise 11.8.

11.10 Let $\boldsymbol{FF}'$ be a rank-factorization of $\boldsymbol{B}$ and $\boldsymbol{A} = \boldsymbol{CX}$. We have

$$\begin{aligned}
E[(\boldsymbol{Ty} - \boldsymbol{A\beta})'\boldsymbol{B}(\boldsymbol{Ty} - \boldsymbol{A\beta})] &= \text{tr}[\boldsymbol{F}'E\{(\boldsymbol{Ty} - \boldsymbol{A\beta})(\boldsymbol{Ty} - \boldsymbol{A\beta})'\}\boldsymbol{F}] \\
&= \sigma^2\text{tr}[\boldsymbol{F}'\boldsymbol{TVT}'\boldsymbol{F}] + \text{tr}[\boldsymbol{F}'(\boldsymbol{T} - \boldsymbol{C})\boldsymbol{X\beta\beta}'\boldsymbol{X}'(\boldsymbol{T} - \boldsymbol{C})'\boldsymbol{F}] \\
&\le \sigma^2\text{tr}[\boldsymbol{F}'\boldsymbol{TVT}'\boldsymbol{F}] + \sigma^2\frac{\boldsymbol{\beta}'\boldsymbol{X}'(\boldsymbol{T} - \boldsymbol{C})'\boldsymbol{FF}'(\boldsymbol{T} - \boldsymbol{C})\boldsymbol{X\beta}}{\boldsymbol{\beta}'\boldsymbol{H\beta}} \\
&\le \sigma^2\text{tr}[\boldsymbol{F}'\boldsymbol{TVT}'\boldsymbol{F}] + \sigma^2\|\boldsymbol{F}'(\boldsymbol{T} - \boldsymbol{C})\boldsymbol{XH}^-\boldsymbol{X}'(\boldsymbol{T} - \boldsymbol{C})'\boldsymbol{F}\|.
\end{aligned}$$

The last step follows from Exercise A.32(b). The first inequality holds with equality when $\|\boldsymbol{K}'\boldsymbol{\beta}\| = \sigma$, where $\boldsymbol{KK}'$ is a rank-factorization of $\boldsymbol{H}$. The second inequality holds with equality when $\boldsymbol{K}'\boldsymbol{\beta}$ is the eigenvector corresponding to the largest eigenvalue of $\boldsymbol{K}^-\boldsymbol{X}'(\boldsymbol{T} - \boldsymbol{C})'\boldsymbol{FF}'(\boldsymbol{T} - \boldsymbol{C})\boldsymbol{X}(\boldsymbol{K}^-)'$.

11.11 (a) The result is proved along the lines of Exercise 11.10, with $\boldsymbol{B} = \boldsymbol{pp}'$.

(b) Let $\boldsymbol{KK}'$ be a rank-factorization of $\boldsymbol{H}$. We have

$$\begin{aligned}
&E[(\boldsymbol{Ty} - \boldsymbol{A\beta})(\boldsymbol{Ty} - \boldsymbol{A\beta})'] \\
&\quad = \sigma^2[\boldsymbol{TVT}'] + [(\boldsymbol{T} - \boldsymbol{C})\boldsymbol{X\beta\beta}'\boldsymbol{X}'(\boldsymbol{T} - \boldsymbol{C})'] \\
&\quad \le \sigma^2[\boldsymbol{TVT}' + (\boldsymbol{T} - \boldsymbol{C})\boldsymbol{X\beta\beta}'\boldsymbol{X}'(\boldsymbol{T} - \boldsymbol{C})'/\boldsymbol{\beta}'\boldsymbol{KK}'\boldsymbol{\beta}] \\
&\quad = \sigma^2[\boldsymbol{TVT}' + (\boldsymbol{T} - \boldsymbol{C})\boldsymbol{X}(\boldsymbol{K}^{-L})'\boldsymbol{P}_{\boldsymbol{K}'\boldsymbol{\beta}}\boldsymbol{K}^{-L}\boldsymbol{X}'(\boldsymbol{T} - \boldsymbol{C})'] \\
&\quad \le \sigma^2[\boldsymbol{TVT}' + (\boldsymbol{T} - \boldsymbol{C})\boldsymbol{X}(\boldsymbol{K}^{-L})'\boldsymbol{K}^{-L}\boldsymbol{X}'(\boldsymbol{T} - \boldsymbol{C})'] \\
&\quad = \sigma^2[\boldsymbol{TVT}' + (\boldsymbol{T} - \boldsymbol{C})\boldsymbol{XH}^-\boldsymbol{X}'(\boldsymbol{T} - \boldsymbol{C})'].
\end{aligned}$$

The equality does not hold for any particular matrix, but no matrix smaller than $\sigma^2[\boldsymbol{TVT}'+(\boldsymbol{T}-\boldsymbol{C})\boldsymbol{XH}^-\boldsymbol{X}'(\boldsymbol{T}-\boldsymbol{C})']$ satisfies the inequality. Hence, the latter matrix is the required supremum.

(c) Let $\boldsymbol{AX}^-\boldsymbol{X}\widehat{\boldsymbol{\beta}}_m = \boldsymbol{T}_0\boldsymbol{y}$. By part (b), we have

$$\begin{aligned}
&\sup_{\boldsymbol{\beta}:\ \boldsymbol{\beta}'\boldsymbol{H\beta}\le\sigma^2} E[(\boldsymbol{AX}^-\boldsymbol{X}\widehat{\boldsymbol{\beta}}_m - \boldsymbol{A\beta})(\boldsymbol{AX}^-\boldsymbol{X}\widehat{\boldsymbol{\beta}}_m - \boldsymbol{A\beta})'] \\
&\qquad = \sigma^2[\boldsymbol{T}_0\boldsymbol{VT}_0' + (\boldsymbol{T}_0 - \boldsymbol{C})\boldsymbol{XH}^-\boldsymbol{X}'(\boldsymbol{T}_0 - \boldsymbol{C})'], \\
&\sup_{\boldsymbol{\beta}:\ \boldsymbol{\beta}'\boldsymbol{H\beta}\le\sigma^2} E[(\boldsymbol{Ty} - \boldsymbol{A\beta})(\boldsymbol{Ty} - \boldsymbol{A\beta})'] \\
&\qquad = \sigma^2[\boldsymbol{TVT}' + (\boldsymbol{T} - \boldsymbol{C})\boldsymbol{XH}^-\boldsymbol{X}'(\boldsymbol{T} - \boldsymbol{C})'].
\end{aligned}$$

Since

$$\begin{aligned}
&\sigma^2\boldsymbol{p}'[\boldsymbol{T}_0\boldsymbol{VT}_0' + (\boldsymbol{T}_0 - \boldsymbol{C})\boldsymbol{XH}^-\boldsymbol{X}'(\boldsymbol{T}_0 - \boldsymbol{C})']\boldsymbol{p} \\
&\qquad \le \sigma^2\boldsymbol{p}'[\boldsymbol{TVT}' + (\boldsymbol{T} - \boldsymbol{C})\boldsymbol{XH}^-\boldsymbol{X}'(\boldsymbol{T} - \boldsymbol{C})']\boldsymbol{p}
\end{aligned}$$

for all $\boldsymbol{p}$, we have

$$\begin{aligned}
&\sigma^2[\boldsymbol{T}_0\boldsymbol{VT}_0' + (\boldsymbol{T}_0 - \boldsymbol{C})\boldsymbol{XH}^-\boldsymbol{X}'(\boldsymbol{T}_0 - \boldsymbol{C})'] \\
&\qquad \le \sigma^2[\boldsymbol{TVT}' + (\boldsymbol{T} - \boldsymbol{C})\boldsymbol{XH}^-\boldsymbol{X}'(\boldsymbol{T} - \boldsymbol{C})'].
\end{aligned}$$

This proves (11.7).

11.12 We have, from Proposition 11.38 and (11.8), the following expressions for the MILEs in cases (a) and (b).

$$\widehat{\boldsymbol{\beta}}_M = [1 + h\mathrm{tr}((\boldsymbol{X}'\boldsymbol{V}^{-1}\boldsymbol{X})^{-1})](\boldsymbol{X}'\boldsymbol{V}^{-1}\boldsymbol{X})^{-1}\boldsymbol{X}'\boldsymbol{V}^{-1}\boldsymbol{y},$$
$$\widehat{\boldsymbol{\beta}}_m = (\boldsymbol{X}'\boldsymbol{V}^{-1}\boldsymbol{X} + h\boldsymbol{I})^{-1}\boldsymbol{X}'\boldsymbol{V}^{-1}\boldsymbol{y}.$$

In order that these are equal almost surely for all $\boldsymbol{y}$, we must have $(\boldsymbol{X}'\boldsymbol{V}^{-1}\boldsymbol{X} + h\boldsymbol{I})\widehat{\boldsymbol{\beta}}_M = (\boldsymbol{X}'\boldsymbol{V}^{-1}\boldsymbol{X} + h\boldsymbol{I})\widehat{\boldsymbol{\beta}}_m$, which simplifies to

$$(\boldsymbol{X}'\boldsymbol{V}^{-1}\boldsymbol{X})^{-1}\boldsymbol{X}'\boldsymbol{V}^{-1}\boldsymbol{y} = \mathrm{tr}[(\boldsymbol{X}'\boldsymbol{V}^{-1}\boldsymbol{X})^{-1}]\boldsymbol{X}'\boldsymbol{V}^{-1}\boldsymbol{y}$$

for almost all $\boldsymbol{y}$, i.e. $(\boldsymbol{X}'\boldsymbol{V}^{-1}\boldsymbol{X})^{-1} = \mathrm{tr}[(\boldsymbol{X}'\boldsymbol{V}^{-1}\boldsymbol{X})^{-1}]\boldsymbol{I}$. However, the ratio of the traces of the two matrices is $\rho(\boldsymbol{X})$.

11.13 Let the MILE mentioned in the problem be $\boldsymbol{a}'\widehat{\boldsymbol{\beta}}_m$. Assume that $\boldsymbol{a}'\widehat{\boldsymbol{\beta}}_m = \boldsymbol{a}'\widehat{\boldsymbol{\beta}}_M$ for almost all $\boldsymbol{y}$. Then, $E(\boldsymbol{a}'\widehat{\boldsymbol{\beta}}_m - \boldsymbol{a}'\widehat{\boldsymbol{\beta}}_M) = 0$, that is,

$$\begin{aligned}
0 &= \boldsymbol{a}'(\boldsymbol{X}'\boldsymbol{V}^{-1}\boldsymbol{X} + h\boldsymbol{I})^{-1}\boldsymbol{X}'\boldsymbol{V}^{-1}\boldsymbol{X}\boldsymbol{\beta} - \frac{\boldsymbol{a}'\boldsymbol{\beta}}{1 + h\mathrm{tr}[(\boldsymbol{X}'\boldsymbol{V}^{-1}\boldsymbol{X})^{-1}]} \\
&= \boldsymbol{a}'(\boldsymbol{I} + \boldsymbol{B})^{-1}\boldsymbol{\beta} - \boldsymbol{a}'\boldsymbol{\beta}/(1 + \mathrm{tr}(\boldsymbol{B})) \\
&= \boldsymbol{a}'(\boldsymbol{I} + \boldsymbol{B})^{-1}\left[\boldsymbol{I} - (\boldsymbol{I} + \boldsymbol{B})/(1 + \mathrm{tr}(\boldsymbol{B}))\right]\boldsymbol{\beta} \\
&= \boldsymbol{a}'(\boldsymbol{I} + \boldsymbol{B})^{-1}[\boldsymbol{I} - \boldsymbol{B}/\mathrm{tr}(\boldsymbol{B})]\boldsymbol{\beta}/(1 + 1/\mathrm{tr}(\boldsymbol{B})),
\end{aligned}$$

where $\boldsymbol{B} = h(\boldsymbol{X}'\boldsymbol{V}^{-1}\boldsymbol{X})^{-1}$. However, any matrix of the form $\boldsymbol{I} - \boldsymbol{B}/\mathrm{tr}(\boldsymbol{B})$, for symmetric positive definite $\boldsymbol{B}$, is positive definite. Therefore, the above expression cannot be equal to 0.

11.14 (a) When $\boldsymbol{V}$ is nonsingular, the Kuks-Olman estimator of $\boldsymbol{X}\boldsymbol{\beta}$ can be written as $\boldsymbol{X}\widehat{\boldsymbol{\beta}}_m = \boldsymbol{X}\boldsymbol{H}^-\boldsymbol{X}'(\boldsymbol{V} + \boldsymbol{X}\boldsymbol{H}^-\boldsymbol{X}')^{-1}\boldsymbol{y}$. However,

$$\begin{aligned}
\boldsymbol{X}\boldsymbol{H}^-\boldsymbol{X}' &= \boldsymbol{X}(\boldsymbol{X}'\boldsymbol{V}^{-1}\boldsymbol{X} + \boldsymbol{H})^-(\boldsymbol{X}'\boldsymbol{V}^{-1}\boldsymbol{X} + \boldsymbol{H})\boldsymbol{H}^-\boldsymbol{X}' \\
&= \boldsymbol{X}(\boldsymbol{X}'\boldsymbol{V}^{-1}\boldsymbol{X} + \boldsymbol{H})^-\boldsymbol{X}'\boldsymbol{V}^{-1}\boldsymbol{X}\boldsymbol{H}^-\boldsymbol{X}' \\
&\quad + \boldsymbol{X}(\boldsymbol{X}'\boldsymbol{V}^{-1}\boldsymbol{X} + \boldsymbol{H})^-\boldsymbol{X}' \\
&= \boldsymbol{X}(\boldsymbol{X}'\boldsymbol{V}^{-1}\boldsymbol{X} + \boldsymbol{H})^-\boldsymbol{X}'\boldsymbol{V}^{-1}[\boldsymbol{X}\boldsymbol{H}^-\boldsymbol{X}' + \boldsymbol{V}].
\end{aligned}$$

Hence, $\boldsymbol{X}\widehat{\boldsymbol{\beta}}_m = \boldsymbol{X}(\boldsymbol{X}'\boldsymbol{V}^{-1}\boldsymbol{X} + \boldsymbol{H})^-\boldsymbol{X}'\boldsymbol{V}^{-1}\boldsymbol{y}$.

(b) When $\boldsymbol{V}$ and $\boldsymbol{U}$ are nonsingular, the BLE of Proposition 11.34 is $\boldsymbol{U}\boldsymbol{X}'(\boldsymbol{V} + \boldsymbol{X}\boldsymbol{U}\boldsymbol{X}')^{-1}\boldsymbol{y}$. Proceeding as in part (a) with $\boldsymbol{H}$ replaced by $\boldsymbol{U}^{-1}$ and all the g-inverses replaced by inverses, we have $\boldsymbol{U}^{-1}\boldsymbol{X}' = (\boldsymbol{X}'\boldsymbol{V}^{-1}\boldsymbol{X} + \boldsymbol{U}^{-1})^{-1}\boldsymbol{X}'\boldsymbol{V}^{-1}[\boldsymbol{X}\boldsymbol{U}\boldsymbol{X}' + \boldsymbol{V}]$. The result follows.

11.15 Let $\boldsymbol{a} = \boldsymbol{X}'\boldsymbol{c}$. Following the proof of Proposition 11.34, we obtain the Bayes risk of the estimator $\boldsymbol{t}'\boldsymbol{y}$, for a given value of σ^2, as $\sigma^2[\boldsymbol{t}'\boldsymbol{V}\boldsymbol{t}+(\boldsymbol{t}-\boldsymbol{c})'\boldsymbol{X}\boldsymbol{U}\boldsymbol{X}'(\boldsymbol{t}-\boldsymbol{c})]$. On the other hand, the maximum risk subject to the constraint $\boldsymbol{\gamma}'\boldsymbol{H}\boldsymbol{\gamma} \le 1$ is $\sigma^2[\boldsymbol{t}'\boldsymbol{V}\boldsymbol{t} + (\boldsymbol{t} - \boldsymbol{c})'\boldsymbol{X}\boldsymbol{H}^-\boldsymbol{X}'(\boldsymbol{t} - \boldsymbol{c})]$ (see the proof of Proposition 11.37).

The average risk coincides with the maximum risk when $\boldsymbol{U} = \boldsymbol{H}^-$. According to the discussion of page 559, the corresponding prior must be the least favourable prior, and the BLE and MILE should coincide in such a case.

11.16 Note that the projection $\boldsymbol{P}_{A|B}\boldsymbol{l}$ must be unique (see discussion preceding Definition 11.39).

(a) Let $\boldsymbol{P}_1$ and $\boldsymbol{P}_2$ be two distinct choices of $\boldsymbol{P}_{A|B}$. Then $(\boldsymbol{P}_1 - \boldsymbol{P}_2)\boldsymbol{l} = \boldsymbol{0}$ for every $\boldsymbol{l} \in \mathcal{C}(\boldsymbol{A} : \boldsymbol{B})$. When $(\boldsymbol{A} : \boldsymbol{B})$ has full row rank, this would mean $(\boldsymbol{P}_1 - \boldsymbol{P}_2)\boldsymbol{l} = \boldsymbol{0}$ for all $\boldsymbol{l}$, i.e. $\boldsymbol{P}_1 = \boldsymbol{P}_2$.

(b) Uniqueness of the projection implies that $\boldsymbol{P}_{A|B}\boldsymbol{l} = \boldsymbol{l}$ for every $\boldsymbol{l} \in \mathcal{C}(\boldsymbol{A})$. If $(\boldsymbol{A} : \boldsymbol{B})$ has full rank, we can use this argument for $\boldsymbol{l} = \boldsymbol{P}_{A|B}\boldsymbol{u}_i$, $\boldsymbol{u}_i$ being the ith column of the appropriate identity matrix. Thus we have $\boldsymbol{P}_{A|B}\boldsymbol{P}_{A|B}\boldsymbol{u}_i = \boldsymbol{P}_{A|B}\boldsymbol{u}_i$ for all i up to the number of rows of $\boldsymbol{A}$. Consequently $\boldsymbol{P}_{A|B}^2 = \boldsymbol{P}_{A|B}$.

(c) If $(\boldsymbol{A} : \boldsymbol{B})$ does not have full row rank, then there is a matrix $\boldsymbol{C}$ such that $\boldsymbol{C}'(\boldsymbol{A} : \boldsymbol{B}) = \boldsymbol{0}$ and $(\boldsymbol{A} : \boldsymbol{B} : \boldsymbol{C})$ has full row rank. Then $\boldsymbol{P}_{A|(B:C)}$ and $\boldsymbol{P}_{(A:C)|B}$ are distinct choices of $\boldsymbol{P}_{A|B}$, as $\boldsymbol{P}_{A|(B:C)}\boldsymbol{C} = \boldsymbol{0}$ and $\boldsymbol{P}_{(A:C)|B}\boldsymbol{C} = \boldsymbol{C}$. Yet another choice, $\frac{1}{2}[\boldsymbol{P}_{A|(B:C)} + \boldsymbol{P}_{(A:C)|B}]$ is non-idempotent, since $\frac{1}{2}[\boldsymbol{P}_{A|(B:C)} + \boldsymbol{P}_{(A:C)|B}]\boldsymbol{C} = \frac{1}{2}\boldsymbol{C}$ and $\frac{1}{4}[\boldsymbol{P}_{A|(B:C)} + \boldsymbol{P}_{(A:C)|B}]^2\boldsymbol{C} = \frac{1}{4}\boldsymbol{C}$.

Appendix A

A.1 Partition $\boldsymbol{I}_{n\times n}$ as $(\boldsymbol{u}_1 : \cdots : \boldsymbol{u}_n)$. Then $\boldsymbol{P} = (\boldsymbol{u}_2 : \boldsymbol{u}_1 : \boldsymbol{u}_3 : \cdots : \boldsymbol{u}_n)$ and $\boldsymbol{Q} = \boldsymbol{P}'$.

A.2 $\boldsymbol{P} = \boldsymbol{Q}^{-1}$.

A.3(a) If $\boldsymbol{A}$ is positive definite, then for all $\boldsymbol{v} \neq \boldsymbol{0}$, we have $\boldsymbol{v}'\boldsymbol{A}\boldsymbol{v} > 0$, i.e. $\boldsymbol{A}\boldsymbol{v} \neq \boldsymbol{0}$. Hence, $\rho(\boldsymbol{A}) = n$ and $\boldsymbol{A}$ is nonsingular.

(b) If $\boldsymbol{A}$ is symmetric and positive semidefinite, then it can be factorized as $\boldsymbol{C}\boldsymbol{C}'$ and there is a $\boldsymbol{v} \neq \boldsymbol{0}$ such that $\boldsymbol{v}'\boldsymbol{A}\boldsymbol{v} = 0$. It follows that $\|\boldsymbol{C}'\boldsymbol{v}\| = 0$, i.e. $\boldsymbol{C}'\boldsymbol{v} = \boldsymbol{0}$. Therefore $\boldsymbol{C}$ does not have full row rank, and so $\boldsymbol{A}$ is singular.

(c) The matrix $\begin{pmatrix} 2 & 3 \\ 1 & 2 \end{pmatrix}$ is positive semidefinite but nonsingular.

A.4 The result is proved by direct verification.

A.5 Yes. $\boldsymbol{A}'(\boldsymbol{A}^-)'\boldsymbol{A}' = (\boldsymbol{A}\boldsymbol{A}^-\boldsymbol{A})' = \boldsymbol{A}'$. If $\boldsymbol{A}$ is symmetric and $\boldsymbol{A}^-$ is any g-inverse of it, then $\frac{1}{2}[\boldsymbol{A}^- + (\boldsymbol{A}^-)']$ is a symmetric g-inverse of $\boldsymbol{A}$.

A.6 Let $\boldsymbol{G}$ be a g-inverse of $\boldsymbol{A}$. If $\boldsymbol{A}$ has full column rank, then the relation $\boldsymbol{A}(\boldsymbol{G}\boldsymbol{A} - \boldsymbol{I}) = \boldsymbol{0}$ cannot hold unless $\boldsymbol{G}\boldsymbol{A} - \boldsymbol{I} = \boldsymbol{0}$.

A.7 The result follows from the identity

$$\begin{pmatrix} \boldsymbol{I} & \boldsymbol{0} \\ -\boldsymbol{C}\boldsymbol{A}^{-1} & \boldsymbol{I} \end{pmatrix} \begin{pmatrix} \boldsymbol{A} & \boldsymbol{B} \\ \boldsymbol{C} & \boldsymbol{D} \end{pmatrix} \begin{pmatrix} \boldsymbol{I} & -\boldsymbol{A}^{-1}\boldsymbol{B} \\ \boldsymbol{0} & \boldsymbol{I} \end{pmatrix} = \begin{pmatrix} \boldsymbol{A} & \boldsymbol{0} \\ \boldsymbol{0} & \boldsymbol{D} - \boldsymbol{C}\boldsymbol{A}^{-1}\boldsymbol{B} \end{pmatrix},$$

which is similar to (A.7), and the fact that the pre- and post-multiplying matrices on the left-hand side are both nonsingular.

A.8 Using (A.6), we can write

$$\begin{aligned} M^- &= \begin{pmatrix} I & A^-B \\ 0 & I \end{pmatrix}^- \begin{pmatrix} A & 0 \\ 0 & C - B'A^-B \end{pmatrix}^- \begin{pmatrix} I & 0 \\ B'A^- & I \end{pmatrix}^- \\ &= \begin{pmatrix} I & -A^-B \\ 0 & I \end{pmatrix} \begin{pmatrix} A^- & 0 \\ 0 & T^- \end{pmatrix} \begin{pmatrix} I & 0 \\ -B'A^- & I \end{pmatrix} \\ &= \begin{pmatrix} A^- + A^-BT^-B'A^- & -A^-BT^- \\ -T^-B'A^- & T^- \end{pmatrix}. \end{aligned}$$

A.9 Let $u_1, \ldots, u_k$ and $v_1, \ldots, v_p$ be bases of $\mathcal{S}$, and $p > k$. Then for $i = 1, \ldots, p$ there is l_i such that $v_i = (u_1 : \cdots : u_k)l_i$. Let $L = (l_1 : \cdots : l_p)$. Since $k < p$, we have $\rho(L) < p$. Hence, there is a vector a such that $La = 0$. Thus $(v_1 : \cdots : v_p)a = 0$, i.e. $v_1, \ldots, v_p$ cannot be linearly independent.

A.10 (a) Let $\dim(\mathcal{S}_1 \cap \mathcal{S}_2) = m$, $\dim(\mathcal{S}_1) = m + j$ and $\dim(\mathcal{S}_2) = m + k$. Let $u_1, \ldots, u_m$ be a basis of $\mathcal{S}_1 \cap \mathcal{S}_2$, $u_1, \ldots, u_m, v_1, \ldots, v_j$ be a basis of $\mathcal{S}_1$ and $u_1, \ldots, u_m, w_1, \ldots, w_k$ be a basis of $\mathcal{S}_2$. We shall show that $u_1, \ldots, u_m, v_1, \ldots, v_j, w_1, \ldots, w_k$ is a basis of $\mathcal{S}_1 + \mathcal{S}_2$. It is easy to see that every vector of $\mathcal{S}_1 + \mathcal{S}_2$ is a linear combination of the proposed 'basis'. We only have to show the linear independence of the 'basis' vectors. To prove this by contradiction, let

$$\sum_{i=1}^{m} \alpha_i u_i + \sum_{i=1}^{j} \beta_i v_i + \sum_{i=1}^{k} \gamma_i w_i = 0.$$

Since $\sum_{i=1}^m \alpha_i u_i + \sum_{i=1}^j \beta_i v_i \in \mathcal{S}_1$ and $-\sum_{i=1}^k \gamma_i w_i \in \mathcal{S}_2$ and these two vectors are equal to one another, we have

$$-\sum_{i=1}^{k} \gamma_i w_i \in \mathcal{S}_1 \cap \mathcal{S}_2.$$

Therefore, $-\sum_{i=1}^k \gamma_i w_i$ can be expressed as $\sum_{i=1}^m \delta_i u_i$, i.e. $\sum_{i=1}^m \delta_i u_i + \sum_{i=1}^k \gamma_i w_i = 0$, i.e. $u_1, \ldots, u_m, w_1, \ldots, w_k$ cannot be a basis set of $\mathcal{S}_2$.

(b) Let $u \in \mathcal{S}_1^\perp \cap \mathcal{S}_2^\perp$. Then u is orthogonal to every vector in $\mathcal{S}_1$ and $\mathcal{S}_2$ and therefore to any linear combination of such vectors. Hence, $u \in (\mathcal{S}_1 + \mathcal{S}_2)^\perp$. Conversely, if $u \in (\mathcal{S}_1 + \mathcal{S}_2)^\perp$, then u is orthogonal to every vector in $\mathcal{S}_1 + \mathcal{S}_2$, and in particular, to those in $\mathcal{S}_1$ and $\mathcal{S}_2$. Thus, $u \in \mathcal{S}_1^\perp \cap \mathcal{S}_2^\perp$.

(c) Let $\dim(\mathcal{S}_1) = k$ and $u_1, \ldots, u_k$ be a basis of $\mathcal{S}_1$. Then $u_1, \ldots, u_k$ are linearly independent vectors in $\mathcal{S}_2$. Since $\dim(\mathcal{S}_2) = k$, these vectors must also form a basis of $\mathcal{S}_2$. Any vector of $\mathcal{S}_2$ is a linear combination of $u_1, \ldots, u_k$, and therefore must be in $\mathcal{S}_1$.

A.11 Let $\boldsymbol{u}_1, \ldots, \boldsymbol{u}_k$ be $p \times 1$ vectors forming a basis of a vector space $\mathcal{S}$, and let $k > p$. Let $\boldsymbol{U}_{p\times k} = (\boldsymbol{u}_1 : \cdots : \boldsymbol{u}_k)$. The row rank (and the column rank) of $\boldsymbol{U}$ is less than or equal to p. Thus, $\boldsymbol{U}$ has at most p independent columns. Since $p < k$, the vectors $\boldsymbol{u}_1, \ldots, \boldsymbol{u}_k$ cannot be linearly independent.

A.12 Let $\boldsymbol{v}_a$ and $\boldsymbol{v}_b$ be projections of $\boldsymbol{v}$ on $\mathcal{S}$. Consequently $\boldsymbol{v}_a \in \mathcal{S}$, $\boldsymbol{v}_b \in \mathcal{S}$, $(\boldsymbol{v} - \boldsymbol{v}_a) \in \mathcal{S}^\perp$ and $(\boldsymbol{v} - \boldsymbol{v}_b) \in \mathcal{S}^\perp$. Therefore, $(\boldsymbol{v}_a - \boldsymbol{v}_b) \in \mathcal{S}$ and $[(\boldsymbol{v} - \boldsymbol{v}_b) - (\boldsymbol{v} - \boldsymbol{v}_a)] \in \mathcal{S}^\perp$. It follows that $\boldsymbol{v}_a - \boldsymbol{v}_b$ is in $\mathcal{S} \cap \mathcal{S}^\perp$, i.e. $\boldsymbol{v}_a - \boldsymbol{v}_b = \boldsymbol{0}$.

A.13 Let $\boldsymbol{P}_1$ and $\boldsymbol{P}_2$ be two orthogonal projection matrices of the vector space $\mathcal{S}$, and $\boldsymbol{u}$ be any vector having the same order as those in $\mathcal{S}$. It follows from Exercise A.12 that $(\boldsymbol{P}_1 - \boldsymbol{P}_2)\boldsymbol{u} = \boldsymbol{0}$. Since this holds for *all* $\boldsymbol{u}$ of appropriate order, we can stack together different versions of this identity by choosing $\boldsymbol{u}$ as successive columns of the identity matrix, to obtain $\boldsymbol{P}_1 - \boldsymbol{P}_2 = \boldsymbol{0}$.

A.14(a) Let $\boldsymbol{P}$ be an idempotent matrix and $\mathcal{S} = \mathcal{C}(\boldsymbol{P})$. It is obvious that for any vector $\boldsymbol{u}$ of appropriate order, $\boldsymbol{P}\boldsymbol{u} \in \mathcal{S}$. Further, whenever $\boldsymbol{u} \in \mathcal{S}$, we can write $\boldsymbol{u}$ as $\boldsymbol{P}\boldsymbol{l}$ for some vector $\boldsymbol{l}$, so that $\boldsymbol{P}\boldsymbol{u} = \boldsymbol{P}^2\boldsymbol{l} = \boldsymbol{P}\boldsymbol{l} = \boldsymbol{u}$. Hence, $\boldsymbol{P}$ is a projection matrix of $\mathcal{S}$.

(b) A matrix is a projection matrix if and only if it is idempotent. We have to show that a projection matrix is orthogonal if and only if it is symmetric. Let $\boldsymbol{P}$ be an orthogonal projection matrix. Then for all vectors $\boldsymbol{u}$ and $\boldsymbol{v}$ of appropriate order, $\boldsymbol{P}\boldsymbol{u}$ and $(\boldsymbol{I} - \boldsymbol{P})\boldsymbol{v}$ are orthogonal to one another. Thus, $\boldsymbol{v}'(\boldsymbol{I}-\boldsymbol{P})'\boldsymbol{P}\boldsymbol{u} = 0$ for all $\boldsymbol{u}$ and $\boldsymbol{v}$, i.e. $(\boldsymbol{I}-\boldsymbol{P})'\boldsymbol{P} = \boldsymbol{0}$. Consequently $\boldsymbol{P} = \boldsymbol{P}'\boldsymbol{P}$, which is symmetric.

Now suppose $\boldsymbol{P}$ is a symmetric projection matrix of the vector space $\mathcal{S}$. Therefore, for every $\boldsymbol{v} \in \mathcal{S}^\perp$ we have $\boldsymbol{v}'\boldsymbol{P}\boldsymbol{u} = 0$ for arbitrary $\boldsymbol{u}$. Therefore, $\boldsymbol{v}'\boldsymbol{P} = \boldsymbol{0}$, i.e. $\boldsymbol{P}\boldsymbol{v} = \boldsymbol{0}$, and hence $(\boldsymbol{I} - \boldsymbol{P})\boldsymbol{v} = \boldsymbol{v}$. Also, for any vector $\boldsymbol{v}$ of appropriate order, $\boldsymbol{u}'\boldsymbol{P}'(\boldsymbol{I} - \boldsymbol{P})\boldsymbol{v} = \boldsymbol{u}'\boldsymbol{P}(\boldsymbol{I} - \boldsymbol{P})\boldsymbol{v} = 0$ for all $\boldsymbol{u}$, i.e. $\boldsymbol{P}(\boldsymbol{I} - \boldsymbol{P})\boldsymbol{v} = \boldsymbol{0}$, and hence $(\boldsymbol{I} - \boldsymbol{P})\boldsymbol{v} \in \mathcal{S}^\perp$. Thus, $\boldsymbol{I} - \boldsymbol{P}$ is a projection matrix of $\mathcal{S}^\perp$, i.e. $\boldsymbol{P}$ must be the orthogonal projection matrix of $\mathcal{S}$.

A.15 Let $\boldsymbol{u} \in \mathcal{S}_1 \oplus \mathcal{S}_2$. We can write $\boldsymbol{u}$ as $\boldsymbol{u}_1 + \boldsymbol{u}_2$ where $\boldsymbol{u}_1 \in \mathcal{S}_1$, $\boldsymbol{u}_2 \in \mathcal{S}_2$ and $\boldsymbol{u}_1'\boldsymbol{u}_2 = 0$. Therefore,

$$\left(\boldsymbol{P}_{\mathcal{S}_1} + \boldsymbol{P}_{\mathcal{S}_2}\right)\boldsymbol{u} = \boldsymbol{P}_{\mathcal{S}_1}\boldsymbol{u} + \boldsymbol{P}_{\mathcal{S}_2}\boldsymbol{u} = \boldsymbol{P}_{\mathcal{S}_1}\boldsymbol{u}_1 + \boldsymbol{P}_{\mathcal{S}_2}\boldsymbol{u}_2 = \boldsymbol{u}_1 + \boldsymbol{u}_2 = \boldsymbol{u}.$$

Further, for a general $\boldsymbol{u}$, we have $(\boldsymbol{P}_{\mathcal{S}_1} + \boldsymbol{P}_{\mathcal{S}_2})\boldsymbol{u} = \boldsymbol{P}_{\mathcal{S}_1}\boldsymbol{u} + \boldsymbol{P}_{\mathcal{S}_2}\boldsymbol{u} \in \mathcal{S}_1 \oplus \mathcal{S}_2$. Thus, $\boldsymbol{P}_{\mathcal{S}_1} + \boldsymbol{P}_{\mathcal{S}_2}$ is a projection matrix of $\mathcal{S}_1 \oplus \mathcal{S}_2$. Being symmetric, it must be the orthogonal projection matrix of $\mathcal{S}_1 \oplus \mathcal{S}_2$ (see Exercise A.14).

A.16 The condition '$\boldsymbol{A}\boldsymbol{x} = \boldsymbol{0}$ implies $\boldsymbol{p}'\boldsymbol{x} = 0$' is equivalent to '$\boldsymbol{x} \in \mathcal{C}(\boldsymbol{A}')^\perp$ implies $\boldsymbol{x} \in \mathcal{C}(\boldsymbol{p})^\perp$', i.e. $\mathcal{C}(\boldsymbol{A}')^\perp \subseteq \mathcal{C}(\boldsymbol{p})^\perp$. The latter condition in turn is equivalent to $\mathcal{C}(\boldsymbol{p}) \subseteq \mathcal{C}(\boldsymbol{A}')$ or $\boldsymbol{p} \in \mathcal{C}(\boldsymbol{A}')$.

A.17 If $\boldsymbol{B}$ is invertible, then $\rho(\boldsymbol{A}\boldsymbol{B}) \le \rho(\boldsymbol{A}) = \rho(\boldsymbol{A}\boldsymbol{B}\boldsymbol{B}^{-1}) \le \rho(\boldsymbol{A}\boldsymbol{B})$, so that $\rho(\boldsymbol{A}\boldsymbol{B}) = \rho(\boldsymbol{A})$. A similar argument holds when $\boldsymbol{A}$ is invertible.

If $\boldsymbol{U}\boldsymbol{D}\boldsymbol{V}'$ is as described, then using the above argument twice, we have $\rho(\boldsymbol{U}\boldsymbol{D}\boldsymbol{V}') = \rho(\boldsymbol{U}\boldsymbol{D}) = \rho(\boldsymbol{D})$.

A.18 Since $\boldsymbol{C}$ has full row rank, it has a right-inverse. Let $\boldsymbol{C}^{-R}$ be a right-inverse of $\boldsymbol{C}$. Then $\boldsymbol{B} = \boldsymbol{B}\boldsymbol{C}\boldsymbol{C}^{-R} = \boldsymbol{A}\boldsymbol{C}^{-R}$, which implies that $\mathcal{C}(\boldsymbol{B}) \subseteq \mathcal{C}(\boldsymbol{A})$. The reverse inclusion is obvious.

A.19 It is easy to see that for a given g-inverse $\boldsymbol{A}^-$, the matrix $\boldsymbol{A}^- + (\boldsymbol{I} - \boldsymbol{P}_{A'})\boldsymbol{U} + \boldsymbol{V}(\boldsymbol{I} - \boldsymbol{P}_A)$ is also a g-inverse of $\boldsymbol{A}$ for arbitrary $\boldsymbol{U}$ and $\boldsymbol{V}$ of appropriate order. If $\boldsymbol{B}\boldsymbol{A}^-\boldsymbol{C}$ does not depend on the g-inverse, then $\boldsymbol{B}\boldsymbol{A}^-\boldsymbol{C} + \boldsymbol{B}(\boldsymbol{I} - \boldsymbol{P}_{A'})\boldsymbol{U}\boldsymbol{C} + \boldsymbol{B}\boldsymbol{V}(\boldsymbol{I} - \boldsymbol{P}_A)\boldsymbol{C}$ should not depend on $\boldsymbol{U}$ and $\boldsymbol{V}$. Therefore, $\boldsymbol{B}(\boldsymbol{I} - \boldsymbol{P}_{A'})\boldsymbol{U}\boldsymbol{C} = \boldsymbol{0}$ for all $\boldsymbol{U}$ and $\boldsymbol{B}\boldsymbol{V}(\boldsymbol{I} - \boldsymbol{P}_A)\boldsymbol{C} = \boldsymbol{0}$ for all $\boldsymbol{V}$. These identities imply that $\boldsymbol{B}(\boldsymbol{I} - \boldsymbol{P}_{A'}) = \boldsymbol{0}$ and $(\boldsymbol{I} - \boldsymbol{P}_A)\boldsymbol{C} = \boldsymbol{0}$, i.e. $\mathcal{C}(\boldsymbol{B}') \subseteq \mathcal{C}(\boldsymbol{A}')$ and $\mathcal{C}(\boldsymbol{C}) \subseteq \mathcal{C}(\boldsymbol{A})$.

A.20 The identity of part (a) follows along the lines of Exercise A.7, where the inverse is replaced by a g-inverse, and using the results of Proposition A.19(b) and Exercise A.19. The condition of part (b) implies that the matrix $\begin{pmatrix} \boldsymbol{A} & \boldsymbol{B} \\ \boldsymbol{B}' & \boldsymbol{C} \end{pmatrix}$ is nonnegative definite. It follows that the matrix $\begin{pmatrix} \boldsymbol{A} - \boldsymbol{B}\boldsymbol{C}^-\boldsymbol{B}' & \boldsymbol{0} \\ \boldsymbol{0} & \boldsymbol{C} \end{pmatrix}$ is nonnegative definite and that $\mathcal{C}(\boldsymbol{B}') \subseteq \mathcal{C}(\boldsymbol{C})$.

A.21(a) Let $\boldsymbol{C}_i\boldsymbol{C}_i'$ be a rank-factorization of $\boldsymbol{V}_i$, $i = 1, 2$. Then $\mathcal{C}(\boldsymbol{V}_i) = \mathcal{C}(\boldsymbol{C}_i) \subseteq \mathcal{C}(\boldsymbol{C}_1 : \boldsymbol{C}_2) = \mathcal{C}((\boldsymbol{C}_1 : \boldsymbol{C}_2)(\boldsymbol{C}_1 : \boldsymbol{C}_2)') = \mathcal{C}(\boldsymbol{V}_1 : \boldsymbol{V}_2)$ for $i = 1, 2$.

(b) Because of the result of part (a), the choice of $(\boldsymbol{V}_1 + \boldsymbol{V}_2)^-$ in the product $\boldsymbol{V}_1(\boldsymbol{V}_1 + \boldsymbol{V}_2)^-\boldsymbol{V}_2$ does not matter. Without loss of generality, let $(\boldsymbol{V}_1 + \boldsymbol{V}_2)^-$ be symmetric. It follows that $\boldsymbol{V}_1(\boldsymbol{V}_1 + \boldsymbol{V}_2)^-\boldsymbol{V}_2 = \boldsymbol{V}_2 - \boldsymbol{V}_2(\boldsymbol{V}_1 + \boldsymbol{V}_2)^-\boldsymbol{V}_2$, which is symmetric. Using the result of Exercise A.20(b) with $\boldsymbol{A} = \boldsymbol{B} = \boldsymbol{V}_2$ and $\boldsymbol{C} = \boldsymbol{V}_1 + \boldsymbol{V}_2$, we know that the matrix $\boldsymbol{V}_2 - \boldsymbol{V}_2(\boldsymbol{V}_1 + \boldsymbol{V}_2)^-\boldsymbol{V}_2$ is also nonnegative definite.

(c) It is easy to see that $\mathcal{C}(\boldsymbol{V}_1(\boldsymbol{V}_1 + \boldsymbol{V}_2)^-\boldsymbol{V}_2) \subseteq \mathcal{C}(\boldsymbol{V}_1) \cap \mathcal{C}(\boldsymbol{V}_2)$. To prove the reverse inclusion, let $\boldsymbol{u} \in \mathcal{C}(\boldsymbol{V}_1) \cap \mathcal{C}(\boldsymbol{V}_2)$, and let $\boldsymbol{l}$ and $\boldsymbol{m}$ be vectors such that $\boldsymbol{u} = \boldsymbol{V}_1\boldsymbol{l} = \boldsymbol{V}_2\boldsymbol{m}$. Then $\boldsymbol{u} = (\boldsymbol{V}_1 + \boldsymbol{V}_2)(\boldsymbol{V}_1 + \boldsymbol{V}_2)^-\boldsymbol{V}_1\boldsymbol{l} = \boldsymbol{V}_1(\boldsymbol{V}_1 + \boldsymbol{V}_2)^-\boldsymbol{V}_2\boldsymbol{m} + \boldsymbol{V}_2(\boldsymbol{V}_1 + \boldsymbol{V}_2)^-\boldsymbol{V}_1\boldsymbol{l} = \boldsymbol{V}_1(\boldsymbol{V}_1 + \boldsymbol{V}_2)^-\boldsymbol{V}_2\boldsymbol{m} + \boldsymbol{V}_1(\boldsymbol{V}_1 + \boldsymbol{V}_2)^-\boldsymbol{V}_2\boldsymbol{l}$, which is in $\mathcal{C}(\boldsymbol{V}_1(\boldsymbol{V}_1 + \boldsymbol{V}_2)^-\boldsymbol{V}_2)$.

A.22 Let $\boldsymbol{U}_1$, $\boldsymbol{U}_2$ and $\boldsymbol{U}_3$ be semi-orthogonal matrices such that the sets of columns of $\boldsymbol{U}_1$, $(\boldsymbol{U}_1 : \boldsymbol{U}_2)$ and $(\boldsymbol{U}_1 : \boldsymbol{U}_3)$ are orthonormal bases for $\mathcal{C}(\boldsymbol{A}) \cap \mathcal{C}(\boldsymbol{B})$, $\mathcal{C}(\boldsymbol{A})$ and $\mathcal{C}(\boldsymbol{B})$, respectively. Then

$$\begin{aligned}
\rho(\boldsymbol{A}'\boldsymbol{B}) &= \rho(\boldsymbol{P}_A\boldsymbol{P}_B) \\
&= \rho((\boldsymbol{U}_1 : \boldsymbol{U}_2)(\boldsymbol{U}_1 : \boldsymbol{U}_2)'(\boldsymbol{U}_1 : \boldsymbol{U}_3)(\boldsymbol{U}_1 : \boldsymbol{U}_3)') \\
&= \rho((\boldsymbol{U}_1 : \boldsymbol{U}_2)'(\boldsymbol{U}_1 : \boldsymbol{U}_3)) = \rho\begin{pmatrix} \boldsymbol{U}_1'\boldsymbol{U}_1 & \boldsymbol{0} \\ \boldsymbol{0} & \boldsymbol{U}_2'\boldsymbol{U}_3 \end{pmatrix} \\
&= \rho(\boldsymbol{U}_1) + \rho(\boldsymbol{U}_2'\boldsymbol{U}_3) \geq \rho(\boldsymbol{U}_1) = \dim(\mathcal{C}(\boldsymbol{A}) \cap \mathcal{C}(\boldsymbol{B})).
\end{aligned}$$

The inequality is strict when $\boldsymbol{A} = \begin{pmatrix} 1 & 0 \\ 0 & 1 \\ 0 & 0 \end{pmatrix}$ and $\boldsymbol{B} = \begin{pmatrix} 1 & 0 \\ 0 & 1 \\ 0 & 1 \end{pmatrix}$.

A.23 The result follows from the identity used to prove the result of Exercise A.7.

A.24 Let $\boldsymbol{CC}'$ be a rank factorization of $\boldsymbol{A}$.

(a) The Löwner order $\boldsymbol{A} \leq \boldsymbol{B}$ implies that $\boldsymbol{I} \leq \boldsymbol{C}^{-1}\boldsymbol{B}(\boldsymbol{C}')^{-1}$, i.e. all the eigenvalues of the latter matrix are greater than or equal to 1. Therefore, all the eigenvalues of $\boldsymbol{C}'\boldsymbol{B}^{-1}\boldsymbol{C}$ are less than or equal to 1. It follows that, $\boldsymbol{v}'\boldsymbol{C}'\boldsymbol{B}^{-1}\boldsymbol{C}\boldsymbol{v} \leq \boldsymbol{v}'\boldsymbol{v}$ for all $\boldsymbol{v}$ and $\boldsymbol{u}'\boldsymbol{B}^{-1}\boldsymbol{u} \leq \boldsymbol{u}'(\boldsymbol{C}')^{-1}\boldsymbol{C}^{-1}\boldsymbol{u}$ for all $\boldsymbol{v}$. Hence, $\boldsymbol{B}^{-1} \leq (\boldsymbol{C}')^{-1}\boldsymbol{C}^{-1} = \boldsymbol{A}^{-1}$.

(b) Note that

$$\begin{pmatrix} \boldsymbol{A} & \boldsymbol{A} \\ \boldsymbol{A} & \boldsymbol{B} \end{pmatrix} = \begin{pmatrix} \boldsymbol{A} & \boldsymbol{A} \\ \boldsymbol{A} & \boldsymbol{A} \end{pmatrix} + \begin{pmatrix} \boldsymbol{0} & \boldsymbol{0} \\ \boldsymbol{0} & \boldsymbol{B} - \boldsymbol{A} \end{pmatrix}.$$

As each of the matrices on the right-hand side is nonnegative definite, so is the matrix on the left-hand side. The stated result follows from Exercise A.20(a). Propositions A.22(a) and A.10(f) ensure that $\boldsymbol{AB}^{-}\boldsymbol{A}$ does not depend on the choice of the g-inverse.

A.25 Choose $\boldsymbol{A} = \boldsymbol{UU}'$ and $\boldsymbol{B} = \frac{1}{2}\boldsymbol{UU}' + \boldsymbol{VV}'$, where $\boldsymbol{U}$ and $\boldsymbol{V}$ are arbitrary matrices of appropriate order, with $\boldsymbol{U}'\boldsymbol{V} = \boldsymbol{0}$. Then $\mathcal{C}(\boldsymbol{A}) = \mathcal{C}(\boldsymbol{U}) \subseteq \mathcal{C}(\boldsymbol{U} : \boldsymbol{V}) = \mathcal{C}(\boldsymbol{B})$, but $\boldsymbol{v}'\boldsymbol{A}\boldsymbol{v} = 2\boldsymbol{v}'\boldsymbol{B}\boldsymbol{v}$ whenever $\boldsymbol{v} \in \mathcal{C}(\boldsymbol{U})$.

A.26 Let $\mathcal{I}_1(\boldsymbol{\theta})$ and $\mathcal{I}_2(\boldsymbol{\theta})$ be two information matrices such that $\mathcal{I}_1(\boldsymbol{\theta}) < \mathcal{I}_2(\boldsymbol{\theta})$. It follows from Proposition B.14 and Exercise A.24 that

$$\begin{aligned} \boldsymbol{G}(\boldsymbol{\theta})\mathcal{I}_1^{-}(\boldsymbol{\theta})\boldsymbol{G}'(\boldsymbol{\theta}) &= \boldsymbol{G}(\boldsymbol{\theta})\mathcal{I}_1^{-}(\boldsymbol{\theta})\mathcal{I}_1(\boldsymbol{\theta})\mathcal{I}_1^{-}(\boldsymbol{\theta})\boldsymbol{G}'(\boldsymbol{\theta}) \\ &\geq \boldsymbol{G}(\boldsymbol{\theta})\mathcal{I}_1^{-}(\boldsymbol{\theta})\mathcal{I}_1(\boldsymbol{\theta})\mathcal{I}_2^{-}(\boldsymbol{\theta})\mathcal{I}_1(\boldsymbol{\theta})\mathcal{I}_1^{-}(\boldsymbol{\theta})\boldsymbol{G}'(\boldsymbol{\theta}) \\ &= \boldsymbol{G}(\boldsymbol{\theta})\mathcal{I}_2^{-}(\boldsymbol{\theta})\boldsymbol{G}'(\boldsymbol{\theta}). \end{aligned}$$

A.27(a)

$$\begin{aligned} \boldsymbol{P}_{A\otimes B} &= (\boldsymbol{A}\otimes\boldsymbol{B})[(\boldsymbol{A}\otimes\boldsymbol{B})'(\boldsymbol{A}\otimes\boldsymbol{B})]^{-}(\boldsymbol{A}\otimes\boldsymbol{B})' \\ &= (\boldsymbol{A}\otimes\boldsymbol{B})[(\boldsymbol{A}'\otimes\boldsymbol{B}')(\boldsymbol{A}\otimes\boldsymbol{B})]^{-}(\boldsymbol{A}'\otimes\boldsymbol{B}') \\ &= (\boldsymbol{A}\otimes\boldsymbol{B})[(\boldsymbol{A}'\boldsymbol{A})\otimes(\boldsymbol{B}'\boldsymbol{B})]^{-}(\boldsymbol{A}'\otimes\boldsymbol{B}') \\ &= (\boldsymbol{A}\otimes\boldsymbol{B})[(\boldsymbol{A}'\boldsymbol{A})^{-}\otimes(\boldsymbol{B}'\boldsymbol{B})^{-}](\boldsymbol{A}'\otimes\boldsymbol{B}') \\ &= [\boldsymbol{A}(\boldsymbol{A}'\boldsymbol{A})^{-}\boldsymbol{A}']\otimes[\boldsymbol{B}(\boldsymbol{B}'\boldsymbol{B})^{-}\boldsymbol{B}'] \;=\; \boldsymbol{P}_A\otimes\boldsymbol{P}_B. \end{aligned}$$

(b) Suppose $\boldsymbol{A}_{m\times n}\otimes\boldsymbol{B}_{p\times q}$ does not have full column rank. Then there is a nontrivial matrix $\boldsymbol{L}_{n\times q}$ such that $(\boldsymbol{A}\otimes\boldsymbol{B})\text{vec}(\boldsymbol{L}) = \boldsymbol{0}$, i.e. $\boldsymbol{BLA}' = \boldsymbol{0}$. Therefore, both $\boldsymbol{A}$ and $\boldsymbol{B}$ cannot have full column rank. (If $\boldsymbol{A}$ has full column rank, then $\boldsymbol{LA}'$ is not $\boldsymbol{0}$, and hence, $\boldsymbol{B}$ cannot have full column rank.) Thus, whenever $\boldsymbol{A}$ and $\boldsymbol{B}$ have full column rank, $\boldsymbol{A}\otimes\boldsymbol{B}$ also has full column rank.

(c) Assume initially that $\boldsymbol{A}$ and $\boldsymbol{B}$ are symmetric and nonnegative definite. Let $\boldsymbol{A}_1\boldsymbol{A}_1'$ and $\boldsymbol{B}_1\boldsymbol{B}_1'$ be rank-factorizations of $\boldsymbol{A}$ and $\boldsymbol{B}$, respectively. Then $\rho(\boldsymbol{A}\otimes\boldsymbol{B}) = \rho((\boldsymbol{A}_1\boldsymbol{A}_1')\otimes(\boldsymbol{B}_1\boldsymbol{B}_1')) = \rho((\boldsymbol{A}_1\otimes\boldsymbol{B}_1)(\boldsymbol{A}_1'\otimes\boldsymbol{B}_1'))$. The last quantity is equal to $\rho(\boldsymbol{A}_1\otimes\boldsymbol{B}_1)$. Since $\boldsymbol{A}_1$ and $\boldsymbol{B}_1$ have full column rank, we have

$$\rho(\boldsymbol{A}\otimes\boldsymbol{B}) = \rho(\boldsymbol{A}_1\otimes\boldsymbol{B}_1) = \rho(\boldsymbol{A}_1)\rho(\boldsymbol{B}_1) = \rho(\boldsymbol{A})\rho(\boldsymbol{B}).$$

If $\boldsymbol{A}$ and $\boldsymbol{B}$ are any pair of (possibly rectangular) matrices, then using the result of part (a), we have

$$\rho(\boldsymbol{A} \otimes \boldsymbol{B}) = \rho(\boldsymbol{P}_{A \otimes B}) = \rho(\boldsymbol{P}_A \otimes \boldsymbol{P}_B) = \rho(\boldsymbol{P}_A)\rho(\boldsymbol{P}_B) = \rho(\boldsymbol{A})\rho(\boldsymbol{B}).$$

(d) This result follows from parts (b) and (c).

A.28 The result can be easily seen to hold for diagonal matrices. In general, let $\boldsymbol{V}_1\boldsymbol{\Lambda}_1\boldsymbol{V}_1'$ and $\boldsymbol{V}_2\boldsymbol{\Lambda}_2\boldsymbol{V}_2'$ be spectral decompositions of $\boldsymbol{A}$ and $\boldsymbol{B}$, respectively. Then it can be verified that the matrix $(\boldsymbol{V}_1 \otimes \boldsymbol{V}_2)(\boldsymbol{\Lambda}_1 \otimes \boldsymbol{\Lambda}_2)(\boldsymbol{V}_1' \otimes \boldsymbol{V}_2')$ is a spectral decomposition of $\boldsymbol{A} \otimes \boldsymbol{B}$. The determinant of the latter matrix is equal to $|\boldsymbol{\Lambda}_1 \otimes \boldsymbol{\Lambda}_2|$. The result follows.

A.29 Let $\boldsymbol{B} = (\boldsymbol{b}_1 : \ldots : \boldsymbol{b}_p)$ and $\boldsymbol{C}$ be a $p \times q$ matrix. Then

$$\begin{aligned}
\mathrm{vec}(\boldsymbol{ABC}) &= \mathrm{vec}\left(\boldsymbol{A}\sum_{i=1}^{p}\boldsymbol{b}_i c_{i,1} : \cdots : \boldsymbol{A}\sum_{i=1}^{p}\boldsymbol{b}_i c_{i,q}\right) \\
&= \begin{pmatrix} \sum_{i=1}^{p} c_{i,1}\boldsymbol{A}\boldsymbol{b}_i \\ \vdots \\ \sum_{i=1}^{p} c_{i,q}\boldsymbol{A}\boldsymbol{b}_i \end{pmatrix} = \begin{pmatrix} c_{1,1}\boldsymbol{A} & \cdots & c_{p,1}\boldsymbol{A} \\ \vdots & \ddots & \vdots \\ c_{1,q}\boldsymbol{A} & \cdots & c_{p,q}\boldsymbol{A} \end{pmatrix} \begin{pmatrix} \boldsymbol{b}_1 \\ \vdots \\ \boldsymbol{b}_p \end{pmatrix} \\
&= (\boldsymbol{C}' \otimes \boldsymbol{A})\mathrm{vec}(\boldsymbol{B}).
\end{aligned}$$

A.30 The consistency condition is $\boldsymbol{b} \in \mathcal{C}(\boldsymbol{A})$, which is equivalent to the given condition because of the result of Exercise A.16.

A.31 The sufficiency of the condition is obvious. In order to prove the necessity, observe that $\boldsymbol{ABA} = \boldsymbol{0}$ implies $\boldsymbol{P}_A\boldsymbol{B}\boldsymbol{P}_A = \boldsymbol{0}$, i.e. $\boldsymbol{P}_A\boldsymbol{B} = \boldsymbol{K}(\boldsymbol{I} - \boldsymbol{P}_A)$ for some matrix $\boldsymbol{K}$. Using Proposition A.23 for each column of $\boldsymbol{B}$, we find that $\boldsymbol{B}$ must be of the form $\boldsymbol{P}_A\boldsymbol{K}(\boldsymbol{I} - \boldsymbol{P}_A) + (\boldsymbol{I} - \boldsymbol{P}_A)\boldsymbol{L}$ for some matrix $\boldsymbol{L}$. Therefore, we can write the symmetric matrix $\boldsymbol{B}$ as

$$\boldsymbol{B} = \frac{1}{2}(\boldsymbol{B} + \boldsymbol{B}') = \boldsymbol{C} - \boldsymbol{P}_A\boldsymbol{C}\boldsymbol{P}_A,$$

where $\boldsymbol{C} = \frac{1}{2}\boldsymbol{P}_A(\boldsymbol{K} - \boldsymbol{L}) + \frac{1}{2}(\boldsymbol{K} - \boldsymbol{L})'\boldsymbol{P}_A + \frac{1}{2}(\boldsymbol{L} + \boldsymbol{L}')$.

A.32 Assume without loss of generality that $\boldsymbol{A}$ is symmetric, and that $\boldsymbol{CC}'$ is a rank-factorization of $\boldsymbol{A}$.

(a) Let $\boldsymbol{a} = \boldsymbol{Am}$. Then

$$\max_{\boldsymbol{l}} \frac{(\boldsymbol{l}'\boldsymbol{a})^2}{\boldsymbol{l}'\boldsymbol{A}\boldsymbol{l}} = \max_{\boldsymbol{l}} \frac{\boldsymbol{l}'\boldsymbol{A}\boldsymbol{m}\boldsymbol{m}'\boldsymbol{A}'\boldsymbol{l}}{\boldsymbol{l}'\boldsymbol{A}\boldsymbol{l}} = \max_{\boldsymbol{u}} \frac{\boldsymbol{u}'(\boldsymbol{C}'\boldsymbol{m}\boldsymbol{m}'\boldsymbol{C})\boldsymbol{u}}{\boldsymbol{u}'\boldsymbol{u}},$$

which is the largest eigenvalue of the rank-1 matrix $\boldsymbol{C}'\boldsymbol{m}\boldsymbol{m}'\boldsymbol{C}$. The latter is equal to $\boldsymbol{m}'\boldsymbol{C}'\boldsymbol{C}\boldsymbol{m}$, which simplifies to $\boldsymbol{a}'\boldsymbol{A}^{-}\boldsymbol{a}$.

(b) Let $\boldsymbol{B} = \boldsymbol{A}\boldsymbol{M}$. Proceeding as in part (a), we have the maximum given by the largest eigenvalue of $\boldsymbol{C}'\boldsymbol{M}\boldsymbol{M}'\boldsymbol{C}$. Also,

$$\begin{aligned}\|\boldsymbol{C}'\boldsymbol{M}\boldsymbol{M}'\boldsymbol{C}\| &= \|\boldsymbol{C}'(\boldsymbol{C}\boldsymbol{C}')^{-}\boldsymbol{C}\boldsymbol{C}'\boldsymbol{M}\boldsymbol{M}'\boldsymbol{C}\|\\ &= \|\boldsymbol{M}'\boldsymbol{C}\boldsymbol{C}'(\boldsymbol{C}\boldsymbol{C}')^{-}\boldsymbol{C}\boldsymbol{C}'\boldsymbol{M}\| \;=\; \|\boldsymbol{B}'\boldsymbol{A}^{-}\boldsymbol{B}\|.\end{aligned}$$

Appendix B

B.1 The joint density of $\boldsymbol{y}$ and z is

$$(2\pi z)^{-n/2}\exp\left(-\frac{1}{2z}\sum_{i=1}^{n}(y_i-\theta)^2\right).$$

The conditional distribution of $\boldsymbol{y}$ given $\left(n^{-1}\boldsymbol{1}'\boldsymbol{y} : z\right)' = (y_0, z_0)$ is $N(y_0\boldsymbol{1}, z_0\left(\boldsymbol{I} - n^{-1}\boldsymbol{1}\boldsymbol{1}'\right))$, which is free of θ (see Example B.1). Thus, the statistic $\left(n^{-1}\boldsymbol{1}'\boldsymbol{y} : z\right)'$ is sufficient. Let $\bar{y} = n^{-1}\boldsymbol{1}'\boldsymbol{y}$. The joint density of the sufficient statistic $(\bar{y} : z)'$ is

$$\left(\frac{2\pi z}{n}\right)^{-1/2}\exp\left(-\frac{n}{2z}(\bar{y}-\theta)^2\right).$$

Then the likelihood ratio

$$\begin{aligned}&\frac{\left(\frac{2\pi z_1}{n}\right)^{-1/2}\exp\left(-\frac{n}{2z_1}(\bar{y}_1-\theta)^2\right)}{\left(\frac{2\pi z_2}{n}\right)^{-1/2}\exp\left(-\frac{n}{2z_2}(\bar{y}_2-\theta)^2\right)}\\ &\quad= \left(\frac{z_2}{z_1}\right)^{1/2}\exp\left(-\frac{n}{2}(\bar{y}_1-\theta)^2\left(\frac{1}{z_1}-\frac{1}{z_2}\right)\right)\end{aligned}$$

is the same for all θ if and only if $\bar{y}_1 = \bar{y}_2$ and $z_1 = z_2$. Hence, $(\bar{y} : z)'$ is minimal sufficient (see Schervish, 1995, p. 92 for details of this argument). It follows from Example B.1 that given z, $\bar{y}$ is sufficient for θ.

B.2 First part is easy. For $n \geq 3$, the separation between any pair of order statistics is ancillary.

B.3 Note that $D(\boldsymbol{t}(\boldsymbol{y})) - \boldsymbol{G}(\boldsymbol{\theta})\mathcal{I}^{-}(\boldsymbol{\theta})\boldsymbol{G}'(\boldsymbol{\theta})$ is the mean squared prediction error matrix of the BLP of $\boldsymbol{t}(\boldsymbol{y})$ in terms of $\boldsymbol{s}(\boldsymbol{y})$ (see Exercise 2.10). This matrix is a null matrix if and only if $\boldsymbol{t}(\boldsymbol{y})$ is almost surely equal to a linear function of $\boldsymbol{s}(\boldsymbol{y})$, and vice versa. Thus, we can write $\boldsymbol{s}(\boldsymbol{y})$ as $\boldsymbol{A}(\boldsymbol{\theta})\boldsymbol{t}(\boldsymbol{y}) + \boldsymbol{b}(\boldsymbol{\theta})$. Consequently, $\log f_{\theta}(\boldsymbol{y})$ must be of the form $\boldsymbol{A}_*(\boldsymbol{\theta})\boldsymbol{t}(\boldsymbol{y}) + \boldsymbol{b}_*(\boldsymbol{\theta}) + \boldsymbol{t}_*(\boldsymbol{y})$. It follows from the factorization theorem that $\boldsymbol{t}(\boldsymbol{y})$ is sufficient for $\boldsymbol{\theta}$. The converse does not hold, as observed in Example B.15.

B.4 Let $\boldsymbol{t}(\boldsymbol{y})$ be an unbiased estimator of $\boldsymbol{g}(\boldsymbol{h}^{-1}(\boldsymbol{\eta}))$, and

$$\boldsymbol{s}_*(\boldsymbol{y}) = \frac{\partial \log f_{\boldsymbol{\theta}}(\boldsymbol{y})}{\partial \boldsymbol{\eta}}.$$

Then $\boldsymbol{s}(\boldsymbol{y}) = \boldsymbol{T}(\boldsymbol{\theta})\boldsymbol{s}_*(\boldsymbol{y})$ where $\boldsymbol{T}(\boldsymbol{\theta}) = \partial\boldsymbol{\eta}/\partial\boldsymbol{\theta}$. We have from the proof of Proposition B.14, $\boldsymbol{G}(\boldsymbol{\theta}) = \boldsymbol{T}(\boldsymbol{\theta})\boldsymbol{G}_*(\boldsymbol{\eta})$ and $\mathcal{I}(\boldsymbol{\theta}) = \boldsymbol{T}(\boldsymbol{\theta})\mathcal{I}_*(\boldsymbol{\eta})\boldsymbol{T}'(\boldsymbol{\theta})$, where $\boldsymbol{G}_*(\boldsymbol{\eta})$ and $\mathcal{I}_*(\boldsymbol{\eta})$ are analogues of $\boldsymbol{G}(\boldsymbol{\theta})$ and $\mathcal{I}(\boldsymbol{\theta})$, respectively, with $\boldsymbol{\theta}$ replaced by $\boldsymbol{\eta}$. Therefore, $\boldsymbol{G}(\boldsymbol{\theta})\mathcal{I}^-(\boldsymbol{\theta})\boldsymbol{G}'(\boldsymbol{\theta}) = \boldsymbol{G}_*(\boldsymbol{\eta})\mathcal{I}_*^-(\boldsymbol{\eta})\boldsymbol{G}_*'(\boldsymbol{\eta})$.

B.5 Let $t(\boldsymbol{y})$ be a complete sufficient statistic for the parameter $g(\boldsymbol{\theta})$, $t_1(\boldsymbol{y})$ an unbiased estimator and $t_2(\boldsymbol{y})$ the UMVUE of $f(\boldsymbol{\theta})$. We have for any loss function $L(\cdot,\cdot)$ which is convex in the second argument

$$\begin{aligned} E[L(g(\boldsymbol{\theta}), t_1(\boldsymbol{y}))] &= E[E\{L(g(\boldsymbol{\theta}), t_1(\boldsymbol{y}))|t(\boldsymbol{y})\}] \\ &\geq E[L(g(\boldsymbol{\theta}), E\{t_1(\boldsymbol{y})|t(\boldsymbol{y})\})] = E[L(g(\boldsymbol{\theta}), t_2(\boldsymbol{y}))] \end{aligned}$$

by Jensen's equality and the Lehmann-Scheffé theorem.

B.6 The joint distribution of $(\bar{y} : y_1)'$ is bivariate normal with mean vector $(\mu : \mu)'$ and dispersion matrix $\begin{pmatrix} 1/n & 1/n \\ 1/n & 1 \end{pmatrix}$. The conditional distribution of y_1 given $\bar{y}$ is obtained by simplifying (2.5) and (2.6).

An unbiased estimator of θ is y_1. The risk of this estimator is its variance, 1. Its 'improvement' by Rao-Blackwell theorem is $\bar{y}$. The risk of the latter estimator is its own variance, $1/n$. This is only a fraction of the risk of y_1, in conformity with the Rao-Balckwell theorem. The difference between the risks is $E[(y_1 - \bar{y})^2] = (1 - 1/n)$.

B.7 Let $\boldsymbol{y} = (y_1, \ldots, y_n)'$. The joint distribution of $\boldsymbol{y}$ and μ is normal. Hence the posterior distribution of μ is normal too. It follows from Proposition B.19 that the Bayes estimator is $E(\mu|\boldsymbol{y})$, which simplifies to the given expression.

B.8(a) According to the result of Exercise B.4 that the Fisher information of η is

$$\mathcal{I}(\theta) \Big/ \left(\frac{\partial h(\theta)}{\partial \theta}\right)^2 \Bigg|_{\theta = h^{-1}(\eta)}.$$

(b) It follows from part (a) that Jeffreys' prior for η has density proportional to the positive square-root of the above expression.

(c) When θ has Jeffreys' prior distribution, the implied prior of η (obtained by transformation rule) coincides with the density of part (b).

B.9 It is easily seen that $E(y) = \theta$; so y is unbiased for θ. However, y is inadmissible as $R(\theta, y) = \theta^2$ and $R(\theta, y/2) = \theta^2/2$. An admissible estimator can be found via a unique Bayes estimator. Let $\lambda = 1/\theta$ and the prior distribution of λ have density $\pi(\lambda) = \beta^\alpha \lambda^{\alpha-1} e^{-\lambda\beta}/\Gamma(\alpha)$, $\lambda > 0$, where α and β are positive parameters. Then the marginal density of y

is $\alpha\beta^\alpha(y+\beta)^{-(\alpha+1)}$, and the posterior distribution of λ given y has density $\pi(\lambda|y) = (y+\beta)^{\alpha+1}\lambda^\alpha e^{-\lambda(y+\beta)}/\Gamma(\alpha+1)$. Therefore, the unique Bayes estimator is $E(\theta|y) = E(1/\lambda|y) = (y+\beta)/\alpha$.

B.10 The family of distributions $N(\mu\mathbf{1}, \boldsymbol{I})$ is MLR in the statistic $t(\boldsymbol{y}) = \bar{y}$, the average of the n elements of $\boldsymbol{y}$. It is easy to see that $\bar{y} \sim N(\mu, 1/n)$. According to the Neyman-Pearson lemma, the most powerful test for $\mathcal{H}_0$ against the *simple* alternative hypothesis $\mu = \mu_1$ is given by the likelihood ratio test, which (because of the MLR property) simplifies to

$$\varphi_c(\boldsymbol{y}) = \begin{cases} 1 & \text{if } \bar{y} > c, \\ 0 & \text{if } \bar{y} < c, \end{cases}$$

where $c = n^{-1/2}z_\alpha$ and z_α is the $(1-\alpha)$ quantile of the standard normal distribution, α being the level of the test. Since this test is identical for all μ_1 contained in the range $\boldsymbol{\Theta}_1 = (0, \infty)$, it must be UMP.

In this case the GLRT statistic of (B.4) simplifies to

$$\ell(\boldsymbol{y}) = \begin{cases} \exp[-\bar{y}^2/2] & \text{if } \bar{y} > 0, \\ 1 & \text{if } \bar{y} \le 0. \end{cases}$$

Thus, the GLRT amounts to rejecting $\mathcal{H}_0$ for large values of $\bar{y}$, and therefore it coincides with the UMP test. The power of this test is

$$P(n^{1/2}\bar{y} > z_\alpha) = 1 - \Phi(z_\alpha - n^{1/2}\mu),$$

where Φ is the standard normal distribution function. The power is an increasing function of $n^{1/2}\mu$ and is always greater than the size α.

Note that the likelihood ratio $f_0(\boldsymbol{y})/f_{\mu_1}(\boldsymbol{y})$ is a decreasing function of $\bar{y}$ when $\mu_1 > 0$ and an increasing function elsewhere. The MP test for $\mathcal{H}_0$ against the simple hypothesis $\mu = \mu_1$ depends on the sign of μ_1. Therefore, no single test is UMP for $\mu \neq 0$. Here, the GLRT statistic is $\exp[-\bar{y}^2/2]$. Thus, the GLRT is amounts to rejecting $\mathcal{H}_0$ when $n\bar{y}^2 > z_{\alpha/2}$. The power of the GLRT is

$$P(n\bar{y}^2 > z^2_{\alpha/2}) = \Phi(-z_{\alpha/2} - n^{1/2}|\mu|) + 1 - \Phi(z_{\alpha/2} - n^{1/2}|\mu|).$$

The power is an increasing function of $n^{1/2}|\mu|$, and is always greater than the size α (even though the power is smaller than that of the one-sided test). Therefore, the test is unbiased. It can also be shown to be UMPU.

B.11 It follows from the discussion of Section B.5 and the result of Exercise B.10 that the level $(1-\alpha)$ UMA confidence region, obtained from the level $(1-\alpha)$ UMP test, is $[0, \bar{y} + n^{-1/2}z_\alpha]$. The level $(1-\alpha)$ UMAU confidence region, obtained from the level $(1-\alpha)$ UMPU test, is $[\bar{y} - n^{-1/2}z_{\alpha/2}, \bar{y} + n^{-1/2}z_{\alpha/2}]$.

Bibliography and Author Index

(Italicized numbers within parentheses indicate page numbers where the source is cited.)

Abramowitz, M. and Stegun, I.A. (2012) *Handbook of Mathematical Functions*, Dover, New York. (*147*)

Aitken, A.C. (1935) On least squares and linear combination of observations. *Proc. Roy. Soc. Edinburgh Sect. A* **55**, 42–48. (*354*)

Alalouf, I.S. and Styan, G.P.H. (1979) Characterizations of estimability in the general linear model. *Ann. Statist.* **7**, 194–200. (*79*)

Albert, A. (1972) *Regression and the Moore-Penrose Pseudoinverse*, Mathematics in Science and Engineering, **94**, Academic, New York. (*592*)

Anscombe, F.J. (1973) Graphs in statistical analysis. *Amer. Statistician* **27**, 17–21. (*182*)

Arnold, S.F. (1981) *The Theory of Linear Models and Multivariate Analysis*, Wiley Series in Probability and Mathematical Statistics, Wiley, New York. (*520*, *532*)

Atkinson, A.C. (1987) *Plots, Transformations, and Regression: An Introduction to Graphical Methods of Diagnostic Regression Analysis*, Oxford Statistical Science Series, Oxford University Press, Oxford. (*210*)

Bahadur, R.R. (1957) On unbiased estimates of uniformly minimum variance. *Sankhyā Ser. A* **18**, 211–224. (*618*, *541*)

Baille, R.T. (1979) The asymptotic mean squared error of multistep prediction from the regression model with autoregressive errors. *J. Amer. Statist. Assoc.* **74**, 175–184. (*439*)

Baksalary, J.K. (2004) An elementary development of the equation characterizing best linear unbiased estimators. *Linear Algebra Appl.* **388**, 3–6. (*349*)

Baksalary, J.K. and Kala, R. (1981) Linear transformations preserving best linear unbiased estimators in a general Gauss-Markoff model. *Ann. Statist.* **9**, 913–916. (*537*)

Baksalary, J.K. and Markiewicz, A. (1988) Admissible linear estimators in the general Gauss-Markov model. *J. Statist. Plann. Inference* **19**, 349–359. (*553*)

Baksalary, J.K. and Markiewicz, A. (1990) Admissible linear estimators of an arbitrary vector of parametric functions in the general Gauss-Markov model. *J. Statist. Plann. Inference* **26**, 161–171. (*555*)

Baksalary, J.K., Markiewicz, A. and Rao, C.R. (1995) Admissible linear estimation in the general Gauss-Markov model with respect to an arbitrary quadratic risk function. *J. Statist. Plann. Inference* **44**, 341–347. (*555*)

Baksalary, J.K. and Mathew, T. (1990) Rank invariance criterion and its application to the unified theory of least squares. *Linear Algebra Appl.* **127**, 393–401. (*363*)

Baksalary, J.K. and Pordzik, P.R. (1989) Inverse-partitioned-matrix method for the general Gauss-Markov model with linear restrictions. *J. Statist. Plann. Inference* **23**, 133–143. (*371*)

Baksalary, J.K., Rao, C.R. and Markiewicz, A. (1992) A study of the influence of the "natural restrictions" on estimation problems in the singular Gauss-Markov model. *J. Statist. Plann. Inference* **31**, 335–351. (*348*)

Baksalary, O.M. and Trenkler, G. (2009) A projector oriented approach to the best linear unbiased estimator. *Statist. Papers* **50**, 721–733. (*573*)

Banerjee, S. and Roy, A. (2014) *Linear Algebra and Matrix Analysis for Statistics*, Chapman and Hall, London. (*583*)

Barnard, G.A. (1963) The logic of least squares. *J. Roy. Statist. Soc. Ser. B* **25**, 124–127. (*537*)

Bartlett, M.S. (1937a) Some examples of statistical methods of research in agriculture. *J. Roy. Statist. Soc. Suppl.* **4**, 137–183. (*317, 495*)

Bartlett, M.S. (1937b) Properties of sufficiency and statistical tests. *Proc. Roy. Soc. London Ser. A* **160**, 268–282. (*337*)

Basu, D. (1958) On statistics independent of sufficient statistics. *Sankhyā* **20**, 223–226. (*619*)

Bates, D.M. and Watts, D.G. (1988) *Nonlinear Regression Analysis and its Applications*, Wiley Series in Probability and Mathematical Statistics, Wiley, New York. (*19*)

Bekir, E. (1988) A unified solution to the singular and nonsingular linear minimum-variance estimation problem. *IEEE Trans. Automatic Control* **33**, 590–591. (*343*)

Belsley, D.A. (1991) *Conditioning Diagnostics: Collinearity and Weak Data in Regression*, Wiley Series in Probability and Mathematical Statistics, Wiley, New York. (*249*)

Belsley, D.A., Kuh, E. and Welsch, R.E. (2005) *Regression Diagnostics: Identifying Influential Data and Sources of Collinearity*, Wiley Series in Probability and Mathematical Statistics, Wiley, New York. (*203, 238, 240, 251*)

Benjamini, Y. and Hochberg, Y. (1995) Controlling the false discovery rate: A practical and powerful approach to multiple testing. *J. Roy. Statist. Soc. Ser. B* **57**, 289–300. (*295*)

Benjamini, Y. and Yekuteli, D. (2001) The control of the false discovery rate in multiple testing under dependency. *Ann. Statist.* **29**, 1165–1188. (*295*)

Bhaumik, D. and Mathew, T. (2001) Optimal data augmentation for the estimation of a linear parametric function in linear models. *Sankhyā Ser. B* **63**, 10–26. (*466*)

Bhimasankaram, P. and Jammalamadaka S.R. (1994a) Recursive estimation and testing in general linear models with applications to regression diagnostics. *Tamkang J. Math.* **25**, 353–366. (*478*)

Bhimasankaram, P. and Jammalamadaka S.R. (1994b) Updates of statistics in a general linear model: A statistical interpretation and applications. *Comm. Statist. Simulation Comput.* **23**, 789–801. (*451, 459, 478, 489*)

Bhimasankaram, P. and SahaRay, R. (1997) On a partitioned linear model and some associated reduced models. *Linear Algebra Appl.* **264**, 329–339. (*379*)

Bhimasankaram, P. and Sengupta, D. (1991) Testing for the mean vector of a multivariate normal distribution with a possibly singular dispersion matrix and related results. *Statist. Probab. Lett.* **11**, 473–478. (*517, 530*)

Bhimasankaram, P. and Sengupta, D. (1996) The linear zero functions approach to linear models. *Sankhyā Ser. B* **58**, 338–351. (*351, 580*)

Bhimasankaram, P., Sengupta, D. and Ramanathan, S. (1995) Recursive inference in a general linear model. *Sankhyā Ser. A* **57**, 227–255. (*451, 458, 478, 480*)

Bich, W. (1990) Variances, covariances and restraints in mass metrology. *Metrologia* **27**, 111–116. (*343*)

Billingsley, P. (2012) *Probability and Measure*, anniversary edition, Wiley, New York. (*37*)

Bischoff, W. (1993) On D-optimal designs for linear models under correlated observations with an application to a linear model with multiple response. *J. Statist. Plann. Inference* **37**, 69–80. (*403*)

Björk, Å. (1996) *Numerical Methods for Least Squares Problems*, Society for Industrial and Applied Mathematics, Philadelphia. (*452*)

Bloomfield, P. and Steiger, W.L. (1983) *Least Absolute Deviations: Theory, Applications and Algorithms*, Birkhäuser, Boston. (*47*)

Bloomfield, P. and Watson, G.S. (1975) The inefficiency of least squares. *Biometrika* **62**, 121–128. (*409*)

Boisbunon, A., Canu, S., Fourdrinier, D., Strawderman, W. and Wells, M.T. (2014) Akaike's information criterion, C_p and estimators of loss for elliptically symmetric distributions. *Int. Statist. Rev.* **82**, 422–439. (*271*)

Boldin, M.V., Simonova, G.I. and Tyurin, Yu.N. (1997) Sign-based methods in linear statistical models (Translated from Russian manuscript by D.M. Chibisov). Translations of Mathematical Monographs, **162**, American Mathematical Society, Providence, RI. (*246*)

Borokov, A.A. (1999) *Mathematical Statistics*, Gordon and Breach, Amsterdam. (*265*)

Bose, N.K. and Rao, C.R. (1993) *Handbook of Statistics, Vol. 10 (Signal Processing and its Applications)*, North-Holland, Amsterdam. (*446*)

Bose R.C. (1949) *Least Squares Aspects of Analysis of Variance*, Inst. Stat. Mimeo. Ser. **9**, Chapel Hill, NC. (*ix*)

Box, G.E.P. and Cox, D.R. (1964) An analysis of transformations. *J. Roy. Statist. Soc. Ser. B* **26**, 211–252. (*211, 310*)

Box, G.E.P. and Draper, N.R. (1987) *Empirical Model-Building and Response Surfaces*, Wiley Series in Probability and Mathematical Statistics, Wiley, New York. (*14*)

Box, G.E.P., Jenkins, G.M., Reinsel, G.C. and Ljung, G.M. (2015) *Time Series Analysis: Forecasting and Control*, fifth edition, Wiley, New York. (*437*)

Box, G.E.P. and Tidwell, P.W. (1962) Transformation of the independent variables. *Technometrics* **4**, 531–550. (*211*)

Breiman, L., Friedman, J., Olshen, R. and Stone, C. (1984) *Classification and Regression Trees*, Chapman and Hall, London. (*212*)

Brockwell, P.J. and Davis, R.A. (2016) *Introduction to Time Series and Forecasting*, third edition, Springer Texts in Statistics, Springer-Verlag, New York. (*438*)

Broemeling, L.D. (1984) *Bayesian Analysis of Linear Models*, CRC Press, Boca Raton. (*255*)

Brown, P.J. (1993) *Measurement, Regression and Calibration*, Oxford Statistical Science Series, Clarendon, Oxford. (*13*)

Brown, R.L., Durbin, J. and Evans, J.M. (1975) Methods of investigating whether a regression relationship is constant over time (with discussion). *J. Roy. Statist. Soc. Ser. B* **37**, 149–192. (*454, 456*)

Brownlee, K.A. (1965) *Statistical Theory and Methodology in Science and Engineering*, second edition, Wiley, London. (*117*)

Bunke, O. (1975) Minimax linear, ridge and shrunken estimators for linear parameters. *Math. Operationsforsch. Statist.* **6**, 697–701. (*561*)

Bunke, H. and Bunke, O. (1974) Identifiability and estimability. *Math. Operationsforsch. Statist.* **5**, 223–233. (*81*)

Buser, S.A. (1977) Mean-variance portfolio selection with either a singular or nonsingular variance-covariance matrix. *J. Financial Quant. Anal.* **12**, 347–361. (*342*)

Card, A., Moore, M.A. and Ankeny, M. (2006) Garment washed jeans: Impact of launderings on physical properties. *Int. J. Clothing Sc. Tech.* **18**, 43–52. (*13, 70*)

Carlson, S.M. (1998) *Uniform Crime Reports: Monthly Weapon-Specific Crime and Arrest Time Series, 1975-1993*, ICPSR06792-v1, Inter-university Consortium for Political and Social Research, Ann Arbor, MI. (*116*)

Carroll, R.J. (1982) Adapting for heteroscedasticity in linear models. *Ann. Statist.* **10**, 1224–1233. (*444*)

Carroll, R.J. and Ruppert, D. (1988) *Transformation and Weighting in Regression*, Chapman and Hall, London. (*444*)

Cattaneo, M.D., Jansson, M. and Newey, W.K. (2018) Inference in linear regression models with many covariates and heteroscedasticity. *J. Amer. Statist. Assoc.* **113**, 1350–1361. (*255*)

Chambers, J.M. (1975) Updating methods for linear models for the addition or deletion of observations. In *A Survey of Statistical Design and Linear Models*, ed. J.N. Srivastava, North-Holland, Amsterdam, 53–65. (*451*)

Chatterjee, S. and Hadi, A.S. (1988) *Sensitivity Analysis in Linear Regression*, Wiley, New York. (*238*)

Chatterjee, S. and Hadi, A.S. (2012) *Regression Analysis by Example*, fifth edition, Wiley, New York. (*238*)

Chaubey, Y.P. (1982) Best minimum bias linear estimators in Gauss-Markoff model. *Comm. Statist. Theory Methods* **11**, 1959–1963. (*567*)

Chen, J.H. and Shao, J. (1993) Iterative weighted least squares estimators. *Ann. Statist.* **21**, 1071–1092. (*442*)

Chib, S., Jammalamadaka, S. Rao, and Tiwari, R. (1987) Another look at some results on the recursive estimation in the general linear model. *Amer. Statistician* **41**, 56–58. (*478*)

Chipman, J.S. (1964) On least squares with insufficient observations. *J. Amer. Statist. Assoc.* **59**, 1078–1111. (*566*)

Chow, S.C. and Shao, J. (1991) Estimating drug shelf-life with random batches. *Biometrics* **47**, 1071–1079. (*447*)

Christensen, R. (1991) *Linear Models for Multivariate, Time Series and Spatial Data*, Springer-Verlag, New York. (*419, 441, 533*)

Christensen, R. (2011) *Plane Answers to Complex Questions: The Theory of Linear Models*, fourth edition, Springer, New York. (*149, 317, 567*)

Cochran, W.G. (1957) Analysis of covariance: Its nature and uses. *Biometrics* (special issue on Analysis of covariance) **13**, 261–281. (*324*)

Cohen, A. (1966) All admissible linear estimates of the mean vector. *Ann. Math. Statist.* **37**, 458–463. (*554*)

Cook, R.D. and Weisberg, S. (1994) *An Introduction to Regression Graphics*, Wiley Series in Probability and Statistics, Wiley, New York. (*239*)

Cressie, N.A.C. (2015) *Statistics for Spatial Data*, revised edition, Wiley Series in Probability and Statistics, Wiley, New York. (*440*)

Daniel, W.W. and Cross, C.L. (2013) *Biostatistics: A Foundation for Analysis in the Health Sciences*, tenth edition, Wiley Series in Probability and Statistics, Wiley, New York. (*164*)

Dasgupta, P. (2015) *Physical Growth, Body Composition and Nutritional Status of Bengali School Aged Children, Adolescents and Young Adults of Calcutta, India: Effects of Socioeconomic Factors on Secular Trends.* Report **158**, Neys-van Hoogstraaten Foundation, The Netherlands, `http://www.neys-vanhoogstraten.nl/wp-content/uploads/2015/06/Academic-Report-ID-158.pdf`. (*3*)

Dasgupta, A. and Das Gupta, S. (2000) Parametric identifiability and model-preserving constraints, *Calcutta Statist. Assoc. Bull.* **50**, 207–221. (*98, 134*)

Davidian, M. and Carroll, R.J. (1987) Variance function estimation. *J. Amer. Statist. Assoc.* **82**, 1079–1091. (*444*)

Davidson, R. and MacKinnon, J.G. (1993) *Estimation and Inference in Econometrics*, Oxford University Press, Oxford. (*437*)

Davies, S.L., Neath, A.A. and Cavanaugh, J.E. (2006) Estimation optimality of corrected AIC and modified Cp in linear regression. *Int. Statist. Rev.* **74**, 161–168. (*194*)

Dobson, A.J. and Barnett, A.G. (2018) *An Introduction to Generalized Linear Models*, fourth edition, Chapman and Hall, London. (*270*)

Dodge, Y. (1985) *Analysis of Experiments with Missing Data*, Wiley Series in Probability and Mathematical Statistics, Wiley, Chichester. (*317*)

Drygas, H. (1983) Sufficiency and completeness in the general Gauss-Markov model. *Sankhyā Ser. A* **45**, 88–98. (*537, 542, 543*)

Drygas, H. (1985) Minimax prediction in linear models. In *Linear Statistical Inference* (Poznań, 1984), eds. T. Caliński and W. Klonecki, Lecture Notes in Statistics **35**, Springer, Berlin-New York, 48–60. (*564*)

Drygas, H. (1996) Spectral methods in linear minimax estimation. *Acta Appl. Math.* **43**, 17–42. (*564*)

Duncan, D.B. and Horn, S.D. (1972) Linear dynamic recursive estimation in the general linear model. *J. Amer. Statist. Assoc.* **67**, 815–821. (*467, 469*)

Eaton, M.L. (1985) The Gauss-Markov theorem in multivariate analysis. In *Multivariate Analysis, Part VI*, ed. P.R. Krishnaiah, North-Holland, Amsterdam, 177–201. (*419*)

Efron, B. and Tibshirani, R.J. (1993) *An Introduction to the Bootstrap*, Chapman and Hall, London. (*154, 237*)

Fang, K.-T., Kollo, T. and Parring, A.-M. (2000) Approximation of the non-null distribution of generalized T^2-statistics. *Linear Algebra Appl.* **321**, 27–46. (*524*)

Farebrother, R.W. (1988) *Linear Least Squares Computations*, CRC Press, Boca Raton. (*452*)

Fisher, R.A. (1926) The arrangement of field experiments. *J. Ministry Agr.* **33**, 503–513 (also included in *Contributions to Mathematical Statistics* by R.A. Fisher, Wiley, New York, 1950). (*282*)

Fisher, R.A. (1936) The use of multiple measurements in taxonomic problems. *Ann. Eugenics* **7**, 179–188. (*534*)

Fomby, T.B., Hill, R.C. and Johnson, S.R. (1984) *Advanced Econometric Methods*, Springer-Verlag, New York. (*21*)

Fox, J. (1991) *Regression Diagnostics: An Introduction*, Sagc, Newbury Park, CA, 257–291. (*239*)

Fu, Y.L. and Tang, S.Y. (1993) Necessary and sufficient conditions that linear estimators of a mixed effects linear model are admissible under matrix loss function. *Statistics* **24**, 303–309. (*554*)

Fuller, W.A. and Rao, J.N.K. (1978) Estimation for a linear regression model with unknown diagonal covariance matrix. *Ann. Statist.* **6**, 1149–1158. (*442*)

Gaffke, N. and Heiligers, B. (1989) Bayes, admissible and minimax linear estimators in linear models with restricted parameter space. *Statistics* **20**, 487–508. (*558*)

Galecki, A. and Burzykowski, T. (2013) *Linear Mixed-Effects Models Using R: A Step-by-Step Approach*, Springer, New York. (*436*)

Galpin, J.S. and Hawkins, D.M. (1984) The use of recursive residuals in checking model fit in linear regression. *Amer. Statistician* **38**, 94–105. (*462*)

Galton, F. (1886) Regression towards mediocrity in hereditary stature. *J. Anthropological Inst.* **15**, 246–263. (*5*)

Gelders, S., Ewen, M., Noguchi, N. and Laing R. (2005) *Price, Availability and Affordability: An International Comparison of Chronic Disease Medicines*, Background report prepared for the WHO Planning Meeting on the Global Initiative for Treatment of Chronic Diseases, Cairo, December 2005, `http://www.who.int/medicines/publications/PriceAvailAfordability.pdf`. (*11*)

Gnot, S. (1983) Bayes estimation in linear models: A coordinate-free approach. *J. Multivariate Anal.* **13**, 40–51. (*558*)

Goldman, A.J. and Zelen, M. (1964) Weak generalized inverse and minimum variance unbiased estimation. *J. Research Nat. Bureau of Standards* **68B**, 151–172. (*366*)

Golub, G.H. and Van Loan, C.F. (2013) *Matrix Computations*, fourth edition, Johns Hopkins University Press, Baltimore, MD. (*57*, *592*, *595*)

Gragg, W.B., LeVeque, R.J. and Trangenstein, J.A. (1979) Numerically stable methods for updating regressions. *J. Amer. Statist. Assoc.* **74**, 161–168. (*452*)

Greenberg, B.G. (1953) The use of analysis of covariance and balancing in analytical surveys. *Amer. J. Pub. Health* **43**, 692–699. (*324*)

Gross, J. (2004) The general Gauss-Markov model with possibly singular dispersion matrix. *Statist. Papers* **45**, 311–336. (*341*)

Gross, J. and Markiewicz, A. (2004) Characterizations of admissible linear estimators in the linear model. *Linear Algebra Appl.* **388**, 239–248. (*562*)

Gruber, M.H.J. (2010) *Regression Estimators: A Comparative Study*, second edition, Johns Hopkins University Press, Baltimore, MD. (*558*, *561*)

Gruber, M.H.J. (1998) *Improving Efficiency by Shrinkage: The James-Stein and Ridge Estimators*, Mercel Dekker, New York. (*260*)

Gujarati, D.N. and Sangeetha (2007) *Basic Econometrics*, fourth edition, Tata McGraw-Hill, New Delhi. (*271*)

Gumedze, F.N. and Dunne, T.T. (2011) Parameter estimation and inference in the linear mixed model. *Linear Algebra Appl.* **435**, 1920–1944. (*436*)

Guy, W. (1859) On the duration of life as affected by the pursuits of literature, science and art. *J. Statist. Soc. London* **22**, 337–361. (*2*).

Hahn, G.J. and Hendrickson, R.W. (1971) A table of percentage points of the distribution of the largest absolute value of k student t variates and its applications. *Biometrika* **58**, 323–332. (*157*)

Hallum, C.R., Lewis, T.O. and Boullion, T.L. (1973) Estimation in the restricted general linear model with a positive semidefinite covariance matrix. *Comm. Statist.* **1**, 157–166. (*566*)

Hannan, E. (1970) *Multiple Time Series*, Wiley, New York. (*404*)

Härdle, W. (1990) *Applied Nonparametric Regression*, Cambridge University Press, London. (*212*)

Härdle, W., Müller, M., Sperlich, S. and Werwatz, A. (2004) *Nonparametric and Semiparametric Models*, Springer-Verlag, Berlin. (*212*)

Hart, J.D. (1997) *Nonparametric Smoothing and Lack-of-Fit Tests*, Springer, New York. (*212*)

Harter, H.L. (1960) Tables of range and studentized range. *Ann. Math. Statist.* **31**, 1122–1147. (*295*)

Harvey, A.C. and Phillips, D.A. (1979) Maximum likelihood estimation of regression models with autoregressive-moving average disturbances. *Biometrika* **66**, 49–58. (*438, 472, 496*)

Harville, D.A. (1981) Unbiased and minimum-variance unbiased estimation of estimable functions for fixed linear models with arbitrary covariance structure. *Ann. Statist.* **9**, 633–637. (*351*)

Haslett, J. (1999) A simple derivation of deletion diagnostic results for the general linear model with correlated errors. *J. Roy. Statist. Soc. Ser. B* **61**, 603–609. (*481*)

Haslett, J. and Haslett, S.J. (2007) The three basic types of residuals for a linear model. *Int. Statist. Rev.* **75**, 1–24. (*462*)

Haslett, S. (1985) Recursive estimation of the general linear model with dependent errors and multiple additional observations. *Austral. J. Statist.* **27**, 183–188. (*451, 457, 459*)

Haslett, S. (1996) Updating linear models with dependent errors to include additional data and / or parameters. *Linear Algebra Appl.* **237/238**, 329–349. (*473*)

Haslett, S.J., Isotalo, J., Liu, Y. and Puntanen, S. (2014) Equalities between OLSE, BLUE and BLUP in the linear model. *Statist. Papers* **55**, 543–561. (*401*)

Haslett, S.J. and Puntanen, S. (2010) Effect of adding regressors on the equality of the BLUEs under two linear models. *J. Statist. Plann. Inference* **140**, 104–110. (*401*)

Hastie, T., Tibshirani, R. and Wainwright, M. (2015) *Statistical Learning with Sparsity: The Lasso and Generalizations*, Chapman and Hall, London. (*255*)

Hauke, J., Markiewicz, A. and Puntanen, S. (2012) Comparing the BLUEs under two linear models. *Comm. Statist. Theory Methods* **41**, 2405–2418. (*401*)

Hawkins, D.M. (1991) Diagnostics for use with regression recursive residuals. *Technometrics* **33**, 221–234. (*462*)

Haykin, S. (1991) *Advances in Spectrum Analysis and Array Processing, Vol. II*, Prentice-Hall, Englewood Cliffs, NJ. (*446*)

Hedayat, A.S. and Majumdar, D. (1985) Combining experiments under Gauss-Markov models. *J. Amer. Statist. Assoc.* **80**, 698–703. (*443*)

Hettmansperger, T.P. and McKean, J.W. (1998) *Robust Nonparametric Statistical Methods*, Kendall's Library of Statistics, **5**, Arnold, London and Wiley, New York. (*246*)

Hoaglin, D.C., Mosteller, F. and Tukey, J.W. (1991) *Fundamentals of Exploratory Analysis of Variance*, Wiley Series in Probability and Mathematical Statistics, Wiley, New York. (*338*)

Hochberg, Y. and Tamhane, A.C. (2009) *Multiple Comparison Procedures*, Wiley, New York. (*149, 295*)

Hocking, R.R. (2013) *Methods and Applications of Linear Models*, third edition, Wiley, New York. (*149*, *195*, *316*, *321*, *430*)

Hoerl, A.E. and Kennard, R.W. (1970a) Ridge regression: Biased estimation for nonorthogonal problems. *Technometrics* **12**, 55–67. (*258*)

Hoerl, A.E. and Kennard, R.W. (1970b) Ridge regression: Applications to nonorthogonal problems. *Technometrics* **12**, 69–82. (*258*)

Hoffman, K. (1996) A subclass of Bayes linear estimators that are minimax. *Acta Appl. Math.* **43**, 87–95. (*564*)

Hooper, P.M. (1993) Iterative weighted least squares estimation in heteroscedastic linear model. *J. Amer. Statist. Assoc.* **88**, 179–184. (*442*)

Hosmer, D.W., Lemeshow, S. and Sturdivant, R.X. (2013) *Applied Logistic Regression*, third edition, Wiley, New York. (*7*)

Hotelling, H. (1951) A generalized T-test and measure of multivariate dispersion. In *Proc. Second Berkeley Symp. Math. Statist. Prob.*, Univ. of California Press, Berkeley, 23–41. (*519*)

Hubble, E. (1929) A relation between distance and radial velocity among extra-galactic nebulae. *Proc. Nat. Acad. Sc.* **15**, 168–73. (*10, 64*)

Humason, M.L. (1936) The apparent radial velocities of 100 extra-galactic nebulae. *Astrophys. J.* **83**, 10–22. (*175*)

Isotalo J., Markiewicz A. and Puntanen S. (2018) Some properties of linear prediction sufficiency in the linear model. In *Trends and Perspectives in Linear Statistical Inference*, M. Tez and D. von Rosen, eds., Springer, Cham, 111–129. (*543*)

Isotalo, J. and Puntanen, S. (2009) A note on the equality of the OLSE and the BLUE of the parametric function in the general Gauss-Markov model. *Statist. Papers* **50**, 185–193. (*401*)

Izenman, A.J. (2013) *Modern Multivariate Statistical Techniques: Regression, Classification, and Manifold Learning*, Springer, New York. (*533*)

James, W. and Stein, C. (1961) Estimation with quadratic loss. In *Proc. Fourth Berkeley Symp. Math. Statist. Prob.* **1**, Univ. of California Press, Berkeley, 361–379. (*552*)

Jammalamadaka, S.R. and Sengupta, D. (1999) Changes in the general linear model: A unified approach. *Linear Algebra Appl.* **289**, 225–242. (*451, 457, 477*)

Jeyaratnam, S. (1982) A sufficient condition on the covariance matrix for F tests in linear models to be valid. *Biometrika* **69**, 679–680. (*403*)

Jones, M.C. and Sibson, R. (1987) What is projection pursuit?, *J. Roy. Statist. Soc. Ser. A* **150**, 1–36. (*212*)

Judge, G.G., Griffiths, W.E., Hill, R.C. and Lee, T.C. (1985) *The Theory and Practice of Econometrics*, second edition, Wiley, New York. (*259*)

Judge, G.G. and Takayama, T. (1966) Inequality restrictions in regression analysis. *J. Amer. Statist. Assoc.* **61**, 166–181. (*375*)

Kala, R. and Klaczyński, K. (1988) Recursive improvement of estimates in a Gauss-Markov model with linear restrictions. *Canad. J. Statist.* **16**, 301–305. (*490*)

Kala, R., Markiewicz, A. and Puntanen S. (2017) Some further remarks on the linear sufficiency in the linear model. In *Applied and Computational Matrix Analysis: MAT-TRIAD 2015*, ed. N. Bebiano, Springer Proceedings in Mathematics & Statistics **192**, Springer, Cham, 275–294. (*543*)

Kala, R. and Pordzik, P.R. (2009) Estimation in singular partitioned, reduced or transformed linear models. *Statist. Papers* **50**, 633–638. (*341*)

Kala, R., Puntanen, S. and Tian, Y. (2017) Some notes on linear sufficiency. *Statist. Papers* **58**, 1–17. (*537*)

Kalman, R.E. (1960) A new approach to linear filtering and prediction problem. *ASME Trans. J. Basic Engrg.* **82-D**, 35–45. (*467*)

Kalman, R.E. and Bucy, R.S. (1961) New results in linear filtering and prediction theory. *ASME Trans. J. Basic Engrg.* **83-D**, 95–108. (*467*)

Kariya, T. (1980) Note on a condition for equality of sample variances in a linear model. *J. Amer. Statist. Assoc.* **75**, 701–703. (*403*)

Kay, S.M. (1999) *Modern Spectral Estimation: Theory and Application*, Prentice Hall, Englewood Cliffs, N.J. (*445*)

Kempthorne, O. (1952) *The Design and Analysis of Experiments*, Wiley, New York. (*343*)

Khuri, A.I. and Cornell, J.A. (1996) *Response Surfaces: Designs and Analyses*, second edition, Statistics: Textbooks and Monographs **152**, Marcel Dekker, New York. (*14*)

Khuri, A.I., Mathew, T. and Sinha, B.K. (1998) *Statistical Tests for Mixed Linear Models*, Wiley Series in Probability and Statistics, Wiley, New York. (*437*)

Kianifard, F. and Swallow, W. (1996) A review of the development and application of recursive residuals in linear models. *J. Amer. Statist. Assoc.* **91**, 391–400. (*457, 462*)

Klonecki, W. and Zontek, S. (1988) On the structure of admissible linear estimators. *J. Multivariate Anal.* **24**, 11–30. (*554*)

Knott, M. (1975) On the minimum efficiency of least squares. *Biometrika* **62**, 129–132. (*409*)

Koch, K.-R. (1999) *Parameter Estimation and Hypothesis Testing in Linear Models*, second edition, Springer-Verlag, Berlin. (*446*)

Koenker, R. (2005) *Quantile Regression*, Cambridge University Press, Cambridge. (*47*)

Kohn, R. and Ansley, C.F. (1983) Fixed interval estimation in state-space models when some of the data are missing or aggregated. *Biometrika* **70**, 683–688. (*343*)

Kornacki, A. (1998) Stability of quadratically and linearly sufficient statistics in general Gauss-Markov model. *Random Oper. Stochastic Equations* **6**, 51–56. (*543*)

Kourouklis, S. and Paige, C.C. (1981) A constrained least squares approach to the general Gauss-Markov linear model. *J. Amer. Statist. Assoc.* **76**, 620–625. (*366, 452*)

Krämer, W. (1980) A note on the equality of ordinary least squares and Gauss-Markov estimates in the general linear model. *Sankhyā Ser. A* **42**, 130–131. (*401*)

Krämer, W. and Donninger, C. (1987) Spatial autocorrelation among errors and the relative efficiency of OLS in the linear regression model. *J. Amer. Statist. Assoc.* **82**, 577–579. (*409, 439*)

Kshirsagar, A.M. (1983) *A Course in Linear Models*, Marcel Dekker, New York. (*482*)

Kuks, J. and Olman, V. (1971) Minimax linear estimation of regression coefficients (In Russian). *Izv. Akad. Nauk Eston. SSR* **20**, 480–482. (*561*)

Kuks, J. and Olman, V. (1972) Minimax linear estimation of regression coefficients II (In Russian). *Izv. Akad. Nauk Eston. SSR* **21**, 66–72. (*560, 561*)

Kutner, M.H., Nachtsheim, C.J. and Neter, J. (2004) *Applied Linear Regression Models*, fourth edition, McGraw-Hill Irwin, New York. (*250*)

LaMotte, L.R. (1978) Bayes linear estimators. *Technometrics* **20**, 281–290. (*558*)

Läuter, H. (1975) A minimax linear estimator for linear parameters under restrictions in form of inequalities. *Math. Operationsforsch. Statist. Ser. Statist.* **6**, 689–696. (*564*)

Lawley, D.N. (1938) A generalization of Fisher's Z-test. *Biometrika* **30**, 180–187. (*519*)

Lehmann, E.L. and Casella, G. (1998) *Theory of Point Estimation*, Springer Texts in Statistics, Springer-Verlag, New York. (*620*)

Lehmann, E.L. and Romano, J.P. (2005) *Testing Statistical Hypotheses*, third edition, Springer, New York. (*136, 633, 635*)

Lewis, T.O. and Odell, P.L. (1966) A generalization of the Gauss-Markov theorem. *J. Amer. Statist. Assoc.* **61**, 1063–1066. (*566*)

Li, Z.-H. and Begg, C.B. (1994) Random effects models for combining results from controlled and uncontrolled studies in a meta-analysis. *J. Amer. Statist. Assoc.* **89**, 1523–1527. (*448*)

Li, F. and Lu, Y. (2018) Lasso-type estimation for covariate-adjusted linear model. *J. Appl. Statist.* **45**, 26–42. (*255*)

Liew, C.K. (1976) Inequality constrained least-squares estimation. *J. Amer. Statist. Assoc.* **71**, 746–751. (*375, 377*)

Lin, C.T. (1993) Necessary and sufficient conditions for the least square estimator to be the best estimator in a general Gauss-Markov model. *J. Math. Res. Exposition* **13**, 433–436. (*401*)

Liu, A. (1996) Estimation of the parameters in two linear models with only some of the parameter vectors identical. *Statist. Probab. Lett.* **29**, 369–375. (*443*)

Liu, Y. (2009) On equality of ordinary least squares estimator, best linear unbiased estimator and best linear unbiased predictor in the general linear model. *J. Statist. Plann. Inference* **139**, 1522–1529. (*401*)

Lovell, M.C. and Prescott, E. (1970) Multiple regression with inequality constraints: Pretesting bias, hypothesis testing and efficiency. *J. Amer. Statist. Assoc.* **65**, 913–925. (*377*)

Lunn, A.D. and McNeil, D.R. (1991) *Computer-Interactive Data Analysis*, Wiley, Chichester. (*535*)

Markiewicz, A. and Puntanen, S. (2009) Admissibility and linear sufficiency in linear model with nuisance parameters. *Statist. Papers* **50**, 847–854. (*555*)

Mathew, T. (1983) Linear estimation with an incorrect dispersion matrix in linear models with a common linear part. *J. Amer. Statist. Assoc.* **78**, 468–471. (*401*)

Mathew, T. (1985) On inference in a general linear model with an incorrect dispersion matrix. In *Linear Statistical Inference* (Poznań, 1984), eds. T. Caliński and W. Klonecki, Lecture Notes in Statistics **35**, Springer, Berlin-New York, 200–210. (*401*)

Mathew, T. and Bhimasankaram, P. (1983a) On the robustness of the LRT with respect to specification errors in a linear model. *Sankhyā Ser. A* **45**, 212–225. (*404*)

Mathew, T. and Bhimasankaram, P. (1983b) On the robustness of the LRT in singular linear models. *Sankhyā Ser. A* **45**, 301–312. (*401, 404*)

Mathew, T., Rao, C.R. and Sinha, B.K. (1984) Admissible linear estimation in singular linear models. *Comm. Statist. Theory Methods* **13**, 3033–3045. (*554*)

Mathew, T., Sinha, B.K. and Zhou, L. (1993) Some statistical procedures for combining independent tests. *J. Amer. Statist. Assoc.* **88**, 912–919. (*443*)

Mayer, L.S. and Wilke, T.A. (1973) On biased estimation in linear models. *Technometrics* **15**, 497–508. (*259*)

McCullagh, P. and Nelder, J.A. (1989) *Generalized Linear Models*, second edition, Monographs on Statistics and Applied Probability, Chapman and Hall, London. (*270*)

McGilchrist, C.A. and Sandland, R.L. (1979) Recursive estimation of the general linear model with dependent errors. *J. Roy. Statist. Soc. Ser. B* **41**, 65–68. (*451, 456, 459*)

McGilchrist, C.A., Sandland, R.L. and Hennessy, J.L. (1983) Generalized inverses used in recursive estimation of the general linear model. *Austral. J. Statist.* **25**, 321–328. (*462*)

Miller, A. (2002) *Subset Selection in Regression*, second edition, Chapman and Hall, London. (*202*)

Miller, R.G. (1981) *Simultaneous Statistical Inference*, second edition, Springer Series in Statistics, Springer-Verlag, New York. (*158, 161, 168, 295*)

Mitra, S.K. (1971) Another look at Rao's MINQUE of variance components. *Int. Statist. Inst. Bull.* **44(2)**, 279–283. (*432*)

Mitra, S.K. and Bhimasankaram, P. (1971) Generalized inverses of partitioned matrices and recalculation of least squares estimators for data and model changes. *Sankhyā Ser. A* **33**, 395–410. (*451, 454*)

Müller, J., Rao, C.R. and Sinha, B.K. (1984) Inference on parameters in a linear model: A review of recent results. In *Experimental Design, Statistical Models, and Genetic Statistics*, ed. K. Hinkelmann, Statistics **50**, Dekker, New York, 277–295. (*542*)

Müller, J. (1987) Sufficiency and completeness in the linear model. *J. Multivariate Anal.* **21**, 312–323. (*543*)

Nanayakkara, N. and Cressie, N.A.C. (1991) Robustness to unequal scale and other departures from the classical linear model. In *Directions in Robust Statistics and Diagnostics, Part II*, eds. W. Stahel and S. Weisberg, IMA Volumes in Mathematics and its Applications **34**, Springer, New York, 65–113. (*579*)

Neuwirth, E. (1985) Sensitivity of linear models with respect to the covariance matrix. In *Linear Statistical Inference* (Poznań, 1984), eds. T. Caliński and W. Klonecki, Lecture Notes in Statistics **35**, Springer, Berlin-New York, 223–230. (*396*)

Nieto, F.H. and Guerrero, V.M. (1995) Kalman filter for singular and conditional state-space models when the system state and the observational error are correlated. *Statist. Probab. Lett.* **22**, 303–310. (*473*)

Nordström, K. (1985) On a decomposition of the singular Gauss-Markov model. In *Linear Statistical Inference* (Poznań, 1984), eds. T. Caliński and W. Klonecki, Lecture Notes in Statistics **35**, Springer, Berlin-New York, 231–245. (*548, 575*)

Olea, R.A. (1999) *Geostatistics for Engineers and Earth Scientists*, Kluwer Academic Publishers, Boston. (*440*)

Okamoto, M. (1973) Distinctness of the eigenvalues of a quadratic form in a multivariate sample. *Ann. Statist.* **1**, 763–765. (*509*)

Oktaba, W., Kornacki, A. and Wawrzosek, J. (1988) Invariant linearly sufficient transformations of the general Gauss-Markoff model: Estimation and testing. *Scand. J. Statist.* **15**, 117–124. (*543*)

Ord, K. (1975) Estimation methods for models of spatial interaction. *J. Amer. Statist. Assoc.* **70**, 120–126. (*439*)

Pearce, S.C. (1983) *The Agricultural Field Experiment*, Wiley, Chechester. (*340*)

Peixoto, J.L. (1986) Testable hypothesis in singular fixed linear models. *Comm. Statist. Theory Methods* **15**, 1957–1973. (*141*)

Pillai, K.C.S. (1955) Some new test criteria in multivariate analysis. *Ann. Math. Statist.* **26**, 117–121. (*519*)

Pilz, J. (1986) Minimax linear regression estimation with symmetric parameter restrictions. *J. Statist. Plann. Inference* **13**, 297–318. (*564*)

Placket, R.L. (1950) Some theorems in least squares. *Biometrika* **37**, 149–157. (*451, 454*)

Pordzik, P.R. (1992a) A lemma on g-inverse of the bordered matrix and its application to recursive estimation in the restricted model. *Comput. Statist.* **7**, 31–37. (*458*)

Pordzik, P.R. (1992b) Adjusting of estimates in general linear model with respect to linear restrictions. *Statist. Probab. Lett.* **15**, 125–130. (*490*)

Press, S.J. (2005) *Applied Multivariate Analysis: Using Bayesian and Frequentists Methods of Inference*, second edition, Dover, Mineola, NY. (*13*)

Puntanen, S. (1987) On the relative goodness of ordinary least squares estimation in the general linear model (Ph.D. dissertation), *Acta Univ. Tamper. Ser. A* **216**, University of Tampere, Finland. (*409*)

Puntanen, S. (1997) Some further results related to reduced singular linear models. *Comm. Statist. Theory Methods* **26**, 375–385. (*379*)

Puntanen, S. and Styan, G.P.H. (1989) The equality of the ordinary least squares and the best linear unbiased estimator (with discussion). *Amer. Statistician* **43**, 153–163. (*401*)

Rao, A.R. and Bhimasankaram, P. (2000) *Linear Algebra*, second edition, Hindustan Book Agency, New Delhi. (*583, 586, 588, 593, 605*)

Rao, C.R. (1967) Least squares theory using an estimated dispersion matrix and its application to measurement of signals. In *Proc. Fifth*

Berkeley Sympos. Math. Statist. and Probability, Vol. I: Statistics, Berkeley, Calif., 1965, eds. L.M. Le Cam and J. Neyman, Univ. of California Press, Berkeley, Calif., 355–372. (*401*, *413*)

Rao, C.R. (1973a) Representations of best linear unbiased estimators in the Gauss-Markoff model with a singular dispersion matrix. *J. Multivariate Anal.* **3**, 276–292. (*346*, *351*)

Rao, C.R. (1973b) Unified theory of least squares. *Comm. Statist. Theory Methods* **1**, 1–8. (*359*)

Rao, C.R. (1973c) *Linear Statistical Inference and its Applications*, second edition, Wiley Series in Probability and Mathematical Statistics, Wiley, New York. (*592*, *364*, *517*, *533*, *566*)

Rao, C.R. (1974) Projectors, generalized inverses and the BLUE's. *J. Roy. Statist. Soc. Ser. A* **36**, 442–448. (*573*)

Rao, C.R. (1976) Estimation of parameters in a linear model. *Ann. Statist.* **4**, 1023–1037. Correction (1979) **7**, 696. (*554*)

Rao, C.R. (1978) Least squares theory for possibly singular models. *Canad. J. Statist.* **6**, 19–23. (*371*)

Rao, C.R. (1979) Estimation of parameters in the singular Gauss-Markoff model. *Comm. Statist. Theory Methods* **8**, 1353–1358. (*351*)

Rao, C.R. and Kleffe, J. (1988) *Estimation of Variance Components and Applications*, North-Holland Series in Statistics and Probability **3**, North-Holland, Amsterdam. (*422*, *431*, *436*)

Rao, C.R. and Mitra, S.K. (1971) *Generalized Inverse of Matrices and its Applications*, Wiley, New York. (*591*, *611*, *615*)

Rao, C.R., Mitra, S.K. and Bhimasankaram, P. (1972) Determination of a matrix by its subclasses of generalized inverses. *Sankhyā Ser. A* **34**, 5–8. (*615*)

Rao, C.R. and Toutenburg, H. (1999) *Linear Models: Least Squares and Alternatives*, second edition, Springer Series in Statistics, Springer-Verlag, New York. (*246*, *373*)

Rao, P.S.R.S. (1997) *Variance Components Estimation: Mixed Models, Methodologies and Applications*, Monographs on Statistics and Applied Probability **78**, Chapman and Hall, London. (*427*)

Rawlings, J.O., Pantula, S.G. and Dickey, D.A. (1998) *Applied Regression Analysis: A Research Tool*, second edition, Springer-Verlag, New York. (*198*)

Rousseeuw, P.J. and Leroy, A.M. (2003) *Robust Regression and Outlier Detection*, Wiley Series in Probability and Mathematical Statistics: Applied Probability and Statistics, Wiley, New York. (*245*, *246*)

Rowley, J.C.R. (1977) Singularities in econometric models of wage determination based on time series data. In *ASA Proceedings of Business and Economic Statistics Section*, 616–621. (*343*)

Roy, S.N. (1953) On a heuristic method of test construction and its use in multivariate analysis, *Ann. Math. Statist.* **24**, 220–238. (*517*)

Ruppert, D. and Aldershof, B. (1989) Transformations to symmetry and homoscedasticity, *J. Amer. Statist. Assoc.* **84**, 437–446. (*232*)

Ryan, T.P. (2009) *Modern Regression Methods*, second edition, Wiley Series in Probability and Statistics, Wiley, New York. (*195*)

Schaffrin, B. (1999) Softly unbiased estimation I: The Gauss-Markov model. *Linear Algebra Appl.* **289**, 285–296. (*567*)

Schall, R. and Dunne, T.T. (1988) A unified approach to outliers in the general linear model. *Sankhyā Ser. B* **50**, 157–167. (*495*)

Scheffé, H. (1959) *The Analysis of Variance*, Wiley, New York. (*307*)

Schervish, M.J. (1995) *Theory of Statistics*, Springer Series in Statistics, Springer-Verlag, New York. (*618*, *619*, *628*)

Schönfeld, P. and Werner, H.-J. (1987) A note on C. R. Rao's wider definition BLUE in the general Gauss-Markov model. *Sankhyā Ser. B* **49**, 1–8. (*351*)

Scott, A.J., Rao, J.N.K. and Thomas, D.R. (1990) Weighted least-squares and quasi-likelihood estimation for categorical data under singular models. *Linear Algebra Appl.* **127**, 427–447. (*343*)

Searle, S.R. (1994) Extending some results and proofs for the singular linear model. *Linear Algebra Appl.* **210**, 139–151. (*351*)

Searle, S.R. (2016) *Linear Models for Unbalanced Data*, second edition, Wiley, New York. (*316*).

Searle, S.R., Casella, G. and McCulloch, C.E. (2006) *Variance Components*, second edition, Wiley Series in Probability and Mathematical Statistics, Wiley, New York. (*430*)

Searle, S.R. and Khuri, A.I. (2017) *Matrix Algebra Useful for Statistics*, second edition, Wiley, New York. (*583*).

Seber, G.A.F. and Wild, C.J. (2003) *Nonlinear Regression*, Wiley Series in Probability and Mathematical Statistics, Wiley, New York. (*19*)

Sen, P.K. and Singer, J.M. (1993) *Large Sample Methods in Statistics: An Introduction with Applications*, Chapman and Hall, New York. (*575*, *578*)

Sengupta, D. (1995) Optimal choice of a new observation in a linear model. *Sankhyā Ser. A* **57**, 137–153. (*343*, *464*, *464*, *466*)

Sengupta, D. (2004) On the Kalman filter with possibly degenerate and correlated errors. *Linear Algebra Appl.* **388**, 327–340. (*473*)

Sengupta, D. and Bhimasankaram, P. (1997) On the roles of observations in collinearity in the linear model. *J. Amer. Statist. Assoc.* **92**, 1024–1032. (*254*)

Shaffer, J.P. (1995) Multiple Hypothesis testing. *Ann. Rev. Psychol.* **46**, 561–576. (*295*)

Shah, K.R. and Deo Sheela S. (1991) Missing plot technique in linear models. *Comm. Statist. Theory Methods* **20**, 3239–3252. (*482*)

Shah, K.R. and Sinha, B.K. (1989) *Theory of Optimal Designs*, Springer-Verlag, New York. (*283*)

Shaked, U. and Soroka, E. (1987). A simple solution to the singular linear minimum-variance estimation problem. *IEEE Trans. Automatic Control* **32**, 81–84. (*343*)

Shang, S.F. and Zhang, L. (1993) Linear sufficiency in the general Gauss-Markov model with restrictions on parameter space. *Northeast. Math. J.* **9**, 235–240. (*543*)

Shao, J. and Tu, D. (1996) *The Jackknife and Bootstrap*, Springer Series in Statistics, Springer, New York. (*154*, *237*)

Shinozaki, N. (1975) *A Study of Generalized Inverse of Matrix and Estimation with Quadratic Loss*, Ph.D. dissertation, Keio University, Japan. (*554*)

Sidak, Z. (1968) On multivariate normal probabilities of rectangles. *Ann. Math. Statist.* **39**, 1425–1434. (*158*)

Snedecor, G.W. and Cochran, W.G. (1967) *Statistical Methods*, Iowa State University, Ames. (*7*, *125*)

Stahlecker, P. and Lauterbach, J. (1989) Approximate linear minimax estimation in regression analysis with ellipsoidal constraints. *Comm. Statist. Theory Methods* **18**, 2755–2784. (*564*)

Stepniak, C. (1989) Admissible linear estimators in mixed linear models. *J. Multivariate Anal.* **31**, 90–106. (*554*)

Strand, O.N. (1974) Coefficient errors caused by using the wrong covariance matrix in the general linear model. *Ann. Statist.* **2**, 935–949. (*396*)

Štulajter, F. (1990) Robustness of the best linear unbiased estimator and predictor in linear regression models. *Appl. Math.* **35**, 162–168. (*396*)

Styan, G.P.H. (1973) When does least squares give the best linear unbiased estimate? In *Multivariate Statistical Inference (Proc. Res. Sem., Dalhousie Univ., Halifax, N.S., 1972)*, eds. D.G. Kabe and R.P. Gupta, North-Holland, Amsterdam, 241–246. (*401*)

Subrahmanyam, M. (1972) A property of simple least squares estimates. *Sankhyā Ser. B* **34**, 355–356. (*113*)

Sun, Q., Zhu, H., Liu, Y. and Ibrahim, J.G. (2015) SPReM: Sparse projection regression model for high-dimensional linear regression, *J. Amer. Statist. Assoc.* **110**, 289–302. (*533*)

Swindel, B.F. (1968) On the bias of some least-squares estimators of variance in a general linear model. *Biometrika* **55**, 313–316. (*410*)

Thomson, A. and Randall-Maciver, R. (1905) *Ancient Races of the Thebaid*, Oxford University Press, Oxford. (*504*)

Tian, Y. (2007) Some decompositions of OLSEs and BLUEs under a partitioned linear model. *Int. Statist. Rev.* **75**, 224–248. (*401*)

Tian Y. and Puntanen, S. (2009) On the equivalence of estimations under a general linear model and its transformed models. *Linear Algebra Appl.* **430**, 2622–2641. (*401*)

Tian, Y. and Wang, C. (2017) On simultaneous prediction in a multivariate general linear model with future observations. *Statist. Probab. Lett.* **128**, 52–59. (*530*)

Tilke, C. (1993) The relative efficiency of OLS in the linear regression model with spatially autocorrelated errors. *Statist. Papers* **34**, 263–270. (*409*)

Titterington, D.M. and Sedransk, J. (1986) Matching and linear regression adjustment in imputation and observational studies. *Sankhyā Ser. B* **48**, 347–367. (*14*)

Toutenburg, H. (1982) *Prior Information in Linear Models*, Wiley Series in Probability and Mathematical Statistics, Wiley, New York. (*564*)

Toyooka, Y. (1982) Prediction error in a linear model with estimated parameters. *Biometrika* **69**, 453–459. (*437*)

Tukey, J.W. (1949) One degree of freedom for non-additivity. *Biometrics* **5**, 232–242. (*305*)

Ullah, A., Srivastava, V.K., Magee, L. and Srivastava, A. (1983) Estimation of linear regression model with autocorrelated disturbances. *J. Time Ser. Anal.* **4**, 127–135. (*419*)

Valliant, R., Dorfman, A.H. and Royall, R.M. (2000) *Finite Population Sampling and Inference: A Prediction Approach*, Wiley, New York. (*388*)

van der Genugten, B.B. (1991) Iterated weighted least squares in heteroscedastic linear models. *Statistics* **22**, 495–516. (*444*)

Vehkalahti, K., Puntanen, S. and Tarkkonen, L. (2007) Effects of measurement errors in predictor selection of linear regression model. *Comput. Statist. Data Anal.* **52**, 1183–1195. (*195*)

Verbeek, M. (2017) *A Guide to Modern Econometrics*, fifth edition, Wiley, Hoboken, NJ. (*16*, *437*)

von Rosen, D. (1990) A matrix formula for testing linear hypotheses in linear models. *Linear Algebra Appl.* **127**, 457–461. (*141*)

Wang, S.-G. and Chow, S.-C. (1994) *Advanced Linear Models: Theory and Applications*, Marcel Dekker, New York. (*404*, *418*)

Wang, S.Q. and Li, M.Q. (2011) A characterization of admissible linear estimator of regression coefficients in variance component models. *Appl. Mech. Materials* **58-60**, 1162–1167. (*554*)

Watson, G.S. (1967) Linear least squares regression. *Ann. Math. Statist.* **38**, 1679–1699. (*409*)

Werner, H.J. (1990) On inequality constrained generalized least-squares estimation. *Linear Algebra Appl.* **127**, 379–392. (*375*, *376*)

Werner, H.J. and Yapar, C. (1996) On inequality constrained generalized least squares selections in the general possibly singular Gauss-Markov model: A projector theoretical approach. *Linear Algebra Appl.*, Special issue honouring C.R. Rao **237/238**, 359–393. (*375*)

Wilkie, D. (1962) A method of analysis of mixed level factorial experiments. *Appl. Statist.* **11**, 184–195. (*297*)

Williams, E.J. (1959) *Regression Analysis*, Wiley, New York. (*339*)

Wu, J.-H. (2008) Admissibility of linear estimators in multivariate linear models with respect to inequality constraints. *Linear Algebra Appl.* **428**, 2040–2048. (*555*)

Wu, Q.-G. (1992) On admissibility of estimators for parameters in linear models. In *The Development of Statistics: Recent Contributions from China*, eds. X.R. Chen, K.T. Fang and C. Yang, Pitman Research Notes in Mathematics Series **258**, Longman Sci. Tech., Harlow, co-published in the US with Wiley, New York, 179–198. (*554*)

Yang, W.L., Cui, H.J. and Sun, G.W. (1987) On best linear unbiased estimation in the restricted general linear model. *Statistics* **18**, 17–20. (*390*)

Zhang, F. (2005) *The Schur Complement and Its Applications*, Springer, New York. (*593*)

Zhang, F. (2013) *Matrix Theory: Basic Results and Techniques*, Springer, New York. (*610*)

Zhang, S., Liu, G. and Gui, W. (2009) Admissible estimators in the general multivariate linear model with respect to inequality restricted parameter set. *J. Inequalities Appl.* **2009**, `https://doi.org/10.1155/2009/718927`. (*555*)

Zhang, X., Wang, H., Ma, Y. and Carroll, R.J. (2017) Linear model selection when covariates contain errors, *J. Amer. Statist. Assoc.* **112**, 1553–1561. (*195*)

Zhou, L. and Mathew, T. (1993) Combining independent tests in linear models. *J. Amer. Statist. Assoc.* **88**, 650–655. (*443*)

Zimmerman, D.L. and Cressie, N.A.C. (1992) Mean squared prediction error in the spatial linear model with estimated covariance parameters. *Ann. Inst. Math. Statist.* **44**, 27–43. (*441*)

Zinde-Walsh, V. and Galbraith, J.W. (1991) Estimation of a linear regression model with stationary ARMA(p, q) errors. *J. Econometrics* **47**, 333–357. (*438*)

Zyskind, G. (1967) On canonical forms, non-negative covariance matrices and best and simple least squares linear estimators in linear models. *Ann. Math. Statist.* **38**, 1092–1109. (*401*)

Zyskind, G. (1975) Error structure, projections and conditional inverses in linear model theory. In *A Survey of Statistical Design and Linear Models*, ed. J.N. Srivastava, North Holland, Amsterdam. (*343*)

Index

A-optimality, 283
abbreviations, xix
accelerated failure time, 17
acceptance region, 631
added variable plot, 52, 104, 207, 272
  for correlated data, 494
adjusted R-square, 193
admissible estimator, 628, 629
admissible linear estimator (ALE), 552, 580
affine estimator, 113, 554
  Bayes, 555
affine function, 43
AIC, 194
Aitken estimator, 354
alternative hypothesis, 631
analysis of covariance (ANCOVA), 322, 495, 532
  adjustment for covariates, 330
  balanced two-way classified data, 331
  estimation of parameters, 324
  multivariate, 532
  tests of hypotheses, 327, 332
  uses of, 323
analysis of variance (ANOVA), 142, 281
  p-way classified data, 317, 334
  in general linear model, 381
  latin square design, 334
  multivariate, 531
  nested model, 318, 321, 335
  one-way classified data, 284, 292
  two-way classified data, 296
    multiple observations per cell, 312
    single observation per cell, 301
    with limited interaction, 307
  with missing observations, 316
ancillary statistic, 119, 617, 619
  linear, 538
  linearly maximal, 538
ARIMAX model, 437
asymptotic normality, 576
autoregressive (AR) model, 20, 438
autoregressive moving average (ARMA) model, 20, 437
average risk, 628

Bahadur's result, 618
  linear version, 541
baseline effect, 285
basis of a vector space, 594
  orthogonal, 595
  orthonormal, 595
basis set of BLUEs, 90, 542, 543
  standardized, 90, 545, 548
basis set of LZFs, 90, 545
  standardized, 90, 545
Basu's theorem, 619
  linear version, 539
Bayes affine estimator, 555, 564

Bayes estimator, 628–630
Bayes linear estimator (BLE), 555
  homogeneous, 555
Bayes risk, 628
Bayesian information criterion (BIC), 195
best linear estimator (BLE), 565
best linear minimum bias estimator (BLIMBE), 565
best linear predictor (BLP), 49, 54, 58, 162, 538
  in general linear model, 383, 582
  in multivariate linear model, 58
best linear unbiased estimator (BLUE), 61, 82, 540
  additivity, 119
  as function of fitted values, 84
  basis set of, 89
  distribution, 121
  existence, 83
  generating set of, 114
  geometric view, 567
  in general linear model, 348, 354, 361
  in multivariate linear model, 501, 502
  large sample properties, 575
  LZF turning into, 315
  relation with LSE, 85
  relation with LZF, 82
  standardized basis set of, 114
  uniqueness, 84
best linear unbiased predictor (BLUP), 162
  in general linear model, 383
  in mixed effects model, 436
  in multivariate linear model, 528
best quadratic unbiased estimator, 435
best subsets regression, 198
bias of an estimator, 621
block, 296
block effect, 297
blocking, 296
Bonferroni confidence interval, 156
Bonferroni inequality, 155, 526
Bonferroni test, 148
bootstrap for non-normal regression, 234
bound
  Cramer-Rao, 627
  on efficiency of LSE, 404, 405
  on estimated variance of LSE, 410
  on prediction error variance, 463
  on type I error probability, 632
Box-Cox transformation, 211, 231

calibration, 13
Cauchy-Schwarz inequality, 601
centered data, 349, 352, 356
central limit theorem, 10
change point, 24
Chebyshev's inequality, 345
chemical balance with bias, 115
chi-square distribution, 34
  noncentral, 35
Cobb-Douglas model, 24, 114, 176
coefficient of determination, 129
collinearity, 109, 246
  condition number, 251
  consequences of , 169
  exact, 113
  involving intercept, 249, 254
  VIF, 249
    intercept augmented, 249
  VP table, 251
column rank, 586
column space, 597
  of a dispersion matrix, 37
column vector, 585
complete sufficient statistic, 119, 618, 619
  for exponential family, 620
  linear, 538
completely randomized design (CRD), 284
component of a vector, 601
component plus residual plot, 207, 272
composite hypothesis, 631
concomitant variable, 323
condition index, 251

condition number, 251
confidence band for regression surface, 159, 174
confidence interval
  for a single linear model parameter, 151
  for error variance, 179
  for ratio of LPFs, 173, 174
  simultaneous, 155
confidence region (set), 633
  in general linear model, 381
  in linear model, 151, 153
  in multivariate linear model, 527
  link with testing, 634
consistency
  of linear equations, 611
  of multivariate linear model, 513
  of singular linear model, 344
consistent linear unbiased estimator (CLUE), 567
constrained least squares approach, 365
contrast, 103, 120, 287
convergence in distribution, 576
Cook's distance, 239, 241, 480, 481
  plot, 242
correlation
  multiple, 33, 53
  partial, 34, 51
covariate, 323
COVRATIO, 240, 241, 498
Cramer-Rao lower bound, 627
  for general linear model parameters, 367
  for linear model parameters, 105
    non-normal case, 109
credible set, 634, 635
critical value, 633
CUSUM plot, 462

D-optimal design, 403
D-optimality, 283
data
  adipose tissue, 164, 165, 179, 180, 213, 219, 230, 232
  age at death, 1, 6, 66, 73, 78, 80, 85, 87, 90, 137, 143
  air speed experiment, 297, 298, 337
  apple yield with cropping under tree, 340
  birth weight of babies, 6, 7, 129, 142, 152, 280
  blood samples in ELISA test for HIV, 339
  brown trout hemoglobin, 336
  charpy v-notch test, 286, 289, 293, 295
  compressive strength of hoop trees, 339
  Egyptian skulls, 504, 509, 520, 524
  Fisher's Iris, 534, 535
  for illustrating diagnostics, 182, 206, 227, 234, 278
  for illustrating heteroscedasticity, 215, 217
  for illustrating linearity plots, 208, 211
  Galton's family, 5, 12, 136, 176, 177
  growth of girls, 2–4, 118
  IMF world economic outlook, 197, 198, 240, 242, 250, 252
  jeans abrasion, 13, 70, 74, 78, 80, 85, 94, 96, 102, 107, 131, 132, 134, 144, 149, 153, 154, 156, 171, 313
  kink bands in rocks, 319, 321
  leprosy drugs, 7, 124, 125, 326, 328
  Los Angeles crimes, 116, 117, 176, 179
  medicine prices, 11, 278
  olympic sprint time, 536
  space shuttle Challenger, 268
  speed of galaxies, 10, 63, 64, 73, 75, 124, 160, 168
    updated, 174, 175
  stack loss, 117, 393
  survival times of poisoned animals, 309, 338
  wind tunnel, 302, 303, 307
  world population, 27, 178, 280

world record times, 26, 117, 118, 178, 179, 337
data exclusion and variable inclusion, 494
decorrelation, 55, 623
for data exclusion in linear model, 473
for data inclusion in linear model, 453
for obtaining restricted BLUE, 370, 374
for variable exclusion in linear model, 485
for variable inclusion in linear model, 491
from linear zero functions, 83
geometric view, 56
in general linear model, 351
in missing plot substitution, 483
in multivariate linear model, 514
reduction of variance through, 59
degrees of freedom, 93
error, 93, 356
deleted residual, 205, 272, 462
deleted studentized residual, 272
deletion diagnostics, 479
design augmentation, 462
design matrix, 16, 281
designed experiment, 281, 531
determinant, 585
DFBETAS, 238, 241, 242, 479, 481
DFFITS, 239, 241, 480
diagnostics for regression
added variable plot, 52, 104, 207
Cook's distance, 239, 241, 242, 480, 481
correlated observations, 224
COVRATIO, 240, 241, 498
CUSUM plot, 462
DFBETAS, 238, 241, 242, 479, 481
DFFITS, 239, 241, 480
Durbin-Watson test, 226, 273, 278
heteroscedasticity, 213
leverage, 73, 202, 237, 239, 272, 498
model inadequacy, 207, 462
non-normality, 229
nonlinearity, 207
residual, 66, 202, 207, 272
VIF, 249
intercept augmented, 249
VP table, 251
diagonal matrix, 584
dimension of a vector space, 594
direction of arrival estimation, 446
dispersion matrix, 15, 30
singular, 341
distribution
chi-square, 34
exponential family, 620
F, 34
multivariate t, 157, 294
multivariate normal, 10, 31
of quadratic forms, 35
prior, 628
singular normal, 37
spherically symmetric, 89, 113
student's t, 34
univariate normal, 31
Wilks' Λ, 517
Wishert, 517
dual model, 580
Durbin-Watson test, 226, 273, 278
dynamic model, 437

E-optimality, 283
efficiency, 627
of LSE, 404
of LUE, 388
error
approximation, 18
due to ignored factors, 2
measurement, 2
multiplicative and additive, 24
observational, 2
error function (*see* linear zero function), 78
error space, 85, 550, 580
characterization, 550
error sum of squares, 92
in general linear model, 355
error variance
MLE of, 358

natural unbiased estimator of, 75, 92, 355, 356
REML estimator of, 450
UMVUE, 75, 358
errors in variables, 25
estimability of a parameter
characterization, 79
in general linear model, 345, 347
in linear model, 79
in multivariate linear model, 501
in variance components model, 420
relation with identifiability, 81
with nuisance parameters, 102, 377
estimation space, 85, 550, 580
characterization, 550
estimator, 621
admissible, 628, 629
affine, 554
Bayes, 628–630
LAD, 245
least squares, 62
linear, 76, 554
LTS, 246
maximum likelihood, 624
minimax, 630
UMVU, 622
unbiased, 621
uniformly minimum variance unbiased, 636
WLS, 217, 354, 358
exclusion of observations, 473
exclusion of variables, 484
exogeneity, 16
expansion estimator of population total, 387
expected value, 15, 30
experimental unit, 282
explanatory variable, 3
stochastic or deterministic, 9
exponential family, 620

F-distribution, 34
noncentral, 35
factor, 3
factorization theorem, 619
finite population sampling, 343, 385, 392, 393
Fisher's scoring, 264
Fisher-Cochran theorem, 35
fitted values
in general linear model, 350
in linear model, 65
in multivariate linear model, 505
Frobenius norm, 588
full column rank, 586
full rank matrix, 586

Gauss-Markov Theorem, 84, 85
converse, 86
general linear model, 16, 341
Aitken estimator, 354
analysis of variance, 381
arising from multivariate normal distribution, 43
BLUE, 348, 354
dispersion of, 352
methods for obtaining, 361
canonical decomposition, 545
checking for consistency, 344
confidence region for parameters, 381
constrained parameter space, 346
effect of linear restrictions, 369
error sum of squares, 355
error variance estimation, 355
estimability and identifiability, 345
fitted values, 350
inclusion/exclusion of observations or variables (*see* updates in linear model), 451
inequality constraints, 375
information matrix for parameters, 366
linear restrictions, 372
maximum likelihood estimation, 357
nuisance parameters, 377
prediction through, 383
reduced normal equation, 378
residuals, 350
dispersion of, 352

stochastic restriction, 373
tests of hypotheses, 379
updates (*see* updates in linear model), 451
uses of, 342
virtually linear estimators in, 351
WLS estimator, 358
general regression (GREG) estimator, 388
generalized inverse (g-inverse) of a matrix, 591
generalized likelihood ratio test (GLRT), 633
in general linear model, 380
in linear model, 140
in multivariate linear model, 515
power of, 146
generalized linear model (GLM), 19, 223, 260
MLE, 263
generating set of BLUEs, 89, 542, 548
generating set of LZFs, 89
normalized, 506
gradient vector, 263, 611, 625
Gram-Schmidt orthogonalization, 595
growth model, 532

hat-matrix, 65
Henderson's Method III, 429
Hessian matrix, 263, 611, 625
heteroscedasticity, 213, 441
systematic, 443
homogeneous linear estimator, 554
homoscedastic linear model, 16, 61
honestly significant difference (HSD), 295
Hotelling's T^2, 522
hypothesis, 631
general linear (*see* linear hypothesis), 122

idempotent matrix, 596
identifiability of a parameter
in general linear model, 345, 348
in linear model, 79, 81
in multivariate linear model, 501
in variance components model, 420
relation with estimability, 81
identity matrix, 585
inclusion of observations, 452
inclusion of variables, 490
indefinite matrix, 589
index plot
of casewise diagnostics, 242
of residuals, 224
inequality constraint, 375
inference, 617
information inequality, 627
information matrix, 626
in general linear model, 366
in linear model, 104
information of single LPF, 105
inner product of vectors, 588
intercept augmented VIF (IVIF), 249, 251, 273, 274
intra-class correlation structure, 398
inverse of a matrix, 586, 591
inverse partitioned matrix (IPM) approach, 363, 458, 464, 478
inversion formulae of matrices, 592
invertible matrix, 586

James-Stein estimator, 260
Jeffreys' prior, 636

Kalman filter, 466
Kolmogorov-Smirnov test, 230
Kronecker product, 44, 297, 500, 588, 593, 616
Kuks-Olman estimator, 561, 581

Löwner order, 59, 88, 190, 258, 554, 566, 608
lack of fit, 172
ladder of transformations, 210
lag plot of residuals, 224
lasso, 255
latent variable, 266
latin square design, 334
Lawley-Hotelling test, 519
least absolute deviation (LAD) estimator, 245

least favourable prior, 559, 564, 582, 630
least median of squares estimator, 246
least squares estimator (LSE), 62, 63
dispersion, 72
efficiency of, 404, 409
large sample properties, 575
ordinary, 217
weighted, 217, 354
least trimmed squares (LTS) estimator, 246
left-inverse of a matrix, 590
Lehmann-Scheffé theorem, 623
level of significance, 632
leverage, 73, 202, 238, 474, 498
as case influence indicator, 237, 239
in diagnostic plots, 242
properties, 271, 272
relation with residuals, 272
likelihood equation, 625
likelihood function, 624
likelihood ratio test (LRT), 633
linear equations, 610
linear estimation, 76
linear hypothesis, 122
decomposition of sum of squares, 138
GLRT, 140, 380
nested, 150
single degree of freedom, 135
testability, 131
testable and untestable, 133
linear minimum bias estimator (LIMBE), 566
linear model, 3
analysis of variance, 142
arising from multivariate normal distribution, 10, 43
assumptions, 15
Bayesian methods, 255
BLUE, 82
calibration through, 13
canonical decomposition, 89
change point in, 24
collinearity in, 109, 113, 169, 246
complete sufficient statistic in, 119
confidence band for regression surface, 159
confidence region for parameters, 151
control in, 13
correlation in, 224
distribution of estimators, 121
dual, 580
error in, 9
error space, 85, 550
error variance estimation (*see* error variance), 74
estimability and identifiability, 79
estimation in, 61
estimation space, 85, 550
fitted values and residuals, 65
general (*see* general linear model), 341
generalized (*see* generalized linear model), 19
heteroscedasticity in, 213
homoscedastic, 16, 61
in broader sense, 19
information matrix for parameters, 104
linear restriction in, 96
linearity assumption in, 207
LSE, 62
matrix-vector form, 15
mixed effects (*see* mixed effects model), 20
MLE, 88
multivariate (*see* multivariate linear model), 499
normality in, 229
notations, 14
nuisance parameters in, 102
obtained through linearization, 17
prediction through, 12, 161
reasons for choosing, 9
reparametrization, 94, 114
robust methods, 246
significance of coefficients, 122
singular (*see* general linear model), 97, 341
tests of linear hypotheses, 122

UMVUE, 75, 84
uses of, 10
linear parametric function (LPF), 76
ALE, 552
BLE, 555, 565
BLIMBE, 565
BLUE, 82
CLUE, 567
confidence interval, 151
estimability and identifiability, 79
inequality constraint on, 376
LSE, 62
minimax linear estimator, 558
MLE, 88, 89
principal components estimator, 256
ridge estimator, 258
shrinkage estimator, 259
subset estimator, 184
test of significance, 135
UMVUE, 84
linear prediction, 20
linear regression, 16, 49
arising from multivariate normal distribution, 43
linear restriction, 96
in general linear model, 369, 372
in multivariate linear model, 512
leading to singular model, 342
sequential, 490
linear unbiased estimator (LUE), 76
characterization, 77
efficiency, 388
in general linear model, 345, 346
in multivariate linear model, 501
linear zero function (LZF), 22, 61, 76
as function of residuals, 84
basis set of, 355
BLUE turning into, 114, 138, 292, 316, 513
characterization, 77
gained from exclusion of variables, 486
gained from inclusion of observations, 454
generating set of, 113, 139
in general linear model, 345, 346
in multivariate linear model, 501
lost from exclusion of observations, 475
lost from inclusion of variables, 492
normalized, 506, 533
standardized basis set of, 114
linearity
in explanatory variables, 17
in parameters, 17
linearization, 17
of Cobb-Douglas model, 24
of polynomial regression model, 17
linearly ancillary statistic, 538
characterization, 551
linearly complete statistic, 538
characterization, 551
linearly independent vectors, 586
linearly maximal ancillary, 538
characterization, 551
linearly sufficient statistic, 538, 582
characterization, 551
invariant, 543
link function, 19, 262
lmreg function
basis, 597
binaries, 67, 80
cisimult, 156
cisngl, 152
cisv, 253
compbasis, 600
confelps, 154
frob, 589
ganova, 144
hanova, 143
hypsplit, 134
hyptest, 137
intsectbasis, 602
is.included, 80, 601
ivif, 250
multcomp, 149
proj, 600
supplbasis, 602
tr, 587
yX, 298
yXm, 310, 315

  yXn, 319
LOESS, 212, 215, 220
logistic regression, 28, 265
loglinear regression, 262
loss function, 621
  convex, 622
  quadratic, 552, 580, 630
  squared error, 552, 621, 629

M-estimator, 245
Mahalanobis distance, 531
Mallows's C_p, 194, 271, 276
matrix, 583
  blocks of, 586
  column rank of, 586
  column space of, 597
    orthogonal projection matrix, 600
  decompositions, 602
  diagonal, 584
  dispersion, 30
  full column rank, 586
  full rank, 586
  full row rank, 586
  g-inverse of, 591
  idempotent, 596
  identity, 585
  inverse of, 586, 591
  inversion formulae, 592
  invertible, 586
  Kronecker product, 588
  Löwner order, 608
  left-inverse of, 590
  long vector form, 588
  Moore-Penrose inverse of, 591
  multiplication, 584
  nonnegative definite, 589
  nonsingular, 586, 591
  norm of, 613
  notations, xxi
  null space, 597
  order of, 583
  orthogonal, 592
  parallel sum, 615
  rank deficient, 586
  rank of, 586, 598, 603
  rank-factorization, 603
  right-inverse of, 590
  row rank of, 586
  row space of, 597
  semi-orthogonal, 592
  singular, 586
  spectral decomposition, 604
  SVD, 603
  symmetric, 584
    spectrum of, 604
  trace of, 584
  transpose of, 584
  variance-covariance, 30
maximal ancillary statistic, 617
  linear, 538
maximum likelihood estimator (MLE), 624
  in general linear model, 357
  in general linear model with unknown dispersion, 413
  in linear model, 88
  in mixed effects model, 422
  in multivariate linear model, 510
maximum modulus-t confidence interval, 158
mean squared error (MSE), 39, 621
mean squared error matrix, 372, 622
mean squared error of prediction (MSEP), 161, 384
meta-analysis, 441, 448
minimal sufficient statistic, 617
  linear, 538
minimax estimator, 630
minimax linear estimator (MILE), 558, 581
minimum mean squared error, 39
minimum norm quadratic estimator (MINQE), 431
minimum norm quadratic unbiased estimator (MINQUE), 430, 432
minimum variance quadratic unbiased estimator (MIVQUE), 435
missing data, 316, 324, 482
missing plot substitution, 316, 482
misspecified error dispersion matrix, 396

effect on estimated variance of LSEs, 410
efficiency of LSE, 404
exact inference with, 398
mixed effects model, 9, 20, 400, 419, 447
ANOVA methods, 428
application to signal processing, 446
best quadratic unbiased estimator, 435
BLUP, 436
Henderson's method III, 429
identifiability and estimability, 420
MINQE, 431
MINQUE, 430, 432
MIVQUE, 435
ML and REML methods, 422
testing of hypothesis, 437
model
accelerated failure times, 17
analysis of covariance (*see* analysis of covariance), 322
ARIMAX, 437
autoregressive (AR), 20, 438
autoregressive moving average (ARMA), 20, 437
Cobb-Douglas, 24
conditional, 16
dynamic, 437
errors in variables, 25
general linear (*see* general linear model), 341
generalized linear, 260
generalized linear (*see* generalized linear model), 19
growth, 532
linear (*see* linear model), 3
linear regression, 16
logistic regression, 28, 265
loglinear, 262
mixed effects (*see* mixed effects model), 419
multivariate linear (*see* multivariate linear model), 499
nested, 318
nonlinear regression, 18
one-way classification (*see* one-way classified data), 284
piecewise linear, 24
polynomial regression, 17, 26, 184
probit regression, 266
random effects (*see* mixed effects model), 419
response surface, 28
seemingly unrelated regression (SUR), 399
simultaneous equations, 21
singular linear (*see* general linear model), 341
state-space, 9, 20
time series, 9
two-way classification (*see* two-way classified data), 296
variance components, 420
model building, 494
model matrix, 16
model-preserving constraint, 98
monotone likelihood ratio (MLR), 632
Moore-Penrose inverse, 591
formula for, 592, 606
most powerful test, 632
multicollinearity (*see* collinearity), 110, 246
multiple comparisons, 147
in general linear model, 380
in multivariate linear model, 526
multiple correlation coefficient, 33, 53, 55
sample, 129, 276
multiple linear regression, 63
multiple R-square, 129, 192
multiple regression, 63, 181
multivariate ANOVA (MANOVA), 531
multivariate linear model, 499
arising from multivariate normal distribution, 533
best linear unbiased estimator (BLUE)
dispersion of, 505

BLUE, 501
confidence regions, 527
consistency of linear restrictions, 513
effect of linear restrictions, 512
error dispersion estimation, 506, 510, 512
error sum of squares and products, 508
estimability and identifiability, 501
fitted values, 505
MANOVA, 531
MLE, 510
model description, 500
normalized LZF, 506, 533
one-sample problem, 530
prediction through, 527
residuals, 505
dispersion of, 505
tests of hypotheses, 515
two-sample problem, 530
multivariate normal distribution, 31
conditional, 32
leading to general linear model, 43
singular case, 37

negative definite matrix, 589
nested hypotheses, 150
nested model, 318, 335, 449
Neyman-Pearson lemma, 632
non-normal data, 89
bootstrap for, 234
non-normal distribution, 107, 246, 435
noncentrality parameter, 35
nonlinear regression, 18
nonnegative definite matrix, 589
nonsingular matrix, 586
norm of a matrix, 613
Frobenius, 588
norm of a vector, 588
normal equation, 62
reduced, 325
normal plot, 229
normalized LZF (NLZF), 506, 533
BLUE turning into, 513
nuisance parameter, 102
in designed experiment, 282
in general linear model, 377
reduced normal equation, 378
leading to singular model, 343
null hypothesis, 631
null space, 599

oblique projection, 570
oblique projector, 582
observational studies, 324
observations, 14
independent, 16
omitted variable, 489
one-sample problem, 530
one-way classified data, 66, 284
analysis of variance, 291, 292
estimation of parameters, 287
with between-groups heterogeneity, 398
optimal design, 283
optimization of quadratic forms and functions, 611
order of a matrix, 583
ordinary least squares (OLS), 217
orthogonal complement of a vector space, 594
orthogonal decomposition of a vector, 595
orthogonal matrix, 592
orthogonal projection matrix, 596
orthogonal vector spaces, 594
orthogonal vectors, 594
outlier
dealing with, 245
location-shift, 205
plots, 242
x-, 204
y-, 204, 205, 230

p-value, 632
parallel sum of matrices, 615
parameter, 3
partial correlation, 34, 51
sample, 104, 208
partial regression plot, 52, 104, 207

partial residual plot, 207
piecewise linear model, 24
Pillai's test, 519
plot
  added variable, 104, 207
  box, 201
  component plus residual, 207
  Cook's distance, 242
  CUSUM, 462
  dot, 290
  index, 224, 242
  lag, 224
  normal, 229
  partial regression, 104, 207
  partial residual, 207
  QQ, 229
  residual vs. leverage, 242
  residual vs. predicted, 219
  residual vs. regressor, 214
  scatter, 2, 183
point estimation, 621
polynomial regression, 17, 26, 184
positive definite matrix, 589
positive semidefinite matrix, 589
posterior distribution, 635
power of a test, 631
prediction
  through general linear model, 383
  through linear model, 161
  through multivariate linear model, 527
prediction interval, 163, 384
  simultaneous, 166
prediction matrix, 65
predictor, 3
  best, 161
  best linear, 49, 54, 162
  best linear unbiased, 162, 383, 528
PRESS, 194, 276
principal components estimator, 256, 260, 274
principle of substitution, 86
prior distribution, 628
probit regression, 266
profile analysis, 525, 533
projection matrix, 596
  formula for, 596, 606
  oblique, 571
  orthogonal, 596
projection of a vector, 595
  oblique, 570
protected least significant difference (PLSD), 294
pure error, 172

QQ plot, 229
quadratic form, 589
  distribution of, 35
  optimzation of, 611
quadratic loss function, 630
quadratically sufficient statistic, 543

R-square
  adjusted, 193
  multiple, 129, 192
random effects model (*see* mixed effects model), 419
random vector, 30
randomized block design (RBD), 297
rank of a matrix, 586
rank-deficient matrix, 586
rank-factorization, 603, 615
Rao-Blackwell theorem, 622
  linear version, 539
ratio estimator of population total, 388
recursive group residual, 457
recursive residual, 454, 456
reduced normal equation, 378
regression, 5, 38
  bets subsets, 198
  coefficients, 16
  confidence band for surface, 159
  diagnostics (see diagnostics for regression), 183
  linear, 16, 49
  logistic, 28, 265
  loglinear, 262
  mean, 39
  median, 45
  nonlinear, 18
  parameters, 16

polynomial, 13, 17, 26, 184
probit, 266
quantile, 45
robust, 245
stepwise, 198
regression diagnostics (see diagnostics for regression), 183
regression estimator of population total, 387
regression line
confidence band for, 160, 174
equality of, 178
paralelity of, 179
regression sum of squares, 128
regressor, 3
regularization, 255
rejection region, 631
reparametrization, 94, 114
general form, 95
residual, 65, 66, 202, 238, 474
as function of model errors, 74
decomposition, 93
decorrelated, 494
deleted, 205, 272, 462
deleted studentized, 272
dispersion of, 72
in general linear model, 352
geometric view, 567
in estimation of error variance, 75
in general linear model, 348, 350
in multivariate linear model, 505
maximum likelihood, 416
recursive, 454, 456
relation with leverage, 272
relation with LZF, 76, 84
standardized (*see* standardized residual), 204
studentized (*see* studentized residual), 204
variance, 72
residual sum of squares, 92
residual sum of squares and products, 510
response, 3, 14
multivariate, 47, 499
response surface, 14, 28, 174
restricted/residual maximum likelihood (REML) estimator, 416, 447
in multivariate linear model, 512
ridge estimator, 258, 260, 274
right-inverse of a matrix, 590
risk function, 621, 622
robust regression, 245
row rank, 586
row vector, 585
row-column design, 317, 334
Roy's union-intersection test, 517
rstudent (*see* studentized residual), 204

S-estimator, 246
saturated model, 304
scalar, 585
Scheffé confidence interval, 156
Scheffé test, 149
Schur complement, 593, 608
seemingly unrelated regression (SUR) model, 399
selection bias, 200
semi-orthogonal matrix, 592
semivariogram, 440
sequential linear restrictions, 490
serial correlation, 224
Durbin-Watson test, 226, 273
model for, 414, 437
Shapiro-Wilk test, 230
shrinkage estimator, 259, 275
side-condition, 291, 311
signal detection, 26, 444
simple hypothesis, 631
simple linear regression, 63, 66, 72, 181
simultaneous confidence intervals, 155
Bonferroni, 156
honestly significant difference, 295
maximum modulus-t, 158
PLSD, 294
Scheffé, 156
simultaneous equations model, 21
singular dispersion matrix, 30, 36, 341

singular linear model (*see* general linear model), 341
uses of, 342
singular matrix, 586
singular value decomposition (SVD), 603
size of a test, 632
small area estimation, 394
Snell's law, 4
solutions of linear equations, 610
spatial correlation, 439, 449
spectral decomposition, 604
spectrum of a symmetric matrix, 604
spherically symmetric distribution, 89, 113
spring balance, 105, 119, 336
spring balance with bias, 115, 119
SRSWOR, 387, 393
standard error, 75, 123
standardized basis set of BLUEs, 90, 544–546, 548
standardized basis set of LZFs, 90, 355, 546
normalized, 506
standardized residual, 204, 242, 497
as diagnostic for fit, 239
for detecting heteoscedasticity, 214, 219
for detecting non-normality, 229
for detecting serial correlation, 224
state-space model, 20, 466
leading to singular linear model, 343
statistic
ancillary, 617, 619
complete, 618
complete sufficient, 119, 619
linearly ancillary, 538
linearly complete, 538
linearly maximal ancillary, 538
linearly minimal sufficient, 538
linearly sufficient, 538
maximal ancillary, 617
minimal sufficient, 617
sufficient, 617, 619
stepwise regression, 198
stochastic restriction, 373
strongly consistent, 578
student's t-distribution, 34
noncentral, 35
studentized residual, 204, 242, 497
as diagnostic for fit, 239
for detecting heteoscedasticity, 214, 219
for detecting non-normality, 229
for detecting serial correlation, 224
subset estimator, 184, 255, 270, 276
criteria for selection, 271, 276
sufficient statistic, 617, 619, 622
conditional, 635
linear, 538
linearly minimal, 538
sum of squares
between-groups, 292
corrected for covariates, 332
decomposition of, 93, 138, 141, 282, 357
due to block difference, 300
due to deviation from hypothesis, 305, 333
due to treatment difference, 300
error, 92, 282
lack of fit, 172
pure error, 172
regression, 128, 282
residual, 92
total, 128, 282, 292
within-group, 292
sum of squares and products, 330
error, 508
supplementary variable, 323
symmetric matrix, 584

t-distribution, 34
noncentral, 35
test of hypothesis, 631
in general linear model, 379
in linear model, 122
in multivariate linear model, 515
time series model, 9
autoregressive (AR), 19, 438

autoregressive moving average (ARMA), 20, 437
state-space, 20, 466
tolerance interval, 167
total sum of squares, 128
trace of a matrix, 584
transformation
Box-Cox, 211, 231
ladder of, 210
linear, 31, 50
linearization, 17
log, 24
power, 232
variance stabilizing, 219
translation invariance, 415
transpose of a matrix, 584
treatment, 282, 296
treatment contrast, 103, 120, 287, 298
treatment effect, 285
Tukey's one-degree of freedom test, 306, 338
two-sample problem, 530
two-way classified data, 69, 296
example
ANOVA with interaction, 313
BLUE, 85
confidence interval, 153
Cramer-Rao lower bound, 107
eliminating nuisance parameters, 102
elliptical confidence region, 154
identifying testable part of hypothesis, 134
linear zero function, 78
multiple comparisons, 149
non-estimable parameter, 80
non-reparametrizing linear restriction, 96, 100
non-testable hypothesis, 131, 132
reparametrization, 94
reparametrizing linear restriction, 96, 98
simultaneous confidence intervals, 156
test of homogeneity of treatment effects, 144
interaction in, 304
multiple observations per cell
balanced case, 309
unbalanced case, 315
single observation per cell, 297
treatment contrast, 120
with interaction and between-groups heterogeneity, 399
with missing observations, 316
type I and Type II errors, 631

UMVUE, 119, 622
linear analogue, 84, 540
uniquesness, 623
unbalanced data, 315, 495
unbiased confidence region, 634
unbiased test, 632
unified theory of least squares estimation, 361
uniformly most accurate (UMA)
confidence region, 634
unbiased (UMAU), 634
uniformly most powerful (UMP) test, 632–634
unbiased (UMPU), 136, 633, 634
unit vector, 588
unknown error dispersion matrix, 395, 412
MLE of unknown parameters, 413
REML estimator, 415
special case of variance components, 419
special cases with correlated error, 437
special cases with uncorrelated error, 441
two-stage estimator, 417
use of prior information, 412
update equations
for exclusion of observations, 477
for exclusion of variables, 488
for inclusion of observations, 457
for inclusion of variables, 493
updates in linear model, 451

application to
Kalman filter, 466
deletion diagnostics, 479
design augmentation, 462
missing plot substitution, 482
model building, 489, 494
model diagnostics, 462
data exclusion and variable inclusion, 494
exclusion of observations, 473
exclusion of variables, 484
inclusion of observations, 452
inclusion of variables, 490

variable
criterion, 3
dependent, 3
endogenous, 3
exogenous, 3
explanatory, 3, 14
controlled, 16
random, 16
independent, 3
response, 3, 14
variance, 17
variance components model, 420
application to signal processing, 446
variance inflation factor (VIF), 249
intercept augmented, 249, 251, 273, 274
variance proportions (VP) table, 251
variance stabilizing transformation, 219
variogram, 440
vector, 585
column space of, 601
orthogonal projection matrix, 601
component of, 601
inner product, 588
linearly dependent, 586
linearly independent, 586
norm of, 588
order of, 585
orthogonal decomposition of, 595
orthogonality, 594
random, 30
vector space, 593
basis of, 594
dimension of, 594
intersection, 593
orthogonal basis of, 595
orthogonal complement, 594
orthogonal projection matrix, 596
orthogonality, 594
orthonormal basis, 595
projection matrix, 596
sum, 594
virtually disjoint, 594
virtually linear estimators, 351

weighing design
chemical balance, 115
spring balance, 105, 115, 119, 336
weighted least squares (WLS)
estimator, 217, 354, 358
Wilks' Λ statistic, 516
distribution, 517
Wishart distribution, 517

x-outlier, 204

y-outlier, 204, 205, 230
yield, 282

CPSIA information can be obtained
at www.ICGtesting.com
Printed in the USA
JSHW021022270920
8258JS00005B/132

9 789811 229282